Harold W. P

HANDBOOK OF PHYSIOLOGY

SECTION 1: Neurophysiology, VOLUME I

HANDBOOK OF PHYSIOLOGY

A critical, comprehensive presentation

of physiological knowledge and concepts

SECTION 1: # Neurophysiology

VOLUME I

Editor-in-Chief: JOHN FIELD

Section Editor: H. W. MAGOUN

Executive Editor: VICTOR E. HALL

American Physiological Society, WASHINGTON, D. C., 1959

Foreword

The original literature in the field of physiology has become so vast and is growing so rapidly that the retrieval, correlation and evaluation of knowledge has become with each passing year a more complex and pressing problem. Compounding the difficulties has been the inevitable trend toward fragmentation into smaller and smaller compartments, both of knowledge and of research skills. This trend is not only inevitable, but it is necessary to healthy growth. It must, however, be accompanied by the development of mechanisms for convenient and reliable re-integration in order that knowledge shall not be lost and research effort wasted.

The American Physiological Society has enlisted the cooperation of physiological scientists over the world in attempting to provide a mechanism in this *Handbook of Physiology* series for providing a comprehensive but critical presentation of the state of knowledge in the various fields of functional biology. It is intended to cover the physiological sciences in their entirety once in about ten years, and to repeat the process periodically thereafter.

Board of Publication Trustees
MAURICE B. VISSCHER, *Chairman*
WILLIAM F. HAMILTON
PHILIP BARD

Preface

This *Handbook of Physiology*, like its predecessors from von Haller on, is designed to constitute a repository for the body of present physiological knowledge, systematically organized and presented. It is addressed primarily to professional physiologists and advanced students in physiology and related fields. Its purpose is to enable such readers, by perusal of any Section, to obtain a working grasp of the concepts of that field and of their experimental background sufficient for initial planning of research projects or preparation for teaching.

To accomplish this purpose the editors have planned a book which would differ from textbooks in being more complete, more analytical and more authoritative. It would differ from a series of monographs in being organized on a consistent plan without important gaps between topics and with as nearly as possible the same relation of intensity of coverage to importance of topic throughout. It would differ from publications emphasizing new developments in that the background of currently accepted or classical concepts would be set forth, newer ideas receiving not more than their due proportion of emphasis relative to the whole body of knowledge in the field. Finally it would differ from a collection of original papers on a series of topics in that it would provide an integrated condensation and evaluation of the material contained therein. Moreover, the overall plan provides that the key experimental findings in the development of each field of investigation be described and discussed in sufficient detail (with appropriate illustrations, quantitative data and adequate documentation) to make clear their nature, validity and significance for the fundamental concepts of the field. The success of this endeavor must be left to the reader's judgment.

This *Handbook* stands as the current representative of an historic series of efforts to collect and systematize biological knowledge—a series continued when the Board of Publication Trustees of the American Physiological Society decided in 1953 to sponsor the present undertaking. A brief list of notable predecessors may interest some readers. First known of the series is a brief Sumerian 'pharmacopeia' dating from perhaps 2100 B.C. Later examples included several Egyptian papyri such as the *Ebers* and the *Edwin Smith*. Far more extensive compilations characterized the Greco-Roman period. Outstanding among those were the Hippocratic collection (written by several authors) and the encyclopedic writings associated with the names of Aristotle, Theophrastus, Celsus and Galen (Pliny's work is useful chiefly to the student of folklore). These treatises systematized knowledge of the day over a wide range and set forth new information based on the authors' observations. Thus they combined the roles of handbook and scientific journal, a pattern that persisted until development of scientific journals (in the seventeenth century). Other important compilations were made by the writers of the 'Moslem Renaissance' such as Rhazes and Avicenna, to whom much of the Greco-Roman literature was available.

European biological compendia of the Christian era, from the fourth century *Physiologus* to the extensive biological encyclopedias of the sixteenth and seventeenth centuries, differed greatly in character from Greco-Roman and 'Moslem Renaissance' work. Marked by strong theological and anthropocentric orientation, they lacked the descriptive accuracy and rational approach of the ancients. *Scientia* was considered ancillary to *sapientia*. Nature was studied chiefly to obtain illustrations for moral tales and religious dogmas, not to gain knowledge or insight, or to learn how to manipulate and control the environment. Writers showed little critical capacity and failed to distinguish between the true and the fabulous, the important and the trivial. These elements are still evident in such major sixteenth century biological encyclopedias as Gesner's *Historiae Animalium* (5 volumes, 1551–1587), and Aldrovandi's *Opera Omnia* (13 volumes, 1599–1677). In both the mark of the medieval *Bestiary* is strong.

However, the tide was turning in the sixteenth century despite these notable examples of medieval *Weltanschauung*. The range and precision of anatomical knowledge were greatly extended by publication in 1543 of Vesalius' *De Humani Corporis Fabrica*. It is interesting to note that increasingly accurate handbooks of descriptive botany began to appear. At about this time the great transition from the medieval to the modern outlook (the 'scientific revolution of 1500–1800') was under way. This has been succinctly described by Raven: "Little by little, nonsense was recognized, fables were exploded, superstitions were unmasked and the world outlook built up out of these elements fell to pieces. The seemingly irrelevant labors of men like Turner or Penny to identify and name and describe bore fruit in a refusal to accept tradition on authority and in an insistence that statements must be based upon observation and capable of verification" (C. E. Raven. *English Naturalists from Neckam to Ray*. 1947, p. 227).

The rise of the mechanical philosophy in the seventeenth century and the rationalism of the eighteenth furnished an intellectual climate favorable for science. This was reflected in the papers, monographs and compendia produced. In the spirit of the time, Diderot, d'Alembert and their associates prepared the *Encyclopédie ou Dictionnaire Raisonné Des Sciences, Des Arts et Des Métiers* (35 volumes, Paris, 1751–1780). While the major contribution of this influential work was to diffuse the rationalist interpretation of the universe in mechanistic terms, it included many contributions in the biological sciences. Together these constitute a transitional stage of biological handbook —quite modern in spirit but not in respect of fact or concept.

While the *Encyclopédie* was in preparation in Paris, the Swiss savant Albrecht von Haller was compiling the *Elementa Physiologiae Corporis Humani* (8 volumes, Lausanne, 1757–1765). This comprised both a handbook of anatomy and physiology and a vehicle for publication of much original work by the author. Compared to earlier work the writing shows impressive critical capacity, detailed familiarity with the achievements of others, ability to distinguish the trivial and the important and over-all scientific insight. This was the first of the great series of German *Handbuch* of physiology.

The vast increase in scientific activity, with multiplication of investigators, laboratories and journals, that characterized the nineteenth century led to more frequent collection and systematization of knowledge in the several active fields. This was naturally centered in Germany where scientific activity was greatest. Notable examples of handbooks of physiology were R. Wagner's *Handwörterbuch der Physiologie mit Ruchsicht auf Physiologisches Pathologie* (Braunschweig, 1842–1853); L. Hermann's *Handbuch der Physiologie* (Leipzig, 1879–1883); C. Richet's unfinished *Dictionnaire de Physiologie* (Paris, 1895–1928); E. A. Schäfer's *Text-Book of Physiology* (Edinburgh and London, 1898–1900); W. Nagel's *Handbuch der Physiologie des Menschen* (Leipzig, 1905–1910); the massive *Handbuch der Normalen und Pathologischen Physiologie, mit Berücksichtigung der Experimentellen Pharmakologie*, edited by A. Bethe, G. von Bergmann, G. Embden and A. Ellinger (Berlin, 1926–1932); and our immediate predecessor, G.-H. Roger and L. Biñet's *Traité de Physiologie Normale et Pathologique* (Paris, 1933–1940). Characteristically these handbooks comprised the contributions of many authors and, in the last two, collaboration of several editors as well. These, with comparable compilations in cognate fields such as K. von Bardeleben's *Handbuch der Anatomie des Menschen* (Jena, 1896–1911) and E. Abderhalden's *Handbuch der Biologischen Arbeitsmethoden* (Berlin, 1925–1939), have provided a corpus of collected and systematized scientific knowledge. A notable feature of all handbooks, including the present one, is their increasingly international character, reflecting the broadening base of the world of science.

Survey of these codifications from the earliest on provides a basis for Abraham Flexner's trenchant comment on the history of medicine. "From the earliest times medicine has been a curious blend of superstition, empiricism, and that kind of sagacious observation which is the stuff out of which ultimately science is made. Of these three strands—superstition, empiricism and observation—medicine was constituted in the days of the priest-physicians of Egypt and Babylonia; of the same three strands it is still composed. The proportions have, however, varied significantly; an increasingly alert and determined effort, running through the ages, has endeavored to expel superstition, to narrow the range of empiricism and to enlarge, refine and systematize the scope of observation. . . . The general trend of medicine has been away from magic and empiricism and in the direction of rationality and definiteness" (A. Flexner. *Medical Education. A Comparative Study*. New York, 1925). We trust that continuation of this trend is reflected in this *Handbook*.

It is difficult to acknowledge properly the devoted and effective work which has made this vast under-taking possible. Its success is due alike to the contributors, to the editorial staff and to the Board of Publication Trustees of the American Physiological Society. Alike to all of these is due the gratitude of the world of physiologists for a task well done.

JOHN FIELD

Editor-in-Chief, 1954–1958

Preface to the Section on Neurophysiology

As the Editor-in-Chief has pointed out, the decision of the American Physiological Society to sponsor a *Handbook of Physiology* continues an historic series of efforts to collect and systematize knowledge in more readily available forms. Although sharing many of the features of its predecessors, the present *Handbook of Physiology* is likely to be less formidable than most of them. Its goal, like that of chariot racing, has been to secure a balanced perch astride the rushing progress of investigative advance. It attempts to survey the status of physiology just past the mid-mark of the twentieth century. In the case of each topic, the compilative accumulation of analytic data is either introduced or concluded by synthesizing comments of an 'elder statesman' still active in the field. Thus a balance is sought between the presentation of specific information and conceptualization appropriate to it.

Appropriately also, the *Handbook* begins with consideration of the nervous system by which the activities of other portions of the body are coordinated and controlled. The nervous system remains the last organ of the body still formidably to resist investigative attack; many fundamental concepts of its function lie waiting in the future. Views proposing a spiritual basis for neural function have obtained since classical antiquity. Only in the past century have materialistic outlooks been effectively introduced, first with respect to the nerve impulse, then in reflex function and, most recently, in Russian views applying concepts of reflex physiology to an understanding of higher activities of the brain. In this latter area, however, subjective experience and the mind still receive major attention in the West from the disciplines of psychology and psychiatry, a testimony to continuing dualistic points of view regarding function of the neural organ. In contemporary studies of physiological psychology the gap between brain and mind seems most rapidly to be closing; prominent representation of this field is probably the most novel feature of the table of contents of the present Neurophysiology Section.

More than customarily, appreciation should be expressed to the contributing authors of this *Handbook*. Each has been willing to add to the many energy-draining burdens of a busy career the difficult task of surveying a field of investigative specialty both for the benefit of associates and for the general welfare of physiological science. The remarkably fine series of articles testifies to the generosity and skill of each contributor. It is to be hoped that reader appreciation may compensate these authors.

Special gratitude should be expressed also for the efforts of the Executive Editor, Victor Hall. His background of editorial experience with the *Annual Review of Physiology* enabled the manifold labors of this 'sweet-blooded' man to be performed so deftly as perhaps to escape the attention of the general reader.

Hopefully, all who use this *Handbook* will wish as I do to thank, if only silently, the contributing authors and the Executive Editor for their generous efforts and to applaud them for such a fine accomplishment.

H. W. MAGOUN

Section Editor

Contents

CHAPTER I

The historical development of neurophysiology

MARY A. B. BRAZIER | *Massachusetts General Hospital, Boston, Massachusetts*

EARLY CONCEPTS OF NERVOUS ACTIVITY

IN CONTRAST TO MEDICINE, a science demanding synthesis of observations, experimental physiology, with its reliance on analysis and laboratory work, has little significant history before 1600. Leaders in medicine developed and practiced its therapies for many centuries before they felt the need to understand the nature and functions of the body's parts in any truly physiological sense and, when the urge for this knowledge first arose, it was to come as much from the philosophers as from the healers of the sick.

Neurophysiology (a term not to come into use until centuries later) had as a legacy from the ancients only their speculative inferences and their primitive neuroanatomy. Aristotle had confounded nerves with tendons and ligaments, had thought the brain bloodless and the heart supreme, not only as a source of the nerves but as the seat of the soul. Herophilos and Erisistratos had recognized the brain as the center of the nervous system and the nerves as concerned both with sensation and movement. However, preliminary to all disciplines was the development of the scientific method and in this Aristotle was a forerunner. If Aristotle is to be evaluated as a scientist, it must be admitted that he was almost always wrong in

every inference he made from his vast collections of natural history and numerous dissections; yet in spite of the stultifying effect of the immoderate worship given him by generations to follow, he stands out as a pioneer in the background of every scientific discipline. He owes this position to his invention of a formal logic, and although his system lacked what the modern scientist uses most, namely hypothesis and induction, his was a first step towards the introduction of logic as a tool for the scientist. Unfortunately Aristotle did not use his logic for this purpose himself.[1] As Francis Bacon put it, Aristotle "did not consult experience in order to make right propositions and axioms, but when he had settled his system to his will, he twisted experience round, and made her bend to his system."

In the second century A.D., Galen's experimental work added little to establish the functions of the animal structures he dissected, though the hypotheses he suggested were put forward so authoritatively that they remained unchallenged for nearly 1500 years. To the intervening centuries, dominated as they were by the Christian church, the teleology implicit in Galen's approach was attractive. Early Western acquaintance with his writings depended entirely upon Latin translations of Arabic. It was only after the fall of the Byzantine Empire and the expulsion of the Greek monks from the area of Turkish conquest that the Greek language began to be read at

[1] The fragments of Aristotle's writings that exist (probably his lecture notes) were not collected until more than 200 years after his death. His *Opera* were among the early scientific works to be printed (in Latin, 1472), nearly 1800 years after his death. English translations (*The Works of Aristotle*) were published by the Clarendon Press, Oxford, in several volumes between 1909 and 1931, edited by J. A. Smith and W. A. Ross.

all generally by scholars in Western Europe (1, 2). In the sixteenth century Thomas Linacre (3), physician to Henry VIII, who had taught Greek to Erasmus at Oxford, translated some of Galen's works into Latin directly from the Greek. The copies he gave to Henry VIII and to Cardinal Wolsey can be seen in the British Museum. Erasmus, commenting on Linacre's translations, said, "I present you with the works of Galen, by the help of Linacre, speaking better Latin than ever they spoke Greek."

Galen's emphasis, in spite of his dissection of animals, was not so much on the structures he found as on the contents of the cavities within them. Function, according to his doctrine, was mediated by humors which were responsible for all sensation, movement, desires and thought, and hence pathology was founded on humoral disturbance. The role of the organs of the body was to manufacture and process these humors. His teaching about the nervous system was that the blood, manufactured in the liver and carrying in it natural spirits, flowed to the heart where a change took place converting them into vital spirits. These travelled to the *rete mirabile* (the terminal branches of the carotid arteries at the base of the brain) where they were changed into animal spirits,[2] a subtle fluid which then flowed out to the body through hollow nerves. Some of these ideas Galen developed from those of his predecessors (such as Alcmaeon, Herophilos, Erisistratos), some were inspired by his dissection of animals, but all were hypothetical, none had any experimental proof or

even partial support, yet some of them were to last well into the nineteenth century.

The sixteenth century gave to physiology its first textbook.[3] This was the contribution of Jean Fernel, physician and scholar, who in 1542 published his *De Naturali Parte Medicinae* (4). This was so well received that it saw many editions. In the ninth of these Fernel changed the title to *Medicina* (5) and named the first section of the revised book *Physiologia*. According to Sherrington (6) this was the first use of the term 'physiology.' There is, however, a manuscript in the Danish Royal Library entitled *Physiologus* that deals with animals and monsters. This copy is an Icelandic version of an apparently much-copied treatise; it is a kind of bestiary. For some time after Fernel's revival of it, the term 'physiology' was still used by most writers to mean natural philosophy. An example of this usage is to be found in the full title of Gilberd's book on the magnet published in 1600. Although still grounded in a classification derived from the four elements of the ancients, Fernel's physiology nevertheless shows dawning recognition of some of the automatic movements which we now know to be reflexly initiated for, although only the voluntary muscles were known to him, he realized that sometimes they moved independently of the will.

Before the seventeenth century opened, a technical achievement in another field laid a foundation on which physiology was to spread. Lagging about 50 years after the invention of printing came the development of copper plate engraving and accurate reproductions of anatomists' drawings became more widely distributed. Supreme, however, among the woodcuts contemporary with the early engravings were those made from the drawings of Jan Stephen of Calcar for the anatomical studies of Vesalius (7–9). These, published in 1543, were to draw the praise of John Evelyn in his treatise on chalcography.[4] After

1. GALEN (130–200 A.D.). *Opera Omnia (in aedibus Aldi et Andrea Asulani)* (in Greek). Venice, 1525. 5 vol.
2. GALEN. *Opera Omnia* (in Greek). Basle, 1538.
3. GALEN. *De Facultatibus naturalibus*, Latin translation by Thomas Linacre. London: Pynson, 1523; English translation by A. J. Brock, Loeb Classical Library. London: Heineman, 1916.

[2] The usage of the term 'animal spirits' throughout the centuries carries the connotation of the Latin *anima* meaning soul and has no reference to the modern meaning of the word 'animal.'

[3] No other was to appear until the beginning of the eighteenth century when Johann Gottfried von Berger (1659–1736) published his textbook entitled *Physiologa Medica sive natura humana*. Wittenberg: Kreusig, 1701.

[4] "Nor lesse Worthy of Commendation are the Gravings. . . those eleven pieces of Anatomie made for Andrea Vessalius design'd by Calcare the Fleming, an Excellent painter, and which were afterwards engraven in Copper by Valverdi in little." Evelyn, John. *Sculptura: or the History, and Art of Chalcography.* London, 1662. The reference is to the plagiarism of the Spaniard, Juan Valverde. *Vivae Imagines Partium Corporis Humani.* Antwerp: Plantin, 1566. (His artist was Becerra.)

4. FERNEL, JEAN (1497–1558). *De Naturali Parte Medicinae.* Paris: Simon de Colines, 1542.
5. FERNEL, J. *Medicina.* Paris: Wechsel, 1554. *Physiologia*, translated into French by Charles de Saint Germain, *Les VII Livres de la Physiologie, composés en Latin par Messire Jean Fernel.* Paris: Guignard, 1655.
6. SHERRINGTON, C. S. *The Endeavour of Jean Fernel.* Cambridge: Cambridge, 1946.
7. VESALIUS, ANDREAS (1514–1564). *De Humani Corporis Fabrica.* Basle: Oporinus, 1543; translated into English by J. B. de C. M. Saunders and C. D. O'Malley. New York: Schuman, 1947.
8. VESALIUS, A. *Epitome.* Basle: Oporinus, translated into English by L. R. Rind. New York: Macmillan, 1949.
9. VESALIUS, A. *Tabulae Sex.* Venice, 1538.

centuries in which human dissection could only be done relatively furtively, a more liberal view had grown up in Italy and among a number of contemporary anatomists, Vesalius is pre-eminent. In themselves, however, with the exception of an experiment showing that the nerve sheath is not vital for conduction, his studies made no contribution to the dynamics of function. Although an opponent of Galen and an exposer of his anatomical errors, Vesalius had no more satisfactory concept of nervous activity to offer than that of animal spirits flowing from the brain down pipe-like nerves to the muscles. Yet for the study of the nervous system, as for other branches of physiology, the publication of *De Humani Corporis Fabrica* is the outstanding contribution of the sixteenth century, the earlier chalk drawings of Leonardo Da Vinci (1452–1519) not being widely known to his contemporaries. The major contributions of Vesalius were not in physiology but in anatomy and in the demonstration that Galen was capable of error (though he himself was not without error).

At the opening of the seventeenth century the important event for all science was the appearance (in 1600) of William Gilberd's[5] classic book *De Magnete* (10, 11). The significance of this work was not only as a landmark for the future of the physical sciences and of electrophysiology through its dawning recognition of a difference between electricity and magnetism; it was the first book to advocate empirical methods and in this way heralded the scientific ferment of the eighteenth century. If one overlooks the last two chapters of *De Magnete*, the book is revolutionary in its experimental approach. It stood out alone in an age when scholasticism was concerned with classification on qualitative lines without measurement and without validation. Authoritative statements of the ancients were the guides, and induction from experiment was virtually unknown. Gilberd's book makes a plea for "trustworthy experiments and demonstrated arguments" to replace "the probable guesses and opinions of the ordinary professors of philosophy."

Gilberd was physician to Queen Elizabeth (whom

he only just survived) and a sketch identified as a portrait of him appears in the contemporary drawing (now in the British Museum) made by William Camden, the Court Herald, of her funeral procession in 1603. A contemporary oil portrait of him painted in 1591 has been lost and remains to us only in engravings. Gilberd was born and lived part of his life in his father's house in Colchester in East Anglia; a portion of this house still stands and, at the time of writing, is being restored. This flowering of the scientific method came during the golden age of Elizabethan England; among Gilberd's contemporaries were Shakespeare, Walter Raleigh, Philip Sydney, John Donne, Christopher Marlow and Francis Bacon.

Francis Bacon has a place in the history of all sciences, for he took scientific method a step farther, to observation he added induction and to inference he added verification. Scientists before him were content with performing an experiment in order to make an observation; from this observation a series of propositions would follow, each being derived from its predecessor, not by experiment but by logic. (Bacon somewhat unjustly criticizes Gilberd for proceeding in this way.) Bacon's contribution to scientific method was to urge, in addition, the rigorous application of a special kind of inductive reasoning proceeding from the accumulation of a number of particular facts to the demonstration of their interrelation and hence to a general conclusion. This was indeed a new instrument, a *Novum Organum* (12). By its application he overthrew reliance on authority of the ancients and opened the way for planned experiment. Although he had no place in his method for the working hypothesis, and his forms of induction and deduction are scarcely those of the modern methodology, they were of considerable influence in its development. The intelligent lines of Bacon's face can be seen in his portraits. John Aubrey (13) tells us that he "had a delicate, lively hazel eie" and that "Dr. Harvey told me it was like the eie of a viper."

The first major work in physiology exemplifying

10. GILBERD, WILLIAM (1540 (or 1544)–1603). *De Magnete, Magnetisque corporibus; et de magno magnete tellure; Physiologica nova plurimis et argumentis et experimentis demonstrata.* London: Peter Short, 1600; translated into English by the Gilbert Club, *William Gilbert of Colchester, physician of London.* London: Chiswick Press, 1900.

11. *Ibid.* (2nd ed.) (posthumous). Gotzianio in Stettin, 1633. This book, far rarer than the first edition, carries more plates than the original, and has some additions by Wolfgang Lochmann of Pomerania (1594–1643).

12. BACON, FRANCIS (1561–1626). *Novum Organum.* 1620; translated into English by Kitchin. Oxford, 1855.

13. AUBREY, JOHN (1626–1697). *Brief Lives set Down 1669–1696*, edited by Andrew Clark. Clarendon Press, 1898, vol. 2.

---

[5] The spelling of Gilberd's name follows the form seen on his portrait and memorial tablet; his name on his book is spelled Gilbert.

FIG. 1. Portrait of William Gilberd from an oil painting on wood, found by Silvanus P. Thompson in an antiquary's shop. The artist and the authenticity of the date on this portrait are unknown. The portrait is now in the possession of Miss Helen G. Thompson, by whose courtesy it is reproduced here. The photograph of 'Tymperleys,' Gilberd's home at Colchester, was taken in 1957 when the house was undergoing extensive restoration. A portion only of the house dates from Gilberd's time. (Photograph by courtesy of Dr. G. Burniston Brown.)

Bacon's methodology was not on the nervous system but on the circulation of the blood. Harvey's magnificent treatise *De Motu Cordis* (14) was a model for workers in all branches of physiology to follow. This small book (it has only 72 pages) was the first major treatment of a physiological subject in dynamic rather than static terms. By experiment Harvey disproved the Galenist doctrine that the motion of the blood in the arterial and venous systems was a tidal ebb and flow, independent except for some leakage through 'pores' in the interventricular septum. By further designed experiments Harvey proved his own hypothesis "that the blood in the animal body is impelled in a circle, and is in a state of ceaseless motion." Harvey had advanced this hypothesis in 1616 but,

as a forerunner of modern scientific method, had proceeded to verify it before publishing his book. But even this triumph of the empirical method did not unseat in Harvey's thinking the belief in a soul located in the blood ('anima ipsa esse sanguis') (15). Harvey was Galenist enough to accept the *rete mirabile* as the destination of the blood within the cranium, although doubt as to its existence in man had already been raised by Berengario da Carpi (16, 17) a hundred years before. Harvey (18) had his own views of nervous function. "I believe," he said, "that in the nerves there is no progression of spirits, but irradiation; and that the actions from which sensation and

14. HARVEY, WILLIAM (1578–1657). *Exercitatio anatomica de motu cordis et sanguinis in animalibus*. Frankfurt: Fitzeri, 1628; translated into English by Willius and Keys, Cardiac Classics, 1941, p. 19.

15. HARVEY, W. *Praelectiones anatomiae universalis*. London: Churchill, 1886. (Reprint of Harvey's Lumleian lecture 1616.)

16. BERENGARIO DA CARPI, GIACOMO (1470–1550). *Commentaria cum amplissimus additionibus super anatomia Mundini*. Bologna: Benedictis, 1521.

17. BERENGARIO DA CARPI, G. *Isagogae breves, perlucidae*. In: *Anatomiam humani corporis, ad suorum scholasticorum preces in lucem editae*. Bologna, 1522; translated into English by H. Jackson, under the title *A description of the Body of Man, being a practical Anatomy*. London, 1664.

18. HARVEY, W. *Praelectiones Anatomiae Universalis*, autotype reproduction edition. Philadelphia: Cole, 1886.

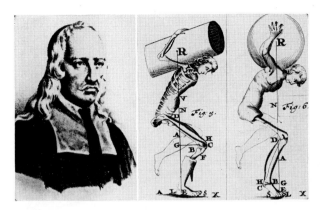

FIG. 2. Borelli and one of his sketches to show the center of gravity of man when carrying a load. (From Borelli, G.A. *De Motu Animalium*, 2nd ed., Leyden: Gaesbeeck, 1685.)

motion result are brought about as light is in air, perhaps as the flux and reflux of the sea."

That nerves might play a role in the working of the heart as a mechanical pump was first suggested by Borelli the Neapolitan, professor of mathematics at Pisa and later at Florence, who applied the reasoning of his discipline to physiology and evolved mechanical models for various bodily functions. His concept of the innervation of muscle was an initiation by the nervous fluid ('succus nerveus') of a fermentation in the muscle swelling it into contraction, for there were still many years to go before a dynamic concept of muscle was to emerge in spite of Harvey's demonstrations on the heart. Peripheral muscles were still regarded as passive structures rather like balloons to be inflated by nervous fluid or gaseous spirits reaching them through canals in the nerves. Borelli, by an ingenious experiment in which he submerged a struggling animal in water and then slit its muscles, demonstrated that the spirits could not be gaseous since no bubbles appeared in spite of the violent contractions. It was this experiment that led him to the suggestion of a liquid medium from the nerve, mixing in the muscle to cause a contraction by explosive fermentation ('ebullitio et displosio') (19).

Giovanni Alphonso Borelli was a member of the group of experimental scientists banded together in the Accademia del Cimento under the patronage of the science-loving Medici brothers in Florence. This small scientific society, successor to the Lincei, existed for only a decade but was typical of the independent groups centered on laboratory experiment that were to spring up in independence of the universities where the scholars had still not looked up from their books. Few as they were (there were only nine members) these laboratory scientists of the Accademia were to have a far-reaching though delayed influence on European thought, for in the final year of the academy's existence they published their proceedings (20). Founded entirely on empirical methodology, this was a truly scientific text. It was, however, written in Italian although soon translated into English, and it did not reach the scientific world at large until Petrus van Musschenbroek of Leyden made a Latin translation (21). It was this book that, for example, influenced Stephen Hales so greatly in his experimental work. The volume included only one series on animal experimentation, but almost all the rest deals with the physics which are basic to the work a physiologist does in his laboratory.

To his contemporary, Descartes, Borelli owed his application of mathematics to muscular action. This pungent philosopher, who rarely did an experiment, wrote a text that was to influence all experimenters, *The Discourse on Method* (22). It is not experimental method that he discusses, but his own method of thought, his theory of knowledge.[6] Scientists had just begun to look around them to observe nature and to let the statements about her by the ancients lie in the books when they had to meet a new and brilliant challenge; mathematics was the tool they were to use. Mathematics would not only elucidate the laboratory experiment but would provide the basis for an all-embracing theory of science.

This great man bred in the gentle landscape of Touraine was to devote his life to a search for the truth, seeking for himself a quiet environment for free thinking.[7] This he found for 25 years in the

19. BORELLI, GIOVANNI ALFONSO (1608–1679). *De motu animalium* (published posthumously). Rome: Bernado, 1680–1; a small section has been translated into English by Michael Foster. *Lectures on the History of Physiology.* Cambridge: Cambridge, 1901.

20. *Saggi di naturali esperienza fatte nell Accademia del Cimento,* edited by L. Magalotti. Florence, 1667; translated into English by Richard Waller. *Essayes of Natural Experiments made in the Accademie del Cimento.* London, 1684.

21. VAN MUSSCHENBROEK, PETRUS (1692–1761). *Testamina Experimentorium Naturalium captorum in Accademia del Cimento.* Leyden, 1731.

22. DESCARTES, R. *Discours de la Méthode.* 1637; English translation by E. S. Haldane and G. R. T. Ross. *Philosophical Works of Descartes.* Cambridge: Cambridge, 1904.

[6] "Méthode de bien conduire sa raison, pour trouver la verité dans les sciences."

[7] "Cum nil dignum apud homines scientia sua invenisset, eremum ut Democritus aliique veri Philosophi elegit sibi juxta Egmundum in Hollandia, sibique solitarius in villula per 25 annos remansit, admirandaque multa meditatione sua detexit" (Borel, p. 9).

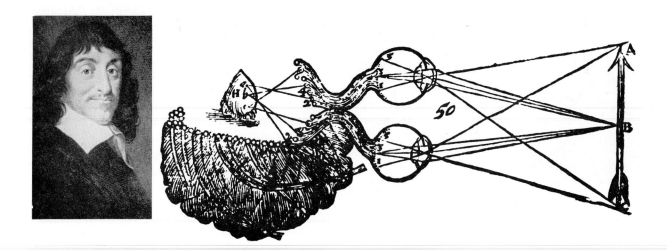

FIG. 3. René Descartes and his concept of the pineal gland. The photograph is from the portrait by Franz Hals in the Louvre, and the diagram is taken from de la Forge, Louis. *Traité de l'Esprit de l'Homme, de ses Facultéz, de ses Fonctions, et de son Union avec le Corps. Suivant les principes de Mr. Descartes.* Geneva: Bousquet, 1725.

village of Egmond in liberal Holland, though even here he could not entirely escape being hounded by bigots. The mistake he made that the world regrets was to leave a milieu so congenial to his philosophic nature for the cold of Sweden and the exacting demands of Queen Christina. There, within a year, he died. His striking face with the intelligent eyes and quizzical eyebrow has been preserved for us in the fine portrait by Franz Hals that hangs in the Louvre.

A great man has many 'lives' written about him but those set down by his contemporaries usually have a special flavor. In the case of Descartes, the short account of his life and his philosophy written by Borel (23) (the microscopist) in 1669 gives one the feeling of bridging the centuries. Borel gives a list of the manuscripts found in Stockholm at Descartes's death in 1650, including the early treatise he wrote on music when he was only 22. Several of his letters were found, some of which Borel reproduces. The letters date from 1632 and give an intimate glimpse of the struggle Descartes had to face in overcoming resistance to his theories among some of his contemporaries.

Descartes (24, 25), having become convinced that in mathematics lay the tool for a unified theory of all science, had now to explain its role in physiology. It followed logically that the animal body and all its workings was a machine, the operation of this machine being directed from a control tower. In the brain with its bilateral development, the singly represented pineal body was chosen by Descartes to play this master role and (in man) it was given the added responsibility of housing the soul. In the concept of the body as a machine, energized not by an immaterial anima[8] but by the external world impinging on it, lies a germ of the idea of reflex activity.

To coming generations of neurophysiologists Descartes bequeathed the notion that impressions from the external world were conveyed by material animal spirits to the ventricles and there directed by the pineal gland into those outgoing tubular nerves that could carry them to the part of the body the subsequent action of which would be the appropriate one. In animals this was presumed to be a purely mechanical action, but in man the soul, resident in the pineal, could have some say in the direction taken by this

23. BOREL, PIERRE (1620–1689). *Vitae Renati Cartesii, Summi Philosophi Compendium.* Frankfurt: Sigismund, 1676.

[8] "It is an error to suppose the soul supplies the body with its heat and its movements." *Passions de l'Âme*, Article 5.

24. DESCARTES, RENÉ (1596–1650). *Passions de l'Âme.* Amsterdam, 1649.
25. DESCARTES, R. *De homine figuris, et latinate donatus a Florentio Schuyl,* posthumous Latin version by Schuyl. Leyden: Moyardum & Leffen, 1662; first French edition, *Traité de l'Homme,* 1664; second French edition, 1677.

central relay. Descartes recognized, however, that perhaps some of these actions lay outside the control of the will, citing as examples involuntary blinking and the withdrawal of the hand on burning.

To neurophysiologists Descartes bequeathed another seed—what was later to be known as the reciprocal innervation of antagonist muscles. In order to ensure that while animal spirits were flowing into one set of muscles the opposing set should relax, he argued that the latter must have their supply of spirits blocked and he postulated that this must be effected by valves. Whether or not he was influenced in his thinking by Harvey's explanation of the valves of the veins is not known, although he was certainly aware of, and had commented on, Harvey's discoveries.[9] Descartes was a member of what a subsequent irreverent generation was to call 'the balloonists.' Apparently unaware of Borelli's experiments, he thought the animal spirits to be "like a wind or a very subtle flame" and that "when they flow into a muscle they cause it to become stiff and swollen, just as air in a balloon makes it hard and stretches the substance in which it is contained."

A young contemporary of Descartes, though less directly influenced by him than was Borelli, was William Croone who was working on muscle action. He too thought that the nervous 'juice' must interact in some way with the muscle (26). The "spiritous liquid" flowed in, mixed with "the nourishing juice of the muscle," and then the muscle "swell'd like a Bladder blown up." Later (27) Croone was to modify this to a number of small bladders for each muscle fiber. Just as Borelli had been a founding member of a scientific society, so was Croone. He was one of the original group who in England formed the Royal Society, a society which unlike the Cimento has continued to flourish and in which to this day eminent scientists not only discuss but demonstrate their experiments before the members. The Royal Society has several distinguished lectureships, among which is the Croonian Lecture founded by the widow of William Croone.

The Royal Society of London received its charter in 1662, being founded for the promotion of 'Natural Knowledge,' and it numbered among the founding members many whose contributions are fundamental

to physiology. The moving spirit was Robert Boyle, the 'father of chemistry' (whose first published work was, however, on *Seraphick Love*). Famous for his law (28) of gaseous pressures, he made his most directly physiological experiments on the respiration of animals. It was still many years before physiologists were to elucidate the effects of anoxia on the nervous system, and another hundred years were to pass before Priestley's and Lavoisier's work on oxygen, but Boyle, by using an ingenious compression chamber, demonstrated that air is essential for life. Almost unnoticed at the time, but since then perhaps overpraised, were the observations of John Mayow (29) on the chemistry of respiration. His publication preceded (although his work was contemporary with) the somewhat similar experiments of the Accademia del Cimento.

In the early seventeenth century emphasis on the search for a chemical foundation for living phenomena characterized for the most part work in Holland and England in contrast to the physical and mathematical approach of the Italians and the French. The two contrasting schools of thought were long to be known by the clumsy names of the iatrochemical and iatromechanical schools. Iatrochemistry, on the rather shaky foundations given to it by van Helmont (1577–1644) and by Sylvius (de La Boë) (1614–1672), provided the approach to the study of the nervous system of Thomas Willis, Sedleian Professor of Natural Philosophy at Oxford (30). Willis, whose clinical achievements outshone his scientific acumen, is recognized in neurology for his description of the circle of Willis and his dissection of the spinal accessory nerve. (Galen had identified only seven pairs of cranial nerves.) Willis was a close colleague at Oxford of Richard Lower, the Cornishman, champion of the theory that spirits flowing into the heart from

28. BOYLE, ROBERT (1627–1691). *New experiments physico-mechanical, touching the spring of the air, and its effects, made, for the most part, in a new pneumatical engine.* Oxford: W. Hall, 1660.

29. MAYOW, JOHN (1645–1679). *Tractus Duo, quorum prior agit De Respiratione: alter De Radutiones.* Oxford: Hall, 1668.

30. WILLIS, THOMAS (1621–1675). *Cerebri anatome: cui accessit nervorum descriptio et usus. (De systemate nervoso in genere),* illustrated by Sir Christopher Wren. London: Flesher, 1664; translated into English by S. Pordage. London: Dring, Harper and Leigh, 1683.

26. CROONE, WILLIAM (1633–1684). *De ratione motus musculorum* (published anonymously). London: Hayes, 1664.

27. CROONE, W. *An Hypothesis of the Structure of the Muscle, and the Reason of its Contraction.* Hooke's Philosophical Collections, No. 11. London, 1675.

[9] Letter to Mersenne dated 1632, quoted in *Oeuvres Complètes de Descartes,* edition of Adam and Tannery, Paris: Cerf, 1897–1910, vol. II, p. 127.

its nerves were what caused it to beat (31). Lower's more spectacular achievement was the apparent transfusion of blood, first in dog and then in man (32, 33). We are surprised today that the man survived as long as he did, for the blood donor was a sheep.

Thomas Willis had added to the prevalent Galenic ideas of nervous function the concept that the soul had two parts which he likened to a flame in the vital fluid of the blood and a light in the nervous juice. When they met in the muscle, they formed a highly explosive mixture which inflated the muscle. Yet even before the seventeenth century had run out, a voice was raised against such visionary explanations. Stensen (34), the great Danish anatomist, writing from Florence in 1667, stated unequivocally that "Animal spirits, the more subtle part of the blood, the vapour of blood, and the juice of the nerves, these are names used by many, but they are mere words, meaning nothing."

The seventeenth century, or *grand siècle* as it was known to Europe, had been gloriously opened by the *De Magnete* and gone on to the achievements of Galileo, Kepler, Huygens, Leibniz and Newton, and, although these were essentially achievements in mathematics, physics and astronomy, all branches of science were fermenting with the implications of these discoveries. The break with dogma was now more than a crack, though the *Index Librorum Prohibitorum* fought a delaying action. The men of the arts were liberal in their championship of the scientists. John Milton's *Areopagitica* (35) is a clarion call for freedom of knowledge and distribution of books. Milton was a young contemporary of Galileo and went to see him in his old age. There is a poignancy about this visit to the old blind astronomer from the poet about to become blind.

The students of the nervous system had the hardest fight against dogma for in their province lay the structures most suspect as being the guardians of man's soul. But ranked behind them and influential on them were some of the greatest philosophers of their time. Prominent among these was Locke (36), the father of empiricism. Born in the West of England and trained as a physician, this man with his colorless personality and his clumsy prose was to channel the efforts of the next several generations of workers on the nervous system into a search for the physiology of the mind. For his *Essay on Humane Understanding* he received immediate recognition and monetary reward, obtaining for it more than was paid to John Milton for *Paradise Lost*.

Straddling like a colossus the division between the seventeenth and eighteenth centuries is Newton, friend and correspondent of Locke, though to scientists it is perhaps a bit disappointing to find that the subject of their correspondence was the interpretation of the New Testament (biblical history was a life-long interest of Newton). Newton's insight into the movement and forces of nature led him to make some tentative suggestions about the working of the nervous system, and these were noted by the physiologists of the time. There is scarcely a single neurophysiologist of the eighteenth century who does not explicitly attempt to align his findings with these conjectures of Newton.

In the General Scholium (37) which he added to the second edition of the *Principia* (26 years after its first publication), Newton included a speculation. This was the idea of an all-pervading elastic aether "exceedingly more rare and subtle than the air," which he again suggested in the form of a question in the series of Queries added to the second English edition of his *Opticks* (38). Applying this suggestion to the nervous system, he said, "I suppose that the Capillamenta of the Nerves are each of them solid and uniform, that the vibrating Motion of the Aetherial Medium may be propagated along them from one End to the other uniformly, and without interruption. . . ." It is easy to understand how eagerly such a statement would be received by those who accepted the idea of a nervous principle running down the nerves but were worried that they knew of no fluid sufficiently swift and invisible. Newton's rather sketchy suggestion was therefore eagerly embraced by many of his contemporaries, one of whom, Bryan Robinson,

31. LOWER, RICHARD (1631–1691). *Tractatus de Corde item de Motu & Colore Sanguinis et Chyli cum Transitu.* London: Allestry, 1669; English translation by K. J. Franklin. *Early Science in Oxford.* Oxford, 1932, vol. 9.

32. LOWER, R. The method observed in transfusing the blood out of one live animal into another. *Phil. Trans.* 1: 353, 1665-6.

33. LOWER, R. AND E. KING. An account of the experiment of transfusion, practised upon a man in London. *Phil. Trans.* 2: 1557, 1667.

34. STENSEN, NICHOLAS (1638–1686). *Elementorum myologiae specimen.* Florence: Stella, 1667, p. 83.

35. MILTON, JOHN (1608–1674). *Areopagitica. A speech for the Liberty of Unlicensed Printing to the Parliament of England.* 1644.

36. LOCKE, JOHN (1632–1704). *An Essay concerning Humane Understanding.* London: Holt, 1690.

37. NEWTON, ISAAC (1642–1727). *Principia.* London: 1687; edition with General Scholium, 1713.

38. NEWTON, I. *Opticks* (2nd ed., 24th Query). London: 1717.

Regius Professor of Physic at the University of Dublin, even went so far as to claim that "Sir Isaac Newton discovered the Causes of Muscular Motion and Secretion" (39).

At the opening of the eigthteenth century the science of the nervous system had reached different levels in the various countries of Europe. In Germany in the first half of the century the Thirty Years War had brought science almost to a standstill, and in the fields of chemistry and physiology this stagnation developed into a retrogression owing to the emergence of an extremely influential figure, Georg Ernst Stahl. In opposition to both the chemical and mathematical schools, Stahl set back the clock by the reintroduction of an immaterial anima which he held to be the sole activating principle of the body parts (40). The latter were regarded as having no dynamic properties of their own, being essentially passive structures. Since the search for an immaterial agent lies outside the scope of science, Stahl's doctrines, promulgated with arrogance and dogmatism, virtually extinguished experimental inquiry among his followers. Yet even writers sympathetic to his viewpoint granted that in attempting to follow his arguments one became "involved in a labyrinth of metaphysical subtlety" (41). The metaphysical approach of Stahl later came under criticism from Vicq d'Azyr (42) who suggested that the invention of an imaginary soul to resolve those phenomena that could not yet be explained by the laws of physics and chemistry was merely a cloak for ignorance. van Helmont did not escape the same criticism.

In opposition to humoral or vitalistic concepts of nervous and muscular activity was a prominent champion of a 'solidist' theory, Giorgio Baglivi. This young man, whom Pope Innocent XII had appointed to be professor of the theory of medicine and anatomy at Rome, put emphasis on the fibers of the muscles and the nerves, and so foreshadowed the importance that was to be given in the eighteenth century to the intrinsic structural properties of these tissues. He de-

FIG. 4. Giorgio Baglivi rising like a phoenix from the flames.

veloped a theory (43) of an oscillatory movement of nerve fibers in order to account for both efferent and afferent activity and envisaged the dura mater as the source of these movements and the recipient of the returning oscillation.

The leading medical center in Europe at this time was the University of Leiden. The empirical approach was urged by the physicist S'Gravesande (44) who advised that "It is Nature herself that should be examined as closely as possible . . . progress may be slow, but what we find will be certain." Petrus van Musschenbroek (45), who had come to the Chair of Physics at Leiden from Utrecht in 1740, had in a discourse on scientific method emphasized that physics should stand apart from metaphysics, that experimental analysis should antecede synthesis, that in the collection of evidence the exception should not be ignored, and that argument by analogy was fraught with danger. Yet it was essentially by analogy that the early eighteenth century viewed the func-

39. ROBINSON, BRYAN (1680–1754). *A treatise of the Animal Oeconomy* (3rd ed.). London: Innys, 1738.

40. STAHL, GEORG ERNST (1660–1734). *Theoria Medica Vera Physiologiam et Pathologium, tanquam Doctrinae Medicae Partes veres Contemplativas e Naturae et Artis veris fundamentis.* Halle, 1708.

41. BOSTOCK, JOHN (1773–1846). *Sketch of the History of Medicine from its origin to the commencement of the nineteenth century.* London: Sherwood, Gilbert & Piper, 1835.

42. VICQ D'AZYR, F. (1748–1794). *Oeuvres de Vicq d'Azyr.* Paris, 1805, vol. 4.

43. BAGLIVI, GIORGIO (1668–1707). De fibra motrice et morbosa. In: *Opera Omnia.* Leyden: Antonii Servant, 1733.

44. S'GRAVESANDE, WILHELM JACOB (1688–1742). *Physices Elementa Mathematica Experimentis confirmata sive Introductio ad Philosopham Newtonianam.* 2nd ed., 1725; 3rd ed., 1742, 2 vols. Leiden.

45. VAN MUSSCHENBROEK, PETRUS (1692–1761). *Discours à l'Organisation de l'Expérience.* 1730. (His swansong as Rector at the University of Utrecht.)

FIG. 5. Boerhaave giving a class in botany. (From the engraving by Jacob Folkema, reproduced by permission of the Rijksuniversiteit in Leiden.)

tions of the nervous system; the brain was analogous to the heart and the nerves analogous to the arteries. In the one case the content was blood; in the other, nervous fluid. Some writers even spoke of "the systole of the brain . . . whereby the animal Juices are forcibly driven into Fibres of the Nerves" (46).

van Musschenbroek had been a pupil of Hermann Boerhaave who came to the Chair of Medicine in Leiden in 1701. Boerhaave, essentially a chemist and a clinician, had an almost legendary fame as a teacher, which must, one feels, have been due to his personality, for he was not an experimenter and his doctrines were not at all progressive. He added little if anything new to the existing body of physiological

knowledge. In his lectures (47, 48) on the nervous system he taught that "The Ventricles of the Brain have also many Uses or Advantages in Life, such as the perpetual Exhalation of a thin Vapour, or moist Dew." Himself a chemist, he made no experiments in physiology and was content to teach that "Tho' the nervous Juice or Spirits separated in the Brain are the most subtile and moveable of any Humour throughout the whole Body, yet are they formed like the rest from the same thicker Fluid the Blood, passing thro' many Degrees of Attenuation, till its Parts become small enough to pervade the last Series of Vessels in the Cortex, and then it becomes the subtile Fluid of the Brain and Nerves." His authority for this doctrine which he handed on to his eighteenth century pupils was the works of Galen who had died in 200 A.D. These teachings are difficult to reconcile with the exhortation expressed in his *Aphorismi* (49) that attention to facts and observations is the best means of promoting medical knowledge.

Yet among his pupils Boerhaave numbered nearly all the prominent students of the nervous system in the eighteenth century: Haller, van Swieten, Monro, Cullen, de Haen, Pringle. His pre-eminence lay in the clinical field, and there can be no doubt that he had the greatest gift of a teacher, that of lighting the fire of enthusiasm in his students. It was two of them, Haller (50) and van Swieten (51), who were responsible for the wider publication of his lectures, for on his own initiative he published little.

van Swieten, who as a Catholic had little chance of advancement at the University of Leiden, went to Austria under the patronage of Maria Theresa and there founded the 'Old Vienna School,' patterning it on the medical clinic at Leiden. He was an advocate of a spare diet and active exertion and quoted in support of his views "the case of a rich priest, who had

46. ROBINSON, NICHOLAS. *A new system of the Spleen, Vapours, and Hypochondriak Melancholy.* London, 1729, p. 262.

47. BOERHAAVE, HERMANN (1668–1738). *Institutiones Medicae in usus animal exercitationis domesticae.* Leyden, 1708; anonymous English translation. *Academical Lectures on the Theory of Physic, being a genuine translation of his Institutes, and Explanatory Comment.* London: Innys, 1743. 5 vol.

48. BOERHAAVE, H. *Praelectiones Academicae de Morbis Nervorum. Quas ex Auditorum Manuscriptis collectas edi curavit,* Jacobus van Eems. Leyden: van der Eyk & Pecker, 1761. 2 vol.

49. BOERHAAVE, H. *Aphorismi de cognoscendis et curandis morbis.* Leyden: van der Linden, 1709.

50. VON HALLER, ALBRECHT (1708–1777). *Commentarii ad Hermann Boerhaave Praelectiones Academicae in proprias Institutiones Rei Medicae.* 1739–1744. 7 vol.

51. VAN SWIETEN, GERHARD L.B. (1700–1772). *Commentaria in Hermanni Boerhaave, aphorismos, de cognoscendis et curandis morbis.* Leiden: Verbeek, 1742–1776. 6 vol.

FIG. 6. Albrecht von Haller, the greatest physiologist of the eighteenth century, and de La Mettrie whose treatise *L'homme machine*, addressed to Haller, caused a controversy that highlighted the question as to whether the soul lay in the province of the physiologist. The portrait of Haller is from the frontispiece of his *Elementa Physiologiae* and is an engraving by Tardieu; that of de La Mettrie is from an engraving in the Bibliothèque Nationale (reproduced here with permission), the original painting being a pastel by Maurice Quentin La Tour.

enjoyed a fat living and long been a martyr to gout, chancing to be carried into slavery by a Barbary corsair, and kept for two years to hard labour and spare diet in the gallies lost his gout and his obesity together. . . ." His master, Boerhaave, a martyr to gout, had died 34 years before, corpulence hastening his end.

We have a contemporary description (52) of Boerhaave's habits and also of his looks. "He had a large head, short neck, florid complexion, light brown hair (for he did not wear a wig), and open countenance, and resembled Socrates in the flatness of his nose. . . ." We are told that he rose at four in the morning, but in the cold Dutch winters he allowed himself an extra hour in bed before settling to work in his unheated study. His chief relaxation was music and he played several instruments of which his favorite was the lute.

It is at about this period—the middle of the eighteenth century—that experimental work on the nervous system began to be channeled into three main divisions: *a*) the elucidation of peripheral nerve

physiology and its differentiation from that of muscle, *b*) the recognition of the function of the spinal cord together with the development of ideas about reflex action, and *c*) the growth of knowledge about the brain as a neural structure unencumbered by dogma concerning the soul.

EXCITABILITY AND TRANSMISSION IN NERVES

In the field of physiology Boerhaave's most prominent pupil was Albrecht von Haller. Haller, a Swiss, was born in Berne and studied at Tübingen but was drawn to Leiden by the magnet of Boerhaave's teaching. After taking his medical degree he returned to Switzerland where he divided his time between medicine, poetry and botany. In 1736 George II of England, Elector of Hanover, appointed him to the chair of the mixed sciences Anatomy, Surgery and Botany at Göttingen, a newly-founded university. It was here that Haller spent the experimental phase of his life as a scientist.

Unlike his master Boerhaave, Haller was a great laboratory worker as well as a phenomenal scholar

52. BURTON, WILLIAM. *An account of the Life and Writings of Hermann Boerhaave*. London: Lintot, 1743.

FIG. 7. Two men whose ideas of irritability anteceded those of Haller. Glisson's concept (1677) included a psychic stage between stimulus and contraction thereby differing from Haller's which postulated a purely peripheral reaction. Johannes de Gorter's proposal of irritability based on mechanical movement was published in 1734. The portrait of Glisson is an engraving from the original painting in the Royal College of Physicians. That of de Gorter is photographed from an engraving, the generous gift of the Director of the National Museum of Science in Leiden. The original painting was by J. M. Quinkhard, the artist of the portrait of van Musschenbroek reproduced in figure 11.

and was the author of the most famous of the eighteenth century textbooks of physiology, the *Elementa Physiologiae* (53). Although these volumes came into print after Haller's retirement to Berne, he had while teaching at Göttingen brought out his *Primae Lineae Physiologiae* (54) for, as he proceeded with his anatomical and experimental studies, his master's texts became less and less useful to him. In the preface to his own work he remarks that, since the time of Boerhaave, anatomy had developed so greatly as to become almost a new science. Haller had himself brought out an anatomy book (55) with fine engravings, and anatomy was one of the four subjects on which he compiled bibliographies (56–59) that are a

great source of information for the medical historian. They contain tens of thousands of references.

For neurophysiologists Haller's most interesting work is his development of the concept of irritability. An earlier student of Boerhaave's at Leiden was Johannes de Gorter who later became physician to the Empress Elizabeth of Russia. He had in 1737 published a volume (60) in which he brought out of obscurity the idea of the intrinsic irritability of tissues that had been postulated by Francis Glisson in the previous century. It is not clear whether de Gorter owed any of his ideas to Glisson. He mentions him only once (in *De Motu vitale*, paragraph 58, p. 40) and this only in reference to the capsula hepatis. In any

53. VON HALLER, ALBRECHT (1708–1777). *Elementa Physiologiae corporis humani*. Lausanne: Marci-Michael Bousquet et Soc., 1757–1765. 8 vol.

54. VON HALLER, A. *Primae lineae physiologiae in usum praelectionium academicarium*. Göttingen: Vandenhoeck, 1747.

55. VON HALLER, A. *Icones anatomicae*. Göttingen: Vandenhoeck, 1743–1756.

56. VON HALLER, A. *Bibliotheca Botanica*. Zurich: Orell, 1771–1772.

57. VON HALLER, A. *Bibliotheca Chirurgica*. Basle: Schweighauser, 1774; Berne: E. Haller, 1775.

58. VON HALLER, A. *Bibliotheca Anatomica*. Zurich: Orell, 1774–1777.

59. VON HALLER, A. *Bibliotheca medicinae practicae*. Basle: Schweighauser, 1776; Berne: E. Haller, 1778.

60. DE GORTER, JOHANNES (1689–1762). *Exercitationes medicae quatuor*. I: *De motu vitale*, 1734; II: *Somno et vigilia*; III: *De fame*; IV: *De Siti*. Amsterdam, 1737.

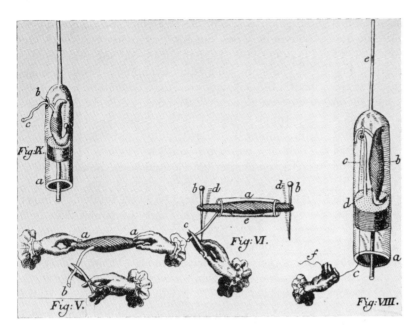

FIG. 8. Swammerdam's experiments including the one by which he proved that muscles were no swollen by an influx of nervous fluid when they contracted. *Fig. V* is of an experiment to show the change in shape of a muscle when stimulated by pinching its nerve. *Fig. VI* illustrates the pulling together of the pins holding the tendons when the muscle contracts. *Fig. VIII* is the crucial one in which a drop of water is imprisoned in the narrow tube projecting from the vessel enclosing the muscle. Swammerdam found that when he stimulated the nerve by pulling it down by a wire, the muscle contracted but the drop of water did not move. He concluded that the volume of the muscle did not expand on contraction. It is the fact that the wire was made of silver (filium argenteum) and the loop of copper (filium aeneum) that has credited Swammerdam with the use of bimetallic electricity as a stimulus to nerve. Some authors however interpret the action in this experiment as the mechanical pull on the nerve. Some originals of Swammerdam's plates can be seen at the National Museum of the History of Science in Leiden. (From *Biblia Naturae*. Amsterdam, 1738).

case his concept of intrinsic irritability differed from that of Glisson in being part of a dynamic scheme in which movements of muscles and nerves acted mechanically on each other (61). Glisson (62) had been among the few scientists of the seventeenth century to test experimentally the Galenist doctrine that muscular contraction was due to an inflow of nervous fluid inflating the muscle. He had demonstrated by immersion of a man's arm in water that the level did not rise on contraction. Swammerdam,[10] in Holland, reached the same conclusion from experiments on frogs (fig. 8). From such experiments, Glisson had gone on to develop a concept of intrinsic irritability varying in kind for the different nervous functions. As Regius Professor of Physic at Cambridge, Glisson

was to a certain extent bound by the statutes governing these professorships to teach the doctrines of Hippocrates and of Galen, and this may have limited him in the development of this new idea of irritability.

In Haller's hands the idea blossomed into a concept that was to dominate physiology for over a century. His theory differed from Glisson's in that he omitted the intermediate element of psychic perception between the irritation and the contraction. The first expression of his theory of the relationship of contractility to irritability is found in 1739 in his commentaries on Boerhaave's lectures and a fuller development in his *Elementa Physiologiae*, but it is in his

61. DE GORTER, J. *Exercitationes Medica Quinta V: De actione viventium particulari*. Amsterdam, 1748.
62. GLISSON, FRANCIS (1597–1677). *Tractatus de ventriculo et intestinis*. London: Henry Brome, 1677.

[10] No known portrait of Swammerdam exists. In the nineteenth century a publisher took one of the heads from Rembrandt's *Anatomy Lesson* and put out a lithograph which he labelled with Swammerdam's name. This was a stroke of imagination rather than fact.

Göttingen lectures (63) given in 1752 (and published the following year) that the concept is most fully developed and supported by experimentation. Haller's own definitions for the dual properties of irritability and sensibility were as follows: "I call that part of the human body irritable, which becomes shorter on being touched; very irritable if it contracts upon slight touch, and the contrary if by a violent touch it contracts but little. I call that a sensible part of the human body, which on being touched transmits the impression of it to the soul; and in brutes, in whom the existence of a soul is not so clear, I call those parts sensible, the Irritation of which occasions evident signs of pain and disquiet in the animal."

One sees immediately the bogey of the early physiologists raising its head—the necessity, on invoking the soul, for differentiating processes in man from those in animals. Haller describes his technique for determining sensibility as follows: "I took living animals of different kind, and different ages, and after laying bare that part which I wanted to examine, I waited till the animal ceased to struggle or complain, after which I irritated the part, by blowing, heat, spirit of wine, the scalpel, lapis infinalis, oil of vinegar, and bitter antimony. I examined attentively, whether upon touching, cutting, burning, or lacerating the part, the animal seemed disquieted, made a noise, struggled, or pulled back the wounded limb, if the part was convulsed, or if nothing of all this happened."

Haller recognized that nerves are "the source of all sensibility," but applied his dichotomy of irritability and sensibility to various types of nerves, noting that all nerves are not irritable according to his definition (with its insistence on resultant contraction). He thus approached the differentiation of motor and sensory nerves. Still incorporated in his hypothesis was the 1600-year-old concept of a nervous fluid within the nerves. It might be thought that once the microscope had been invented, the question of whether or not the nerves were hollow pipes might have been quickly settled. Indeed in 1674 Leeuwenhoek (64), with the limited magnification of his simple microscope, had specifically searched for cavities in the nerves of a cow but his results were equivocal. One hundred years later this issue was still unresolved.

The only competing hypothesis, which received but little support, was that the nerves were cords that communicated sensation to the brain by their vibrations (rejected by Boerhaave as "repugnant to the Nature of the soft, pulpy and flaccid nerves"). This view was also rejected by Haller.

In considering how a fluid could possibly flow as swiftly as nerves can be observed to act, Haller proposed that it must indeed be a very subtle fluid imperceptible to the eye yet more substantial than heat, aether, electricity or magnetism. In another comment he granted that electricity was a most powerful stimulus to nerves but that he thought it improbable that the natural stimulus was electrical. Thinking always in terms of electricity flowing as down a wire, Haller, like so many physiologists after him, felt the lack of insulation around the nerve to be a critical argument against nervous influence being electrical.

However, the notion of electricity as a transmitter of nervous activity kept cropping up at about this time. Alexander Monro (65), Professor of Medicine and Anatomy in the University of Edinburgh, a pupil of Boerhaave and first of the great dynasty of Monros, pointed out that no cavities could be seen in nerves, that no drops of fluid came out when a nerve was cut, and that the nerve did not swell when ligated; and he rather cautiously skirted the possibility of electricity being the agent. But he too considered it only in terms of electricity running down a wire and, like Haller, was bothered that the nerve was inadequately insulated to prevent loss. "We are not sufficiently acquainted," he said, "with the properties of aether or electrical effluvia pervading everything, to apply them justly in the animal oeconomy; and it is difficult to conceive how they should be retained or conducted in a long nervous cord."

Electricity had also been suggested by Stephen Hales (66) in refuting a suggestion that the swelling of muscles was due to inflow of blood. This country clergyman, without formal scientific or medical training, by his experimental skill and keen observation became one of the outstanding contributors to knowledge of the circulation. In writing of the nerves he said, "From this very small Force of the arterial Blood

63. von Haller, A. De partibus corporis humani sensibilibus et irritabilibus. *Comment. Soc. reg. Sci. Göttingen* 2: 114, 1753; English translation by M. Tissot, M.D. *A dissertation on the sensible and irritable parts of animals*, from a treatise published in the *Transactions of the Royal Society of Göttingen* and read in the Academy of Göttingen by Haller on April 22, 1752. Printed by J. Nourse at the Lamb opposite Katherine-street in the Strand, 1755.

64. van Leeuwenhoek, Antonj (1632–1723). *Phil. Trans.* 9: 178, 1674.

65. Monro, Alexander (1697–1762). *The works of Alexander Monro* (collected by his son). Edinburgh: Charles Eliot, 1781.

66. Hales, Stephen (1677–1761). *Statical Essays.* London: Innys and Manby, vol. I, 1726; vol. II, 1732.

FIG. 9. The Abbé Nollet and some of his experiments in which he electrified plants and animals. The portrait, which shows the Abbé in his study at La Mouette, is from the oil painting by Jacques de Lajoue that hangs in the Musée Carnavalet in Paris and is reproduced by kind permission of the Conservateur, M. Charageat. The illustration on the right is from Nollet's book, *Recherches sur les Causes Particuliers des Phénomènes Électriques*. Paris, 1749.

among the muscular Fibres we may with good reason conclude, how short this Force is of producing so great an Effect, as that of muscular Motion, which wonderful and hitherto inexplicable Mystery of Nature, must therefore be owing to some more vigorous and active Energy, whose Force is regulated by the Nerves; but whether it be confined in Canals within the Nerves, or acts along their surfaces like electrical Powers, is not easy to determine."

At the end of the century came Galvani. His famous *Commentary*, published first in 1791, appeared at a time of intense interest in electricity. The demonstration by Stephen Gray (67) in England that the human body could be electrified had been taken up and popularized by the Abbé Nollet (68) at the French Court and by Hausen (69), the Professor of Mathematics in Leipzig. Each had copied Gray's experiment in which he suspended a boy by ropes from the ceiling, bringing a flint-glass tube that had been charged by friction close to his feet and watching the attraction of a leaf-brass electroscope to his nose (see fig. 10).

Electroscopes of this primitive type were the only instruments then available for the detection of electricity, the most sensitive one being that developed by the curate of a rural parish in Derbyshire (70). This delicate instrument with its gold leaves was identified by his name as Bennet's electrometer, though it was scarcely a metrical device. Sources of electricity were still the frictional machines, first globes of sulphur, glass or porcelain, and later revolving discs. It was

67. GRAY, STEPHEN (?–1736). Experiments concerning electricity. *Phil. Trans.* 37: 18, 1731.
68. NOLLET, JEAN-ANTOINE (1700–1770). *Essai sur l'électricité des corps.* Paris: Guerin. 1746.
69. HAUSEN, CHRISTIAN AUGUST (1693–1743). *Novi profectus in historia electricitatis.* Leipzig, 1743.
70. BENNET, ABRAHAM (1750–1799). *New Experiments on Electricity.* Derby: John Drewry, 1789.

FIG. 10. The experiment of electrifying a boy, from the French translation of the book by F. H. Winckler (Professor of Greek and Latin at Leipzig) entitled, *Essai sur la Nature. Les effets et les causes avec description de deux nouvelles machines à Électricité.* Paris: Jorry, 1748. (Photographed from the copy in the Wheatland collection by kind permission of Mr. David Wheatland.)

FIG. 11. van Musschenbroek and a Leyden jar. The portrait is from the oil painting by J. M. Quinkhard which hangs in the Museum of the History of Science in Leiden. The jar is an early one, rather large in size, also from the same museum, by the courtesy of which these photographs are reproduced.

not until the development of the Leyden jar by Petrus van Musschenbroek, Professor of Physics in Leiden, that physiologists gained a much more stable and powerful source of electricity.

van Musschenbroek, striving to conserve electricity in a conductor and to delay the loss of its charge in air, attempted to use water as the conductor, insulating it from air in a nonconducting glass jar. However, when he charged the water through a wire leading from an electrical machine, he found the electricity dissipated as quickly as ever. His assistant, Andreas Cuneus, while holding a jar containing charged water, accidentally touched the inserted wire with his other hand and got a frightening shock. With one hand he had formed one 'plate,' the charged water being the other, and the glass jar the intervening dielectric. A condenser was born. On touching the wire with his other hand he had shorted this condenser through his body giving himself such a jolt that he thought "his end had come" (71). van Musschenbroek wrote to Réamur describing a similar experience. Storage of electricity had now become possible and in fact had been achieved independently by almost the same means (an electrified nail dipping into a vial containing liquid) by von Kleist (72) of

71. Quoted in J.-A. NOLLET. *Mémoire de l'Académie Royale de Sciences.* Paris, 1746, p. 1–25.
72. VON KLEIST, EWALD JURGEN (d. 1748). Letter to J. G. Krüger, quoted in *Geschichte der Erde Halle* 1746, p. 177; and letter to Winkler (J. H. Winkler. *Die Eigenschaften der electrischen Materie und des electrischen Feuers.* Leipzig. 1745).

Kamin in Pomerania, yet another of the indefatigable company of eighteenth century clergymen to whom science owes so much.

Both the electroscope and the Leyden jar were used by Galvani in the experiments he had begun not later than 1780. He was also familiar with the fact that some animal forms, notably the marine torpedo and the electric eel, had intrinsic electricity. Scientific studies of this type of animal electricity had begun with the work of John Walsh (73) in 1733 and have continued to this day. In those days the production of a spark was considered a *sine qua non* for full acceptance of the electrical nature of a phenomenon; this was lacking for the fish until after Galvani's time when Matteucci developed a technique for demonstrating it (see fig. 12). For many years before Galvani's day, as demonstrated for example by Swammerdam and by the French anatomist Joseph Guichard Duverney,[11] it had been known that the limbs of a frog could be convulsed by mechanical irritation, and electricity applied directly to the muscle already had been used by many physicians (and quacks) to animate paralytics.

The three chief observations that stand out from the many experiments reported by Galvani in his original *Commentarius* (74) were *a*) that a frog's nerve muscle preparation, although at a distance from a sparking electrostatic machine, would twitch when touched by an observer (in the light of later knowledge this was called induction at a distance, with stimulation occurring by the 'returning stroke' at the moment of sparking); *b*) that atmospheric electricity could be used to stimulate frogs' legs if a long wire were erected (the principle of the lightning conductor); and *c*) that frogs' legs twitched when hung by brass hooks to an iron railing even in the absence of a thunderstorm. This last, the most important discovery in his first set of experiments, was due to the current that flows between dissimilar metals when connected in a circuit, though Galvani did not understand this at the time and attempted to explain all his results as the presence of intrinsic animal electricity.

The *Commentarius* was reprinted three times, twice in 1791 and again in the turbulent year 1792 (the year that France seized Savoy); then it reached scientists

73. WALSH, JOHN (1725-1795). On the electric property of the torpedo. *Phil. Trans.* 63: 461, 1773.

74. GALVANI, A. (1737-1798). De viribus electricitatis in motu musculari. *Commentarius De Bononiensi Scientiarum et Artium Instituto atque Academia Commentarii* 7: 363, 1791; English translation of 2nd reprinting of Galvani's Commentary by M. G. Foley. In: *Galvani: Effects of Electricity on Muscular Motion.* Norwalk: Burndy Library, 1954.

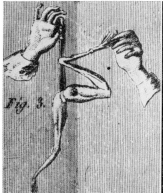

FIG. 12. Galvani and the experiment on muscle contraction in the absence of any metals. The portrait is from the contemporary oil painting in the Library of the University of Bologna (reproduced by courtesy of Dr. G. Pupilli). The experiment in which one leg is being stimulated by touching the nerves from the severed spinal column is reproduced from Aldini's book, *Essai sur le Galvanisme.* Paris: Piranesi, 1804.

outside Italy. Through the great controversy stirred up by Volta which continued after Galvani's death in 1798 (Galvani's less prudent nephew Aldini championing his cause), two extremely important areas of knowledge developed from the original observations. One was the recognition and elucidation of the electrical properties of muscle and nerve which were to lead directly to the discovery (by du Bois-Reymond in the next century) of the action potential of nerve, and the other was the development (by Volta) of bimetallic electricity into the electric battery, one of the major technological steps in the history of science.

Volta had striven to explain all the frog experiments by bimetallic currents, insisting that to produce electricity three substances were always necessary, two heterogeneous metals and a third conducting material

[11] This, one of the early public demonstrations of the stimulation of muscle through irritation of its nerve, was made before the Académie Royale de Sciences in Paris in 1700, and is reported for that year as follows: "M. Du Verney shewed a frog just dead, which in taking the nerves of the belly of this animal which go to the thighs and legs, and irritating them a little with a scalpel, trembled and suffered a sort of convulsion. Afterwards he cut these nerves in the belly, and holding them a little stretched with his hand, he made them do so again by the same motion of the scalpel. If the frog has been longer dead this would not have happened, in all probability there yet remained some liquor in these nerves, the undulation of which caused the trembling of the parts where they corresponded, and consequently the nerves are only pipes, the effect whereof depends upon the liquor which they contain." *History and Memoirs of the Roy. Acad. Sci. Paris.* Translated and abridged by John Martyn and Ephraim Chambers. London: Knapton, 1742, p. 187.

Casa Galvani Settembre 1786.

FIG. 13. Volta and the experiment of Galvani that led to the development of the Voltaic pile. The engraving of Volta is from the drawing by Roberto Focasi. Volta was an admirer of and was honored by Napoleon, one of whose gestures he seems to have caught. Behind him is a Voltaic pile. The sketch at the right was composed by an artist from a drawing made by du Bois-Reymond when he visited Galvani's house 54 years after the latter's death. It depicts the experiment (designed to test atmospheric electricity) in which Galvani stumbled on the phenomenon of bimetallic electricity. (From *Reden von Emil du Bois-Reymond*, 1887, vol. 2.)

to complete the circuit. If this third material were a frog's muscle, it would by virtue of its irritability react to the flow of bimetallic electricity, but its role (according to Volta) was solely that of an electroscope (75). When Aldini (76) demonstrated by dipping ends of nerve and muscle in mercury that the same effect could be obtained with a single metal, Volta replied that the surface in contact with the air suffered a change that made it heterogeneous with the depth. This tortuous argument was disproved by von Humboldt (77).

Before Galvani's death an anonymous (78) tract was published, almost certainly with his collaboration, in which an experiment was described on the twitching of muscles in the absence of any metals or external

source of electricity. A contraction was demonstrated when the cut end of a frog's spine fell over onto its muscle or when one limb was drawn up to touch the exposed sciatic nerve (see fig. 12). In this case the source of electricity was what we now recognize as the current of injury. Even after this demonstration (79) Volta tried to explain the current flow as the result of heterogeneity of tissues (muscle and nerve).

The design of Humboldt's experiments and the clarity of his reasoning are a pleasure to study in the welter of acrimonious controversy that greeted Galvani's findings. Without bias towards either protagonist Humboldt repeated their experiments, examined their interpretations, designed new experiments to test their hypotheses and came to the conclusion that Galvani uncovered two genuine phenomena (bimetallic electricity and intrinsic animal electricity) and that these were not mutually exclusive. Humboldt demonstrated that both great scientists erred in their interpretations of their experiments; however, from these were to grow the science of electrophysiology on the one hand and, on the other, the brilliant development of the electric battery. Not only does Humboldt expose the erroneous parts of Galvani's and of Volta's interpretations but also

75. VOLTA, ALESSANDRO (1745–1827). On electricity excited by the mere contact of conducting substances of different kinds. *Phil. Trans.* 90: 403, 1800.

76. ALDINI, GIOVANNI (1762–1834). *De animali Electricitate dissertationes duae.* Bologna, 1794.

77. VON HUMBOLDT, FREDERICK ALEXANDER (1769–1859). *Versuche über die gereizte Muskel- und Nervenfasser.* Posen und Berlin, 1797.

78. ANONYMOUS. *Dell'uso e dell'attivita dell'Arco conduttore nelle contrazioni del muscoli.* With *Supplemento.* Bologna: S. Tommaso Aquino, 1794; part of the *Supplemento* has been translated into English by M. Tschou in: B. Dibner. *Galvani-Volta.* Norwalk: Burndy Library, 1952.

79. VOLTA, A. *Phil. Mag.* 4: 163, 1799.

those of the writers who rushed in so precipitately to take up arms for one or the other protagonist—Pfaff (80), Fowler (81), Valli (82), Schmuck (83), each received his rebuke. He tells us that he thought some of the problems out while sitting at the foot of Mt. Bernard reading de Saussures' *Voyages dans les Alpes* (84). Humboldt was a great traveller (especially at a period when he was an inspector of mines) but did not let this interfere with his experiments, for he took his apparatus along with him, even on horseback.

The pursuit of research in animal electricity was carried on in many countries, the most valuable contributions coming first from the Italian scientists. Their task was made easier for them by Oersted's discovery of electromagnetism and its development by Nobili into a useful form of galvanometer. Oddly enough Oersted's researches (85, 86) that led to his important experimental demonstration of the relationship between electricity and magnetism were motivated by a metaphysical belief in the universality of nature, a faith inspired by his adherence to Natürphilosophie. This romantic doctrine with its façade of facts was very powerful in Germany from about 1810 to 1840 and was derived from Kant's rejection of empiricism and his philosophy of universal laws known *a priori* by intuition. Oersted's own *a priori* belief was so strong that he did not hesitate to make his first experimental test of it in the classroom during a lecture to advanced students at the University of Copenhagen. The experiment worked; when current flowed in a single loop of bent wire, a magnet below it moved. This great discovery led to the development of instruments with multiple windings and to moving coil galvanometers. The contribution of Nobili, Professor of Physics

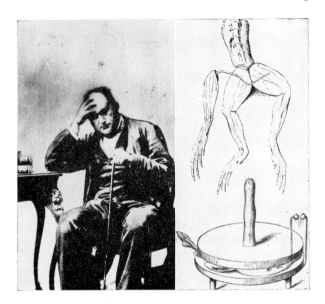

FIG. 14. Matteucci and two of his experimental procedures. The portrait is reproduced from the old yellowing photograph in the Schola Normale Superiore in Pisa (by courtesy of Dr. G. Moruzzi). Above on the right is Matteucci's illustration of his rheoscopic frog, and below is his experiment demonstrating that the discharge of a marine torpedo can make a spark cross a gap.

and Natural History at Florence, was the astatic galvanometer (87) in which two coils of wire wound in opposite directions cancelled the effect of the earth's own magnetism.

It was Matteucci, the Professor of Physics at Pisa, who laid the groundwork of muscle electrophysiology that was to be developed so exhaustively by du Bois-Reymond. Carlo Matteucci (88) was one of the prominent figures in the Risorgimento. A great liberal and a great patriot, he attempted to coordinate the efforts of all European liberals when the 1848 revolution broke out. When Italy was united in 1859, he was made a Senator. He was one of the early Ministers for Public Instruction in Italy. His contributions have never received adequate recognition, mainly owing to the acrimonious attacks made on his work by du Bois-Reymond who came near to diminishing his own stature by his sour polemics. Matteucci had raised the question as to where in the nerve-muscle

80. PFAFF, CHRISTOPHE-HENRI (1773–1858). Abhandlung über die sogennante thierische Electrizität. *Gren's J. Physik.* 8(2): 196, 1798.

81. FOWLER, RICHARD. *Experiments and observations relative to the influence lately discovered by M. Galvani, and commonly called Animal Electricity.* Edinburgh: Duncan, 1793.

82. VALLI, EUSÈBE (1755–1816). *Experiments in Animal Electricity.* London: Johnson, 1793.

83. SCHMUCK, EDMUND JOSEPH. *Beiträge zur neuern Kenntniss der thierische Elektricität.* Mannheim, 1792.

84. DE SAUSSURES, H. B. *Voyages dans les Alpes.* Neuchatel, 1796.

85. OERSTED, HANS CHRISTIAN (1777–1851). Expériences sur un effet que le courant de la pile excite dans l'aiguille aimantée. *J. Phys. Chim.* 91: 72, 1820; English translation in *Ann. Phil.* 16: 273, 1820. The earliest announcement of Oersted's discovery was in a four-page pamphlet (now rare) entitled *Experimenta circa effectum conflictus electrici in acum magneticum.* Copenhagen, 1820 (copy in the Wheeler collection, New York).

86. OERSTED, H. C. Galvanic magnetism. *Phil. Mag.* 56: 394, 1820.

87. NOBILI, C. LEOPOLD (1784–1835). Über einen neuen Galvanometer. *J. Chem. u. Phys.* 45: 249, 1825.

88. MATTEUCCI, CARLO (1811–1865). *Leçons sur les Phénomènes Physiques des Corps Vivants,* translated by Clet. Paris: Masson, 1847; English translation by Jonathan Periera. *Lectures on the physical phenomena of living beings.* Philadelphia: Lea and Blanchard, 1848.

FIG. 15. Johannes Müller and his famous pupil von Helm-holtz. The delicate chalk drawing of Müller was at one time in the Surgeon General's Library (now the National Library of Medicine). The picture of von Helmholtz shows him as a young man in the period when he made his major contribu-tions to the physiology of peripheral nerve.

preparation the electricity lay and had thought that muscle alone could produce it. The preparation used by Matteucci was a frog's leg complete be-low the knee with only the isolated nerve above it. Galvani's frogs retained a piece of the vertebral column with the insertion of the nerve into its portion of the spinal cord. Matteucci's contribu-tions in brief were a) the galvanometric detection of a current flow between the cut surface of a muscle and its undamaged surface, demonstrated in both animal and man (89, 90); b) the multiplication of current by serial arrangement of cut muscles so that the transverse section of each touched the longitudinal section of the next; c) the decrease in this current dur-ing tetanus caused by strychnine (90) (the germ of the

discovery of the action current); and d) the ability of a frog's muscle contraction to generate enough electricity to stimulate the nerve of another nerve-muscle preparation when laid across it (the rheo-scopic frog) (91, 92). Matteucci was inconsistent in his interpretation of this finding and showed his characteristic vacillation between an explanation in terms of electricity and one based on nervous force. He named the effect the 'secondary contraction.' Matteucci (93) also noted such important laboratory phenomena as the difference in stimulating effect of 'make' and 'break' shocks, and the polarizing effects of prolonged flow of current on electrodes. He noted that polarization could occur inside the muscle and thus laid the ground for all the work that was to follow on polarization and electrotonus.

du Bois-Reymond, of French name and Swiss descent, lived all of his working life in Berlin. He was a pupil of the greatest physiologist of the time, Johannes Müller. Müller, professor first at Bonn and then at Berlin, was a gifted teacher who could count among his pupils von Helmholtz, von Brücke and Sechenov. His *Handbuch der Physiologie* (94) was the great textbook of the nineteenth century, and the journal he founded, *Müller's Archives für Anatomie und Physiologie*, as a successor to Reil's first physiological journal, was the main outlet for the stream of research that was coming from the German schools at that time. His own interests lay mostly in sensory physiology where his name is always associated with the 'Law of Specific Nerve Energies,' although this concept in fragmentary form had certainly occurred to others before him, including notably Charles Bell[12] and John Hunter.[13] By this law Müller formulated the findings that wherever along its course a sensory nerve was stimulated, the resultant sensation was that appropri-ate to the sense organ it served. On the issue of elec-tricity in nerve, Müller took the position that it was indeed an artificial excitant but had no part in natural excitation. He reached this conclusion largely from an experiment in which he mashed the nerve and demon-

89. MATTEUCCI, C. Sur le courant électrique de la grenouille. *Ann. chim. et phys.* 68: 93, 1838.

90. MATTEUCCI, C. Deuxième mémoire sur le courant élec-trique propre de la grenouille et des animaux à sang chaud. *Ann. chim et phys.* 80: 301, 1842.

[12] ". . . while each organ of sense is provided with a capacity o. receiving certain changes to be played upon it, as it were, yet each is utterly incapable of receiving the impression destined for another organ of sensation." Quoted from Bell, Charles (1774-1842). *Idea of a new anatomy of the brain, submitted for the observation of his friends.* Privately printed, 1811.

[13] "It is more probable that every nerve so affected as to communicate sensation, in whatever part of the nerve the impression is made, always gives the same sensation as if affected at the common seat of the sensation of that particular nerve. . . ." Quoted in *The Works of John Hunter* edited by J. F. Palmer. London: Longmans, 1835. 4 vol.

91. MATTEUCCI, C. Sur une phénomène physiologique produite par les muscles en contraction. *Compt. rend. Acad. sc., Paris* 4: 797, 1842.

92. MATTEUCCI, C. AND F. H. A. HUMBOLDT. Sur le courant électrique des muscles des animaux vivants ou récemment tués. *Compt. rend. Acad. sc., Paris* 16: 197, 1843.

93. MATTEUCCI, C. *Compt. rend. Acad. sc., Paris* 52: 231, 1861; 53: 503, 1861; 56: 760, 1863; 65: 131, 1867.

94. MÜLLER, JOHANNES (1801-1858). *Handbuch der Physiologie des Menschen.* Coblentz: Hölscher, vol. I, 1833; vol. II, 1840; English translation by William Baly. vol. I, 1838; vol. II, 1842.

strated that, although electricity passed through the damaged zone, mechanical stimulation of the nerve above the injury provoked no twitch.

During the era of intense concentration on electrophysiology in the Italian and German schools, laboratories in other countries were developing a different approach. Among these was that of Claude Bernard (95), pupil of Magendie. Claude Bernard made use of curare as a blocking agent, interpreted by him as a nerve poison that spared the muscle. He found that in a curarized preparation the muscle would not twitch if he stimulated it directly and hence concluded that normally transmission could not be electrical either. In these experiments he used the ingenious little stimulator built from a Voltaic pile of alternate copper and zinc plates that is shown in figure 16. He did not recognize that his failure to evoke a contraction by direct stimulation of the muscle was due to his 'pile' giving too feeble a current.

Müller was the last of the great physiologists to retain a trace of vitalism in his thinking. This he probably owed to his exposure as a student at Bonn to Natürphilosophie and the influence of its leader, Schelling (96). Although more extensively indoctrinated in this sterile philosophy than Oersted had been, Müller was later able to free himself more easily from its stultifying effects, and he eagerly encouraged the physical and chemical approaches to biological experiment. Not a trace of vitalism is found in his pupils.

Towards the half-century a marked swing away from the metaphysics of Natürphilosophie characterized neurophysiology. du Bois-Reymond considered himself (and with some right) to be the champion of this movement which strove to explain all physiology on chemical and physical grounds. And in fact, as we have seen, it was the physicists of the period who were contributing most of the new experiments and concepts of muscle and peripheral nerve action. Before this, neurophysiologists had reached a stage in their work in which progress was hampered by lack of sufficiently sensitive instruments. The physicists came to their help and indeed were themselves intrigued by the types of physical phenomena that biological preparations provided.

In 1841 du Bois-Reymond received from his

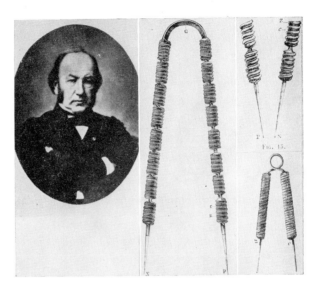

FIG. 16. Claude Bernard at the age of 53, and the ingenious stimulators he used in his electrophysiological studies of nerve. They were miniature voltaic piles built up of alternate discs of copper and zinc. Just before use they were moistened with vinegar. Such devices were made obsolete by the du Bois-Reymond induction coil and it is rather surprising to find Bernard still advocating them in his day. Although adequate for nerve stimulation, they gave too feeble a current to stimulate a muscle directly; from this Bernard concluded that the nervous effect on muscle could not be electrical.

master a copy of Matteucci's book *Essai sur les Phénomènes Électriques des Animaux* (97), together with the suggestion that he repeat and extend Matteucci's experiments. By November of that year he had already completed a preliminary note (98), but his major work, the *Thierische Elektricität* (99), did not appear until 1848. The first part of this long and detailed book, unlike its later sections, shows little originality in scientific ideas, the author with a chip on his shoulder being carried along in the wake of Matteucci of whose publications he was outspokenly critical. However, where du Bois-Reymond shines, and what makes his book a classic, is his skill in instrumentation, far surpassing that of Matteucci, so that he was able to extend and improve on these earlier observations. Moreover, not being hampered (as Matteucci was) by residual traces of a belief in

95. BERNARD, CLAUDE (1813–1878). *Leçons sur la physiologie et la pathologie du système nerveux.* Paris: Baillière, 1858. 2 vol.

96. SCHELLING, FREDERICK WILHELM JOSEPH (1775–1854). *Sammtliche Werke.* Stuttgart and Augsburg, 1856–1861, 14 vol.; English translation of vol. III by T. Davidson. In *J. Speculat. Philos.* 1: 193, 1867.

97. MATTEUCCI, C. *Essai sur les Phénomènes électriques des Animaux.* Paris: Carilian-Goeury and Dalmont, 1840.

98. DU BOIS-REYMOND, EMIL (1818–1896). Vorläufiger Abriss, einer Untersuchung über den elektromotorischen Fische. *Ann. Physik. Chem.* 58: 1, 1843.

99. DU BOIS-REYMOND, E. *Untersuchungen über thierische Elektricität.* Berlin: Reimer, vol. I, 1848; vol. II, 1849.

FIG. 17. du Bois-Reymond and one of the schemata he postulated for transmission at the end plate.

'nerve force,' he brought clearer inductive reasoning to the interpretation of his observations.

du Bois-Reymond confirmed Matteucci's demonstration that not only nerve-muscle preparations but muscles themselves could produce electricity and, with some acerbity, claimed priority for naming this the 'muscular current' (Muskelström). Both Matteucci and du Bois-Reymond distinguished muscular current from the 'frog current' (la correnta propria della rana), so named by Nobili to describe the current flow between the feet of the prepared frog and any other part of the animal. Neither Nobili (100) nor Matteucci, nor even du Bois-Reymond at this time, recognized that the so-called frog current was an injury current consequent to their having transsected their frogs. Nobili had thought it was a thermoelectric effect due to differential cooling times of nerve and muscle.

du Bois-Reymond, using faradic stimulation, also confirmed Matteucci's finding that the muscle current was reduced during tetanic stimulation and named this the negative variation. It is what is now called the action current of muscle. du Bois-Reymond went on to demonstrate the same negative variation in nerve during activity and thus discovered the action current of nerve which Matteucci had failed to find with his less sensitive instruments. du Bois-Reymond made the following claim, "If I do not greatly deceive myself, I have succeeded in realizing in full actuality (albeit under a slightly different aspect) the hundred years' dream of physicists and physiologists, to wit, the identity of the nervous principle with electricity." His great contemporary Carl Ludwig (101) was unwilling to accept this for, thinking still in terms of the nerve as a telegraph wire, he held

(among other objections) that its resistance was too great and its insulation too poor for it to be a good conductor.

Pflüger (102) tried to overcome some of these difficulties by his 'liberation hypothesis.' In this he stated that nervous transmission was "not a simple advancing undulation in which the sum of the living forces is not increased" but a situation in which "new tension forces are set free by the living forces of the stimulus and become in turn living forces with each onward step." In spite of the obscurity of the terminology (this is Morgan's translation), one can detect a foreshadowing of the ideas held by today's physiologists.

du Bois-Reymond elaborated a theory that all undamaged muscle had a resting potential between the middle (positive) and the tendons (negative) and that during activity this decreased, thus giving the 'negative variation.' He was still not clear on the role of injury currents for he thought injury merely intensified the resting potentials. On this point he entered into acrimonious dispute with his pupil Hermann who was equally stubborn in insisting that there were no resting potentials in the absence of injury and that all current flow in muscle and nerve was due to damage (103). Hermann therefore introduced the term 'demarcation currents' to describe them. Later experimentation has shown both men to have been partially right and partially wrong.

du Bois-Reymond's conception of regularly oriented 'electromotive particles' arranged along the surface of muscle and of nerve was the forerunner of the schemata of polarization that were to be developed more fully and more accurately by his pupil Bernsstein (104) and that lie at the core of modern theory. The critical issue as to whether the negative variation in nerve potential was identical with the excitatory process (i.e. the nerve impulse) was taken up by Bernstein who set out, at du Bois-Reymond's suggestion, to compare their velocities. von Helmholtz, one of the same brilliant group schooled in Müller's famous laboratory, had in a triumph over primitive apparatus succeeded in measuring the velocity of

100. NOBILI, L. *Ann. chim. et phys.* 38: 225, 1828; 44: 60, 1830.

101. LUDWIG, CARL (1816–1895). Über die Krafte der Nervenprimitivenrohr. *Wien. med. Wchnschr.* 46: 47, 1861.

102. PFLÜGER, E. (1829–1910). *Untersuchungen über die Physiologie des Electrotonus.* Berlin: Hirschwald, 1859.

103. HERMANN, LUDIMAR (1838–1914). Weitere Untersungen über die Ursache der electro-motorischen Erscheinungen an Muskeln und Nerven. *Arch. ges. Physiol.* 3: 15, 1870.

104. BERNSTEIN, JULIUS (1839–1917). *Untersuchungen über den Erregungsvorgang im Nerven- und Muskelsysteme.* Heidelberg: Winter, 1871.

the excitatory processes (105) in the frog. In his success he had proved his old teacher wrong. In 1844 Müller had said, "The time in which a sensation passes from the exterior of the brain and spinal cord and thence back to the muscle so as to produce a contraction, is infinitely small and immeasurable." von Helmholtz's technique was as follows: the moment of nerve stimulation, by the break shock of an induction coil, was signalled by the closing of the primary circuit. The resultant muscle contraction lifted a contact in the same circuit, thus breaking it. The break signalled the arrival of the nerve impulse in the muscle. By timing this interval, with stimulation at measured distances along the nerve, von Helmholtz was able to calculate its conduction velocity. This simplified description masks the extreme ingenuity of the original experiment. In technique von Helmholtz had come a long way from Haller's attempt to discover the velocity of nervous action. Haller had read parts of *The Aeneid* aloud, timing himself, counting the syllables and calculating the length of the nervous paths used in reading and speaking. In some way that is not entirely clear, he arrived at a figure of 50 m per sec.

The conduction rate found by Bernstein (approximately 29 m per sec.) tallied sufficiently well with von Helmholtz's final results, 27 to 30 m per sec., for him to be satisfied with the inferred identity of the impulse and the negative variation. Bernstein's experiments, using for stimulation a rheotome devised by himself with a galvanometer for detection of response, enabled him to plot the time course of what we now call the nerve's action potential and to determine its latency, rise-time and decay. One of the pregnant observations he made was that the negative variation caused a deflection of his galvanometer that sometimes crossed the base line, thus exceeding the value for the resting nerve potential. In today's terminology, he found the overshoot of the action potential beyond the resting potential level.

Bernstein (106) became widely known for his theory that the membrane of the inactive fiber of nerve or muscle was normally polarized, having positive ions on the outside and negative ions on the inside, and that the action potential was a self-propagating depolarization of this membrane. This was based on his assumption that the membrane is selectively permeable to potassium ions. His explanation of injury currents was that they were the result of a break in the membrane.

In the later nineteenth century, after a long hiatus, physiology in England was again coming into its own. At the half-century, which saw such brilliance in the German schools, there was virtually no physiological work in progress in England. There were no physiological laboratories and there was no systematic physiological research. A dual chair in anatomy and physiology had been created in 1836 at University College, London, and had been given to the anatomist William Sharpey. Such teaching as he gave in physiology was from books and his pupils saw no experiments, yet from among them came the leader of one of the more famous English schools of physiology, Michael Foster (1836–1907), founder of the Cambridge School. Though not himself a neurophysiologist, Foster could count among his pupils some to become later among the most brilliant in the field, Sherrington (1857–1952), Gaskell (1847–1914), Langley (1852–1925) and, as descendents from the last, Keith Lucas and in turn Adrian.

This, the late nineteenth century, was an age of great progress in the development of instrumentation and, with their improved tools, physiologists were able to make more accurate observations of stimulus strength, response characteristics and time relationships than had their predecessors. In 1871 Bowditch (107) demonstrated that heart muscle did not respond with graded contractions to graded stimuli. He assumed that the global response he observed was due to a leakage of excitation throughout the fiber population of cardiac muscle. It was in fact the experimental evidence for what was later to be called the 'all-or-nothing law.' Bowditch, an American, did these experiments in Ludwig's laboratory in Leipzig where he worked on the problem with Krönecker, the teacher of Harvey Cushing. On his return to Harvard, Bowditch founded the first laboratory for physiological research in the United States.

Forgotten by Bowditch, or unread, were the writings of Fontana in the eighteenth century in which, in discussing heart muscle, he said, ". . . the irritability of the fibre can be activated by a small cause, and by a feeble impression: but once activated, it has a power proportional to its own forces, which can be

105. VON HELMHOLTZ, H. (1821–1894). Messungen über den zeitlichen Verlauf der Zuchung animalischer Muskeln und die Fortpflanzungsgeschwindigkeit der Reizung in den Nerven. *Arch. Anat. Physiol.* 277, 1850.

106. BERNSTEIN, J. Über den zeitlichen Verlauf der negativen Schwankung des Nervenstroms. *Arch. ges. Physiol.* 1: 173, 1868.

107. BOWDITCH, H. P. (1840–1911). Über die Eigenthumlichkeiten der Reizbarkeit welche die Muskelfasern des Herzens zeigen. *Ber. Konigl. Sachs. Gesellsch. Wiss.* 23: 652, 1871.

much greater than those of the exciting cause. . . ."[14] Fontana (108) went on to a recognition of the refractory period (a term introduced by Marey) in heart muscle which he explained as an exhaustion of irritability resulting from the contraction.

That skeletal muscle might share this property was also foreshadowed by Fontana but did not receive experimental proof until the work of Fick (109), another pupil of Ludwig's, although the finding was not further developed until the ingenious experiments of Keith Lucas (110) at the beginning of this century. In the meantime, an all-or-nothing property in nerve had been detected by Gotch (111), the predecessor of Sherrington in the Chair of Physiology in Liverpool, a finding that was to reach definitive form in the hands of Keith Lucas' pupil, Adrian (112, 113). That the law applied to sensory as well as to motor nerves was established by Adrian & Forbes (114) in 1922 (in a paper whose title replaced the term 'all-or-none' by the more grammatical one 'all-or-nothing'). This line of work led on to investigations of the refractory period of peripheral nerve and the accurate plotting of the time course of after potentials. The invention of the vacuum tube amplifier and the cathode ray oscilloscope opened the modern era of electrophysiology, and with them the foundations of today's techniques were laid by Gasser & Erlanger (115).

One branch of peripheral nerve physiology remains to be outlined. This is the subject of neuromuscular transmission. Its history is short for, before the latter half of the nineteenth century, continuity between nerve and muscle was assumed, the neuron theory had not been formulated and neuroneural synapsis had not been conceived. The 1700-year-old hypothesis of a nervous fluid implied humoral transmission in structures having continuity and only at mid-nineteenth century, when this was finally abandoned, did the possibility of junctional tissues become a live one.

In 1862 Willy Kühne (116, 117), pupil of von Brücke and later professor of physiology in Heidelberg, published a memoir on the end organs of motor nerves. Noting the histological differences between muscle and its innervating nerve, he suggested that action currents of the nerve by invasion of the muscle caused it to contract. That there was a delay at the neuromuscular junction was noted in du Bois-Reymond's laboratory and the master himself considered the possibility of a chemical influence (the agents he mentioned were ammonia and lactic acid which Leibig had demonstrated in muscle in 1847); he went to great pains, however, to sketch electrical fields in support of what was called the 'modified discharge hypothesis' (as shown in fig. 17).

The controversy surrounding the mode of transmission at the motor end plate was carried into the modern era and, at a time not yet history, essential agreement was reached that transmission at the neuromuscular junction is chemical in nature. The major contribution that settled the issue came from pharmacological experimentation of today's scientists, stemming from the pioneer work of Elliott (118), Dale (119) and Loewi (120) in the early part of the century. Elliott, while a student at Cambridge, noticed that smooth muscle responded to adrenin even when deprived of its sympathetic nerves and this led him

108. FONTANA, FELICE GASPAR FERDINAND (1730–1805). *De Legibus Irritabilitatis.* Lucca: Riccomini, 1767.

109. FICK, ADOLF (1829–1901). *Mechanische Arbeit und Warmeentwicklung bei der Muskelthätigkeit.* Leipzig: Brockhaus, 1882.

110. LUCAS, K. The "all-or-none" contraction of amphibian skeletal muscle. *J. Physiol.* 38: 113, 1909.

111. GOTCH, FRANCIS (1853–1913). The sub-maximal electrical response of nerve to a single stimulus. *J. Physiol.* 28: 395, 1902.

112. ADRIAN, EDGAR D. (1889–   ). On the conduction of subnormal disturbances in normal nerve. *J. Physiol.* 45: 389, 1912.

113. ADRIAN, E. D. The "all-or-none" principle in nerve. *J. Physiol.* 47: 460, 1914.

114. ADRIAN, E. D. AND A. FORBES. All-or-nothing responses in sensory nerve fibres. *J. Physiol.* 56: 301, 1922.

115. GASSER, HERBERT S. (1888–   ) and JOSEPH ERLANGER (1874–   ). A study of the action currents of nerve with a cathode ray oscillograph. *Am. J. Physiol.* 62: 496, 1922.

116. KÜHNE, WILLY (1837–1900). *Über die peripherischen Endorgane der motorischen Nerven.* Leipzig: Engelmann, 1862.

117. KÜHNE, W. On the origin and causation of vital movement. *Proc. Roy. Soc., London. ser. B* 44: 427, 1888.

118. ELLIOTT, THOMAS RENTON (1877–   ). On the action of adrenaline. *J. Physiol.* 32: 401, 1905.

119. DALE, HENRY HALLETT (1875–   ). Transmission of nervous effects of acetylcholine. *Harvey Lectures* 32: 229, 1937.

120. LOEWI, OTTO (1873–   ). Über humorale Übertragbarkeit der Hertznervenwirkung. *Arch. ges. Physiol.* 189: 239, 1921.

[14] Quoted from Hoff, H. E. The history of the refractory period. *Yale J. Biol. & Med.* 14: 635, 1942.

to suggest that adrenin "might then be the chemical stimulant liberated on each occasion when the impulse arrives at the periphery." Langley (121), who was at that time professor of physiology at Cambridge, recognizing that in some smooth muscle the action both of sympathetic nerve stimulation and of adrenin was to produce contraction whereas in others the result was a relaxation, postulated the existence of two kinds of receptor substance—excitatory and inhibitory. That adrenin mimicked sympathetic action was then accepted.

The possibility of a chemical mediator for the vagal action on the heart was explored experimentally in several centers. Bottazzi (122), Martin (123) and Howell (124) thought the agent must be potassium, Dixon (125) that it was muscarine, an alkaloid closely related in structure to the cholines. These substances had been shown to be active in several puzzling ways. In 1906 Hunt & Taveau (126) had demonstrated the extremely potent effect of acetylcholine on arterial pressure, and by 1914 the work of Dale (127) was already pointing so strongly to acetylcholine being the drug involved in parasympathetic action, that he described it as 'parasympathomimetic.' Direct experimental proof was lacking that a chemical substance excreted as a result of nerve stimulation would in fact activate a tissue in a similar way, although the hypotheses both for epinephrine in the sympathetic and acetylcholine in the parasympathetic system seemed highly plausible.

The direct proof came from the brilliant researches of Otto Loewi (128) in which he demonstrated that

121. LANGLEY, JOHN NEWPORT (1852–1906). On the reaction of cells and of nerve-endings to certain poisons, chiefly as regards the reaction of striated muscles to nicotine and to curare. *J. Physiol.* 33: 374, 1905.

122. BOTTAZZI, P. *Arch. Physiol.* 882, 1896.

123. MARTIN, E. G. The inhibitory influence of potassium chloride on the heart, and the effect of variations of temperature upon this inhibition and upon vagus inhibition. *Am. J. Physiol.* 11: 370, 1904.

124. HOWELL, W. H. Vagus inhibition of the heart in its relation to the inorganic salts of the blood. *Am. J. Physiol.* 15: 280, 1906.

125. DIXON, W. E. On the mode of action of drugs. *Med. Mag.* 16: 454, 1907.

126. HUNT, R. AND R. DE M. TAVEAU. On the physiological action of certain cholin derivatives and new methods for detecting cholin. *Brit. M. J.* 2: 1788, 1906.

127. DALE, H. H. The action of certain esters and ethers of choline, and their relation to muscarine. *J. Pharmacol. & Exper. Therap.* 6: 147, 1914.

128. LOEWI, O. Über humorale Übertragbarkeit Herznervenwirkung. *Arch. ges. Physiol.* 189: 239, 1921.

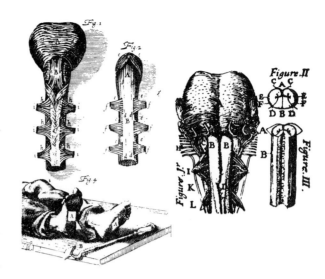

FIG. 18. *Left:* an early representation of spinal roots and tracts as drawn by Domenico Mistichelli in his *Trattato dell'Apoplessia*, 1709 (from the copy in the Boston Medical Library by courtesy of Dr. Henry Viets). Mistichelli is considered to be one of the first workers to recognize the crossing of the pyramids. *Right:* the crossing of the pyramids was described and experimentally demonstrated on injury to the brain in dogs by Pourfour du Petit, a pupil of Duverney. His drawings are from his *Lettres d'un médicin*, 1727. (From the copy in the Bibliothèque Nationale. Reproduction by courtesy of Dr. Auguste Tournay.)

the fluid bathing a frog's heart which had been stimulated through its vagus had an inhibitory action on the beat of another heart. He named the agent 'Vagusstoffe.' From this classic observation, one of the landmarks of physiology, experimentation spread out to the examination of other tissues, other nerves, and other mediators and inhibitors, and forms one of the wide fields of today's research. With the recognition of neuroneural synapses the problem of transmission was carried from the peripheral neuromuscular system into the central nervous system.

SPINAL CORD AND REFLEX ACTIVITY

The functions of the spinal cord long remained an enigma to the early physiologists. For as long as the belief persisted that every nerve in the body required its own canal leading directly from the brain in order to insure its supply of animal spirits, the spinal cord appeared to be merely a bundle of nerve fibers grouped together. In other words, it was a prolongation of the peripheral nervous system channeling into the brain.

The relationship of the spinal cord to peripheral nerves and to the rest of the central nervous system could hardly be understood until the structure of the neuron had been learned. The period that saw the great development of knowledge of cell structure came with the high-power microscopes of the nineteenth century. Before then descriptions of the finer elements necessarily lacked exactness, though in 1767 Fontana had given a good account[15] of the axis cylinder, and there seems little reason to doubt that the bodies Alexander Monro (129) saw in the spinal cord in 1783 were the anterior horn cells. Nerve cells were certainly seen by Dutrochet (130) in 1824 though we do not find a very exact description of them before 1833, when Ehrenberg (131, 132) published his findings on the spinal ganglia of the frog.

The visualization of axis cylinders on the one hand, and of cell bodies on the other, still did not help the physiologist very much in his search for understanding of nervous connections. It was from the botanists that the next lead came. The cell theory had a long history among plant physiologists and its emphasis on the role of the nucleus and the cellular matrix appealed to microscopists who could see similar structures in animal tissues. In 1837 Purkinje (133), working at home for lack of a laboratory at the University of Breslau where he was professor, realized the significance of the observations on plant tissues and suggested that the cell theory might justifiably be extended from botany to zoology. Two years later Schwann (134) marshalled the facts and crystallized the idea in his classic monograph.

For an understanding of function, knowledge of the cell bodies was not enough. The nerve tracts were of primary importance, and during this same period histologists were finding that the medullated axon was not the only kind of fiber. In 1838, in a little book that was one of the last scientific texts to be published in Latin, Remak (135) revealed the existence of nonmedullated nerves. His work is illustrated by many delicate drawings of cells from various parts of the nervous system, mostly taken from ox and man. But by 1865 physiologists knew that in addition to medullated and nonmedullated nerves there were other fibrous processes which Dieter's (136) work (published posthumously) showed to be dendrites. In the same monograph there is a description of the glia. The cell theory did not explain how all these fibrous structures related to the cell body, and a student's thesis was one of the early publications to take this step. In 1842 von Helmholtz (137), in the earliest of the many brilliant contributions he made to physiology, established the connection between peripheral nerve and ganglia in invertebrates using the crab. von Helmholtz was 21 years old when he wrote this inaugural thesis.

The next major advance came in 1850 from Waller (138) with his demonstration that axons degenerate when cut off from their cell bodies and his conclusion that the latter were their source of nutriment. The development by Marchi & Algeri (139) of the osmic acid stain for degenerating myelin sheaths gave the physiologist a technique for tracing the nerve tracts.

129. MONRO, ALEXANDER (secundus) (1733–1817). *Observations on the structure and functions of the nervous system.* Edinburgh: Creech, 1783.
130. DUTROCHET, RENÉ JOACHIM HENRI (1776–1847). *Recherches anatomiques et physiologiques sur la structure intime des animaux et des végétaux.* Paris: Baillière, 1824.
131. EHRENBERG. C. G. Notwendigkeit einer feineren mechanischen Zerlegung des Gehirns und der Nerven. *Ann. Physik. u. Chem.* 104: 449, 1833.
132. EHRENBERG, C. G. *Beobachtung einer unbekannten Structur des Seelesorgans.* Berlin, 1836.
133. PURKINJE, JOHANN EVANGELISTA (1787–1869). Über die gangliöse Natur bestimmter Hirntheile. *Ber. Versamml. deutsch. Naturforsch. Artze, Prague* 1837, p. 175.
134. SCHWANN, THEODORE (1810–1882). *Mikroskopische Untersuchungen über die Übereinstimmung in der Struktur und dem Wachsthum der Thiere und Pflanzen.* Berlin: Sander, 1839; English translation by Sydenham Society, 1847.
135. REMAK, ROBERT (1815–1865). *Observationes anatomicae et microscopicae de systematis nervosi structura.* Berlin: Reimer, 1838.
136. DIETERS, OTTO FRIEDRICH KARL (1821–1863). *Untersuchungen über Gehirn und Rückenmark des Menschen und der Säugetiere.* Brunswick: Vieweg, 1863.
137. VON HELMHOLTZ, H. *De Fabrica systematis nervosi Evertebratorum* (Inaugural Thesis). 1842.
138. WALLER, AUGUSTUS VOLNEY (1816–1870). Experiments on the section of the glossopharyngeal and hypoglossal nerves of the frog, and observations of the alterations produced thereby in the structure of their primitive fibres. *Phil. Trans.* 140: 432, 1850.
139. MARCHI, V. AND C. ALGERI. Sulle degenerazioni discendenti consecutive a lesioni della corteccia cerebrale. *Riv. sper. Fremat* II: 492, 1835.

[15] "Le nerf est formé d'un grand nombre de cylindres transparents, homogènes, uniformes, très-simples. Ces cylindres paroissent formés, comme d'une paroi, ou tunique très subtile, uniforme, remplie, autant l'oeil peut enjuger, d'une humeur transparente, gélatineuse, insoluble dans l'eau. Chacun de ces cylindres reçoit une enveloppe en forme de gaine extérieure, la quelle est composée d'un nombre immense de fils torteux." Fontana. *Traité sur le venin de la Vipère.* Florence, 1781. 2 vol.

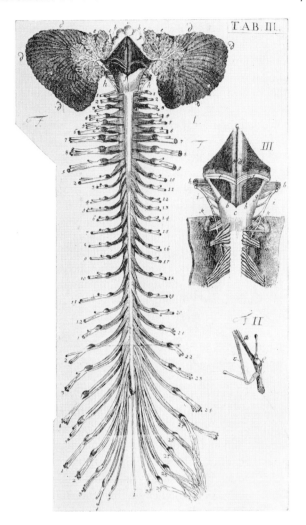

FIG. 19. *Left:* Jiri Prochaska of Prague, the proponent of automatic reflexion in the medulla and spinal cord. *Right:* Prochaska's illustration of the spinal roots and their ganglia.

The definitive study of the relationship of the medullated axon to the nerve cell followed in 1889 and was the work of von Kölliker (140), professor of anatomy in Wurzburg. From this wealth of accumulated knowledge, a generalized concept of neuron behavior became possible and in 1891 a clear formulation was achieved by Waldeyer-Hartz (141). The neuron theory was established. In reviewing these basic steps that had to be taken before any unravelling of central nervous system pathways could proceed with certainty, one is struck by the fact that so many of the contributors (Schwann, Remak, von Helmholtz, Kölliker) were pupils of Johannes Müller.

Another of the early stumbling blocks to an understanding of the spinal cord was the differentiation of motor and sensory function. It was early suspected that the ganglia of the spinal roots were in some way involved in this question. Galen had thought that the presence of a ganglion indicated that the nerve was powerfully motor in action and here the matter rested for some centuries. In 1783 Alexander Monro (129) noted that the spinal ganglia were formed on the

posterior roots and that their coalescence with the anterior roots occurred peripherally to these swellings. But like Galen he thought that they were concerned with 'muscular' nerves and defended them as such against the suggestion by James Johnstone (142) that their action was to cut off sensation. This rather bizarre concept had received some consideration in the mid-eighteenth century.

The presence of ganglia suggested to several minds a specialization of function in the nerves on which they were formed. Both Prochaska (143) and Soemmering (144) had drawn attention to the re-

140. VON KÖLLIKER, RUDOLF ALBERT (1817–1905). *Mikroskopische Anatomie.* Leipzig, 1850–1854.
141. WALDEYER-HARTZ, HEINRICH WILHELM GOTTFRIED (1836–1921). Über einige neuere Forschungen im Gebiete der Anatomie des Centralnervensystems. *Deutsche med. Wchnschr.* 17: 1213, 1244, 1287, 1331, 1352, 1891.

142. JOHNSTONE, JAMES (1730–1802). Essay on the use of the ganglions of the nerves. *Phil. Trans.* 54: 177, 1765.
143. PROCHASKA, JIRI (1749–1820). *De Structura Nervorum.* Prague: Gerle, 1780–1784. 3 vol.
144. SOEMMERING, SAMUEL THOMAS (1755–1830). *De basi encephali et originibus nervorum cranio egredientum.* Göttingen: Vandenhoeck, 1778.

semblance between the ganglia of the fifth cranial nerves and those of the posterior roots, and Bichat (145), the brilliant French pathologist who died so young, had gone so far as to associate all ganglia with the nervous processes of involuntary, unconscious 'organic' life.

The differentiation between the ganglia found in the sympathetic nervous system and those on the roots of the central nervous system was to come later. Charles Bell made the distinction but admitted he did not know what role was played by the sympathetic nerves or by their ganglia (146). His many studies on the fifth and seventh cranial nerves (146-148), illustrated by his own beautiful drawings, are classics, and his demonstrations of the function in the nerves of the face are perpetuated in the name Bell's palsy. Bell had come from Edinburgh to the famous anatomical school that William Hunter had founded in Great Windmill Street near Piccadilly. A brilliant dissector but not primarily an experimentalist, Bell relied heavily on his brother-in-law, John Shaw, in this aspect of his work and suffered a great loss when Shaw died.

In the cord the various columns had been dissected by the anatomists and the grouping together of nerves in such large bundles had certainly seemed suggestive of parcellation of function. But not all anatomists were agreed. Bichat on dissecting out some nerve filaments found them centrally located in the lower cord but more lateral higher up. He therefore concluded that although the filaments had individual properties, the fasciculi were mixed. The idea persisted, however, that the columns and also the spinal roots might have different functions according to whether they were anterior or posterior. An early idea was that the anterior roots carried both motor and sensory supplies for the muscles while the posterior roots gave a sensory service for the skin. An Edinburgh anatomist, Alexander Walker (149), suspected that they might serve separate roles but unfortunately picked the posterior root as the motor and the anterior root as sensory.

In 1811 a small pamphlet was privately printed, entitled *Idea of a new anatomy of the brain submitted for the observation of his friends*. The author was Charles Bell (150). This pamphlet had no general distribution, no more than 100 copies being printed. (Only three are known to exist today, one of which is in the National Library of Medicine in Washington; in England, copies can be seen at the British Museum and at the Royal Society.) Bell stated that the purpose of this pamphlet was to assure his friends that in his dissections of the brain he was investigating its structure and not searching for the seat of the soul. In this work he stated his opinion that nerves owe their differences in properties to their being connected to different parts of the brain. He said that, holding this opinion, he wondered whether the double roots of the spinal nerves might indicate that "nerves of different endowments were in the same cord, and held together by the same sheath." To test this idea experimentally, he cut "across the posterior fasciculus" and noted that there were no convulsive movements of the muscles of the back; but that on touching the anterior fasciculus with the point of a knife, the muscles of the back were immediately convulsed. From this experiment he concluded at that time, "The spinal nerves being double, and having their roots in the spinal marrow, of which a portion comes from the cerebrum and a portion from the cerebellum, they convey the attributes of both grand divisions of the brain to every part, and therefore the distribution of such nerves is simple, one nerve supplying its distinct part."

It may be noted that there is in this pamphlet no suggestion that the posterior columns or roots might be sensory in function. Bell considered the cerebellum to be concerned with involuntary and unconscious functions ("the secret operation of the bodily frame" and "the operation of the viscera") whereas he recognized the cerebrum "as the grand organ by which the mind is united with the body. Into it all the nerves from the external organs of the senses enter; and from it all the nerves which are agents of the will pass out."

145. BICHAT, MARIE FRANCOIS XAVIER (1771–1802). *Anatomie générale, appliquée à la physiologie et à la médecine.* Paris: Brosson, 1801, 2 vol.; English translation by G. Hayward. Boston: Richardson and Lord, 1822. 3 vol.

146. BELL, CHARLES (1774–1842). *The Nervous System of the Human Body as explained in a series of papers read before the Royal Society of London.* Edinburgh: Black, 1836.

147. BELL, C. On the nerves; giving an account of some experiments on their structure and functions, which lead to a new arrangement of the system. *Phil. Trans.* 111: 398, 1821.

148. BELL, C. Of the nerves which associate the muscles of the chest in the actions of breathing, speaking, and expression. Being a continuation of the paper on the structure and functions of the nerves. *Phil. Trans.* 112: 284, 1822.

149. WALKER, ALEXANDER (1779–1852). New anatomy and physiology of the brain in particular, and of the nervous system in general. *Arch. Universal Sc.* 3: 172, 1809.

150. BELL, C. *Idea of a new anatomy of the brain submitted for the observation of his friends.* Privately printed, 1811; reproduced in J. F. Fulton. *Selected Readings in the History of Physiology.* Springfield: Thomas, 1930, p. 251.

In essence, therefore, Bell regarded the cerebellum, posterior columns and posterior spinal roots as concerned with unconscious impressions and involuntary movements; the cerebrum, anterior columns and anterior roots as conveying conscious sensation and willed movements.

On July 22, 1822, François Magendie, member of the Academy of Sciences of Paris (and later to be professor at the Collège de France), read a paper (151) to the Academy as a result of which the following entry was made: "M. Magendie reports the discovery he has recently made, that if the posterior roots of the spinal nerves are cut, only the sensation of those nerves is abolished, and if the anterior roots are cut, only the movements they cause are lost." This report was followed by a fuller account (152, 153) in the journal that Magendie himself had founded. The experiments, made on puppies which survived the surgical procedures, gave Magendie the confidence to state "that the anterior and posterior roots of the nerves which arise from the spinal marrow, have different functions, that the posterior appear more particularly destined to sensibility, whilst the anterior seem more especially allied to motion."

In spite of his not having suggested a function of conscious sensation for the posterior roots in either the privately printed pamphlet or published papers (147) on the fifth and seventh cranial nerves, Bell with a questionable lack of scruple claimed full priority and engaged in a wrangle that invaded the scientific journals for many years. This carried the unpleasant flavor of evidence twisted by hindsight. Bell's 'republications' in 1824 (154) of his earlier writings contained subtle changes in wording that deceived his supporters into believing his claims to be better founded than they were.[16] Among those hoodwinked were Flourens and, at first, Magendie's pupil, Claude Bernard. Posterity gives each some credit by pre-

FIG. 20. The protagonists in the Bell-Magendie controversy. Bell (*left*) and Magendie (*right*) as young men. The portrait of Bell was painted by Antony Stewart of Edinburgh in 1804; that of Magendie (attributed to Guérin) is at the Collège de France.

serving the nomenclature of the Bell-Magendie Law. In spite of his claims, Bell made no move to get experimental proof of the function of the posterior roots and as late as 1832 (155) was stressing that their sensory nature was only inferred. He said in his lectures to the Royal College of Physicians, ". . . as we have proved the anterior column to be the origin of the motor nerves, we may infer the posterior roots are those which render the entire nerve a nerve of sensation." In 1844 Johannes Müller (156) confirmed the law experimentally, something Bell had never done, but the conclusion seems inescapable that the concept in its complete form as well as its experimental proof was first contributed by Magendie.

Magendie, whose youth coincided with the French Revolution, came from surgery into physiology where his urge towards experimentation could give him greater satisfaction. So strongly empiricist was he that he rarely made generalizations from his observations

151. MAGENDIE, FRANÇOIS (1783–1855). Procès-verb, 1822. *Acad. Sc.* 7: 348, 1820–1823.

152. MAGENDIE, F. Expériences sur les fonctions des racines des nerfs rachidiens. *J. physiol. expér. et path.* 2: 276, 1822.

153. MAGENDIE, F. Expériences sur les fonctions des racines des nerfs qui naissent de la moelle épinière. *J. physiol. expér. et path.* 2: 366, 1822. [References 152 and 153 can be read in English in Alexander Walker's translations in: *Documents and dates of modern discoveries in the nervous system* (Pub. anonymously). London: Churchill, 1839.]

154. BELL, C. *An Exposition of the Natural System of the Nerves of the Human Body with a Republication of the Papers Delivered to the Royal Society, on the Subject of Nerves.* London: Spottiswoode, 1824.

155. BELL, C. Lectures on the physiology of the brain and nervous system. Reported in: *Ryan's Med. Surg. J.* 1: 682, 752, 1832.

156. MÜLLER, J. Bestutigung des Bell'schen Lehrsatzes. Notiz. a. d. Geb. d. natur- u. heilk. (Weimar) 30: 113, 1831; this is more readily available in French in *Ann. Sc. Natur.* 23: 95, 1831, and a section is translated into English in W. Stirling. *Some Apostles of Physiology.* London: Waterlow, 1902.

[16] For a detailed comparison of the texts see Flint, A. Considérations historiques sur les propriétés des racines des nerfs rachidiens. *J. de l'anat. et de physiol.* 5: 520, 1868.

in the laboratory which were many and varied. His work on the spinal roots led him to follow the differentiation of function into the spinal tracts where he found that pressure on the posterior columns, but not on the anterior, caused signs of pain. One other aspect of Magendie's work on the spinal cord should be mentioned, his rediscovery of the cerebrospinal fluid (157). Sixty years earlier this had been seen and described by Cotugno (158), at that time a young physician in the Hospital for Incurables in Naples, but his monograph had stirred no general interest though it helped to win him the chair of anatomy at the university. Magendie described the foramen known by his name, but oddly revived a valve-like role for the pineal as controller of this opening. He thought the fluid was secreted by the arachnoid membrane, and it was many years later that its origin in the choroid plexuses was discovered. A later pamphlet by Magendie (159) on the cerebrospinal fluid has some fine illustrations by H. Jacob.

Once the differentiation of function between the anterior and posterior roots had been accepted, the finer points as to which regions were innervated by their fibers began to occupy the physiologists. The question as to whether all the fibers of an anterior root served the same or many muscles was paralleled by its corollary as to whether one muscle received fibers from one or many roots. That the last arrangement is the correct one was first clearly shown by Eckhardt (160) in frogs and by Peyer (161) in rabbits. Both were working in Carl Ludwig's laboratory. The definitive demonstrations came later from Sherrington's (162) careful analyses, mostly in the monkey, from which he concluded that "the position of the nerve-cells sending motor fibres to any one skeletal muscle is a scattered one, extending throughout the whole length of the spinal segments innervating that muscle."

Tracing of the fibers of the sensory roots was intrinsically more difficult. Türck's (163) studies in Vienna had indicated the complexity of sensory innervation in the dog, and Herringham (164) had found the segmental relationship with the vertebrae; but again it was Sherrington (165) who, using the reflex as criterion of the existence of afferent fibers, unravelled the phenomena of overlapping of segmental cutaneous innervation. Until the time of Sherrington it had been thought that the motor fibers to a given muscle were derived from the same spinal segment that received the sensory inflow from the skin surrounding it. This was particularly the view of Krause (166). Sherrington's mapping of myotomes and dermatomes showed this rule to be erroneous.

Sherrington's development of a comprehensive theory of reflex action could scarcely have been envisaged before the sensory endings in muscle had been discovered. This advance was mainly the work of Ruffini (167, 168) who in 1892 identified as sensory organs muscle spindles, tendon organs and Pacinian (169) corpuscles. These structures had been seen and described by others, but their function had not been appreciated. The need for an apparatus for muscle sense had been felt by Charles Bell (170) in order to convey "a sense of the condition of the muscles to the brain," and he postulated "a circle of nerves," saying that "every muscle has two nerves, of different properties supplied to it." That sensations are aroused by

157. MAGENDIE. Mémoire sur la liquide qui se trouve dans le crâne et canal vertébral de l'homme et des animaux mammifières. *J. physiol. expér. et path.* 5: 27, 1825.

158. COTUGNO, DOMENICO (1736–1822). *De Ischiade Nervosa Commentarius.* Naples: Simonios, 1764; a portion has been translated into English. *A Treatise on the Nervous Sciatica, or Nervous Hip Gout.* London: Wilkie, 1775, p. 14.

159. MAGENDIE, F. *Récherches physiologiques et cliniques sur le liquide céphalorachidien ou cérébro-spinal.* Paris: Mequignon-Marvis, 1842.

160. ECKHARDT, C. Über Reflexbewegungender vier letzten Nervenpaare des Frosches. *Ztschr. rat. Med.* (1st series) 1: 281, 1849.

161. PEYER, J. Über die peripherischen Endigungen der motorischen und sensibelen Fasern der in den Plexus brachialis des Kaninchens eintretenden Nerven wurzeln. *Ztschr. rat. Med.* (1st series) 4: 67, 1853.

162. SHERRINGTON, CHARLES SCOTT (1857–1952). Notes on the arrangement of some motor fibres in the lumbosacral plexus. *J. Physiol.* 13: 621, 1892.

163. TÜRCK, LUDWIG (1810–1868). Über die Haut-Sensibilitätsbewirke der enzelnen Rückenmarksnervenpaare. *Denkschr. Akad. Wiss.* 29: 299, 1868.

164. HERRINGHAM, W. P. The minute anatomy of the brachial plexus. *Proc. Roy. Soc., London.* ser. B 41: 423, 1887.

165. SHERRINGTON, C. S. Experiments in examination of the peripheral distribution of the fibres of the posterior roots of some spinal nerves. *Phil. Trans.* 184 B: 641, 1894.

166. KRAUSE, FEDOR (1856–1937). *Beiträge zur Neurologie der oberen Extremität.* Leipzig, 1865.

167. RUFFINI, ANGELO. Di una particolare reticella nervosa e di alcuni corpuscoli del Pacini che si trovano in concessione cogli organi musculo tendinei del gatto. Atti R. Accad. Lincei 1: 12, 1889; French translation in: Sur un réticule nerveux spécial et sur quelques corpuscles de Pacini qui se trouvent en connexion avec les organes musculo-tendineux du chat. *Arch. ital. biol.* 18: 101, 1893.

168. RUFFINI, A. Observations on sensory nerve endings in voluntary muscles. *Brain* 20: 368, 1897.

169. PACINI, FILIPPO (1812–1883). *Nuovi organi scoperti nel corpo humani.* Pistoja: Cino, 1840.

170. BELL, C. On the nervous circle which connects the voluntary muscles with the brain. *Phil. Trans.* 2: 172, 1826.

movements of the limbs is an observation that goes back at least to Descartes' posthumous treatise (171), but that the act of volition in itself could also be 'felt' was an idea espoused by some, including, rather surprisingly, von Helmholtz.[17] But a peripheral rather than a central mechanism had more adherents for, like Bichat, they thought that muscles must be sensitive.

Infiltrating the early work on spinal cord physiology is the gradual development of the idea of the reflex. The eventual emergence of a concept of reflex activity grew out of centuries of attempts to explain animal movements, motion receiving more attention than sensation for it was considered to be the sign of life. Galen had regarded movements as three in kind: natural (such as the pulse), governed by the heart; voluntary, governed by the soul (located in the brain); and unconscious movements of voluntary muscles (such as in respiration). Involuntary muscle was unknown even in the days of Fernel (172) and Descartes (173), both of whom emphasized a distinction between movements dictated by reason and those due to the appetites. The ideas of Fernel and of Descartes have both long been regarded as forerunners of the concept of reflex activity. The claims for Fernel rest on his observation of automatic movements, some of which we now know to be reflexly initiated; but the peripheral origin or the stimulus that caused them was not recognized by him. An ardent supporter of Descartes as the originator was du Bois-Reymond (174) who stressed this claim in his eulogy of Müller, written at the time of the latter's death.

The first suggestion that perhaps the spinal cord could be a center for communication between nerves was made by Thomas Willis (175) who came very close to picturing the reflex. He thought that all voluntary movements came from the cerebrum, all involuntary from the cerebellum and that they were ruled by a soul that resided both in the blood and in the nervous fluid. For Willis the medulla was an appendix of the brain which he likened to a musical organ (30) taking air into its bellows (i.e. animal spirits from the brain) in order to blow them out into the appropriate organ pipes (the nerves). Elsewhere (176) Willis showed his interest in the organ as a musical instrument and gave some description of it.

Where Willis came close to describing reflex action was in stating that sense impressions carried by the animal spirits to the sensorium commune (which he put in the corpus striatum) went on to higher levels of the cerebrum where they were perceived and formed into memories. Some, however, were reflected back towards the muscles ('species alia reflexa'). Although the resultant movement was automatic and although one might be unaware of the sensory stimulus, Willis held that one was conscious of the resultant muscular effect. The example he gives is irritation of the stomach causing vomiting, and it is noticeable that Willis's discussion of 'reflexes' comes in his chapter on knowledge and recognition.

Willis used 'motus reflexus' and the verb 'refluere' in making this proposition and the terms were used again by Baglivi (177) who refers to him. Their usage of 'reflexus' reads as though it were closer to the modern term than Descartes' 'esprits refléchis'.[18] Across the centuries the changing nuances of word meanings make it impossible to catch the exact connotation intended by an author, but Descartes' interest in the reflection of light rays suggests that this may have been the analogy he had in mind.

A mechanism for the mediation of involuntary movements was not the only one for which physiologists were searching. The early workers were much exercised by what they termed 'the sympathy of parts' for they recognized an integration of body mechanisms that eluded nervous influence flowing only from the brain. Some suggested an interaction taking place peripherally in a plexus, an anastomosis of the sensory and motor nerve endings. Winslow (178),

171. DESCARTES, R. *Traité de l'Homme*, first French ed. 1664, chapt. 77.

172. FERNEL, J. *De Naturali Parte Medicinae* (1st ed.). Paris: Simon de Colines, 1542; 2nd ed. *Physiologia.* 1554.

173. DESCARTES, R. *Traité de l'Homme*, first French ed. 1664.

174. DU BOIS-REYMOND, E. *Gedächnissrede auf Johannes Müller.* Berlin, 1858; reprinted in *Reden*, vol. 2. Leipzig: Veit, 1887.

175. WILLIS, THOMAS (1621–1675). *De Anima Brutorum (De Scientia seu Cognitione brutorum).* London: Davis, 1672.

176. Ibid., chapt. 6.

177. BAGLIVI, GIORGIO (1668–1707). *De fibra motrice.* 1700, book 1, chapt. 5.

178. WINSLOW, JAMES BENIGNUS (1669–1760). *Exposition anatomique de la structure du corps humain.* Paris: Duprez and Desessartz, 1732, pt. VI (illustrated by plates from Bartolomeo Eustachius (1520–1574). *Tabulae anatomicae.* Rome: Gonzaga, 1714); English translation by G. Douglas. Edinburgh: Donaldson & Elliot, 1772. 2 vol.

[17] In discussing the sensation of outward movement of an eyeball the external rectus of which is paralyzed, he says, "We feel, then what impulse of the will, and how strong a one, we apply to turn the eye to a given position." von Helmholtz, H. *Handbuch der physiologischen Optik.* Leipzig: Voss, 1867, parts translated into English by William James in his *Principles of Psychology.*

[18] Descartes used this term only once, in *Passions de l'Âme*

working in Paris and later in Copenhagen, thought he had found the clue in the ganglia of the sympathetic chain. These he envisaged as small brains in which intercommunication between nerves could take place, effecting sympathy between various visceral organs. "These ganglions . . . may be looked upon," he said, "as so many origins or germina dispersed through this great pair of nerves, and consequently as so many little brains." This ingenious but erroneous theory has left its name on the structures, the sympathetic ganglia. Winslow illustrated his text with the fine plates of Eustachius that had lain for so long unnoticed in the Vatican Library. These plates do not however show the 'small brains.'

In following the early ideas about 'sympathy between the parts' it must be remembered that, although so much emphasis was laid on the humors by early physiologists, endocrines were unknown and consequently their influence could not be invoked. There were, however, all down the centuries, some who held that the blood was the great integrator. In the eighteenth century, for example, John Hunter (179) was teaching that the blood was the agent of sympathy.[19] He was drawn to this view from his work on inflammation and fevers arising from gunshot wounds in the soldiers he cared for as an army surgeon in the Seven Years' War with France.

Only slowly did the concept of reflex activity gain ground. Hunter's contemporary and fellow Scot, Robert Whytt, was accumulating observations and making experiments that are fundamental to modern physiology, although his descriptions of them are also often cloaked by his terminology. In the first place (180), he recognized the involuntary nature of pupillary contraction and dilation and demonstrated the dependence of this action on the integrity of the corpora quadrigemina, thus anticipating the work of Herbert Mayo (181) in the next century. He went on

to the study of involuntary movements of voluntary muscle systems in decapitated animals. The movements of animals after their heads had been severed was common knowledge to every housewife who had ever killed a chicken and had attracted the attention of scientists since Leonardo's day. Even in the seventeenth century Boyle (182) had recognized the implications of these phenomena, realizing that "these may be of great concernment in reference to the common doctrine of the necessity of unceasing influence from the brain, being so requisite to sense and motion." Boyle's curiosity about the brain and its workings was interwoven with his great interest in theology, although his views on the latter did not please the theologians. Dean Swift was even moved to parody them in a satire called *A Pious Meditation upon a Broomstick in the Style of the Honourable Mr. Boyle.*

Glisson (62) had also distinguished between 'willed' movements and those of decapitated animals. He thought the latter analogous to a class of movements depending on a lower form of perception not reaching the mind. One might become aware of them (*perceptio sensitiva*) but they were not ruled by the mind as were voluntary movements (*perceptio perceptionis*).

Whytt's experiments (183) carried the argument farther for he showed that this type of involuntary motion could not be explained as due to the innate irritability of muscle tissue (Haller's *vis insita*), for preservation of the spinal marrow was essential for it. He was, however, not the first to discover that the spinal cord was essential for this type of movement. He had been anticipated by the Reverend Stephen Hales, whose many and brilliant physiological experiments make one wonder how much time he gave to his parishioners in Teddington. Whytt gives full credit to Hales, for he says, "The late reverend and learned Dr. Hales informed me that having many years since tied a ligature about the neck of a frog to prevent any effusion of blood, he cut off its head . . . the frog also at this time moved its body when stimulated, but that on thrusting a needle down the spinal marrow, the animal was strongly convulsed and immediately after became motionless." Alexander Stuart (184) repeated

179. Hunter, John (1728–1793). *Treatise on the Blood, Inflammation and Gunshot Wounds.* London: Nicol, 1794.

180. Whytt, Robert (1714–1766). *An essay on the vital and other involuntary motions of the animal.* Edinburgh: Hamilton, Balfour and Neill, 1751.

181. Mayo, Herbert (1796–1852). *Anatomical and Physiological Commentaries.* London: Underwood, vol. I, 1822; vol. II, 1823.

---

[19] Samuel Taylor Coleridge's comment on some of John Hunter's writings is perhaps a little harsh: "The light which occasionally flashes upon us seems at other times, to struggle through an unfriendly medium, and even sometimes to suffer a temporary occultation." Coleridge, S. T. *Hints towards the Formation of a more Comprehensive Theory of Life.* Philadelphia: Lea & Blanchard, 1848.

182. Boyle, Robert (1627–1691). *Considerations touching on the Usefulness of Experimental Natural Philosophy.* London 1663.

183. Whytt, R. *Observations on the Nature, Causes and Cure of those Disorders which are commonly called Nervous, Hypochondriac, or Hysteric, to which are prefixed some remarks on the sympathy of the nerves.* Edinburgh: Balfour, 1765.

184. Stuart, A. *Three lectures on muscular motion, read before the Royal Society in the year MDCCXXXVIII.* London Woodward, 1739.

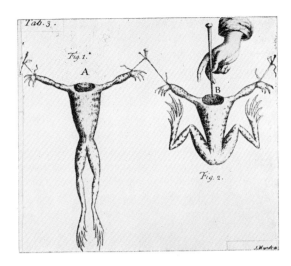 

FIG. 21. *Left:* Alexander Stuart's experiment confirming the observations of Stephen Hales that a decapitated frog convulses on being pithed and then becomes immobile. (From Stuart, A. *Croonian Lectures 1738*. London: Woodward, 1739.) *Right:* Robert Whytt whose experiments demonstrated reflex action in decapitated animals and the effects of spinal shock. (From the portrait in the Royal College of Physicians, Edinburgh, by courtesy of Mr. G. R. Pendrill.)

and confirmed this experiment and described it in a lecture to the Royal Society in 1738.

Whytt in his experiments on the frog came very close to defining the segmental reflex. He also noted spinal shock, for he remarked that a decapitated frog could not be made to move immediately after transection although if one waited about 15 min. it would react to stimuli. But perhaps the most striking of his observations is the one in which he anticipated Sherrington in regard to the stretch reflex. "Whatever stretches the fibres of any muscle so far as to extend them beyond their usual length, excites them into contraction about in the same manner as if they had been irritated by any sharp instrument, or acrid liquor" (183, p. 9).

With the publication of Whytt's work physiologists were divided between regarding the movements of spinal animals as a lingering in the cord of powers originally derived from the brain, and the view that the spinal marrow itself was capable of sensation and movement. Whytt inclined to the latter view in his explanation of the writhings of decapitated and eviscerated snakes. "We are naturally led to conclude," he said, "that they are still in some sense alive, and endued with feeling, i.e. animated by a sentient principle."

Before the end of the century, Whytt's publications had been followed by those of Unzer (185), of Halle

and of his pupil Prochaska (186) who was a practising ophthalmologist in Prague. Both these men contributed more in systematization and formulation at the conceptual level than in the addition of new experimental facts. In England, the Sydenham Society gave both their books to the same translator, Thomas Laycock (the teacher of Hughlings Jackson), and through him the word reflexion became the accepted term. Unzer postulated several sites where reflexion of impressions might take place—in the brain, in the ganglia, in bifurcations of nerves and in plexuses. Only if they reached the brain would these impressions be consciously perceived. Unzer in discussing automatic movements protected himself against the attacks encountered by some of his predecessors by saying that "the animal machines are mysteriously and inscrutably endowed by the Creator."

Prochaska, with one foot in the past, believed in a sensorium commune where automatic reflexion took place and thought this might be in the medulla or the cord but did not agree with Unzer that reflexion might be at the level of the ganglia. He reverted to

Leipzig: Wiedmanns, 1771; English translation by T. Laycock. *Principles of a Physiology of the Nature of Animal Organisms.* London: Sydenham Society, 1851.

186. PROCHASKA, JIRI (1749–1820). Part III: De functionibus systematis nervosi, et observationes anatomico-pathologicae. In: *Adnotationum Academicarum.* Prague: Gerle, 1784; English translation by T. Laycock. *Dissertation on the Functions of the Nervous System.* London: Sydenham Society, 1851.

185. UNZER, JOHANN AUGUST (1727–1809). *Erste Gründe einer Physiologie der eigenlichten thierischen Natur thierischer Kövper*

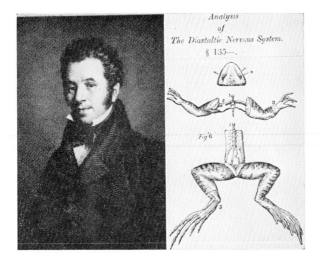

FIG. 22. *Left:* Marshall Hall. *Right:* one of his experiments to demonstrate the three parts of the reflex arc. The arc was broken by any of the following procedures: *a)* skinning the extremity (at *3*) (the 'esodic' nerves); *b)* sectioning of the "brachial or the lumbar or femoral nerve leading to the point irritated" (i.e. the 'exodic nerve' at *2*); or *c)* removing the spinal marrow (the 'spinal centre'). (From Hall, M. *Synopsis of the Diastaltic Nervous System:* being outlines of the Croonian Lectures delivered at the Royal College of Physicians in April 1850.)

the idea of an inherent *vis nervosa* in the nerves that enabled them to function in isolation from the brain and he supported this argument by citing the movements of anencephalic monsters. In his view the 'purpose' of reflex activity was preservation of the individual.

Here the history of reflex activity rested for nearly 30 years and the next advance was a technical rather than a conceptual one. This was the perfection by Legallois (187) of a method for the artificial respiration of mammals and from then on, in many laboratories, heads began to fall. Legallois, by sectioning the neuraxis serially from above and from below, narrowed the center of activity drastically and was so impressed by the amount of sensorimotor function left in a segment that he rather sweepingly concluded that the spinal cord was the principal seat of sensation and the source of voluntary motion. Although this extreme view did not gather many adherents, it was clear that the spinal cord could no longer be thought of as a mere prolongation and bundling together of peripheral nerves. On the contrary, the tendency now

was to regard it as a caudal extension of the brain. Legallois should be remembered for being the first to recognize clearly that the respiratory center lay in the medulla oblongata.

This was the setting of the stage for the man who lifted the whole subject of reflex activity into the framework of modern neurophysiology and into clinical science. Marshall Hall, an Englishmen educated in the great school at Edinburgh where he was a pupil of the third Monro, was a successful practising physician who set up a laboratory in his own house (in Malet Street where the present buildings of London University stand). Here he worked on his animals, mostly frogs and reptiles, collating his observations (188) with those he made on patients (189). His acumen enabled him to perceive several details that had escaped his predecessors. For example, the writhings of the decapitated snake that had led Whytt to a postulate of lingering 'life' within the cord were recognized by Hall as motor responses to the renewed sensory stimuli set up by each movement.

Like Unzer, Hall in his work on the machine-like movements of decapitated animals protected himself from onslaught by stating them to be "all beautiful and demonstrative of the wisdom of Him who fashioneth all things after his own Will." Hall, again like Unzer, realized that the sensory impression that set off a reflex need not be consciously perceived, although he was consistently remiss in acknowledging the contributions of his predecessors. He also ignored the work of his contemporaries, for nowhere does he refer to the great blossoming of knowledge of nerve physiology that was taking place at this time and which has been reviewed in an earlier section of this essay. He seems also to have been unaware of the contractility of involuntary muscle although Baglivi (190) over a hundred years before he had made the distinction between smooth and striated muscle. Hall had many detractors who vigorously accused him of plagiarism, both from Müller and from Prochaska. The first challenge was easier to meet than the second, for Hall's earliest communication (191) antedated Müller's publication (94) on decapitated animals by one year. In the published report of this first paper,

187. LEGALLOIS, JULIEN JEAN CÉSAR (1770–1814). *Expériences sur la principe de la vie, notamment sur celui des mouvements du coeur, et sur le siège de ce principe.* Paris: D'Hautel, 1812.

188. HALL, MARSHALL (1790–1857). *New Memoir on the Nervous System.* London, 1843.

189. HALL, M. *Diseases and Derangements of the Nervous System* London: Baillière, 1841.

190. BAGLIVI, GIORGIO (1668–1707). *Opera omnia medicopractica et anatomica.* Leyden: Anisson & Posuel, 1704.

191. HALL, M. On a particular function of the nervous system. *Proc. Zool. Soc.* part 2, p. 189, Nov. 27, 1832.

which Hall gave to the Zoological Society of London in November 1832, there is, however, no full description of the reflex arc nor does he use these terms. The emphasis is on "a function of the nervous system . . . distinct from sensation and voluntary or instinctive motion," being a "property which attaches itself to any part of an animal, the corresponding portion of the brain and spinal marrow of which is entire."

The attack was pursued by others[20] with great bitterness and its leaders engaged in such unworthy acts as checking on library slips to prove that Hall had borrowed Prochaska's book. (The slips however postdated Hall's original publications.) To the modern worker the battle seems puerile and undignified and one regrets that its protagonists did not spend the time on experiment instead of polemics.[21] Of the men for whom priority was being claimed, Prochaska was dead and it is noticeable that Müller, a truly great man, after making generous acknowledgement to Hall in his Handbuch stood aloof from these bickerings.

In essence Marshall Hall's major contributions to neurophysiology were, first (192), that sensory impressions coming into the medulla spinalis had far reaching effects in the nervous system in addition to the segmental effector response,[22] secondly the recognition that although reflex activity took place at a spinal level it could be influenced by the will[23] and thirdly, the relationship of this fact to the exaggeration of reflex response on removal of the brain (193). These are not the only areas in which he anticipated Sherrington. He gave a preliminary glimpse of the stepping reflex, "In the actions of walking in man, I imagine the reflex function to play a very considerable part, although there are, doubtless facts which demonstrate that the contact of the sole with the ground is not unattended by a certain influence upon the action of certain muscles."

Marshall Hall introduced the word 'arc' to describe the reflex pathway. Many of his other terms have, happily, not been retained by physiologists, for he was a great lover of neologisms, as his definition of the arc shows: "the existence in *Anatomy and Physiology*, of a continuous Diastaltic Nervous Arc including an *Esodic Nerve*, the *Spinal Centre* and *Exodic Nerve* in

essential relation and connection with each other— and of a *series* of such Arcs. . . ." (194). (One recognizes here that Queen Victoria had a rival among her subjects in the use of italics.)

One further contribution of Hall's at the conceptual level should be noted. Implicit, if not explicit, in the theories of the earlier physiologists was the notion that in voluntary movement volition directed a nervous influence towards the individually appropriate muscles. Hall pointed out that the will was more teleological and less specific in its action and not "directed to any muscle or set of muscles, but to an aim, object and purpose of their contraction" (195). Hall's contributions were not evaluated as highly by his contemporaries as they have been by later physiologists, though he himself had no doubts as to how they should be ranked; he stated that they were the greatest advance in medical science since William Harvey.

The impact of the work of the physiologists on the concepts of the psychologists was very great and so disturbing that their literature was filled with controversy for many years. Long before the concept of reflex activity was carried into the brain by Sechenov to explain its higher functions, the psychologists were in distress over the implication for 'sensation,' for 'consciousness' and for 'volition,' of the developing knowledge of spinal reflexes. The most conspicuous controversy was that waged between Eduard Pflüger (196), von Helmholtz's successor at the Physiological

194. HALL, M. *Synopsis of the diastaltic nervous system.* Croonian Lectures, London, 1850.
195. HALL, M. *Memoirs on the Nervous System.* London, 1837.
196. PFLÜGER, EDOUARD (1829–1910). *Die sensorischen Funktionen des Rückenmarks der Wirbelthiere nebst einer neuen Lehre über die Leitungsgesetze der Reflexionen.* Berlin, 1853.

192. HALL, M. On the reflex function of the medulla oblongata and medulla spinalis. *Phil. Trans.* 123: 635, 1833.
193. HALL, M. *On the true spinal marrow, and on the excito-motory system of the nerves.* Lectures given before the Royal Society, privately printed, 1837.

[20] Such as, for example, George, J. D. Contribution to the history of the nervous system. *Lond. med. Gaz.* 22: 40, 93, 1837–1838.

[21] A full account of the controversy (though scarcely an unbiased one) can be found in Longet, F. A. *Traité d'Anatomie de Physiologie du Système Nerveux de l'Homme et des Animaux Vertébrés.* Paris, 1842. 2 vol.

[22] "But the operation of the reflex function is by no means confined to parts corresponding to distinct portions of the medulla. The irritation of a given part may, on the contrary, induce contraction in a part very remote." *Phil. Trans.* 123: 635, 1833.

[23] "The true spinal system is susceptible of modification by volition. . . ." *Memoirs on the Nervous System.* London, 1837, part 2, p. 73. (This part of the observation was anticipated by Whytt.)

Institute at Bonn, and Rudolph Lötze (197), professor of Philosophy at Göttingen. Back and forth the battle raged, swinging from physiology into metaphysics and back again into experiment. The arguments all centered around the problems of whether a spinal animal was sentient and conscious, and whether its movements were purposeful. Was such an animal intelligent? Did it have memory? Pflüger espoused the idea of consciousness in the cord, Lötze denied it; both were dogmatic but to neither can we look for advancement of knowledge of the central nervous system in this context.

In the nineteenth century, while Marshall Hall was still alive, the nature of inhibition became of major interest to physiologists and before the end of the century was to have its role in reflex activity demonstrated by Sherrington. Although the possibility of inhibition had been suggested by several workers, the actual phenomenon had first been observed (and rejected as an error of experiment) by Volkmann (198) in 1838 in relation to the action of the vagus on the heart. It was again observed, and this time accepted, by the Weber brothers (199) in 1845. The elder brother, Ernst, held the joint chair of anatomy and physiology at Leipzig until Carl Ludwig came in 1866 to take over the latter section and set up his famous institute. The technique of the classic experiment that established the existence of vagal inhibition was the stimulation by a voltaic pile of both vagi of the frog. Later the Webers found that unilateral stimulation had the same effect and they confirmed the result by stimulating the vagus of a cat with an induction current. They reported this discovery, one of the landmarks of nerve physiology, at the Congress of Italian Scientists held in Naples in 1845 (which accounts for their publication being in Latin rather than in German). This type of inhibition, like that which was eventually evoked to explain Bernard's (200) observation of the influence of the chorda tympani on the submaxillary blood vessels, seemed simple to later physiologists faced with the complexities of inhibition in the central nervous system. These had to await exploration by Sherrington.

An enduring interest of Sherrington and one exhaustively explored by him in the laboratory was reciprocal innervation of antagonist muscles, and many of his publications were on this subject. The attempt of Descartes (25) in the seventeenth century to reach an explanation based on channeling of vital spirits had no immediate successor. In the early part of the nineteenth century Charles Bell (201) had postulated the existence of peripheral inhibition by insisting on the need for nerves which had the opposite of an excitatory effect on muscle. "The nerves," he said, "have been considered so generally as instruments for stimulating the muscles, without thought of their acting in the opposite capacity, that some additional illustration may be necessary." He went on to describe an experiment in which contraction of a flexor muscle coincided with imposed relaxation of its opponent extensor.

The possibility of a peripherally exerted inhibition of muscle contractility attracted many people at about this time. One of the earliest was a Dr. West (202) of Alford in Lincolnshire (who had heard Bell's lectures at the Royal College of Surgeons). West's suggestion was that contraction was an inherent property of muscle and that the action of the nerve supplying it was not to evoke, but to 'restrain' or 'rein' this innate tendency to contract. He explained a voluntary contraction as a withdrawal of this nervous restraint "so as to allow the peculiar property of muscular fibre to shew itself." The publication of West's hypothesis provoked some expostulation, one anonymous correspondent saying this was "certainly one of the clumsiest contrivances that nature was ever accused of." The mechanism of rigor mortis was not understood at this time and West felt that his theory offered a possible explanation. The idea was also present in the arguments of many others, for example those of Engel (203), of Stannius (204) and of Dugès

197. LÖTZE, RUDOLPH HEINRICH (1817–1881). Instinct. In: R. Wagner. *Handwörterbuch.* pt. 2. Brunswick: Vieweg, 1842–1853.

198. VOLKMANN, ALFRED WILHELM (1800–1871). Über Reflexbewegungen. *Arch. Anat. u. Physiol.* 15, 1838.

199. WEBER, EDUARD FRIEDRICH WILHELM (1806–1871) AND ERNST HEINRICH WEBER (1795–1878). Experimenta, quibus probatur nervos vagos rotatione machinae galvano-magneticae irritatos, motum cordi retardare et adeo intercipare. *Ann. Univ. Med., Milano* 20: 227, 1845.

200. BERNARD, CLAUDE (1813–1878). Recherches anatomiques et physiologiques sur la corde du tympan, pour servir à l'histoire de l'hémiplégie faciale. *Ann. méd.-psychol.* 1: 408, 1843.

201. BELL, C. On the nerves of the orbit. *Phil. Trans.* 113: 289, 1823.

202. WEST, R. UVEDALE. On the influence of the nerves over muscular contractility. *Ryan's Med. Surg. J.* 1: 24, 245, 445, 1832.

203. ENGEL, JOSEPH. Über Muskelreizbarkeit. *Ztschr. Gesellsch. Ärtze, Wien* 1: 205, 252, 1849.

204. STANNIUS, HERMANN (1808–1883). Untersuchungen über die Leistungsfähigkeit der Muskeln u. Todtenstarre. *Vierordt's Arch. physiol. heilk.* 1, 1852.

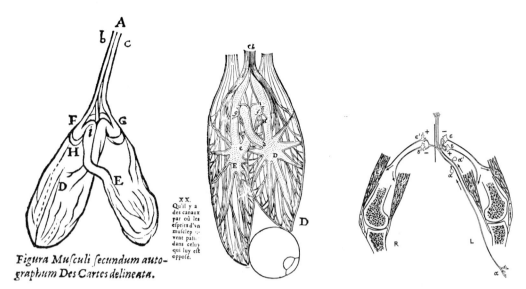

Figura Musculi secundum auto-
graphum Des Cartes delineata.

FIG. 23. *Left:* Descartes' sketch of reciprocal muscles of the eye (*De Homine*, the Latin translation by Schuyl). *Center:* a redrawing showing closure of valves on relaxation, opening on contraction to allow animal spirits to flow in and swell the muscle (*L'Homme*, the French edition of 1677). *Right:* Sherrington's diagram of the connections and actions of two cells of a dorsal root ganglion. The *plus sign* indicates that at the central synapses the afferent impulses excite the ipsilateral flexor muscle and the contralateral extensor, while inhibiting the ipsilateral extensor and the contralateral flexor muscle. (From Sherrington, C. S. *The Integrative Action of the Nervous System*, 2nd ed. Cambridge: Cambridge, 1947.)

(205) in Montpellier. The latter favored a peripherally exerted nervous influence acting against an inherent elasticity of muscle.

In 1868 Hering (206) and Breuer (207) found in the respiratory system a parallel to Bell's experiment whereby distention of the lung acting through the pulmonary branch of the vagus inhibited inspiration while exciting expiration, the well-known Hering-Breuer reflex. And in 1883 Krönecker (208) working on the swallowing reflex in Ludwig's laboratory with his American pupil, Meltzer, demonstrated the inhibitory action of the superior laryngeal nerve on inspiratory muscles during contraction of expiratory ones. The reflex nature of swallowing had been recog-

nized by Marshall Hall (195) in 1823 and the direct afferent nerve for it had been identified by Magendie (209) to be the glossopharyngeal, but the reciprocal effect had not been noted by them.

It is the fact that there are no inhibitory nerves to vertebrate skeletal muscle that drew the whole subject of reflex inhibition into the central nervous system. With the realization that reflex inhibition had its site in the central nervous system, attention was turned to the connection between the incoming sensory element of the arc and the motor component, to the junction between them, in other words, to the synapse (Sherrington's word). That there might be an interaction of a synaptic kind between neurons in the periphery had occurred to several workers, one among whom was Sigmund Freud (210). His work on fresh-water crabs and his illustrative sketches of how he conceived of intercommunication between the axons of their ganglia came close to what is now termed an ephapse, although he pictured transverse crossings that suggest a uniting of fibers rather than a contiguity.

205. DUGÈS, ANTOINE. *Traité de Physiologie Comparée de l'homme et des Animaux.* Montpellier & Paris, 1838; *Compt. rend. Soc. de biol.* March 17, 1847.

206. HERING, KARL EWALD KONSTANTIN (1834–1918). Die Selbststeuerung der Athmung durch den Nervus Vagus. *Sitzber. Akad. Wiss. Wien* 57: 672, 1868.

207. BREUER, JOSEPH (1842–1925). Die Selbsteuerung der Athmung durch den Nervus Vagus. *Sitzber. Akad. Wiss. Wien* 58: 909, 1868.

208. KRÖNECKER, KARL HUGO (1839–1914) and SAMUEL JAMES MELTZER (1851–1920). Der Schluckmechanismus, seine Erregung und seine Hemmung. *Arch. Anat. Physiol.* Suppl.: 328, 1883.

209. MAGENDIE, F. *Leçons sur les fonctions du système nerveux.* Paris, 1839.

210. FREUD, SIGMUND (1856–1939). Über den Bau der Nervenfasern und Nervenzellen beim Flusskrebs. *Sitzber. Akad. Wiss. Wien* 85:9, 1882.

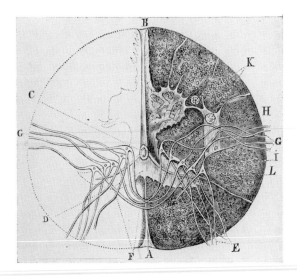

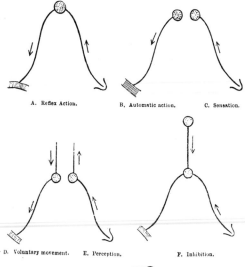

XV. DIAGRAMS ILLUSTRATING THE ELEMENTARY
COMBINATIONS OF THE NERVOUS SYSTEM.

A. Reflex Action.   B. Automatic action.   C. Sensation.

D. Voluntary movement.   E. Perception.   F. Inhibition.

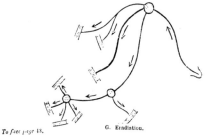

To face page 13.   G. Eradiation.

FIG. 24. *Above:* Schema of the connections between the posterior and anterior roots of the spinal cord as taught to students in the days before the
neuron doctrine and the theory of the synapse. [From Bernard, C. *Leçons
sur la Physiologie et la Pathologie du Système Nerveux.* Paris: Ballière, 1858.)
Right: Connections in the nervous system as taught to students in 1885.
(From Pye-Smith, P. H. *Syllabus of a course of lectures on Physiology delivered at
Guy's Hospital.* London: Churchill, 1885.)

Recognition of the synapse could come only after
the neuron theory had replaced the reticular theory.
According to the latter, strongly championed by
von Gerlach (211), nerve cells were connected with
each other by a diffuse fibrillary network forming an
anastomosis. This hypothesis received support from
Golgi (212), although it was his silver staining technique in the hands of Ramón y Cajal (213) that
finally disproved it, for Ramón y Cajal established
that both axons and dendrites had free endings. Together they shared the Nobel prize in 1906, Golgi
devoting his address to an attack on the neuron theory
that his fellow prize winner had done so much to up-
hold. In modern times, the synapse (an abstraction)
is having to be remodelled in the light of what the
electron microscope is revealing.

The nature of central inhibition, a still incompletely
resolved issue, has evoked many hypotheses. Among
them, those depending on mutual interference of
impulses at the effector component of the reflex arc
form one class. An example is the schema suggested
by Rosenthal (214) in 1862 to explain the effect of
efferent vagus fibers on the respiratory center. He
proposed that an effector system excited into action
by one nerve could have the pulsating rhythm of its
nervous supply disturbed by inflow from another
nerve, the result being a redistribution of previously
grouped impulses into more frequent but less powerful
(and hence inadequate) discharges. Lack of evidence
for a pulse-like time-rhythm in nerve trunks led to the
rejection of this hypothesis by Wundt, Sherrington
and others.

In the 1870's and 1880's attempts to explain inhibition on metabolic effects depending directly on the
cell's response to stimulation being an assimilation of
chemical nutrients were espoused by Gaskell (215)

211. VON GERLACH, JOSEPH (1820–1896). The spinal cord. In:
S. Stricker, *A Manual of Histology* (English translation).
London: New Sydenham Society, 1872.

212. GOLGI, CAMILLO (1844–1926). *Atti Soc. ital. progr. sc.*
3rd réunion. 1910.

213. RAMÓN Y CAJAL, SANTIAGO (1852–1934). Neuron theory
or reticular theory. *Arch. fisiol.* 5, 1908; translation by
Purkiss and Fox. Madrid, 1954.

214. ROSENTHAL, JOSEPH. *Die Atembeweg und ihre Bezichung zum
nervus Vagus.* Berlin, 1862.

215. GASKELL, WALTER HOLBROOK (1847–1914). On the
rhythm of the heart of the frog and of the nature of the
action of the vagus nerve *Phil. Trans.* 173: 993, 1882.

(for the vagus) and Hering (216) (for black-white sensations of the visual sense), by Verworn (217) (in his *Biogenhypothese*). The hypothesis did not survive for long. As Forbes (218) said in his critique, "To assume that increase of anabolism necessarily implies decrease of catabolism, is to suppose that increasing a man's salary ensures decrease of his expenditure." A theory of immobilization of ion transfer during inhibition was proposed by Macdonald (219) in 1905, at a time when the release of potassium from injured nerves was receiving considerable attention.

With the discovery of the refractory period in nerve [by Gotch and Burch (220) in 1889] there was some tendency to regard block of conduction due to excitatory impulses arriving during refractoriness caused by preceding excitation to be the mechanism of inhibition. This is now recognized as a misuse of the term, and in fact Sherrington's demonstration that after discharge persisting after cessation of excitation could be cut short by inhibitory nerve action was an early salutory corrective.

In the course of researches on the inexhaustibility of nerve, a subject which engrossed the early electrophysiologists, Wedensky (221) found that a rapid series of strong stimuli would fail to produce more than a single twitch if the transmission from nerve to muscle were blocked either by fatigue at the end plate or by artificially impairing a section of the nerve by narcosis. If however the frequency or the strength of the tetanus were then reduced, the muscle went immediately into tetanic contraction. Wedensky concluded that the nerve was inexhaustible and that the phenomenon was one of inhibition. This may, however, be regarded as a special usage of the term since the effect he observed was merely a characteristic of the relative refractory period of nerve and its time course as related to strength of stimulus (222).

It was Sherrington's insistence on a central site for the inhibitory mechanisms of skeletal muscle that emphasized the reflex nature of inhibition. The contributions of Sherrington and his school are the basis of modern ideas of the reflex at the spinal level. A great number of findings (223–227) made by Sherrington and brought together into a unifying explanatory scheme included the following major observations: that postural tonus of a muscle is dependent not only on efferent nerves but on afferent nerves from that muscle itself, the stimulus to the latter being from stretch receptors [the myotatic reflex (223)]; that decerebrate rigidity (224) is an exaggerated muscle tonus in the antigravity muscles—a reflex standing ["an harmonious congerie of stretch-reflexes" (225)]; that the afferent nerve from a given muscle can elicit a contraction in that muscle itself (228), without involvement of the opposing muscles of the joint;[24] that the main stimulus for the stepping reflex (229) does not come from contact of the foot with ground, as might be expected;[25] that stimulation causing flexion in one

223. LIDDELL, E. G. T. AND C. S. SHERRINGTON. Reflexes in response to stretch (myotatic reflexes). *Proc. Roy. Soc., London. ser. B* 96: 212, 1924.
224. SHERRINGTON, C. S. Cateleptoid reflexes in the monkey. *Proc. Roy. Soc., London. ser. B* 60: 411, 1897.
225. SHERRINGTON, C. S. Problems of muscular receptivity. Linacre Lecture. *Nature, London* 113: 732, 892, 929, 1924.
226. SHERRINGTON, C. S. *Selected Writings of C. S. Sherrington*, edited by D. Denny-Brown. London: Hamish Hamilton, 1940.
227. SHERRINGTON, C. S. Note on the knee-jerk and the correlation of action of antagonistic muscles. *Proc. Roy. Soc., London. ser. B* 52: 556, 1892–3.
228. SHERRINGTON, C. S. On reciprocal innervation of antagonistic muscle (eighth note). *Proc. Roy. Soc., London. ser. B* 76: 269, 1905.
229. SHERRINGTON, C. S. Flexion-reflex of the limb, crossed extension-reflex, and reflex stepping and standing. *J. Physiol.* 40: 28, 1910.

216. HERING, HEINRICH EWALD (1866–1948). Zur Theorie de Vorgange in der lebendigen Substanz. *Lotos* 9: 35, 1889; translated in *Brain* 20: 232, 1897.
217. VERWORN, MAX. *Die Biogenhypothese*. Jena: Fischer, 1903.
218. FORBES, ALEXANDER. Reflex inhibition of skeletal muscle. *Quart. J. Exper. Physiol.* 5: 149, 1912.
219. MACDONALD, J. S. The structure and function of nerve fibres. *Proc. Roy. Soc., London. ser. B* 76: 322, 1905.
220. GOTCH, F. and G. J. BURCH. The electrical response of nerve to two stimuli. *J. Physiol.* 24: 410, 1899.
221. WEDENSKY, NICHOLAᴵ YEVGENEVICH (1852–1922). Die Erregung, Hemmung und Narkose. *Arch. ges. Physiol.* 100: 1, 1903.
222. ADRIAN, E. D. Wedensky inhibition in relation to the "all-or-none" principle in nerve. *J. Physiol.* 46: 384, 1913.

[24] From a series of 14 articles by Sherrington on reciprocal innervation stretching over the years from 1893 to 1909 (and developed in many other of his writings), the following excerpt may be quoted as one of his crucial experiments: "All the nerves of the limb being severed, except those of the *vasti* and *crureus*, the animal is inverted and the knee then gently but fully extended by raising the foot, the thigh being held vertical. The foot is then released, the anticrus falls, and in doing so is seen to be suddenly checked by exciting a contraction of the extensor of the knee. This contraction is different from a knee-jerk, for it only slowly passes off." Sherrington, C. S. *Proc. Roy. Soc., London. ser. B* 76: 283, 1905.

[25] ". . . in the intact animal (cat, dog), severance of all the nerve trunks directly distributed to all four of the feet up to and above the wrists and ankles impairs walking so little as to make it highly unlikely that the loss of receptivity of the feet destroys any large factor in the reflex basis of these acts" (235).

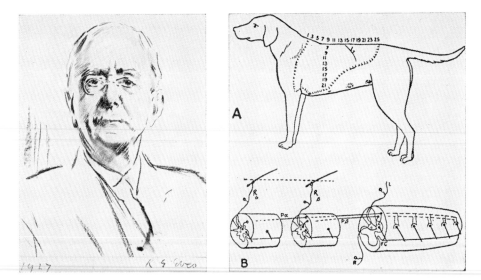

FIG. 25. Charles Scott Sherrington, from the drawing by Reginald Eves (reproduced by permission from *Selected Writings of Sir Charles Sherrington*, edited by D. Denny Brown. New York: Hoeber, 1940). *Right:* Sherrington's classic picture of the areas for the scratch reflex in the dog. (From Sherrington, C. S. *The Integrative Action of the Nervous System.* Cambridge: Cambridge, 1947.)

limb frequently evokes an extensor movement in the contralateral homologous limb [the crossed-extensor reflex (229)]; that this reflex can also be centrally inhibited; and that after prolonged inhibitory stimulation there is, on withdrawal of the stimulus, an increase of contraction ['reflex rebound' (230)]. These are only a few of the reflex phenomena that received elucidation through Sherrington's work.

Out of a vast number of laboratory experiments grew his unifying hypothesis of reflex excitation and reflex inhibition, and hence of an interdependence of reflex arcs resulting in an integrative action of the nervous system. Sherrington's classic book bearing this title was published (231) when he was Professor of Physiology at Liverpool University and was based on lectures he gave at Yale University. The concepts of 'the final common path,' of 'synaptic connections,' of 'central inhibition,' of 'central excitation' and of 'reciprocal innervation' are incorporated in modern physiology which recognizes its debt to Sherrington. The nineteenth century which had opened with only one method for tracing fiber tracts—that of dissecting them out as Bichat had done—gave to physiologists two great new tools, the histological method of

Wallerian degeneration and the technique of electrical recordings. In the hands of Victor Horsley and his associates, Gotch, Beever, Schäfer and others, electrophysiology of spinal-cord systems made great advances which can be followed in the series of papers published in the *Philosophical Transactions* between 1886 and 1891. An overall view of what could be achieved by this new method is given in the Croonian Lecture of Gotch and Horsley in 1891 (232).

Towards the end of the century these techniques were being applied, not only by Horsley, but by many of his contemporaries to the study of the physiology of the brain.

PHYSIOLOGY OF THE BRAIN: DEVELOPMENT OF
IDEAS AND GROWTH OF EXPERIMENT

At the mid-eighteenth century, scientists seeking knowledge of the brain could look back on a history of their field that revealed a gradual evolution of anatomical knowledge about its structure but only conjecture about its physiology.

Among the early Greeks the teachings of Plato had placed man's rational faculties where we would put

230. SHERRINGTON, C. S. Strychnine and reflex inhibition of skeletal muscle. *J. Physiol.* 36: 185, 1907.
231. SHERRINGTON, C. S. *The Integrative Action of the Nervous System.* New York: Scribners, 1906; new edition. Cambridge: Cambridge, 1947.

232. GOTCH, F. AND VICTOR HORSLEY. On the mammalian nervous system, its functions and their localization determined by an electrical method. *Phil. Trans.* B 182: 267, 1891.

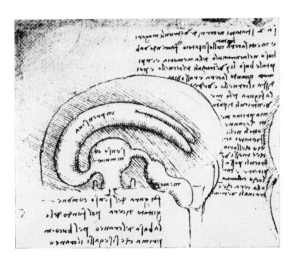

FIG. 26. *Left:* the three ventricles of the brain as envisaged by Albertus Magnus. *Right:* Leonardo da Vinci's wax cast, the first experimental determination of their shape.

them now, in the head; the passions he put in the spinal marrow relating them to the heart, and the lower appetites were given a place in the cord below the diaphragm where they could play upon the liver. For Plato these were the divisions of man's tripartite soul.

Under the influence of Galen the spinal nervous system lost this position of importance, for according to his doctrine other organs of the body, the liver and the heart, were the primary sites for manufacture and transmutation of the spirits. From the Islamic physicians came the emphasis on three ventricles with different functions, an anterior ventricle being the receiver of all incoming spirits, a 'sensus communis,' whereas a posterior ventricle formed the reservoir for the outflow of animal spirits to all muscles through their nerves. In a middle ventricle was to be found man's reason. Similar ideas about triple cavities in the brain and their allotted functions were generally accepted throughout the unenlightened middle ages until finally an anatomist, no less a man than Leonardo da Vinci (233), mapped the true shape of the ventricles by pouring into them melted wax to form a cast.

Throughout the sixteenth and seventeenth centuries, the structure of the brain was being unfolded by the anatomists but still without a parallel investigation of function. It was the cranial nerves that

yielded first and Galen's seven pairs[26] (accepted on his authority for 1400 years) swelled to nine in the seventeenth century. In 1660 Schneider (234) identified the olfactory pair and 2 years later Willis (235) dissected the accessory nerve that bears his name. Today's recognition of 12 pairs of cranial nerves dates from the eighteenth century and the work of von Soemmering (236), whose books are illustrated by engravings rivalled only by those of Charles Bell. von Soemmering wrote copiously on anatomy, illustrating some of his work by his own hand and some by the drawings of his pupil Koeck.

The role played by each pair of cranial nerves was still in some degree obscure, for some nerves appeared to have more than one function, and Whytt (237) was one of the early workers to observe how complex their action might be. He found that the optic nerve

233. DA VINCI, LEONARDO (1452–1519). *On the Human Body; The Anatomical, Physiological, and Embryological Drawings of Leonardo da Vinci,* with translations, emmendations and a biographical introduction by C. D. O'Malley and J. B. deC. M. Saunders. New York: Schuman, 1952.

234. SCHNEIDER, CONRAD VICTOR (1614–1680). *Liber primus de catarrhis.* Wittenberg: Mevius & Schumacher, 1660.

235. WILLIS, THOMAS (1621–1675). *De Anima Brutorum.* In: *Opera Omnia.* Leyden: Huguetan, 1681.

236. SOEMMERING, SAMUEL THOMAS (1755–1830). *De basi encephali et originibus nervorum cranio egredientum.* Göttingen: Vandenhoeck, 1778.

237. WHYTT, ROBERT (1714–1766). *An essay on the vital and other involuntary motions of animals.* Edinburgh: Hamilton, Balfour and Neill, 1751.

[26] According to Galen's numbering, the seven pairs of cranial nerves were: *1)* optic; *2)* oculomotor and abducens taken together; *3)* and *4)* were both parts of what is now called the trigeminal; *5)* facial together with the auditory; *6)* the glossopharyngeal, vagus and accessory nerves; *7)* the hypoglossal.

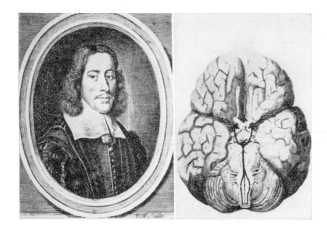

FIG. 27. Thomas Willis and the illustration of the base of the brain taken from his book *De cerebri anatome*. The circle of Willis, named for him, had been depicted by several anatomists before him. Willis was fortunate in having Christopher Wren as his illustrator.

was not solely concerned with vision but that it carried the stimulus that led to the contractile response of the iris to light. In the post-mortem examination on a child with fixed pupils he found a lesion blocking the inflow from the optic nerves to the thalamus and inferred that this impairment of sensory inflow was responsible for the motor deficit that had been the clinical sign. This was indeed the recognition of a reflex arc, and the pupillary reflex was for many years known by his name.

As noted above, Willis had dissected the spinal accessory nerve to its junction with the cord but he believed it to convey voluntary control. Lacking a scientific acumen equal to his skill as a dissector, and influenced by Galen, he thought this nerve anastomosed with the vagus (the 'wandering' nerve). Schneider, on the other hand, had no doubts as to the action of the olfactory nerves for it was his work on the nasal mucosa and olfactory processes that led to his identification of them. Willis also was aware of their function for he called them the 'smelling' nerves. He noted that within the skull they had 'mammillary processes' and said, "As to the Fibres and Filaments or little strings stretching out from the more soft nerves through the holes of the Sieve-like Bone into the caverns of the Nose, these are found in all Creatures who have the mammillary Processes: so it is not to be doubted, but that these Processes, with this appendix and its medullary origine is the Organ of Smell."[27] Willis called in his knowledge of compara-

tive anatomy and noted that "the filaments or little strings" of the organ of smell were "more remarkable in hunting Hounds than in any other Animal whatsoever."

The nerves that had both sensory and motor branches proved the most difficult. Magendie (238) at first thought the fifth nerve was sensory and nutrient to the face, and the seventh nerve entirely motor, since cutting it caused facial paralysis without relieving neuralgia. In 1820 Charles Bell (147), dissecting the nerves of the face, noticed that the fibers of the seventh nerve went to muscle whereas those of the fifth entered the skin. He suspected they served different functions, and being himself an anatomist rather than an experimentalist, asked his brother-in-law, John Shaw, to make a study of the effect of sections of these nerves. Using an unusual experimental animal, the donkey, Shaw was able to demonstrate paralysis in the one case, loss of reaction to touch in the other; neither he nor Bell whose fine drawings illustrate his findings recognized the mixed nature of these nerves. After this beginning several workers added their contributions to the further clarification of the cranial nerves, prominent among these being Mayo (239) (who taught the course in anatomy and physiology at King's College, London).

It was only in the eighteenth century that doubt was first thrown on the assumption that the sympathetic trunk (or 'intercostal' nerve, as it was then called) was an appendage of the brain. This grew from the transection experiments of Pourfour du Petit (240) and his observations on contraction of the pupil. For centuries anatomists had shown this nerve as stemming from the brain. Vesalius (7), in his drawings of the human nervous system, put it in one trunk with the vagus. (In the dog, though not in man, the two nerves lie in the same sheath in the neck region.) Eustachius (241) separated the two, but like many after him, including Willis, he depicted an intracranial origin. These drawings of the anatomists must have been designed to be consistent with Galen-

[27] The quotations are from Pordage's translation (1683) of Willis, T. *Cerebri anatome: cui accessit nervorum descriptio et usus.* London: Flesher, 1664.

238. MAGENDIE, F. *J. physiol. expér. et path.* 4: 176, 302, 1824.
239. MAYO, H. *Anatomical and Physiological Commentaries.* London: Underwood, vol. I, 1822; vol. II, 1823.
240. POURFOUR DU PETIT, FRANÇOIS (1664–1741). Mémoire dans lequel il est demonstré que les nerfs intercostaux fournissent des rameaux que portent des esprits dans les nerfs. *Hist. Acad. roy. Sc. Paris* 1, 1727.
241. EUSTACHIUS, BARTOLOMMEO (1520–1574). *Tabulae anatomicae* (posthumous). Rome: Gonzaga, 1714.

ist doctrine, rather than with observation from dissection. du Petit's experiments came very close to uncovering the action of vasomotor nerves, the subject that was to receive so much investigation in later years from Claude Bernard (242, 243), from Carl Ludwig (244) and from Pavlov's other teacher, Cyon (245). Bernard's experiments were mostly on skin temperature changes due to vasomotor action, although at no time would he relinquish entirely an explanation on a metabolic basis. Ludwig had found the secretory action of the lingual nerve but he did not separate it from the chorda tympani as Bernard did later.

A marked advance in understanding the physiology, not only of the cranial nerves but of the brain itself, came when techniques were developed for ablating and stimulating parts of the central nervous system without the animal succumbing to the procedures. The surgery in the early attempts was frequently so drastic that results were rarely specific. For example, the experimental results of Willis that confirmed his belief in the cerebellum as a vital center were probably due to his animal's having succumbed to injuries near the fourth ventricle. Other early experimenters such as Duverney (246) with his pigeons, Chirac (247) and Perrault (248) with their dogs had to be satisfied with very brief durations of survival.

At the opening of the nineteenth century interest in localization of cerebral function had been widely stirred by the lectures of Franz Gall (249) in Vienna. Unfortunately Gall's reputation as a phrenologist has

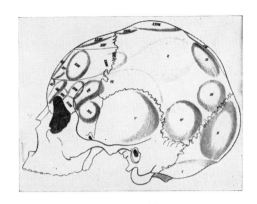

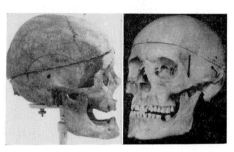

FIG. 28. *Above:* Gall and Spurzheim's map of a skull with certain areas marked for correspondence with different mental acuities. *Below,* for comparison: Gall's skull on the *left,* that of Spurzheim on the *right.* Although Gall's own ideas were channeled into phrenology, they were influential in directing interest to the study of cerebral localization. (The skull of Gall is in the Musée de l'Homme in Paris and is reproduced here by the kindness of Dr. Ardvège; that of Spurzheim is in the Warren Museum at the Harvard Medical School, and has been photographed by permission of Dr. P. I. Yakovlev.)

overshadowed his more important work on the fiber tracts of the white matter of the brain, work which clarified the previously contradictory ideas as to the anatomy of the commissures and of the pyramidal decussation. But, while his contemporaries were concerning themselves with sites for sensory and motor functions, Gall was proposing localization of mental faculties and he may be regarded as a pioneer in emphasizing the importance of the grey matter for intellectual processes. It was when, together with his pupil, Spurzheim (250), he proceeded to assign separate 'organs' in the brain to the different mental faculties and to relate these to bumps on the skull that he began to be challenged. All the same, in spite

242. BERNARD, CLAUDE (1813–1878). Influence du grand sympathique sur la sensibilité et sur la calorification. *Compt. rend. Soc. de biol.* 3: 163, 1851.

243. BERNARD, C. De l'influence de deux ordres de nerfs qui déterminent les variations de couleur du sang veineux dans les organes glandulaires. *Compt. rend. Acad. sc., Paris* 47: 245, 393, 1858.

244. LUDWIG, CARL FRIEDRICH WILHELM (1816–1895). *Mitt. naturforsch. Gessellsch. Zurich* 50, 1851.

245. CYON, ILYA (1842–1912) AND C. F. W. LUDWIG. Die Reflexe eines der sensiblen Nerven des Herzens auf die motorischen der Blutgefässe. *Arb. Physiol. Inst., Leipzig* 1: 128, 1867.

246. DUVERNEY, JOSEPH GUICHARD (1648–1730). *Phil. Trans. Roy. Soc.* 19: 226, 1697 (reported by Preston).

247. CHIRAC, PIERRE (1650–1732). *Du motu cordis analytica.* Montpellier, 1698.

248. PERRAULT, CLAUDE (1613–1688). *Mémoires pour servir à l'histoire des animaux.* Paris: Acad. d. Sci., 1671–1676.

249. GALL, FRANZ JOSEPH (1758–1828) AND JOHANN CASPAR SPURZHEIM (1776–1832). Recherches sur le système nerveux en général, et sur celui du cerveau en particulier. *Mém. Inst. Paris* 1808.

250. GALL, F. J. AND J. C. SPURZHEIM. *Anatomie et physiologie du système nerveux en général et du cerveau en particulier, avec des observations intellectuelles et morales de l'homme et des animaux, par la configuration de leur têtes.* Paris: Schoell 1810–1819 (vols. I & II by Gall & Spurzheim; vols. III & IV by Gall).

FIG. 29. Two investigators of the cerebellum, Pierre Flourens (1794–1867) and Luigi Luciani (1840–1921).

'blind' and 'deaf' and appeared to be asleep although it stirred when poked. Flourens went so far as to say that the bird lost its volition and "even the faculty of dreaming." He noted that it retained the sense of equilibrium and that its pupils still reacted to light. Others repeating Flourens' experiments were unconvinced, for their decerebrate pigeons could be startled by a loud noise and could avoid obstacles.

Since sudden death followed section of the medulla, Flourens concluded that here lay the essential mechanism for respiration and the maintenance of life. In this conclusion he had of course been anticipated by Legallois. Much of Flourens' fame as an experimentalist derived from his observation that extirpation of the cerebellum (in birds and mammals) caused loss of coordinated movement. Flourens, whose interest lay so deeply in the elucidation of the control of voluntary movement, was himself to suffer paralysis for a long period before his death.

In the 1820's when Fluorens was pursuing these experiments, many workers were 'mutilating' animals (to use Gall's phrase) (254), and some jockeying for priority was inevitable. Most of Flourens' observations, particularly those on the cerebellum, had been anticipated by Rolando at Sassari, whose treatise (255) of 1809 (written in the Italian language and printed and illustrated by himself) was therefore republished in French in an abbreviated form in 1824 (256).

Rolando did not succeed in keeping his animals alive. Even his tortoises died after removal of their brains, although Fontana who had been successful with these animals showed him his own technique. Many of Rolando's conclusions (257) were therefore incorrect since he mistook surgical shock for paralysis. Less ruthless extirpations, of the hemispheres only, he found to be compatible with life. Rolando believed the cerebellum to be a kind of 'voltaic pile' and the source of all movement. Flourens thought it merely the regulator. Magendie (258) disagreed, holding cerebellar function to be maintenance of equilibrium.

of its bizarre concepts, phrenology had a surprisingly wide acceptance for a considerable period even among the medical profession. It was to the psychologists (although that term was not yet in use) that phrenology particularly appealed, for it was the first major consideration of mental characteristics as attributes of brain function.

One of the more prominent men to attack Gall's doctrines was Flourens who made a sweeping rejection of all such ideas, denying the brain any discretely localized action. But Flourens' monograph (251) appeared some years after the deaths of Gall and Spurzheim both of whom had built up comfortable careers out of their speciality. Flourens recognized three major functional regions of the brain (the cerebral hemispheres, the medulla and the cerebellum), but within these entities he envisaged their action as global and their roles as being sensory, vital and motor, respectively. Concerning the cerebral hemispheres he said that animals that survive their removal "lose perception, judgment, memory and will ... therefore the cerebral hemispheres are the sole site of perception and all intellectual abilities" (252). He did not hesitate to infer subjective qualities and faculties. In one of the more renowned of his experiments (253) he had kept a pigeon alive after removal of its cerebral hemispheres. The bird was

251. FLOURENS, PIERRE (1794–1867). *Examen de Phrénologie.* Paris, 1842; English translation by D. de L. Meigs. *Phrenology Examined.* Philadelphia, 1846.
252. FLOURENS, P. *Recherches expérimentales sur les propriétés et les fonctions du système nerveux dans les animaux vertébrés.* Paris: Crevot, 1824.
253. FLOURENS, P. *Arch. gén. de méd.* 2: 321, 1823.
254. GALL, F. J. *Sur les fonctions du cerveau et sur celles de chacune de ses parties.* Paris, 1822–1825. 6 vol.
255. ROLANDO, LUIGI (1773–1831). *Saggio sopra la vera struttura del cervello dell' uomo de degl' animali e sopra le funzioni del sistema nervoso.* Sassari, 1809.
256. ROLANDO, L. Expériences sur les fonctions du système nerveux. *J. physiol. expér. et path.* 3: 95, 1823.
257. ROLANDO, L. Osservazioni sul cervelletto. *Mem. reale accad. sc.* Turin 29: 163, 1825.
258. MAGENDIE, F. *Précis élémentaire de Physiologie.* Paris, 1825; English translation by E. Mulligan. Edinburgh: Carfrae, 1826.

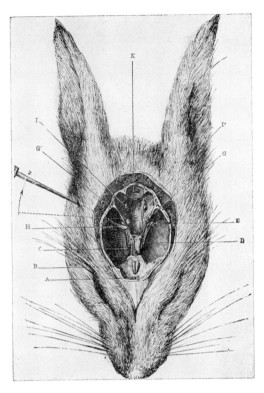

FIG. 30. *Left:* Magendie's technique for sectioning the fifth nerve in the living rabbit. The dissection is to demonstrate the insertion of his instrument. On the rabbit's right, the probe is seen entering the base of the skull and reaching the trunk of the fifth nerve at *H*. On the animal's left, the end of the instrument is seen at *E* and the sectioned nerve at *G*. (From: Bernard, C. *Leçons sur la Physiologie et la Pathologie du Système Nerveux.* Paris: Baillière, 1858. *Right:* pigeon deprived of its cerebral hemispheres in position described by Flourens. (From: Luciani, L. *Human Physiology*, English ed. London: Macmillan, 1915.)

He reached this conclusion from studying the disturbance of gait in a duck[28] from which he had re-removed the cerebellum unilaterally. He followed these experiments with bilateral destructions and noticed forced movements. The great contribution towards our modern knowledge of cerebellar mechanisms came from Luciani of Florence whose book *Il Cervelletto* (259) is a classic, as is also his textbook of physiology (260).

Magendie in the observations he made on decerebrate animals (261) anticipated Sherrington by an accurate and detailed description of decerebrate rigidity in rabbits. This was in the days before the discovery of anesthesia and Magendie was severely criticized for his practice of vivisection. But extirpation experiments on animals could give no clue to the cortical representation of speech. This had to come from clinical observation with studies at autopsy. Gall had placed language in the anterior lobes and the first clinical reports seemed to confirm this. In fact, the great surge of work aiming to establish localized centers in the human brain began with the speech center. In his studies of encephalitis Bouillaud (262), a pupil of Magendie and later Professor of Medicine, had reasoned that the anterior lobes of the brain were necessary for speech and went on to observe that other focal lesions of the brain caused localized im-

259. LUCIANI, LUIGI (1840–1921). *Il Cervelletto.* Florence, 1891.

260. LUCIANI, L. *Human Physiology.* English translation by F. A. Welby. London: Macmillan, 1915.

261. MAGENDIE, F. Sur le siège du mouvement et du sentiment dans la moelle épinière. *J. physiol. expér. et path.* 3: 153, 1823.

262. BOUILLAUD, JEAN BAPTISTE (1796–1881). *Traité clinique et physiologique de l'encéphalite ou inflammation du cerveau.* Paris: Baillière, 1825.

[28] Sherrington in quoting this experiment mistranslated Magendie's word 'canard' as 'water-dog.'

FIG. 31. Goltz and one of his decorticate dogs. (Studio portraits of man and dog are reproduced here by the kind permission of Dr. Paul Dell.)

pairment of muscular movement. The cause of cerebral localization was taken up by his son-in-law, Auburtin (263), who predicted that a lesion would be found in the anterior lobes of an aphasic patient who was at that time in the hospital of Bicêtre under the surgeon Pierre Broca. Autopsy confirmed Auburtin's prediction, pinpointing the lesion in the left anterior lobe. The next aphasic patient on Broca's service was found at autopsy to have an even more discrete lesion—in what is known to this day as Broca's area (264). The name of Auburtin has been forgotten, as has Broca's term 'aphemia' for aphasia.

Broca's speech area (the left third frontal convolution) which he thought to be concerned with articulation was to be challenged by Pierre Marie (265) in the twentieth century, but the new concept of cerebral localization developed like a wave in the later 1800's—a wave that is only now beginning partially to

recede. For the physiologists the impressive experiments were those of Goltz of Strasbourg who, after starting with frogs (266), mastered the technique of keeping warm-blooded animals alive for prolonged periods after drastic extirpations of large portions of their brains (267). Three of his dogs became famous. The first two survived 57 and 92 days respectively, the third being purposely sacrificed at 18 months. Goltz exhibited them at international congresses, killed one of them before an audience and gave their brains to Langley in Foster's laboratory to dissect (268, 269). Sherrington's participation in the necropsy of one of these dogs was the subject of his first published paper (in 1884) (270). All who witnessed the remarkable degree of retention of sensibility and

263. AUBERTIN, ERNST (1825–   ). Considerations sur les localisations cérébrales, et en particulier sur le siège de la faculté du langage articulé. *Gaz. hebd. med. et chir.* 10: 318, 348, 397, 455, 1863.
264. BROCA, PIERRE PAUL (1824–1880). Perte de parole, ramollissement chronique et destruction du lobe antérieur gauche du cerveau. *Bull. soc. anthropol. Paris* 2: 235, 1861.
265. MARIE, PIERRE (1853–1940). Revision de la question de l'aphasie; la troisième circonvolution frontale gauche ne joue aucun rôle spécial dans la fonction du langage. *Sem. méd. Paris* 26: 241, 1906.

266. GOLTZ, FRIEDRICH LEOPOLD (1834–1902). *Beiträge zur Lehre den Funktionen der Nervenzentren des Frosches.* Berlin: Hirschwald, 1869.
267. GOLTZ, F. L. Der Hund ohne Grosshirn. *Arch. ges. Physiol.* 51: 570, 1892.
268. LANGLEY, J. N. Report on the parts destroyed on the right side of the brain of the dog operated on by Professor Goltz. *J. Physiol.* 4: 286, 1883.
269. LANGLEY, J. N. AND A. S. GRUNBAUM. On the degeneration resulting from removal of the cerebral cortex and corpora striata in the dog. *J. Physiol.* 11: 606, 1890.
270. LANGLEY, J. N. AND C. S. SHERRINGTON. Secondary degeneration of nerve tracts following removal of the cortex of the cerebrum in the dog. *J. Physiol.* 5: 49, 1884.

mobility by these animals and who later studied the necropsy findings from the Cambridge laboratory were astounded, and there can be no doubt that these experiments gave a great impetus to neurosurgical procedures in animals and in man.

The physiology of the brain was now beginning to unfold and to reveal itself in dynamic terms after centuries of static representation in the two-dimensional pages of the anatomy books. To clinical observation of impairment by disease states, three experimental techniques were added: regional ablation, stimulation (both mechanical and electrical) and eventually the recording of the brain's own electricity.

Mechanical and chemical irritation of the cortical surface had suggested itself to many investigators down the years, some of the attempts reaching the extremes of the bizarre (see, for example, fig 32). Cabanis (271), the celebrated physician and *idéalogue*, had provoked convulsive movements in muscle groups that seemed to vary with the region irritated. Earlier, Haller (272), searching for irritability, had pricked the brain and applied irritating fluids and concluded that the grey matter was insensitive to stimulation and that the white matter was the seat of sensation and the source of movement.

The Italian physiologists had been more successful. The Abbé Fontana (273) and Caldani (274) (Galvani's predecessor in the chair of anatomy at Bologna) had convulsed their frogs by electrical stimulation inside their brains. Rolando (255), following their lead, extended his experiments to pigs, goats, sheep, dogs and also to birds. The influential Magendie however had failed and had proclaimed the cortex electrically inexcitable; an opinion in which he was backed by Flourens (252). In these days before the neuron had been recognized as the unit of the nervous system, before the pyramidal fibers were known to be processes of cortical cells, there was no *a priori* reason to expect electrical stimulation of the cortical surface to have a peripheral effect, but soon an incontrovertible proof was to be given.

271. CABANIS, PIERRE J.-G. *Rapports du physique et du moral de l'homme.* Paris: Bibliothèque Choisie, 1830.

272. ZINN, JOHANN GOTTFRIED (1727–1759) AND A. HALLER. *Mémoires sur les parties sensibles et irritables du corps animal.* Lausanne: D'Arnay, 1760.

273. FONTANA, FELICE (1720–1805). *Accad. Sc. Ist. Bologna,* 1757.

274. CALDANI, LEOPOLDO (1725–1813). *Institutiones physiologicae et pathologicae.* Leyden: Luchtmans, 1784.

FIG. 32. One of the bizarre experiments of Aldini on two freshly-decapitated criminals. In the center is a voltaic pile, the circuit through the heads being completed by conducting arcs. Aldini, Galvani's impetuous nephew, lacked the sagacity and scientific acumen of his famous uncle. (From Aldini, G. *Essai Théorique et Expérimental sur le Galvanisme.* Paris: Fournier, 1804. 2 vol.)

FIG. 33. Two pioneers in attempts to stimulate the brain: the Abbé Fontana, physician to the Archduke of Tuscany and professor of physics in the University of Pisa; and Caldani, Galvani's predecessor in the chair of anatomy at Bologna. (The portrait of Fontana is reproduced by courtesy of Dr. G. Pupilli.)

The pioneers were Fritsch & Hitzig (275) (two young privatdocents in Berlin) with their now famous experiments in which they used a galvanic current and from which evolved the idea of a 'motor cortex.'

275. FRITSCH, GUSTAV THEODOR (1838–1891) AND EDUARD HITZIG (1838–1907). Über die elektrische Erregbarkeit des Grosshirns. *Arch. Anat. Physiol. wiss. Med. Leipzig* 37: 300, 1870.

FIG. 34. Gustav Fritsch and Edouard Hitzig. (Photographs reproduced by kind permission of Dr. A. E. Walker, for whom Professor Stender of Berlin obtained the picture of Hitzig.)

Ferrier (276–278), a few years later, in a long series of experiments using faradic stimulation in monkeys was able to bring out not merely muscle twitches of an indeterminate kind but also grosser movements. Of course, as we now know, these are imprecise and even athetoid in comparison with movements made by the animal naturally. Benefitting from the parallel development of electrical techniques, Victor Horsley, in a series of papers with Beevor (279, 280) in the next decade, described more closely the motor areas in the monkey cortex. From these experiments there emerged the designation of the precentral gyrus as predominantly motor in function and the postcentral as sensory. Between the two, Beevor & Horsley (281,

282) recognized an area which they called 'the zone of confusion.' An important point that emerged from their use of this technique was that in addition to areas of maximal representation of a given movement, the cortex also has marginal zones that are less specific. In other words, they found no sharp demarcation lines.

With Schaefer (283), Horsley went on to further studies of both motor and sensory function, using ablation as well as electrical excitation. The basic interest was of course in the application of these findings to man, especially in the light of the observations of Hughlings Jackson on the march of symptoms during the epileptic fit (284). Species differences came markedly to light when Beevor & Horsley compared their findings on the bonnet monkey with those in the orangutan. The first pioneers to attempt electrical stimulation of the cortex in man (through holes in the skull) were Bartholow in America in 1874 (285) and Sciamanna 8 years later in Italy (286). These were followed by Keen (287), in his youth an army surgeon in the American Civil War and later professor of surgery at Jefferson Medical College. In 1888, in a patient whose seizures began in the hand, he removed the area the stimulation of which caused movements of the wrist. He used a 'faradic battery,' and with it found areas for hand, elbow, shoulder and face movements. When respiration and circulation became poor, he revived the patient with brandy injected into the forearm. In the same year several other workers applied a similar technique in man but

276. FERRIER, DAVID (1843–1928). The localization of function in the brain. *Proc. Roy. Soc.* 22: 229, 1873–4.

277. FERRIER, D. Experiments on the brain of monkeys. *Phil. Trans.* 165: 433, 1876.

278. FERRIER, D. *The Function of the Brain.* London: Smith Elder, 1876.

279. BEEVOR, C. E. AND V. HORSLEY. A minute analysis (experimental) of the various movements produced by stimulating in the monkey different regions of the cortical centre for the upper limb as defined by Professor Ferrier. *Phil. Trans.* 178: 153, 1887.

280. BEEVOR, C. E. AND V. HORSLEY. A further minute analysis by electrical stimulation of the so-called motor region (facial area) of the cortex cerebri in the monkey. *Phil. Trans.* 185: 39, 1894.

281. BEEVOR, C. E. AND V. HORSLEY. An experimental investigation into the arrangement of the excitable fibres of

the internal capsule of the bonnet monkey. *Phil. Trans.* 181: 49, 1890.

282. BEEVOR, C. E. AND V. HORSLEY. A record of the results obtained by electrical excitation of the so-called motor cortex and internal capsule in the orang-utang. *Phil. Trans.* 181: 129, 1890.

283. HORSLEY, V. AND EDWARD ALBERT SCHAEFER (1850–1935). A record of experiments upon the functions of the cerebral cortex. *Phil. Trans.* 179: 1, 1888.

284. JACKSON, JOHN HUGHLINGS (1835–1911). Unilateral epileptiform seizures, attended by temporary defect of sight. *Med. Times Gaz.* 1: 588, 1863.

285. BARTHOLOW, ROBERTS (1831–1904). Experimental investigations into the functions of the human brain. *Am. J. M. Sc.* 67: 305, 1874.

286. SCIAMANNA, E. Gli avversari delle localizzazioni cerebrali. *Arch. psichiat. Turin* 3: 209, 1882.

287. KEEN, WILLIAM WILLIAMS (1837–1932). Three successful cases of cerebral surgery including (1) The removal of a large intracranial fibroma; (2) Exsection of damaged brain tissue; and (3) Exsection of the cerebral centre for the left hand; with remarks on the general technique of such operations. *Am. J. M. Sc.* 96: 329, 452, 1888.

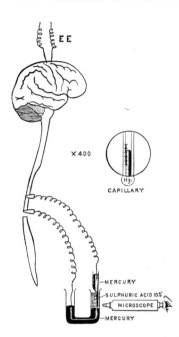

FIG. 35. Victor Horsley and one of his experiments on the localization of the motor cortex. (The latter illustration from *Trans. Congr. Am. Physic. Surg.* 1: 340, 1888.)

systematic exploration had to wait for Cushing, Foerster and Penfield in the modern age of neuro-surgery, and for the development of clinical neurophysiological investigation.

In the light of clinical observation and the results of electrical stimulation, the concept that the cortical grey matter acted as a whole and that motor function had no representation above the basal ganglia began to crumble. At this same period, the birth of a new technique brought yet another method of approach for the investigator. This was the recording of brain potentials evoked by sensory stimulation and the discovery of the brain's own electrical activity, the dawn of electroencephalography.

In 1875 Richard Caton (288), at the Royal Infirmary School of Medicine in Liverpool, while searching for the cerebral counterpart of du Bois-Reymond's action potential in nerve, not only found it, but noticed that when both of his electrodes lay on the cortical surface there was a continuous waxing and waning of potential. This oscillation of the base line was present in the unstimulated animal and Caton proved it to be unrelated to respiratory or cardiac rhythms. He also proved these fluctuations to be biological in origin by showing them to be vulnerable

to anoxia and to anesthesia and to be abolished by death of the animal. In his first work Caton's experimental animal was the rabbit and his detecting instrument was a Thomson's galvanometer. This was in the days before photographic recording of laboratory observations and Caton's first publication of his findings took the form of a demonstration before the British Medical Association (289). Superimposed on these oscillations Caton found potential swings related to sensory stimulation and realized immediately the meaning of this for cerebral localization studies. Caton went on to use monkeys and gave further reports of his results in 1877 and in 1887 (290), the latter at the International Medical Congress held that year in Washington, D. C.

Strangely enough, in spite of the prominent groups before whom Caton gave his demonstrations and the popular medical journal in which he reported them, his work received little attention at the time, even among English-speaking physiologists. Meanwhile in Poland, a young assistant in the physiology department of the University of Jagiellonski in Krakow,

288. CATON, RICHARD (1842–1926). The electric currents of the brain. *Brit. M. J.* 2: 278, 1875.

289. CATON, R. Interim report on investigation of the electric currents of the brain. *Brit. M. J.* 1: Suppl. 62, 1877.

290. CATON, R. Researches on electrical phenomena of cerebral grey matter. *Tr. Ninth Internat. Med. Congr.* 3: 246, 1887.

FIG. 36. Richard Caton, shown in his thirties at the period when he was working in electrophysiology. (From a photograph in possession of the writer, being the generous gift of Miss Anne Caton.)

Adolf Beck, not knowing of Caton's work 15 years earlier, was searching initially for the same phenomenon, namely for electrical signs in the brain of impulses reaching it from the periphery. Like Caton before him he succeeded, but he also found the brain wave. His animals were mostly dogs and he published the protocols of all his experiments in the Polish language for a doctoral thesis (291). In order to reach a wider audience he sent a short account to the most widely read journal in Germany, the *Centralblatt für Physiologie* (292). A spate of claims for priority for finding sensorily evoked potentials followed the German publication of Beck's findings—the first coming from Fleischl von Marxow, Professor of Physiology in Vienna (293), and the next from

Gotch and Horsley (294). It is noticeable that it was the electrical response of the brain to sensory stimulation that drew the most interest, for this was a finding that lay directly in the main stream of current thinking about cortical localization of function. The completely novel idea of a continuously fluctuating electrical potential intrinsic to the 'resting' brain was, at that time, of interest only to its two independent discoverers, Caton and Beck.

The somewhat acrimonious wrangle over priority was based in Fleischl von Marxow's case on work done in 1883. This had not been published but only noted down in a sealed letter which he had deposited with the University and which he asked to have opened after reading Beck's report in 1890. He was solely concerned with response potentials and noted "little or no movement of the base line." He was clearly unaware of Caton's reports and demonstrations. Gotch and Horsley's ignorance of their countryman's work is less easily understood. Caton was a prominent figure at Liverpool, the first holder of the Chair of Physiology in which Gotch was to follow him (and later Sherrington).

The dispute in the columns of the *Centralblatt* over priority for discovery of the electrical currents of the brain was finally stilled by a letter from Caton (295), drawing the attention of the protagonists to his publication of 15 years earlier. By the turn of the century the electrical activity of the brain had reached the textbooks (296). Caton's interests had developed along many lines and he became prominent in several fields of medicine and scholarship as well as in public affairs, becoming in turn President of the Medical Institution and Lord Mayor of Liverpool. Beck (297), who at the age of 32 became professor of Physiology at the University of Lvov, continued to work on the subject into this century, publishing with his old professor Cybulski, and interest was thereby aroused in Germany and in Russia. He met a tragic death during the German occupation of Poland.

291. BECK, ADOLF (1863–1942). *Oznaczenie lokalizacyi w mozgu i rdzeniu za pomoca zjawisk elektry czynch* (Thesis). Krakow: Univ. Jagiellonski, 1890.

292. BECK, A. Die Bestimmung der Localisation der Gehirn und Rüchenmarksfunktionin vermittelst der elektrischen Erscheinungen. *Centralbl. Physiol.* 4: 473, 1890.

293. FLEISCHL VON MARXOW, ERNST. Mittheilung betreffend die Physiologie der Hirnrinde (letter to the editor dated Vienna, Nov. 24, 1890). *Centralbl. Physiol.* 4: 537, 1890.

294. GOTCH, F. AND V. HORSLEY. Über den Gebrauch der Elektricität für die Localzirung der Erregungserscheinungen im Centralnervensystem (letter to the editor received Jan. 17, 1891). *Centralbl. Physiol.* 4: 649, 1891.

295. CATON, R. Die Ströme des Centralnervensystems (letter to the editor received Feb. 22, 1891). *Centralbl. Physiol.* 4: 785, 1891.

296. SCHÄFER, E. A. *Textbook of Physiology.* Edinburgh: Young & Pentland; London: Morrison & Gibb; 1898, 1900. 2 vol.

297. BECK, A. AND NAPOLEON CYBULSKI. Weitere Untersuchungen über die elektrischen Erscheinungen in der Hirnrinde der Affen und Hunde. *Centralbl. Physiol.* 6: 1, 1892.

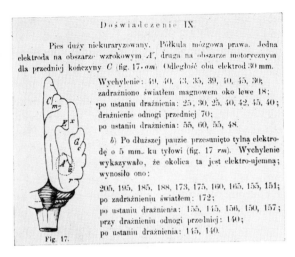

FIG. 37. Beck and protocol from one of the experiments in his original thesis on the electrical phenomena of the brain and spinal cord, 1890. (Obtained through the courtesy of Dr. Andrei Jus of Pruszkow.)

Interest became widespread in 1929 with the first publication on brain potentials in man. In that year Hans Berger (298), a psychiatrist in a hospital in Jena, revealed to the scientific world the results of work he had been pursuing in secretive seclusion for over 5 years. He had repeated and confirmed the findings of Caton (to whom he gave full credit) and had extended them to man. He studied (and named) the electroencephalogram in normal man, finding the two major rhythms, alpha and beta, that Neminski had found in dogs (299). He applied Caton's tests for the biological origin of the potentials he found, showing them to be affected by hypoxia and by anesthesia. He also found them to be changed by sleep.

Berger's outstanding contribution was the foundation of clinical electroencephalography. Having proved that brain waves could be recorded in man through the unopened skull, he went on to demonstrate that their characteristics could be used as an index of brain disease and thus he opened up a new line of approach for the physiologist and the clinician to the study of brain mechanisms. Berger's major discovery in the clinical field was that the electroencephalogram is abnormal in epilepsy. He did not with

298. BERGER, HANS (1873–1941). Über das Elektrenkephalogramm des Menschen. *Arch. Psychiat.* 87: 527, 1929.

299. PRAWDITZ-NEMINSKI, W. W. Zur Kenntnis der elektrischen und der Innervationsvorgänge in den funktionellen Elementen und Geweben des tierischen Organismus. Elektrocerebrogramm der Säugertiere. *Arch. ges. Physiol.* 209: 362, 1925.

FIG. 38. Hans Berger, the first to record electroencephalographic potentials from man, and the founder of clinical electroencephalography. Below is the first published electroencephalogram of man. The subject was Berger's son, Klaus. His alpha rhythm is shown in the upper trace above a 10 per sec. sine wave from an oscillator.

centainty record the spikes that are now associated with the seizure discharge, for with the technique he used there was serious interference by muscle potentials. His instruments were a double-coil galvanometer and a string galvanometer, and in much of his initial work he used only two electrodes, these being large plates fixed one to the forehead and one to the back of the head. He thus missed the localizing potentialities of the EEG, and in addition gathered in all the muscle potentials of the frontalis and trapezius muscles. In later experiments he changed to needle electrodes pushed into the skin. In his early experiments he tried a reference electrode consisting of a silver spoon held in the subject's mouth. The development of concepts about the EEG concomitants of grand mal epilepsy had their grounding in Fischer's (300) recordings during experimentally-induced seizures in dogs.

The demonstration of the 3 per sec. wave-and-spike formation so typical of the petit mal type of epilepsy was the achievement of the team of Lennox, Davis and the Gibbses at the Harvard Medical School (301). This discovery (which Berger came very close to making), together with that of Grey Walter (302) published the following year (1936), namely that brain tumors can be located through the skull by the abnormally slow waves of their surrounding tissue, form the two main foundations of clinical electroencephalography. Altenburg & Foerster (303) had during a brain operation found abnormal potentials associated with a tumor, but Walter's demonstration that neoplasms could be located by the reversal of sign of the slow waves recorded from the unopened head and his confirmation that the tumor itself was electrically silent made this a practical clinical test. The subsequent expansion and development of electroencephalography is part of the continuing story of modern times not yet history.

In the history of electroencephalography one other figure should be mentioned. One year after Caton's discovery, Danilewsky, the Russian neurophysiologist, noted the same phenomenon of oscillating cortical potentials in the absence of applied sensory stimulation in five dogs on which he was experimenting. He did not publish this at the time and reported it only

in retrospect (304) as a confirmation of Caton's original observation. Danilewsky's primary interest lay in the autonomic effects of stimulation of the cortex, such as arterial pressure changes (305), and in the mechanisms of temperature control (306), and he was active in the design of new instrumentation for electrophysiological experimentation (307). Together with his brother (Alexis Y. Danilewsky) he was prominent among the Russian physiologists at the end of the nineteenth century.

In the latter half of the nineteenth century, Russian neurophysiology saw a development that was to influence all future concepts about the brain and behavior. At this period it was usual for Russian physiologists to go to centers in Western Europe for training and experience under the outstanding teachers of the time, and to Müller's laboratory in 1856 came I. M. Sechenov. Sechenov, later to be known as 'the father of Russian neurophysiology' was then 27 years old and during the next 6 years he received training from six of the more outstanding physiologists: Müller, du Bois-Reymond, Ludwig, von Helmholtz, Bunsen and Claude Bernard. The influence of these leaders can be traced in Sechenov's later thought and development. Among them, only one, Müller, retained even a lingering trace of allegiance to the concept of a vital force, and with him Sechenov had the least contact, for Müller was at the end of his life, still lecturing but no longer experimenting.

In neurophysiology the most influential of Sechenov's teachers were du Bois-Reymond and Claude Bernard. Sechenov took du Bois-Reymond's course in animal electricity and in 1860 returned to St. Petersburg with one of his master's induction coil stimulators and a galvanometer and with them introduced electrophysiology into Russian science. Two years later he was back in Western Europe, this time in Claude Bernard's laboratory in Paris, and it was here that the experiments were made that were to mold his thinking and to suggest to him a concept of brain mechanisms later to flower in the hands of Pavlov into the theory that has dominated Russian neuro-

300. FISCHER, MAX H. Elektrobiologische Auswirkungen von Krampfgiften am Zentralnervensystem. *Med. Klin.* (*Munich*) 29: 15, 1933.

301. GIBBS, F. A., H. DAVIS AND W. G. LENNOX. The EEG in epilepsy and in conditions of impaired consciousness. *A. M. A. Arch. Neurol. & Psychiat.* 34: 1133, 1935.

302. WALTER, W. GREY. The location of cerebral tumours by electroencephalography. *Lancet* 2: 305, 1936.

303. FOERSTER, O. AND H. ALTENBURGER. Elektrobiologische Vorgange an der menschlichen Hirnrinde. *Deutsche Ztschr. Nervenh.* 135: 277, 1935.

304. DANILEWSKY, VASILI YAKOVLEVICH (1852–1939). Zur Frage über die elektromotorischen Vorgänge im Gehirn als Ausdruck seines Thätig keitszustandes. *Centralbl. Physiol.* 5: 1, 1891.

305. DANILEWSKY, V. Y. Experimentelle Beiträge zur Physiologie des Gehirns. *Arch. ges. Physiol.* 11: 128, 1875.

306. DANILEWSKY, V. Y. Die Verbrennungswarme der Nahrungsmittel. *Biol. Zentralbl.* 2: 371, 1882.

307. DANILEWSKY, V. Y. A new electrical machine for rhythmically altering the strength of galvanic currents (in Russian). *Vratsch.* 22, 1883.

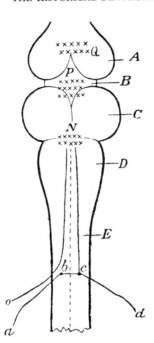

FIG. 39. Ivan Michailovich Sechenov and his diagram illustrating reflex arcs in the spinal cord and brain of the frog. *a-b-c-d* represents a spinal reflex arc with sensory (*a-b*), central (*b-c*) and motor (*c-d*) components. The reflex arc of the brain consists of the sensory nerve (*O*), the central component (*N-c*) and the motor efferent (*c-d*). *P* is the region in the brain stem where Sechenov concluded the inhibitory apparatus lay.

physiology ever since, the theory of conditional reflexes.

Sechenov's experiments that proved so crucial to his future thinking were on the effect on reflex movements of salt crystals placed at various levels of the transected neuraxis (308). His preparation (309) was the decapitated frog, a toe of which he dipped into acid, a procedure that had been developed by Türck. He timed the interval between stimulus and onset of withdrawal of the frog's foot by counting the beats of a metronome. In this way he got some index of the degree to which application of the salt crystal to the brain stem slowed withdrawal. Sechenov interpreted lengthening of withdrawal time as inhibition of reflex activity. The selection of a salt crystal as a stimulus seems strange in the hands of a pupil of du Bois-Reymond's and is reminiscent of Marshall Hall's use of it half a century earlier to study depression and

augmentation of spinal reflexes. Only later (310) did Sechenov use electrical stimulation in his experiments on the 'spontaneous' variations of spinal cord potentials which he regarded as signs of activity in the spinal centers. This was the first experimental approach towards a centrally exerted inhibitory action on skeletal ('voluntary') muscle.

Although at this stage his own experimental evidence seemed slender, Sechenov must have been pondering its meaning in much wider terms, for a year later, on his return to Russia, he published as a series of articles the essay (311) that proved to be so influential in Russian physiology. This essay on the *Reflexes of the Brain* was later (1866) published as a book after a stormy period during which efforts were made to suppress its publication and censure its author. This opposition was stirred by Sechenov's assertion that all higher brain function was a material reflex consisting of three sectors—an afferent initiation by sensory inflow, a central process entirely sub-

308. SECHENOV, IVAN MICHAILOVICH (1829–1905). *Physiologische Studien über die Hemmungsmechanismus für die Reflexthätigkeit des Rückenmarks im Gehirne des Frosches*. Berlin: Hirschwald, 1863.

309. SECHENOV, I. M. Note sur les moderateurs des mouvements reflexes dans le cerveau de la grenouille. *Acad. Sc., Paris* 1863.

310. SECHENOV, I. M. Galvanische Erscheinungen an dem Verlangerten Marke des Frosches. *Arch. ges. Physiol.* 27: 524, 1882.

311. SECHENOV, I. M. *Reflexes of the Brain*. Medizinsky Vestnik, 1863; English translation in *Sechenov's Selected Works*. Moscow-Leningrad: State Publ. House, 1935, p. 263.

ject to physical laws and an efferent component result-ing in a muscular movement. All reactions, however they might be described in common parlance as pleasure, fear, distress or other descriptive terms were, according to him, in essence muscular in expression. During the passage of the inflow through the central portion of the arc there could either be excitation which would augment the reflex motor response (as in so-called emotional states) or inhibition which would decrease the reflex muscular movement, the resultant being 'rational' controlled behavior. It is interesting that Sechenov conceived that inhibition could be learned and that with maturity an increase in the degree of inhibition exerted was achieved.

Thus, according to Sechenov, all human behavior was a balance between inhibition and excitation operating mechanically at the central link of the re-flex arc. A so-called 'willed' movement according to him only apparently lacked the first component of the arc, its afferent inflow being material memory traces left by external stimuli in the past. It was in elaborat-ing this part of his theory that Sechenov approached the concept of the conditional reflex, for he postulated that the memory trace of a past sensory experience could be evoked by the recurrence of any fraction of it even if this fraction were quite insignificant and unrelated in its apparent meaning. This is essentially the principle underlying the formulation of the condi-tional reflex theory, namely the potency of an indiffer-ent external stimulus provided it is repeatedly time-locked to the original experience. One further point should be noted in this early attempt to relate mental processes to brain physiology. Sechenov believed that man had the special faculty of increasing the degree of inhibition exerted at the central link until a level of total inhibition of the efferent discharge was reached, and he held that thought was an example of this condition.

Although terms such as 'cerebral reflexes' and 'psychical reflexes' abound in the nineteenth century literature, they were mostly used by psychologists to describe automatisms. At this period only a few writers had broached the problem of explaining mental processes in physiological terms. Thomas Lay-cock (312), whose belief in cortical localization no doubt influenced his pupil Hughlings Jackson, wrote in 1845 a paper *On the reflex function of the brain*. In this he stated his belief that "the brain although the organ of consciousness, was subject to the laws of reflex ac-tion, and that in this respect it did not differ from other ganglia of the nervous system." He too envisaged a three-component arc, the central link in the brain being one where 'ideagenous' changes took place that influenced the motor output. He came close to antic-ipating one of Sechenov's postulates by stating that the actual sensory impression of an object or the mere idea of it could evoke the same 'ideagenous' change in the brain and result in a similar reflex motor effect. So firmly did Laycock believe in the neuronal basis of ideas that he calculated how many there could be to the square inch of grey matter (the answer was 8000) and argued that "as there must be an immense number of square inches of surface in the grey matter extended through the cerebrospinal axis of man, there is space sufficient for millions." We find echoes of this kind of calculation in some of today's conjectures about the number of possible interconnections in the brain.

Laycock did not test his hypotheses by experiment though he argued from a basis of clinical observation, for he said "an experiment is occasionally made by nature." There is no evidence that Sechenov was aware of Laycock's ideas, although he was influenced by the writings of two other nonexperimentalists, Herbert Spencer (313) and George Henry Lewes (314). These two men, united through their relation-ships with George Eliot, were influential not only on Sechenov but on Pavlov. Their writings, now largely unread, were translated into Russian almost immedi-ately after publication and were everywhere highly regarded. Spencer's work was an argument for cortical representation of mental function, and Hughlings Jackson was one who expressed indebtedness to him. Spencer based much of his argument on comparative evolution though he was writing 4 years before the publication of the *Origin of the Species* by Darwin (315), another writer whose books were extremely influential on Russian thought. Spencer stressed localization of mental processes, saying that "whoever calmly considers the question cannot long resist the conviction that different parts of the brain must in some way or other subserve different kinds of mental action." When we find in his *Autobiography* (316) that

312. LAYCOCK, THOMAS (1812–1876). On the reflex function of the brain. *Brit. & For. Med. Rev.* 19: 298, 1845.

313. SPENCER, HERBERT (1820–1903). *Principles of Psychology.* 1855. 2 vol.

314. LEWES, GEORGE HENRY (1817–1878). *The Physiology of the Common Life.* London: Blackwood, 1859. 2 vol.

315. DARWIN, CHARLES ROBERT (1809–1882). *On the Origin of Species by means of Natural Selection or the Preservation of Favoured Races in the Struggle for Life.* London: John Murray, 1859.

316. SPENCER, H. *An Autobiography.* London: Williams & Norgate, 1904. 2 vol.

FIG. 40. Ivan Petrovich Pavlov (reproduced from Babkin's *Pavlov, A Biography* by permission of the publishers, University of Chicago Press). On the right Pavlov watching an experiment (Sovfoto ⁂319573 Moscow USSR).

he had the bumps on his head read by a phrenologist (with flattering interpretations)[29] we perceive a derivation of his ideas from Gall and Spurzheim. Spencer became hypochondriacal about his own head, believing it to have an inadequate blood supply. To improve the circulation he exercised at rowing and at racquets in 15 min. spurts, dictating his books in the intervals between exertions. His friend, Lewes (317) in his *Physical Basis of Mind* was doubtful about the localization of the various mental processes but convinced of their physiological nature.

Pavlov, the towering figure of Russian neurophysiology, repeatedly throughout his life stressed his indebtedness to Sechenov[30] and to Lewes[31] (whose book on physiology he read when a schoolboy). The influence of these men, one too little known outside Russia, one almost forgotten, was so great that they feature not only in the scientific writings of the times but in Russian fiction. Turgeniev is said to have taken Sechenov as his model for the science student, Bazarov, in *Fathers and Sons* and Dostoievsky cited the reading of Lewes' book as a sign of education in the wife of a drunk in *Crime and Punishment*.

Pavlov dated his interest in the digestive system (318) from reading Lewes, an interest that was to occupy the first 25 years of his working life and to win for him the Nobel Prize. And it was a feature of the digestive system, the salivary apparatus, that was to be drawn by him into the work suggested by Sech-

enov's theories of 30 years before. Fundamental in Pavlov's thinking (319) was the concept of temporary connections established in the cortex by the repetition of external stimuli linked only by a constant time interval, although one gets the impression that he thought more in terms of influence than of specific neuronal connections. Thus, for example, in his classical experiment, the repeated sound of a metronome, at a fixed interval before food was made available to his experimental dogs, caused salivation to begin with shorter and shorter latency and at an increasing rate. Later more complex situations were developed as laboratory procedures, and this type of reflex was used for mapping the response of the cerebral cortex to various sensory inputs, Pavlov (319) naming the areas as 'analyzers' for the various modalities.

The instability and temporary character of the conditioned reflex in contrast to that of the inborn

319. PAVLOV, I. P. *Lectures on Conditioned Reflexes*, English translation by W. H. Gantt. New York: Internat. Pub., 1928.

[29] The opening sentence of the phrenologist's report read: "Such a head ought to be in the Church." When we seek the basis for this statement in the itemized score for Spencer's bumps, we find both Firmness and Self-esteem 'very large;' Language 'rather full,' and Wit and Amativeness only 'moderate.'

[30] See Shaternikov, M. N. The life of I. M. Sechenov. In: *Sechenov, Selected Works.* Moscow-Leningrad: State Publ. House, 1935.

[31] See Babkin, B. P. *Pavlov.* Chicago: Univ. Chicago Press, 1949, p, 214.

317. LEWES, G. H. *The Physical Basis of Mind.* Boston, 1877.
318. PAVLOV, I. P. (1849–1936). *Lectures on the Work of the Principal Digestive Glands* (in Russian). St. Petersburg: Kushnerev, 1897; translated into English by W. H. Thompson. London: Griffin, 1902.

unconditioned reflexes serving instinctual movements for preservation of life led to Pavlov's ideas of cortical inhibition and its relationship to sleep and hypnosis. Pavlov distinguished between natural conditional reflexes learned in early life and the artificially conditional reflexes of the laboratory. Among the first he classed the connections formed in infancy between the smell or sight of food and the salivary response. This observation goes back many centuries and is well described by Whytt (181), who like Laycock after him, recognized that the 'idea' could be as powerful a stimulus as the sensory impression.

Pavlov had in his youth been a student of Ludwig and of Heidenhain; from the former he had brought the insistence on a physical basis for all biological processes and from the latter an interest in secretory mechanisms and the phenomena of hypnosis. The fertility of Pavlov's ideas and his indefatigable energy drew to him an enthusiastic school of workers and by the 1920's he had a large team working under him on the many features of establishment, reinforcement, extinction and inhibition of conditional reflexes. He was a well-loved teacher, though a man of fiery temperament. Sherrington has left a vignette of him at the age of 65 describing him as "overflowing with energy, although an elderly man; he was spare in figure and alert and humourous in manner." Even at the end of a long working day on encountering a stairway he "ran up it rather than walked." Sherrington came away from this visit, made in 1914, with a great enthusiasm for the leader of Russian neurophysiology (320).

Pavlov's ideas of the reflex became more diffuse and more nebulous as he grew older. Experiments to test the modes of behavior of animals to conditioning stimuli were less difficult to design than ones to test the hypothesis advanced to explain them. Temporary neuronal connections in the cortex proved easier to postulate than to prove. Pavlov's own attempts were with decorticate preparations (a technique that had been used before him by Sechenov) and it is only in recent times that the electrophysiologist's tools have been applied to this problem.

320. SHERRINGTON, C. S. Marginalia. In: *Science, Medicine and History. Essays in Honour of C. Singer*, edited by E. A. Underwood. London: Oxford, 1953.

As the second half of the twentieth century unfolds the neurophysiologist in his search for brain mechanisms continues to use the three main categories of experimental procedure: anatomical, ablative and electrical. It is the great advance in electrical stimulation and recording that marks this era of investigation from its predecessors, although it is only through knowledge from all sources that progress can be achieved in an understanding of the brain.

Neurophysiology came into being as a specialized branch of endeavor when the nervous system no longer had to compete with the humors and with the blood as the principal coordinator of the body. With the recognition that sensation and motion were mediated by the nerves their position became unassailable, for movement was regarded as the sign of life. Slowly the concept of neural organization began to be pieced together and levels of integration were postulated, in the spinal cord, in the cortex and in the deeper structures of the brain. The period of analysis of the function of each structural unit, of each sector of the nervous system, was followed by a shift of emphasis towards a synthetic consideration of neural activity. The search began for the physiological mechanisms of mental processes, of consciousness, of memory—all terms and concepts that had belonged to another domain of thought. In the neurophysiology of today we find both angles of approach, ranging from analysis of the intimate physicochemical basis of nervous structure and dynamics to the synthesis of action that we call behavior of the organism.

The writer expresses her great indebtedness to the authors of many articles and books not listed in the abridged bibliography that follows. She adds her thanks to those who have sent her material in correspondence, and in particular would mention appreciatively: Dr. Maria Rooseboom for the use of material and microfilms from the National Museum for the History of Science at Leiden; Dr. Palle Birkelund, Director of the Danish Royal Library; Dr. Auguste Tournay for a photostat copy of Pourfour du Petit's *Letters*; the Institution of Electrical Engineers and Miss Helen G. Thompson for access to material collected by Silvanus P. Thompson on Gilberd; Miss Anne Caton for family photographs and material from the diaries of Richard Caton; Dr. Andrei Jus of Pruszkov for photostats of Adolf Beck's doctoral thesis; and F. Czubalski of Warsaw for information about Beck's works. For details of Beck's life the writer expresses warm appreciation to his daughter, Mme. Jadwiga Zahrzewska.

A SHORT LIST OF SECONDARY SOURCES

Space does not permit the listing of all the articles to whose authors the writer is indebted for information. The following books have been selected for the special interest they may have for the physiologist. Where possible, works in the English language have been chosen.

BENCE JONES, H. *On Animal Electricity*. London: Churchill, 1852.
BETTMANN, O. L. *A Pictorial History of Medicine*. Springfield: Thomas, 1956.
BORING, E. G. *A History of Experimental Psychology*. New York: Appleton, 1929.

BOSTOCK, J. *Sketch of the History of Medicine from its Origin to the Commencement of the Nineteenth Century*. London: Sherwood, Gilbert and Piper, 1835.

BROWN, G. B. *Science, its Method and its Philosophy*. London: Allen & Unwin, 1951.

CANGUILHEM, G. *La Formation du Concept de Réflexe*. Paris: Presses univ. France, 1955.

CASTIGLIONI, A. *Italian Medicine*. New York: Hoeber, 1932, Clio Medica Series, vol. 6.

CASTIGLIONI, A. *A History of Medicine* (2nd ed.). New York: Knopf, 1947.

COMRIE, J. D. *A History of Scottish Medicine*. London: Wellcome Historical Medical Museum, 1932.

CORNER, G. W. *Anatomy*. New York: Hoeber, 1930, Clio Medica Series, vol. 3.

COOKE, J. *A Treatise on Nervous Diseases*. Boston: Wells and Lilly, 1824. (Previously published in England.)

DAMPIER, W. C. *A History of Science*. Cambridge: Cambridge, 1946.

DANA, C. *Textbook of Nervous Diseases*. New York: Wm. Wood, 1925. (Includes a chapter by F. H. Garrison on the history of neurology.)

DAREMBERG, C. *Essai sur la détermination et les caractères des périodes de l'histoire de la médecine*. Gaz. med. Paris, 1850.

FEARING, F. *Reflex Action*. Baltimore: Williams & Wilkins, 1930.

FOSTER, M. *Textbook of Physiology* (1st American ed.), edited by E. T. Reichert. Philadelphia: H. C. Lea's son and Co., 1880. (1st English ed., 1876.)

FOSTER, M. *Lectures on the History of Physiology*. Cambridge: Cambridge, 1901.

FRANKLIN, K. *A Short History of Physiology*. London: Staples, 1949.

FULTON, J. F. *Muscular Contraction and the Reflex Control of Movement*. Baltimore: Williams & Wilkins, 1926.

FULTON, J. F. *Selected Readings in the History of Physiology*. Springfield: Thomas, 1930.

FULTON, J. F. *Physiology*. New York: Hoeber, 1931, Clio Medica Series, vol. 5.

FULTON, J. F. *Physiology of the Nervous System* (3rd ed.). New York: Oxford, 1949.

GARRISON, F. H. *An Introduction to the History of Medicine*. Philadelphia: Saunders, 1929.

HALL, A. R. *The Scientific Revolution 1500–1800*. London: Longmans, 1954.

HAMILTON, W. *The History of Medicine, Surgery and Anatomy from the Creation of the World, to the Commencement of the Nineteenth Century*. London: Colburn and Bentley, 1831.

LENARD, P. *Great Men of Science*, translated by H. S. Hatfield. New York: Macmillan, 1933.

MAJOR, R. *A History of Medicine*. Springfield: Thomas, 1954.

MORGAN, C. E. *Electro-Physiology and Therapeutics*. New York: Wood, 1868.

MORTON, L. T. AND F. H. GARRISON. *A Medical Bibliography* (2nd ed.). London: Grafton, 1954.

NORDENSKIÖLD, E. *History of Biology*, translated by L. B. Eyre. New York: Tudor, 1935.

PETTIGREW, T. J. *Medical Portrait Gallery. Biographical Memoirs of the most Celebrated Physicians, Surgeons, etc.* London: Fisher, 1872. 3 vol.

POTAMIN (BROTHER) AND J. J. WALSH. *Makers of Electricity*. New York: Fordham Univ. Press, 1909.

RENOUARD, P. V. *History of Medicine from its Origin to the Nineteenth Century*, translated by C. G. Comegys. Philadelphia: Lippincott, 1856. 2 vol.

ROTHSCHUH, K. E. *Geschichte der Physiologie*. Berlin: Springer, 1953.

RUSSELL, T. R. *The History of Heroes of the Art of Medicine*. London: Murray, 1861.

SCHÄFER, E. A. *Textbook of Physiology*. Edinburgh and London: Y. J. Pentland, 1898, vol. 1; 1900, vol. 2.

SHRYOCK, R. H. *The Development of Modern Medicine*. New York: Knopf, 1947.

SINGER, C. *A Short History of Medicine*. New York: Oxford, 1928.

SINGER, C. J. *Essays on the History of Medicine*. London: Oxford, 1924.

SINGER, C. J. *The Evolution of Anatomy; a Short History of Anatomical and Physiological Discovery to Harvey*. London: Paul, Trench, Trubner, 1925.

SOURY, J. *Le Système nerveux central. Structure et Fonctions*. Paris: Carré et Naud, 1899.

SPRENGEL, K. *Histoire de la Médecine*, translated and abridged from the 2nd German ed. by A. J. L. Jourdan. Paris: Deterville, 1792–1803. 2 vol.

STIRLING, W. *Some Apostles of Physiology*. London: Waterlow, 1902.

SUDHOFF, K. *Essays in the History of Medicine*, English translation edited by F. H. Garrison. New York: Medical Life Press, 1926.

WHEWELL, W. *History of the Inductive Sciences*. London: Parker 1857. 3 vol.

WHITTAKER, E. T. *History of the Theories of Aether and Electricity from the Age of Descartes to the Close of the Nineteenth Century*. London and New York: Longmans, Green and Co., 1910, revised 1951, second volume added 1953.

WIGHTMAN, W. P. D. *The Growth of Scientific Ideas*. New Haven: Yale Univ. Press, 1951.

WILKINSON, C. H. *Elements of Galvanism in Theory and Practice*. London: Murray, 1804.

WOLF, A. *A History of Science, Technology and Philosophy in the 16th and 17th Centuries* (2nd ed.). London: Allen and Unwin, 1950.

WOLF, A. *A History of Science, Technology and Philosophy in the 18th Century* (2nd ed.). London: Allen and Unwin, 1952.

BIOGRAPHIES

For each of the following scientists one biographical study only has been listed. Again the choice has been made on the grounds of interest to the physiologist and, where possible, text in the English language.

ARISTOTLE. Taylor, A. E. *Aristotle*. London: Nelson, 1943.

BACON, FRANCIS (1561–1626). Farrington, B. *Francis Bacon, Philosopher of Industrial Science*. New York: Schuman, 1949.

BAGLIVI, GIORGIO (1668–1707). Stenn, F. Giorgio Baglivi. *Ann. Med. Hist.* (3rd ser.) 3: 183, 1941.

BELL, CHARLES (1774–1842). Pichot, A. *The Life and Labours of Sir Charles Bell*. London: Bentley, 1880.

BERGER, HANS (1873–1942). Ginzberg, R. Three years with Hans Berger. A contribution to his biography. *J. Hist. Med.* 4: 361, 1949.

BERNARD, CLAUDE (1813–1878). Olmsted, J. M. D. and E. H.

Olmsted. *Claude Bernard, Physiologist, and the Experimental Method in Medicine.* New York: Schuman, 1952.

BICHAT, MARIE FRANCOIS XAVIER (1771–1802). Busquet, P. *Les Biographies Médicales* I: 37, 1927.

BOERHAAVE, HERMANN (1668–1738). Burton, W. *An Account of the Life and Writings of Hermann Boerhaave.* London: Lintot, 1743.

COTUGNO, DOMENICO (1736–1822). Levinson, A. Domenico Cotugno. *Ann. Med. Hist.* 8: 1, 1936.

DA VINCI, LEONARDO (1452–1519). O'Malley, C. D. and J. B. deC. M. Saunders. *Leonardo da Vinci on the Human Body.* New York: Schuman, 1952.

DESCARTES, RENÉ (1596–1650). Haldane, E. *The Life of René Descartes.* London, 1905.

FERNEL, JEAN (1497–1558). Sherrington, C. S. *The Endeavour of Jean Fernel.* Cambridge: Cambridge, 1946.

FONTANA, FELICE (1730–1805). Marchand, J. F. and H. E. Hoff. Felice Fontana. The Laws of Irritability. *J. Hist. Med.* 10: 197, 302, 399, 1955.

GALEN (130–200). Sarton, G. *Galen of Pergamon.* Lawrence: Univ. Kansas Press, 1954.

GALL, FRANZ JOSEPH (1758–1828). Temkin, O. Gall and the phrenological movement. *Bull. Hist. Med.* 21: 275, 1947.

GALVANI, ALOYSIUS (1737–1798). Fulton, J. F. and H. Cushing. A biographical sketch of the Galvani and Aldini writings on animal electricity. *Ann. Sci.* 1: 239, 1936.

GILBERD, WILLIAM (1540 or 1544–1603). Waldron, F. G. *Biographical Mirrour.* London: Harding, 1795.

HALES, STEPHEN (1677–1761). Burget, G. E. Stephen Hales, 1677–1761. *Ann. Med. Hist.* 7: 109, 1925.

HALL, MARSHALL (1790–1857). Hall, Charlotte. *Memoirs of Marshall Hall.* London, 1861.

HARVEY, WILLIAM (1578–1657). Chauvois, L. *William Harvey. His Life and Times: his Discoveries: his Methods.* London: Hutchinson, 1957.

HORSLEY, VICTOR ALEXANDER HADEN (1857–1916). Paget, S. *Sir Victor Horsley, a Study of his Life and Work.* New York: Harcourt Brace, 1920.

HUNTER, JOHN (1728–1793). Paget, S. *John Hunter.* London: Fisher Unwin, 1897.

LINACRE, THOMAS (1460–1524). Johnson, J. N. *The Life of Thomas Linacre.* London, 1835.

LUDWIG, CARL FRIEDRICH WILHELM (1816–1895). Lombard, W. P. The Life and Work of Carl Ludwig. *Science* 44: 363, 1916.

MAGENDIE, FRANÇOIS (1783–1855). Olmsted, J. M. D. *François Magendie.* New York: Schuman, 1944.

MONRO, ALEXANDER (1697–1762) AND MONRO, ALEXANDER

SECUNDUS (1733–1817). Inglis, J. A. *The Monros of Auchinbowie.* Edinburgh, 1911.

MÜLLER, JOHANNES (1801–1858). Häberling, W. *Johannes Müller.* Leipzig, 1924.

NOLLET, JEAN ANTOINE. Torlais, J. *Un Physicien au Siècle des Lumières: Abbé Nollet.* Paris: Siprico, 1954.

OERSTED, HANS CHRISTIAN (1770–1851). Stauffer, R. C. Speculation and experiment in the background of Oersted's discovery of electromagnetism. *Isis* 48: 33, 1957.

PAVLOV, IVAN PETROVICH (1849–1936). Babkin, B. P. *Pavlov.* Chicago: Univ. Chicago Press, 1949.

PROCHASKA, JIRI (1749–1820). Laycock, T. Introduction. To: *The Principles of Physiology.* London: Sydenham Society, 1851, p. ix.

RAMÓN Y CAJAL, SANTIAGO (1852–1934). Cannon, D. *Explorer of the Human Brain.* New York: Schuman, 1949.

SECHENOV, IVAN MIHAILOVICH (1829–1905). Shaternikov, M. N. The life of I. M. Sechenov (in English). In: *Sechenov, Selected Works.* Moscow-Leningrad: State Publ. House, 1935.

STAHL, GEORG ERNST (1660–1734). Metzger, H. *Newton, Stahl, Boerhaave et la doctrine chimique.* Paris: Alcan, 1930.

STENSEN, NICHOLAS (1638–1686). *Nicolaus Steno and His Indice,* edited by G. Scherz. Copenhagen: Munksgaard, 1958.

UNZER, JOHANN AUGUST (1727–1799). Laycock, T. Introduction. To: *The Principles of Physiology.* London: Sydenham Society, 1851, p. i.

VAN LEEUWENHOEK, ANTONJ (1672–1723). Dobell, C. *Antony van Leeuwenhoek and his "Little Animals."* New York: Harcourt Brace, 1932.

VESALIUS, ANDREAS (1514–1564). Cushing, H. *A Bio-bibliography of Andreas Vesalius.* New York: Schuman, 1943.

VOLTA, ALESSANDRO (1745–1827). Cohen, I. B. Introduction. To: Galvani's *Commentary,* English translation by M. G. Foley. Norwalk: Burndy Library, 1954.

VON GUERICKE, OTTO (1602–1686). Hoffmann, F. W. *Otto von Guericke.* Magdeburg, 1874.

VON HALLER, ALBRECHT (1708–1777). Klotz, O. Albrecht von Haller 1708–1777. *Ann. Med. Hist.* 8: 10, 1936. Also: Hemmeter, J. C. Albrecht von Haller, his scientific, literary and poetic activity. *Bull. Johns Hopkins Hosp.* 19: 65, 1908.

VON HELMHOLTZ, HERMANN LUDWIG FERDINAND (1821–1894). McKendrick, J. G. *H. L. F. von Helmholtz.* London: Unwin, 1899.

VON HUMBOLDT, FREDERICK ALEXANDER (1769–1859). de Terra, H. *The Life and Times of Alexander von Humboldt.* New York: Knopf, 1955.

WHYTT, ROBERT (1714–1766). Seller, W. *Memoir of the Life and Writings of Robert Whytt, M. D.* Edinburgh: Neill, 1862.

WILLIS, THOMAS (1621–1675). Miller, W. S. Thomas Willis (1621–1675). *Bull. Soc. Med. Hist. Chicago* 3: 215, 1923

CHAPTER II

Neuron physiology—introduction

J. C. ECCLES | *Department of Physiology, Australian National University, Canberra, Australia*

CHAPTER CONTENTS

MORPHOLOGICAL FEATURES OF THE NEURON

THE CONCEPT that the nervous system is composed of discrete units or nerve cells was first proposed in 1886-7 by His and Forel, later it was strongly supported by van Gehuchten and Cajal, and finally in 1891 it was given an appropriate nomenclature, 'neuron' and 'neuron-theory', by Waldeyer. Although all the great neurohistologists of that classical era were ranged for or against the neuron theory, it was pre-eminently the achievement of Cajal to establish the fact that the functional connections between individual nerve cells, or neurons, are effected by close contacts and not by continuity in a syncytial network, as was proposed in the rival reticular theory of Gerlach and Golgi. Appropriately, Cajal's last great contribution (11) was devoted to a critical survey of the evidence for and against the neuron theory, which has not been seriously challenged since that time, at least for the vertebrate nervous system.

Neurons have the most diverse forms, yet there are certain features that are common to all. The nucleus always lies in an expanded part, the soma or cell body, from which the axon takes origin and often runs for long distances before breaking up into the synaptic terminals that make contact either with other neurons or with effector cells such as muscles, glands or electric organs. Under physiological conditions of operation, axons (with the exception of primary afferent axons) transmit impulses only in the centrifugal direction and thus constitute the effector apparatus of the nerve cell. The different types of nerve cells show much more variation in their other branches, the dendrites, which normally share with the soma the receptive function for the nerve cell. Pyramidal cells of the cerebral cortex and the Purkinje cells of the cerebellum have the most extensively branched dendrites, but most neurons of the central nervous system have fairly elaborate dendritic structures. By contrast, in the dorsal root ganglion cells the receptive structure is remotely located in the receptor organs which are connected to the soma by a long axon-like fiber that normally conducts in the centripetal direction, and which we may call the primary afferent axon.

Very great functional significance is attached to the surface membrane of the neuron. This membrane must not be confused with the fibrous, glial and myelin structures which contribute a sheath to neurons, providing them with mechanical strength and electrical insulation. Until the advent of electronmicroscopy the surface membrane had not been observed directly; yet it was an essential postulate in explanations of the electrical properties of the surface of the neuron and of the manner in which its interior was maintained at a very different composition from the exterior, particularly in respect to such ionic species as sodium, potassium and chloride. It also provided a structural basis for explaining such fundamental processes as the conduction of the impulse and the operation of excitatory and inhibitory synaptic junctions. Recently, numerous electronmicroscopic studies (21, 22, 23, 48, 66, 67, 70) have revealed it as a boundary membrane of uniform thickness, about 50 Å, which stands out with remarkable clarity from the interior of the neuron and its surround. There is much more uncertainty with respect to the chemical composition of the membrane, which generally is supposed to be a thin, probably bimolecular, layer of mixed phospholipids and cholesterol, supported by a protein framework. It is further postulated that the transport of molecules and ions across this membrane is largely a diffusion process, the respective net movements being determined by the electrochemical potentials. However, metabolic energy must also be made available for net transport against the electrochemical gradients of such ions as sodium and potassium. With some membranes, it is also necessary to postulate that specific permeability functions are 'built in'; for example, in all membranes giving the self-regenerative responses that are characteristic of impulses, depolarization initiates a brief permeability to sodium ions; and at excitatory synapses the excitatory transmitter substance probably causes the membrane to become like a sieve with pores permeable to all small ions, while at inhibitory synapses the inhibitory substance causes much more selective ion permeability, which may, however, be due to a still finer sieve-like structure.

It will emerge in the subsequent sections on neuron physiology that as yet very little functional significance can be attached to all the detailed structural features occurring within neurons, which are well described in a recent review by Young (79). At the present level of understanding, the behavior of neurons is explained in terms of the properties of their surface membranes, including the specialized surface membranes of the synaptic regions. The interior is assigned a function merely on account of its ionic composition and its specific conductance. Doubtless this unsatisfactory state of affairs will be remedied as new insights are gained into the metabolic functions of the nerve cell and their integration with the membrane functions.

Some beginnings have already been made. For example, energy derived from metabolic processes in the neuron is necessary in order to move ions across the surface membrane against their electrochemical potentials. There is now evidence that, with the linked transfer of sodium outwards and potassium inwards, the rate of this ionic pump is determined by the internal concentration of sodium ions (15, 16, 53, 54). Another correlation between the neuron interior and the surface membrane is beginning to emerge in relation to the synaptic vesicles in the presynaptic

terminals. There is evidence supporting the postulate that these vesicles are concerned in the quantal emission of transmitter from the presynaptic terminals of the neuromuscular junction (26, 63, 70); and that the level of the membrane potential of the presynaptic terminals determines the rate of emission of quanta therefrom, the rate rising by more than a million-fold during a nerve impulse. Thus it has been postulated that in some way the properties of the surface membrane are able to influence profoundly the state of relatively large structures (spheres of 300 to 500 Å in diameter) in the immediately adjacent cytoplasm (26, 63); and, by analogy, a similar postulate has been suggested for the synaptic vesicles which also form characteristic features of all synaptic junctions that on other grounds are regarded as functioning by chemical transmission (21, 29, 67).

The internal structure of neurons is profoundly altered in pathological states induced, for example, by section of the axon or by the action of toxins (4). There is good evidence that such a striking feature as the Nissl substance or ergastoplasm is concerned in the protein manufacture that occurs during growth and regeneration (58). But as yet there is little understanding of the 'trophic' action which the cell body exercises on the axon, apparently by maintaining an intra-axonic pressure and a continual transfer of material along the fiber (79).

Electronmicroscopy has already contributed much information that is of the greatest value in interpreting the mode of operation of synapses. Despite the very wide range in the grosser features of synapses, at the electronmicroscopic level there is a remarkable similarity between all synapses that are believed to work by a chemical transmitter mechanism (fig. 1). Essentially, in these structures considerable areas of the presynaptic and postsynaptic membranes are separated by a very narrow cleft that shows a remarkable uniformity in width for any one type of synapse and that varies in width from 150 to 500 Å with different types. Presumably, this accurate apposition of the two membranes is maintained by some structural linkage across the cleft, which appears in electronmicrophotographs as a granular material. The presynaptic and postsynaptic membranes are continuous with the surface membranes of their respective cells, neurons or effector cells, and as yet have not been shown to have any distinctive structural features except the deep transverse folds that distinguish the subsynaptic muscle membrane at the neuromuscular junction (figs. 1D, E) (19, 69, 70). Finally, in all chemical-transmitting synapses the presynaptic termi-

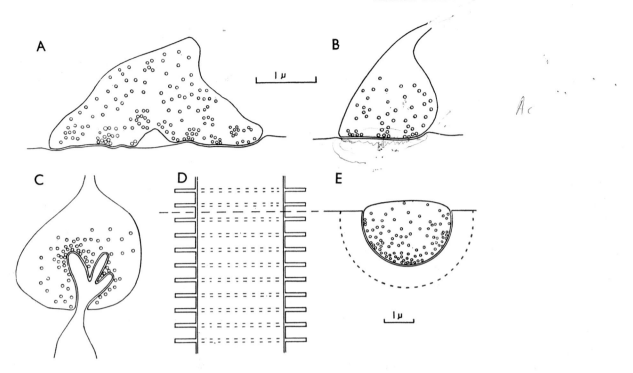

FIG. 1. Drawings showing dimensions and form of various types of synaptic junctions as revealed by electronmicroscopy. In all transverse sections the presynaptic terminals are shown above and the postsynaptic element below. In addition the presynaptic terminals can be identified by the contained synaptic vesicles. The synaptic cleft is seen as the narrow space between the juxtaposed presynaptic and subsynaptic membranes and is shown communicating at the sides of the synapse with the interstitial spaces. A. A large synapse on a motoneuron of the abducens nucleus. [From Palay (67).] B. Synapse in the ventral acoustic ganglion of the guinea pig. [From de Robertis (21).] C. Synapse between red receptor and postsynaptic cell in the rabbit retina. [From de Robertis & Franchi (23).] D, E. Elongated nerve terminal of amphibian muscle as seen from above (D) and in transverse section (E). The naturally occurring irregularities of the junctional folds are neglected in order to give a regular geometrical diagram with approximately equivalent dimensions. A junctional fold is shown by a broken line in E. [From data and figures of Couteaux & Taxi (19) and Robertson (70).]

nals contain the characteristic synaptic vesicles which are 300 to 500 Å across and which are often clustered close to the synaptic region.

The word synapse, as proposed by Sherrington (71), may be applied to the presynaptic terminal with its contained synaptic vesicles, the synaptic cleft of 150 to 500 Å, and the subsynaptic membrane with its special receptive and reactive mechanism. Later, when the mode of operation of synapses is discussed, it will appear that much of the old morphological characterization of synaptic endings is of little significance, at least for many types of neurons. Thus the various localizations designated axosomatic, axodendritic and axoaxonic would be almost equipotent in their action except for those neurons that have very elongated dendrites, as for example the pyramidal cells of the cortex. Furthermore, there can be little

significance in the detailed form of synapses as described by such terms as *boutons terminaux* and *en passant*, giant club endings, basket-type endings, etc. [cf. Bodian (3).]

PHYSIOLOGICAL PROPERTIES OF SURFACE MEMBRANES OF NEURONS

By inserting an electrode within a nerve fiber or the soma of a neuron and analyzing the potential changes produced by current pulses, it has been shown that the surface membrane has a high electrical resistance, corresponding to its low ionic permeability, and a high electrical capacity, as would be expected for a membrane no more than 50 Å thick. The electrical resistance shows wide variations with different types of nerve fibers and neurons, the values ranging from 1000 to approximately 10,000$\Omega \cdot$cm^2 for squid and sepia giant fibers, respectively (49, 77), and it probably lies within the range of 500 to 1000$\Omega \cdot$cm^2 for mammalian motoneurons (15, 29, 44). Values for specific capacitance of giant fiber membranes range from 1 to 1.5 μF per cm^2 and for mammalian motoneurons are probably at least 3 μF per cm^2. In addition, there is a considerable potential difference across the surface membranes of neurons, including all their branches, the inside being -50 to -80 millivolts relative to the exterior under normal resting conditions.

It may be claimed that only one hypothesis, which may be termed the membrane ionic hypothesis, attempts to account quantitatively for propagation within neurons both of impulses and of the events which control the generation of impulses, and also for transmission across synapses. The earliest ionic hypothesis was proposed by Bernstein (2) in 1902. For the modern version of this ionic hypothesis, as applied to the responses within a neuron, reference may be made to Hodgkin (49, 50), to Hodgkin & Huxley (52) and to Huxley (57). Its application to synaptic transmission has been specially developed for neuromuscular junctions and the synapses on mammalian motoneurons (15, 16, 17, 26, 28, 29, 38, 41).

Essentially it is postulated that the resting membrane potential of neurons and muscle fibers (-50 to -100 mv) is due to the relatively free diffusion of the small ions, K$^+$ and Cl$^-$, across the membrane, while the Na$^+$ permeability is of a much lower order. For example, in the giant axons of squid the resting K$^+$ and Na$^+$ conductances are, respectively, about 0.5 and of the order of 0.01 mmho per cm^2. As a consequence, an electrical potential difference is set up across the membrane so that there is little or no electrochemical potential gradient of the freely diffusing ions, K$^+$ and Cl$^-$, across the membrane despite the very large concentration differences that obtain, $(K_i)/(K_o)$ and $(Cl_o)/(Cl_i)$, both being of the order of 20 to 50. It may be noted that subsidiary hypotheses, such as the ionic pump mentioned in the preceding section, are required in order to explain how these concentration differences are maintained along with the very low internal sodium concentration. It is further postulated that, if the resting potential of the membrane is suddenly reduced by a considerable amount (say from -50 mv to 0), both the Na$^+$ and K$^+$ conductances undergo characteristic increases. As summarized by Huxley (57), the conductance "for Na ions rises in one or two tenths of a millisecond to perhaps 15 mmho/cm^2, and then falls to a low value with a time constant of about 1 msec. That for K ions does not change noticeably at first, but rises along an S-shaped curve, becoming appreciable as the Na conductance falls from its peak, and eventually flattening out and remaining at about 20 mmho/cm^2 as long as the membrane potential difference is held at zero. When the membrane potential difference is restored to its ordinary resting value, the K conductance returns to its resting value along an exponential decay curve, without an S-shaped start. The Na conductance remains low, but the 'inactivation' which caused it to fall after its peak during the period at zero membrane potential difference persists, decaying exponentially with about the same time constant as the K conductance." Meanwhile the Na and K ions have been moving down their electrochemical gradients. For a giant axon there is a gain in Na of 3 to 4 $\times$ 10^{-12} moles per cm^2 per impulse and a loss of an equivalent amount of K.

According to the ionic hypothesis, the membrane may be represented by an electrical diagram (fig. 2) in which the membrane capacitance (a) is shown in parallel with two battery-resistance elements (b and c) representing, respectively, the K and Na diffusion channels across the membrane. The respective batteries are at the approximate equilibrium potentials for K and Na ions, and the resistances which represent reciprocals of the respective conductances are both capable of variation over a wide range. For the squid axon the respective resistances of the resting membrane are about 2 $\times$ 10$^3\Omega$ cm^2 and 10$^5\Omega$ cm^2, while during activity the values are as low as 25Ω cm^2 and 10Ω cm^2.

On the basis of quantitative studies of the time courses of the conductance changes as produced by a wide range of membrane potential changes, it has been possible (52) to set up differential equations which relate three parameters to the membrane potential changes, viz. the 'turning on' of the Na conductance, the 'turning on' of the K conductance and the 'inactivation' of the Na conductance, and in which all the coefficients are experimentally determined. These equations give a very satisfactory quantitative account of a wide range of performance of the giant fibers from which the coefficients were derived. It will suffice to show how the propagation of the nerve impulse is explained.

The explanation of the propagation of the nerve impulse is based on measurements of the cable properties of the nerve fiber in addition to the differential equation relating the ionic conductances to the

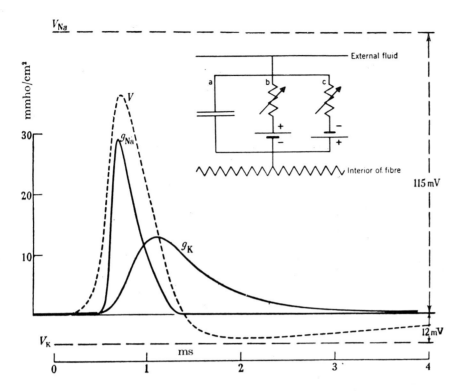

FIG. 2. Theoretical action potential (V) and membrane conductance changes g_{Na} and g_K obtained by solving the equations derived by Hodgkin & Huxley (52) for the giant axon at 18.5°C. *Inset* shows diagram of an element of the excitable membrane of a nerve fiber—*a*, constant capacity; *b*, channel for K^+; *c*, channel for Na^+. [From Hodgkin & Huxley (52); Huxley (57).]

membrane potential. At any instant the nerve impulse will be extended as a potential change along the nerve fiber as shown in figure 3B. According to the ionic hypothesis, there will be a net inward movement of Na ions during the rising phase of the impulse (figs. 2, 3A) because the Na conductance has been greatly increased by the depolarization so that Na ions move freely down their electrochemical gradient carrying positive charges inwards, thus adding to the depolarization and hence to the Na conductance. In this self-regenerative manner, when the level of depolarization of any element of the nerve membrane increases above a critical value, it causes the membrane potential to be carried almost up to the Na equilibrium potential which is about +50 mv, i.e. internally positive (fig. 2). The delayed development of the other two ionic processes checks this potential change and eventually restores the resting membrane potential; the Na conductance is inactivated and the K conductance increases so that, during the falling phase of the impulse, the membrane potential is dominated by the flux of K ions moving outwards along their electrochemical gradient across the

membrane (figs. 2, 3A), which eventually is restored to its original resting potential close to the potassium equilibrium potential. Propagation occurs because of the cable properties of the nerve fiber, current flowing outwards across the membrane ahead of the impulse in the circuits, as shown diagrammatically in figure 3C. This current effects a discharge of the membrane capacitance so that in the zone ahead of the impulse the membrane is depolarized sufficiently to initiate the regenerative increase in Na conductance, by which time the impulse may be said to have arrived at this new zone, which will in turn go through the conductance changes outlined above. It will be appreciated that propagation will be a continuous and uniform process along a stretch of nerve with uniform properties. The propagation velocity calculated from the differential equation and the measured cable properties of a nerve fiber is not only of the correct order, but is in very close agreement with that actually observed (52). Saltatory propagation along the nodal structure of a medullated nerve also can be satisfactorily explained by the occurrence of essentially similar processes at each node. This propagation

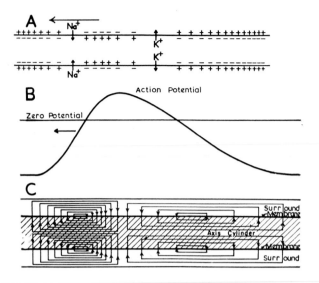

FIG. 3. *A.* Diagram showing postulated movement of sodium and potassium ions across the membrane during an impulse advancing in the direction of arrow, and the resulting alteration of charge on the membrane and its recovery. *B.* Potential distribution of the impulse along a nerve or muscle fiber. *C.* Resulting flow of electric current both in the external medium and within the fiber. Note the reversal of membrane potential during the spike. Figure 3B is drawn so that the impulse is at approximately the same position as in figure 3A and C.

is treated very fully in the following chapter by Tasaki.

After the events depicted in figures 2 and 3, the ionic hypothesis would predict that a length of nerve fiber would have gained a quantity of Na ions that was at least adequate to displace the charge on its capacitance so that there is the maximum change in the membrane potential, and that there would also have been an equivalent loss of K ions in the recharging process. The actually observed values have been several times larger, which is to be expected because the periods of Na entry and K emission overlap so that much of the ionic influx cancels out as far as the membrane potential is concerned. Thus the immediate energy source for the propagation of the impulse derives from the concentration batteries for Na and K ions, and metabolic energy is only later required in order to restore the ionic composition. However, the ionic flux per impulse is so small relative to the ionic composition of the fiber that, even in the absence of a restorative process, many thousands of impulses can be propagated along large nerve fibers without

significantly changing the effectiveness of the concentration batteries.

The ionic hypothesis can also explain satisfactorily a great many other properties of nerve fibers [(cf. Hodgkin (49); Hodgkin & Huxley (52)], for example the subthreshold and threshold phenomena including the all-or-nothing behavior, the refractory period following the impulse, the effects of anelectrotonus and catelectrotonus, including accommodation, the effects produced on the nerve impulse and the other responses by changing the Na or K concentrations, or both, in the external medium and in the axoplasm (54). This is such an immensely impressive performance that the ionic hypothesis of the nerve fiber must rank as one of the great conceptual achievements in biology.

It is admitted that as yet the ionic hypothesis, in so far as it has been formulated, does not give a complete description of the behavior of the nerve membrane. For example the nature of the specific changes in Na and K conductance is not explained, the intensity-time courses of changes are merely measured and utilized in the explanations. The effect of external calcium ions on these conductances also is not yet understood. Again, nothing is known about the manner in which metabolic energy is employed to drive sodium and potassium ions across the membrane against their electrochemical gradient.

As would be expected, such a comprehensive and precisely formulated hypothesis has been subjected to much critical attack. However much of this criticism has been based on imperfectly controlled experiments. For example deviations from the predicted effects of variations in the external potassium concentrations on the resting membrane potential probably have been largely due to secondary changes in the internal potassium. In this context great significance attaches to the recent experiments of Hodgkin & Horowicz (51) on the membrane potential of isolated single muscle fibers. Extracellular diffusion time is thus reduced to a minimum, so that a steady membrane potential is observed within a second of changing the external ionic composition and thus before there is any appreciable change in the internal composition. Under such conditions, with changes in (K_o), the observed membrane potentials agree very closely with those predicted by the ionic hypothesis. It was also remarkable that, making use of the anomalous rectification in K ionic diffusion across the membrane [cf. Katz (59)], it was possible by changing the internal composition of the muscle fiber to have a membrane the potential of which was virtually controlled by the $(Cl_o)/(Cl_i)$ ratio and then later to restore the normal ionic composition of the fiber, as revealed by a normal behavior of the membrane potential to variations in (K_o).

In conclusion it may be stated that, though detailed modifications and developments of the ionic hypothesis are required in order to explain such phenomena as the falling phases of the action potentials of medullated nerve fibers and cardiac muscle fibers and the effect thereon of repolarizing currents, in essentials the ionic membrane hypothesis has survived the most severe tests and remains as the only conceptual framework for our discussion of the electrical events that are so essentially concerned in all activities of the neuron. It will therefore be pertinent to consider now the mode of operation of synapses in the light of the ionic hypothesis

TRANSMISSION BETWEEN NEURONS

The synapse is a device for the transmission of information from one neuron to another. Excitatory synaptic action is effective only in so far as it leads to the discharge of an impulse by the postsynaptic neuron, for only under such conditions does this neuron in turn exert effective action on other neurons. It may be provisionally concluded from the available experimental evidence that any neuron, other than a primary sensory neuron, requires excitatory synaptic action in order to generate an impulse. In the absence of an afferent input even the most complex assemblages of neurons remain silent, as may be seen in the isolated cortical slabs of Burns (10).

On the other hand, inhibitory synaptic action attempts to suppress the discharge of impulses and is effective in so far as it diminishes or shortens the discharge produced by any given synaptic excitation. Inhibition can be thought of as exercising a sculpturing role on what would otherwise be the massive incoordinate activity of a convulsing nervous system, thus reducing it to the organized responses characteristic of normal nervous activity. However, just as with the excitatory synapses, inhibitory synapses require activation by presynaptic impulses. Hence, an investigation of the transmission between neurons can be reduced to a study of the mode of operation of excitatory and inhibitory synapses. It will emerge that the ionic hypothesis of the nerve membrane

provides the basis for our attempts to understand both these types of synaptic activity.

Excitatory Synaptic Action

Excitatory synaptic action on neurons is exhibited in its simplest form by the monosynaptic action which afferent impulses from the annulospiral endings of muscle spindles exert on motoneurons. When recorded by an intracellular electrode, the monosynaptic action by a single volley generates a depolarizing potential, the excitatory postsynaptic potential (EPSP), that runs virtually the same time course regardless of volley size (fig. 4A to C). This observa-

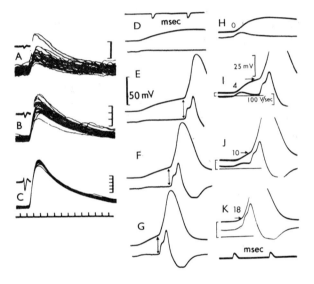

FIG. 4. A to C. EPSP's obtained in a biceps-semitendinosus motoneuron with afferent volleys of different size. Inset records at the left of the main records show the afferent volley recorded near the entry of the dorsal nerve roots into the spinal cord. They are taken with negativity downward and at a constant amplification for which no scale is given. Records of EPSP are taken at an amplification that decreases in steps from A to C as the response increases. Separate vertical scales are given for each record of EPSP. All records are formed by superposition of about 40 faint traces. D to G. Intracellularly-recorded potentials of a gastrocnemius motoneuron (resting membrane potential, -70 mv) evoked by monosynaptic activation that was progressively increased from D to G. The lower traces are the electrically differentiated records, the double-headed arrows indicating the onsets of the IS spikes in E to G. H to K. Intracellular records evoked by monosynaptic activation that was applied at 12.0 msec. after the onset of a depolarizing pulse whose strength is indicated in mμa. A pulse of 20 mμa was just below threshold for generating a spike. H shows control EPSP in the absence of a depolarizing pulse. Lower traces give electrically differentiated records. Note that the spikes are truncated. [From Coombs et al. (14).]

tion indicates that each excitatory presynaptic impulse generates in the postsynaptic neuron a potential change of this same time course, and that the recorded EPSP's of figure 4A to C are produced by a simple summation of these elemental EPSP's. It thus provides an illustration of the classical concept of spatial summation (72, 73).

As shown in figure 4D to G, if the EPSP is increased beyond a critical threshold level, it causes the neuron to discharge an impulse, the latency being briefer the larger the EPSP. In figure 4E, F, G the increase of the EPSP to above threshold was brought about by increasing the size of the presynaptic volley, but, as would be expected, the EPSP can also be made to generate an impulse by conditioning procedures that change the membrane potential towards the critical threshold level. For example in figure 4I to K the same EPSP as in figure 4H was made effective by the operation of a background depolarizing current which was commenced 12 msec. before and which changed the membrane potential by the amount shown in each record. The impulse is seen to arise (at the arrows) at a total level of depolarization of about 18 mv, which is made up in varying proportions by the conditioning depolarization and the super-

imposed EPSP. The threshold level of depolarization may be attained also by superimposing an EPSP on the depolarization produced by a preceding EPSP (temporal summation), as is illustrated by Grundfest (Chapter V, fig. 17).

All these investigations conform with the hypothesis that synaptic excitatory action is effective in generating an impulse solely by the depolarization of the neuron, i.e. by producing the EPSP (17, 28, 29, 44). As far as the generation of an impulse by the EPSP is concerned, the same processes obtain as with the propagation of an impulse from one part of a neuron to another.

In order to produce the EPSP, the activated synapses must cause an electric current to be generated which depolarizes the postsynaptic membrane. Thus, as shown in figure 5B, a current must flow inwards immediately under the activated synapses, i.e. across the subsynaptic membrane, in order that a return current may flow outward across the remainder of the postsynaptic membrane, so depolarizing it. When a brief current pulse is applied across the membrane, it builds up a potential difference that on cessation of the current decays considerably faster than the EPSP (12). Hence it is postulated that the current producing

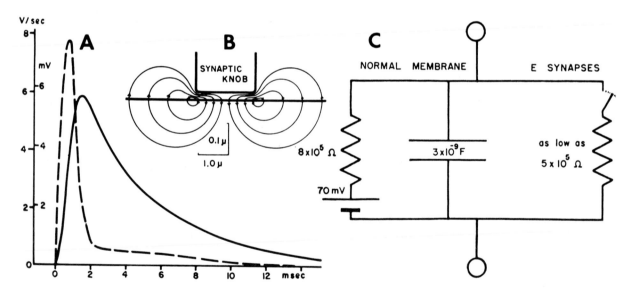

FIG. 5. A. The continuous line is the mean of several monosynaptic EPSP's, while the broken line shows the time course of the subsynaptic current required to generate this potential change. B. Diagram showing an activated excitatory knob and the postsynaptic membrane. As indicated by the scales for distance, the synaptic cleft is shown at 10 times the scale for width as against length. The current generating the EPSP passes in through the cleft and inward across the activated subsynaptic membrane. [From Coombs *et al.* (12).] C. Formal electrical diagram of the membrane of a motoneuron with, on the right side, the circuit through the subsynaptic areas of the membrane that are activated in producing the monosynaptic EPSP. Maximum activation of these areas would be indicated symbolically by closing the switch.

the EPSP is not suddenly switched off after the summit of the EPSP, but that, as shown in the analysis of figure 5A (broken line), a small residual current continues to flow and thus delays the repolarization during the decline of the EPSP (continuous line). It will be appreciated that the EPSP's of figures 4 and 5A are produced by the operation on the neuron of the postsynaptic currents generated by many synaptic knobs that have been activated simultaneously by the afferent volley.

By passing an extrinsic current across the neuronal membrane it has been possible even to reverse the potential across it, its interior then being positive to the exterior. When this occurs, the EPSP is also reversed in sign (cf. Grundfest, Chapter V, fig. 3B), which indicates a reversal of the postsynaptic currents shown in figure 5B and of the ionic flux across the subsynaptic membrane (17). The effects on the EPSP of diminution and reversal of the membrane potential and of changes in the ionic composition of the neuron are explicable by the postulate that the activated subsynaptic membrane becomes permeable to all small ions, such as Na^+, K^+ and Cl^-. The time course of this permeability change is given by the broken line of figure 5A, and its effect on the membrane potential can be derived from the electrical diagram of figure 5C. A similar investigation on the endplate potential of the neuromuscular junction (24, 26; Fatt, Chapter VI) has shown that reversal occurs at a membrane potential of about -15 mv, which would be close to the liquid-junction potential between the muscle fiber and its environment. More accurate investigations on the EPSP may likewise reveal that a battery of about -15 mv should be inserted in the synaptic component of the diagram in figure 5C.

It can now be taken as established that transmission across synapses occurs not by the spread of electrical currents, but by the specific chemical substances which impulses cause to be liberated from the presynaptic membranes (29, 38, 43). These substances alter the ionic permeability of the subsynaptic membrane and consequently initiate specific ionic fluxes across this membrane. These fluxes in turn are responsible for the postsynaptic currents that cause the transient depolarizations or hyperpolarizations of the postsynaptic membrane which are produced respectively by excitatory or inhibitory action (16, 17). Since it gives the time course of the ionic permeability change, the broken line of figure 5A may be taken to give the time course of action on the subsynaptic membrane of the brief jet of excitatory transmitter substance that a presynaptic impulse causes to be emitted from the presynaptic knob. Acetylcholine is the transmitter substance at a few types of central synapse, but the excitatory transmitter has not yet been identified for the great majority.

Impulses can also be generated in a nerve cell by another method that is of particular value in relation to the problem of locating the site at which impulses arise in nerve cells. When the axon of a nerve cell is stimulated, an impulse travels antidromically up to the nerve cell and usually invades it, generating an antidromic spike potential as in figure 6A. When thus recorded by a microelectrode in the soma, the antidromic spike potential has two main components, as shown by the step on the rising phase which is greatly accentuated in the electrically differentiated record lying immediately below the potential record in figure 6A. Evidence from recent intensive investigations (1, 7, 13, 39, 40, 46) can all be satisfactorily explained by the postulate that the initial small spike is generated by the impulse in the initial segment of the neuron (axon hillock plus nonmedullated axon), while the later large spike is produced when the impulse invades the soma-dendritic membrane (13, 46). The two spikes may therefore be called the IS and SD spikes.

When the neuronal spike potentials generated by synaptic or direct stimulation are recorded at sufficient speed, they are likewise seen to be compounded of IS and SD spikes, particularly in the differentiated records (fig. 6B), though the separation is always less evident than with the corresponding antidromic spike potential. It must therefore be postulated that the EPSP produced by the activation of synapses covering the soma and dendrites is effective not by generating an impulse in these regions, but by the electrotonic spread of the depolarization to the initial segment, as is illustrated by the lines of current flow in figure 6C. By recording the impulse discharged along the motor nerve fiber in the ventral root it is found that usually this impulse started to propagate down the medullated axon about 0.05 msec. after the initiation of the IS spike, i.e. the medullated axon is usually excited secondarily to the initial segment (14). The critical level of depolarization for generating an impulse thus gives the threshold for the IS membrane, as marked by the horizontal arrow labelled IS in figure 6B, and not of the SD membrane. An approximate measure of the threshold for the SD membrane is given by the membrane potential obtained at the first sign of inflection produced by the incipient SD spike, as is indicated by the differentiated records in figure 6A and B. This potential is measured

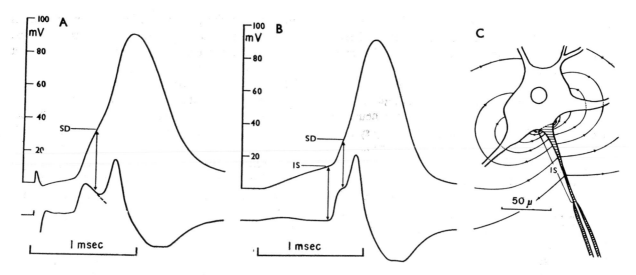

FIG. 6. Tracings of intracellularly recorded spike potentials evoked by antidromic (*A*) and mono-synaptic (*B*) stimulation of a motoneuron, respectively. [From Coombs *et al.* (14).] The lower traces show the electrically differentiated records. Perpendicular lines are drawn from the origins of the IS and SD spikes, as indicated in the differentiated records, the respective threshold depolarizations being thus determined from the potential records and indicated by horizontal lines labelled respectively IS and SD. *C.* Diagram showing the lines of current flow that occur when a synaptically induced depolarization of the soma-dendritic membrane electrotonically spreads to the initial segment.

at the levels of the horizontal SD arrows and is approximately the same for the antidromically and synaptically evoked spikes, as illustrated in figure 6*A* and *B*. Synaptic excitatory action thus generates an SD spike not directly by its depolarizing action, but only indirectly through the mediation of the IS spike which lifts the depolarization of the SD membrane to threshold by currents that flow in the reverse direction to those drawn in figure 6*C*.

With normal motoneurons the threshold level of depolarization has always been, as in figure 6*A* and *B,* much higher for the SD membrane than for the IS membrane. There has been a considerable range in the threshold values for motoneurons that are shown by their resting and spike potentials to be in good condition. The IS threshold has ranged from 6 to 18 mv, and the SD threshold from 20 to 37 mv (14). However, for any one motoneuron the SD threshold has been about two to three times the IS threshold. Several other types of neurons in the central nervous system also reveal a threshold difference between the IS and SD membranes. The functional significance of these distinctive threshold areas of neurons will be considered after synaptic inhibitory action has been considered.

The difference in threshold between the IS and SD membranes must not be confused with the concept that membranes excited by chemical transmitter are inexcitable electrically (cf. Grundfest, Chapter V). This concept would be applicable merely to the sub-synaptic areas of the SD membrane and not to the whole of that membrane. It should be noted that the receptor membrane of the bare nerve ending in the Pacinian corpuscle also appears to be inexcitable electrically, though acting as a primary focus for depolarizing the first node of the medullated axon (27; Gray, Chapter IV). There is some analogy here with the SD membrane acting to depolarize the IS membrane, so generating an impulse there; but the analogy does not hold for subsequent events because the impulse in the IS membrane usually invades the SD membrane, whereas with the Pacinian corpuscle there is no such antidromic invasion.

Inhibitory Synaptic Action

Strictly, the concept of inhibition is restricted to depressions of neuronal excitability which occur independently of any conditioning excitatory synaptic activity on that neuron, and also independently of any depression of the excitatory synaptic bombardment that is employed in testing for the suspected inhibition. It may be noted that conditioning by large afferent volleys causes a fairly prolonged depression in the size of the primary afferent volley and hence depresses its excitatory action (8, 45, 55). This effect has been attributed to the dorsal root reflex and the dorsal root potential set up by the powerful conditioning volley (8) and probably is of little significance with more physiological types of afferent input. Apart from this effect it has been shown that inhibitory actions on motoneurons are explained satisfactorily by the transient increase which is produced in their membrane potentials and which has been designated the inhibitory postsynaptic potential, IPSP (6, 16, 18). A comparable synaptic inhibitory action has been observed with crustacean stretch receptor cells (60), and has also been recorded on the neurons of Clarke's column by Curtis, Eccles & Lundberg (19a).

As shown in figure 7B to H, a single volley in the afferent fibers from annulospiral endings in quadriceps muscle evokes a hyperpolarizing response, the inhibitory postsynaptic potential (IPSP) in a motoneuron of the antagonist muscle (biceps-semitendinosus). The IPSP is observed to be increased in a series of stages as the afferent volley is increased in size, but it is not altered in time course, showing that a simple spatial summation occurs when several inhibitory synapses on the same neuron are simultaneously activated. With the maximum spatial summation in figure 7E the membrane potential was increased from −60 to −63.5 mv.

In order to produce the observed hyperpolarization, current must be flowing inward across the motoneuronal membrane in general, and there must be a corresponding outward current in the region of the activated inhibitory synapses (fig. 8A, inset). As with the excitatory synaptic action in figure 5A, the time course of the current that produces the IPSP may be determined if the time constant of the membrane is known. The broken line in figure 8A plots the time course so determined and shows that the high intensity phase has virtually the same time course as with excitatory synaptic action, though there is much less

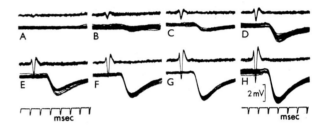

Fig. 7. A to H. Lower records give intracellular responses of a biceps-semitendinosus motoneuron to a quadriceps volley of progressively increasing size, as is shown by the upper records which are recorded from the sixth lumbar dorsal root by a surface electrode (downward deflections indicating negativity). All records are formed by the superposition of about 40 faint traces.

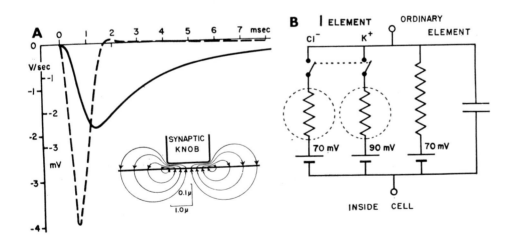

FIG. 8. A. Continuous line plots the mean time course of the IPSP set up in a biceps-semitendinosus motoneuron by a single quadriceps Ia volley. The measured time constant for the membrane was 2.8 msec. The broken line gives the time course of the inhibitory subsynaptic current that would produce the IPSP, the calculation being similar to that used in deriving figure 5A. Inset shows lines of postsynaptic current flow in relationship to an inhibitory synaptic knob. B. Diagrammatic representation of the electrical properties of an ordinary element on the neuronal membrane and of an inhibitory element with K+ and Cl− ion components in parallel. Further description in the text.

residual action. By investigating the effects of varying the membrane potential by current applied through the microelectrode (cf. Grundfest, Chapter V, fig. 12), it has been shown that the IPSP is produced by a process of ionic diffusion across the subsynaptic membrane that has an equilibrium potential at about 10 mv more hyperpolarized than the resting membrane potential, i.e. at about −80 mv (16). Furthermore, it has been shown by ionophoretic injection through the microelectrode that this ionic diffusion is satisfactorily explained by the hypothesis that the inhibitory synaptic transmitter increases the permeability of the subsynaptic membrane to ions below a critical size, e.g. to K^+ and Cl^-, and not to somewhat larger ions, e.g. to Na^+ (16; Grundfest, Chapter V, fig. 12). This type of ionic mechanism appears to occur with all types of central inhibition so far investigated and also with the IPSP of the crustacean stretch receptor cells (37, 60). It is remarkable that a somewhat similar ionic mechanism explains the vagal inhibitory action on the heart (25, 56, 76) and probably for the inhibitory action on crustacean muscle (42).

The electrical diagram in figure 8C illustrates the hypothesis that the inhibitory transmitter increases the conductance of the subsynaptic membrane to both K^+ and Cl^- ions, which have the equilibrium potentials indicated by the respective batteries, and so causes the flow of a current (fig. 8B) which tends to hyperpolarize the rest of the neuronal membrane to about −80 mv, which is the mean of the equilibrium potentials for K^+ and Cl^- ions.

Factors Controlling Impulse Generation

The currents which flow from the subsynaptic membrane to exert a hyperpolarizing action on the motoneuronal membrane and set up an IPSP (fig. 8A, inset) also effectively hyperpolarize the membrane of the initial segment. However the currents generated by this ionic mechanism are even more effective in checking depolarization (18). On this account, with any of the three methods of stimulation, synaptic, direct or antidromic, there is an increased difficulty in generating an impulse in the motoneuron. All the various types of inhibitory action can be sufficiently explained by the increased ionic conductance produced by the inhibitory transmitter substance and the consequent flow of postsynaptic currents that oppose the excitatory currents [fig. 8; cf. Coombs *et al.* (18); Eccles (29)].

The low threshold of the initial segment relative to the soma-dendritic membrane accounts for the observation that with normal motoneurons impulses are always generated in the initial segment. As a consequence the motoneuron acts as a far better integrator of the whole synaptic excitatory and inhibitory bombardment than would be the case if impulses were generated anywhere over the whole soma-dendritic membrane. If these latter conditions obtained, a special strategic grouping of excitatory synapses [cf. Lorente de Nó (65)] could initiate an impulse despite a relative paucity of the total excitatory synaptic bombardment and a considerable inhibitory bombardment of areas remote from this focus. As it is, both excitatory and inhibitory synaptic action are effective only in so far as they affect the membrane potential of the initial segment. It is here that the conflict between excitation and inhibition is joined, not generally over the motoneuronal surface, as was envisaged by Sherrington in his concept of algebraic summation.

In the account so far given the soma-dendritic surface functions merely as a generating area for the postsynaptic currents that are effective only in so far as they act on the initial segment either in generating an impulse or in preventing it. If an impulse so generated invades the soma-dendritic membrane, it does so after the discharge has occurred along the axon (14). It might thus appear that the invasion of the soma-dendritic membrane is of no consequence in the essential function of the neuron in discharging impulses down its axon. However, in contrast to the initial segment and the medullated axon of neurons, the soma-dendritic membrane of many species of neurons develops after an impulse a large and prolonged after-hyperpolarization (15, 68). This after-hyperpolarization delays the generation of the next impulse by the neuron and thus very effectively slows the frequency of the rhythmic discharges of neurons [cf. Eccles (28), pp. 174–8]. This frequency control by the soma-dendritic membrane is very important in limiting the frequency with which motoneurons activate muscles. Recently it has been shown that the motoneurons supplying the slow postural muscles have much more prolonged after-hyperpolarizations than those supplying the fast phasic muscles (30).

Central Inhibitory Pathways

It may be taken as established that at least some afferent fibers, e.g. those from annulospiral endings and tendon organs, act as pathways both for excitatory and inhibitory actions on motoneurons, and in addition exert excitatory actions directly on other neurons in the spinal cord (31, 32, 33, 35, 61, 62). Until recently values for the central conduction time of the so-called direct inhibitory pathway (annulospiral afferent fibers to motoneurons of antagonist action) were derived by measurements of the shortest interval at which an inhibitory volley can precede a monosynaptic excitatory volley and yet be effective in inhibiting the reflex discharge. Since such intervals approximated to zero, it was erroneously concluded that the latency of direct inhibitory action approximated to that of monosynaptic excitatory action, and hence that the inhibitory pathway was also monosynaptic, i.e. that the annulospiral afferents of muscle had inhibitory synaptic endings on motoneurons (5, 28, 61, 64). However the IPSP generated under such conditions has a latent period at least 0.8 msec. longer than the monosynaptic excitatory action of a comparable pathway (35), which is just the interval that would be expected if there were a synaptic relay on the inhibitory pathway. It has further been found that the annulospiral afferents establish a synaptic relay in the intermediate nucleus which conforms in every respect with the properties of the direct inhibitory pathway (35). Of particular significance is the recent observation that the summed action of impulses in several annulospiral fibers is required before any IPSP is produced by them, which contrasts with their monosynaptic excitatory pathway, where the individual impulses are independently effective in generating EPSP (36). Evidently the spatial summation of the inhibitory impulses also requires the synaptic relay station that has been found in the intermediate nucleus and that is required in explaining the long central latency of the 'direct' inhibitory pathway. The same additional latency and interneuronal relay are observed for the IPSP generated through the contralateral inhibitory pathway which Wilson & Lloyd (78) have discovered in the S2 and S3 segmental levels (20). Finally, the monosynaptic excitatory action of afferent impulses from the quadriceps and gracilis muscles on soleus and biceps-semitendinosus motoneurons, respectively, (32) provides a sufficient explanation of Sprague's observation (74) that some afferent fibers entering by the L5 dorsal root establish synaptic connections directly with motoneurons of the L7 and S1 segments [cf. Eccles (29), p. 156]. It may therefore be taken as established that a single interneuron is interpolated on the direct inhibitory pathway, as shown diagrammatically in figure 9A. Similarly there is a single interneuron on the inhibitory pathway from motor axon collaterals

to motoneurons (34), as is shown diagrammatically in figure 9B. By a systematic study of the IPSP's produced by afferent impulses in the fibers of Golgi tendon organs, it has recently been found that there is always at least one interneuron on the inhibitory pathway, though sometimes two are interpolated (33).

Inhibitory and Excitatory Transmitter Substances

Strychnine has been found to have a highly specific and rapid action in depressing inhibitory synaptic action (cf. Grundfest, Chapter V, fig. 12), at least with the five types of inhibitory action that have so far been investigated in the spinal cord (5, 18, 29). Similarly, tetanus toxin very effectively depresses all these inhibitory synaptic actions (9). In fact the clinical effects of both strychnine and tetanus toxin can be sufficiently explained by these actions. Since the activation of the inhibitory interneurons is not affected when synaptic inhibitory action has been virtually abolished by strychnine or tetanus toxin, it may be concluded that these agents exert their depressant action on the inhibitory synapses, as indicated in figure 9A and B. On account of the rapidity and effectiveness of its action it seems likely that strychnine acts competitively with the inhibitory transmitter for the receptor patches of the inhibitory subsynaptic membrane. Certainly the highly specific actions of tetanus toxin and strychnine indicate that inhibitory synaptic action is mediated by a specific inhibitory transmitter substance.

The interneuron on the inhibitory pathways (cf. fig. 9A and B) can be regarded as being introduced in order to change over from a neuron that manufactures and liberates an excitatory transmitter substance to one that operates through the inhibitory transmitter substance. It is, therefore, postulated that any one transmitter substance always has the same synaptic action, i.e. excitatory or inhibitory, at all synapses on nerve cells in the mammalian central nervous system. According to this principle, any one class of nerve cells in the mammalian central nervous system will function exclusively either in an excitatory or in an inhibitory capacity at all of its synaptic endings, i.e. it is postulated that there are functionally just two types of nerve cells, excitatory and inhibitory. The interneurons illustrated in figure 9A and B are examples of 'inhibitory neurons'. On the other hand, the dorsal root ganglion cells with their primary afferent fibers, probably the neurons of all the long tracts both ascending and descending, the motoneurons, and many interneurons belong to the class

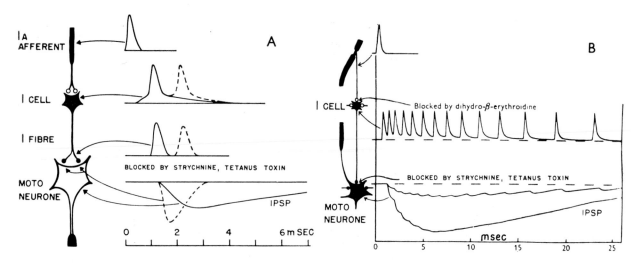

FIG. 9. *A.* Schematic drawing of the anatomical and physiological features of the direct inhibitory pathway. It shows the events in the primary afferent fiber, in its excitatory synaptic connections with an intermediate neuron (I cell) and finally in the inhibitory synaptic connection of this neuron with a motoneuron, where the inhibitory subsynaptic current is shown by a broken line and the IPSP by a continuous line (cf. fig. 6*A*). *B.* Diagram summarizing the postulated sequence of events from an impulse in a motor axon to the inhibition of a motoneuron. All events are plotted on the time scale shown below and the corresponding histological structures are shown diagrammatically to the left (note indicator arrows). The four plotted time courses are from above downwards for the following events: the electrical response of impulse in motor-axon collateral; the electrical response evoked in a Renshaw cell by the cumulative effect of acetylcholine at many synapses, showing impulses superimposed on a background depolarization; the IPSP generated in the motoneuron by the Renshaw cell discharge; and the aggregate IPSP evoked in a motoneuron that is bombarded repetitively by many Renshaw cells, which become progressively more asynchronous, so smoothing the latter part of the ripple. The structural diagram to the left shows converging synapses on the Renshaw cell and on the motoneuron. [From Eccles *et al.* (34).]

excitatory neurons'. Conceptually, by this subdivision of nerve cells into excitatory and inhibitory types, a great simplification is produced in the physiology of central synaptic mechanisms, for all branches of any one neuron can be regarded as having the same synaptic function, i.e. as being uniformly excitatory or uniformly inhibitory. Terzuolo & Bullock (75) give experimental evidence that this principle of neuronal specificity does not hold for the cardiac ganglion of Limulus.

In attempting to understand the operation of any neuronal system in the mammalian central nervous system, a useful provisional postulate would be that all inhibitory cells are short-axon neurons lying in the grey matter, while all transmission pathways including the peripheral afferent and efferent pathways are formed by the axons of excitatory cells. Such a postulate would be of most direct application in relation to such simple problems as the modes of termination of the descending tracts, but eventually it may be applicable also to more complex situations in the brainstem and even in the cerebellar and cerebral cortices. In all these situations there is as yet no infor-

mation on the structural features of the inhibitory mechanisms.

It will be sufficiently evident from the above account of nerve cells that interactions between nerve cells are attributed to synaptic contacts which operate by a specific chemical transmitter mechanism. The alternate postulate is that, at least in part, interaction between neurons is attributable to the flow of electric currents generated by active neurons. There is at present no experimental evidence that the nervous system of vertebrates operates in this way. The flow of electric currents between neurons is far too small to have any significant effect, even in experiments using the unphysiological procedure of large synchronous volleys. In contrast it should be mentioned that some synapses in crustacea do operate by electrical transmission, there being special permeability and rectification properties of the apposed synaptic membranes (47). Such a mechanism would have been detected if it were operative at any of the central synapses of vertebrates that have been systematically investigated.

REFERENCES

1. ARAKI, T. AND T. OTANI. *J. Neurophysiol.* 18: 472, 1955.
2. BERNSTEIN, J. *Arch. ges. Physiol.* 92: 521, 1902.
3. BODIAN, D. *Cold Spring Harbor Symp. Quant. Biol.* 17: 1, 1952.
4. BODIAN, D. AND R. C. MELLORS. *J. Exper. Med.* 81: 469, 1945.
5. BRADLEY, K., D. M. EASTON AND J. C. ECCLES. *J. Physiol.* 122: 474, 1953.
6. BROCK, L. G., J. S. COOMBS AND J. C. ECCLES. *J. Physiol.* 117: 431, 1952.
7. BROCK, L. G., J. S. COOMBS AND J. C. ECCLES. *J. Physiol.* 122: 429, 1953.
8. BROOKS, C. McC., J. C. ECCLES AND J. L. MALCOLM. *J. Neurophysiol.* 11: 417, 1948.
9. BROOKS, V. B., D. R. CURTIS AND J. C. ECCLES. *J. Physiol.* 135: 655, 1957.
10. BURNS, B. D. *J. Physiol.* 111: 50, 1950.
11. CAJAL, S. R. *Trab. Lab. Invest. Biol. Univ. Madrid* 29: 1, 1934.
12. COOMBS, J. S., D. R. CURTIS AND J. C. ECCLES. *Nature, London* 178: 1049, 1956.
13. COOMBS, J. S., D. R. CURTIS AND J. C. ECCLES. *J. Physiol.* 139: 198, 1957.
14. COOMBS, J. S., D. R. CURTIS AND J. C. ECCLES. *J. Physiol.* 139: 232, 1957.
15. COOMBS, J. S., J. C. ECCLES AND P. FATT. *J. Physiol.* 130: 291, 1955.
16. COOMBS, J. S., J. C. ECCLES AND P. FATT. *J. Physiol.* 130: 326, 1955.
17. COOMBS, J. S., J. C. ECCLES AND P. FATT. *J. Physiol.* 130: 374, 1955.
18. COOMBS, J. S., J. C. ECCLES AND P. FATT. *J. Physiol.* 130: 396, 1955.
19. COUTEAUX, R. AND J. TAXI. *Arch. Anat. Microsc. Morph. Exper.* 41: 352, 1952.
19a. CURTIS, D. R., J. C. ECCLES AND A. LUNDBERG. *Acta physiol. scandinav.* In press.
20. CURTIS, D. R., K. KRNJEVIC AND R. MILEDI. *J. Neurophysiol.* 21: 319, 1958.
21. DE ROBERTIS, E. D. P. *J. Biophys. & Biochem. Cytol.* 2: 503, 1956.
22. DE ROBERTIS, E. D. P. AND H. S. BENNETT. *J. Biophys. & Biochem. Cytol.* 1: 47, 1955.
23. DE ROBERTIS, E. D. P. AND C. M. FRANCHI. *J. Biophys. & Biochem. Cytol.* 2: 307, 1956.
24. DEL CASTILLO, J. AND B. KATZ. *J. Physiol.* 125: 546, 1954.
25. DEL CASTILLO, J. AND B. KATZ. *J. Physiol.* 129: 48P, 1955.
26. DEL CASTILLO, J. AND B. KATZ. *Prog. Biophys. & Biophys. Chem.* 6: 121, 1956.
27. DIAMOND, J., J. A. B. GRAY AND M. SATO. *J. Physiol.* 133: 54, 1956.
28. ECCLES, J. C. *The Neurophysiological Basis of Mind: The Principles of Neurophysiology.* Oxford: Clarendon Press, 1953.
29. ECCLES, J. C. *The Physiology of Nerve Cells.* Baltimore: Johns Hopkins Press, 1957, 270 pp.
30. ECCLES, J. C., R. M. ECCLES AND A. LUNDBERG. *Nature London* 179: 866, 1957.
31. ECCLES, J. C., R. M. ECCLES AND A. LUNDBERG. *J. Physiol.* 136: 527, 1957.
32. ECCLES, J. C., R. M. ECCLES AND A. LUNDBERG. *J. Physiol.* 137: 22, 1957.
33. ECCLES, J. C., R. M. ECCLES AND A. LUNDBERG. *J. Physiol.* 138: 227, 1957.
34. ECCLES, J. C., P. FATT AND K. KOKETSU. *J. Physiol.* 126: 524, 1954.
35. ECCLES, J. C., P. FATT AND S. LANDGREN. *J. Neurophysiol.* 19: 75, 1956.
36. ECCLES, R. M. AND A. LUNDBERG. *Nature, London* 179: 1305, 1957.
37. EDWARDS, C. AND S. W. KUFFLER. *Fed. Proc.* 16: 34, 1957.
38. FATT, P. *Physiol. Rev.* 34: 674, 1954.
39. FATT, P. *J. Neurophysiol.* 20: 27, 1957.
40. FATT, P. *J. Neurophysiol.* 20: 61, 1957.
41. FATT, P. AND B. KATZ. *J. Physiol.* 115: 320, 1951.
42. FATT, P. AND B. KATZ. *J. Physiol.* 121: 374, 1953.
43. FELDBERG, W. *Physiol. Rev.* 25: 596, 1945.
44. FRANK, K. AND M. G. F. FUORTES. *J. Physiol.* 134: 451, 1956.
45. FRANK, K. AND M. G. F. FUORTES. *Fed. Proc.* 16: 39, 1957.
46. FUORTES, M. G. F., K. FRANK AND M. C. BECKER. *J. Gen. Physiol.* 40: 735, 1957.
47. FURSHPAN, E. J. AND D. D. POTTER. *Nature, London* 180: 342, 1957.
48. GEREN, B. B. AND F. A. SCHMITT. *Proc. Nat. Acad. Sc., Wash.* 40: 863, 1954.
49. HODGKIN, A. L. *Biol. Rev.* 26, 339, 1951.
50. HODGKIN, A. L. *Proc. Roy. Soc., London. ser. B* 148: 1, 1958.
51. HODGKIN, A. L. AND P. HOROWICZ. *J. Physiol.* 137: 30P, 1957.
52. HODGKIN, A. L. AND A. F. HUXLEY. *J. Physiol.* 117: 500, 1952.
53. HODGKIN, A. L. AND R. D. KEYNES. *J. Physiol.* 128: 28, 1955.
54. HODGKIN, A. L. AND R. D. KEYNES. *J. Physiol.* 131: 592, 1956.
55. HOWLAND, B., J. Y. LETTVIN, W. S. McCULLOCH, W. PITTS AND P. D. WALL. *J. Neurophysiol.* 18: 1, 1955.
56. HUTTER, O. F. AND W. TRAUTWEIN. *J. Physiol.* 129· 48P, 1955.
57. HUXLEY, A. F. In: *Ion Transport across Membranes.* New York: Acad. Press, 1954.
58. HYDÉN, H. *Acta physiol. scindinav.* 6: suppl. 17, 1943.
59. KATZ, B. *Arch. Sc. Physiol.* 3: 285, 1949.
60. KUFFLER, S. W. AND C. EYZAGUIRRE. *J. Gen. Physiol.* 39: 155, 1955.
61. LAPORTE, Y. AND D. P. C. LLOYD. *Am. J. Physiol.* 169: 609, 1952.
62. LAPORTE, Y., A. LUNDBERG AND O. OSCARSSON. *Acta physiol. scindinav.* 36: 188, 1956.
63. LILEY, A. W. *J. Physiol.* 134: 427, 1956.
64. LLOYD, D. P. C. *J. Neurophysiol.* 9: 421, 1946.
65. LORENTE DE NÓ, R. *J. Neurophysiol.* 1: 195, 1938.
66. PALADE, G. E. AND S. L. PALAY. *Anat. Rec.* 118: 335, 1954.
67. PALAY, S. L. *J. Biophys. & Biochem. Cytol.* Suppl., 2: 193, 1956.
68. PHILLIPS, C. G. *Quart. J. Exper. Physiol.* 41: 58, 1956.
69. REGER, J. F. *Anat. Rec.* 122: 1, 1955.
70. ROBERTSON, J. D. *J. Biophys. & Biochem. Cytol.* 2: 381, 1956.
71. SHERRINGTON, C. S. In *A Text Book of Physiology* (7th ed.), edited by M. Foster. London: Macmillan, 1897.
72. SHERRINGTON, C. S. *Proc. Roy. Soc., London. ser. B* 97: 519, 1925.

73. SHERRINGTON, C. S. *Proc. Roy. Soc., London. ser. B* 105: 332, 1929.

74. SPRAGUE, J. M. *XX Internat. Physiol. Congr., Abstr. of Communic.:* 849, 1956.

75. TERZUOLO, C. A. AND T. H. BULLOCK. *Arch. ital. biol.* 96: 117, 1958.

76. TRAUTWEIN, W., S. W. KUFFLER AND C. EDWARDS. *J. Gen. Physiol.* 40: 135, 1956.

77. WEIDMANN, S. *J. Physiol.* 114: 372, 1951.

78. WILSON, V. J. AND D. P. C. LLOYD. *Am. J. Physiol.* 187: 641, 1956.

79. YOUNG, J. Z. *Endeavour* 15: 5, 1956.

CHAPTER III

Conduction of the nerve impulse

ICHIJI TASAKI | *Laboratory of Neurophysiology, National Institute of Neurological Diseases and Blindness, National Institutes of Health, Bethesda, Maryland*

CHAPTER CONTENTS

THE MODERN DEVELOPMENT of the concept of the nerve impulse may be said to have started with the measurement of the velocity of the nerve impulse by von Helmholtz (141) in 1850. He measured the time interval between delivery of an electric shock to the nerve of a nerve-muscle preparation and the start of contraction of the muscle by two different methods. The first method used was to start a constant current through a ballistic galvanometer at the time of delivery of the shock and to interrupt the current automatically by a switch opened by the twitch of the muscle. The second method he used was based on graphical registration of the muscular contraction on a moving surface. He compared the time intervals measured by stimulating the nerve near its two extreme ends.

Helmholtz's finding and the subsequent confirmation and expansion of his observation by a number of investigators established the fact that a nerve impulse travels along the nerve at a rate far slower than that of light or sound in a similar medium but substantially faster than the process of transportation of substances by streaming or diffusion in a slender tube like a nerve fiber. Later, in 1908, Lucas (80) found that the velocity of the nerve impulse doubles with a rise in temperature of about 10 degrees. The question of whether or not the nerve impulse is associated with any chemical reactions, however, was not solved until Tashiro (138), Parker (98), Fenn (32) and Gerard (40) established the increase in production of carbon dioxide and consumption of oxygen related to nervous activity. The demonstration of heat production associated with propagation of nerve impulses by Downing *et al.* (24) gave a further strong support to the view that chemical reactions underlie the process of nervous conduction.[1]

An entirely different line of approach to the study of the processes underlying nervous conduction originates with Hermann (47). He worked on a 'core-conductor model' of nerve which is the predecessor of the passive iron model (75). The basic idea

[1] Some investigators are of the opinion that all the chemical reactions take place late in the recovery phase and not during the period in which electrical signs of activity can be observed [e.g. Hodgkin & Huxley (59)]

developed from the observations on the model is that nervous conduction may be mediated by a flow of electric current between successive portions of the nerve, i.e. by local circuits. Through very extensive investigations of bioelectricity by Matteucci (86), Du Bois-Reymond (25), Biedermann (12) and others, it became known that a transient potential variation is generated by a stimulation of a nerve between the portion of the nerve or the muscle carrying an impulse and the killed or resting portion. The existence of a local circuit is therefore a logical consequence of the direct observations on the bioelectricity of the nerve.

A direct demonstration of the decisive role played by a local circuit in the propagation of an impulse was brought forward, a long time after Hermann's prediction, first by Osterhout & Hill (95) who worked not on the nerve but on a large plant cell, *Nitella*. They found that propagation of an impulse along this elongated cell can be reversibly blocked under certain experimental conditions by removing or reconnecting a salt bridge which constituted a part of the local circuit. Later, similar observations were made both on isolated invertebrate nerve fibers (52) [cf. also (50)] and on single nerve fibers of the toad (117).

The development of the concept of the all-or-none relationship between the intensity of stimulus and the 'size of the response' followed a long, confusing course. In 1871, Bowditch (16) found that the magnitude of contraction in an excised heart muscle of the frog is independent of the intensity of the shock used; a weak shock, if effective at all, causes a contraction which is as large as that caused by a strong shock. A similar quantal relationship between the twitch and stimulus intensity was demonstrated in individual muscle fibers of the frog sartorius muscle (101) and also in a nerve-muscle preparation of the frog containing a small number of nerve fibers (81). In these cases the 'size of the response' represents the magnitude of muscular contraction observed at some distance away from the site of stimulation.

Attempting to expand the concept of 'size of response' to include the response in the nerve itself, Lucas (82) and Adrian (1) introduced the idea of measuring the nerve impulse by its ability to stimulate the adjacent portion of nerve, or by its capability to travel across a narcotized region of nerve—the logic being analogous to measuring the power of a man by his ability to cross a desert. Through a number of ingenious experiments, Lucas and Adrian concluded that the size of the nerve impulse in individual nerve fibers was independent of the way it was elicited. Kato (69) and his associates and also

Davis *et al.* (23) pointed out that there was an erroneous assumption in this argument as to the mechanism of narcotic action. However, the conclusion that a propagated nerve impulse obeyed the all-or-none law turned out to be perfectly correct.

Another series of somewhat controversial arguments was evoked among investigators when the concept of 'local' or 'subthreshold' response was introduced in physiology. In 1937 Rushton (105) predicted the existence of a local response in nerve by the following argument. If propagation of a nerve impulse is due to successive stimulation of a resting portion of nerve by the neighboring active (responding) area, a definite minimum area of a nerve has to be excited by the stimulating current in order that the response at the site of stimulation can generate a propagated all-or-none response. In other words, he stipulates that there should be a 'response' at the site of stimulation that is too small to initiate a full sized propagating response.

Soon after Rushton's prediction, Hodgkin (51) obtained clear-cut records indicating the existence of 'subthreshold responses' in the invertebrate nerve fiber. However, it was found later that Hodgkin's demonstration did not prove the legitimacy of Rushton's argument. Cole & Curtis (19) proved that the resistance of the surface membrane of the squid nerve fiber decreases at the peak of its response to about $\frac{1}{200}$ of the resistance at rest; a responding area of the squid axon behaves like a battery with no appreciable internal resistance. Under ordinary experimental conditions, it is practically impossible to elicit a full-sized response in an area too small to initiate a propagated impulse. Furthermore, these subthreshold responses were demonstrated in squid axons of which a large area was subjected uniformly to a stimulating current. Later we shall discuss similar phenomena observed in the myelinated nerve fiber (p. 98).

We have discussed up to this point the course of development of some of the basic concepts concerning the nature of the nerve impulse. We shall describe on the following pages the main experimental facts known about the nerve fiber and its ability to carry impulses. Emphasis will be placed on the data obtained from invertebrate and vertebrate single nerve fibers. There is good reason to believe that, at least in this field of physiology, the behavior of an assembly of many nervous elements can be understood if the behavior of individual fibers under simple, well-defined, experimental conditions is known. It is generally extremely difficult to infer the behavior of individual fibers from observations on the nerve trunk.

COMPOUND CHARACTER OF PERIPHERAL NERVE

Soon after the first World War, Forbes & Thacher (34) introduced a condenser-coupled vacuum tube amplifier into the field of electrophysiology. Aided by the continued development of electronic engineering, Gasser & Erlanger (38) in 1922 took the first photograph of a nerve response recorded with an instrument ideal in being inertialess. They started using a cathode ray oscillograph to register the time course of responses of the nerve.

The standard technique of recording electric signs of activity of a whole nerve trunk is to kill (ordinarily by crushing) one end of a nerve and to place one of the recording electrodes on this killed end (see fig. 1A). The other electrode needed to measure the potential difference is placed on the intact part of the nerve near the killed end. Ordinarily, either lightly chlorided silver wire (abbreviated as Ag-AgCl) or calomel half cells (Hg-HgCl) are used for recording for they are nonpolarizable. Stimulating electrodes (S in fig. 1) can be either the Ag-AgCl Ringer type or a pair of plain platinum wires. A precaution has to be taken to 'isolate' the stimulus from ground, namely, to eliminate metallic connection of the stimulating electrodes with ground. The main reason for the necessity of stimulus isolation is to prevent flow of stimulating (and other) currents between the stimulating and ground electrodes. The electrodes and the nerve are generally mounted in a moist chamber to prevent evaporation of water from the surface of the nerve.

The arrangement of the recording electrodes just described is called a 'monophasic lead' and a response of the nerve recorded with this arrangement is referred to as a 'monophasic action potential'. The traditional picture illustrating the principle of this method of recording action potentials is as follows. The portion of nerve carrying an impulse is 'electrically negative' to the portion at rest. When an impulse started by a stimulus emerges in the region of the recording electrode E_1, the potential difference between E_1 and E_2 undergoes a transient variation which makes the potential at E_2 more positive (or less negative) to that at E_1. Since the impulse does not reach the region of E_2, a potential variation representing the nervous activity at E_1 is recorded monophasically.

The modern picture illustrating the principle of monophasic recording (83, 124) is slightly different from the classical one. Attention is now focused upon the nerve fibers and the intercellular space in the nerve trunk. When a nerve fiber carries an impulse, it generates a transient flow of current in the surrounding fluid medium. In the region of E_1 and E_2, this transient current in the intercellular space is directed from E_2 to E_1, raising the potential at E_2 relative to E_1 for a short period of time. The currents produced simultaneously by many fibers in the nerve are superposed in the intercellular space and give rise to a large compound action potential. In this modern picture, the 'electrical negativity' in

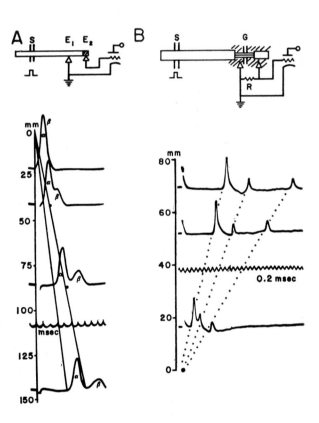

FIG. 1. A. Demonstration of the constant velocity of propagation of the α- and β-waves in the action potential of the sciatic nerve of the bullfrog. S, the stimulating electrodes; E_1 and E_2, recording electrodes, the latter at the killed end of the nerve. The distance from the site of stimulation to the recording electrode E_1 is indicated on the vertical line. The starting points of the oscillograph trace show the distances at which the records were taken. Abscissa, time. [From Gasser & Erlanger (38).] B. A similar observation made on a three-fiber preparation of the toad. The diameters of the fibers were 13, 9 and 5 μ. The strength of the stimulating shocks employed was twice the threshold for the smallest fiber. [From Tasaki (124).]

the classical picture[2] is clearly defined as an *IR* drop in the intercellular space.

We shall now proceed to discuss the time course of the action potential of a bullfrog sciatic nerve recorded with this arrangement. When the distance from the stimulating electrode (S) to the recording electrodes (E_1) is relatively large and the shock is strong enough to stimulate most of the fibers in the nerve, an action potential with several separate peaks is observed (fig. 1*A*, bottom). As the distance is altered, the time intervals between the peaks are found to alter, indicating that separate elevations in the potential record represent processes travelling along the nerve at different velocities. Gasser, Erlanger, Bishop and others (13, 38) interpreted these findings as resulting from differences in the conduction velocity of the different fibers in the nerve trunk.

In figure 1*B*, a set of records is presented showing the validity of the interpretation just mentioned. Here, the connective tissue sheath around the sciatic nerve is removed near its distal end and all except three nerve fibers are cut (for the detail of this operation, cf. 113, 124). The two recording electrodes are placed in two small pools of Ringer's solution separated by a narrow air gap (0.1 mm wide) across which the exposed nerve fibers are mounted. Under these circumstances, the electric currents which the nerve fibers produce when the impulses arrive at the site of recording inevitably flow through the resistor (*R* in the figure) connected between the electrodes. The *IR* drop thus produced is amplified and recorded with an oscillograph.

It is seen in the records that the number of peaks observed is equal to the number of the fibers left uncut. Three fibers are now generating three separate potential variations. It is also clear that each fiber carries an impulse at a rate which is approximately constant for the whole length of the sciatic nerve.

It is simple to demonstrate the statistical rule formulated by Erlanger and Gasser that the conduction velocity increases with increasing fiber diameter. If only one large fiber is left uncut, we find a high conduction velocity; a weak electric shock is sufficient to excite it. If one small fiber is

[2] It is important to distinguish a negative potential from a negative electric charge. The potential along a uniform electric conductor is inevitably related by Ohm's law to a flow of current in the conductor; it has to be expressed as a potential difference between the two points on the conductor, for instance, 'the potential of E_1 is 10 mv below (or above) that of E_2' but not 'E_2 is negative and E_1 is positive.'

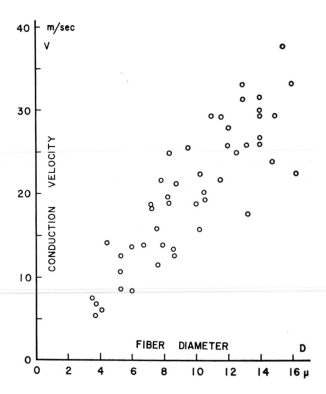

FIG. 2. Conduction velocity of individual nerve fibers, *V*, plotted against fiber diameter, *D*. Single fibers were isolated from sciatic-gastrocnemius preparations of the bullfrog. The outside diameter of the fiber was measured at the operated region near the muscle. Temperature, 24°C. [From Tasaki *et al.* (131).]

isolated in the region of recording, we find a small response which arrives at the site of recording after a long delay; a strong shock is needed to stimulate such a fiber.

In figure 2 the conduction velocities of about 50 different fibers in the bullfrog sciatic nerve are plotted against their outside diameter. There is a rough proportionality between the fiber diameter and the conduction velocity, the correlation coefficient between the two being 0.92 in this measurement. The relation between the minimum effective intensity or threshold of shock and the fiber diameter determined by this method can be found elsewhere (124).

It is well-known that the internodal length (the distance between the two neighboring nodes of Ranvier) increases with the fiber diameter. For the fibers in the bullfrog sciatic nerve, the relation between the diameter *D* and the internodal length *L* was found to be expressed by the formula

$$L = 0.146 \times 10^3 D,$$

the correlation coefficient between the two being 0.62. The relation between the conduction velocity V (expressed in m per sec.) and the diameter (in μ) presented in figure 2 can be expressed by

$$V = 2.50D$$

(at 24°C). From the two formulae above, it follows immediately that

$$\frac{L}{V} = 0.059 \text{ (msec.)}.$$

The ratio L/V represents the average conduction time for one internodal length. The last expression indicates that, statistically speaking, the internodal conduction time is roughly independent of the fiber diameter.

In the experiments involving electric stimulation of whole nerve trunks, it is customary to designate groups of nerve fibers of different conduction velocities as α, β, γ, (δ), B and C. Group α represents the fastest myelinated nerve fibers in the nerve with velocities of 20 to 30 m per sec. in the frog, while B fibers are the slowest group (5 m per sec. or less) at room temperature. The first three (or four) groups are often included in A. Group C represents non-myelinated fibers. This classification is somewhat arbitrary.

The distribution of the fiber sizes in a nerve trunk generally shows several peaks of numerical predominance. Reflecting this situation, action potentials recorded at some distance away from the site of stimulation develop several peaks. However, because of the difference in size and duration of the action potentials among different fibers, it requires a tedious calculation to predict the configuration of the action potential of a whole nerve trunk on the basis of its fiber size distribution. A detailed treatment of this problem is found in a monograph by Gasser & Erlanger (38).

GENERAL CHARACTER OF THE NERVE IMPULSE

In the preceding section we have seen an example of simplicity and clarity of the experiments done with isolated single nerve fibers. It was Adrian & Bronk (5) in 1928 who made the first successful attempt to reduce operatively the number of active fibers in a nerve to record single fiber responses. The operation of isolating single nerve fibers of the frog and the toad was developed in Kato's laboratory (70).

Another successful approach to single fiber experiments was achieved by the use of nerve preparations of invertebrates, such as crabs, lobsters, crayfish or squid. The operative procedure of obtaining single fibers in these invertebrate nerves is simpler than the dissection of a single frog nerve fiber, since some of the fibers in these lower animals are larger than 100 μ in diameter. So-called squid giant axons, which Young (146) has introduced to electrophysiologists, are as large as 400 to 900 μ in diameter and are an excellent material for investigating the potential inside the axoplasm.

Through the use of single fiber preparations, the demonstration of some of the basic properties of the propagated nerve impulse has become extremely simple and direct. The following properties are common to all the nerve fibers examined, vertebrate and invertebrate.

a) All-or-none law. The historical aspect of the development of this law has been mentioned in the introduction of this chapter. This law may be stated as follows: with other factors constant, the size and shape of any electrical sign of a propagated nerve impulse is independent of the intensity of stimulus employed to initiate the impulse.

It has been mentioned that a definite threshold intensity is needed to initiate an impulse in a nerve fiber. As signs of an impulse, one may take the current developed by the fiber, the action current, or the potential changes inside the axoplasm, or any other electrical response of the fiber. When the stimulus intensity is varied, these signs may appear slightly earlier or later; but the whole time course remains uninfluenced by how far above threshold the stimulus intensity is.

The records presented in figure 3 show the time course of the action currents produced by a single nerve fiber of a toad in response to electric shocks of varying intensities. The shocks were applied to the sciatic nerve trunk and the current associated with an impulse traveling along a single nerve fiber in the nerve was recorded by the technique described in the discussion of the experiment of figure 1B. At threshold (the lowest trace), the action current of the fiber started after a long and variable delay. The time course of this action current, however, was identical with that of the other responses to stronger shocks.

It is possible to modify the time course of the electric response of a fiber by changing physical or chemical environmental conditions, such as temperature or composition of the fluid around the fiber. This fact should not be regarded as a violation of the all-or-

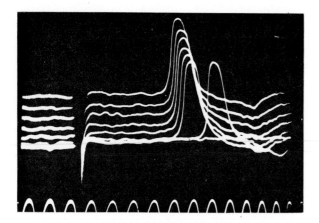

FIG. 3. Demonstration of the all-or-none behavior of the electric response (binodal action current) of a single myelinated fiber. The distance between the stimulating electrodes and the site of recording was 20 mm. The strengths of the stimulating shocks were, from the bottom upward, 100, 105, 150, 200, 250, 300 and 350 per cent of threshold, respectively. Time marker, 5000 cycles per sec. Temperature, 20.5°C. [From Tasaki (124).]

none law. This law refers to the identity of the responses obtained by changing only the stimulus intensity and nothing else.

The all-or-none law is not applicable, at least not in as strict a form as described above, to electrical responses recorded at the site of stimulation (cf. p. 98).

b) The refractory period. The time course of the response of a nerve fiber is not influenced by the rate at which the stimulating shocks are repeated as long as the rate is less than about 10 per sec. When, however, the repetition rate is increased up to about 100 per sec. at room temperature, it is found that the responses are different in their size and shape from the responses obtained at lower frequencies. During a short period of time after an impulse has swept over the fiber, the 'condition' of the fiber is different from that of a normal resting fiber. This period is called the refractory period of the nerve fiber.

It is customary to investigate the properties of a nerve fiber in the refractory period by using a series of paired stimuli, a brief conditioning shock followed by a brief test shock at an adjustable interval. The response of the fiber to the first conditioning shock has the normal configuration, while the response to the second test shock varies with the time interval between the paired shocks. The threshold for the second shock is known to undergo a pronounced change during the early stage in the refractory period.

The curve representing the time course of the

gradual change in threshold with increasing shock intervals is generally called a 'recovery curve'. In the first recovery curve published by Adrian & Lucas (6) in 1912, the reciprocal of threshold, the 'excitability', was plotted against the interval between the two shocks. The thick continuous line in figure 4 shows a recovery curve determined by using the propagated impulses of a single nerve fiber as the index. The threshold for the test shock alone (measured 1 sec. or more after the conditioning shock) is taken as unity. The observed data indicate that, as the interval between the conditioning and test shocks decreases, the threshold for the test shock rises first gradually and then more rapidly. There is a sharp break in the curve at the moment when the threshold is about 2.5 to 3 times the normal value, namely, when the excitability is about 30 to 40 per cent of the normal level.

This break in the recovery curve indicates that, in the period following initiation of a propagated nerve impulse in a nerve fiber, there is a definite period during which the fiber is incapable of carrying a second impulse. This period was designated by previous workers as the 'absolutely refractory period', but more recently the term the 'least (or critical) interval' between two effective stimuli (124, 136) is preferred. The reason for this recommendation is the fact that, when one determines the recovery curve at the site of stimulation, a continuous curve without a break is obtained. The term 'functional' absolutely refractory period has also been recommended to describe this period (103).

The period during which the excitability recovers continuously is called the 'relatively refractory period'. Following this period there is often a period of heightened excitability which is called the supernormal phase. During the 'supernormal phase', the size of the action potential and the conduction velocity are practically normal.

The thin line in figure 4 shows the recovery curve for the same fiber determined at low temperature. The temperature-dependence of the recovery curve is pronounced, the Q_{10} being about 3.5 (2, 119). The effect of temperature change is reversible.

The conduction velocity is known to be subnormal during the relatively refractory period. This is shown in figure 5, in which the shock response intervals for two impulses were plotted against the distance between the site of stimulation and the site of recording. The two impulses were set up at an interval slightly longer than the least interval of the fiber. It is seen in the figure that the shock response interval for the first impulse increases proportionately with the con-

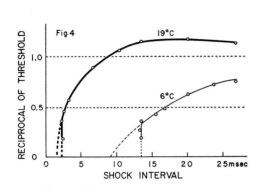

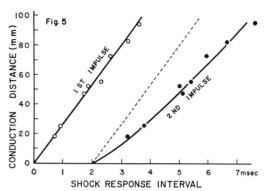

FIG. 4. Recovery curves of a toad nerve fiber determined at two different temperatures. [From Tasaki (119).]

FIG. 5. Relation between the conduction distance and the shock response interval for two impulses elicited at an interval of 2 msec. A motor nerve fiber of 11 μ in diameter innervating the flexor digitorum brevis of the toad. Temperature, 23°C.

duction distance. Evidently, the first impulse travels along the fiber at a normal constant rate.

If the second impulse had travelled at the normal velocity, the shock response interval for the second impulse should be represented by the dotted line in the figure which has the same slope as the straight line for the first impulse. Actually, it is seen that the observed shock response interval increases with increasing conduction distance more rapidly than that for the first impulse.

It is easy to figure out the space-time pattern of the two impulses based on the experimental data present in figure 5. Evidently, the tangent (slope) of the curve in the figure represents the velocity of the second impulse at that moment. At the point where the two impulses were initiated, the velocity of the second impulse is approximately 50 per cent of the velocity of the first impulse. Because of this large difference in velocity between the two impulses, the second impulse lags, spatially and temporally, behind the first as they travel along the fiber. As separation between the two impulses increases, however, the second impulse gains more speed because of increasing recovery from the refractoriness left behind the first impulse. Thus, as they travel along a nerve fiber, the interval between the two impulses approaches asymptotically a constant value which is independent of the initial interval at which they started.

c) Two-way conduction. It is simple to demonstrate that a nerve fiber is capable of carrying impulses in both directions, from its proximal end toward the distal and also in the reverse direction. An observation illustrated by figure 6 shows this. Here a squid giant axon is used. An entirely analo-

gous observation has been made on the vertebrate myelinated nerve fiber.

The axon is placed in a pool of fresh sea water on a glass plate. Near each of the two ends of the axon a pair of stimulating electrodes is placed. A recording electrode, a glass pipette of about 1 μ at the tip filled with isosmotic potassium chloride solution in this case, is pushed into the axoplasm of the axon through its surface membrane. The grounded sea water is taken as a reference point for measuring the action potential. A stimulus applied at one end, A in the figure, gives rise to a response of the all-or-none type, indicating that the impulse starting at A travels toward B. When another stimulating shock is applied at the other end, B, sometime after the impulse from A has swept over the fiber, the impulse arising at B can be recorded by the pipette in the middle of the axon (see the top record in fig. 6). Since the recording pipette can be placed anywhere between A and B with essentially the same result, this observation proves that the axon is capable of carrying impulses in both directions.

When the time interval between the shocks at A and B is reduced below a certain limit (see the record in the middle), the second shock becomes ineffective. The explanation of this fact is simple. Soon after region B of the axon is traversed by the impulse arising at A, this region becomes refractory and does not respond to the second shock.

What happens if two shocks are applied simultaneously at the two ends A and B? There is no refractoriness at the site of stimulation in this case since these regions have not been traversed by any impulse. Hence, an impulse should be initiated at A propagating toward B. Simultaneously, another impulse starting at B should travel toward A. Then, the impulses are bound to undergo a collision at a point about half way between the two sites of stimulation of the axon. After such a head-on collision, it should be impossible for the two impulses to travel further since the region where the impulse from A is heading is freshly traversed by the impulse from B and is consequently incapable of carrying another impulse. The same thing can be said of the region on the other side of the site of collision.

In the bottom record of figure 6, the two stimulating shocks are delivered in such a way that the two impulses collide exactly at the site of recording. This is accomplished by adjusting the delays of the two shocks after the start of the sweep of the oscillograph beam in such a manner that the response to shock A alone appears at the same spot on the oscillograph screen as the response to shock B alone. Delivery of two shocks under these conditions elicits, as can be seen in the figure, only one response which has almost the same configuration as the response to one shock. The shock response interval is known to be slightly reduced by collision. A further discussion on this topic may be found elsewhere (120).

d) Multiplication of impulses at the branching point of a nerve fiber. Histological studies indicate that vertebrate motor nerve fibers frequently undergo dichotomy or ramification at nodes of Ranvier, one mother fiber giving rise to two (or more) daughter fibers [cf. e.g. Eccles & Sherrington (26)]. During the course of isolating single nerve fibers innervating the toad gastrocnemius muscle, such branching motor fibers are sometimes encountered. It has been shown in such preparations that the muscle tension developed by stimulation of the mother fiber (with two daughter fibers intact) is nearly twice as great as the tension observed after severing one of the daughter fibers. Obviously, this indicates that the impulse travelling down the mother fiber invades the two daughter fibers. By this process of successive dichotomy, an impulse travelling along a motor nerve fiber multiplies itself before it reaches a large number of muscle fibers.

Sensory nerve fibers generally dichotomize as they approach their peripheral endings. They also branch off many collaterals in the spinal cord. It is generally believed that impulses multiply themselves at these bifurcating points. In the squid axons, multiplication of impulses at bifurcation points has also been observed.

e) Interaction between nerve fibers. When a group of fibers in a nerve trunk carries nerve impulses, it never happens, under ordinary experimental conditions, that these impulses are transmitted to the other surrounding nerve fibers. This can be shown by the following simple observation.

The gastrocnemius muscle of the toad or frog is innervated by a small nerve twig branching off from the large tibial nerve which innervates also plantar muscles and the skin of the foot. Stimulation of the tibial nerve at a point distal to the exit of the muscle nerve to the gastrocnemius does not evoke any potential variation in the muscle nerve nor any contraction in the muscle. Such a stimulus sets up a 'volley of impulses' in the majority of the fibers in the tibial nerve, but these impulses do not spread to the nerve fibers entering the muscle.

It has been found, however, that there is a very weak, barely detectable interaction between the nerve fibers in a common nerve trunk. Otani (96) found that, when the peroneal branch of the sciatic nerve carries a volley of impulses, the threshold for the fibers from the tibial branch undergoes a transient change. This observation was confirmed and expanded by several investigators, notably by Marrazzi & Lorente de Nó (85). This result is now interpreted on a purely electrical basis: when a group of fibers carries impulses, the fluid in the intercellular space is traversed by action currents developed by these active fibers. If a stimulating current pulse is delivered in this region of nerve, the effect of the stimulus is modified when it is superposed on or antagonized by the action currents. The maximum change in threshole is of the order of 10 per cent.

If the mechanism of interaction between nerve fibers is electrical in nature, it would be expected that the interaction should be greatly enhanced by reducing the shunting effect of the fluid medium around the nerve fiber. Katz & Schmitt (73) have shown that this is actually the case.

The diagram at the top of figure 7 illustrates their experimental arrangement. Two nerve fibers of the crab were immersed in a pool of mineral oil. Fiber I was stimulated with electrodes A and B and its response was observed by means of the recording electrodes D and E in the figure. At about the time of arrival of an impulse from B at the site of recording, testing current pulses were delivered through electrodes C and D to determine changes in threshold of fiber II at D. The triphasic curve at the bottom of figure 7 is the time course of the threshold changes observed. Katz & Schmitt explained these results, with good reason, as due to the flow of the action cur-

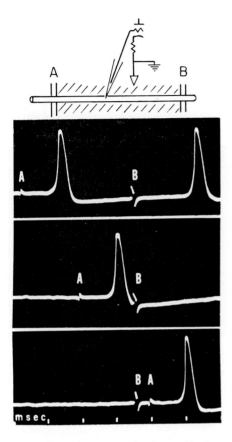

FIG. 6. Action potentials of a squid giant axon elicited by stimulating shocks at the two ends, A and B, of the axon. The recording micropipette was pushed into the axoplasm through the axon membrane. Demonstration of two-way conduction (*top*), refractoriness (*middle*) and collision of impulses (*bottom*). Temperature, 20°C. (Discussion in text.)

rent developed by fiber I through the surface membrane of fiber II. They also demonstrated that the velocity of an impulse in fiber II is affected by the impulse in fiber I when the amount of the fluid is reduced and when the two impulses are not spatially far apart.

Arvanitaki (9) and Tasaki (124) showed that, under special experimental conditions, it is possible to make an impulse jump from one fiber to another by leading the action current of one fiber through the other.

CABLE PROPERTIES OF THE INVERTEBRATE AXON

It is easy to introduce a small glass pipette or a set of metal wires longitudinally into a squid giant axon. By using such internal electrodes, electric properties of the giant axon have been extensively investigated

by a number of physiologists. We shall discuss in this section some of the basic observations which serve to clarify electric properties of the resting giant axon (fig. 8).

When a glass pipette electrode of about 100 μ in diameter is inserted longitudinally into a giant axon, it is found that the potential of this electrode (relative to the large ground electrode in the surrounding sea water) goes down gradually as the pipette electrode is advanced along the axis of the axon. The potential inside the axon is negative to (i.e. lower than) that of the surrounding fluid medium. When the electrode is advanced more than about 10 mm from the point of insertion on the surface membrane, the potential level of the axoplasm is practically independent of the position of the tip of the pipette. In other words, the space occupied by the axoplasm is practically equipotential. The potential difference between the surrounding fluid medium and the axoplasm determined by this or other similar methods is called the 'resting membrane potential'.

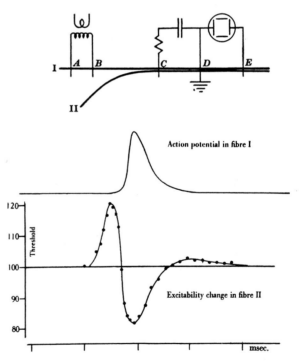

FIG. 7. *Top*: Electrode arrangement used for demonstration of excitability changes in a single nerve fiber of the crab caused by the passage of an impulse in the adjacent fiber. A, B, leads for stimulation of fiber I; C, D, leads for stimulation of fiber II; D, E, recording leads connecting with amplifier and cathode ray oscillograph. *Bottom*: Excitability changes in fiber II during the passage of an impulse in fiber I. Abscissae: time in msec. Ordinates: threshold intensity of fiber II in percentage of its resting threshold. [From Katz & Schmitt (73).]

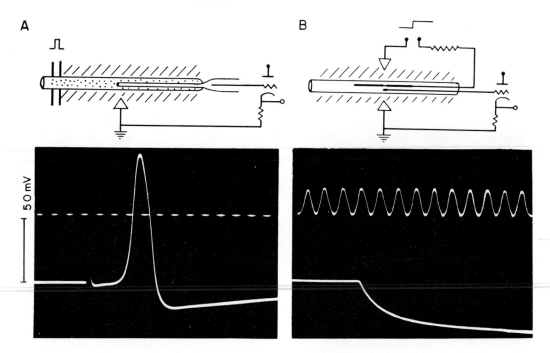

FIG. 8. *A*. Resting and action potential of the squid giant axon recorded with an intracellular glass pipette electrode. Time marker (0.5 msec.) indicates the potential level observed when the recording electrode was in the surrounding sea water. Temperature, 23°C. *B*. Exponential variation in the membrane potential caused by passage of a constant current through the membrane of a squid giant axon with a long intracellular silver wire electrode. The thick portions of the wire in the diagram on the top show the exposed surface of the electrodes. Time marker, 1000 cycles per sec. Temperature, 20°C. (The axons in the diagrams are disproportionately thick and short.)

The fact that the potential level is the same everywhere in the axoplasm indicates, according to Ohm's law, that there is no measureable flow of electric current in the axoplasm at rest. It also proves that the resting potential represents, as in the frog muscle fiber (76) and in other nervous elements, a sharp drop of electric potential across the space occupied by the thin surface membrane of the cell. The resting potential of an excised squid giant axon is known to be 50 to 60 mv; it is considerably smaller than that of vertebrate skeletal muscle and nerve cells.

When a pulse of stimulating current is applied to a giant axon with an internal recording electrode, there occurs a transient rise of 100 to 120 mv in the potential of the axoplasm referred to ground (fig. 8*A*). The magnitude of the action potential measured by this method is practically independent of the position of the electrode tip in the axoplasm. If the tip of the internal electrode touches or pierces the surface membrane, both the resting and action potentials are profoundly diminished or completely eliminated. The action potential represents, therefore, a transient variation of the potential difference across the surface

membrane of the axon. It is important to distinguish this 'membrane action potential' from those recorded with external electrodes.

When it was discovered that the membrane action potential is substantially larger than the resting potential of the membrane (22, 56), some investigators who believed the membrane hypothesis of Bernstein (10) were greatly surprised. In 1902 Bernstein postulated, without clear supporting evidence, that the action potential may be a mere diminution or disappearance of the resting membrane potential (see p. 117). The finding that the inside potential rises above the outside potential near the peak of the action potential, therefore, conflicts with this postulate of the membrane hypothesis.

Besides the role in maintaining a potential difference, the surface membrane of the resting axon plays another important part in electrophysiology of the nerve fiber. The resting membrane has a high resistance to a direct current. This can be shown by the use of the arrangement of figure 8*B*, in which a set of two metal wire electrodes was used instead of a glass pipette.

The electrode set shown in the figure consists of one wire with a long (about 12 mm) exposed surface and the other with a short (1 mm) exposed surface. The long wire is used to send a constant current into the axon and the other for recording potential changes caused by the current. The short electrode has its exposed (uninsulated) surface in the middle of the long one. The remaining surface of each electrode is insulated with a layer of enamel. A pulse of constant current can be generated by connecting a high voltage source to the current electrode through a high resistance.

When the sign of the applied current is such that the axon membrane is traversed by an inward directed current, the potential inside the membrane is found to be lowered by the current. However, as can be seen in the record in the figure, the potential change at the onset of the current is gradual—mathematically speaking, exponential. The potential change varies roughly proportionately with the intensity of the applied current. When the current is reversed, the sign of the potential change is simply reversed, provided that the change in the resting potential does not exceed about 5 mv.

This behavior of the axon can be readily understood if one assumes that the axon membrane consists of a condenser with a parallel resistance (fig. 9A). As is well known, the current flowing through a condenser of a capacity, C, is given by $C \, dV/dt$, where dV/dt is the rate of change in the potential difference, V, across the condenser. The current, I, through a system of a condenser and a parallel resistance is

given by the expression

$$I = C \frac{dV}{dt} + \frac{V}{R}, \qquad (4 \cdot 1)$$

i.e. by the sum of the capacitative current and the ohmic current. When the current, the capacity and the resistance, R, are all constant, the time course of the potential is given by

$$V = IR \left(1 - e^{-t/RC} \right), \qquad (4 \cdot 2)$$

where t is the time after the onset of the current. By comparing equation (4-2) with the observed result of figure 8B, the values of R and C can be determined. The capacity, C, of the giant axon membrane determined by this method is approximately 1 $\mu f/cm^2$ and the membrane resistance is between 1 and 2.5 $k\Omega \cdot cm^2$. [cf. Hodgkin et al. (61), p. 440]. The time constant of the membrane, RC, is, therefore, 1 to 2.5 msec.[3]

In the argument developed above, the resistances of both the axoplasm and the sea water have been ignored. Cole & Hodgkin (20) and Schmitt (106) have shown that the axoplasm is a homogeneous conductor with a specific resistance of about 40 ohm·cm at 20°C. The specific resistance of the sea water is approximately 20 ohm·cm at the same temperature. These resistances are too small to have any observable effect upon the measurement of figure 8B.

Now the question arises of how the voltage source representing the resting membrane potential fits in the system of a capacity and a parallel resistance of figure 9A. It is possible to draw a continuous current from the resting membrane; therefore, it is legitimate to represent the source of the resting potential by a battery. There are obviously two simple ways, B and C in the figure, of connecting a battery in the circuit of A. Both ways fit with the observed data. There is at present no direct experimental procedure that can serve to determine which one of them represents the axon membrane better. In the sodium theory (cf. p. 118), the electromotive force of the membrane is assumed to be connected in parallel with the condenser as in B.

As the result of the above discussion, it has become clear that a squid axon behaves like the core-conductor of Hermann (see p. 75) or like a submarine cable. Using elementary calculus, we may proceed slightly

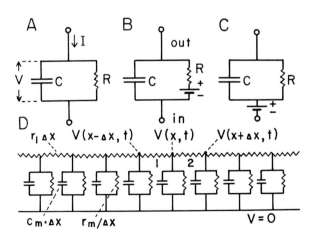

FIG. 9. Structure of the squid giant axon revealed by the use of intracellular electrodes. C, capacity, and R, resistance of the membrane. Two possible ways of connecting the source of the resting potential in the circuit of R and C are shown by diagrams B and C. (Further detail in text.)

[3] These figures were obtained by eliminating the effect of the current flowing near the end of the current electrode by the technique described by Marmont (84). The reader is reminded in this connection to pay attention also to the dimensions of these figures.

further to discuss the spread of electricity along a uniform resting axon.

In figure 9D, the electric properties of an axon immersed in a large volume of sea water are represented by a network of resistances and capacities. Since we are interested only in the change of potentials, the batteries are omitted in the figure. The resistance of the axoplasm of a unit length is represented by r_i; it is related to the specific resistance of the axoplasm R_i by the expression

$$r_i = \frac{R_i}{\pi(\frac{1}{2}D)^2}, \qquad (4\text{-}3)$$

where D is the diameter of the fiber.

Symbols r_m and c_m denote, respectively, the resistance and the capacity of the membrane covering the axoplasm of a unit length. They are related to the corresponding figures for a unit area, R_m and C_m, by the formulae

$$r_m = \frac{R_m}{\pi D}, \qquad (4\text{-}4)$$

$$c_m = \pi D C_m. \qquad (4\text{-}5)$$

Let $V(x, t)$ denote the potential of the axoplasm, referred to the potential of the surrounding fluid medium, at position x and time t. Then the symbols $V(x - \Delta x, t)$ and $V(x + \Delta x, t)$ can be used to denote the potentials at position $(x - \Delta x)$ and at $(x + \Delta x)$, respectively. The axon is now imaginatively divided into a series of segments of a length Δx. The axoplasm resistance (to a longitudinal current) of such a segment is then $r_i \Delta x$. Similarly, the membrane capacity and the resistance of one segment are given by $c_m \Delta x$ and $r_m/\Delta x$, respectively. By applying Ohm's law, it is found that the longitudinal current in the section labelled 1 is equal to $[V(x, t) - V(x - \Delta x, t)]/(r_i \Delta x)$. Similarly, the longitudinal current through section 2 is equal to $[V(x + \Delta x, t) - V(x, t)]/(r_i \Delta x)$. The difference between the current through 1 and that through 2 is equal to the membrane current, which has the form given by equation (4-1). This us to the equation

$$\frac{V(x + \Delta x, t) - V(x, t)}{r_i \Delta x} - \frac{V(x, t) - V(x - \Delta x, t)}{r_i \Delta x}$$
$$= c_m \Delta x \frac{\partial V(x, t)}{\partial t} + \frac{V(x, t)}{r_m/\Delta x}.$$

By taking the limit Δx to zero, we obtain the well known cable equation:

$$\frac{r_m}{r} \frac{\partial^2 V(x, t)}{\partial x^2} = c_m r_m \frac{\partial V(x, t)}{\partial t} + V(x, t). \qquad (4\text{-}6)$$

It is obvious that the spread of currents in other non-myelinated nerve fibers and in a uniform muscle fiber can be described by the same equation.

In the steady state the potential is a function of position x alone. Equation (4-6) is then reduced to

$$\frac{r_m}{r_i} \frac{d^2 V(x)}{dx^2} = V(x), \qquad (4\text{-}7)$$

in which $V(x)$ represents $V(x, \infty)$. The general solution of this equation is

$$V(x) = A e^{-x/\lambda} + B e^{+x/\lambda}, \qquad (4\text{-}8)$$

where λ, the 'space constant', is related to the membrane resistance and the axoplasm resistance by the expression

$$\lambda = \sqrt{\frac{r_m}{r_i}} = \sqrt{\frac{D R_m}{4 R_i}}. \qquad (4\text{-}9)$$

Constants A and B in equation (4-8) depend on the boundary conditions.

In a special case where a constant current of intensity I_0 is sent into the axon at $x = 0$, constant B has to be equal to zero; otherwise, $V(x)$ approaches infinity as x increases. At $x = 0$ where the current is sent into the axon, $dV(x)/dx$ is equal to $-\frac{1}{2} r_i I_0$, the factor $\frac{1}{2}$ being introduced to meet the situation where the current spreads on both sides of the point $x = 0$. From these boundary conditions, it is found that $A = \frac{1}{2} r_i \lambda I_0$ and $B = 0$. The solution of equation (4-7) for this special case is, therefore,

$$V(x) = \frac{1}{2} r_i \lambda \cdot I_0 e^{-x/\lambda} \qquad (4\text{-}10)$$

The 'effective' resistance $\frac{1}{2} r_i \lambda$ can be expressed by virtue of equation (4-9) as $\frac{1}{2} \sqrt{r_m r_i}$. The space constant, λ, is a measure of the spread of electricity along the axon; the greater the value of λ, the more extensive is the spread. In the squid giant axon, λ is of the order of 0.6 cm (20). Solutions of the general cable equation for several special cases have been achieved (30, 63, 130).

CABLE PROPERTIES OF THE MYELINATED NERVE FIBER

Large nerve fibers in the vertebrate nerve have a thick layer of fatty substance, the myelin sheath, between the cylinder of the axoplasm and the outermost layer of connective tissue, the neurilemma or the sheath of Schwann. The myelin sheath is broken at so-called nodes of Ranvier where the surface of the axis cylinder is covered directly by the neurilemma.

The width of the nodal membrane uncovered by the myelin sheath is roughly 0.5 to 1 μ. The distance between the nodes has been discussed on p. 78.

The first experimental evidence indicating that the myelin sheath has a high resistance to a direct current was obtained in Tokyo in 1934 [Kubo, Ono & Tasaki cited in (70)]. When the threshold of an isolated single nerve fiber was determined with a small electrode placed near the fiber, it was found that the threshold varied regularly with the distance from the nodes of the fiber (fig. 10). In these early experiments the threshold was determined by taking twitches of the muscle innervated by the isolated fiber as an index that a nerve impulse had been initiated in the fiber. Later, measurements were made by taking electric responses of the fiber as an index [e.g. fig. 1 in Tasaki (123)]. All these experiments indicate that the threshold is lowest when the small electrode (stimulating cathode) is placed directly on one of the nodes (the other electrode placed in the fluid medium away from the fiber), and is highest when the electrode is at the point half way between two neighboring nodes. These findings have been interpreted as indicating that, because of the high (d.c.) resistance of the myelin sheath, the stimulating current enters and leaves only at the nodes and consequently that the nerve fiber is excited only at the nodes. A further discussion on this subject may be found elsewhere (71, 124).

It was found later that the myelin sheath is not a perfect insulator but that short current pulses can flow readily through this sheath (66, 124, 125, 136). To illustrate this point, we shall mention an observation published in Germany during World War II (136). The diagram in figure 11A illustrates the experimental arrangement used.

A single nerve fiber of the toad is mounted across three small pools of Ringer's solution divided by two narrow air gaps of 0.1 to 0.3 mm width. The pool in the middle is about 1 mm wide and contains only the myelin covered part of the fiber. All the nodes (N_1, N_2 and others) are kept in the larger, lateral pools. In

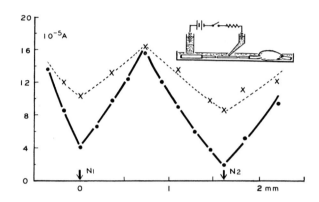

FIG. 10. Threshold strength of a long stimulating current (in amperes) plotted against distance from a node of Ranvier, N_1. Motor nerve fiber of the toad immersed in a shallow pool of Ringer. Black circles show the results obtained with the cathode of the battery connected to the microelectrode, and the crosses with current flowing in the opposite direction. Temperature, 23°C. [From Tasaki (124).]

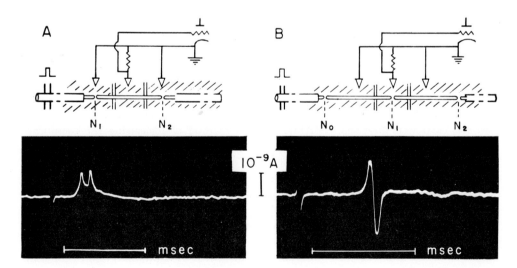

FIG. 11. A. Membrane current led through 1 mm long myelin covered portion of toad motor nerve fiber. B. Similar to A; there is a node (N_1) in the middle pool. The fibers were stimulated through the electrode on the nerve trunk. Note that the action potential at the node is about 0.9 msec. duration at 24°C. (The nerve fiber in the diagram is disproportionately thick and short.)

each of the pools, a nonpolarizable electrode is immersed. The electrodes in the lateral pools are directly grounded and the one in the middle pool is grounded through a resistor of 0.1 to 0.3 megohms. The currents produced by the fiber in response to an electric shock applied to the fiber near its cut end are recorded by amplifying the IR drop across the resistor.

If the myelin sheath were a perfect insulator of electricity, no flow of current should be recorded with this arrangement. Actually, a relatively strong flow of current is observed through the myelin sheath. As can be seen in the records of figure 11A, the membrane current led through the myelin sheath has clear double peaks of an outward flow, followed by a long phase of a weak inward current.

When a node of Ranvier is introduced into the middle pool (fig. 11B), an entirely different result is obtained. The flow of current through the membrane of the fiber in the middle pools is triphasic, first outward, then inward and finally outward (weak). Comparing the two records in figure 11, it is found that a strong flow of inward current takes place only at the nodes of Ranvier. Since the total amount of current leaving a fiber at any moment has to be equal to the sum of the current entering the fiber at the same moment, the peaks of the outward current through the myelin sheath (record A) should correspond roughly to the peaks of inward current at the neighboring nodes (N_1 and N_2). The effects of more distant nodes are naturally far smaller than those of the neighboring nodes.

That the first peak in record A of figure 11 is caused by the response at node N_1 and the second peak by the response at N_2 has been shown in the following manner. When a few drops of cocaine-Ringer's solution are introduced in the lateral pool in which N_2 is immersed, the height of the second peak is immediately reduced. When the same cocaine-Ringer's solution is applied to the portion of the nerve fiber in the middle pool, no change in the current is observed. Finally, when the narcotizing solution is introduced gradually into the pool of N_1, the height of the first peak is gradually reduced, while the second peak remains unchanged until it disappears suddenly at the moment when the propagation of the impulse is blocked.

Further evidence indicating that electric responses of a myelinated nerve fiber are evocable only at the nodes of Ranvier has been obtained by narcotizing the portions of the fiber located in the lateral pools and stimulating the fiber through two of the electrodes (124, 132). When there is one node in the middle pool (as in the diagram of fig. 11B), a full-sized action current can be recorded from a short (1 mm) nonnarcotized portion of the nerve fiber. But, when no node is left in the normal Ringer's solution in the middle pool (as in fig. 11A), no action current can be elicited from the fiber.

The size of the membrane action potential at the node was estimated by Tasaki & Takeuchi (135) by measuring the action current and the resistance of the single fiber preparation. Huxley & Stämpfli (67) estimated it by compensating the action current with an external voltage source (assuming that the myelin sheath is a perfect insulator). Later, a direct method of recording the action potential of the nodal membrane was developed (128). All these indirect and direct methods give a figure between 95 and 115 mv at the peak of activity. Later, we shall discuss the difference between the shape of the nodal action potential and that of the squid action potential.

If one assumes that the myelin sheath behaves like a condenser with a parallel resistance as shown by the diagram of figure 9A, the flow of current through the myelin sheath should be described by equation (4-1) in the preceding section. The voltage V in the equation can be either an applied voltage or an action potential developed at the nodes. The two peaks in the current flowing through the myelin sheath (fig. 11A), therefore, are indicative of the situation in which the voltage inside the myelin sheath rises in two steps, one step at the beginning of the action potential at N_1 and the other step when N_2 is also activated. Actually, the time interval between the two peaks is close to the internodal conduction time discussed previously on p. 79.

It requires a slight mathematical treatment of the data to separate the current led through the myelin sheath into its capacitative and ohmic components and to determine the absolute values for the capacity, c_m, and the resistance r_m, of the myelin sheath (125). Although this method of measuring the membrane capacity and the resistance is not as direct as that for the squid axon, the accuracy of the measurement is fairly high (the probable error being about 10 per cent). The results of recent measurements of these membrane constants are listed in the uppermost column of table 1. The observed values of c_m and r_m were converted into the values for myelin sheath of a unit area (represented by capitalized figures) by using equations (4-4) and (4-5) in the preceding section.

The capacity and the resistance of the nodal membrane given in table 1 were determined by measuring the current through node (N_1) in the middle pool of

TABLE 1. *Resistances and Capacities of the Myelin Sheath, the Squid Axon and the Nodal Membrane*

	c_m farad/cm	C_m farad/cm²	r_m ohm·cm	R_m ohm·cm²
Myelin sheath (fiber diameter 12 μ)	1.6×10^{-11}	5×10^{-9}	2.9×10^7	10^5
Squid giant axon (diameter 500 μ)	1.6×10^{-7}	10^{-6}	$(6-15) \times 10^3$	$(1-2.5) \times 10^3$
Nodal membrane	$1.5 \ \mu\mu f^*$	$(3-7) \times 10^{-6}$	$41 \ M\Omega^*$	$8-20$

Data from references (20, 61, 125).
* Values for one whole node of Ranvier of the toad motor nerve fiber.

figure 11*B*, after treating this node with a sodium-free Ringer's solution or with a dilute cocaine-Ringer's solution. The details of the principle of the method can be found elsewhere (125). Since it is difficult to estimate the area of the nodal membrane, the figures for a unit area of the nodal membrane are somewhat inaccurate. For comparison, the membrane constants of the squid giant axon are also listed in the same table.

It is interesting to note that the capacity of both the myelin sheath and of the nodal membrane is extremely insensitive to changes in the temperature and the chemical composition of the surrounding fluid medium, while their resistance can be strongly modified by slight changes in the environment (124, 125). There is, however, one simple way of increasing the capacity of the myelin sheath, that is, by dissolving the fatty substance of the myelin sheath by an application of a saponin-Ringer's solution or some other detergent solution. During the early stage of a saponin treatment of the myelin sheath, the capacity increases as the resistance decreases, the product $c_m r_m$ remaining almost unchanged. This fact strongly suggests that the capacity of the myelin sheath is dielectric in nature, determined by the thickness of the sheath and the dielectric constant of the myelin substance. The dielectric constant of the myelin sheath is known to be similar to that of many other fatty compounds (66, 125).

CONDUCTANCE OF THE MEMBRANE DURING ACTIVITY

We have seen in the preceding section that the development of the action potential represents a transient variation in the potential difference across the surface membrane of the nerve fiber. In 1939, Cole & Curtis (19) demonstrated in the squid giant axon that this variation in the membrane potential is associated with a pronounced change in the resistance of the membrane. Tasaki & Mizuguchi (133) showed a similar change in the membrane at the node of Ran-

vier. We shall discuss the principle of measuring the membrane impedance during activity under relatively simple experimental conditions. The method to be described is slightly different from that employed by Cole & Curtis but the principle is the same.

In the arrangement shown in the upper part of figure 12, a long silver wire electrode about 100 μ in diameter is thrust into a squid axon immersed in sea water. This internal electrode and a large electrode immersed in sea water surrounding the axon are connected to one arm of an alternating current

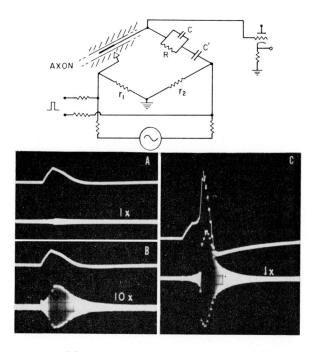

FIG. 12. Measurement of the membrane impedance of a squid giant axon during activity with an a.c. impedance bridge. The bridge was balanced for the impedance of the resting membrane. The two records on the left were taken at nearly the same stimulus intensity, but the bridge output was amplified 10 times the normal (1x) in the lower record. The upper trace in the records displays the unfiltered bridge output; the potentials recorded are slightly reduced and distorted by the bridge. The bridge a.c., 20 kc per sec.; temperature, 22°C. (Further discussion in text.)

Wheatstone bridge. The ratio arms, r_1 and r_2 in the figure, consist of ohmic resistors, $r_2:r_1$ being $10:1$ or larger. The remaining arm consists of condensers (C' and C) and a resistor (R). When a high frequency alternating current is applied to the bridge, a sinusoidal potential variation is produced across the membrane. By proper adjustment of the variable resistance and the capacity, however, it is possible to reduce the a.c. output of the bridge to zero.

As has been mentioned above (p. 85) the axon membrane can be represented by a condenser and parallel resistance. The relationship between the potential difference (V) across the membrane and the current (I) through the membrane is expressed by equation (4-1) which can be rewritten as

$$I = C \frac{dV}{dt} + GV, \qquad (6\text{-}1)$$

where G is the conductance of the membrane, i.e. the reciprocal of resistance R in equation (4-1). We are now interested in the relation between a steady sinusoidal current and a sinusoidal voltage that satisfies equation (6-1). We denote the current by

$$I = I_0 \sin \omega t \qquad (6\text{-}2a)$$

and the voltage by

$$V = V_0 \sin (\omega t + \theta), \qquad (6\text{-}2b)$$

where I_0 and V_0 are the current amplitude and the voltage amplitude, respectively, ω is 2π times the frequency and θ the phase difference between the current and the voltage. Introducing (6-2a and b) into (6-1), we find that

$$\begin{aligned} I_0 \sin \omega t &= V_0 \omega C \cos (\omega t + \theta) + GV_0 \sin (\omega t + \theta) \\ &= V_0 (G \cos \theta - \omega C \sin \theta) \sin \omega t \\ &\quad + V_0 (G \sin \theta + \omega C \cos \theta) \cos \omega t \end{aligned}$$

The last equation is satisfied when (and only when) the coefficient of $\cos \omega t$ is zero and simultaneously when the coefficients of $\sin \omega t$ on both sides of the equation are equal. This leads to the relations

$$\tan \theta = -\frac{\omega C}{G} \qquad (6\text{-}3a)$$

and

$$I_0 = V_0 (G \cos \theta - \omega C \sin \theta).$$

From equation (6-3a) it follows that

$$\sin \theta = \frac{-\omega C}{\sqrt{\omega^2 C^2 + G^2}}, \qquad \cos \theta = \frac{G}{\sqrt{\omega^2 C^2 + G^2}}$$

Therefore,

$$I_0 = V_0 \sqrt{\omega^2 C^2 + G^2}$$

or

$$V_0 = I_0 \frac{1}{\sqrt{\omega^2 C^2 + G^2}}. \qquad (6\text{-}3b)$$

When the impedance bridge in the upper part of figure 12 is roughly balanced for a given intensity of the bridge a.c., the current I through the axon membrane is determined by the variable condensers and the variable resistance of the bridge, because $r_2 \gg r_1$. Under these conditions, the amplitude V_0 is proportional to the impedance, $1/\sqrt{G^2 + \omega^2 C^2}$, of the membrane. When G increases during activity, V_0 decreases. In the method involving use of the impedance bridge, small changes in the membrane impedance are detected by balancing the bridge with the membrane impedance at rest and recording small unbalances after a high amplification. Under such circumstances, not only a change in the amplitude V_0 but also any change in the phase θ brings about a bridge unbalance. When the bridge is at balance, the voltage between the two electrodes across the axon membrane is completely cancelled by the voltage across r_1. A change in the phase θ or in the amplitude V_0, makes this cancellation imperfect.

[In order to detect changes in the membrane impedance during activity, it is necessary to make the frequency of the bridge a.c. high enough so that in the period to be examined there are a number of full cycles of the a.c. The time resolution in the impedance measurement is affected also by the characteristic of the filter circuit in the recording system.]

After the Wheatstone bridge has been accurately balanced for the membrane impedance at rest, a short pulse of outward current is passed through the axon membrane. If this pulse is well below the threshold, the potential trace (the upper trace in the records of fig. 12) shows an exponential decay of the membrane potential after the end of the pulse; in this case there is very little or no bridge unbalance detectable. When the pulse intensity approaches the threshold, the fall of the membrane potential after termination of the pulse becomes slow and erratic (see p. 98); concomitantly there is a sign of a decrease in the membrane impedance (record A) which can be recorded distinctly by increasing the amplification of the a.c. bridge output (record B). With suprathreshold pulse intensities, large unbalances of the bridge are observed (record C), indicating that there is a marked reduction in the membrane impedance associated with production of an action potential.

The temporal relation between the action potential and the bridge unbalance shown in record C is similar to that observed by Cole & Curtis with their external impedance electrodes. They explained their data as indicating that at the peak of activity there occurs a 200-fold increase in the membrane conductance. In the squid giant axon, the membrane conductance stays above the resting level for some time after the end of the falling phase of the action potential.

In the myelinated nerve fiber of the frog, the impedance measurement is complicated by the fact that the change in the membrane impedance takes place only at the node (133). An example of simultaneous recording of the action current and of the membrane impedance in a single node is shown in figure 13. A quantitative analysis of this data is complicated by the fact that the bridge a.c. flows readily through the myelin sheath because of its capacity. Some quantitative information in regard to the conductance at the peak of activity can be obtained by passing testing current pulses through the node and comparing the change in the membrane potential due to the current pulse before and during activity. It has been shown by this method that at the peak of activity the membrane conductance increases approximately 10 times. In the nodal membrane, there is a close parallelism between the time course of the action potential and the time course of the loss in the membrane impedance (129, 133); in this respect the nodal membrane is in sharp contrast with the squid axon membrane.

More recently, Hodgkin, Huxley & Katz (57, 58,

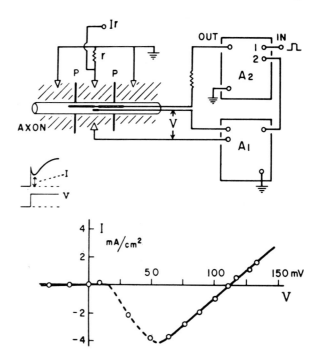

FIG. 14. *Upper:* Arrangement used for clamping the membrane potential of a squid giant axon along rectangular time courses. This circuit is slightly different from that used by Hodgkin *et al.* (61), but the principle is the same. A_1 is a low-gain differential amplifier; A_2, a high-gain differential amplifier (1000 times). The thick portions of the lines in the axon represent the exposed surface of the metal wire electrodes. The distance between the two partitions (P) was 8 mm. (The diameter of the axon and the wire drawn in the diagram is disproportionately large.) Resistance r was 2.5 (sometimes 50 or 250) ohms. *Lower:* Relation between the membrane depolarization (V) and the membrane current at the peak of the inward surge (I). Near $V = 0$, the V-I relationship is roughly linear, but its slope is about $\frac{1}{250}$ of that of the straight line on the right-hand side. Temperature, 22°C. The labile portion of the V-I relation shown by the broken line represents either all-or-none (probably nonsynchronous) responses in some parts of the membrane (the patch theory), or a partial increase in the conductance uniformly all over the membrane (the sodium theory).

61) measured in a series of beautiful experiments the conductance of the squid axon membrane by a very direct, theoretically simple method, often referred to as the 'method of voltage clamp'. The diagram in the upper part of figure 14 illustrates the principle of the method.

A giant axon is placed across three pools of sea water separated by two narrow partitions. A pair of metal wire electrodes is thrust through the axon; one is used for measuring the membrane potential (V) and the other for passing currents through the axon

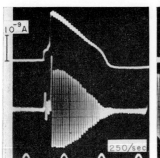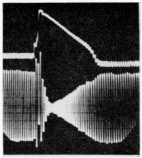

FIG. 13. Simultaneous recording of action potentials and changes in the membrane impedance during activity of a single node of Ranvier. In the left-hand record, the bridge was balanced for the impedance at rest; in the right-hand record, the best balance was obtained near the peak of activity. [From Tasaki & Freygang (129).]

membrane. The two lateral pools are directly grounded with large silver wire electrodes. The middle pool is also grounded but through a resistor (r) of a few ohms. When a current is sent through the long internal electrode, this resistor (r) is traversed by a current (I) passing through the axon membrane in the middle pool; the small potential drop (Ir) is amplified and is taken as the measure of the membrane current. The membrane potential is measured across the axon membrane in the middle pool. The circuits connected to the axon are constructed in such a manner that the membrane potential (V) can be maintained at any desired level by an automatic adjustment of the membrane current (I).

The principle of the automatic control of the membrane current by the feed-back mechanism is as follows. In the diagram of figure 14, A_1 is a preamplifier which transmits the membrane potential (V) at its input to one of the inputs of a differential amplifier A_2. The other input of A_2, marked 1 in the figure, is connected to a source of rectangular (or other) voltage pulses. The output of amplifier A_2 has the same phase as that of input 1 and opposite to that of input 2.

First let us consider the case in which input 1 is grounded. When membrane potential (V) tends to rise by some intrinsic process in the axon, the potential of input 2 starts to rise immediately. This potential is then amplified and, after reversing its polarity, transmitted to the long wire electrode in the axon. This immediately causes a flow of an inward membrane current which lowers the membrane potential (V). As a consequence, if the gain of A_2 is sufficiently high, any change in the membrane potential (V) can be almost completely suppressed by an automatic control of the membrane current (I). In practice, the over-all gain of this feed-back amplifier was 1000 to 3000.

Next, we consider the case in which the potential of input 1 of amplifier A_2 varies along a rectangular time course. At the moment when the potential of input 1 starts to rise, there is a sudden flow of an outward current through the axon membrane. This flow immediately raises the membrane potential (V). The rise in V is transmitted to input 2, tending to lower the output voltage of A_2. In the steady state there is a flow of a constant membrane current which is sufficient to maintain the membrane potential at the constant level. If the gain of A_1 is unity, the time course of the membrane potential (V) reproduces the potential applied to input 1 fairly accurately.

The records furnished in figure 15 show the rela-

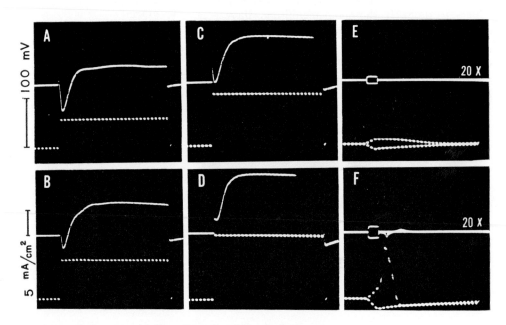

FIG. 15. Relationship between the membrane potential (dotted trace) and the membrane current (continuous trace) observed with the arrangement of fig. 14. In records A to D, the membrane potential was 'clamped' along rectangular time courses by automatic adjustment of the membrane current. In E and F, rectangular current pulses were applied through the current electrode and the variation in the membrane potential was recorded with the other internal electrode; the deflection sensitivity of the current trace is 20 times as high as in other records. Blanking of the potential trace indicates 0.25 msec. Temperature, 22 °C.

tionship between the membrane potential and the membrane current as revealed by the method of voltage clamp. When the membrane potential is raised suddenly from its resting level to a new level slightly above the ordinary threshold (i.e. above 12 to 15 mv) and is maintained at this constant level (record A), it is found that the membrane is traversed by a current which flows first outward, then inward and finally outward again. The first phase of the outward current is so short that it is seen as a mere break in the upper (current) trace in the record. The second phase of an inward current is seen as a downward deflection in the record. The third phase of a steady flow of an outward current is shown by the current trace staying above the zero level in the right-hand side of the record.

The obvious explanation of the time course of the membrane current in records A and B is as follows. The axon membrane has a capacity of the order of 1 μf per cm² (p. 85). In order to shift the membrane potential suddenly by an amount V, a total charge of $C \cdot V$ (where C is the capacity of the membrane in the middle pool) has to be supplied by the current electrode. This capacitative flow of current takes place within the extremely short period of time during which the membrane potential is actually rising. The second phase is related to the ability of the membrane to produce an action potential in response to a sudden rise in the axoplasm potential. If the membrane potential had not been clamped (as in fig. 15F), the potential inside the axon should start a rapid rise; an inward membrane current is needed to counteract this potential rise during activity and to maintain the membrane potential at the constant level. The third phase of the membrane current reflects the situation in which a relatively strong continuous current is needed to maintain the membrane at a steady 'depolarized' level.

When the voltage step in the clamping rectangular pulse is increased, the intensity of the inward membrane current is found to decrease. The relation between the depolarizing voltage step and the peak of the inward surge of current is plotted in the lower part of figure 14. When the voltage step is approximately equal to the peak value of the membrane action potential, the peak of the inward surge is found to reach zero (fig. 15C). As the voltage step is increased further, the peak stays above the zero level; i.e. even at the peak of the inward surge of current, the membrane current is in the direction imposed by the applied voltage. As can be seen in the figure, the relation between the voltage step V

and the current I at the peak of the inward surge is represented by a straight line in a wide range of voltage.

The fact that the voltage-current relation is linear can be taken as indicating that, in this range of membrane depolarization, the axon membrane behaves like a 'battery' with a definite electromotive force (emf) and a definite internal resistance. The voltage at which there is no current flow represents the emf of this battery and the slope of the voltage-current straight line corresponds to the internal resistance. The membrane emf at the peak of the inward surge of current coincides with the peak of the membrane action potential. In the experiments of Hodgkin & Huxley (57, p. 465), the membrane resistance determined from the slope of the V-I relation is about 30 ohm·cm². The figure obtained recently by several investigators from the National Institutes of Health is 7 to 12 ohm·cm² (at 15 to 22 °C). The resistance of the resting membrane, measured with small voltage steps (less than 5 mv or negative voltages) is 2 to 3 kΩ·cm² (61, p. 440). At the peak of activity, therefore, the membrane conductance is increased by a factor of one to three hundred.[4]

In agreement with the notion that the inward surge of current is associated with the ability of the membrane to develop an action potential, narcosis of the axon with ethanol or urethane is known to eliminate the inward surge reversibly. A recently popularized method of reversible elimination of the action potential is to reduce the sodium concentration of the surrounding sea water.

The finding that sodium ions are necessary in the process of excitation is not new. More than half a century ago, Overton (97) pointed out that the frog nerve-muscle preparation loses its ability to respond to stimuli unless there are sodium or lithium ions in the medium. He also pointed out that chloride ions in Ringer can be replaced with bromide, nitrate, acetate, salicylate, etc. without eliminating the excitability. Recently Hodgkin & Katz (62) have shown the importance of sodium ions in a more quantitative manner [cf. also Huxley & Stämpfli (68)]. They have found that the spike amplitude of the squid giant axon

[4] Quite recently similar voltage-clamp experiments were carried out on single node preparations of the toad. It was observed that the voltage-current relationship obtained was similar to that shown in figure 14 except that the labile portion of the curve indicated by the broken line was limited in a narrower voltage range. The membrane conductance determined by this method was approximately 10 times as high as that of the resting nodal membrane.

decreases with the logarithm of the external sodium concentration, the proportionality constant being very close to 58 mv which is the coefficient of Nernst's equation (cf. p. 117).

Based on this and other experimental facts, Hodgkin & Huxley (59) formulated a hypothesis in which the inward surge is interpreted as the consequence of an increase in the membrane permeability specific to sodium ions. We shall discuss this point later (p. 118).

THRESHOLD AND SUBTHRESHOLD PHENOMENA

In the early part of this century when physiologists had no way of directly observing the potential difference across the excitable membrane, a great number of articles were published dealing with the problem of threshold excitation of the nerve or the muscle. At first, physiologists were charmed by the elegant physicomathematical scheme of the ionic theory of nerve excitation formulated by Nernst (91). He derived the relation between the threshold intensity of current and its duration on the assumption that excitation took place when the concentration of some ion reached a certain critical level near the semipermeable membrane of the nerve. Nernst argued that the passage of an electric current through a uniform electrolytic conductor in the nerve cannot bring about any electrochemical changes (except for raising temperature) that might be responsible for initiation of an impulse. His argument is based upon the principles of electrolytic conductors and undoubtedly it is still valid at present. Nevertheless, physiologists soon abandoned Nernst's approach to the problem and accepted more formal, physicochemically vague arguments which reached a climax with Monnier-Rashevsky-Hill theory of nerve excitation (48, 88, 102).

At present it is possible to pass rectangular pulses of current uniformly through the excitable membrane of the nerve fiber, and to determine how the membrane potential behaves when the stimulus reaches threshold. The assumptions adopted by previous investigators can thus be subjected to direct tests.

Threshold Membrane Potential

The excitable membrane at the node of Ranvier of the vertebrate myelinated nerve fiber is a narrow ring-shaped band. Its width (0.5 to 1 μ) is far smaller than the diameter of the fiber at the node or than the distance between neighboring nodes. It is possible to

record potential changes across this membrane by the use of a positive feed-back amplifier [e.g. McNichol & Wagner (87)].

At the top of figure 16 is shown the experimental arrangement used to study the behavior of the nodal membrane in threshold excitation. The fiber is mounted across three pools of saline solution separated by two air gaps. The large pool, where node N_0 in the figure is immersed, is filled with a dilute cocaine-Ringer's solution. The pool in the middle, where the node under study, N_1, is located, is filled with normal Ringer's solution. In the small pool, filled with cocaine-Ringer's or an isosmotic potassium chloride solution, the small portion of the nerve fiber including N_2 is immersed. The electrode in the large pool is connected to a source of a square voltage pulse. The middle pool is grounded, and the smallest pool is connected to the high impedance input of a positive feed-back amplifier. Since there is practically no current in the portion of the fiber in the air gap between N_1 and N_2, the potential measured by the amplifier approximates the potential drop across the nodal membrane of N_1. A rectangular voltage pulse

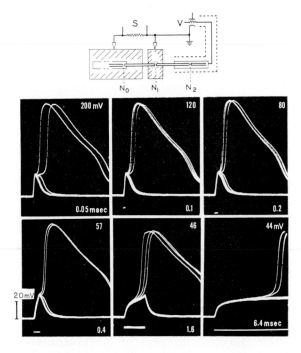

FIG. 16. Demonstration of the constancy of the threshold membrane potential in stimulation of a single node of Ranvier (N_1) with rectangular voltage pulses (S). Nodes N_0 and N_2 are inexcitable. V indicates the input of a positive feed-back amplifier for recording the membrane potential. In each record the stimulus intensity and duration used are given. [From Tasaki (126).]

applied between N_0 and N_1 sets up through the membrane of N_1 a current, the time course of which is distorted by current flow through the myelin sheath.

The records in figure 16 show the behavior of the membrane potential at threshold as observed with this arrangement. The duration of the stimulating pulse was varied in the range between 0.05 and 6.4 msec. At every stimulus duration the stimulus intensity was adjusted to threshold, and without changing the intensity, five to seven sweeps of the oscillograph beam were superposed on each record. Because of spontaneous variation in the property of the nerve fiber (14, 99), the node sometimes responded with a full-sized action potential and sometimes failed to produce an action potential.

We may define the 'threshold membrane potential' as the highest potential level of the membrane which, after the end of the applied stimulating pulse, decays without producing an action potential (63, 126). The level of the threshold membrane potential measured from the resting potential level is often called the threshold (or critical) depolarization.' It is seen in the records that the threshold depolarization is practically independent of the stimulus duration. When the duration is short (e.g. 0.05 msec.), a very large voltage (200 mv) is needed to excite the node; the observed fact is that this high a voltage is required to raise the membrane potential within a short period of time to the threshold level, which is about 15 mv above the resting potential. This is exactly what has been assumed in most of the classical theories of nerve excitation.

As we have discussed in a previous section, the surface membranes of the nerve fiber, both the myelin sheath and the nodal membrane, have relatively large capacities. Consequently, in order to raise the membrane potential by a constant amount, higher stimulus intensities are required at shorter stimulus durations.

However, there is in this type of experiment one complication that has not been fully understood by previous investigators who worked only on nerve trunks. It is the gradual rise in the membrane potential that precedes the rapid rising phase of the action potential in stimulation by a long pulse (see fig. 16, record for 6.4 msec.). In response to a long stimulating pulse, an action potential either appears within a few msec. (within 10 msec. at the most) after the start of the pulse or fails to appear at all. When the action potential fails to appear, the behavior of the membrane potential does not diverge from what is expected from the physical constants of the resting nerve fiber. When the membrane potential starts to diverge distinctly from the simple time course, provided that the applied pulse has not been withdrawn within 5 msec. or so, there is always (at least in a normal node) an action potential.

Action potentials evoked by long stimulating pulses have a more-or-less gradual rising phase followed by a phase of rapid potential rise. If the applied stimulating pulse is withdrawn before the start of the rapid potential rise, the production of a full-sized action potential is prevented. Such a gradual potential rise followed by a sudden potential fall caused by a withdrawal of the applied pulse is seen in the record labelled 46 mv (1.6 msec.) in figure 16.

The nonlinear phenomenon just described is considered at present to indicate the following. The production of an action potential is a kind of 'regenerative' or 'autocatalytic' process similar to the explosion induced by heating of a mass of gunpowder (105). The heat applied from outside causes combustion in only some of the gunpowder particles; the heat arising from these particles in turn induces combustion in other neighboring particles. Similarly, when the stimulus duration is sufficiently long, the start of a 'response' (the start of combustion in the analogy above) tends to raise the membrane potential (temperature) together with the applied stimulus (applied heat). If the external source of current (heat) is maintained, this process eventually raises the membrane potential (temperature) to a critical explosive point. If, however, the applied pulse is withdrawn before the critical level of the membrane potential is reached, the potential returns to its resting level along a variable time course. With very short current pulses, the membrane potential has to be raised by the external source up to the critical level.[5]

In the excitation of the invertebrate axon with rectangular current pulses, results similar to those in figure 16 have been obtained by several investigators [e.g. Hodgkin & Rushton (63)]. To stress the similarity between the vertebrate myelinated nerve fiber and the squid axon, unpublished records obtained by Hagiwara and others are presented in figure 17. The arrangement of the stimulating and recording electrodes used is similar to that in figure 14; two metal wires about 30 mm in length were inserted along the axis of an axon. Pulses of constant current

[5] It should be pointed out that some physiologists have slightly different viewpoints in regard to the statement made in this sentence (104, 107).

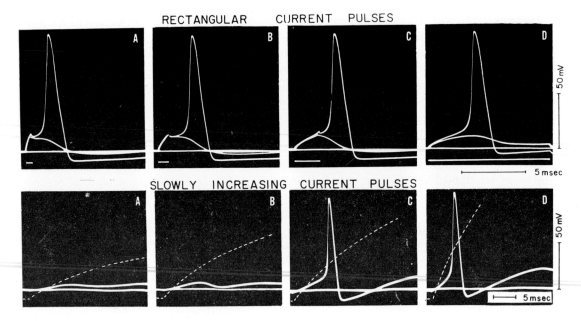

FIG. 17. *Upper portion:* Stimulation of a squid giant axon by rectangular current pulses applied through a long intracellular metal electrode. The membrane potential was recorded with another intracellular electrode. Stimulus durations used are indicated by the bars in the records. *Lower portion:* Stimulation of a squid giant axon by slowly rising current pulses. The time courses of the current pulses used are indicated by the broken lines. [From S. Hagiwara *et al.*, unpublished.]

were applied through one of the internal wire electrodes and the change in the membrane potential was recorded with the other electrode. Under these experimental conditions, the axon membrane is traversed by the applied current uniformly over the whole area under investigation. The intensity of the stimulating pulses was adjusted to the threshold at every stimulus duration.

It is seen in the figure that the threshold membrane potential defined as the highest subthreshold level of the membrane potential is approximately constant (within about 5 per cent), irrespective of the stimulus duration. As in the nodal membrane of the toad myelinated nerve fiber, the decay of the membrane potential in barely subthreshold stimulation is extremely variable. In response to long current pulses (see record *D*), however, a phenomenon we have not discussed before is seen. A barely subthreshold, long current pulse sets up an approximately exponential change at the beginning; later, in spite of maintained flow of the constant current, the membrane potential is found to fall gradually. This is the behavior of the membrane associated with the phenomenon classically known as 'accomodation' [see Erlanger & Blair (27)]. In the nodal membrane, the process of accommodation progresses more slowly than in the squid axon and is not apparent in figure 16.

It has been known for many decades (79) that a slowly increasing current fails to excite a nerve fiber even when its intensity rises well above the rheobase.[6] Evidently, this phenomenon is related to the 'accommodative fall in the membrane potential' just mentioned. This point is illustrated by the records in the lower part of figure 17. When the rate of current increase is greater than a certain critical value, a full-sized action potential starts when the membrane potential reaches the threshold level. When the membrane current rises slower than the critical rate, the potential begins to fall while the current intensity is increasing. Once such an accommodative fall in the membrane potential has taken place, the potential can rise well above the ordinary threshold level without initiating an action potential.

Now, let us turn to the corresponding observation on the toad myelinated nerve fiber. Figure 18 shows the behavior of the nodal membrane in threshold stimulation by linearly rising voltage pulses. The experimental arrangement used is the same as that used in the experiment of figure 16. Since there is a high ohmic resistance in the axis-cylinder between

[6] This is the threshold for a long rectangular pulse. For pulses longer than 5 msec., the threshold is practically independent of duration.

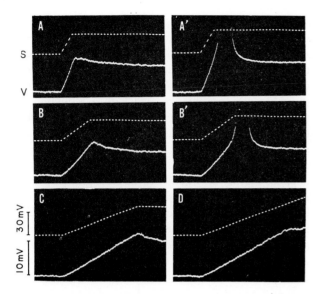

FIG. 18. Variations of the membrane potential of a single node (V) caused by linearly rising voltage pulses (S). The arrangement of fig. 16 was used. In records A' and B' the missing portions of the potential trace (V) indicate production of action potentials of about 100 mv in amplitude. The trace for the stimulating voltage (S) was blanked at 100 cps. Large motor nerve fiber of the toad. Temperature, 11 °C. [From Tasaki (127).]

nodes N_0 and N_1 and since the time constant of the membrane is far shorter than the time scale employed in these observations, the time course of the current through the nodal membrane is similar to that of the applied voltage. In records A, B, C and D, an accommodative fall in the membrane potential is evident. Each of the paired records, A-A' or B-B', was taken at almost the same stimulus intensity; in one (A or B) the node failed to respond, and in the other (A' or B') a large action potential was evoked. The peak value of the subthreshold membrane potential in these cases is more erratic than in the experiment of figure 16; it is roughly independent of the rise time of these stimuli.

In most classical theories of nerve excitation [e.g. Hill (48)], the process of accommodation has been regarded as a gradual rise in the threshold level of the nerve during the period of prolonged d.c. stimulation. The direct observations mentioned above indicate that this is not exactly the case. It is due to a secondary change in the property of the membrane which decreases the effectiveness of the current to raise the membrane potential. Undoubtedly, this is related to the phenomenon of delayed rectification described first by Cole (18); he found that the axon membrane of the squid shows a resistance to an outward directed maintained current far smaller than

that measured with an inward current [see also Hodgkin (53)]. Hodgkin & Huxley (59) attributed this process mainly to an increased permeability of the membrane to potassium ions. In the nodal membrane, there is some evidence indicating that there is a change in the resting potential when the membrane undergoes an accommodative change (127).

Strength-Duration Relation

The relation between the threshold intensity of a stimulus and its duration is called a strength-duration or intensity-time relation. In the squid giant axon excited by means of a long internal metal wire electrode, the significance of this relation is now very clear. When a rectangular pulse of current is applied to the membrane through the internal electrode, the membrane potential rises exponentially as described by equation (4-2). If a stimulus which lasts no longer than about 2 msec.[7] (at 14 °C) is to initiate an action potential, the membrane potential has to reach the critical level, V_c, at the end of the pulse. This leads to the relation

$$V_c = IR \left(1 - e^{-T/RC}\right),$$

in which T is the duration of the current pulse, I is the current intensity and RC the time constant of the membrane. Rearranging the terms, we have

$$T = RC \log \frac{I}{I - (V_c/R)}.$$

This is known as Blair's equation for strength-duration relation (15). Because of the interaction between the stimulating current and the response of the membrane mentioned above, this equation is only a poor approximation near the rheobase.

Stimulation of a squid giant axon through a glass pipette can be treated in a similar fashion by using the solution of the cable equation for the corresponding conditions. Again the rheobase will be slightly (20 to 30 per cent) smaller than that expected from the space and time constants of the resting axon membrane. When the duration becomes far shorter than the membrane time constant, another complication (related to the phenomenon of abolition of an action potential to be discussed in the next section) probably sets in. When the current pulse is extremely short, the uncharged membrane on both sides of the site of stimulation is expected to prevent a further rise in potential at the site of stimulation and to suppress the start of an action potential. These factors have not yet been carefully investigated.

[7] This figure was kindly supplied by Dr. S. Hagiwara.

In the myelinated nerve fiber, the strength-duration relation is determined primarily by the complicated network formed by the nodal membrane, the axis cylinder and the myelin sheath. Because of the interaction between the applied current and the start of a response, the rheobase is 20 to 30 per cent smaller than that expected from the membrane properties at rest (see fig. 16). So far, no one has derived the equation describing the distribution of the membrane potential caused by a rectangular voltage applied at one point between two neighboring nodes. In practice, however, the strength-duration relation is expressed by a purely empirical formula:

$$S = b \left(1 + \frac{\sigma}{T} \right),$$

in which S is the threshold voltage, b the rheobase voltage and σ a constant which has a dimension of time and is known as 'chronaxie'. It is known that the chronaxie for a node varies markedly with the distance between the node under study and the stimulating partition (65).

Subthreshold Response

It has been shown in the explanations of figures 16 and 17 that the membrane potential raised by a brief shock of barely subthreshold intensity decays along a variable time course which is far slower than that expected from the physical properties of the resting nerve fiber. This delay in the fall of the membrane potential is said to be due to a 'subthreshold response' or a 'local response'. Such delay occurs only when the stimulus intensity is greater than 80 to 90 per cent of the threshold (in single node preparations). This phenomenon is more marked in a preparation with high threshold and a poor action potential than in a fresh normal preparation. The phase of the potential rise in these cases is determined by the physical properties of the resting membrane. The subthreshold response is considered as a sign of the beginning of the regenerative process which has subsided without growing into a full-sized response. The historical aspect of the concept of the subthreshold response has been discussed in the introduction of this chapter.

A subthreshold 'response' is different from an ordinary full-sized response in that it does not leave behind it a clear refractoriness. In the period during which the membrane potential stays above the level of the resting potential, the threshold for the second shock (necessary to evoke a full-sized response) is

lower than the threshold at rest. (In the squid axon, a subthreshold response is followed by a small 'undershoot', during which the membrane potential is below the resting level; the threshold is higher in this period than at rest.) Like an ordinary response, a subthreshold response is associated with a reduction in the membrane impedance; the reduction is, however, far smaller than that associated with a full-sized response (see fig. 12).

The amplitude of the full-sized action potential depends slightly on whether or not it is preceded by a marked subthreshold response. It is seen in the records of figure 16 that the action potentials preceded by a slow gradual potential rise are consistently smaller than those preceded by an abrupt potential rise. Because of this variation in the amplitude of the response and of the subthreshold responses, the response recorded at the site of stimulation is said to be only approximately all-or-none.

In the experiments of figures 16 and 17, the stimulating current is applied uniformly through the excitable membrane. It is not possible, therefore, to interpret the subthreshold response as an action potential localized in a small area subjected to a strong stimulating current (see p. 76). This area hypothesis of the subthreshold response can be saved if one assumes that the surface of the excitable membrane is not uniform but that there are spots or patches where the sensitivity to electric stimuli is higher than at the remaining surface. In the sodium theory (59), a subthreshold response is attributed to a small increase in the sodium conductance of the membrane.

When a nerve fiber is excited by a stimulating current distributed nonuniformly over the membrane, the time course of the subthreshold response is complicated by the spatial factor. Especially when the state of the nerve fiber has been altered locally by the stimulating or recording electrode or when there are large stimulation artifacts, pictures very different from those in figures 16 and 17 can be obtained. Because of these complications, there have been a number of confusing reports on this topic.

Measurement of Excitability by Using Test Shocks

In classical physiology writers used to speak of measuring the 'excitability' of the nerve by test shocks. Insofar as we define the excitability as the reciprocal of the threshold (p. 80), this procedure of measuring the excitability is simple and straightforward. It seems, however, that to old physiologists the term 'excitability' or 'irritability' had some anthropomorphized meaning [e.g. Verworn (140)] and the procedure of measuring it was more-or-less comparable to determining a man's ability by mental tests. Such a concept of excitability has no clear physiological meaning.

Here, we shall discuss the significance of the method of using test shocks to explore the state of the nerve fiber. This method has been used mainly on vertebrate nerve fibers.

In the arrangement illustrated in the inset in figure 19, an isolated nerve fiber is mounted across two pools of Ringer's solution. The narrow air gap is located between nodes N_1 and N_2. Through the electrodes immersed on the pools, short pulses superposed on long rectangular voltage pulses are applied to the fiber. The intensity of the short pulse, S, the voltage of the long pulse, v, and the time interval, t, from the beginning of the long pulse to the start of the short pulse are three variables in this experiment. The data presented in A were obtained by fixing voltage, v, at one of four different values (-20, -10, 10 and 20 mv) and adjusting S to make the composite stimulating pulses barely effective in eliciting a nerve impulse at varying values of t. The data in B were obtained by fixing t at 2 msec. and adjusting v and S to make the pulses barely effective. Thresholds were determined by taking the response of the muscle innervated by the nerve fiber as an index of initiation of an impulse; the same result, however, can be obtained by

taking the action potential of the nerve fiber as an index.

In B, the observed point for $S = 0$ is at $v = 30$ to 31 mv, indicating that the rheobasic voltage of the fiber under these experimental conditions was about 30 mv. The threshold for the brief shock depends on the duration of the shock; for durations shorter than about 30 μsec., the threshold rises inversely as the duration. The shock used in the present experiment was within this range and its threshold was taken as unity.

The curves in A show how the threshold for the test shock, S, is modified by the subthreshold pulse, v. At any fixed value of t, the change in S is roughly proportional to v, except when v is greater than about 50 per cent of the rheobase (B). One thing that looks strange in this figure at first sight is the change in threshold observed at $t = 0$ and for negative values of t. This is a constant finding in single fiber experiments and has also been observed by Erlanger & Blair in their experiments with nerve trunks (27). If the test shocks measure the state of the nerve fiber at the moment when the shocks are delivered, it is obviously absurd that the threshold starts to change before the beginning of the subthreshold pulse used to modify the state of the fiber.

There are two factors that serve to explain this strange fact. One factor is the time required for the spread of membrane potential along the myelin sheath, and the other factor is the production of a

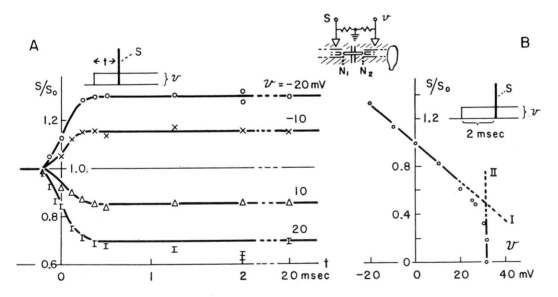

FIG. 19. Changes in threshold for a brief shock (S) caused by application of a subthreshold rectangular voltage pulse (v). The sign of the stimulating voltage pulse is positive when the pulse induces an outward current through node N_2 in the diagram. S_0 represents the threshold for the brief shock alone.

subthreshold response. We shall first discuss the time factor.

When a rectangular pulse of voltage is applied across the air gap in the arrangement of figure 19, the membrane potential at the nearest node (N_1 and N_2) rises (or falls) along a sigmoid curve. This sigmoid time course arises from the situation that both the myelin sheath and the nodal membrane have a capacity which delays spread of the membrane potential. The problem of spread of potential along a uniform cable is discussed in some detail on p. 86. The situation in the myelinated nerve fiber is complicated by the discontinuities at the nodes, and unfortunately no rigorous mathematical solution of the problem is at present available. It is certain, however, that both V (the membrane potential at the node) and dV/dt are zero at $t = 0$, and V rises first gradually, then faster and finally approaches the plateau.

The variation in the membrane potential caused by a brief voltage pulse is given by the derivative, dV/dt, times a constant, because a brief pulse can be regarded as a difference between two long rectangular pulses of the same intensity but starting in succession at a small time interval. From this it follows that the maximum of the membrane potential change caused at the node by the test shock is reached a certain period of time, τ_0, after the delivery of the shock [see curve $\tau/4$ on p. 492 of Lorente de Nó (77)]. This time (τ_0) depends on the distance from the stimulating partition to the node under study (122). Now, in the range of voltage, v, where the relationship between S and v is expressed by straight line I in figure 19B, action potentials are elicited when the algebraic sum of the potentials caused by v and S reaches the critical level. Therefore, the origin of time has to be shifted to the left by τ_0 if the curves are to represent the change in the state of the fiber caused by the subthreshold pulse, v. The argument along this line was developed first by Erlanger & Blair (14, 38) and later by Tasaki (118, 122).

Next, we discuss the second factor that has to be taken into consideration in the analysis of the curves in A of figure 19. When the test shock, S, precedes the start of the subthreshold pulse, v, the change in the threshold of S is small. It has been mentioned that, when a brief shock is close to its threshold, the fall in the membrane potential at the node is far slower than that expected from the physical constants of the resting nerve fiber. If a weak (positive) rectangular pulse (v) follows such a barely subthreshold test pulse, it is possible that the membrane potential is raised to the critical level, thus initiating a full-sized response.

This can account for a decrease in threshold in the region where t is negative and v is positive. Katz (72) developed this argument to explain the results of his experiments in which the effect of a brief shock was tested by another brief shock. His argument is not entirely correct since he ignored the first (time) factor mentioned above. Erlanger & Blair as well as Tasaki neglected the second factor arising from the subthreshold phenomenon; their argument, therefore, has to be partly modified.

Finally, we shall discuss the significance of the break in the v-S relation in the experiment of figure 19B. Some physiologists believe that this break is a sign of the development of subthreshold response to a subrheobasic rectangular pulse alone [e.g. Niedergerke (92)]. As we see, however, in the lower right part of figure 16, this is not exactly the case. The continuous transition from straight line I to II is evidently due to the interplay of the two stimuli related to the development of 'the slowly rising phase of the membrane potential' which precedes a full-sized action potential.

ABOLITION OF THE ACTION POTENTIAL

Initiation of an action potential can be regarded as a transition of the membrane from its resting state into the active state which is characterized by a low membrane resistance and a high potential level. The reverse process, i.e. a transition from the active state of the membrane to the resting state, was first demonstrated in the cardiac muscle of the kid (142), then in the toad nodal membrane (126) and finally very recently in the squid axon membrane. The action potential of the cardiac muscle is associated with a systolic contraction. The fact that this contraction can be abolished by a strong (anodal) current pulse in an all-or-none manner has been known since the time of Biedermann (12, pp. 257–264).

The regenerative process of initiating an action potential is set off by a change (rise) in the membrane potential up to a certain level. In an analogous manner, the process of abolition of an action potential is set off by a change (fall) in membrane potential down to a critical level. This is shown in figure 20. These records were obtained from a single node preparation of the toad. The arrangement of the stimulating and recording electrodes used is similar to that for the experiment of figure 16. The first pulse of outward membrane current raises the membrane potential to the level slightly above the critical po-

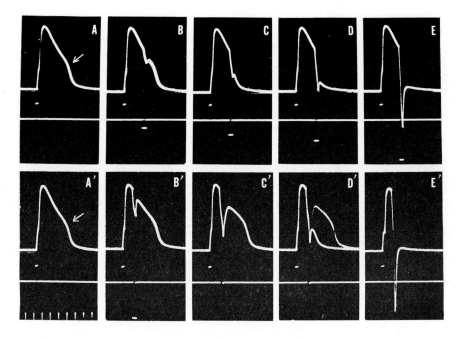

FIG. 20. Abolition of the action potential of a single node by pulses of inward membrane current. The lower trace in each record indicates the time course of the voltage applied between N_0 and N_1 in the diagram of fig. 16, *top*. The amplitude of the recorded action potential was approximately 100 mv. Time marks in msec. A toad nerve fiber at 10°C. [From Tasaki (126).]

tential necessary to initiate an action potential. The second pulse of inward current is applied during the falling phase of the action potential and lowers the membrane potential down to various levels.

When the change in the membrane potential caused by the second pulse is slight (records B, B′, C′), the potential rises after the end of the pulse back to the level which might have been reached if the second current pulse had not been applied. When the membrane potential is lowered by the second pulse below a certain critical level (records C, D), the potential does not rise after the end of the pulse but falls further to the potential level of the resting membrane. At the critical intensity of the second pulse (record D′), the membrane potential in some instances rises to the level of the active membrane and in others falls to the level of the resting potential. A further increase in the intensity of the second pulse lowers the membrane potential below the resting potential (record E, E′); however, after the end of the pulse, the membrane potential rises and settles usually at the level of the resting potential.

Similar records of abolition of action potentials have been taken from a squid giant axon which has been treated with intracellularly injected tetraethylammonium chloride. This chemical when applied ex-

ternally is known to prolong the duration of the action potential of the frog nerve and muscle fiber (46, 78). Prolonged action potentials of the squid or of the toad motor nerve fiber show a remarkable resemblance to the action potential of the heart muscle. When the action potential is prolonged as it is in these cases, the time constant of the membrane is far shorter than the duration of the action potential and the demonstration of the phenomenon of abolition is thereby made easy.

It is seen that the critical potential level for abolition gradually rises during activity. Toward the end of the prolonged action potential, the critical level for abolition is close to the level of the 'shoulder' of the action potential at which the membrane potential starts to fall rapidly.

It is an interesting fact that the action potential which has been abolished in its very early phase leaves behind it no refractory period. This is shown by the superposed record in figure 21. Record *A* in the figure is an ordinary unabolished action potential of a single node of the toad motor fiber. When this action potential is abolished in its later stages by a pulse of inward current through the node (record *B*), there is a relatively refractory period following this prematurely terminated response; a strong current

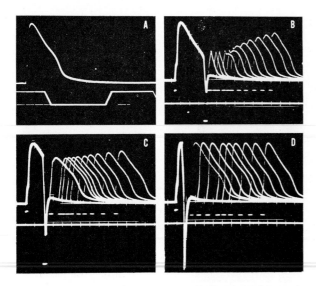

FIG. 21. Recovery of the amplitude of the action potential following abolition of a response of a single node. The arrangement shown by the diagram in the upper part of fig. 16 was used. *A.* Action potential of a single node (*top*) and a truncated 60 cycle wave indicating 100 mv level in applied stimulating and abolishing pulses (*bottom*). *B, C* and *D.* Superposed recordings showing recovery after an abolished response. Temperature, 10°C. [From Tasaki (126).]

pulse is needed to initiate a second action potential and the amplitude of the second response decreases continuously with decreasing interval between the two responses. Record *D* shows that, following the action potential abolished at its peak, the node exhibits no refractoriness to the following stimulating pulse. In record *C*, the action potential has been abolished after the potential has fallen slightly from the peak; it is seen that the amplitude of the second response is slightly subnormal at the beginning and recovers gradually.

These observations reveal how the process responsible for the refractoriness progresses during the falling phase of the action potential. As was pointed out by Adrian (2) in 1921, the end of the action potential coincides roughly with the beginning of the relatively refractory period [cf. Tasaki (119, 124)]. When the action potential is abolished in the middle of its falling phase, the recovery in the amplitude of the second response starts in the middle of the normal recovery curve (126). It has been suggested therefore that the refractoriness is due to some chemical product which accumulates during the falling phase of the action potential. In the sodium theory (see p. 118) a different explanation is given to the origin of the refractoriness.

The rapid falling phase following the shoulder of a normal action potential appears to be a transition of the membrane from the active state to the resting state resulting from the gradually rising critical level for abolition reaching the level of the continuously falling potential level of the membrane.

NERVOUS CONDUCTION ALONG UNIFORM AXONS

We are now ready to discuss nervous conduction as a process that involves production of action potentials in successive portions of the surface membrane of the nerve fiber in an orderly fashion. In the squid giant axon, the rise in the membrane potential[8] at the peak of the action potential is 100 to 120 mv and the critical depolarization necessary to initiate an action potential is 12 to 15 mv. Furthermore, the resistance of the membrane in the active area is far smaller than that of the membrane at rest (see p. 89). Therefore, when a portion of an axon membrane is thrown into action by a pulse of stimulating current, the adjacent portion of the membrane is automatically brought to action by the restimulating effect of the local circuit between the active and resting area of the axon. By a repetition of this process of stimulation by the local circuit, the activity spreads indefinitely on both sides of the site of initial stimulation.

The local circuit cannot be closed if there is no conducting fluid medium outside the nerve fiber. Therefore, nervous conduction is expected to stop if the saline solution outside the fiber is completely removed. In practice, it is not possible to remove the fluid outside the fiber completely, but it is easy to reduce it by immersing a cleaned single nerve fiber in mineral oil. Hodgkin (52) has found that, when an isolated nerve fiber of the crab is immersed in mineral oil, the velocity of the nerve impulse is markedly reduced. This is a clear-cut demonstration of the importance of the local circuit in the process of propagation of a nerve impulse.

In figure 22 a set of records from Hodgkin's paper is reproduced. The velocity of the crab nerve fiber in normal sea water was 4 to 5 m per sec. This was reduced by 20 to 40 per cent when the fiber was transferred into a bath of mineral oil. This reduction in the

---

[8] The membrane potential is defined as the energy required to transfer a unit charge across the membrane from the external medium to the axoplasm. If the potential difference between the fluid in the intracellular micropipette and the axoplasm (which is probably small but indeterminable) is ignored, this coincides with the potential of an intracellular electrode referred to the medium. Since the membrane potential at rest is a negative quantity, a small rise in the membrane potential represents a decrease in its absolute magnitude.

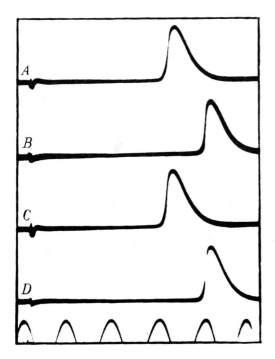

FIG. 22. Demonstration of the dependence of the conduction velocity of a crab nerve fiber upon the resistance of the external medium. *A* and *C*. Action potential recorded with sea water covering 95 per cent of the intermediate conduction distance. *B* and *D*. Fiber completely immersed in oil. Conduction distance, 13 mm. Time in msec. [From Hodgkin (52).]

velocity was prompt and completely reversible; there seems to be little doubt, therefore, that the effect is due to the increased electric resistance of the surrounding medium.

The velocity of a nerve impulse is determined by a mechanism involving the interplay of many factors. In a uniform axon immersed in a large volume of highly conducting fluid medium, the mechanism determining the conduction velocity is as follows. In the inactive area of the axon ahead of the active area, the membrane is traversed by an outward current (see fig. 23) the intensity of which depends on the velocity of the impulse. This current is supplied by the active area immediately behind the active-inactive boundary. The membrane current in the active area is inward (see fig. 23), and this inward current tends to delay the rate of potential rise in the active region. If the membrane is capable of developing an action potential rapidly in spite of the existence of a strong inward current, the velocity tends to be high. If the capacity and the conductance of the resting membrane are large, the active area of the membrane has to supply a strong current to bring the membrane potential of the inactive area up to the critical level, and conse-

quently the velocity tends to be small. A large longitudinal resistance (small fiber diameter) is expected to have the same effect upon the velocity as an increased external resistance.

Hodgkin & Huxley (59) determined the relation between the membrane potential and the membrane conductance on the squid axon. By using the cable equation and a set of empirical formulae relating the membrane potential and the membrane conductance, they calculated the velocity and obtained a solution of the right order of magnitude.

We have discussed in a previous section (see p. 83) the cable properties of a uniform invertebrate axon. In a uniform axon carrying an impulse of a constant velocity, there are certain features that deserve further discussion. First of all, it should be pointed out that there is an inseparable relationship between the spatial distribution of the membrane potential and the time course of the action potential. A diagram representing the time course of an action potential can be converted into a diagram showing the spatial distribution simply by converting the time scale into the distance scale by using the conduction velocity as a conversion factor. This and the following statements are not applicable to axons with any macroscopic nonuniformity along their length in regard to the size and shape of the action potential.

Next to be discussed is the relationship between the spatial distribution of the action potential and the distribution of the longitudinal and the membrane current of the axon. According to Ohm's law, the longitudinal current in the axoplasm is proportional to the gradient of the potential in the axoplasm, i.e.

$$I_i = \frac{-1}{r_i} \frac{\partial V}{\partial x} \qquad (9\text{-}1a)$$

$$= \frac{-1}{r_i v} \frac{\partial V}{\partial t}, \qquad (9\text{-}1b)$$

where I_i is the longitudinal current, r_i the axoplasm resistance per unit length of axon, V the potential of the axoplasm (as a function of time, t, and distance along the axon, x) and v the conduction velocity. A variation in the longitudinal current with respect to space is associated with the membrane current, I_m, (Kirchoff's law), i.e.

$$I_m = -\frac{\partial I_i}{\partial x} \qquad (9\text{-}2a)$$

$$= \frac{1}{r_i} \frac{\partial^2 V}{\partial x^2} \qquad (9\text{-}2b)$$

$$= \frac{1}{r_i v^2} \frac{\partial^2 V}{\partial t^2} \qquad (9\text{-}2c)$$

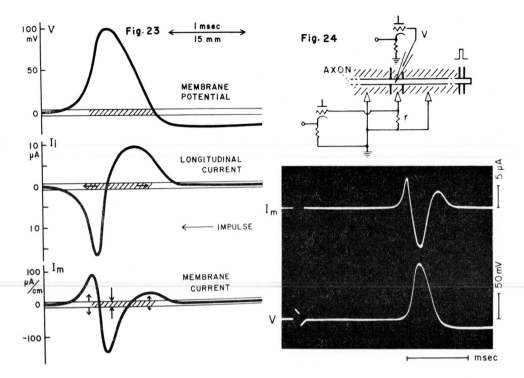

FIG. 23. Diagrams showing the spatial and temporal distribution of the membrane potential, V, the longitudinal current, I_i, and the membrane current, I_m. The curves for I_i and I_m were obtained from the upper curve for V by the graphical method of determining derivatives.

FIG. 24. Simultaneous recording of the membrane action potential (V) and the membrane current (I_m). The width of the middle pool was about 2 mm. The potential drop across the resistor r was taken as the measure of the membrane current. Temperature, 20°C.

These equations show that the membrane current of a uniform axon is proportional to the second derivative (with respect to either time or space) of the membrane action potential [cf. Katz & Schmitt (73)]. It should be pointed out in this connection that equations (9-2) were derived without any assumption as to the behavior of the resting or active membrane. These equations fail to hold only when the axoplasm disobeys Ohm's law or when the propagation of the impulse is macroscopically nonuniform.

Figure 23 shows the space and time patterns of the membrane potential, the longitudinal current and the membrane current as calculated by equations (9-1) and (9-2). To emphasize the similarity between the space pattern and the time course of the action potential, the impulse is assumed in this figure to travel from the right-hand end of the axon to the left. The resistance r_i is assumed to be 1.5×10^4 ohm per cm [cf. Schmitt (106)] and the velocity to be 15 m per sec. It is seen that the longitudinal current is diphasic and the membrane current is triphasic. It is simple to prove that the total area under the curve for the longi-

tudinal current or under the curve for the membrane current has to be equal to zero.

The upper part of figure 24 shows an approximate method of recording the membrane current of the giant axon of the squid. A giant axon is mounted across three pools of sea water separated by two narrow partitions. The large lateral pools are directly grounded, and the small middle pool is grounded through a small resistor. The membrane current flowing through the portion of the fiber in the middle pool is measured by amplifying a small potential drop across the resistor between the middle pool and ground. In order to obtain a simultaneous recording of the membrane action potential, a microelectrode is inserted into the portion of the axon in the middle pool. The axon is excited by a shock applied near its end. The record presented in the figure shows that the temporal relation between the action potential and the membrane current is very similar to what has been expected from the results of the calculations in figure 23.

We shall now discuss the field of potential in the

surrounding fluid medium produced by the triphasic membrane current just mentioned. If the space-time pattern of the membrane current is given, the problem of finding the potential field in a volume conductor is a purely physical problem, namely, an application of Ohm's law to the electrolytic conductor around the axon.

The simplest example of problems of this type is the case in which a uniform axon is surrounded throughout its length by a conducting fluid of a uniform thickness (fig. 25A). We assume that the volume of fluid is not so small as to modify the spatial distribution of the membrane current discussed above. Let s denote the resistance per unit length of the surrounding fluid medium; in the present case, $s \ll r_i$, where r_i is the resistance per unit length of the axoplasm. We express the potential difference across the axon membrane at point x and time t explicitly as $V(x + vt)$, indicating that the variation in the membrane potential travels leftward at a constant velocity, v. Similarly, the longitudinal current and the membrane current are functions of $(x + vt)$.

It is simple to show that the total current flowing through the whole cross section of the surrounding fluid medium at any point, x, at any moment, t, is equal and opposite to the longitudinal current in the axon at the same x and t. To the present one dimensional approximation, the current in the medium at x and time t is given by $-I_i(x + vt)$. Denoting the

potential at x_2 in the medium referred to that at x_1 by U_{2-1}, it is found that

$$U_{2-1} = \int_{x_1}^{x_2} s\,I_i(x + vt)\,\mathrm{d}x$$

$$= \frac{-s}{r_i} V(x_2 + vt) - \frac{-s}{r_i} V(x_1 + vt). \tag{9-3}$$

[Note that the integral above represents a summation of the IR drops along the fluid medium at a given moment t.] The action potential recorded externally with electrodes placed at x_1 and x_2, U_{2-1}, consists of two terms, one representing the activity at x_2, $V(x_2 + vt)$, and the other, the activity at x_1, $V(x_1 + vt)$. The amplitude of the observed potential variation is reduced by a factor of s/r_i. Equation (9-3) is a mathematical expression of what is known as 'diphasic recording' of the action potential. Because of the negative sign in front of $V(x_2 + vt)$, it was believed that the surface of the active portion of an axon was 'electrically negative' to the surface at rest. It should be borne in mind, however, that, if the surrounding medium is not uniform, the potential on the active surface is not always negative to that on the resting surface.

The next simple example of the volume conductor problems is the case in which the resistance per unit length of the conducting fluid medium changes at x' suddenly from s_1 to s_2 (fig. 25B). Expressing s as a function of x, it is found that

$$U_{2-1} = \int_{x_1}^{x_2} s(x) I_i(x + vt)\,\mathrm{d}x$$

$$= \frac{-1}{r_i} \int_{x_1}^{x_2} s(x)\, \frac{\partial V(x + vt)}{\partial x}\,\mathrm{d}x$$

$$= \frac{-s_2}{r_i} V(x_2 + vt) - \frac{-s_1}{r_i} V(x_1 + vt)$$

$$+ \frac{s_2 - s_1}{r_i} V(x' + vt). \tag{9-4}$$

[The last step of the calculation above was accomplished by integration by parts.] The right-hand member of equation (9-4) contains three terms, the first term representing the activity at x_2, the second term that at x_1 and the third term arising from the activity at x'. The third term changes its sign, depending on whether $s_2 < s_1$ or $s_2 > s_1$; it vanishes when $s_2 = s_1$. If s_1 is nearly zero, i.e. if the amount of fluid around the axon is very large on one side of x', the second term in equation (9-4) vanishes and the equation indicates that the electrode at x_1 effectively records the potential variation at x'.

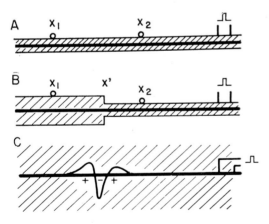

FIG. 25. A. A uniform axon immersed in a conducting fluid medium of uniform diameter; the action potential recorded with electrodes at x_1 and x_2 is given by the equation (9-3). B. The case in which the diameter of the fluid medium changes at x'; the action potential recorded is given by equation (9-4). C. A uniform axon immersed in a large volume of fluid; the potential near the axon is given by the triphasic curve in the diagram.

The final case to be discussed is the potential field produced by a uniform axon suspended in a large volume of conducting fluid. In this case, the potential in the fluid at a great distance away from the axon is not influenced by the nerve impulse; therefore, the electrode on such a point is truly 'indifferent'. Under such circumstances, the potential in the space is inversely proportional to the distance from the source of current. Since there is a line source in the present case, the potential at point P in the fluid medium is given by

$$U_{\mathrm{p}} = \frac{S}{4\pi} \int \frac{I_{\mathrm{m}}(x + vt)}{R_{\mathrm{p}}(x)}\, \mathrm{d}x,$$

where S is the specific resistance of the fluid medium and $R_{\mathrm{p}}(x)$ is the distance between point P and point x. If point P is on the surface of the axon (at $x = p$),

$$U_{\mathrm{p}} \propto I_{\mathrm{m}}(p + vt),$$

since the source in the immediate neighborhood of the recording electrode is expected to have an overwhelmingly large effect in determining U_{p}. The time course of U_{p} is now triphasic as is the time course of the membrane current in figures 23 and 24. Under these circumstances it is incorrect to say that the surface of the active region of the axon is 'electrically negative'.

More complicated cases of the volume conductor problems can be solved by finding the solution of Laplace's equation $\Delta V = 0$ under the boundary condition described roughly by $(-1/S)\,(\partial V/\partial n) = I_{\mathrm{m}}(x + vt)$, where n is the normal to the surface of the axon. To apply this concept of volume conductors to the potential field in the body, one has to consider both the nonuniformity of the excitable tissues and the nonhomogeneity of the conducting medium. The arguments described above on the potential field caused by nerve impulses are based on the work of Craib (21), Marmont (83), Lorente de Nó (77), Tasaki & Takeuchi (136) and others.

NERVOUS CONDUCTION IN MYELINATED NERVE FIBER (SALTATORY CONDUCTION)

The mode of propagation of a nerve impulse in the vertebrate myelinated nerve fiber is expected to be somewhat different from that in the invertebrate nerve fiber because of the structural discontinuities along the myelinated nerve fiber. We have seen that the myelin sheath of the vertebrate nerve fiber shows an extremely high electric resistance to a direct current (p. 87). We have also become acquainted with the experimental evidence indicating that the electric response of the nerve fiber derives from physiological activity localized at nodes of Ranvier of the fiber (p. 88). The myelinated nerve fiber has a cable structure; when one of the nodes of the fiber is thrown into action, there is a local current which tends to raise the membrane potential of the adjacent node to a level higher than the threshold potential. When all the nodes of the fiber are excitable, therefore, it is expected that the activity will spread from node to node indefinitely along the fiber. We shall examine the line of evidence indicating that this is actually the mode of nervous conduction in the mylinated nerve fiber.

Effect of Increase of External Resistance

It is a fairly difficult problem to demonstrate that an increase in the resistance of the external fluid medium does affect propagation of a nerve impulse in the myelinated nerve fiber. The reason is that the resistance per unit length of the axis cylinder is very high (150 to 250 MΩ per cm) even in the largest nerve fiber in the frog sciatic nerve. Unless the external resistance is raised above this level of the internal resistance, it would not be possible to demonstrate a clear effect upon the process of nervous conduction.

The first piece of evidence along this line was obtained in the nerve fiber of which a portion was rendered inexcitable by narcosis (117, 135). The upper part of figure 26 shows the experimental arrangement employed. An isolated nerve fiber of the toad is mounted across three pools of Ringer's fluid separated by two narrow air-gap partitions. A portion of the fiber, including two nodes of Ranvier, is introduced into the small middle pool, and the remaining portions of the fiber are immersed in the large lateral pools. In each of the three pools, an electrode of Ag-AgCl Ringer (agar) type is immersed. The electrode in one of the lateral pools is connected to a low input amplifier, and the remaining two electrodes are grounded.

With all three pools filled with normal Ringer's solution, the nerve impulse arising at E in the figure always travels across the two narrow partitions (record A). When the portion of the fiber in the middle pool is treated with a cocaine-Ringer's solution (0.2 per cent), the impulse fails in some preparations to propagate beyond the narcotized region (record B). When the electrode in the small middle pool is

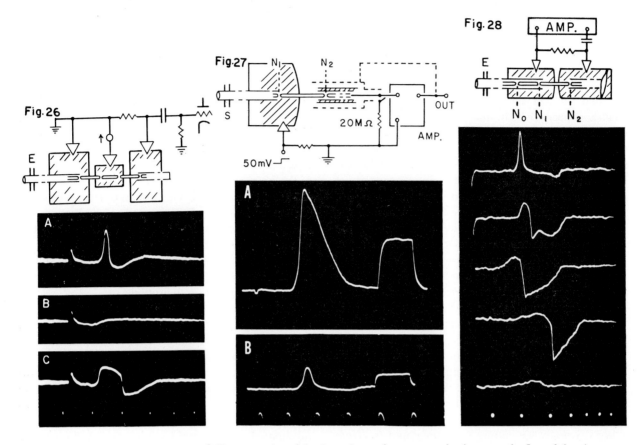

FIG. 26. Demonstration of the dependence of nervous conduction upon the flow of electric current outside the fiber. *A*. Action current recorded with an amplifier connected between the middle and the distal pools; stimulus given at E. *B*. Block of conduction caused by replacing the fluid in the middle pool with an 0.2 per cent cocaine-Ringer's solution. *C*. Restoration of conduction by lifting the middle electrode from the surface of the fluid. Time marks, 1 msec. apart. [From Tasaki (123).]

FIG. 27. Demonstration of the effect of a shunting resistance of 20 megohms across the insulated internode upon nervous conduction. AMP represents a high input-impedance preamplifier. Record *A* was taken with the resistance disconnected; Record *B* with the resistor connected. [From Tasaki & Frank (128).]

FIG. 28. Measurement of the safety factor in nervous conduction by narcosis. *Top record:* Normal binodal action current. *Second through fourth records:* 3, 7, 38 and 38.1 minutes after introduction of a 3 per cent urethane-Ringer's solution into the proximal pool. [From Tasaki (124).]

lifted above the surface of the saline at this moment, there occurs a marked increase in the recorded current and, at the same time, the time course of the current becomes diphasic (record *C*). In a motor nerve fiber with its innervating muscle left intact, it is seen that the diphasicity in the recorded current is always associated with propagation of an impulse across the narcotized region in the middle pool.

The mechanism of restoration of conduction in this experiment is as follows. The portion of the fiber in the middle pool treated with cocaine is inexcitable. The activity of the portion of the fiber in the lateral pool induces a current that spreads along the fiber in the middle pool, but this spreading current is too weak to excite the portion of the fiber beyond the middle pool. When the electrode in the middle pool is removed, the leakage of the spreading current through the portion of the fiber in the middle pool is reduced and, consequently, the current that reaches the other side of the middle pool is increased. Thus, the spreading current becomes suprathreshold for the portion of the fiber beyond the middle pool.

The question has been raised (37, 66, 128, 145) as to whether it is possible to block propagation of a nerve impulse by insulating a nerve fiber between the two neighboring nodes. First, we must discuss a troublesome factor related to the experiment designed to answer this question.

In order to detect propagation of nerve impulses across an insulating air gap, it is necessary to have an amplifier or the innervated muscle attached to the single fiber preparation. Stimulating electrodes and a muscle or recording electrodes connected to the two sides of the insulating gap introduced an electric capacity which, under ordinary experimental conditions, is large enough to establish a local circuit (by this capacitative pathway). The resistance of a single fiber preparation mounted across a wide air gap is of the order of 50 MΩ. If there is a capacity of about 2 μμf between the two portions across the gap, the local circuit between the two portions of the preparation will be very effectively closed by the capacitative pathway for a period of about 0.1 msec. In fresh single fiber preparations, it is actually impossible to demonstrate a conduction block at an insulating air gap if muscular contractions are taken as an index of such conduction[9] (128, 145).

The capacitative coupling between the two insulated portions of a single fiber preparation can be markedly reduced by the use of a positive feed-back amplifier. In the diagram of figure 27 the small portion of the preparation on one side of the insulating air gap is connected to the input of a unity-gain preamplifier and is completely enclosed in a metallic shield driven by the output of the preamplifier. (Note that, when the potential of the insulated portion rises above the ground potential, the potential of the shield around the fiber rises to the same extent and, consequently, no electric charge is induced between the insulated portion of the preparation and ground. The input impedance of the preamplifier can be made as high as 1000 MΩ.)

It is surprising to see that most single-fiber preparations mounted as shown in this figure are still capable of carrying impulses across the air gap (128). Washing the surface of the internode in the gap with a nonelectrolyte solution does not generally help to bring about a block at the insulating air gap. Probably, the cell of Schwann on the surface of the nerve fiber does not permit us to raise the external resistance high enough to cause a conduction block in fresh preparations.

Record *A* in figure 27 was obtained after circulating dry air around the portion of the fiber on the air gap for a short period of time. This causes a rapid evaporation of water from the surface of the fiber followed by a slow desiccation of the axis cylinder. The monophasicity of the response indicates that the block has actually taken place. Record *B* in the figure was taken while the small insulated portion of the preparation was grounded through the 20 MΩ resistor in the figure. The response is now diphasic (or rather binodal), indicating that conduction was restored by the shunting resistance. A similar reversible restoration of conduction can be obtained by reducing the feed-back voltage to the driven shield, thereby increasing the capacity of the insulated portion of the preparation to ground.

The observation just described indicates that the ability of the nerve impulse to excite the adjacent resting region is very large. As a consequence, a reversible conduction block by increasing the external resistance has been demonstrated so far in preparations with a somewhat reduced safety margin. However, it seems safe to conclude from the observations described above that nervous conduction in the myelinated nerve fiber does depend on the electric pathway outside the myelin sheath.

Safety Factor

The safety factor in nervous conduction may be defined as the ratio of the action current of the nerve fiber to the minimum current intensity necessary for nervous conduction. If an action current generated at one point of the nerve fiber acts as an electric stimulus to the adjacent point, it should be possible to measure the action current in terms of the normal threshold.

The first attempt to determine the safety factor was made by using a dilute narcotic solution to reduce the action current from one portion of a nerve fiber and by measuring the minimum intensity of the current necessary to excite the adjacent portion of the fiber (135). In the uppermost part of figure 28 is shown the experimental setup used. A motor nerve fiber of the toad is mounted across two pools of Ringer's fluid separated by a narrow air gap. The muscle innervated by the fiber is left uncut, and twitches in the muscle resulting from stimulation of the fiber near its proximal end are taken as an index of nervous conduction. An ohmic resistor (of about

---

[9] There are somewhat controversial viewpoints on this subject in the literature. Huxley & Stämpfli (66) reported that conduction was blocked when the external resistance was raised. Wolfgram & van Harreveld (145) failed to demonstrate a block under similar experimental conditions and expressed the view that their experimental results were inconsistent with the concept of saltatory conduction. Frankenhauser & Schneider (37) reported that they could demonstrate a block with a 20 MΩ shunting resistance across the insulating air gap. For a further discussion on this point, see Tasaki & Frank (128).

0.2 MΩ) is connected between the two electrodes immersed in the pools; this resistor serves to close the external pathway of the local circuit and also to measure the longitudinal current flowing through the axis cylinder bridging the air gap.

When the two pools are filled with normal Ringer's solution, a familiar action current which we often refer to as a 'binodal' action current is recorded. Based upon the arguments described on earlier pages (p. 88), this action current is explained as deriving mainly from activity at the nodes (N_1 and N_2 in the figure) in the immediate neighborhood of the recording partition. The rapid rising phase of the action potential at N_1 develops a large gradient of potential along the axis cylinder between node N_1 and N_2; the phase of a strong (2 to 3 times 10^{-9} amp.) current flow in the binodal action current is the period during which N_1 is active but N_2 is still inactive. When the action potential starts also at node N_2, the potential gradient along the axis cylinder is greatly diminished, resulting in a sudden fall in the longitudinal current between N_1 and N_2. At the end of the action potential of a single node (fig. 16), the membrane potential falls very rapidly. The abrupt end in the binodal action current is related to the difference in the time of termination of the action potential at N_1 and N_2. Because of the capacities of the nodal membrane and of the myelin sheath, the spread of current from N_0 to the internode between N_1 and N_2 prior to the start of activity at N_1 is very small.

When a urethane-Ringer's solution barely strong enough to block nervous conduction is introduced into the proximal pool (in which N_1 is immersed), the upward deflection in the record (representing positivity of the right-hand electrode in the diagram) gradually decreases, indicating that the current arising at N_1 (partly from N_0) is reduced by narcosis. When the upward deflection is reduced to one-fifth to one-seventh of the original size, the downward deflection which has gradually increased during narcosis suddenly drops out and, simultaneously, conduction across the recording internode fails (the lowermost record in fig. 28). From these observations, it is found that the safety factor is between five and seven in large myelinated nerve fibers of the toad.

The safety factor can be estimated from the measurement of the threshold membrane potential and the nodal action potential. It has been shown that the action potential of a normal node is approximately 110 mv at the peak. When a membrane potential of this size is developed at node N_1, the adjacent node N_2 is subjected to a strong outward current which would raise the membrane potential by 50 to 60 mv if N_2 had been made inexcitable (124). Since the threshold depolarization of a fresh node is 10 to 15 mv, it is found that the safety factor estimated by this method is about five. There are other methods of estimating the safety factor (124). They all give a figure between four and seven.

As the result of this large safety factor in nervous conduction, a nerve impulse can travel across one or sometimes two completely narcotized nodes (124). In the experiment of figure 26 it is often seen that conduction across the middle pool remains unsuspended after introduction of a strong narcotic solution. A nerve impulse cannot travel across three inexcitable nodes.

Does the Nerve Impulse Jump from Node to Node?

In 1925 Lillie (75) found that, when his iron wire model of a nerve was covered with glass tubing broken at regular intervals, the activation process jumped from one break to the next. On the basis of this observation, he pointed out the possibility that the nerve impulse in the myelinated nerve fiber may jump from node to node as in the model. This model of 'saltatory conduction' has the following two features: (a) the electrochemical changes underlying the process of 'conduction' are localized at the 'nodes' and (b) the time required for the conduction of the impulse is determined solely by the rapidity of the process at the node. In the model, therefore, the role of the internodal segment is simply to provide an ohmic conductance to the local circuit.

We have described the main line of evidence indicating that, in the vertebrate myelinated nerve fiber, the physiological process responsible for producing action potentials is localized at the nodes. We have also seen that, although the d.c. resistance of the myelin sheath is very high, the capacity of the myelin sheath is large enough to have a marked effect upon the threshold of the nerve fiber measured with short current pulses (p. 99). This capacity of the myelin sheath, therefore, sets a certain limitation to the analogy between propagation of the activation wave in the iron-wire model and the actual process of nervous conduction in the myelinated nerve fiber.

The upper part of figure 29A illustrates the arrangement to demonstrate saltatory conduction in the model nerve fiber. An iron wire covered with glass tubings except at the 'nodes' is immersed in a bath of nitric acid. When the wire in the passive state is stimulated at one end, the process of activation as

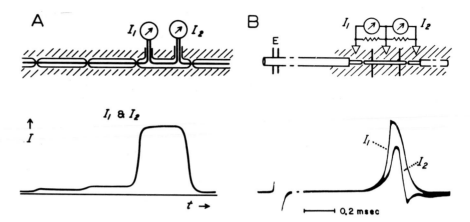

FIG. 29. *A.* Time courses of the longitudinal current at two points in one internode of Lillie's salta-tory nerve model. [From Franck (35).] *B.* Time courses of the longitudinal current recorded at two extreme ends in one internode of a frog nerve fiber. Stimulus at E. [From Hodler *et al.* (64).]

recognized by color changes and bubbling on the surface spreads from node to node. The trace repro-duced in the figure is the time course of the longitudi-nal current taken from a recent article by Franck (35). Since the glass tubing is a perfect insulator of elec-tricity, the time courses of the longitudinal currents recorded at two different points in one internode are undoubtedly the same.

Figure 29*B* shows a corresponding observation on the real myelinated nerve fiber. By the arrangement illustrated at the top, the longitudinal current is re-corded at two points in one internodal segment. As can be seen in the tracing below, there is a large dif-ference between the longitudinal currents recorded at two points which are about 1.5 mm apart in this case. The difference between the two longitudinal currents represents the double peaked membrane cur-rent recorded through the myelin sheath (fig. 11*A*).

We see in figure 29*B* that the two longitudinal currents recorded at two different points in one internode rise at different rates, reach the peaks at different moments and fall at different rates. This is a direct consequence of the existence of a large capaci-tative flow of current through the myelin sheath. Like a signal travelling along a submarine cable, the longitudinal current spreads along the axis cylinder at a finite rate.[10] Because of this slow spread of the membrane potential (cf. p. 100) and of the longi-

[10] A different viewpoint is stated in a previous paper by Huxley & Stämpfli (66). The slight difference between their experimental results and the results described in the text is probably due to their use of a high input resistance in their amplifier which tends to lower the time resolution in recording [cf. footnote on p. 11, Tasaki (124)].

tudinal current along the internode, it is not legiti-mate to state that a nerve impulse jumps from node to node without spending any time in the internode. This point has been stressed in an article by Hodler *et al.* (64) [cf. also Stämpfli (114)]. It has been pointed out (125) that the major portion of the temperature dependence of the conduction velocity (Q_{10} of about 1.8) can be attributed mainly to a change in the cable properties of the nerve fiber [cf. also Schmitt (106)].

Field of Potential Produced by a Nerve Impulse

We have discussed in the preceding section the field of potential produced in the surrounding fluid medium by a nerve impulse travelling along a uni-form invertebrate nerve fiber. Because of the struc-tural discontinuities along the myelinated nerve fiber, the statements made in the preceding section are not in a strict sense applicable to the myelinated nerve fiber. However, there is a special case in which the effect of the discontinuities is very small.

Let us consider the case in which a single nerve fiber of a uniform diameter is enclosed in a glass tubing of a uniform diameter filled with Ringer's solution (as in fig. 25*A*). In this case, the longitudinal current at one point along the fiber is equal in in-tensity and opposite in sign to the current flowing through the medium at the same point. From the argument described in the preceding section, it is found that the spatial distribution of the potential along the fluid medium in the glass tubing is a mir-ror image of the potential inside the axis cylinder, its absolute value being determined by the ratio of the resistance per unit length of the outside fluid to that of the axis cylinder (equation 9-3). This field of potential travels along the fiber at the average velocity of the impulse. Insofar as one disregards the variations in the potential that occur within one internodal distance (about 2 mm) or within one internodal conduction time (about 0.1 msec.), the potential field produced by a myelinated nerve fiber in the fluid medium is similar to that produced by a uniform invertebrate axon.

The distribution of the potential on the surface of a uniform nerve trunk produced by a nerve impulse travelling along a single nerve fiber in the trunk can be regarded as analogous to the case described above. To the approximation that the potential variations within 0.1 msec. are disregarded, therefore, the principle of 'diphasic recording of the action potential' described in the preceding section is applicable to this case. A further discussion on this problem can be found elsewhere (124). Frankenhauser (36), Hodler *et al.* (64), Stämpfli & Zotterman (115) and others have investigated the details of the potential variations occurring within one internodal conduction time and also within one internodal length.

When a myelinated nerve fiber is immersed in a two-dimensional or three-dimensional volume conductor, the potential field produced by a nerve impulse is very different from the field produced by an impulse of a uniform invertebrate axon. As has been shown in figure 11, strong sinks of electric current are localized at the nodes while the sources are distributed along the internodes as well as at the nodes. Therefore, the time course of the potential picked up by a recording electrode placed near one of the nodes is expected to be very different from the record obtained with the electrode on the myelin covered portion of the fiber.

Figure 30 shows the time courses of the action potentials recorded with a metal microelectrode placed at various points near a node of Ranvier of an isolated single nerve fiber immersed in a thin layer of Ringer's solution. The vertical straight line in the middle of the figure represents the course of the fiber, and the center of the two concentric circles represents the position of the node under study. It is seen in the figure that the largest negative potential is observed when the recording electrode is placed in the immediate neighborhood of the node. The amplitude of the negative component of the action potential decreases as the distance from the node increases, and this decrease is roughly independent of the direction in which the electrode is moved away from the

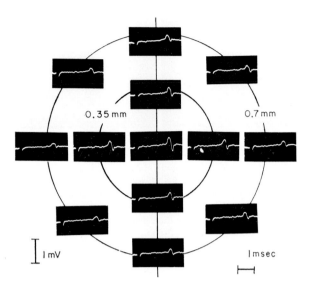

FIG. 30. Records of action potentials taken with a small metal electrode placed around a node of Ranvier. The nerve fiber was immersed in a shallow layer of Ringer's solution. The vertical line represents the nerve fiber, and the center of the two concentric circles the node under study. The impulse travels downward. Five records on the vertical line were taken with the electrode along the fiber and slightly to one side. Other nodes of the fiber were not exposed in the operated region of the preparation. The conduction distance was about 45 mm. Temperature, 20°C. [From Tasaki (137).]

fiber. For further details of this experiment see Tasaki (124).

Conduction in a Polarized Nerve Fiber

When a direct current is applied to a nerve trunk through a pair of nonpolarizable electrodes in contact with its surface, the portion of the nerve fiber near the anode is traversed by a continuous inward membrane current, and the region near the cathode is subjected to an outward membrane current. The behavior of the nerve impulse in such 'polarized' regions of the nerve fiber was discussed by Pflüger (100) more than a half century ago. A nerve fiber modified by a constant current is said to be in an 'electrotonic' state. In order to understand the behavior of a nerve impulse in the nerve fiber under 'electrotonus', it is desirable to investigate the behavior of a single node preparation under influence of a constant current.

Figure 31 shows the effect of a passage of a short rectangular current pulse upon the threshold and the action potential of the single node. The arrangement employed is the same as that for figure 16 (p. 94).

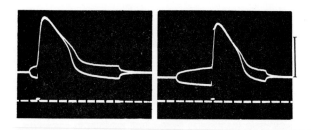

FIG. 31. Effect of short polarizing current pulses upon the action potential of a single node of Ranvier. The arrangement shown in the upper part of fig. 16 was used. The action potential was initiated by a short stimulating pulse approximately 1 (*left*) and 4 msec. (*right*) after the start of the polarizing pulse. Voltage calibration, 50 mv; time marks, 1 msec. A toad nerve fiber at 11 °C. [From Tasaki (126).]

When a pulse of outward subthreshold current is applied through the nodal membrane, the potential inside the node rises above the resting level, resulting in an upward deflection in the record. The threshold membrane potential measured during the period of current flow (of about 10 msec.) is nearly identical with the level before the start of the subthreshold pulse. In other words, a weak additional current, which is sufficient to raise the membrane potential from the new level reached by application of the subthreshold pulse to the normal threshold level, releases a full-sized action potential. The membrane potential at the peak of the action potential is also unaffected by the constant current.

When the polarity of the constant current is reversed, a stronger additional stimulating pulse is required to raise the membrane potential to the threshold level. The membrane potential at the peak of the action potential is not affected by application of a constant inward current of about 10 msec. duration.

In the experiment just described, if one regards the threshold for the short (additional) current pulse as a function of the rectangular polarizing current, one finds that the threshold is lowered by an outward polarizing current and raised by a current of opposite polarity. Similarly, if one measures action potentials from the level immediately before the delivery of the short stimulating pulse, it is found that the amplitude is reduced by an outward (or cathodally polarizing) current and increased by an inward (or anodally polarizing) current. This is the direct, or primary effect of the polarizing current upon the threshold and the action potential.

A long polarizing current brings about a secondary change in the membrane. A strong maintained cathodal polarization caused an additional decrease in the amplitude of the action potential (cathodal depression) accompanied by changes in the membrane conductance and probably in its emf. The effect of a strong anodal polarization is somewhat obscured by the strong stimulating current required to raise the membrane potential up to the threshold level. Using intact sciatic nerves, Lorente de Nó (77) made an extensive investigation on the changes in the membrane potential caused by long polarizing currents.

Now let us discuss in this connection the well-known experiment by Erlanger & Blair (28) who in 1934 discovered the electric sign of the discontinuous nature of nervous conduction in the myelinated nerve fiber. They applied anodal polarization to the portion of the nerve under the recording electrode (monophasic lead) and found that, when the intensity of the polarizing current was gradually increased, the configuration of the action potential of a single nerve fiber in the nerve underwent a sudden discontinuous change. Figure 32 furnishes an example of their record. In record *B* the intensity of the polarizing current was maintained at the critical level for the discontinuous change. The action potential showed in one sweep a distinct notch in its rising phase, and in the next sweep (superposed on the same film)

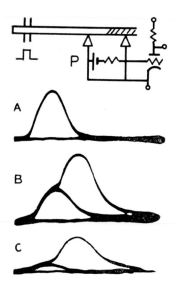

FIG. 32. Changes in the configuration of a monophasic action potential of a single nerve fiber in an intact nerve trunk produced by anodal polarization at the proximal recording lead. *A.* The normal spike potential. *B.* The spike under anodal polarization just strong enough to block at the most accessible node; two action potentials superposed. *C.* Further increase in the polarizing current to the next critical strength. [From Erlanger & Blair (28).]

the component of the action potential above the notch dropped out completely.

They did not consider this observation as indicating the saltatory nature of nervous conduction in the myelinated nerve fiber. However, they correctly explained this discontinuity as being related to the existence of nodes along the myelinated nerve fiber. Takeuchi & Tasaki (116) repeated this observation on isolated single nerve fibers and obtained substantially the same result.

The explanation of the discontinuous change in the single fiber response (fig. 32) is as follows. When the threshold membrane current of the anodally polarized node under the recording electrode rises above the membrane current caused by the activity of the adjacent node, the response of the node under study drops out and a small potential variation arising from the activity of the adjacent node is observed. A further discussion on this subject may be found elsewhere (124).

Pflüger's Law of Contraction

The law of contraction formulated by Pflüger (100) in 1859 is at present of almost historical interest only. To demonstrate this law one has to use a pair of nonpolarizable electrodes, e.g. long chlorided silver wires imbedded in 2 per cent agar-Ringer's gel filled in glass tubings or classical electrodes of the Zn-$ZnSO_4$ type. A sciatic-gastrocnemius preparation of the frog or toad is the standard material used for this demonstration. When pulses of constant current (of about 10 sec. duration) are applied to the nerve trunk through the nonpolarizable electrodes, one generally finds that contractions of the muscle, if there are any, occur only immediately following the onset or following the end of the pulse but not during the period of constant current flow. The presence or absence of contraction depends upon the intensity of the current and also upon the arrangement of the anode and the cathode of the stimulating electrodes with respect to the muscle. In table 2 an example is presented of the results of this type of observation. The symbol + indicates the presence and − the absence of a muscular contraction. The appearance of a contraction is a sign of arrival of nerve impulses in the muscle.

If one takes nerve impulses carried to the muscle by a single nerve fiber as an index, one obtains a result somewhat different from that stipulated by the classical law. The result obtained after cutting all but one fiber near the muscle is also shown in

TABLE 2. *Demonstration of Pflüger's Law of Contraction*

Current Intensity μA	Cathode-Anode-Muscle (Ascending)		Anode-Cathode-Muscle (Descending)	
	Make	Break	Make	Break
4.5	+(−)	−	+(−)	−
6	+	−	+	−
18	+	−	+	−
30	+	−	+	−
52	+	+(±)	+	+(−)
75	+(−)	+(±)	+	+(−)
98	+(−)	+	+	+(±)
120	+(−)	+(±)	+	+(±)
144	+(−)	+(±)	+	+(−)
166	−	+(±)	+	±(−)
188	−	+(−)	+	−

This table indicates the presence, +, or the absence, −, of a muscular contraction on make or break of long current pulses applied to the nerve trunk of a sciatic-gastrocnemius preparation of the toad. The orifice of the electrodes (Ag-AgCl type) was about 6 mm in diameter and the space between the two electrodes was also about 6 mm. The resistance of the nerve between electrodes was approximately 10 kilohms. The results obtained after cutting all the nerve fibers near the muscle except one large motor fiber are presented in parenthesis, and is mentioned only when it is different from that for the whole nerve preparation.

table 2. There are more negative signs in this case than in the case for the whole nerve trunk. This difference arises from the situation that there are in the nerve trunk many fibers which are situated in different parts of the potential field (produced by the applied current). The existence of the small motor nerve fibers which produce slow muscular contractions (134) in the nerve trunk makes also some difference between a single fiber and a nerve trunk experiment.

If one applies current pulses directly to the isolated portion of a single motor nerve fiber in this type of observation, one finds more negative signs than in the two previous cases. In this type of direct stimulation of a single nerve fiber, it is very difficult to demonstrate excitation of the fiber on break of an applied current. Break excitation which is readily observable in the nerve trunk is evidently due mainly to the capacities of the myelin sheath and of the connective tissues. These elements in the nerve trunk tend to generate outward membrane currents at the nodes of the fibers on withdrawal of the applied current.

The mechanism of anodal block of nerve conduction has been discussed on previous pages. The absence of a contraction on 'make' of a strong 'ascending' current pulse in the table indicates that the nerve impulse initiated under the cathode could not pass through the anodally polarized region of the nerve between the cathode and the muscle.

Effect of Narcosis upon Nervous Conduction

It has been pointed out that narcotics, such as cocaine, urethane, ethanol and others, depress or eliminate electric responses of the nerve fiber when they are applied to the nodes of Ranvier of the fiber (p. 109). The action of these chemicals, as well as the effect of low sodium in the medium, progresses with surprising rapidity; an equilibrium between the single fiber and the surrounding fluid medium containing these chemicals is established within one second (68, 71, 124).

It is well known that the action of these narcotics upon the whole nerve trunk is extremely slow and gradual, as emphasized by Winterstein (144). Evidently the time required for diffusion of the chemical into the nerve trunk accounts for the slow action of these chemicals upon it. The diagram in figure 33 illustrates this great difference in the rapidity of action of urethane between the intact sciatic nerve and

the exposed nerve fibers. The circles in the figure represent the times required for conduction block at various concentrations of urethane-Ringer's solution in intact sciatic nerves. The narcotic was applied to a 15 mm long uniform portion of the sciatic nerve of the toad, and the disappearance of muscular contraction was taken as an index of block. The relationship between the time required for conduction block and the concentration of urethane is given by a smooth curve.

When a single nerve fiber preparation or a few fiber preparations with a 15 mm long exposed region are used in this type of experiment, an entirely different result is obtained. For concentrations lower than about 1.8 per cent, conduction through the narcotized region remains unblocked for an hour or more; and for concentrations higher than about 2.2 per cent, conduction block sets in within one second. At the critical concentration, which was approximately 2 per cent in this experiment, conduction block occurs within about 1 minute. The relationship between the concentration and the time required for blocking is, therefore, given by the thick line (bending at almost a right angle) in the figure.

We have pointed out that a nerve impulse can jump across one or two complete inexcitable nodes. If one reduces the length of the narcotized region down to about 5 mm or less, a longer time is required to block conduction since time must be allowed for diffusion of the narcotic along the nerve. This fact was once taken as evidence for 'decremental conduction' in the narcotized region of the nerve (23, 69, 82).

Narcotizing solutions of below the critical concentration applied to a node raise the threshold and lower the amplitude of the response. The magnitude of this narcotizing effect depends on the concentration used. Based on the experimental data on the effects of narcosis on single nodes, it is possible to explain many phenomena related to narcosis of the nerve. The detail of the accounts along this line may be found elsewhere (124).

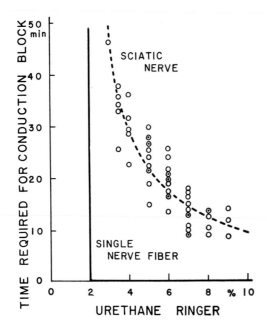

FIG. 33. Relation between the concentration of urethane (*abscissae*) and the time required for conduction block (*ordinates*) in a single fiber preparation (*continuous line*) and in the whole sciatic nerve (*circles*). [From Tsukagoshi, cited by Tasaki in (124).]

AFTER-POTENTIALS AND RHYTHMICAL ACTIVITY

We shall devote this section to two subjects which are less clearly understood at present than those previously discussed, namely after-potentials and rhythmical activity of the nerve fiber. The relationship between after-potentials and rhythmical activity is not a direct one, but in some cases they are clearly related to each other.

After-Potentials

The term 'after-potential' was introduced by Gasser and his associates [cf. Gasser & Erlanger (38); Gasser & Graham (39)] to describe the small, slowly declining potential change that follows the large, short 'spike-potential' in the monophasic action potential of a nerve trunk. The records furnished in the left column of figure 34 show monophasic action potentials of the nerve trunk taken at slow sweep speeds. The action potential of A-fibers (top) shows very little after-potentials, but the responses of B- and C-fibers manifest large after-potentials following the sharp spike-potentials. These potentials were recorded with extracellular electrodes (fig. 1) from three different nerve trunks of the cat.

Let us next discuss the after-potentials recorded from single fiber preparations. In the right-hand column of figure 34 are shown the time courses of the action potentials of three different kinds of excitable elements. An upward deflection in these records represents a rise in the intracellular potential (referred to the potential of the surrounding fluid medium). The 'retention' of a higher potential level

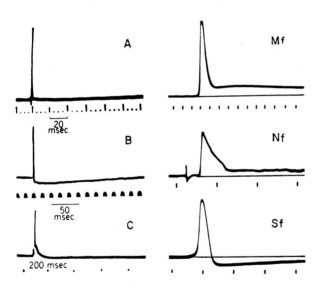

FIG. 34. After-potentials in nerve trunks (*left*) and in single fibers (*right*). *A.* Response of mammalian A-fibers. *B.* Response of mammalian B-fibers. *C.* Response of mammalian C-fibers. [The three records on the left are from Grundfest (43).] *Mf.* Action potential of a toad muscle fiber, recorded intracellularly. *Nf.* Response of a toad nerve fiber poisoned with veratrine. *Sf.* Action potential of a squid giant axon. Time marks on the right in msec.

in the upper two records is often called a 'negative' after-potential, because an action potential was considered in the classical physiology as a 'negative' variation of the potential of the nerve surface (cf. p. 105). Evidently, the term 'negative' after-potential is at present confusing and inadequate.

The after-potential of the frog (or toad) muscle fiber (fig. 34, right top) seems to decay roughly at the time constant of the membrane (30). This after-potential is not associated with any measurable change in the membrane resistance. These facts suggest that, following one whole cycle of activity of the muscle fiber membrane, there is an excessive charge of electricity remaining in the large capacity of the membrane and this charge is dissipated through the membrane resistance. In the nodal membrane of the toad (or frog) nerve fiber, the time constant of the membrane is far shorter than the duration of the spike potential (table 1, p. 89); therefore, an after-potential of this type does not exist in the amphibian nerve fiber.

The after-potential of the frog nerve fiber shown in figure 34, right center, was induced by poisoning the fiber with veratrine, an alkaloid which is known to cause rhythmical activity in the muscle and nerve. Gasser & Graham (39) have shown that this chemical greatly enhances the (negative) after-potential of the nerve trunk. The after-potential of this type is associated with a concomitant decrease in the membrane resistance (108, 133).

The after-potential in the squid giant axon (fig. 34, right bottom) is often referred to as an 'undershoot': the membrane potential stays, after the end of the main spike potential, below the initial level of the resting potential. As we have seen in the record of figure 12, this after-potential is associated with a pronounced decrease in the membrane resistance. Grundfest et al. (45) found that there is a phase of slightly increased membrane impedance following the period of decreased membrane impedance. In the sodium theory (p. 118), the undershoot in the squid giant axon is attributed to an increase in the potassium permeability of the membrane.

The nature of the after-potentials in B- and C-fibers in the vertebrate nerve is not clear. Further discussions on the after-potentials of the nerve trunk are found in the monograph by Gasser & Erlanger (38).

Rhythmical Activity

In excitable tissues in living organisms, action potentials appear, as a rule, in more-or-less rapid succession. Thus motor nerve cells in the vertebrate spinal cord discharge impulses repetitively over a wide range of frequency depending on the state of the cell. Similarly, sensory nerve fibers carry a series of impulses toward the spinal cord in response to sensory stimuli delivered to their endings. There is at present a large amount of data concerning the pattern of impulse discharge obtained by the method of recording single fiber responses originated by Adrian (3, 4).

In many excitable tissues, application of a long constant current generates a train of action potentials, as shown by Arvanitaki (8), Fessard (33), Erlanger & Blair (29), Katz (72) and others. The records furnished in figure 35 show repetitive firing of action potentials in the squid giant axon induced by constant outward membrane currents of four different intensities. The stimulating pulses are sent into the axon through a long intracellular metal wire electrode, and the responses are recorded with another intracellular electrode. It is difficult to maintain repetitive firing indefinitely under these experimental conditions. It is to be observed that each action potential is preceded by a slowly rising phase of the membrane potential. This slowly rising phase has been demonstrated at the sites of naturally induced repetitive responses in the automatically beating cardiac muscle [cf. Weidmann (143)].

The site at which impulses are initiated repetitively is called a 'pacemaker'. At present, it is not clear how sensory nerve endings or the motor nerve cells become pacemakers. However, there is one thing that can be inferred from the mechanism of the nervous conduction in the peripheral nerve fiber. As has been discussed on previous pages, nervous conduction is effected through excitation of each segment (or node of Ranvier) by the electric current generated by the adjacent active segment. From this one can infer that a sensory stimulus or a natural stimulus for the motor nerve cell has to be transformed eventually into an electric stimulus in order that it initiates a propagated impulse. (If the size and shape of the electric current generated by a sensory stimulus are similar to those of the ordinary action current, the statement just made has no meaning; however, it is generally accepted that the first electrical sign of the response to a sensory stimulus is variable in size and very different from the ordinary all-or-none response.) Since a constant current applied to a peripheral nerve fiber can give rise to a repetitive firing of impulses, it is generally believed that natural pacemakers resemble in some respect an artificial one induced by application of a constant current (fig. 35).

The mechanism of repetitive firing proposed by Adrian (3, 4) to interpret the injury and sensory discharges of impulses is as follows. An electric stimulus of a constant intensity sets up the first action potential in accordance with the law of electric excitation. Then, the nerve fiber falls into the refractory period which makes the stimulus totally ineffective. As the fiber recovers from this refractoriness, the stimulus becomes effective again and the second action potential is set up. The second response leaves behind it another refractory period. The nerve fiber thus exhibits a kind of oscillatory phenomenon similar to that in a neon lamp connected to a battery, a condenser and a resistor.

It is simple to express Adrian's concept in terms of the membrane potential and the threshold depolarization. At the beginning of the refractory period, the critical membrane potential is close to the level of the shoulder of the action potential (see fig. 20).

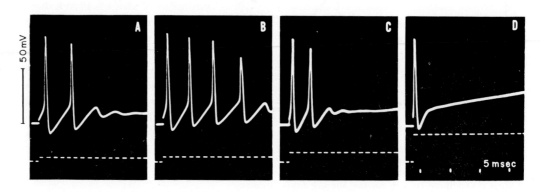

FIG. 35. Repetitive firing of action potentials in a squid giant axon. The relative intensities of the stimulating currents used are indicated by the broken lines. Both stimulating and recording electrodes were long intracellular metal wires. [From S. Hagiwara *et al.*, unpublished.]

During the relatively refractory period there is a continuous recovery in the threshold membrane potential. This concept of Adrian seems to explain many facts known about repetitive firing. In tissues with a time constant which is much longer than the duration of the action potential, however, not only the recovery process, but also the time required to charge the membrane capacity is considered to influence the rhythm of repetitive firing (54). It is also known that the oscillation in the membrane potential at subthreshold levels (8, 9) plays an important role in production of rhythmical activity in some tissues.

In connection with the pacemaker mechanism, there is an interesting phenomenon which seems to deserve a short discussion. That is 'resetting' of the rhythm of the repetitive response by an 'extra impulse' reaching the pacemaker. In 1936 Gilson (41) examined the effect of an artificial (electric) stimulation of the sinus of the turtle heart upon the rhythm of the heart beat. He found that the time interval between the artificially induced response and the following (natural) response is approximately equal to the normal interval of the automatically induced responses, regardless of the interval between the artificially induced response and the preceding one. Similar phenomena have been demonstrated in natural and artificial pacemakers in the sensory nerve fiber and in the motor nerve fiber [cf. Tasaki (121)].

CURRENT THEORIES OF THE RESTING AND
ACTION POTENTIALS

In the last section of this chapter, we shall briefly discuss the current theories dealing with the mechanism whereby the resting and action potential of the nerve or muscle fiber is generated. This problem has been extensively and authoritatively reviewed by many recent investigators in a symposium *Electrochemistry in Biology and Medicine*, edited by Shedlovsky (111). The great variety of the views maintained by recent investigators toward the present problem indicates that the current theories to be described below are not yet accepted as unequivocal. We shall make an attempt to explore the sources of equivocalities and controversies in the present problem.

Resting Potential

Twenty years before the turn of the century, Biedermann (12, p. 354) discovered that application of an isosmotic potassium chloride solution to a portion of a muscle generates a large potential difference between the site of application and the remaining surface of the muscle. Later, Höber (49) extended this observation and found that the ability of various cations to affect the resting potential of the muscle increases in the following series: Li, Na, Mg, Cs, NH_4, Rb, K. Höber found also that the corresponding series for anions is CNS, NO_3, I, Br, Cl, acetate, HPO_4, SO_4, tartarate.

In 1902 Bernstein (10) published the so-called 'membrane theory' in which he postulated *a*) that the resting potential is pre-existent at the plasma membrane of the cell (prior to injury or application of potassium salts), and *b*) that the resting potential is maintained by virtue of the semipermeability of the plasma membrane. At that time, the pre-existence of ions in the electrolyte solution (Arrhenius, 1883) was known, and osmotic phenomena in the membrane of some plant cells and in artificial membranes (Pfeffer, 1877) were also well understood. Nernst's book on theoretical chemistry dealing with concentration cells had just appeared at that time (1900).

A present, there is no doubt about the validity of the membrane theory in the form described above. There are in Bernstein's theory two additional postulates. He speculated that the resting potential is a diffusion potential resulting from the difference in the mobility of potassium and phosphate ions through the membrane and also that the action potential is caused by a reduction of the resting potential resulting from a nonspecific increase of permeability of the membrane during activity.

Later on, a large volume of work was published showing that, within a certain limit, the relationship between the resting potential, E_r, and the external potassium concentration, $[K]_o$, can be expressed by the Nernst equation

$$E_r = 58 \log \frac{[K]_o}{[K]_i} \text{ (mv)} \qquad (12\text{-}1)$$

where $[K]_i$ represents the concentration of potassium in the protoplasm (7, 55, 68, 76, 94). However, the validity of equation (12-1) does not by itself prove that the process of diffusion of potassium ions is responsible for the resting potential.

Equation (12-1) represents the theoretical maximum (absolute) value of the resting potential that can be attained if the concentration gradient of potassium were the cause of the resting membrane potential. If, therefore, it happens under any circumstances that the observed membrane potential exceeds the value given by equation (12-1), one is forced to believe that the resting potential is generated primarily by some electrochemical mechanism other than the diffusion of the potassium ion. This type of evidence against the potassium theory has been expressed by several investigators though not in a written form until the recent work of Shaw *et al.* (109).

The electrochemical nature of the plasma membrane is not yet clearly understood. Osterhout (94), Beutner (11) and others assume that the resting potential is maintained across an oil (nonaqueous) layer. Teorell (139), Sollner (112) and others have developed the concept of a charged porous membrane as the site of bioelectric potential. Shedlovsky (110) stressed the asymmetry of the membrane with respect to two surfaces and the possible role of protons in generation of the bioelectric potentials.

To explain the divergence of the observed resting potential from the Nernst equation, Hodgkin (55) used the modified Goldman equation (42). There is some doubt as to the applicability of this equation to living cells, because of the assumption of a uniform field (i.e. no charge in the membrane) adopted in deriving this equation (139, p. 338). Boyle & Conway (17) found that the ratio of chloride across the muscle fiber membrane is close to the ratio $[K]_o/[K]_i$ and argued that the resting potential of the skeletal muscle fiber is a Donnan potential. There are, however, some arguments against this notion (44).

Action Potential

There is at present only one widely accepted theory of action potential production. That is the so-called sodium theory postulated by Hodgkin & Huxley (57, 58, 59). Previously Nachmansohn (89) advanced a theory in which acetylcholine is assumed to play a decisive role in action potential production. Recently, however, he shifted his effort toward an attempt to supply a biochemical basis for the sodium theory (90).

This theory started with the development of the modern technique of recording and controlling the intracellular potential. When it was found that the amplitude of the membrane action potential is substantially larger than the resting potential across the membrane (p. 84), physiologists realized that Bernstein's postulate as to the origin of the action potential (p. 117) is incorrect. The finding of Hodgkin & Katz (62) that the amplitude of the action potential

of the squid giant axon varies with approximately 58 mv times the logarithm of the concentration of sodium in the external medium (p. 93) has led these British physiologists to postulate that the membrane potential at the peak of activity is determined by the concentration gradient of the sodium ion across the axon membrane. (According to this postulate, the amplitude of the action potential should vary with 58 mv times the logarithm of the intracellular concentration of sodium; however, it is difficult in practice to alter the sodium concentration in a wide range.)

Hodgkin & Huxley (59) elaborated this concept further and explained the mechanism of action potential production by assuming that the increase in the membrane conductance during activity (p. 89) is a specific increase of permeability to sodium ions. They tried to substantiate this idea by voltage clamp experiments (p 91). Their success in reconstructing the action potential from the data obtained by the voltage clamp technique is often regarded as sufficient proof of the sodium theory.

The diagram in figure 36, right, shows the equivalent circuit of the excitable membrane postulated in the theory. When the membrane is at rest, the conductance of the membrane is maintained by the permeability of the membrane to potassium ions; i.e. $g_K \gg g_{Na}$, where g_K is the 'potassium conductance' and g_{Na} the 'sodium conductance' of the membrane. This situation should bring the potential of the resting membrane close to E_K which is defined by equation (12-1). E_{Na} in the diagram represents the 'sodium equilibrium potential' defined by the equation of the type of equation (12-1) for the sodium ion; the polarity of E_{Na} is opposite to that of E_K. If g_{Na} increases at the peak of activity to a value well above g_K, the membrane potential should approach

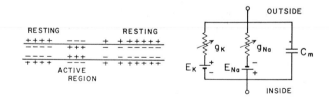

FIG. 36. *Right:* The equivalent circuit proposed by Hodgkin & Huxley to represent the membrane of the squid giant axon. *Left:* The state of an axon carrying an impulse proposed by the same authors. The signs + and − indicate the electric charges on the capacity which are assumed to determine the membrane potential. Note that this concept of charges on the condenser determining the membrane potential is inapplicable to the circuit diagram of fig. 9C.

E_{Na}; this explains the reversal of the membrane potential during activity. If g_{Na} is increased to some extent by a stimulating current pulse, a further increase in g_{Na} can be brought about by a regenerative process; an increase in g_{Na} causes a rise in the membrane potential which in turn gives rise to a further increase in g_{Na}. The theory is self-consistent. The readers who are interested in this beautiful scheme are referred to the original article (59).

It may be worth pointing out that there are in the sodium theory a number of assumptions that are not directly proved by experiments. They assume in the first place that the axon membrane under voltage clamp is spatially uniform; this may not be a safe assumption. They assume also that the capacity of the membrane is connected in parallel to the emf of the membrane (p. 85). They did not exclude the possibility that the sodium ions bound in the substance of the membrane (instead of the free sodium ions in the medium) exert direct influence upon the amplitude of the action potential. There are several more assumptions in the theory. Although most of these assumptions appear to be reasonable, it is also true that one can make a set of entirely different assumptions and explain almost the same amount of experimental data.

There is at present a large volume of work dealing with the movement of sodium or potassium ions across the excitable membrane. The principal findings

pertinent to the discussion in this chapter are a) a steady outward current through the axon membrane is carried almost exclusively by potassium ions (60), and b) there is an exchange of intracellular potassium with extracellular sodium associated with repetitive excitation of the axon (74). It is generally agreed that the amount of the Na-K exchange associated with repetitive excitation observed in invertebrate axons is close to the value expected from the sodium theory.

It should be kept in mind in this connection that there are excitable tissues which do not require any sodium ion in the medium to produce action potentials. Crustacean muscles studied by Fatt & Katz (31) are a well-known example, and the plant cell, *Nitella*, investigated by Osterhout and his associate (93, 94) is another. This fact suggests that the role of the sodium ion in the medium might be only indirectly connected with the process of action potential production. The alternative explanation of this fact is that the mechanism of action potential production is very different in different tissues.

The author wishes to express his gratitude to the following colleagues who have kindly read the manuscript of this chapter and have given many important suggestions: Dr. M. Fuortes, Dr. S. Hagiwara, Prof. A. L. Hodgkin and Dr. C. S. Spyropoulos. The manuscript was prepared with the valuable help of Mrs. Mary Allen, Mrs. Claire Mayer and Mrs. Lydia N. Tasaki, to whom the author also wants to express his appreciation.

REFERENCES

1. ADRIAN, E. D. *J. Physiol.* 45: 389, 1912.
2. ADRIAN, E. D. *J. Physiol.* 55: 193, 1921.
3. ADRIAN, E. D. *The Basis of Sensation.* London: Christophers, 1928.
4. ADRIAN, E. D. *The Mechanism of Nervous Action.* Philadelphia: Univ. Pennsylvania Press, 1932.
5. ADRIAN, E. D. AND D. W. BRONK. *J. Physiol.* 66: 81, 1928.
6. ADRIAN, E. D. AND K. LUCAS. *J. Physiol.* 44: 68, 1912.
7. ADRIAN, R. H. *J. Physiol.* 133: 631, 1956.
8. ARVANITAKI, A. *Propriétés Rythmiques de la Matière Vivante. Variations graduées d' la polarisation et rythmicités.* Paris: Hermann, 1938.
9. ARVANITAKI, A. *J. Neurophysiol.* 5: 89, 1942.
10. BERNSTEIN, J. *Elektrobiologie.* Braunschweig: Vieweg, 1912.
11. BEUTNER, R. *Biochem. Ztschr.* 137: 496, 1923.
12. BIEDERMANN, W. *Elektrophysiologie.* Jena: Fischer, 1895. (English translation by F. A. Welby. London: Macmillan, 1896, 1898.)
13. BISHOP, G. H., P. HEINBECKER AND J. L. O'LEARY. *Am. J. Physiol.* 106: 647, 1933.
14. BLAIR, E. A. AND J. ERLANGER. *Am. J. Physiol.* 114: 309, 1935/36.
15. BLAIR, H. A. *J. Gen. Physiol.* 15: 709, 1932.
16. BOWDITCH, H. P. 1871. (Cited in J. F. Fulton. *Muscular Contraction.* Baltimore: Williams & Wilkins, 1926, p. 48.)
17. BOYLE, P. J. AND E. J. CONWAY. *J. Physiol.* 100: 1, 1941.
18. COLE, K. S. *J. Gen. Physiol.* 25: 29, 1941.
19. COLE, K. S. AND H. J. CURTIS. *J. Gen. Physiol.* 22: 649, 1939.
20. COLE, K. S. AND A. L. HODGKIN. *J. Gen. Physiol.* 22: 671, 1939.
21. CRAIB, W. H. *J. Physiol.* 66: 49, 1928.
22. CURTIS, H. J. AND K. S. COLE. *J. Cell. & Comp. Physiol.* 15: 147, 1940.
23. DAVIS, H., A. FORBES, D. BRUNSWICK AND A. McH. HOPKINS. *Am. J. Physiol.* 76: 448, 1926.
24. DOWNING, A. C., R. W. GERARD AND A. V. HILL. *Proc. Roy. Soc., London. ser. B* 100: 223, 1926.
25. DU BOIS-REYMOND, E. *Untersuchungen über Thierische Elektricität.* Berlin: G. Reimer, 1848/49.
26. ECCLES, J. C. AND C. S. SHERRINGTON. *Proc. Roy. Soc., London. ser. B* 106: 326, 1930.
27. ERLANGER, J. AND E. A. BLAIR. *Am. J. Physiol.* 99: 129, 1931/32.

28. Erlanger, J. and E. A. Blair. *Am. J. Physiol.* 110: 287, 1934.

29. Erlanger, J. and E. A. Blair. *Am. J. Physiol.* 114: 328, 1935/36.

30. Fatt, P. and B. Katz. *J. Physiol.* 115: 320, 1951.

31. Fatt, P. and B. Katz. *J. Physiol.* 120: 171, 1953.

32. Fenn, W. O. *J. Gen. Physiol.* 10: 767, 1927.

33. Fessard, A. *Propriétés Rythmiques de la Matière Vivante.* Paris: Hermann, 1936, Part I (p. 99), Part II (p. 66).

34. Forbes, A. and C. Thacher. *Am. J. Physiol.* 52: 409, 1920.

35. Franck, U. F. *Prog. Biophys. & Biophys. Chem.* 6: 171, 1956.

36. Frankenhauser, B. *J. Physiol.* 118: 107, 1952.

37. Frankenhauser, B. and D. Schneider. *J. Physiol.* 115: 117, 1951.

38. Gasser, H. S. and J. Erlanger. *Electrical Signs of Nervous Action.* Philadelphia: Univ. Pennsylvania Press, 1937.

39. Gasser, H. S. and H. T. Graham. *Am. J. Physiol.* 101: 316, 1932.

40. Gerard, R. W. *Physiol. Rev.* 12: 469, 1932.

41. Gilson, A. S. *Am. J. Physiol.* 116: 358, 1936.

42. Goldman, D. E. *J. Gen. Physiol.* 27: 37, 1943.

43. Grundfest, H. In: *Modern Trends in Physiology and Biochemistry,* edited by E. S. G. Barron. New York: Acad. Press, 1952.

44. Grundfest, H. In: *Electrochemistry in Biology and Medicine,* edited by T. Shedlovsky. New York: Wiley, 1955, p. 141.

45. Grundfest, H., A. M. Shanes and W. Freygang. *J. Gen. Physiol.* 37: 25, 1953.

46. Hagiwara, S. and A. Watanabe. *J. Physiol.* 129: 513, 1955.

47. Hermann, L. *Arch. ges. Physiol.* 75: 574, 1899.

48. Hill A. V. *Proc. Roy. Soc., London. ser. B* 119: 305, 1936.

49. Höber, R. *Arch. ges. Physiol.* 106: 599, 1905.

50. Hodgkin, A. L. *J. Physiol.* 90: 183, 1937.

51. Hodgkin, A. L. *Proc. Roy. Soc., London. ser. B* 126: 87, 1938.

52. Hodgkin, A. L. *J. Physiol.* 94: 560, 1939.

53. Hodgkin, A. L. *J. Physiol.* 106: 319, 1947.

54. Hodgkin, A. L. *J. Physiol.* 107: 165, 1948.

55. Hodgkin, A. L. *Biol. Rev.* 26: 339, 1951.

56. Hodgkin, A. L. and A. F. Huxley. *Nature, London* 144: 710, 1939.

57. Hodgkin, A. L. and A. F. Huxley. *J. Physiol.* 116: 449, 1952.

58. Hodgkin, A. L. and A. F. Huxley. *J. Physiol.* 116: 473, 1952.

59. Hodgkin, A. L. and A. F. Huxley. *J. Physiol.* 117: 500, 1952.

60. Hodgkin, A. L. and A. F. Huxley. *J. Physiol.* 121: 403, 1953.

61. Hodgkin, A. L., A. F. Huxley, and B. Katz. *J. Physiol.* 116: 424, 1952.

62. Hodgkin, A. L. and B. Katz. *J. Physiol.* 108: 37, 1949.

63. Hodgkin, A. L. and W. A. H. Rushton. *Proc. Roy. Soc., London. ser. B* 133: 444, 1946.

64. Hodler, J., R. Stämpfli and I. Tasaki. *Am. J. Physiol.* 170: 375, 1952.

65. Hodler, J., R. Stämpfli and I. Tasaki. *Helvet. physiol. et bharmacol. acta* 10: C54, 1952.

66. Huxley, A. F. and R. Stämpfli. *J. Physiol.* 108: 315, 1949.

67. Huxley, A. F. and R. Stämpfli. *J. Physiol.* 112: 476, 1951.

68. Huxley, A. F. and R. Stämpfli. *J. Physiol.* 112: 496, 1951.

69. Kato, G. *The Theory of Decrementless Conduction in Narcotized Region of Nerve.* Tokyo: Nankodo, 1924.

70. Kato, G. *The Microphysiology of Nerve.* Tokyo: Maruzen, 1934.

71. Kato, G. *Cold Spring Harbor Symp. Quant. Biol.* 4: 202, 1936.

72. Katz, B. *Electric Excitation of Nerve.* London: Oxford, 1939.

73. Katz, B. and O. H. Schmitt. *J. Physiol.* 97: 471, 1940.

74. Keynes, R. D. *J. Physiol.* 114: 119, 1951.

75. Lillie, R. S. *J. Gen. Physiol.* 7: 473, 1925.

76. Ling, G. and R. W. Gerard. *J. Cell. & Comp. Physiol.* 34: 383, 1949.

77. Lorente de Nó, R. *A Study of Nerve Physiology* (Parts I and II). New York: Rockefeller Inst. Med. Res. 1947.

78. Lorente de Nó, R. *J. Cell. & Comp. Physiol.* 33: Suppl. 1, 1949.

79. Lucas, K. *J. Physiol.* 36: 253, 1907.

80. Lucas, K. *J. Physiol.* 37: 112, 1908.

81. Lucas, K. *J. Physiol.* 38: 113, 1909.

82. Lucas, K. *The Conduction of the Nervous Impulse.* London: Longmans, 1917.

83. Marmont, G. *Am. J. Physiol.* 130: 392, 1940.

84. Marmont, G. *J. Cell. & Comp. Physiol.* 34: 351, 1949.

85. Marrazzi, A. S. and R. Lorente de Nó. *J. Neurophysiol.* 7: 83, 1944.

86. Matteucci, Carlo. *Compt. rend. Acad. Sc. Paris* 14: 310, 1842.

87. McNichol, E. F. and H. Wagner. *Naval Med. Res. Inst. Project Report,* Vol. 12, p. 97–118, 1954.

88. Monnier, A. M. *L'Excitation Electrique des Tissues.* Paris: Hermann, 1934.

89. Nachmanoshn, D. *The Harvey Lectures.* Series XLIX. New York: Acad. Press, 1955.

90. Nachmansohn, D. and I. B. Wilson. In: *Electrochemistry in Biology and Medicine,* edited by T. Shedlovsky. New York: Wiley, 1955, p. 167.

91. Nernst, W. *Arch. ges. Physiol.* 122: 275, 1908.

92. Niedergerke, R. *Arch. ges. Physiol.* 258: 108, 1953.

93. Osterhout, W. J. V. *J. Gen. Physiol.* 24: 7, 1941.

94. Osterhout, W. J. V. In: *Electrochemistry in Biology and Medicine,* edited by T. Shedlovsky. New York: Wiley, 1955, p. 213.

95. Osterhout, W. J. V. and S. E. Hill. *J. Gen. Physiol.* 13: 547, 1930.

96. Otani, T. *Jap. J. Med. Sc. III Biophys.* 4: 355, 1937.

97. Overton, E. *Arch. ges. Physiol.* 92: 346, 1902.

98. Parker, G. H. *J. Gen. Physiol.* 8: 21, 1925.

99. Pecher, C. *Compt. rend. Soc. de biol.* 122: 87, 1936.

100. Pflüger, E. F. W. *Untersuchungen über die Physiologie des Elektrotonus.* Berlin, 1859.

101. Pratt, F. H. and J. P. Eisenburger. *Am. J. Physiol.* 49: 1, 1919.

102. Rashevsky, N. *Mathematical Biophysics.* Chicago: Univ. Chicago Press, 1938.

103. ROSENBLUETH, A., J. A. ALANIS AND J. MANDOKI. *J. Cell. & Comp. Physiol.* 33: 405, 1949.

104. ROSENBLUETH, A. AND J. V. LUCO. *J. Cell. & Comp. Physiol.* 36: 289, 1950.

105. RUSHTON, W. A. H. *Proc. Roy. Soc., London. ser. B* 124: 210, 1937.

106. SCHMITT, O. H. In: *Electrochemistry in Biology and Medicine,* edited by T. Shedlovsky. New York: Wiley, 1955, p. 91.

107. SCHOEFFLE, G. M. AND J. ERLANGER. *Am. J. Physiol.* 167: 134, 1951.

108. SHANES, A. M., H. GRUNDFEST AND W. FREYGANG. *J. Gen. Physiol.* 37: 39, 1953.

109. SHAW, F. H., S. E. SIMON, B. M. JOHNSTONE AND M. E. HOLMAN. *J. Gen. Physiol.* 40: 263, 1956.

110. SHEDLOVSKY, T. *Cold Spring Harbor Symp. Quant. Biol.* 17: 97, 1952.

111. SHEDLOVSKY, T. (editor). *Electrochemistry in Biology and Medicine.* New York: Wiley, 1955.

112. SOLLNER, K. In: *Electrochemistry in Biology and Medicine,* edited by T. Shedlovsky. New York: Wiley, 1955, p. 33.

113. STÄMPFLI, R. *Ergebn. Physiol.* 47: 70, 1952.

114. STÄMPFLI, R. *Physiol. Rev.* 34: 101, 1954.

115. STÄMPFLI, R. AND Y. ZOTTERMAN. *Helvet. physiol. et pharmacol. acta* 9: 208, 1951.

116. TAKEUCHI, T. AND I. TASAKI. *Arch. ges. Physiol.* 246: 32, 1942.

117. TASAKI, I. *Am. J. Physiol.* 127: 211, 1939.

118. TASAKI, I. *Arch. ges. Physiol.* 245: 665, 1942.

119. TASAKI, I. *Biochim. et biophys. acta* 3: 498, 1949.

120. TASAKI, I. *Biochim. et biophys. acta* 3: 665, 1949.

121. TASAKI, I. *Cytologia* 15: 205, 1950.

122. TASAKI, I. *Jap. J. Physiol.* 1: 75, 1950.

123. TASAKI, I. *Cold Spring Harbor Symp. Quant. Biol.* 17: 37, 1952.

124. TASAKI, I. *Nervous Transmission.* Springfield: Thomas, 1953.

125. TASAKI, I. *Am. J. Physiol.* 181: 639, 1955.

126. TASAKI, I. *J. Gen. Physiol.* 39: 377, 1956.

127. TASAKI, I. In: *Microphysiologie Comparée des Eléments Excitables.* Colloques Internationaux du Centre National de la Recherche Scientifique No. 67, Paris, 1957, p. 1.

128. TASAKI, I. AND K. FRANK. *Am. J. Physiol.* 182: 572, 1955.

129. TASAKI, I. AND W. H. FREYGANG, JR. *J. Gen. Physiol.* 39: 211, 1955.

130. TASAKI, I. AND S. HAGIWARA. *Am. J. Physiol.* 188: 423, 1957.

131. TASAKI, I., K. ISHII AND H. ITO. *Jap. J. Med. Sc. III Biophys.* 9: 189, 1943.

132. TASAKI, I. AND K. MIZUGUCHI. *J. Neurophysiol.* 11: 295, 1948.

133. TASAKI, I. AND K. MIZUGUCHI. *Biochem et biophys. acta* 3: 484, 1949.

134. TASAKI, I. AND K. MIZUTANI. *Jap. J. Med. Sc. III Biophys.* 10: 245, 1944.

135. TASAKI, I. AND T. TAKEUCHI. *Arch. ges. Physiol.* 244: 696, 1941.

136. TASAKI, I. AND T. TAKEUCHI. *Arch. ges. Physiol.* 245: 764, 1942.

137. TASAKI, I. AND N. TASAKI. *Biophys. et biochim. acta* 5: 335, 1950.

138. TASHIRO, S. *Am. J. Physiol.* 32: 107, 1913.

139. TEORELL, T. *Prog. Biophys. & Biophys. Chem.* 3: 305, 1953.

140. VERWORN, M. *Irritability.* New Haven: Yale, 1913.

141. VON HELMHOLTZ, H. *Arch. Anat. Physiol.* 71, 1850. (Cited in Biedermann, 12.)

142. WEIDMANN, S. *J. Physiol.* 115: 227, 1951.

143. WEIDMANN, S. *Elektrophysiologie der Herzmuskelfaser.* Bern und Stuttgart: Huber, 1956.

144. WINTERSTEIN, H. *Die Narkose.* Berlin: J. Springer, 1926.

145. WOLFGRAM, F. J. AND A. VAN HARREVELD. *Am. J. Physiol.* 171: 140, 1952.

146. YOUNG, J. Z. *Cold Spring Harbor Symp. Quant. Biol.* 4: 1, 1936.

CHAPTER IV

Initiation of impulses at receptors

J. A. B. GRAY | *Department of Physiology, University College, London, England*

CHAPTER CONTENTS

IN THE INTACT ORGANISM impulses are set up in primary afferent fibers as a result of activity in those receptors with which the fibers are associated. These receptors may consist solely of specialized terminations of the afferent nerve fibers, or the nerve endings may be associated with other cells which play a significant role in the initiation of impulses. In either instance, the role of the receptor is to record the state of, or changes in, the physical or chemical environment by the initiation of impulses which are then conducted in the primary afferent fibers to the central nervous system. A primary afferent fiber may be connected with a single receptor or with many; but even when it is supplied by numerous receptors, a single afferent fiber remains a single channel into the central nervous system and must be considered as such. When dealing with the activity in such a fiber it is necessary to consider the fiber and all its peripheral connections as a whole, that is as a sensory unit. It is the purpose of this section to consider something of the general behavior of sensory units and of the mechanisms by which individual receptors initiate impulses in the primary afferent neurons.

GENERAL PROPERTIES

A few words should first be said concerning classification. Sensory units can be described by reference to the properties of the specific stimulus, the nature of the activity and the site and distribution of the receptive field. All these factors, together with the conduction velocity of the fiber, are measurable quantities and a precise description of a sensory unit is thus possible. It seems better in this context to avoid terms such as warmth, pain or red; these terms describe sensations which depend on the activity of the whole nervous system, not just on the properties of one sensory unit.

Type of Energy Required to Excite Receptors

In most animal organisms there are receptors that respond to the following forms of energy: mechanical, thermal, electromagnetic (as light) and chemical. With the exception of one important group, it appears that nearly all receptors are especially sensitive to one form of energy and either completely or relatively insensitive to all others. The excepted group consists of those receptors that have a low sensitivity to all types of energy, but will respond to any form of energy that reaches a damaging or near damaging level; these receptors are of course those that give rise to defensive reflexes and are associated with the sensation of pain. The specificity of receptors to a particular form of energy was first propounded in modern times by Müller (76). As a whole this concept is not seriously challenged, but recently an attack has been made on its application to receptors situated in the skin (99). The objections are based both on the finding that there are areas of human skin in which morphologically specialized endings are not found but from which all modalities of sensation can be elicited (39), and on the results of certain sensation experiments (65, 66). There need be no rigid correlation between morphological and functional specializations; it is indeed interesting to note that the bulk of the direct evidence for the functional specificity of sensory units has come from preparations of frog and toad skin which contain few morphologically differentiated nerve endings (24). As regards to sensation experiments it must be realized that sensations are the end result of complicated processes and that such experiments, while giving information about sensations and their specificity, cannot weigh heavily against direct evidence on the properties of sensory units.

Direct evidence of the specificity of units has been obtained by recording the responses of single ones to different stimuli. In the earlier experiments of this type single fibers were not isolated in an anatomical sense, but small bundles of nerve fibers were used so that the activity of individual units could be identified and analyzed; using this technique it was possible to show that thermal and near-damaging stimuli only excited activity in small fibers and did not produce activity in the larger fibers which responded only to mechanical stimuli (2, 50, 103, 104). This type of work has now been carried a stage further by isolating and recording from single afferent fibers that have their receptive fields in the skin of toads and of cats (73). Results of such experiments show that mechanically sensitive units are not easily excited by thermal stimuli [though this has been shown to happen in the cat's tongue (45)] or by acid; that thermally sensitive units do not normally respond to mechanical stimulation [the rattlesnake pit organ is an exception (15)]; and that units responding to acid, prick or burning do not respond to small mechanical or thermal stimuli.

The specificity of sensory units is not confined, however, to a simple distinction between different types of energy but involves distinctions between other properties of the stimulus. Of these properties, those connected with its time course are perhaps the most obvious; the different rates of adaptation exhibited by different units is an example which will be considered again. Specificity to a particular band of frequencies of a periodic function is another example; thus there is evidence that different units in the retina respond to different frequencies of light waves (31, 91) and that primary units from the mammalian cochlea have particular characteristics in relation to the frequency of the sound waves (93). In both these instances the sensory units are displaying a specificity, but there is clearly a difference in the way this specificity is brought about. In the retina it seems probable that individual receptors are different, but in the cochlea it is the mechanical properties of the system that are mainly responsible for the results. Such a distinction between the properties of the receptor and the properties of the supporting tissues is one that arises in other situations but is one that is irrelevant in the context of describing the properties of sensory units. The examples of specificity so far given in this paragraph are concerned with time factors, but there are others. Thus there are two types of thermal unit found in the cat's tongue; in both types the frequency of the impulse discharge depends on the temperature of the receptors, but in one group the maximum frequency is found at a temperature of 30 to 32°C (46), while in the other it occurs at 37.5 to 40°C (22). Again, units in the cat's tongue responding to chemical stimuli, and presumably responsible for the sensation of taste, can be grouped in respect to the substances that are able to set up activity in them (82).

Adaptation

When a piece of tissue containing a receptor sensitive to mechanical stimuli is subjected to an abrupt increase in the forces applied to it and the new situation is then maintained, the sensory unit will discharge impulses at a frequency, which starts at a relatively high value and then decreases with time (4, 74, 75) (fig. 1). This decline in frequency is known as adaptation and may be slow or rapid. In those units that are described as tonic, the frequency of the impulse discharge declines relatively slowly to a steady value which is characteristic of the applied force (fig. 1); the frequency of the discharge from other units, those called phasic, adapts more rapidly and finally falls to zero (5). In an extreme case a sensory unit may only discharge a single impulse during the change in the applied forces and will then remain silent until another change takes place. Adaptation is also observed in sensory units specifically sensitive to forms of energy other than mechanical.

Adaptation is a word that describes the response of a sensory unit to a particular function of the type of energy concerned. When adaptation is rapid, it can be said that the unit is not signalling a pressure, a temperature or a concentration; but it does not tell us what particular function in respect to time is signalled.

To say that a function is signalled means that a constant value of the function gives rise to a constant and repeatable frequency of impulse discharge in the fiber of the sensory unit. In most situations it is very difficult to maintain a constant velocity or acceleration for a sufficiently long time to see whether or not a constant frequency of discharge is in fact set up [a notable exception has appeared in the experiments on the semicircular canals using constant angular velocities and accelerations (72)]. Even if such experiments were performed it is by no means certain that simple relations would be found. This is therefore a situation in which it is necessary to continue to use an empirical description.

It should be noted that in the first sentence of this section, reference is made to the tissue surrounding the receptors. Even in the instances in which a receptor has been isolated, e.g. the muscle spindle and Pacinian corpuscle, there is far more supporting tissue than active element. These supporting tissues may be of fundamental importance in the adaptation of 'simple' receptors in the same way as the structures of the middle ear and cochlea cause 'adaptation' of the ear to steady pressures applied to the tympanic membrane. This problem will be considered at a later stage when all the relevant evidence has been discussed.

Receptive Fields

A sensory unit has a particular situation and particular size of receptive field, i.e. the area from which the single afferent fiber receives branches. The size of these receptive fields can vary quite considerably, for example up to 9 by 5 cm, not mm, in cat's skin (73) and up to 100 sq. mm in frog's skin (3); while other sensory units have receptive fields which comprise only a single end organ. Variation of size of receptive fields occurs with different types of unit in skin and also in specialized organs such as the eye. There is wide overlap of receptive fields and it is clear that spatial discrimination must depend on the coordination of information supplied through a considerable number of primary channels.

Information

Sensory units constitute independent channels which signal to the central nervous system information about the physical and chemical environment of the organism. This information is conveyed by the pattern of activity in any one unit and by the characteristics and organization of each channel. These factors can be classified as follows:
- a) Factors related to time
  - i) Interval between impulses
  - ii) Duration of activity
- b) Factors related to the properties of units
  - i) Characteristics of the 'normal' stimulus, e.g. the nature of the energy and other relevant factors
  - ii) Size and position of the receptive field
  - iii) Sensitivity of the unit

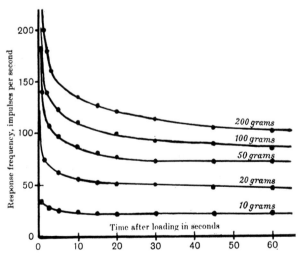

FIG. 1. Response of cat muscle spindle to stretch. *Abscissa:* time in sec. *Ordinate:* impulses frequency per sec. Each curve for a different force. [From Matthews (75).]

REPETITIVE RESPONSES AND TONIC RECEPTORS

Stimulus-Frequency Relations

There are many sensory units, the function of which is to signal to the central nervous system the properties of a steady state, e.g. temperature, concentration or intensity of illumination. At any time, except shortly after an abrupt change from one state to another, the frequency of the impulse discharge of the unit will depend on the value of the physical or chemical function in question; and a particular frequency will, in the working range of any one unit, be consistently related to a particular value. One example is seen in figure 2 where the frequency of impulse discharge in five single fibers from pressure receptors of the carotid sinus is plotted against pressure in the sinus. Another example appears in figure 22 of Chapter XVIII on Thermal Sensations in this volume (p. 452), in which the impulse frequencies in two units from the cat's tongue responding to thermal stimuli are plotted against temperature. The curves in the two figures are clearly quite different; the pressure units, while showing individual variations, all start to fire at a certain pressure above which the frequency of discharge increases as the pressure increases until an upper limit of frequency is reached (12, 60). The temperature units on the other hand both show maxima in their temperature-frequency relationship, but these maxima occur at two widely different temperatures. The two types of response represent the activity of two distinct groups of units found in cats (22, 46) and it is presumed that the

activity of these two types of unit bears a close causal relationship with the subjective sensations of cold and warmth.

Looking at the two examples shown, it would seem improbable that any relationship between 'stimulus' and frequency having general relevance to sensory units of all types could be found. This is strictly true, but there is a relationship that has been found to describe reasonably well the response characteristics of certain types of unit in their working range. This is what is known as the Weber-Fechner law. This law derives from an observation made by Weber that the smallest difference in the weight of two objects bears a constant relation to the weight of the objects. It is usually given as $\Delta I/I = C$, where I is intensity of stimulus, ΔI the smallest detectable difference in intensity and C a constant. Fechner developed this observation in a theoretical way by making the assumption that each discriminable step of stimulus intensity corresponds to a unit increase in sensation, that is to say he stated that $\Delta I/I = k\Delta S$ where ΔS is the increase in sensation. From this it follows that $dS/dI = 1/kI$ and $S = a \log I + b$. This equation was originally put forward in an attempt to quantitate sensation, a thing we are not concerned with here; however, we are concerned with its relevance to 'stimulus'-frequency relations. The relation between the applied force and impulse frequency recorded from a frog's muscle spindle has been found to be consistent with this relationship (95). The corresponding relationship between intensity of illumination and response from an ommatidium of the eye of *Limulus* is also consistent with the equation under certain specific conditions (41). These findings have inevitably raised the question of whether this relationship indicates anything about the mechanisms involved in the initiation of impulses or whether it must be regarded simply as an empirical description (31). The fit between equation and experiment is not sufficiently good to suggest that the fundamental processes depend on a simple logarithmic relationship, but if, as seems possible, these processes are related to ionic equilibria across cell membranes, a logarithmic term might be expected to appear in the relationship.

Effect of a Reduction of Excitation

It has already been pointed out that while a tonic sensory unit will respond to a certain steady state with a certain frequency, a sudden increase in, for

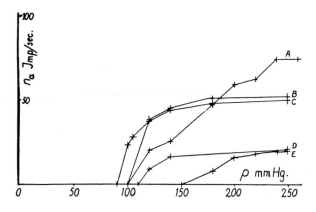

FIG. 2. Responses of five single pressure sensitive units (*A* to *E*) from the cat's carotid sinus. *Abscissa:* intrasinusal pressure in mm Hg. *Ordinate:* impulse frequency per sec. [From Landgren (60).]

instance, the applied force will cause a relatively large increase in the frequency of the discharge, an increase which will then decline until the correct frequency for the new steady state has been reached. A similar process occurs if there is a sudden decrease in, again for instance, the applied force. In this instance the frequency falls abruptly to a value below that expected for the new steady state and then increases with time. Thus, if a muscle spindle is discharging rhythmically and the muscle in which it lies is stretched for a time and then suddenly returned to its resting length, the frequency of the discharge from the spindle falls well below its resting value, possibly to zero; after a time the resting rhythm re-establishes itself (75). Similar changes can be observed in other types of unit, for example in temperature sensitive units (46), and the pressure sensitive units of the cat's carotid sinus (60). It should be noted that the behavior of such units contrasts with that of phasic units which are considered in another section below.

Nature of Repetitive Firing

Ideas on the mechanisms by which firing takes place started with the proposals of Adrian (1). Essentially these were that special nonaccommodating regions of nerve exist at sensory nerve endings and that repetitive activity is initiated in these regions; the frequency of the discharge depends on the refractory period which may be longer here than in other parts of the nerve. Broadly speaking, work on the nature of repetitive firing by sensory receptors has followed two lines. The first has attacked the problem of nerve accommodation and the other, the mechanism that determines the interval between impulses.

Many investigations have been carried out on the rate of accommodation of nerve and these have shown that accommodation need not be rapid and that in crustacean (49), amphibian (26) and mammalian (32, 89) nerve it is in fact possible to obtain maintained repetitive firing during the passage of a constant current. Further it has been found that most experimental procedures tend to increase the rate of accommodation (81); it is possible that the common effect of all these procedures is to lower the membrane potential, a reduction of which is known to increase the rate of accommodation (94). These findings led to the view that the mechanism of repetitive firing from sensory receptors could be explained on the known properties of nerve fibers. This view was elaborated in particular by certain Scandinavian workers (9, 30) who suggested that the receptor develops a 'generator potential' which causes current to flow in the nerve fiber so acting like a constant current stimulus in setting up a train of impulses. This idea has remained the basis of most subsequent work on the subject.

The concept that the intervals between the impulses of a train are dependent on the rate of recovery after an impulse is faced with the difficulty that rhythmic discharges of very low frequency, a few impulses per second, can be observed. These intervals are much longer than the total duration of the recovery process as known in nerve. Investigations on the repetitive firing of crustacean nerve during the passage of a constant current have introduced another idea (49), that the intervals between impulses are determined by the response time. That is to say the intervals are determined in the same manner as the latency from the beginning of a current stimulus to the initiation of the first impulse.

The passage of a constant current through a crustacean axon sets up a repetitive discharge as shown in figure 3. Several points can be seen in this figure; the frequency of discharge is related to the current strength; the interval between the beginning of the current and the first impulse is always closely related to the intervals between the other impulses; these intervals are all dependent on the development of the local response, an impulse being initiated whenever this local response reaches the critical potential; the critical potential at which the impulses are set up is the same with all but the greatest strengths of current and all but the highest frequencies of impulses. Apart from this direct evidence that it is the time course of the development of the local response that sets the interval between impulses, the recovery time of these axons is such that it cannot explain the frequencies observed. These crustacean axons have long response times and can therefore give regular low frequency discharges.

The events taking place in certain stretch receptors in crustacea are very similar (27). A microelectrode in the cell body of one of these primary sensory neurons is able to detect a receptor potential generated in the terminals and, superimposed on it, a discharge of nerve impulses. The receptor potential will be considered in a later section. Here it is sufficient to point out that after an impulse the membrane potential builds up again in a manner very similar to that shown in figure 3, and the next impulse is set up when this potential reaches the critical value. The

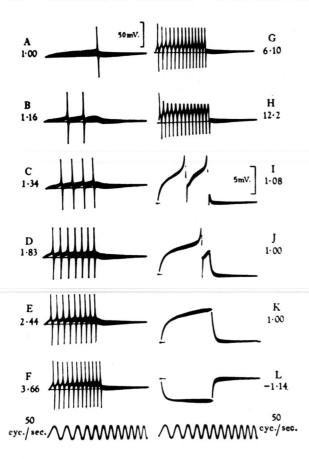

FIG. 3. Responses at the cathode of single carcinus axons to constant currents. *A–H:* increasing currents as indicated. *I–K:* near threshold currents at higher amplification and faster sweep speed. *L:* potential change at anode, conditions as *I–K.* [From Hodgkin (49).]

critical potential remains the same at all but the highest values of impulse frequency.

The initiation of impulses by the receptor potential generated in the muscle spindle of the frog has also been observed (58). In this preparation the critical potential remains constant for all except the first impulse in a discharge at a constant frequency, but the value is different for different frequencies; in fact there is a direct and linear relationship between the value of the critical potential and the frequency of the discharge. An explanation of this phenomenon has been given as follows (58): recovery after a nerve impulse depends on two processes *a)* a restoration of membrane resistance and *b)* a return of excitability (see 48). If the first of these processes is the more rapid in the frog muscle spindle fibers, but not in the crustacean fiber, then results such as have been observed would be expected.

Modification of Afferent Discharges by Current

Afferent discharges can be modified by the application of currents to the regions in which such discharges are set up. This can be seen in the frog's muscle spindle (25); if the spindle is made to discharge at a suitable frequency by stretch and a current is applied between an electrode on the afferent nerve and another on the muscle, the frequency is increased if the electrode on the muscle is the cathode and decreased if this electrode is the anode. The increase or decrease of frequency is related to the intensity of current, though the relation is not a simple one. Other preparations exhibit similar effects. Current passed through the nerve terminals of the isolated labyrinth of the ray causes an increase in the frequency of discharge in these fibers when the cathode is on the tissue surrounding the sensory endings and the anode on the afferent nerve fibers; a current in the opposite direction causes a reduction in the discharge frequency (71). These changes caused by the flow of current summate with those due to angular acceleration in the appropriate direction. Similar results can be observed by polarization of the lateralis organs of *Xenopus laevis*. It has been shown that when the applied current flows along the nerve fiber, as in the instances already described, an increase in frequency occurs when the cathode is on the terminal and the anode on the nerve; however, if the current flows between electrodes placed on either side of the skin, the frequency is increased when the cathode is on the inside and the anode on the outside (77). The frequency of discharge in the nerve fibers from the lateral line organ of the Japanese eel is also increased by a current passed between an anode on the outside of the skin and a cathode on the inside (55); the passage of a current in the same direction has been shown to excite afferent fibers from touch receptors in frog skin (73). Currents can also modify the discharge from a compound eye (40).

These results are important in two respects. First, depolarization of the terminal parts of the axon membrane can summate with end organ activity which suggests that the latter involves a depolarization of the terminals. This is in fact known to occur in many instances which will be considered below. Second, it can be argued from the results obtained with currents passed across the skin instead of along the nerve that, during sensory activity, impulses are initiated away from the terminal (77). Direct evidence that this is so in certain instances will be given later.

EXCITATION OF IMPULSES BY CONTROLLED PULSES AND PHASIC RECEPTORS

In the last section stimulus-frequency relations were considered. Such relations give important information about units that signal the values of steady states by indicating them as particular and repeatable frequencies of impulses. That is to say these relations are important for nonadapting or tonic units. On the other hand, the response of phasic units, and the adapting part of responses of tonic units, are dependent on the time course of the stimulus; in particular the rates of change at the beginning and end of the pulse are important. To investigate these phasic units in detail, it is therefore important to use stimuli of known time course. It is also important that the stimulus should be adequately damped. The importance of this can be shown by an example: Pacinian corpuscles have thresholds of a few tenths of a micron and, for the amplitude threshold to be minimal, the displacement must be complete in less than a millisecond (34); if large displacements of tens of microns are used, it only requires a one per cent oscillation to give rise to what appears to be a repetitive response. Various techniques have been used for this purpose. Thus for mechanical receptors, electromagnetic (6, 57) and crystal transducers (34, 35) have been used. The former have bigger displacements, but generally have a slower time course than the latter which can have a damped rise time of 0.2 msec. and a displacement of 10 to 20 μ. It should be noted that even 0.2 msec. is not very short compared with the latency from the beginning of the stimulus to the impulse.

Quantitative Aspects of Excitation

Using such methods, the latencies for impulse initiation in Pacinian corpuscles and frog skin receptors have been measured (34, 35). In the Pacinian corpuscle latencies after the onset of mechanical deformations of any duration are longer (i.e. 0.5 to 3.0 msec.) than those following the beginning of a constant current stimulus to the receptor's own nerve fiber within a millimeter of the ending. After mechanical stimulation of frog skin even longer latencies have been observed. The latency observed in the Pacinian corpuscle can be shown to be due to the time taken for the receptor potential to develop (37); it seems likely, therefore, that the longer latencies found with frog skin receptors indicate even more prolonged receptor processes. Curves of recovery after the ini-tiation of an impulse by a short mechanical pulse to a Pacinian corpuscle have been shown to be similar to the curves of recovery obtained after electrical excitation of the ending's own nerve fiber close to the corpuscle and of nerves in general (34). Thus, in this instance at least, there is direct evidence that the time course of recovery at the site of impulse initiation is not much different from that in other parts of nerves.

The change of amplitude threshold with change of stimulus velocity has also been measured, and the minimum velocity of stimulus necessary for excitation found. Thus, just as there is a critical slope in the excitation of nerve by a linearly increasing current, so there is a critical slope in the excitation of phasic receptors by linearly increasing displacements. Such measurements give a quantitative measure of the adaptation of such receptors. Thus the critical slope for a Pacinian corpuscle is given as 1200 rheobases per sec. (36) and that for receptors in frog's skin 61 rheobases per sec (35).

As a means of investigating the fundamental mechanisms of receptors, such measurements have been superseded by direct recording of receptor potentials; but they are still of use in certain types of quantitative investigation (53).

On and Off Responses

At least some phasic receptors respond with one or a few impulses to a change from one state to another; this response is not qualitatively dependent on the sign of this change. Thus many photoreceptors respond when the intensity of illumination on them is suddenly raised from one level to another and again when the intensity is suddenly reduced (30). The same type of response to change of state is seen in receptors in toad and cat skin (73). Measurements of the threshold amplitude for on and off responses to rectangular displacements have been made for Pacinian corpuscles and frog skin receptors; in the former the threshold for a compression (the 'on response') is usually slightly lower than that for a decompression (the 'off response'), but not infrequently the reverse is true (34); on the other hand the excitability of the frog's cutaneous receptors to a compression is much greater than the excitability to the decompression (35). These differences may well be due to the mechanics of the systems, for in these experiments compression is a result of an externally applied force, while decompression depends solely on the restoring forces inherent in the tissue; it is likely that restoration is a much more rapid process in a Pacinian corpuscle than in frog's skin.

Summation

Two subthreshold short pulses applied to a phasic receptor within a suitable interval of each other can summate and set up an impulse; the essential point in this experiment is that the first pulse is over before the beginning of the second and the summation takes place in the receptor. Further discussion of this point will be left to the next section where receptor potentials are discussed. One particular case can, however, be discussed here. It is possible to observe summation between the subthreshold activity evoked by a small short mechanical pulse and a brief electrical test shock. Such a test shock can be used to measure the excitability of the receptor at different times after the application of the mechanical pulse; in this way indirect evidence of the time course of a receptor potential has been obtained (34).

RECEPTOR POTENTIALS AND OTHER GENERATOR POTENTIALS

It is now widely held that the immediate cause of impulse initiation in receptors and sense organs is the development of an electrical potential change which is graded according to certain characteristics of the stimulus and which is confined to the region of the receptor or organ. Such potentials have now been found in a number of situations of different types and these findings, together with supporting evidence such as summation results from other sites, form the justification for such a generalization.

In this section I shall use the term 'generator potential' to describe any graded potential change occurring in a sensory receptor or in a complex sense organ that can reasonably be supposed to be a cause of the initiation of an impulse. The term 'receptor potentials' I will confine to those generator potentials occurring in a single receptor. Thus the cochlea microphonic is a generator potential but not a receptor potential.

Generator Potentials in Complex Organs

These lie outside the scope of this particular chapter but are included briefly for completeness. The cochlea is the best example of this group. In this organ there is a potential difference maintained between the endolymph and the perilymph (96). During the application of a sound wave, an alternating potential can be recorded and shown to have its greatest intensity at the point on the basilar membrane at which the hair cells are situated (16). This potential is directly related to the sound pressure wave (100). There is reason to suppose that this microphonic potential, as it is called, is the cause of impulse initiation (16). 'Microphonic' potentials have also been found in other sites, e.g. the lateral line organs (54) and sacculus (105). These potentials serve a similar function to the receptor potentials of neurons but, in the cochlea at least, they represent changes of potential between multicellular compartments instead of across cell membranes. It is not improbable that there are common factors in the development of these two types of potential, but we cannot expect to find close parallels.

Receptor Potentials Generated in Nerve Terminals

Such potentials have been recorded from certain mechanically excitable receptors (6, 27, 37, 58), from photoreceptors (42, 79) and from olfactory receptors (78). In all these instances the receptor potential has been recorded at a distance from its source, and in no case has the membrane potential of the receptor region been recorded directly. In each of the three mechanical examples on which we have information at present, the records were obtained by recording the currents flowing along the nerve fiber, the nerve fiber behaving as a pair of passive concentric conductors. The changes in these currents must have been related to changes in potential across the membrane of the terminal portions of the afferent nerve fiber, since all currents recorded must have crossed the membrane peripheral to the recording region; this does not prove of course that the changes are actively generated across the terminal membrane. Reasons for believing that the receptor potentials are in fact actively generated at this site are given in the last section of this chapter.

Examples of receptor potentials are shown in figure 4. Figure 4A and B are records from muscle spindles from the frog (58); in both experiments the preparations had been procainized to prevent impulse activity. Figure 4A shows the changes that occur at the beginning of a maintained stretch; it can be seen that there is a relatively large initial change of potential and that this is followed by a small but maintained potential change. The earlier phase, called the dynamic phase, is related to the velocity of the stretch. The smaller maintained change of potential

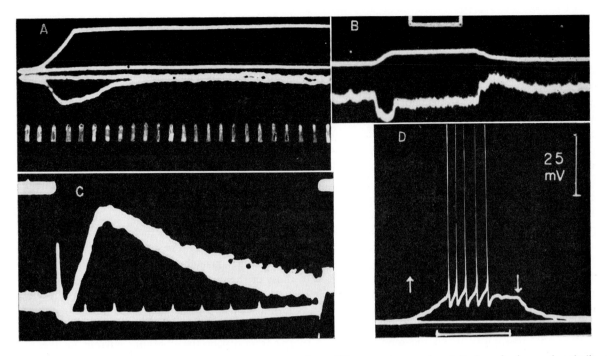

FIG. 4. Receptor potentials from different receptors. *A* and *B*: from frog's muscle spindle, procainized. *Top:* stretch. *Bottom:* receptor potential. Time, A, 500 cps; B, 0.1 sec. [From Katz (58).] *C:* from cat's Pacinian corpuscle, procainized. *Upper trace (at start):* amplitude and duration of displacement and time in msec. Note that this trace crosses the other trace during displacement. *Lower trace (at start):* receptor potential record. [From Gray & Sato (37).] *D:* from crayfish stretch receptor. Arrows mark duration of stretch. Time, 1 sec. [From Eyzaguirre & Kuffler (27).]

depends only on the amplitude of the stretch. Figure 4B shows also the events occurring when the stretch is released. It can be seen that there is a change of potential in the opposite direction to the other deflections, that is the electrode near the receptor goes positive to the distant electrode. The time course of this deflection tends to be slower than that of the initial dynamic phase, but it must be remembered that relaxation of the muscle depends on the restoring forces in the tissue while the stretch is actively imposed. The three phases of the receptor potential correspond to the initial burst, to the maintained discharge and to the reduced discharge that follows the end of a stretch.

Figure 4C (37) shows a receptor potential from a Pacinian corpuscle and with it the voltage pulse applied to the crystal transducer that was used to stimulate; impulse activity has been prevented with procaine. This potential differs in several respects from that found in the muscle spindle. There is no maintained plateau, the potential declining to zero once the peak is past. The shape of the receptor potential is nearly or completely the same whether excited by a short pulse of say 0.3 msec. duration, by the be-

ginning of a long pulse (fig. 4C) or by the end of a long pulse. As in the case of the muscle spindle these results are consistent with the results of experiments on the excitation of impulses by these receptors. These two examples illustrate contrasting types of receptor potential, the one associated with tonic behavior and the other with phasic behavior. In particular it is worth noting that a receptor potential, and with it an impulse, is set up by decompression of a Pacinian corpuscle, while relaxation of a muscle spindle is associated with a positive going receptor potential and an inhibition of the impulse discharge.

The receptor potential in figure 4D is that of a slowly adapting stretch receptor from the crayfish (27). This was recorded by means of a microelectrode in the cell body of the neuron which, in this instance, lies in the periphery close to the muscle; the receptor part of the cell lies still further to the periphery in the terminations that ramify in the receptor muscle. The record shows a steady depolarization well maintained throughout the stretch; there is no marked dynamic phase, even when the early part of the potential is not obscured by spikes, as in figure 4D, though there is some initial decline in the level of the depolarization;

at the end of the stretch the potential simply returns to its resting level. This difference from the muscle spindle potentials may be due to the effective velocity of the stretch. In this record, unlike those that are illustrated in figure 4A, B and C, the impulse discharge has not been interfered with and five spikes are shown arising from the receptor potential. It can be seen that each impulse is preceded by a relatively slow decrease in membrane potential (the prepotential) and that when this decrease reaches a critical value the impulse is discharged.

Receptor potentials are not confined to mechanically excited receptors. It has long been known that slow potentials could be obtained from the retina and from compound eyes (31). There has been reason to suppose that part at least of these potentials represented activity of the receptors themselves. Direct evidence that single ommatidia produce receptor potentials has now been obtained. In the single isolated ommatidium of *Limulus* (42) a receptor potential builds up rapidly when the ommatidium is illuminated. The potential then dies away, but with suitable recording conditions some depolarization appears to remain as long as the receptor is illuminated. The cessation of illumination is not accompanied by hyperpolarization. The olfactory mucosa of the frog produces slow potential changes when excited by air containing a suitable agent (78). The distribution in area and in depth of these potentials and their relative insensitivity to cocaine suggest that they are due to synchronous activity of the olfactory receptors.

Relation of Receptor Potentials to Impulse Initiation

There can be little doubt that receptor potentials are the immediate cause of the initiation of impulses. They always precede the impulse and the impulses appear when a critical potential has been reached. In the crustacean stretch receptor this critical level remains constant under a variety of conditions. With the frog's muscle spindle the critical potential depends on the frequency of the discharge, an observation which has been discussed above. In this preparation the frequency of discharge is linearly related to the amplitude of the receptor potential, a fact which suggests that the receptor potential is causally related to the impulse discharge. That such a relationship is not immediately visible in the results obtained from the crustacean stretch receptor does not mean, of course, that the frequency of the impulse discharge is not related to the amplitude of the receptor potential.

This is perhaps best explained by considering the steps involved in the initiation of the impulse. There are reasons, which will be considered below, for supposing that the impulses are initiated at a point which is near but not identical with that at which the receptor potential is generated. Currents due to the receptor potential will then flow through and discharge the membrane of the neighboring parts of the nerve fiber; this part of the membrane will develop local responses (48, 56), and if the membrane potential falls to the critical level an impulse will be discharged. This sequence of events is essentially the same as that found during the repetitive firing of a carcinus axon in response to an externally applied constant current (49). The slowly rising prepotentials of the crayfish stretch receptor (fig. 4D) are similar to those of the current excited carcinus axon (fig. 3). In both these examples the recording conditions are such that what is recorded is related to the membrane potential at the point of impulse initiation and not to the intensity of the charging current or the potential of the source supplying this current. In consequence what is seen is the passive discharging and local response of the membrane at the site of initiation followed by the impulse if and when the membrane potential falls to a critical level; this part of the membrane is then repolarized and the cycle starts again. The rate of discharging of the membrane and hence the frequency of the impulses depends on the intensity of the discharging current which in turn depends on the size of the receptor potential; this, however, is masked during a train of impulses. If the amplitude of the receptor potential could be measured during the impulse discharge a relationship between receptor potential amplitude and frequency would no doubt be found, and this might be similar to the relation between applied current and frequency in the carcinus axon. A relation was found in the case of the frog's muscle spindle because, between impulses, conditions were such that the full amplitude of the receptor potential was recorded; this was proved by subsequent procainization. Possible reasons for this behavior have already been considered.

Quantitative Relations Between Stimulus and Receptor Potential

The amplitudes of the receptor potentials of the muscle spindle and Pacinian corpuscle increase with the amplitude of the displacement up to a certain point and then level off to a maximum. An example is shown in figure 5. This particular example was ob-

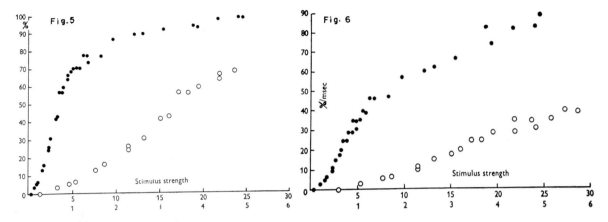

FIG. 5. Receptor potential amplitude in relation to the displacement of the mechanical stimulus with velocity constant in a Pacinian corpuscle. *Abscissa:* stimulus strength in arbitrary units. *Ordinate:* receptor potential amplitude as percentage of maximum. ○ same points as ●, but stimulus strength scale expanded five times. [From Gray & Sato (37).]

FIG. 6. Receptor potential rate of rise in relation to the displacement of the mechanical stimulus with velocity constant in a Pacinian corpuscle. *Abscissa:* stimulus strength in arbitrary units. *Ordinate:* receptor potential rate of rise as percentages of maximum amplitude per msec. ○ same points as ●, but stimulus strength scale expanded five times. [From Gray & Sato (37).]

tained from a Pacinian corpuscle (37), but a similar relationship has been observed in the muscle spindle of the frog (58). The value of the receptor potential reaches a constant level with large displacements; this is not conclusively proved by the published data, partly because of the limits to the size of stimulus used and partly, in the Pacinian corpuscle experiments, because the biggest stimuli introduced artifacts that tended to sum with the response. The question of the absolute amplitude of this maximum is considered in a later section.

The rate of rise of the potential is also related to the size of the exciting displacement (37). This is shown in figure 6. There is a change in the slope of this graph at that level of stimulus strength above which the amplitude increase is limited, but even above this point the rate of rise of the potential continues to increase with stimulus strength. That this is a genuine effect is supported by the fact that the time of rise of the potential continues to shorten over this range of stimuli. Since the recorded potential is a result of a potential change across the terminal membrane (whether or not the potential is actively generated at this site), the rate of rise of the receptor potential will reflect the rate at which current flows in to the capacity of this membrane. In other words these results suggest that the current across the membrane of the nerve fiber terminal continues to increase

as the stimulus increases even though the peak potential has reached a maximum value.

The amplitude of certain receptor potentials, for example those of the Pacinian corpuscle and the early phase of that of the frog's muscle spindle (fig. 4A), is also dependent on the velocity of the displacement. Indirect evidence shows that this is also true of other receptors responding to other forms of energy, for example thermal receptors (46). Figure 7 illustrates the change in relative amplitude of the receptor potential that accompanies change in the velocity of the mechanical stimulus, the amplitude of the stimulus being kept constant. It is immediately clear that the amplitude of the receptor potential, while independent of velocity at high values, is over a certain range closely related to the velocity of the stimulus. The 'angle' of this curve occurs, for the Pacinian corpuscle, at a compression velocity of about 1 mm per sec. (i.e. about 5 thresholds per msec.). This means that many physiological stimuli may be expected to lie within the velocity-sensitive range.

The time course of the receptor potential is in most instances dependent on the properties of the stimulus. It has already been pointed out that the rate of rise of the potential varies with stimulus amplitude and this change in the rate of rise of the potential change is accompanied by a change in the time of rise (37, 58). The rate of rise of the potential change may also be affected by the velocity (or comparable time

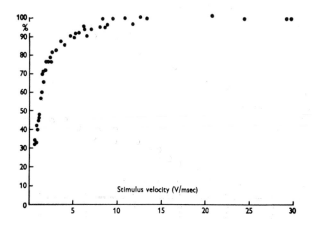

FIG. 7. Receptor potential amplitude in relation to the velocity of the mechanical stimulus with displacement constant in a Pacinian corpuscle. *Abscissa:* stimulus velocity in arbitrary units. *Ordinate:* receptor potential amplitude as percentage of maximum. [From Gray & Sato (37).]

function of the relevant form of energy) of the pulse used to excite; thus the rate of rise of the receptor potential of the frog's muscle spindle gets less as the velocity of the stimulus is reduced. In the Pacinian corpuscle there may be some change in rate of rise, but often there is no effect attributable specifically to the stimulus velocity; that is to say that, though the rate of rise of the potential change increases as its amplitude increases, the time course of a receptor potential of a given amplitude is often the same whether it is produced by a small displacement having a high velocity or by a larger displacement of lower velocity. In other words there are many mechanical pulses having different values of amplitude and velocity that are equivalent as 'stimuli'.

The duration of static receptor potentials, e.g. that of the frog's muscle spindle and the slowly adapting stretch receptor of the crayfish, is directly dependent on the duration of the applied force. The rate of decay of those potentials, which are velocity sensitive, may possibly depend on the duration of the applied force under certain circumstances; however, the rate of decay of the receptor potentials of the Pacinian corpuscle, the only end organ in which this particular point has been investigated, is normally independent of the duration of the stimulus (37). Off responses have the same time course as on responses.

Absolute Magnitude of the Receptor Potential

Receptor potentials reach a maximum at a certain value of stimulus strength. It is of considerable theo-

retical importance to know the absolute value of this potential change. Up to the present, it has been possible to make only a rough estimate of its value in the Pacinian corpuscle (20). This has been done by recording the external current flowing along the axon between the second and third nodes of Ranvier during activity of each of these nodes and of the receptor potential. By the use of blocking techniques and by taking differences, these components were obtained separately and measured. Under suitable conditions these currents will be proportional to the driving potentials. The results given are that the receptor potential amplitude is 59 per cent (n = 6, S.D. = 14 per cent) of the amplitude of the impulse at node 2 and 38 per cent (n = 5, S.D. = 17 per cent) of the amplitude of the impulse at node 3. The difference between the figures is due to a decline in the impulse amplitude as the terminal is approached. The attenuation per internode of the receptor potential is likely to be less than the 0.5 for large myelinated fibers of toads (92), so the absolute value of the receptor potential can be considered as of the same order of magnitude as the resting and action potentials. This conclusion is supported by results from the crayfish stretch receptor (27). The amplitude of the recorded receptor potential at threshold ranges from 8 to 25 mv depending on the type of receptor. It has been estimated that the loss due to passive conduction along the nerve fiber will have reduced the true value of the receptor potential by 20 to 80 per cent; also a maximum receptor potential must be appreciably greater than a threshold one. The ratio for the Pacinian corpuscle is 10 to 1 (37).

Summation of Receptor Potentials

If, during a maintained receptor potential, the receptor is subjected to increase in the stimulus strength the final value of the receptor potential will correspond to the final value of the stimulus. In this instance both the stimulus and the receptor potential have summed. With short pulse excitation it has been shown that summation of receptor potentials occurs after the stimulus is over (6, 37) as shown in figure 8. This summation appears similar to that found with endplate potentials and synaptic potentials. A special case of summation occurs when an 'on' response summates with an 'off' response (37). Summation of subthreshold receptor potentials can in this way set up impulses (6) and it seems likely that this process is of

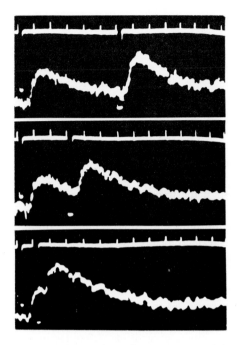

FIG. 8. Summation of receptor potentials with different intervals between stimuli. *Upper trace:* stimulus signal and time in msec. *Lower trace:* receptor potentials. [From Gray & Sato (37).]

considerable functional importance in determining maximum sensitivities. It is probably also important in determining the thresholds for sensation at different frequencies of vibration (83).

Depression

After the production of one receptor potential by a Pacinian corpuscle a subsequent one, occurring within a few milliseconds, is depressed. This is most easily seen with a preparation in which impulse activity has been prevented; it can then be seen that the depression of the test responses increases as the conditioning stimulus is increased and decreases as the interval between the conditioning and test pulses is increased (18, 37). Depression of the receptor potential is also caused by an impulse set up as a result of mechanical stimulation; this depression is much greater than that produced by a threshold receptor potential alone, though it does not appear to be as great as the depression caused by really large mechanical stimuli, whether an impulse is present or not. Antidromically conducted impulses also cause depression of a subsequent receptor potential, though for any given time interval after the impulse the depression is slightly less

than when the conditioning impulse is excited mechanically. At the time of writing there are a number of problems which require elucidation and on which the evidence is conflicting.

Depression has not been described for other receptor potentials, but this is not surprising as the stimulating conditions have been very different. It would be interesting to know, however, if any part of the initial decline of other receptor potentials were due to the same cause as this depression; the decline of the Pacinian corpuscle potential appears to be due to other and more rapid processes.

SITE OF IMPULSE INITIATION

There is evidence from the rapidly adapting type of stretch receptor of the crayfish that impulses are set up in the cell body (27). The records in these experiments were made through an electrode that was inside the cell body and it was found that the change of membrane potential required to excite an impulse was the same whether this change was brought about by a receptor potential spreading from the periphery or by current spread from an antidromically conducted impulse that had been blocked before it invaded the cell body. If the receptor potential set up impulses peripheral to the cell body, the apparent threshold value of the receptor potential, as recorded by this method, would be less than the true value by the amount of decrement occurring between the site of initiation and the cell body; this is in fact what occurs in the slowly adapting stretch receptors of the same species. Direct distortion of the cell body and the larger dendrites does not produce any potential changes; receptor potentials are produced only by stretching the muscle fibers in which the finer terminals of the neuron ramify. It therefore seems certain that while the impulses are initiated in the cell body of the rapidly adapting receptor, the receptor potentials are developed peripheral to this in the finer dendritic terminals.

A similar state of affairs appears to occur in the Pacinian corpuscle (20). In this receptor a straight nonmyelinated fiber of $2~\mu$ diameter runs down the central core of the corupscle; at the end of this central core the axon becomes myelinated. One node of Ranvier is regularly found inside the corpuscle about half way between the end of the central core and the point at which the axon leaves the capsule, and the second occurs near the latter point (86). The immediate surroundings of the nonmyelinated terminal have been shown to be specialized (85), and it must be supposed that it is in this region that the receptor potential is generated. By recording across a barrier surrounding the internode between the second and third nodes of Ranvier, it was found possible to record distinct phases of activity due to each of the first two nodes if the thresholds of these nodes were raised by anodal polarization. No phase of impulse activity could be found attributable to the nonmyelinated terminal even though thresholds were raised by an amount that, on theoretical grounds, should have been quite adequate to reveal such impulse activity if it existed. It therefore appears that after a mechanical stimulus the impulse is set up at the first node of Ranvier.

Indirect evidence that impulses are not initiated in the terminations of the afferent nerve fibers of certain other preparations has already been considered in the section on the effects of applied currents.

Not only is there evidence that impulses are, in some receptors at least, set up away from the terminals in which the receptor potentials are generated, but there is also evidence that such terminals are not invaded by antidromically conducted impulses. In the crayfish stretch receptor the receptor potential is not abolished by an antidromic action potential; if the impulse invaded the membrane that is involved in the production of the receptor potential one would expect a complete short circuiting of this membrane and the temporary abolition of the receptor potential (28). A similar observation has been made with the olfactory mucous membrane of the frog (78); stimulation of the olfactory nerve at different strengths and frequencies had no effect on the response of the olfactory membrane to an exciting substance. As has already been stated in the last section, an antidromic impulse causes slightly less depression of the receptor potential in the Pacinian corpuscle than does an impulse set up by a mechanical pulse. It has already been argued that an impulse initiated in this receptor by a mechanical stimulus starts at the first node of Ranvier; if an antidromically conducted impulse invaded the nonmyelinated terminal then it would be expected to produce a greater depression of the receptor potential. This is not the case and it seems, therefore, that antidromic impulses do not invade the nonmyelinated terminal (18).

Evidence that impulses set up by physiological stimuli to receptors do not start in the receptor region might simply mean that all-or-nothing impulses cannot occur there during receptor activity. That antidromic impulses do not invade the terminals might be a result of block at regions of low safety factor, though from parallel situations elsewhere this does not seem very likely. The most probable explanation of all these results is that those regions of membrane that are not invaded are different from the rest of the neuron surface and are not capable of producing a regenerative all-or-nothing response.

When a frog's muscle spindle is discharging at low frequency small all-or-nothing potentials can be seen. These are much smaller than the propagated impulse and may occur in a number of discrete sizes (57). They disappear if the frequency of discharge of full-size impulses is increased and also if the receptor is bombarded antidromically. After a full-size impulse there is always a delay before the next all-or-nothing event, whether full-size or small, but after one of the small all-or-nothing potentials the interval may be quite short. An explanation of these events may be that impulses are set up in the terminal branches of this type of receptor, but an impulse in a single branch is unable to pass the regions of low safety factor that occur where the branches join (57). A full-size impulse would then only be set up if there were sufficient synchrony in the activity of the terminal branches. On the same argument all-or-nothing activity in a single branch would fail to invade other branches and therefore would not depress their activity, while a full-size antidromic impulse would invade them all.

EFFECT OF PROCAINE AND SODIUM LACK ON
RECEPTOR POTENTIALS

In the frog's muscle spindle concentrations of procaine from 0.1 to 0.3 per cent abolish impulse activity but leave the receptor potential apparently unaffected. Higher concentrations of procaine reduce the amplitude of the receptor potential, affecting the static phase more than the dynamic (58). Similar results can be obtained with the Pacinian corpuscle of the cat. The impulse is abolished by concentrations of 0.1 to 0.5 per cent procaine in the bathing fluid, but if the procaine is washed out after about 10 min. there is no reduction in the amplitude of the receptor potential. Prolonged soaking in these concentrations causes a reduction of the receptor potential amplitude (37).

Similar effects can be obtained in both these preparations if they are soaked in sodium-free solutions. Ten minutes soaking in such a solution abolishes repetitive firing from the muscle spindle while thirty minutes is enough to abolish the initial spike (58).

Thirty minutes soaking is about the time needed to abolish the impulse from a Pacinian corpuscle preparation (37). In neither instance is the receptor potential effected.

The times of action of these solutions are remarkably similar for the two preparations and in both instances are very long compared with the time such solutions take to act on isolated single nerve fibers. It seems likely that diffusion times play an important part. It is known from direct experiments with labelled sodium, potassium and bromine that diffusion through the capsules of the Pacinian corpuscle is slow (38).

In the Pacinian corpuscle, however, it is possible to perfuse the receptor through the capillary loop that enters the corpuscle with the axon and ramifies in its proximal pole (19). Using a perfused preparation of this kind it is found that procaine in a concentration of 0.02 to 0.05 per cent in the perfusion fluid abolishes the impulse; 0.05 per cent and higher concentrations of procaine cause a reduction of the receptor potential amplitude. The abolition of the impulse occurs within 1.5 min.

If these preparations of the Pacinian corpuscle are perfused with a sodium-free solution the amplitude of the receptor potential falls and after about 20 min. the amplitude is constant and very small. This is illustrated in figure 9. This reduction in amplitude occurs whether the sodium chloride of the physiological solution is replaced by choline chloride or by sucrose. The effect, under favorable conditions, is reversible and recovery occurs on changing the perfusion fluid back to a physiological solution. When different concentrations of sodium are perfused it is found that the amplitude of the receptor potential, measured after a constant level has been reached, is related in a graded manner to the concentration of sodium. When sodium is absent there is a small remnant of the receptor potential; it is probable that this represents a genuine property of the receptor (19).

The receptor potentials of other types of receptor have also been found to be resistant to local anesthetics. Cocaine (0.5 per cent) applied externally has little or no effect on the potentials of the olfactory mucous membrane, though the same application abolishes the responses of the olfactory bulb (78). Procaine in concentrations of 0.05 to 0.1 per cent in the bathing fluid abolishes the impulses but not the receptor potential of the crayfish stretch receptor.

The position at the present time seems to be that while receptor potentials are more resistant than

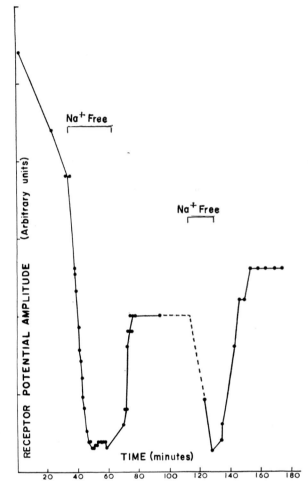

FIG. 9. Effect of perfusion with a sodium-free solution on receptor potential amplitude. *Abscissa:* time in min. *Ordinate:* receptor potential amplitude, arbitrary units. Sodium chloride was replaced with sucrose and changes in recording resistance have been corrected for. Impulses were abolished with procaine but were allowed to reappear during the period marked by the dotted line. [From Diamond, J., J. A. B. Gray & D. Inman. Unpublished figure.]

impulses to procaine, in the Pacinian corpuscle at least quite low concentrations (0.05 per cent) do affect the receptor potential if the diffusion barriers are avoided by perfusion. Perfusion also reveals that the receptor potential is almost completely abolished in the absence of sodium.

TRANSMISSION OF ENERGY TO THE RECEPTOR ELEMENTS

It has long been recognized that there are factors in the transmission of the exciting energy to the receptors that are important in the functioning of the more specialized sense organs. For example the ability of the cochlea of the higher vertebrates to act as a frequency analyzer is due to its mechanical properties (97). In compound eyes the distribution of absorbing pigments affects the distribution of light on the receptors so as to increase either the sensitivity or the discrimination of the eye (84). The same situation can be seen if the skin is taken as a whole. It has been shown that thermal receptors respond to the temperature at a given point at a given time (106); the distribution, both in time and space, of temperature in the skin, and consequently the nature of sensation aroused, will depend on the physical properties of the whole system. Another, and rather different, example of the effect of external physical factors is the decrease in the rate of adaptation of mechanical receptors in frog's skin that occurs as a result of stretching the skin (68).

All the examples mentioned in the last paragraph refer to the physical properties of a whole tissue or organ and their effect on the behavior of a population of receptors. The factors involved in the transmission of energy inside what is normally described as a single ending can also be of fundamental importance. The Pacinian corpuscle consists of a central core surrounded by thin laminae which form the boundaries of coaxial spheroids; the spaces between the laminae are filled with fluid. When the ending is squeezed displacements of the laminae occur and these can be recorded from photographs taken with short flashes (51, 52). During and immediately after the onset of a compression, relatively large displacements of the laminae occur (fig. 10 *left*); but these decline rapidly to a steady value which is maintained as long as the corpuscle is compressed. This maintained displacement varies with the position of the lamina measured, those near the periphery of the corpuscle showing large displacements while those near the center show none; figure 11 is a plot of maintained displacement against distance from the center of the corpuscle. The time course of the compression can be recorded and therefore the displacement that would be expected at any instant, if the response of the system were independent of time, can be calculated. Subtraction of

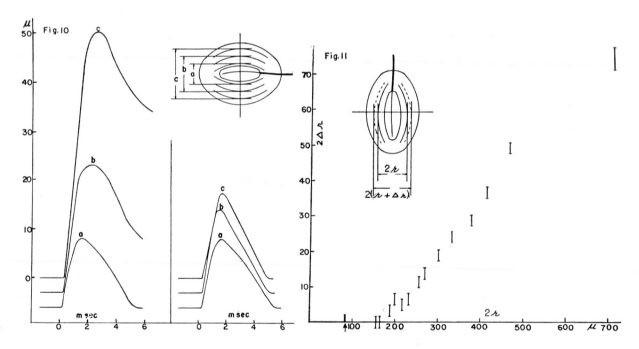

FIG. 10. Mechanical properties of the Pacinian corpuscle. *Left:* time course of displacements of 3 laminae (see inset) during a compression that started at $t = 0$, rose linearly to $t = 2.6$ msec. and then remained constant. *Right:* 'dynamic component' of displacement. See text. [By courtesy of S. J. Hubbard.]

FIG. 11. Mechanical properties of the Pacinian corpuscle. *Abscissa:* diameter in the transverse plane (2r). *Ordinate:* maintained displacement of laminae as functions of transverse diameters (2Δr). ↑ marks edge of the central core. Bars indicate ±2 × standard error. [By courtesy of S. J. Hubbard.]

this theoretical displacement from that observed (fig. 10 *left*) leaves a 'dynamic component' (fig. 10 *right*); it can be seen that this component is transmitted with less attenuation to the center of the end organ, and also that its time course is similar to that of a receptor potential (fig. 4C). It seems therefore that the rapid adaptation of this receptor is primarily a mechanical phenomenon. Since neither a change in axon length nor a bending of the axon has been detected, it seems that radial displacements of the axon itself, or of the tissues immediately surrounding it, are responsible for activating the receptor.

EFFECTS OF 'TRANSMITTER' SUBSTANCES

A number of investigations into the actions of acetylcholine, epinephrine, histamine and related compounds have been carried out. These investigations have in general had one of two objectives: one, to see if these substances are normally involved in the initiation of impulses by receptors; the other, to see if there is specialization of the membrane of the terminal part of the sensory axon.

Action of Acetylcholine

Acetylcholine has been shown to increase or initiate a discharge of impulses from a variety of sensory receptors. These include mechanical receptors from the skin of the cat and the dog (13, 23), from the cat's carotid sinus (17, 64), from the crayfish stretch receptor (102), the cat's tongue (62) and from the frog's skin (53); also thermal receptors in the cat's tongue (21) and chemical receptors of the cat's tongue (62) and carotid body (98). Succinylcholine has been found to increase the activity of mammalian muscle spindles (33). Finally acetylcholine has been found to effect and even initiate sensations in the human subject; these include pain (7, 44, 90) and thermal (10) sensations. Many of these investigations include control experiments designed to show that these are direct effects on the sensory pathway and are not secondary to contractions of smooth or striated muscle and do not result from excitation of the autonomic nervous system. It seems clear therefore that acetylcholine does have an action on some part of the sensory pathway, and since similar applications of acetylcholine to nerve fibers (53, 70) or to preganglionic nerve terminals (11, 14) are ineffective, it seems likely that these results represent a direct action of the substance on the receptor mechanism itself. The dosage and pharmacological pattern of these responses vary from one preparation to another. The most common picture is that represented by the experiments on the mechanical receptors of cats and frogs in which responses were recorded directly from the primary sensory nerve fibers. These responses are produced by doses of the same order of magnitude as those required to excite the skeletal neuromuscular junction. They are unaffected by atropine, but are blocked by curare or excess nicotine; smaller doses of nicotine behave like acetylcholine. The picture is thus very similar to that of the acetylcholine action at synapses and the skeletal neuromuscular junction. The main divergence from this pattern is that atropine blocks the acetylcholine effect in the crayfish stretch receptor (102). Atropine has also been found to raise the thresholds for the sensations of pain (90) and of cold (10) in the human; its mode of action in these instances is not at present clear.

There has been some difference of opinion as to whether acetylcholine can act independently or whether it merely sensitizes the receptor to the natural stimulus; it is possible that the action may be different in different preparations. In some preparations, as shown in figure 12, there is no doubt that acetylcholine can initiate a discharge (17) and that the action of acetylcholine summates with the physiological stimulus (17, 53). In the frog's skin acetylcholine does not effect the time course of excitation or recovery but does lower the threshold and increase the rate of adaptation (53). The most likely explanation of the action of this substance is that it depolarizes the membrane of the terminal portions of the sensory nerve fiber and that this action is confined to those parts that take part in the generation of the receptor potential. This conclusion might lead one to suppose that acetylcholine plays some part in the normal response to a physiological stimulus. This, however, seems very doubtful in the light of results obtained with blocking agents and anticholinesterases.

Action of Blocking Agents and Anticholinesterases

It has been stated above that the action of acetylcholine on sensory receptors is blocked by curare. It is also blocked by hexamethonium (17, 23), and large doses of nicotine (13). While these substances block the action of a subsequent dose of acetylcholine or nicotine, they have no effect, in most preparations, on the normal response to a physiological stimulus. Thus the mechanical receptors of the carotid sinus of the

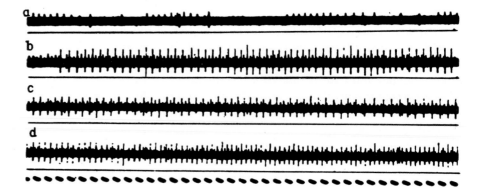

FIG. 12. Acetylcholine excitation of pressure receptors in the cat's carotid sinus. *a:* pressure in sinus, 25 mm Hg; injection of 0.5 ml saline. *b:* same pressure; injection of 0.5 ml of 10^{-4} g per ml acetylcholine. *c:* pressure, 111 mm Hg; 1.0 ml saline. *d:* same pressure; 1.0 ml acetylcholine 10^{-5} g per ml. Time, 0.1 sec. All records made 9.5 sec. after injection. [From Diamond (17).]

cat are still able to produce a normal frequency-pressure curve when perfused with 1 per cent hexamethonium (fig. 13), although the acetylcholine effect is blocked by a concentration of 10^{-6} hexamethonium (17). In the case of the carotid body, the chemical receptors of which appear particularly sensitive to acetylcholine, large doses of blocking agents diminish the response to low oxygen tensions (61).

Physostigmine does not affect the response of mechanical receptors in cat's and dog's skin to mechanical stimulation (13), nor does it alter the pressure-frequency relationship of the pressure receptors of the cat's carotid sinus (17). In two types of chemical receptor, anticholinesterases do enhance the response to the physiological stimulus; thus physostigmine and prostigmine increase the activity of chemical receptors of the cat's carotid sinus and prostigmine increases that of chemical receptors in the cat's tongue.

These results suggest that acetylcholine cannot be an intermediary in the normal process of excitation at many types of receptor. Against this evidence, it has been argued that the blocking agents do not have access to the critical region; however, all these agents block the acetylcholine effect and nicotine is both an exciting and blocking agent. Such arguments can only be valid if it is argued that there is a third region on the sensory pathway that differs from the main part of the neuron in its sensitivity to these substances and from the receptor region in that it is not involved in the production of receptor potentials. There is no evidence that acetylcholine is present in receptors (13), but there is evidence of the presence of cholin-esterase in the Pacinian corpuscle (8, 43) and Meissner's corpuscle (8); in the former this appears to be all pseudocholinesterase and its destruction does not appear to effect function in any way during an acute experiment (Diamond, J. & J. A. B. Gray, unpublished observations).

The arguments against the participation of acetylcholine as an intermediary in the normal process of excitation of some types of receptor do not exclude the possibility that local concentrations of acetylcholine may modify the excitability of receptors under physiological conditions. There is no evidence for such an action of acetylcholine, but there is evidence that a parallel action can occur with epinephrine.

Effects of Sympathetic Stimulation and Epinephrine

Stimulation of the sympathetic supply to the skin of the frog has been shown to increase the excitability of the cutaneous receptors (67). Stimulation of the sympathetic in these preparations increases the response to a standard mechanical stimulus applied to the skin surface; also if the skin is stretched but not otherwise stimulated mechanically so that there is no discharge in the afferent fibers, stimulation of the sympathetic may initiate a discharge. These results are paralleled by the application of epinephrine to the skin. The effects of epinephrine and sympathetic stimulation add to those of mechanical stimulation of the skin and the application of currents to it. These results have been obtained in preparations which have been subsequently sectioned and shown to contain no smooth muscle except that associated with the blood vessels

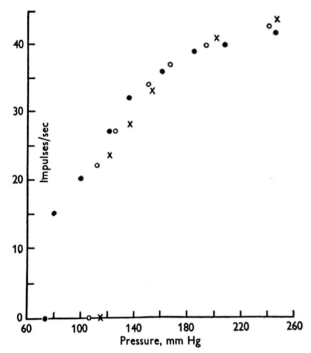

FIG. 13. Effects of hexamethonium on the pressure-response relationship of cat's carotid sinus receptors. *Abscissa:* Pressure in sinus in mm Hg. *Ordinate:* impulse frequency per sec. ○, ✕ normal curves, ● perfusion with 1 per cent hexamethonium. [From Diamond (17).]

and they appear to be due to a direct effect of epinephrine on the receptor. Epinephrine can also increase the size of the receptor potential of the Pacinian corpuscle in response to a given stimulus; this results in a lowering of the threshold (69). In the carotid sinus of the cat there is also an effect of epinephrine, but in this instance the effect appears to be secondary to its action on the muscle of the sinus (17, 63).

These results show that the activity of receptors may be modified by centrifugal activity. The idea is not, of course, new because the effects of stimulating the efferent fibers to the muscle spindles are well known (59). Centrifugal influences on the activity of the ear (29) and eye (31) are also under investigation, but whether or not these operate at receptor level is not yet clear. This topic is discussed also by Livingston (Chapter XXXI) on central effects on afferent activity in this work.

Other Substances

Histamine is a substance that has been much investigated in relation to receptors, especially those con-

cerned with the sensation of pain in man. Discussion of this problem belongs to another chapter. Many other agents have also been investigated (80) and special mention should be made of the sensitization of receptors by anesthetics (88, 101).

MINUTE STRUCTURE OF RECEPTORS

Electronmicroscopical studies have begun to throw some light on those structural relationships that may be of importance in explaining the genesis of the receptor potential in mechanical receptors. Sections of muscle spindles from the frog and of Pacinian corpuscles from the cat's mesentery have been investigated.

In the muscle spindle the finer branches of the afferent fiber which are nonmedullated lie in close relation to the intrafusal muscle fiber. These fibers, as they approach their termination, lose their Schwann cell sheath and come into direct contact with the muscle fibers; the continuation of the Schwann cell also runs in contact with the muscle but is separated from the axon. Smaller axons, which may represent the final terminations, are also seen in close relation to, but not in contact with, the muscle surface. The terminal parts of the afferent fibers contain many mitochondria, though with no apparent orientation (fig. 14A) (87).

In the Pacinian corpuscle the axon is nonmyelinated from the point at which it enters the central core (86). At this point it has a diameter of 2 μ which it maintains until it ends. Over the whole of this nonmyelinated section there are certain characteristic features (85) (fig. 14B). There appears to be no Schwann cell sheath; there are numerous mitochondria inside the nerve fiber arranged as a palisade around the fiber just beneath its surface membrane. The axon itself is not round but an ellipse in cross section and is surrounded by a complex cellular structure. This cellular structure is divided into two D-shaped parts separated from each other, in the middle by the axon, and on either side by gaps that continue the plane of the long axis of the elliptical nerve fiber.

At this stage of such investigations, the most striking feature of these results is that both types of mechanical receptors show the terminal axon without a Schwann cell sheath.

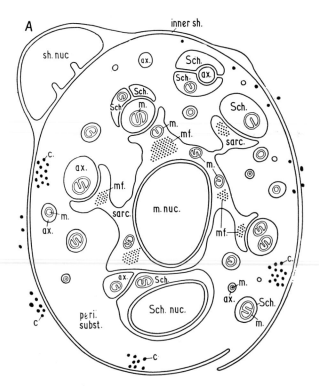

FIG. 14A. Diagram of a cross section of a portion of a frog's muscle spindle, at resting length, in the region of the sensory innervation. Inner sh., intrafusal muscle fiber inner sheath; m.nuc., muscle nuclei; mf., myofilaments; sarc., sarcoplasm; m., mitochondria; peri. subst., perimuscular substance; ax., axons; Sch., Schwann cells. [By courtesy of J. D. Robertson.]

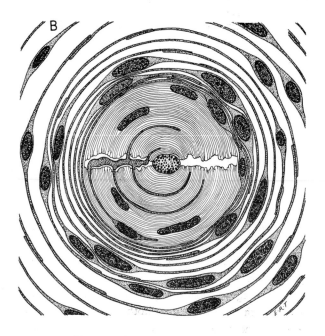

FIG. 14B. Diagram of a transverse section of the central core of a Pacinian corpuscle based on electronmicrographs. [By courtesy of A. Quilliam.]

HYPOTHESES CONCERNING THE MECHANISMS OF RECEPTORS

Many of our present ideas on the mechanisms involved in the initiation of impulses by receptors stem from the idea of nerve as a model sense organ (9). This concept involves two parts; first that a constant current would excite repetitive discharges in a nerve fiber, and secondly that such currents are produced in nerves under physiological conditions by the development of generator potentials in the receptors.

It is now known that many receptors produce receptor potentials and it is probably safe to assume that this is a generalization that applies widely. There is good evidence, which has already been considered, that these receptor potentials are the immediate cause of the impulse discharges. At present there is no evidence or need to suppose that the part of the afferent fiber in which the impulses are set up differs from other parts of nerve fibers in its response to a flow of current, whether this be a flow of current due to a receptor potential, to an external source or to the summated effects of both. There is evidence that has already been considered which indicates that in the Pacinian corpuscle impulses are set up at the first node of Ranvier and that the terminal nonmyelinated portion of the nerve fiber does not appear capable of conducting impulses. Similar conclusions can be drawn for the stretch receptor of the crayfish, though in this instance it is not possible to put such clear anatomical limits to impulse conduction. It may well be a general property of receptors that impulses are set up at a point central to the sensitive terminals by currents which are generated elsewhere. The summation noted between natural stimuli and externally applied currents would result from a passive summation of the discharging process in this region of the membrane.

The results just considered further suggest that the part of the nerve fiber that is unable to conduct a nerve impulse is the site at which the receptor potential is generated. This view is supported by the fact that the conditions under which receptor potentials have been recorded from the three mechanical receptors indicate that the current must have crossed the nerve fiber membrane peripheral to the point of recording. Estimates of the absolute value of the maximum receptor potentials suggest that it is unlikely that those currents that traverse the membrane of the nerve terminal are secondary to activity in an external source. Furthermore the fine structure of these terminals shows certain distinctive features. Thus, to take the specific example of the Pacinian corpuscle, the nonmyelinated terminal appears unable to conduct impulses and this same region is structurally specialized, in particular in not having a Schwann cell sheath. The estimated potential change that occurs across the membrane of this part of the fiber during a maximum receptor potential is of the same order of magnitude as the resting and action potentials. Many receptors are sensitive to acetylcholine, though it is not known whether or not the Pacinian corpuscle is sensitive. It is tempting to suggest that the inability to conduct impulses, the sensitivity to acetylcholine, the ability to produce receptor potentials and the absence of the Schwann cell sheath are all connected. There is not however enough evidence at present to support such an assertion.

Olfactory receptors appear to fall in line with much of what has been said in the last few paragraphs. To some extent photoreceptors may as well, but these considerations belong to other chapters. For the rest of this discussion consideration will be given almost entirely to simple mechanical receptors as it is from receptors of this type that the relevant evidence is at present available.

The next point to be considered is the immediate source of energy utilized in the production of a receptor potential. Maintained receptor potentials that last for minutes have been recorded; and if it is assumed that receptor potentials are responsible for the initiation of impulses in certain other receptors, for example the mechanical receptors in the carotid sinus of the cat, receptor potentials must remain constant for hours (17). Such potentials cannot be maintained across a biological membrane without the continual utilization of energy; such energy clearly cannot be provided by the work done during the deformation of the receptor. Since this is so, an internal store of energy must be available. It has already been argued that receptor potentials are generated across the membrane of the terminal portions of the afferent nerve fiber. Across this membrane is a store of energy in the form of the electrochemical gradients of the principal ions. It seems likely that it is this energy which is utilized during the activity of the receptor. In all slowly adapting receptors some such internal store of energy must be available; this does not necessarily follow for rapidly adapting processes such as the receptor potential of the Pacinian corpuscle and the dynamic phase of the muscle spindle potential. While it seems reasonable that all mechanical receptors of the relatively simple group under consideration should have fundamentally the same mechanism, there is no conclusive evidence that this is so. In fact it has been suggested (58) that the static and dynamic phases of the muscle spindle receptor potential may have different mechanisms.

During receptor activity the potential across this membrane must alter. One suggestion discussed as an explanation of the dynamic phase of the muscle spindle receptor potential was that the potential change was a result of a change of membrane capacity, the total charge remaining constant; it was, however, pointed out that there were quantitative difficulties in this explanation (58). Similar calculations for the Pacinian corpuscle demand large increases in surface area which are known not to occur. A more likely explanation of receptor activity is that ions transfer charge across the membrane by moving down their electrochemical gradients as a result of changes in the permeability of the membrane to one or more ion species (37, 58). If charge is to be transferred in such a direction as to explain the observed potential changes, cations must enter the fiber or anions leave it. The internal anions of nerve fibers are mostly large and less likely to move than the external cations which are almost entirely sodium. If the mechanism in question were something of the kind suggested, it would then be expected that the receptor potential would be nearly abolished in the absence of sodium. This is in fact what has been observed in the Pacinian corpuscle. Another observation that can be explained on this hypothesis is that the rate of rise of the receptor potential continues to increase with increasing stimulus strength at a level of stimulus strength at which the amplitude of the potential change remains practically constant. This can be explained by assuming that the permeability of the membrane continues to increase, so increasing the rate at which charge is transferred, while the final potential reached is limited by the equilibrium potentials of the ionic gradients concerned.

If the hypothesis put forward be accepted for the time being, the next problem is to consider how the changes of membrane permeability are brought about. This might be due to a distortion of the membrane or displacements in relation to surrounding structures, it might be due to a change of pressure in and around the axon or there may be chemical intermediaries outside or inside the axon. The last alternative still leaves the problem of how the mechanical energy produces the chemical intermediaries. At present there are no grounds for choosing between these mechanisms. However, if there are chemical intermediaries in the Pacinian corpuscle, the time course of their action (the latency often being less than 0.2 msec.) and their ability to function at room temperature (37) show that they have quite different properties from mammalian synaptic transmitters. Other evidence has been presented in an earlier section which suggests that at many mechanical receptors acetylcholine does not act as a chemical transmitter.

The adaptation of receptors is a subject that has stimulated many hypotheses (47, 74). Until recently these have been based mostly on the concept that the adaptation of receptors is closely related to the accommodation of nerve fibers. It would certainly be expected that this factor would play a part if impulses are set up in the nerve fiber as a result of currents generated by receptor activity in the terminals. This factor cannot be entirely discounted, but there are now very good reasons for supposing that other factors may be more important. The time courses of all the receptor potentials so far observed are in general agreement with the corresponding time courses of the impulse discharge. Thus the short receptor potential of the Pacinian corpuscle corresponds to the single impulse produced by relatively large stimuli, the dynamic and static phases of the receptor potential of the muscle spindle correspond to the initial high frequency burst and the maintained discharge of impulses and the receptor potentials found in the two types of stretch receptor investigated in the crayfish correspond to the fast and slow adaptation of the two endings. The adaptation of the receptor potential may simply reflect changes in the mechanical events going on in the

terminals. This seems to be the case in the Pacinian corpuscle where only a brief wave of distortion can be found in the central core during a maintained deformation of the outside of the endorgan. In the crustacean stretch receptors, the difference between the slow and fast cells has been attributed to differences in the mechanical attachments between the dendrites of the two types of cell and the muscle fibers in which they ramify (27). The change in the rate of adaptation of receptors in frog skin, when the skin is stretched, is another example of the importance of mechanical factors. It is impossible to say whether or not such factors can account for the whole phenomenon of adaptation of the receptor potential. It is possible that there may be some mechanism that reduces the effectiveness of a stimulus as time passes; such a mechanism might conceivably be related to the depression of the receptor potential observed in the Pacinian corpuscle.

Many of our ideas on the mechanisms of receptors are at the present time speculative. Definite ideas on these problems may develop as work goes deeper into the mechanisms of those few receptors which are particularly well adapted for such investigations. Also when results, that have already been obtained on some receptors, are repeated or contradicted by work on other types, it may be possible to say how far we may generalize from such results as have been obtained.

REFERENCES

1. ADRIAN, E. D. *The Basis of Sensation.* London: Christophers, 1928.
2. ADRIAN, E. D. *Proc. Roy. Soc., London, ser. B.* 109: 1, 1931.
3. ADRIAN, E. D., McK. CATELL AND H. HOAGLAND. *J. Physiol.* 72: 377, 1931.
4. ADRIAN, E. D. AND Y. ZOTTERMAN. *J. Physiol.* 61: 151, 1926.
5. ADRIAN, E. D. AND Y. ZOTTERMAN. *J. Physiol.* 61: 465, 1926.
6. ALVAREZ-BUYLLA, R. AND J. RAMIREZ DE ARELLANO. *Am. J. Physiol.* 172: 237, 1953.
7. ARMSTRONG, D., R. M. L. DRY, C. A. KEELE AND J. W. MARKHAM. *J. Physiol.* 120: 236, 1953.
8. BECKETT, EVELYN B., G. H. BOURNE AND W. MONTAGNA. *J. Physiol.* 134: 202, 1956.
9. BERNHARD, C. G., R. GRANIT AND C. R. SKOGLUND. *J. Neurophysiol.* 5: 55, 1942.
10. BING, H. I. AND A. P. SKOUBY. *Acta physiol. scandinav.* 21: 286, 1950.
11. BRINK, F., D. W. BRONK AND M. LARRABEE. *Ann. New York Acad. Sc.* 47: 457, 1946.
12. BRONK, D. W. AND G. STELLA. *Am. J. Physiol.* 110: 708, 1935.
13. BROWN, G. L. AND J. A. B. GRAY. *J. Physiol.* 107: 306, 1948.
14. BROWN, G. L. AND F. C. MACINTOSH. *J. Physiol.* 96 10P, 1939.
15. BULLOCK, T. H. AND F. P. J. DIECKE. *J. Physiol.* 134: 47, 1956.
16. DAVIS, H., I. TASAKI AND R. GOLDSTEIN. *Cold Spring Harbor Symp.* 17: 143, 1952.
17. DIAMOND, J. *J. Physiol.* 130: 513, 1955.
18. DIAMOND, J., J. A. B. GRAY AND D. R. INMAN. *J. Physiol.* 141: 117, 1958.
19. DIAMOND, J., J. A. B. GRAY AND D. R. INMAN. *J. Physiol.* 142: 382, 1958.
20. DIAMOND, J., J. A. B. GRAY AND M. SATO. *J. Physiol.* 133: 54, 1956.
21. DODT, E., A. P. SKOUBY AND Y. ZOTTERMAN. *Acta physiol. scandinav.* 28: 101, 1953.
22. DODT, E. AND Y. ZOTTERMAN. *Acta physiol. scandinav.* 26: 345, 1952.
23. DOUGLAS, W. W. AND J. A. B. GRAY. *J. Physiol.* 119: 118, 1953.
24. ECKER, A. AND R. WIEDERSHEIN. *Anatomie des Frosches.* Braunschweig: Vieweg, 1896.
25. EDWARD, C. *J. Physiol.* 127: 636, 1955.
26. ERLANGER, J. AND E. A. BLAIR. *Am. J. Physiol.* 121: 431, 1938.

27. EYZAGUIRRE, C. AND S. W. KUFFLER. *J. Gen. Physiol.* 39: 87, 1955.

28. EYZAGUIRRE, C. AND S. W. KUFFLER. *J. Gen. Physiol.* 39: 121, 1955.

29. GALAMBOS, R. *XXth Internat. Physiol. Cong., Abstracts of Communications:* 321, 1956.

30. GRANIT, R. *Sensory Mechanisms of the Retina.* London: Oxford, 1947.

31. GRANIT, R. *Receptors and Sensory Perception.* New Haven: Yale, 1955.

32. GRANIT, R. AND C. R. SKOGLUND. *J. Neurophysiol.* 6: 337, 1943.

33. GRANIT, R., S. SKOGLUND AND S. THESLEFF. *Acta physiol. scandinav.* 28: 134, 1953.

34. GRAY, J. A. B. AND J. L. MALCOLM. *Proc. Roy. Soc., London, ser. B* 137: 96, 1950.

35. GRAY, J. A. B. AND J. L. MALCOLM. *J. Physiol.* 115: 1, 1951.

36. GRAY, J. A. B. AND P. B. C. MATTHEWS. *J. Physiol.* 114: 454, 1951.

37. GRAY, J. A. B. AND M. SATO. *J. Physiol.* 122: 610, 1953.

38. GRAY, J. A. B. AND M. SATO. *J. Physiol.* 129: 594, 1955.

39. HAGEN, E., H. KNOCKE, D. C. SINCLAIR AND G. WEDDELL. *Proc. Roy. Soc., London. ser. B* 141: 279, 1953.

40. HARTLINE, H. K., N. A. COULTER AND H. G. WAGNER. *Fed. Proc.* 11: 65, 1952.

41. HARTLINE, H. K., AND C. H. GRAHAM. *J. Cell & Comp. Physiol.* 1: 277, 1932.

42. HARTLINE, H. K., H. G. WAGNER AND E. F. MacNICHOL. *Cold Spring Harbor Symp.* 17: 125, 1952.

43. HEBB, CATHERINE AND K. J. HILL. *Quart. J. Exper. Physiol.* 40: 168, 1955.

44. HELLAUER, H. P. *Ztschr. vergl. Physiol.* 32: 303, 1950.

45. HENSEL, H. AND Y. ZOTTERMAN. *J. Physiol.* 115: 16, 1951.

46. HENSEL, H. AND Y. ZOTTERMAN. *Acta physiol. scandinav.* 23: 291, 1951.

47. HOAGLAND, H. *Cold Spring Harbor Symp.* 4: 347, 1936.

48. HODGKIN, A. L. *Proc. Roy. Soc., London. ser. B* 126: 87, 1938.

49. HODGKIN, A. L. *J. Physiol.* 107: 165, 1948.

50. HOGG, B. M. *J. Physiol.* 84: 250, 1935.

51. HUBBARD, S. J. *J. Physiol.* 132: 23P, 1956.

52. HUBBARD, S. J. *J. Physiol.* 141: 198, 1958.

53. JARRETT, A. S. *J. Physiol.* 133: 243, 1956.

54. JIELOF, R., A. SPOOR AND H. DE VRIES. *J. Physiol.* 116: 137, 1952.

55. KATSUKI, Y. AND S. YOSHINO. *Jap. J. Physiol.* 2: 219, 1952.

56. KATZ, B. *J. Physiol.* 106: 66, 1947.

57. KATZ, B. *J. Physiol.* 111: 248, 1950.

58. KATZ, B. *J. Physiol.* 111: 261, 1950.

59. KUFFLER, S. W., C. C. HUNT AND J. P. QUILLIAM. *J. Neurophysiol.* 14: 29, 1951.

60. LANDGREN, S. *Acta physiol. scandinav.* 26: 1, 1952.

61. LANDGREN, S., G. LILJESTRAND AND Y. ZOTTERMAN. *Acta physiol. scandinav.* 26: 264, 1952.

62. LANDGREN, S., G. LILJESTRAND AND Y. ZOTTERMAN. *Acta physiol. scandinav.* 30: 105, 1954.

63. LANDGREN, S., E. NEIL AND Y. ZOTTERMAN. *Acta physiol. scandinav.* 25: 24, 1952.

64. LANDGREN, S., A. P. SKOUBY AND Y. ZOTTERMAN. *Acta physiol. scandinav.* 29: 381, 1953.

65. LELE, P. P. *J. Physiol.* 126: 191, 1954.

66. LELE, P. P., G. WEDDELL AND C. M. WILLIAMS. *J. Physiol.* 126: 206, 1954.

67. LOEWENSTEIN, W. R. *J. Physiol.* 132: 40, 1956.

68. LOEWENSTEIN, W. R. *J. Physiol.* 133: 588, 1956.

69. LOEWENSTEIN, W. R. AND R. ALTAMIRANO-ORREGO. *Nature, London* 178: 1292, 1956.

70. LORENTE DE NÓ, R. *J. Cell. & Comp. Physiol.* 24: 85, 1944.

71. LÖWENSTEIN, O. *J. Physiol.* 127: 104, 1955.

72. LÖWENSTEIN, O. AND A. SAND. *Proc. Roy. Soc., London. ser. B* 129: 256, 1940.

73. MARUHASHI, J., K. MIZUGUCHI AND I. TASAKI. *J. Physiol.* 117: 129, 1952.

74. MATTHEWS, B. H. C. *J. Physiol.* 71: 64, 1931.

75. MATTHEWS, B. H. C. *J. Physiol.* 78: 1, 1933.

76. MÜLLER, J. *Handbuch der Physiologie des Menschen.* Coblenz: J. Holscher, 1840. (Parts translated by W. Baly. *The Physiology of the Senses, Voice and Muscular Motion.* London: Taylor Walton & Maberly, 1848.)

77. MURRAY, R. W. *J. Physiol.* 134: 408, 1956.

78. OTTOSON, D. *Acta physiol. scandinav.* 35: Suppl. 122, 1956.

79. OTTOSON, D. AND G. SVAETICHIN. *Cold Spring Harbor Symp.* 17: 165, 1952.

80. PAINTAL, A. S. *XXth Internat. Physiol. Cong., Abstracts of Reviews:* 78, 1956.

81. PARRACK, H. O. *Am. J. Physiol.* 130: 481, 1940.

82. PFAFFMANN, C. *J. Cell. & Comp. Physiol.* 17: 243, 1941.

83. PIÉRON, H. *The Sensations. Their Functions, Processes and Mechanisms.* London: Muller, 1952.

84. PROSSER, C. L. (editor). *Comparative Animal Physiology.* Philadelphia: Saunders, 1950.

85. QUILLIAM, T. A. *Fed. Proc.* 15: 147, 1956.

86. QUILLIAM, T. A. AND M. SATO. *J. Physiol.* 129: 167, 1955.

87. ROBERTSON, J. D. *Proc. 1st European Reg. Conf. Electron Microsc.:* 197, 1957.

88. ROBERTSON, J. D., A. A. B. SWAN AND D. WHITTERIDGE. *J. Physiol.* 131: 463, 1956.

89. SKOGLUND, C. R. *Acta physiol. scandinav.* 4: Suppl. 12, 1942.

90. SKOUBY, A. P. *Acta physiol. scandinav.* 24: 174, 1951.

91. SVAETICHIN, G. *Acta physiol. scandinav.* 39: Suppl. 134, 1956.

92. TASAKI, I. *Nervous Transmission.* Springfield: Thomas, 1953.

93. TASAKI, I. *J. Neurophysiol.* 17: 97, 1954.

94. TASAKI, I. AND M. SAKAGUCHI. *Jap. J. Physiol.* 1: 7, 1950.

95. VAN LEEUWEN, S. *J. Physiol.* 109: 142, 1949.

96. VON BÉKÉSY, G. *J. Acoust. Soc. Am.* 24: 72, 1952.

97. VON BÉKÉSY, G. AND W. A. ROSENBLITH. In: *The Handbook of Experimental Psychology,* edited by S. S. Stevens. New York: Wiley, 1951.

98. VON EULER, U. S., G. LILJESTRAND AND Y. ZOTTERMAN. *Acta physiol. scandinav.* 1: 383, 1941.

99. WEDELL, G. *Ann. Rev. Psychol.* 6: 119, 1955.

100. WEVER, E. G. AND C. W. BRAY. *Proc. Nat. Acad. Sc., Wash.* 16: 344, 1930.

101. WHITTERIDGE, D. AND E. BÜLBRING. *J. Pharmacol.* 81: 340, 1944.

102. WIERSMA, C. A. G., E. FURSHPAN AND E. FLOREY. *J. Exper. Biol.* 30: 136, 1953.

103. ZOTTERMAN, Y. *Skandinav. Arch. Physiol.* 75: 105, 1936.

104. ZOTTERMAN, Y. *J. Physiol.* 95: 1, 1939.

105. ZOTTERMAN, Y. *J. Physiol.* 102: 313, 1943.

106. ZOTTERMAN, Y. *Ann. Rev. Physiol.* 15: 357, 1953.

CHAPTER V

Synaptic and ephaptic transmission[1]

HARRY GRUNDFEST | *Department of Neurology, College of Physicians and Surgeons, Columbia University, New York City*

CHAPTER CONTENTS

[1] The researches at the author's laboratory were supported in part by funds from the following sources: Muscular Dystrophy Associations of America, National Institutes of Health (B-389 C), National Science Foundation and United Cerebral Palsy Associations.

b) Polarized ephaptic transmission
Evolutionary Aspects of Ephaptic Transmission
Quasiartificial Synapses

CONTRACTION OF A MUSCLE when an apparently un-
reactive nerve is stimulated, the problem of transmission in its most obvious form, challenged the ingenuity of early physiologists. Electricity quickly
became a relatively familiar force after the invention
of the Leyden jar and was invoked in Galvani's
theory (84). Electric fluid supplied from the central
nervous system, he said, charged the interior of a
muscle as the Leyden jar is charged by an electrostatic machine. Contraction was caused by discharge
of this electrical fluid when the muscle and its nerve
were connected by a metallic arc. The 'discharge
hypothesis' formulated by Krause and Kühne in
the 1860's encompassed as well the data obtained
in the two decades after the foundation of electrophysiology by du Bois-Reymond and others. "A
nerve only throws a muscle into contraction by
means of its currents of action," said Kühne in his
Croönian Lecture of 1888 (133). This electric theory
of transmission (fig. 1) was dominant until very recent
times (98) despite the questions and doubts raised by
du Bois-Reymond himself in 1874 (55), and by Bernstein in 1882 (20). The former suggested that another
mechanism, secretion by the nerve of some chemical
agent, might be the cause of neuromuscular excitation.

Transmission in the central nervous system hardly
offered a problem to the physiologists of the nineteenth century, chiefly for one reason. Nerve and
muscle are distinctly different tissues performing
different functions and obviously joined together at a
specialized region, the endplate. Connections between
nerve cells, however, were thought to be continuous,
the neurofibrils of one penetrating into the body of
another. This reticular theory of Gerlach was challenged only at the end of the nineteenth century when
His, Kölliker and pre-eminently Ramón y Cajal
proposed the neuron theory (169), so named by Waldeyer. Sherrington, in 1897 (181), applied the term
synapse to the region of contact or contiguity at which
transmission takes place from the presynaptic nerve
cell to another, the postsynaptic cell. The present
chapter will use these terms in their general context,
including in this sense the neuromuscular and neuro-
glandular junctions.

The occurrence of demonstrable barriers at the
contacts between neurons, different staining qualities

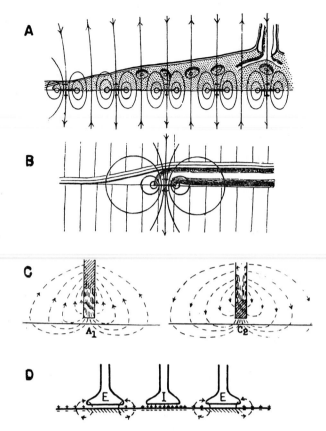

FIG. 1. Models for electrical transmission. *A*, *B*: du Bois-
Reymond's 'modified discharge hypothesis' of 1874 for the
neuromuscular junction. *A*: The current loops produced at a
large endplate surface, which is itself not part of the muscle
fiber, he thought would cause both anodal and cathodal depolarizations. The current fields, indicated by the arrows,
would thus alternate between excitant and depressant actions.
B: du Bois-Reymond suggested that a geometrical arrangement
which excited the muscle at a point contact would be more
effective. [From du Bois-Reymond (55).] *C*: Eccles' model of
1946 proposed an essentially similar arrangement. Before the
impulse of the presynaptic fiber had arrived at the synapse
(*left*), there would be a hyperpolarizing (inward) current flow
in the synaptic membrane. When the impulse reached its
terminus (*right*) it would cause depolarization and excitation.
[From Eccles (57).] *D*: Electrical model for inhibitory synaptic
effects showing interaction of excitatory (E) and inhibitory (I)
synapses. The latter were assumed to be the terminals of a short
axon, Golgi II cell which developed a nonpropagating spike at
its soma. The anodal focus caused by the I knob was supposed
to depress the cathodal excitatory effects of the E knobs. Current flows are simplified in the diagram, loops which are supposed to diminish their excitatory effect are shown only at the
edges of each E knob. [From Brooks *et al.* (28).]

that indicate histochemical differences between pre-
and postsynaptic units and the independent existence
of the latter after destruction of the former (i.e.

absence of transneuronal degeneration) constituted the evidence brought forward by Ramón y Cajal and others in support of the neuron theory.

When the neuron theory became accepted, the electrical theory of transmission, essentially as formulated by Kühne for the neuromuscular synapse, was also generally adopted (cf. 45, 57, 140). Nevertheless, Sherrington's life-long study of the central nervous system emphasized that the physiological actions of the latter were dominated by the properties of synaptic transmission. These, he thought (183), were in many respects fundamentally different from the properties of conductile activity of nerve or muscle fibers, in which all-or-none impulses, spikes, are propagated by electrical local circuit excitation within the confines of a single cell, even though the latter may be very long in extent. A Russian school of physiology headed by Ukhtomsky (cf. 176) also maintained that central nervous phenomena could not be explained solely in terms of all-or-none activity.

The neuron theory incorporates and gives physiological meaning to the doctrine of polarized conduction which is embodied in the Bell-Magendie Law. The presynaptic terminals impinge upon the synaptic, or subsynaptic (cf. 60) membrane of the postjunctional cell with various types of contacts. These are located chiefly, but not exclusively, at the dendrites and soma of neurons, and Ramón y Cajal distinguished the different sites of contact as axodendritic and axosomatic synapses (cf. 169). Contacts between the nerve fibers and the effector cells, muscle or gland, are also made at specialized regions, those of muscle fibers being termed endplates, as noted above. Impulses afferent in a prefiber evoke activity in the postjunctional cell. If the cell is a neuron, its junctional activity may result in a spike which propagates along the latter's axon. At the terminals of this axon, a new transfer may then take place to another neuron or to an effector cell. In some instances unidirectional progression is apparently invalidated, but the general mechanism of these cases is probably by ephaptic transmission (10). This appears to be fundamentally different from synaptic transmission and will be discussed in the last section of this chapter. One recently discovered case of unidirectional conduction (83) produced by an electrical local circuit mechanism will also be discussed at that time.

The concept of unidirectional synaptic transmission rpemitted Ramón y Cajal to deduce many functional aprrperties of the central nervous system from anatomloic data (168). Changes that occur in gross and fine structure, in histochemical properties and in physio-

logical behavior after extirpation or damage of specific elements also give clues to function. The information obtained by these methods relates chiefly, however, to the study of integrative activity which is the subject of later chapters.

While it, too, bears largely on integrative functions, the analysis of reflexes as exemplified in Sherrington's work (cf. 44, 182) nevertheless also provides data on the synaptic processes themselves and discloses phenomena such as cumulative, long-lasting excitatory and inhibitory states. These two synaptic properties endow the central nervous system with its remarkable flexibility and variety of responsiveness. Both characteristics may also be present in simpler peripheral synaptic organizations and are commonly found in the peripheral synaptic structures of invertebrates. Sherrington's basic method, stimulation of selected pathways and study of their effects and interactions, has been refined by application of modern electrophysiological techniques. The combination has given information on the effects of different synaptic inflows, their relative potencies, the temporal and spatial distribution of excitatory and inhibitory actions, particularly in the spinal cord (cf. 140; and later chapters in this volume).

The electrophysiological study of single unit pathways such as nerve-muscle or neuron-neuron provides still more detailed and intimate information on synaptic mechanisms (cf. 62). Microelectrode recording, either from the vicinity of single cells or from their interior, is a recent extension of the technique which can provide the most definitive information (52, 59, 60, 95, 97). In all cases, transmissional activity is found to be associated with a special type of electrical response, the postsynaptic potential or p.s.p. The transmissional electrogenesis at the endplates of skeletal muscle fibers is known as the endplate potential (e.p.p.). Basically, however, the properties of e.p.p.'s are identical with those of p.s.p.'s. A presynaptic potential, occurring at the terminals of dorsal root fibers, has also been described but from indirect evidence only (140).

Pharmacological data provide much of the oldest evidence that synaptic transmission is different from the conductile process. Claude Bernard (18) found that curare, the Indian arrow poison, blocked excitation of a muscle by its nerve. The muscle and nerve individually retain their conductile properties, and the primary effect of the drug is on the transmission process. Attempts to account for the synaptic blockade in terms of electrical transmission were not successful (cf. 98). A host of other chemicals exert actions chiefly wherever synapses occur. These junctional regions also appear to have special biochemical requirements. Transmission, for example, is more easily disrupted by anoxia than is conduction. Pharmacological and biochemical tools, particularly in combination with the techniques of electrophysiology, provide additional data on the processes of synaptic transmission (cf. 96, 99–101, 161–166).

A challenge to the electrical theory was offered by that of chemical transmission which evolved chiefly from the work of Dale, Loewi, Cannon and their associates (cf. 150, 177). According to this view, activity of a presynaptic fiber releases at its synaptic terminals a chemical transmitter agent. That substance excites the electrical activity of the postjunctional cell. By repetition of the secretory process at the terminals of the latter, a new action is started in the next unit of a transmissional chain. The present chapter adopts this view.

The conclusion that synaptic transmission obligatorily involves a chemical mediator derives from a hypothesis based upon a recent examination of data on available synaptic systems (97). All possess a common constellation of properties that are shown in table 1 and discussed in the portion of this chapter devoted to synaptic electrogenesis. The entire group of these distinguishing characteristics appears to be referable to a single fundamental property of synaptic electrogenic membrane, namely that its activity is not initiated by an electrical stimulus. Thus, there arises a profound distinction between the conductile activity of axons or muscle fibers and the transmissional activity at synapses. The former is electrically excitable by an applied stimulus or by the internally generated local circuit of activity. The latter is electrically inexcitable and must be evoked by a specific stimulus which in the context of synaptic structure must be a chemical excitant, or transmitter agent, released by the active presynaptic nerve fibers.

The currently used definition of synapses is still essentially as it developed with Sherrington and Ramón y Cajal, a junction in contiguity between anatomically distinct cells across which activity is nevertheless transmitted, but only in one direction, from the presynaptic cell to the postsynaptic. Many other specifications are now available to distinguish transmissional activity from conductile or ephaptic, and these appear to derive from the one feature, that synaptic activity is electrically inexcitable.

NATURE OF POSTSYNAPTIC POTENTIALS

The earlier studies of p.s.p.'s were made with external recordings from muscle endplates (59, 62, 63, 86), sympathetic ganglia (56) and the spinal cord (57, 58). The muscle synapses being more easily accessible, it was most intensively studied both electrophysiologically and pharmacologically (cf. 62). More recently, this and many other varieties of synapses have been investigated with intracellular recording (cf. 52, 59, 60, 68, 95, 97), and a reasonably coherent and satisfactory description of the principles of synaptic electrogenesis is now available.

Generation Sites of Postsynaptic Potentials

As noted above, p.s.p.'s are associated with the occurrence of transmissional activity at junctions between a pre- and a postunit. Only in a few systems (e.g. neuromuscular and squid giant axon synapses) is the junction confined to a clearly delineated area of the postunit. In these cases it is found that the p.s.p. is largest within the region of the junction and decreases rapidly as the distance of the recording electrode from the junction increases (fig. 2). The form of the potential is also distorted in the manner characteristic of electrotonic spread (114, 141), both facts indicating that the site at which electrogenesis occurs is confined to the synaptic region. As will be described below, the nonpropagating, 'standing' response of p.s.p.'s is a consequence of electrical inexcitability.

When the p.s.p. is recorded with a microelectrode, at first externally and then internally, the sign of the p.s.p. reverses when the electrode penetrates the cell. Like the spike, which also undergoes reversal of sign under the same conditions, the neurally evoked potential is produced at the excitable electrogenic membrane of the postjunctional cell, hence the term p.s.p.

Molecular Structures of Differently Excitable Membranes

The structures of the membranes that are involved in synaptic activity are not as yet known. The presynaptic terminals occur in an immense variety of shapes and sizes. In some of these electron microscopy has indicated the presence of vesicles (54, 174). The latter have been interpreted (cf. 52) as sites of concentration of chemical mediators which presumably are formed in the nerve fibers and ejected during activity into an extracellular synaptic space of about 100 Å. The postsynaptic sites which respond specifically to the chemical transmitter agents cannot, at present, be differentiated structurally from those of electrically excitable membranes. This is perhaps best exemplified

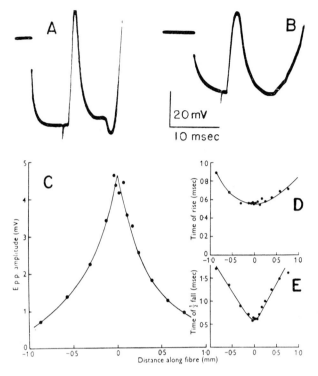

FIG. 2. Some properties of depolarizing postsynaptic potentials. *A, B:* The intracellularly recorded e.p.p. of a mammalian muscle fiber is evoked by neural stimuli during hyperpolarization of the muscle fiber membrane through another intracellular electrode. The impaled hyperpolarized fiber did not respond with a spike or contraction, but others unaffected by the polarizing current and excited by the neural volley contracted. The resulting movement pulled the microelectrode out of the tested muscle fiber producing the artifact seen at the end of each record. The response in *B* is smaller than that in *A,* partly because it is generated at a less hyperpolarized membrane as is described in the text. However, it is also broader than the response in *A,* indicating that the recording microelectrode was probably some distance from the focus of the e.p.p. The effects of recording at various distances from this focus are shown in *C, D* and *E.* The amplitude of the e.p.p. falls sharply (*C*); the rising phase is prolonged somewhat (*D*) and the falling phase even more (*E*) as the electrode is moved farther from the focus. [From Boyd & Martin (23).]

by electron microscopic studies of eel electroplaques (95).

These cells possess three functionally distinct types of membrane. One major surface is composed of membrane that does not respond electrogenically to any type of stimulation and has a very low electrical resistance. The other major surface of each cell is diffusely innervated and, presumably only under the presynaptic terminals, there is excitable membrane of the synaptic type which responds only to neural or to chemical stimuli. Intermingled with this electri-

cally inexcitable membrane component is one that is electrically excitable and produces a spike. Electron microscopy has as yet not been able to discern differences between the two different components of the excitable membrane, nor between their structures and those of the nonresponsive membrane (95, 143).

Two functionally quite different junctions, in squid and crayfish respectively, appear to be similar when observed by electron microscopy (175). However, that activating the giant axon of squid is electrically inexcitable and thus conforms to the extended definition of synapses given above. On the other hand, the junction between a medial giant fiber and the motor giant axon of the crayfish (83), as will be discussed below, appears to resemble the ephaptic junctions of septate giant axons (125).

The inability of present day microscopic techniques to differentiate the structures of membranes which differ profoundly in their functional properties indicates that the differences which determine these properties must be at the molecular level. Probably, as microscopic methods develop, the difficulty of visualizing molecular differences will be overcome. At present, however, the chief tools available for analyzing these structures are electrophysiological observations of function and of the disturbance in function produced by various experimental means, including the use of chemical agents (cf. 99–101; 163).

Types of Postsynaptic Potentials

Synaptic electrogenesis differs from that of the spike by being relatively small and, when more than one nerve fiber is available to excite it, is graded in amplitude depending on the strength of the stimulus to the nerve. Furthermore, two varieties of p.s.p.'s can occur. One, like the spike, tends to decrease the resting potential, hence is a depolarizing p.s.p. The other tends to increase the resting potential and is therefore a hyperpolarizing p.s.p. The two varieties of p.s.p.'s are present in different proportions in different cells. Some cells generate only depolarizing, others only hyperpolarizing p.s.p.'s, while in a third group both types of responses are produced usually, and perhaps always, by stimulation of different neural inflows. All vertebrate muscle fibers thus far known, their embryological relatives the electroplaques of most electric organs and some neurons develop only a depolarizing p.s.p. Certain gland cells are at present known in which a hyperpolarizing p.s.p. is the sole electrogenesis (144, 146). The crayfish stretch receptor, likewise, produces a hyperpolarizing p.s.p. (130), but depolarizing electrogenesis is also evoked, although in this case by stretch of the mechanosensory receptor membrane (66, 67, 94). In other cells, notably neurons of the vertebrate central nervous system (59, 60, 158, 159, 161–167) and some invertebrate muscle fibers (73, 131) and neurons (33, 186), both types of p.s.p.'s are found.

The depolarizing p.s.p., being of the same sign as the effective stimulus for electrical or local circuit production of a spike, can also evoke the latter and is therefore termed an 'excitatory' p.s.p. (59, 60). The spike arises when the p.s.p. is sufficient to depolarize the adjacent electrically excitable, spike-generating membrane to a critical firing level (fig. 3). The latter varies among different cells and is of the order of 10 to 40 mv change from the resting level. The hyperpolarizing p.s.p., by the same criterion, is an 'inhibitory' p.s.p. However, these names are not always appropriate. There are cells, like some electroplaques or muscle fibers (cf. 95, 97), that generate depolarizing p.s.p.'s but no spikes. The depolarizing p.s.p. there-fore may have nothing electrogenic to excite. Like-wise, those gland cells which generate only hyper-polarizing p.s.p.'s also have no spike to inhibit (cf. fig. 20). On the contrary, the hyperpolarizing electro-genesis of the gland cells is associated with activity in the form of secretion (146).

When the two varieties of p.s.p.'s occur in a cell which also generates spikes, they interplay with excitatory and inhibitory influences upon the elec-trically excitable membrane. The inhibitory synaptic action may occur independently of the magnitude and even the sign of the inhibitory p.s.p. As will be described below (p. 160) this p.s.p. may be de-polarizing under certain electrochemical conditions, or the activity of the synaptic membrane may not manifest itself as a potential. Nevertheless, when this synaptic activity is pitted against a depolarizing p.s.p. it always tends to decrease the magnitude of the latter and thereby to diminish or block its ex-citatory effect on the electrically excitable membrane. In some cases, therefore, the term 'inhibitory' p.s.p.

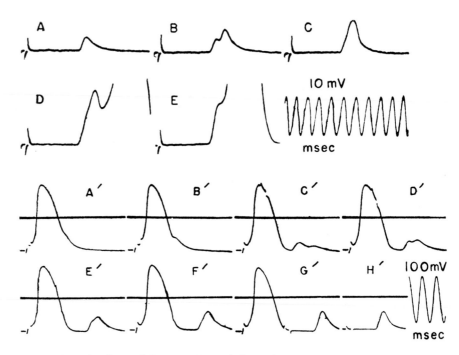

FIG. 3. Synaptic transfer from the p.s.p. to the spike. Intracellular recording, eel electroplaque. *Above:* Increasing stimuli to a nerve produced a stepwise increase of the p.s.p. (*A* to *C*). A still larger stimulus evoked a spike (*D* and *E*). *Below:* The p.s.p. first generates a local, graded response of the electrically excitable spike-generating membrane. When the neural stimulus evokes a p.s.p. during the absolute refractory period (*A′, B′*), the response lacks this component of graded activity of the electrically excitable membrane. Later (*C′* to *G′*) the local response develops, grows, arises earlier and fuses with the p.s.p. The combined response is seen in isolation in *H′*. This series of records was taken at approximately ⅒ the amplification of the upper set. Baseline denotes the zero for the resting potential and for the overshoot of the spikes. [From Altamirano *et al.* (4).]

is more apt than 'hyperpolarizing' p.s.p., but the latter term may be extended to denote a tendency to maintain as well as to increase the resting potential.

Interrelations of Postsynaptic Potentials and Spikes

It has been noted above that the p.s.p. is not actively propagated as is the spike. Thus, the transmissional electrogenesis of a p.s.p. is confined to the synaptic site. While their local electrical activity can be recorded in or about the cells that produce it (cf. 51, 70), p.s.p.'s do not, in general, evoke activity in other cells, their effects being confined to the cell in which they originate.

To elicit 'distant' actions in the next postjunctional cell, the prejunctional cell must generate a spike. Thus, transmissional activity in a synaptically linked chain of units is consummated only if the p.s.p. of each unit evokes a spike. When the depolarizing p.s.p. in one of the linked elements is insufficient to elicit a spike, the transmissional chain is broken. Likewise, if at one synaptic site, inhibitory p.s.p. is sufficiently large to block the spike of that cell, the chain is also broken.

Thus, spikes and p.s.p.'s are functionally interrelated. The former command the secretory activity at presynaptic terminals of their cell, and the released transmitter agent then evokes the p.s.p. of the next cell, which may or may not itself elicit a new spike, to repeat the process. It should be noted that while hyperpolarizing p.s.p.'s can inhibit spike production, they are themselves evoked by an excitatory activity in the presynaptic cell that propagates within the latter and effects the hyperpolarization of the postjunctional synaptic membrane through the secretory activity that it calls forth in the presynaptic terminals. In other words, a p.s.p., whether excitatory or inhibitory, always represents an active process, a response of subsynaptic membrane to an appropriate excitant.

As was noted above, and will be described in more detail below, the electrically inexcitable synaptic electrogenic membrane has different properties from those which generate the spike. The properties even of simple synaptic systems are therefore compounded from and subject to the various properties of the different electrogenic components. The multiplicity of synaptic transfers in the central nervous system makes the synaptic properties a dominant factor, although those of conductile electrogenesis are also important. Since the amount and type of synaptic electrogenesis determines the occurrence or absence of spikes, factors which modify p.s.p.'s are therefore of great significance in the central nervous system. Among these are the effects of pharmacological agents or synaptic drugs, and their use as experimental tools has already been mentioned. However, other agents and physiological conditions may affect production of p.s.p.'s. For example, the synaptic membrane may be altered in its properties by previous activity (cf. 95, 97; and below) and this could affect synaptic electrogenesis. The physiological properties of the presynaptic terminals may also be changed by various conditions, including previous activity. This change might affect the amount or nature of the transmitter agent released under the new circumstances and thereby affect transmission. Thus, the magnesium ion interferes with release of transmitter agents from the presynaptic terminals (cf. 52). Neuromuscular transmission is then depressed or blocked. The calcium ion acts reciprocally and in excess antagonizes the effects of excess magnesium ion.

SPECIFIC PROPERTIES OF SYNAPTIC ELECTROGENESIS

Evidence Against Electrical Stimulation of Postsynaptic Potentials

The existence of varieties of postjunctional cells in which p.s.p.'s are generated without spikes, e.g. in *Torpedo* and *Raia* electroplaques, invertebrate and vertebrate muscle fibers and gland cells (cf. 95, 97), provides one kind of direct evidence for electrical inexcitability of synaptic membrane (figs. 4A, 5; cf. fig. 20). An electrical stimulus which does not fire the presynaptic nerve fibers evokes no electrical activity in these cells. Responses are only produced by afferent neural activity or by chemicals which thus mimic the action of the transmitter agent (fig. 5).

Even in those cells which also generate spikes, the p.s.p. is produced only by neural or chemical stimuli. Direct electrical stimuli applied to the cell, or its local circuit excitation by antidromic invasion, evoke only spikes without p.s.p.'s (fig. 6). Finally, the occurrence of spikes and of absolute refractoriness which is their concomitant does not preclude the independent development of p.s.p.'s. The electrogenesis of the latter then can be superimposed upon that of the spike, i.e. it can be evoked during the absolute refractory period (figs. 6, 7). Together therefore, these three types of data provide direct evidence that the p.s.p.'s are generated by membrane that is not itself electri-

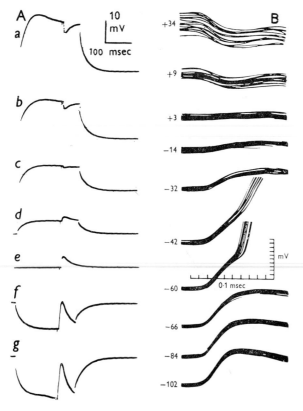

FIG. 4. Differences between electrically inexcitable and excitable membrane. *A:* The slow muscle fiber of the frog is not electrically excitable and produces no spikes, even when the membrane is strongly depolarized at beginning of (*a*). It develops p.s.p. on stimulation of the nerve during the application of the electrical pulse. The response at the resting potential (*e*), a depolarizing p.s.p., is increased when the membrane is hyperpolarized by the applied pulse (*f, g*). The p.s.p. is decreased by depolarizing the membrane (*d*) and is reversed in direction by strongly depolarizing the membrane (*a* to *c*). The magnitude of the reversed depolarizing p.s.p. increases as the interior of the membrane is driven beyond an equilibrium potential given approximately by the pulse in *c*. [From Burke & Ginsborg (35).] *B:* Responses of a cat motoneuron to orthodromic stimuli show essentially the same behavior of the p.s.p.'s, but are complicated by the appearance of a spike and the inactivation of electrically excitable membrane. The response at the resting potential (−66 mv) is a depolarizing p.s.p. which does not elicit a spike. Hyperpolarization of the membrane caused little change in the p.s.p. Depolarizations to −60 mv and −42 mv summed with the excitatory effect of the p.s.p., evoking spikes. These are no longer produced by the p.s.p.'s at the resting potential −32 mv, etc. These depolarizations, after evoking spikes by the electrical stimuli, then inactivated the spike-generating membrane. The p.s.p.'s decreased and at a membrane potential of +3 mv disappeared but reappeared in reversed sign as the internal face of the membrane was made more positive. [From Eccles (60).]

cally excitable. Other properties of p.s.p.'s that distinguish them from spikes are also referable to this

TABLE 1. *Characteristics and Properties of Differently Excitable Electrogenic Membrane*

Spike (Electrically Excitable)	P.S.P.'s (Electrically Inexcitable)
A. Characteristics	
Transducer action:	
(i) Sequential increase of Na⁺ and K⁺ conductances and Na⁺ inactivation	Two types: a) increased conductances for all ions b) specific increase in K⁺ and/or Cl⁻ conductances
(ii) Rates determined by membrane potential	Rates not determined by membrane potential
Electrical response:	
(i) Begins with graded depolarization, develops overshoot	Two types: a) depolarizing b) hyperpolarizing
(ii) All-or-none response	Graded response
B. Direct Evidence for Characteristic Differences	
(i) Spike absent ⎫ (ii) Spike present ⎭	Developed only by neural or chemical stimuli
C. Consequences of Characteristic Differences	
(i) Always in depolarizing direction	Of either sign, electrochemically reversible
(ii) Hindered or blocked by hyperpolarization	Electrochemical gradation
(iii) Excited, then blocked by depolarization	Electrochemical gradation
(iv) Pulsatile, relatively fixed duration independent of stimulus	May be prolonged, sustained while stimulus lasts
(v) Vanishingly brief latency	Appreciable, irreducible latency
(vi) Relatively inert to chemicals	Sensitive in two ways: response may be a) evoked by synapse activators; b) depressed or blocked by inactivators
(vii) Decrementless propagation	Nonpropagated, 'standing' potential

single, fundamental difference in their modes of excitation. These correlations are summarized in table 1, and form the content of this section (cf. also 97).

Mechanisms of Bioelectrogenesis

The means by which a cell can generate electrical activity are restricted in variety by the nature of the physiological and electrochemical systems of living tissues (91, 112, 113). Conductile and transmissional

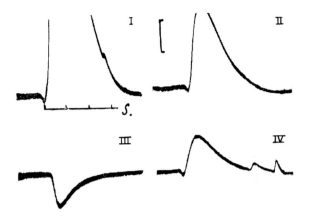

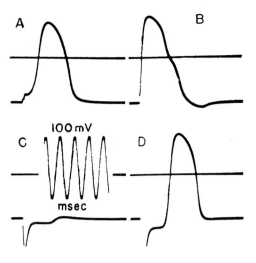

FIG. 5. Electrogenic action of acetylcholine on the electrically inexcitable membrane of *Torpedo* electroplaques. Intraarterial injections of 10 μg (*I*), 5 μg (*II*) and 2.5 μg (*IV*) in the presence of physostigmine produced electrical activity, the larger amounts evoking the larger responses. The neurally evoked discharge of *Torpedo* organ lasts only a few msec. (cf. 95). The long duration of the response produced by injections of acetylcholine presumably is due to sustained depolarization of the electrically inexcitable electroplaques by an excess of the administered transmitter agent. *III* indicates a control in which only perfusion fluid was injected. The electroplaques were probably depolarized in the 'resting' state, and the 'hyperpolarization' seen in this record may have been caused by temporary dilution of the depolarizing excitant. Calibrations: 0.5 mv, and seconds. [From Feldberg & Fessard (74).]

FIG. 6. Some differences between electrically and neurally excitable responses. *A, B:* Weak and strong depolarizing electrical stimuli to the eel electroplaque excited the cell directly, the latter with almost no latency. *C, D:* The stimuli were applied in the reverse direction. These are ineffective for the electrically excitable membrane but stimulate the cell indirectly by way of the nerve terminals supplying the synaptic membrane. The weak indirect stimulus evoked only a p.s.p. after a latency of almost 2 msec. (*C*). The very strong stimulus (*D*) shortened the latency to about 1.7 msec., and the larger p.s.p. evoked a spike with very brief delay. No p.s.p.'s were produced by the direct stimuli. However, the strong direct stimulus (*B*) also excited the nerve fibers which evoked a p.s.p. that occurred with the same latency as in *C* and *D* but appearing this time on the falling phase of the directly elicited spike. The p.s.p. therefore occurred while the electrically excitable membrane was absolutely refractory. [From Altamirano *et al.* (4).]

excitable membranes utilize the electrical polarization or resting potential of the cell. This appears as a potential difference across the cell membrane with its interior negative relative to the exterior. At rest, the membrane has a rather high resistance, indicating that it presents a considerable barrier to the penetration of ions. The physiological electrogenic response of the membrane to an appropriate stimulus, its transducer action (94), is the temporary alteration of its permittivity to ions. The electrical change is its consequence, derived from the prior, metabolically energized unequal distribution of ions and the resting potential.

Whereas the spike is generated by temporally sequential processes comprising first enhanced sodium conductance, then enhanced potassium conductance and sodium inactivation (113),[2] the transducer actions of synaptic membrane involve different ionic events.

[2] Recent data on eel electroplaques (3) indicate that a process of potassium inactivation may be involved in spike production (95). The participation of other, potential-insensitive processes is discussed below in connection with graded responses of electrically excitable membrane.

Depolarizing p.s.p.'s are caused by a general increase of permittivity to all ions (71; cf. 52, 60) which tends to abolish the resting potential. Electrogenesis of hyperpolarizing p.s.p.'s probably involves increased permittivity for K^+ and Cl^- (60, 61; Grundfest *et al.*, in preparation). Each ion species then moves in the direction of its electrochemical gradient, K^+ outward and Cl^- inward. Loss of positive charges and gain of negative thus account for the increased internal negativity.

The immediate consequences of electrical inexcitability of synaptic transducer actions are made apparent by the diagram of figure 8. Depolarization is the stimulus that initiates transducer action of an electrically excitable membrane. The entry of Na^+, forced inward because of the high concentration of this ion in the external medium, causes further depolarization. This electrogenic response to the trans-

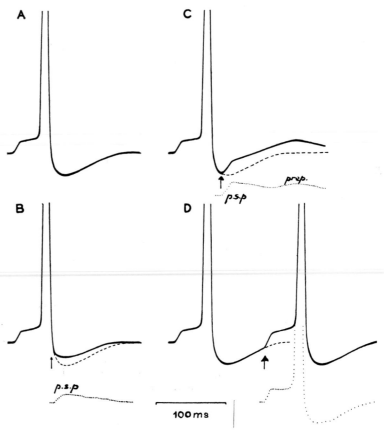

FIG. 7. Absence of refractoriness in postsynaptic responses in the giant neuron of *Aplysia*. *A:* A single shock to the presynaptic nerve first evokes a long-lasting p.s.p. out of which rises the spike of the giant neuron. *B:* A second stimulus, exciting the cell during its refractory period, adds a potential (solid line beginning at arrow) to the initial response (broken line). The difference (dotted line, below) is due to the second p.s.p. *C:* The second stimulus was delivered somewhat later. The added potential also shows a local response (*prep.*) which was initiated by the p.s.p. in the electrically excitable membrane during the relatively refractory period. *D:* At a longer interval, a second stimulus evokes the full response as in *A.* [From Arvanitaki & Chalazonitis (11).]

ducer action of the membrane can then act as a further stimulus to the latter. The positive feedback of the effect leads to a regenerative sequence and to the explosive, all-or-none spike. Since the transducer actions of electrically inexcitable membrane are not affected by the electrogenesis of the p.s.p.'s, feedback either positive (in the case of the depolarizing), or negative (for the hyperpolarizing p.s.p.'s) is lacking. Because of the absence of electrical feedback p.s.p.'s of either sign are thus produced that are graded in proportion to the availability of the specific excitants of the respective transducer actions.

Other Consequences of Electrical Inexcitability

A) SUSTAINED ELECTROGENESIS. The transducer actions of the spike generator are a sequence of potential-determined events, the first (sodium conductance) tending to cause the depolarizing electrogenesis, others (potassium conductance, sodium inactivation) tending to terminate it and to restore the resting potential. The sensitivity of these processes to the changes in membrane potential produced by the electrogenesis itself thus leads to a self-limiting event, the spike, of rather constant duration with which is also associated refractoriness (113). Not being electrically excitable, the transducer actions of the syn-

aptic membrane are relatively insensitive to the changes of membrane potential. Hence, p.s.p.'s may be sustained as long as the excitant of the transducer action is available (fig. 9) since they are not subject to refractoriness (figs. 6, 7) nor inactivation. The transducers of most types of sensory membrane are probably also electrically inexcitable (94, 95, 97). The sustained graded electrogenesis which can develop to a sustained stimulus is the means for transmitting information by a train of pulsatile spikes, coded as to frequency and number in some relation to the intensity and duration of the stimulus (97, 103; fig. 10; cf. fig. 13). The transducers of some mechano-sensitive organs, at least, also have chemical sensitivity (94, 96, 97), indicating further their relations with chemically sensitive synaptic membrane.

Although the postsynaptic membrane, in contrast to the electrically excitable, is capable of sustained electrogenesis, its responsiveness to a steady stimulus may be affected in various ways. These reflect the lability of the membrane in the face of the very chemical agents by which it is excited (95, 96). An example is the gradual diminution or even disappearance of synaptic electrogenesis when a muscle or autonomic ganglion is continuously acted upon by acetylcholine or other agents (123, 127, 129, 187).

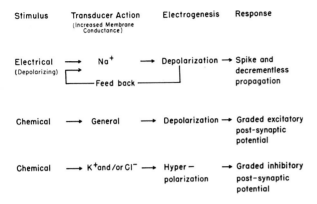

Stimulus	Transducer Action (Increased Membrane Conductance)	Electrogenesis	Response
Electrical (Depolarizing)	Na^+ / Feed back	Depolarization	Spike and decrementless propagation
Chemical	General	Depolarization	Graded excitatory post-synaptic potential
Chemical	K^+ and/or Cl^-	Hyper-polarization	Graded inhibitory post-synaptic potential

FIG. 8. The different ionic mechanisms evoked by transducer actions in electrically excitable and synaptic membranes, and some consequences of the different excitabilities. The depolarization caused by an electrical stimulus is regenerative in the electrically excitable membrane and produces the all-or-none spike. The electrically inexcitable synaptic membrane can produce either depolarizing or hyperpolarizing p.s.p.'s which do not react back on the transducer actions. This insensitivity to electrical effects results in responses graded in proportion to the available chemical stimulus. The depolarizing p.s.p. can act as a stimulus for the electrically excitable membrane, while the hyperpolarizing is inhibitory to the latter. [From Grundfest (96).]

The kinetics of this reversible desensitization have been studied thus far only in frog muscle endplates (fig. 11). The nature of the processes involved (127) is not yet clear, but neither the loss of responsiveness nor its recovery are controlled by the membrane potential.

Desensitization may be slow and unimportant relative to the excitatory events that occur at synapses in response to their normal neural activation. However, it might become a disturbing factor if transmitters are continuously released locally or systemically. This situation could result from the action of drugs or might arise from a pathological state. Rapidly developing desensitization has not yet been described, but it might account for the successively decreased p.s.p.'s sometimes produced by a train of stimuli. This process has been termed 'defacilitation' (33, 186). Decrease in the generator potential of sense organs acted upon by a constant stimulus, such as is seen in the rapidly adapting stretch receptors of crayfish (66), might be accounted for by a desensitization phenomenon.

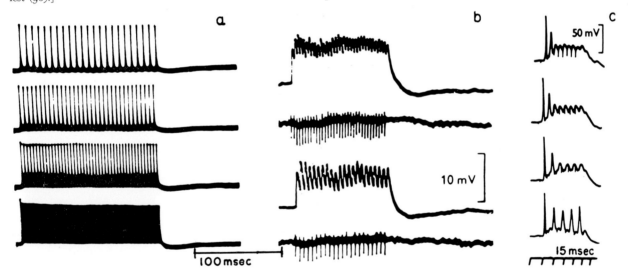

FIG. 9. Some consequences of the differently excitable electrogenic mechanisms in neurons. *a:* The cat motoneuron excited antidromically at high frequencies (140, 205, 280 and 630 per sec.) produces pulsatile spikes, only their after-potentials fusing. [From Brock *et al.* (25).] *b:* The p.s.p.'s produced by orthodromic stimuli (205 and 280 per sec.) summate, a higher average level of the depolarization being produced by the higher frequency of stimulation. The summated response is maintained as long as the afferent stimuli are delivered (lower record of each set). The amplitude calibration applies to the p.s.p.'s of this set which were taken at about 10x the amplification of *a*. [From Brock *et al.* (24).] *c:* Repetitive activity evoked in the rabbit cervical sympathetic neuron by stimulating the preganglionic supply at approximately 80, 100, 120 and 150 per sec. At the time scale of the records the first p.s.p. is not shown (cf. fig. 17C). The p.s.p. evokes a large spike; but even at the lowest frequency, the spikes caused by the subsequent p.s.p.'s are small, while the p.s.p.'s themselves are summed and sustained. This synaptic depolarization, increasing at higher frequencies of afferent drive, inactivates the spike-generating membrane. After the second depressed spike the responses progressively decrease, and at the highest frequency disappear. The p.s.p.'s are generated as long as there is an influx of presynaptic stimuli. [From Eccles (64).]

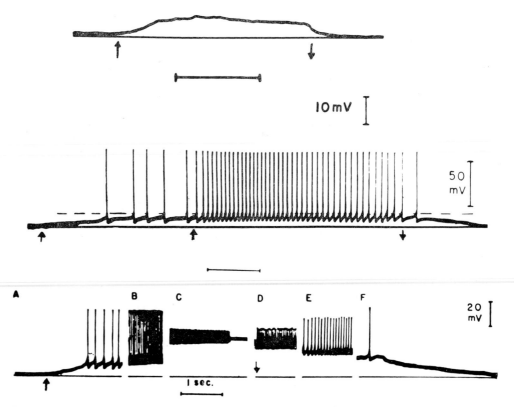

FIG. 10. Depolarizing electrogenesis of crayfish mechanoreceptor sense organ and the effects it evokes in the electrically excitable portion of the cell. *Top:* A weak stretch stimulus (↑) caused a depolarization of about 7 mv across the membrane of the cell body. This was maintained until the stretch was released (↓). *Middle:* Records at lower amplification. A weak stimulus produced a low frequency discharge of spikes. Increased stretch (second arrow) caused a higher frequency discharge which continued with some slowing as long as the stimulus was applied. The spikes generated during the depolarization develop a hyperpolarizing undershoot which is absent when the response is evoked by a single electrical stimulus. *Bottom:* Three increasingly larger stimulations are shown in *A* to *C*. The spikes produced at high frequency by the strongest stimulus (*C*) were diminished in amplitude and at the end were no longer evoked, while the receptor continued to respond with its sustained, summated depolarization. *D* to *F:* The return of responsiveness of the electrically excitable membrane after its inactivation. Note that the average level of the depolarization produced by the mechanoreceptor dendrites is graded with the degree of the stimulus. [From Eyzaguirre & Kuffler (66).]

B) POSTSYNAPTIC POTENTIALS DURING HYPERPOLARIZATION AND DEPOLARIZATION. P.s.p.'s can be produced during hyperpolarization of the cell, while spike electrogenesis may be blocked (fig. 12). These different effects may be ascribed directly to the different modes of excitation of the electrogenic membrane components. The effects produced by depolarization are somewhat more complicated but can also be accounted for on the same basis. Superposition of depolarization by a brief extrinsic electrical stimulus and that of a depolarizing p.s.p. enhances the excitation of the electrically excitable membrane (4, 60, 79). The spike thus arises earlier on the p.s.p. since the critical level of depolarization is thereby attained earlier.

Sustained depolarization, in some cells even when rather small, blocks spike electrogenesis (fig. 13) probably (cf. 95, 96) by the augmentation of sodium inactivation and potassium conductance that it causes in electrically excitable membrane (113). Electrical inexcitability of synaptic transducer action permits the continued development of p.s.p.'s after the spike can no longer be produced by direct or neural stimuli (figs. 11 and 13). Other manifestations of synaptic activity can also be evoked when the spike generating membrane is inactivated by ionically induced depolarization (50). The generator potential of a sense organ (fig. 10) may also continue to be produced even though that sustained depolarization inactivates the electrically excitable membrane and no spikes can

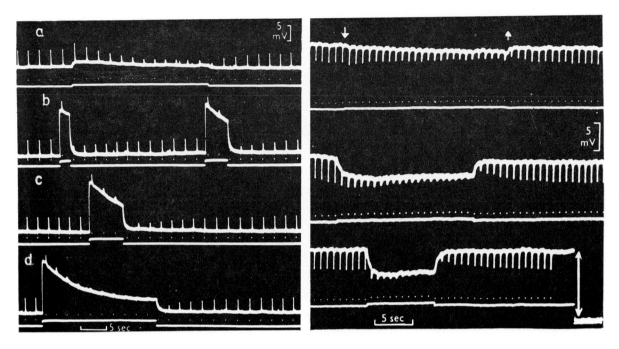

FIG. 11. Desensitization of the synaptic membrane of frog sartorius muscle fibers by sustained applications of acetylcholine. The drug was applied through each of two pipettes close to the surface of the endplate. From one pipette it was released at regular intervals in brief jets of approximately constant quantity. These testing stimuli are signaled by dots on the lower line in each set. The upper line shows the response of the endplate recorded with an internal microelectrode. The e.p.p.'s in these records are compressed on the slow time scale. In the course of the recordings a larger longer-lasting jet of different amounts of acetylcholine was also applied to the endplate as a conditioning stimulus. *Left:* An otherwise normal preparation. *a:* The conditioning stimulus was a weak dose of acetylcholine applied for a long time. *b* to *d:* The concentration was higher, and the drug was applied for different times. The testing responses diminished progressively during the depolarization produced by the conditioning stimulus. Their amplitudes recovered gradually after the conditioning depolarization had ended. Note that the recovery from desensitization is not associated with further change in potential. The recovery process therefore is not controlled by the membrane potential. *Right:* The muscle was immersed in isotonic potassium sulfate which depolarized the fibers and rendered them unresponsive to electrical stimuli. The tested muscle fiber was made inside-positive by about 15 mv by means of an intracellularly applied current. The synaptic membrane remains excitable to acetylcholine following these procedures, but the sign of the response is now reversed for reasons that will be discussed in the third subsection of this portion of this chapter. The membrane still exhibits desensitization to different intensities of the excitant drug (*top* to *bottom*). The desensitization process itself therefore is also not controlled by the membrane potential. At the end of the lower record the internal recording electrode was withdrawn from the muscle fiber (at the arrow), the trace going from a level of internal positivity to that of the reference zero potential. [From Katz & Thesleff (127).]

develop. Thus, the sustained depolarization at sensory receptor terminals or at synaptic junctions, which is a property of electrically inexcitable membrane while initially excitatory for the associated electrically excitable spike generator can, secondarily, inactivate the latter and thereby block further conductile or transmissional activity.

This effect accounts for Wedensky inhibition, the failure of transmission produced by stimulating the presynaptic nerve at high frequency. Summated and

sustained by this synaptic drive, the depolarizing p.s.p.'s at first evoke a few spikes which then cease to develop while the large p.s.p.'s continue to be produced by the afferent stimulation (fig. 9). Although Wedensky inhibition is probably of little importance in physiological activity of organisms, the phenomenon has long interested physiologists because the attempt to explain it in terms of electrical excitability has proved unconvincing (cf. 81, 141). The presence of electrically excitable and inexcitable electrogenesis

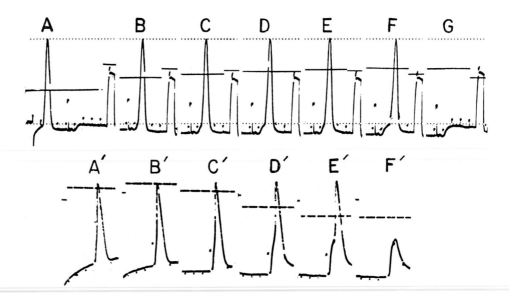

FIG. 12. Different effects on spikes and p.s.p.'s of cat motoneurons produced with different amounts of membrane polarization. The membrane potential was changed by passing an appropriate current through the recording microelectrode. A Wheatstone bridge arrangement balanced out the artifacts caused by this current, but as a consequence absolute levels of the membrane potential could not be measured. *Upper set* (*A* to *G*): Two traces are simultaneously recorded, the upper indicating the amount of current flow through the electrode, the lower showing the recorded potentials. *A* to *C*, decreasing amounts of depolarizing current; *D*, no applied current; *E* to *G*, increasing amounts of hyperpolarizing current. The records are aligned so that the peaks of the spikes coincide (upper broken line). The parallel lower broken line passes through the point at which the spike begins. When the strong depolarizing current was applied in *A*, it quickly evoked a direct spike. A subsequent orthodromic volley evoked a p.s.p. which reached the critical firing level but found the electrically excitable membrane still refractory. Hence, an orthodromically evoked spike was absent. At the end of this and subsequent records is a 50 mv calibrating pulse. *B*, *C*, the depolarizations from the applied current were smaller. They did not elicit a spike; but summing with the depolarization of the p.s.p. evoked a spike earlier than the orthodromic volley alone did (*D*). Hyperpolarization of the membrane operated in the opposite direction, hindering the orthodromically evoked spike which appeared markedly late on the p.s.p. in *F*, and was absent in *G*, although the p.s.p. in the hyperpolarized neuron was larger (compare the p.s.p.'s in *A* and *G*). A small deflection which follows the artifact of the stimulus to the nerve and precedes the p.s.p. by nearly 1 msec. is probably electrotonic pick-up of activity from the presynaptic impulses. Note that it is too small to evoke the spike. *Lower set* (*A'* to *F'*). In this experiment the spikes were elicited by antidromic invasion from the motor axons. *A'* to *C'*, decreasing amounts of membrane depolarization; *D'*, no applied current; *E'* and *F'*, currents applied so as to produce increasing membrane hyperpolarization. The antidromic spike (*D'*) shows an inflection which probably represents a response first in the axon hillock portion, succeeded by involvement of the rest of the cell. Depolarization of the cell body facilitates its invasion by the antidromic spike and minimizes the inflection on the rising phase. It is almost absent when the cell is strongly depolarized (*A'*). Hyperpolarization hinders the invasion of the cell body (*E'*) and when it is strong (*F'*) prevents the response of the soma. The smaller, early component is then seen in isolation as pick-up at the cell body of the response in the axon hillock and nerve fiber. Timing pulses at 1 msec. intervals are injected into the records. [From Frank & Fuortes (79).]

in the same cell also permits blockade of spikes by synaptic depolarization induced by drugs that excite the synaptic membrane (fig. 13). This blockade is frequently useful clinically but it in often misnamed as 'curarization' (cf. 96). Blockade by *d*-tubocurarine and other similarly acting agents operates through an

entirely different mechanism as will be described below.

C) ELECTROCHEMICAL GRADATION AND REVERSAL OF POSTSYNAPTIC POTENTIALS. Although synaptic transducer action is not responsive to electrical stimuli,

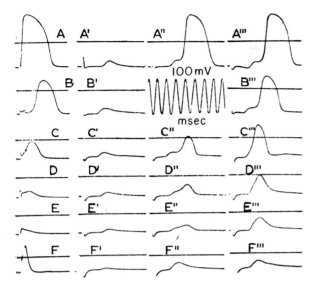

FIG. 13. Differential effects of depolarization on the spike and p.s.p. of the eel electroplaque. Column *A* to *F*, direct stimulation; columns *A'* to *F'*, etc., weak, moderately strong, and very strong stimuli to a nerve. *A* to *A'''*, the response of the normal cell. The resting potential is about 80 mv seen as the deflection of the active trace downward from the zero line (upper trace). The strong direct stimulus evoked a spike with very brief latency (*A*). The weak neural volley caused a p.s.p. (*A'*), the stronger also a spike (*A''* and *A'''*) arising out of the p.s.p. The cell was treated with weak physostigmine (25 μg per ml solution) for 78 min., and weak acetylcholine (1 μg per mg) for the last 58 min. of that period. These drugs had no effect on the potentials; 5 μg per ml acetylcholine were then added. Depolarization developed, the spikes 36 min. later becoming smaller, but the p.s.p. was unaffected (*B* to *B'''*). The diminishing electrically evoked response 9 min. later (*C* to *C'''*) became graded, as seen by its larger size in response to the strong neural volley. These effects progressed during the next 19 min. (*D* to *D'''*) and 11 min. thereafter (*E* to *E'''*). The p.s.p. to the threshold neural volley decreased (*E'*), but was still evident later (*F'*) when the electrically excitable membrane no longer responded to a much stronger direct stimulus (*F*). The p.s.p. to a maximal neural stimulation (*F'''*) was still about as large as initially (*A'''*). This p.s.p. was capable of evoking a small graded response of the electrically excitable membrane, as seen by the delayed additional potential on the falling phase. [From Altamirano *et al.* (6).]

the magnitudes of the p.s.p.'s and also their signs may be affected by changes in the membrane potential (52, 60, 97). These effects, however, are secondary and, indeed, are explicable only by the electrical inexcitability of postsynaptic electrogenic membrane.

Suppose that a transducer action increases solely the permittivity for Cl⁻. More of this ion being present in the external fluid, it tends to flow inward until the increased internal negativity tends to prevent further entry. Thus, the direction and amount of ionic flow is determined both by the chemical concentration gradient and by the electrical potential gradient, the combination being termed the electrochemical gradient. For a given concentration gradient there is a corresponding potential gradient at which the flow of ions is balanced by the opposite force of the electrical charge. If the membrane resting potential is increased by some means, the electrogenesis caused by influx of Cl⁻ would reach the electrochemical potential (E_{Cl^-}) for that ion sooner. The hyperpolarizing p.s.p. would therefore appear to be smaller. If the membrane potential is made more negative than E_{Cl^-}, Cl⁻ in the cell would be forced outward. The p.s.p. would then appear to reverse in sign, depolarizing the hyperpolarized membrane approximately to the level of E_{Cl^-}. This effect is seen in figure 14I.

The p.s.p. can likewise be affected by changing the Cl⁻ concentration either of the interior or of the exterior. For example, suppose that the external Cl⁻ is replaced by another anion which does not penetrate the membrane. During transducer action, Cl⁻ would move out from the cell since it is now more concentrated in the interior. The electrogenesis of hyperpolarizing p.s.p.'s can thus be reversed to depolarization. The effect of increasing internal Cl⁻ is seen in figure 14. Secondary electrochemical effects therefore can change the amplitude or sign of the p.s.p.

In the case of the depolarizing p.s.p.'s, increase of resting membrane potential may lead to increased electrical responses; decrease of the resting potential decreases and eventually reverses the sign of the depolarizing p.s.p.'s. These various conditions for electrochemical grading and reversal of the p.s.p.'s are found experimentally (figs. 4, 11, 14). The grading and reversal of p.s.p.'s are strong evidence that the transducer actions of synaptic membrane are not electrically excitable (97) since the physiological responses are not affected even by violent changes of the membrane potential, though the electrogenesis itself is modified.

Cat motoneuron p.s.p.'s are electrochemically reversible (cf. 60), but anomalies have been observed that are instructive. In theory, as outlined above, the apparent 'depolarization' of a reversed hyperpolarizing p.s.p. should only return the membrane potential to the same level as does the hyperpolarization of the normal p.s.p. The 'depolarization' therefore should not reach the critical firing level for the spike, the membrane in theory still remaining at a hyperpolarized level, and the 'depolarizing' p.s.p. should not become excitatory. Frequently, however, this is not the case when the reversal is produced by changing the ionic concentration gradients of the motoneuron.

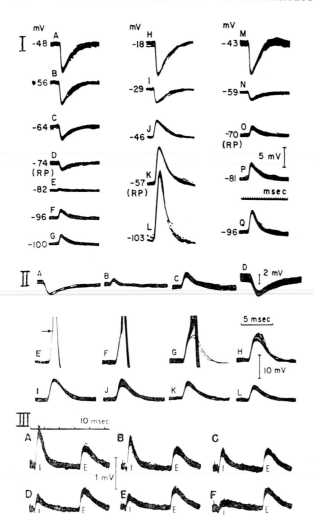

The initial resting potential may then be altered little or not at all, as is also the case with microinjections of ions into squid giant axons (cf. 91, 105). The changed chemical gradient of the motoneuron then causes a reversal of hyperpolarizing p.s.p.'s into depolarization which develops at, or near, the initial resting potential. The reversed 'inhibitory' p.s.p. now may elicit a spike (fig. 14II).

In crustacean muscle fibers (68, 73) and stretch receptors (130) the equilibrium potential for the inhibitory p.s.p. is nearly identical with the resting potential. Stimulating the inhibitory axon therefore may elicit no p.s.p., or the latter may be small, and of either sign. Nevertheless, the membrane potential tends to be clamped at or near the resting potential, particularly if the activity of the inhibitory synaptic membrane increases markedly the permittivity of the membrane for the relevant ions (K^+, Cl^- or both). Excitatory depolarization, elicited at the same time, by p.s.p.'s in muscle fibers or by mechano-sensory dendrites in stretch receptors, therefore tends to be depressed. When the inhibitory synapses of lobster muscle fibers are maximally activated by γ-aminobutyric acid the membrane potential is increased by about 4 mv, but the membrane conductance is increased about 8-fold (Grundfest, Reuben & Rickles, in preparation; cf. 99).

D) LATENCY OF POSTSYNAPTIC POTENTIALS. As mentioned above, the onset of the explosive response of electrically excitable membrane depends upon the attainment of a critical level of depolarization. A strong electrical stimulus, causing rapid depolarization to that level, therefore evokes a spike with vanishingly brief latency (fig. 6), this fact having been established by Bernstein in 1871 (19). In all cases

FIG. 14. Reversals of hyperpolarizing p.s.p.'s. Intracellular recording from biceps-semitendinosus motoneuron of cat; hyperpolarizing p.s.p.'s evoked by stimulating quadriceps nerve. I. A to G: The resting potential was −74 mv (D). Depolarization augmented the p.s.p. (A to C). Hyperpolarization at first diminished the p.s.p., the equilibrium potential for ionic movements without electrogenesis being at −82 mv (E). Further hyperpolarization reversed the sign of the p.s.p. (F, G). The Cl^- content of the motoneuron was then increased and K^+ decreased (H to L). Immediately thereafter (J to L) the p.s.p. was 'depolarizing' at all but the least negative values (H, I) of the membrane potential. M to Q: Recovery toward initial condition not yet complete 3 to 4 min. later. II. Reversal of the sign of the p.s.p. was produced by changing the ionic gradient of Cl^-. Initial response (A) was altered in B and C by increasing intracellular Cl^- as a result of diffusion out of the tip of the microelectrode. Depolarization of the membrane to −27 mv by an applied current restored the sign of the p.s.p. (D). The Cl^- gradient was then changed drastically. The reversals of the p.s.p.'s produced soon thereafter (E to G) occurred without significant change of the resting potential and were sufficient to excite spikes, at first with brief latency (E), then progressively later (F and G). Each record is formed by superposition of many traces. In G it is seen that the depolari-

zation occasionally fell below the critical firing level and continued to decrease in the later records (H to L). III. The membrane generating hyperpolarizing p.s.p.'s maintains its pharmacological individuality, although the electrical response may be reversed and is then indistinguishable from that of a depolarizing p.s.p. Prior to taking this series of records the hyperpolarizing p.s.p. evoked in the biceps-semitendinosus motoneuron by stimulating quadriceps afferents was reversed (by diffusing Cl^- from the electrode into the cell). This response is shown at the beginning of each record (I). Following it is a depolarizing p.s.p. (E) evoked by stimulating afferents in the biceps-semitendinosus nerve. Strychnine salicylate (0.1 mg per kg) was injected after record A and caused progressive diminution of I, but no change in E during the next 4 10-sec. intervals (B to E). The reversed hyperpolarizing p.s.p. almost disappeared after a second injection (F). [From Eccles (60).]

where appropriate data are available (cf. 97) the neurally evoked response arises after an appreciable irreducible latency (fig. 6), or synaptic delay (44; cf. 140).

Between the arrival of the presynaptic impulse and the onset of the p.s.p. of cat motoneurons there is a latency of about 0.3 to 0.4 msec. (59, p. 130). In the eel electroplaque the latency attains 1 to 2.5 msec. (4). This delay is not conducive to, nor consistent with, electrical excitation of synaptic membrane by the action current of the presynaptic impulse (97) as was pointed out by du Bois-Reymond (55) and Bernstein (20).

Presumably, synaptic latency is compounded from the durations required: (*i*) for release of transmitter from the presynaptic terminals; (*ii*) for its transit across a synaptic space of about 100 Å (52, 54, 152, 153, 174, 553); and (*iii*) for development of the electrogenic reactions when the transmitter acts upon the postsynaptic membrane. The details of none of these components are as yet known.

E) ELECTROTONIC EFFECTS OF PRESYNAPTIC IMPULSE UPON POSTSYNAPTIC REGION. Intracellular recording revealed (cf. 59, 60) that the presynaptic spike not only arrived too early, but also that its electrotonic effect was too little to cause electrical excitation of the postsynaptic membrane. Indirect stimulation of the eel electroplaque (fig. 6C, D) excites the terminal fibers innervating the cell membrane. Their spikes must have occurred with vanishingly small latency upon strong stimulation (D). However, no trace of electrotonic effects in the electroplaque was found. The presynaptic impulses could not be observed even at high sensitivity of recording (fig. 3). In other preparations small, brief as well as early electrotonic pick up of the presynaptic spikes is observed (cf. figs. 19, 27A). The magnitudes, 1 or 2 mv, are insignificant for electrical excitation which requires critical depolarizations of some 10 to 40 mv.

Among the possibilities for accounting for the smallness of electrotonic effects across synapses are the following.

1) The resistance of one or both cell membranes may be very high. In most types of synapses the presynaptic terminals making contact with postsynaptic membrane are very small and this alone would decrease the electrotonic effects. However, the contact between the pre- and postfibers in the squid giant axon synapse are broad, yet the electrotonic postjunctional potential is small (fig. 19). Likewise, in the eel electroplaque where the innervation is diffused

widely over the cell membrane electrotonic effects are small.

2) The bulk of the synaptic current may be shunted by the subsynaptic space.

3) If the nerve terminals were themselves electrically inexcitable neurosecretory regions the spike would not invade the nerve proximate to the synapse. The extrinsic current in the synaptic region would thus be already attenuated by electrotonic losses.

F) CHEMICAL SENSITIVITY OF SYNAPTIC MEMBRANE. Many varieties of drugs exert effects upon synapses, but they either do not affect electrically excitable membrane or do so only when applied in high concentrations and for long times (6, 96). The high sensitivity of synaptic membrane to chemicals is probably also a consequence of its chemical excitability. Thus, many drugs cause synaptic electrogenesis, thereby mimicking the effects of the natural transmitter agents. These substances are known as 'depolarizing drugs' but are more properly designated as 'synapse activators' (95, 96) for their action is merely that of excitants. The type of synaptic electrogenesis is determined by the nature of the synapse itself. For example, acetylcholine and its mimetics cause depolarization when applied to muscle endplates or sympathetic ganglia, but when applied to the cardiac pacemaker synapses which are hyperpolarized by vagal stimuli the drugs also cause hyperpolarization (49, 120). A second group of substances, the 'synapse inactivators', hinder or prevent excitation of the membrane by the activator drugs. These are also called 'nondepolarizing competitive inhibitors' (155).

Both types of substances may cause block of transmission. Depolarizing excitatory p.s.p.'s are diminished in amplitude or prevented by the inactivating drugs. The decrease of the p.s.p. below the critical level for discharging spikes is the mechanism of the synaptic blockading action of these drugs. Curare or *d*-tubocurarine act in this way (fig. 15). A general feature of blockade by inactivating drugs is that the electrically excitable membrane is affected little or not at all. Thus, the postjunctional cell can remain directly excitable.

Synapse-activating drugs induce transmissional blockade by an entirely different mechanism which is referrable to the fundamentally different excitabilities of electrogenic membrane. Acting on the synaptic membrane, the drugs evoke depolarization of the excitatory synapses. This electrogenesis, sustained in

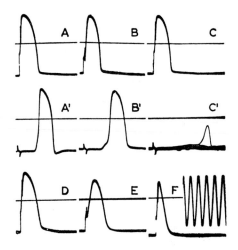

FIG. 15. Effect of nondepolarizing synaptic blocking agents on the responses of the eel electroplaque. Direct stimulation of the cell is represented in *A* to *F*, neural excitation in *A'* to *C'*. The initial responses to both stimuli are shown in *A* and *A'*. At 3 min. after substituting a bathing solution containing 5 mg per ml *d*-tubocurarine, the directly elicited spike was unchanged (*B*), but synaptic excitation was less effective, the spike arising later on the smaller p.s.p. (*B'*). At 5 min. (*C, C'*) the directly elicited response was still unaffected, but the p.s.p. had decreased so much (*C'*) that it was seen only with repetitive stimulation at 50 per sec., and produced a single small 'spike,' after which it could no longer affect the electrically excitable membrane. The latter, however, remained fully responsive to a direct stimulus 41 min. later (*D*), but eventually this responsiveness decreased (96 min. later, *E*; and 110 min. after this, *F*). The resting potential of the cell was unchanged. Calibration 100 mv and msec. [From Altamirano *et al.* (6).]

the presence of the chemical stimulant, leads to inactivation of the spike-generating membrane as described above. The entire cell may then become inexcitable by direct stimuli (fig. 13). In the case of skeletal muscle fibers, the inactivating depolarization is confined to the regions of the endplates and neuromuscular transmission is blocked because these regions do not generate spikes. Neuromuscular blockade evoked by 'depolarizing' synapse activating drugs, and blockade also at neuronal synapses, are usually preceded by a brief period of hyperactivity. The disorganized contraction of muscles, frequently but incorrectly termed 'fasciculation', is due to the initial excitatory effect of the synaptic depolarization, the individual muscle fibers responding to this stimulus before their spikes are inactivated. Blockade by the truly curarizing drugs, the inactivators of synaptic activity, is not preceded by the excitatory effects.

Postsynaptic Potentials as Nonpropagated 'Standing' Potentials

The local circuit current of activity, in combination with electrical excitability, makes possible the conductile property of electrically excitable, regeneratively responsive membrane (fig. 8). The all-or-none character of the spike then leads to decrementless propagation. A consequence of electrical inexcitability is that the p.s.p.'s do not set off activity in other portions of synaptic membrane. The electrogenesis is therefore localized and does not propagate except electrotonically as mentioned earlier (fig. 2). This 'standing' nature of p.s.p.'s has important physiological consequences that will be discussed later. It also introduces a technical complication in the interpretation of potentials recorded from volume conductors. The rules that apply to potentials generated by a travelling impulse (cf. 140, 141) need not hold, particularly since hyperpolarizing as well as depolarizing p.s.p.'s of the 'standing' variety can be produced at various sites (cf. 161–167).[3] It is of more than historical interest to note that Sherrington and his colleagues suggested that the central excitatory state (c.e.s.) "is a specialized manifestation of local excitatory state." (44, p. 43). In the present day contexts, the central excitatory state may be identified in large measure with occurrence of depolarizing p.s.p.'s, and the central inhibitory state with of hyperpolarizing p.s.p.'s. However, phenomena such as desensitization (p. 157) may obscure or eliminate this parallelism between potentials and excitability. Thus, as appears in figure 11, the depolarized but also desensitized endplate may not respond to a stimulus. Such a condition might lead to blockade of transmission although the background is one of depolarization. Desensitization of hyperpolarizing synapses has not yet been described, but its occurrence is not unlikely. If it exists, it could provide cases of lifting of inhibitory blockade in the face of a background of hyperpolarization. It will be shown later that the responsiveness of electrically excitable membrane (its local excitatory state) can change without a parallel change of the membrane potential, although the excitability of this membrane is also a reflection of the action of graded local responses.

[3] An extreme example of localized activity which is therefore highly instructive has been reported in the cat cortex (150, fig. 19). Within a range of 20 μ in the depth of the cerebral cortex the pattern and degree of electrical activity undergoes great modifications.

Interaction of Graded Responses

Generated and propagated in electrically inexcitable membrane, p.s.p.'s can spread only by electrotonus (fig. 2), passively, without evoking new activity and with considerable decrement. As weak depolarizations, p.s.p.'s acting upon adjacent, electrically excitable membrane may evoke graded local responses (figs. 3, 7, 13). The latter are also decrementally propagated, but the decrement may be smaller than in the case of p.s.p.'s. The depolarizing activity of a graded local response at one site may, in turn, give rise to some degree of active response at other sites. Thus, depending upon the local excitability of the membrane and the amount of initial local response, this graded depolarization may spread only passively, or it may propagate with various degrees of active contribution. The ultimate extent of the latter is that which evokes a spike. This explosive process dominates subsequent events since the magnitude of its electrical activity usually far exceeds the requirements for continued local circuit electrical excitation. In other words, when the spike generator has a high safety factor, decrementless propagation is the rule.

The nature of graded local responses of electrically excitable membrane will be discussed below (p. 167) in conjunction with the mechanisms of gradation of p.s.p.'s. Here, it is desired to stress that the two graded responses provide a pathway for summative gradation as a transition to the all-or-none spike (fig. 3).

EVENTS IN SYNAPTIC TRANSMISSION

Functional Interrelations Within Single Cell

A generalized schema of the activities within a single unit in a transmission chain is shown in figure 16. The input of the cell, the synaptic surface in the present context, but which may also be the receptor surface of a sensory cell (cf. 94, 96, 97), is activated by a specific chemical stimulus and develops an electrical response. Only the depolarizing variety, excitatory for the conductile mechanism, need be considered now. The p.s.p. may be brief or long and may give rise to a single spike or to a train of impulses. This conductile activity, arriving at the terminus of the cell, causes secretory activity which releases a transmitter agent that can excite another unit of the transmission chain or an effector.

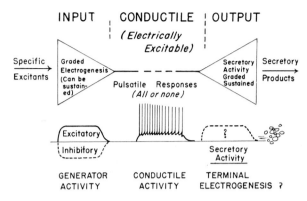

FIG. 16. Diagrammatic representation of functional components and electrical responses of a receptor cell or neuron. The electrically inexcitable input produces electrogenesis graded in proportion to its specific stimulus and sustained as long as the latter is applied. The possibility of hyperpolarizing electrogenesis is shown but is not further considered. The depolarization at the input, operating upon the conductile electrically excitable component, can evoke spikes in the latter coded in number and frequency in proportion to the depolarization. These signals, propagated to the output, there command secretory activity, roughly proportional to the information encoded in their message and sustained as long as the message demands. The transmitter released at the output can initiate a synaptic transfer by operating upon the depolarizing input of another cell. The possibility of a special output electrogenesis is indicated but is not further considered. The lower electrical portion of this diagram may be compared with records from a sense organ (fig. 10). [From Grundfest (97).]

Evolution of Electrogenic Membrane

The occurrence of receptor-effector cells in primitive metazoa suggested to Parker (154) that the nervous system evolved by parcellation of the two functions among separate receptor and effector cells with the interposition of a conductile element extending from the receptor cell. Later in evolution, correlational neuronal cells were presumed to have arisen. This evolutionary schema may also be applied to the individual cells, neurons and muscle fibers as well as receptors (103). The receptor portion of the primitive unit was probably sensitive to specific stimuli and this characteristic is retained at the electrically inexcitable input of the present nerve cell, muscle fiber, gland or receptor (fig. 16). The output likewise may be considered as representing the primitive effector, frankly so in the contractile muscle fibers or in glands. The terminals of the neurons likewise probably embody the secretory capacity of primitive units adapted to a new function, transmission at close contact. Other neurosecretory cells of more general function are also common (179) and the electrically inexcitable secretory cells of the adrenal medulla are regarded as second order autonomic neurons (cf. 177).

The conductile portion of the neuron, generating all-or-none spikes and therefore capable of decrementless propagation, requires electrical excitability for this function. It is probably a later evolutionary development (21) brought about in the course of extension of the cells in the metazoa and of their participation in complexly organized activity. That the conductile activity represents a new evolutionary step, mediated by a structure interposed between the primitive input and output sections, is also suggested by the absence of conductile electrogenesis in gland cells and by their electrical inexcitability (96, 97). The occurrence of muscle fibers which are also not electrically excitable and which generate no spikes (4, 34, 35, 97) reinforces this view. Classifying distinctions with respect to excitability and the types of responses of electrogenic membranes are by no means exhaustive of the different varieties. Pharmacological differences of various kinds specify an even greater diversity amongst excitable, electrogenic membranes. These differences are not to be seen by anatomical methods, nor indeed, by electrophysiological means alone, since pharmacologically distinct varieties of membrane can all generate similar types of electrical responses (fig. 14III).

Transmitter Actions

The varieties of transmitters will be treated below; the present discussion will be confined to the general electrophysiological aspects. From this point of view, the precise chemical natures of the substances are of little moment, the important feature being that they all activate synaptic electrogenesis. It is unlikely that the sign of the p.s.p. is affected by the excitant agent. Thus, as noted above, acetylcholine is a 'depolarizing' substance for excitatory p.s.p.'s but activating inhibitory synapses, as in the pacemaker of the heart it is a 'hyperpolarizing' agent. The characteristics of the transmitters will, however, determine to some extent the character of the p.s.p. *a*) For example, if the transmitter is a large complex molecule, it is unlikely that it would be available in large concentrations at the terminals of the presynaptic element. The amount of total excitant might therefore be limited in proportion to the quantity secreted during a single activity. Thus, a single afferent volley might cause a number of p.s.p.'s, but repetitive activity might rapidly exhaust the available transmitter. *b*) Molecular dimen-

sions and configurations might also determine the rapidity of diffusion of the transmitter from its site of release to its site of action. The distances involved, although probably only about 100 Å are significant in terms of molecules. *c*) The kinetics of interaction between the transmitter and the postsynaptic electrogenic surface may also be in part determined by the transmitter itself. For example, it is conceivable that two different agents might act on similar synaptic sites with different kinetics, giving rise to differences in the p.s.p.'s evoked by each. Studies in kinetics of these interactions are only now beginning (cf. 53, 127) and the nature of interaction is as yet unknown. Analogy with other processes is usually invoked and two models which are at present fashionable, activation processes of enzyme reactions and antigen-antibody combinations, are not necessarily mutually exclusive. The transmitter agent is presumed to combine with some 'receptor' sites of the synaptic membrane (cf. 2, 9, 14). *d*) The chemical properties of the transmitter may also determine the characteristics of the p.s.p. Thus, a labile agent such as acetylcholine may be rapidly destroyed, and it might give rise to shorter p.s.p.'s than would a more stable excitant of the same synaptic site (cf. 53). *e*) Likewise, the degree of chemical binding between the transmitter and the 'receptor' or the stability of the complex may play similar roles in determining the duration of the p.s.p., or in its 'competitive' behavior toward an inactivating synaptic drug. *f*) Although a transmitter agent may activate a given type of receptor it may also be an inactivator of other types. Thus, the transmitter at inhibitory synapses of some invertebrate muscle fibers is thought to be an inactivator of the excitatory synapses (68, 73). *g*) A given synaptic complex might be composed of several varieties of receptors, although all generating the same kind of p.s.p. Yet, one transmitter might inactivate some of the receptors while another transmitter did not, and the p.s.p.'s would vary accordingly.

Two of the factors, the transit time of the transmitter across the synaptic gap (*b* in the preceding) and an induction period (*c* above), probably determine the synaptic latency as noted earlier. Together these two processes may last several milliseconds.

Genesis of Postsynaptic Potentials

Important information on this matter derives from the occurrence of spontaneous 'miniature' p.s.p.'s at muscle endplates. Probably this activity is generated by random releases of transmitter from presynaptic sites (52). The miniature p.s.p.'s are probably quantal in the sense that each is composed of a minimum electrical change generated by a 'packet' of transmitter agent. The random release of packets from presynaptic terminals at different synaptic sites and the electrical inexcitability of the postsynaptic membrane combine to cause local miniature p.s.p.'s generated now at one site, now at another (51).

Depolarization of the presynaptic nerve terminals augments the frequency of miniature e.p.p.'s in frog muscle fibers (52). Similar data (137) on rat diaphragm muscle are even more decisive (fig. 17). Depolarizing electrotonus applied to the phrenic nerve increases the rate of the miniature activity very markedly, while hyperpolarizing the nerve terminals decreases the activity. Excess magnesium, which depresses the release of transmitter agents (cf. 52), depresses or eliminates the effects of the electrotonic currents.

The action of magnesium indicates that the effects produced by the electrotonic potentials are exerted through the medium of the nerve terminals and are

genuinely synaptic in nature. Other tests also lead to this conclusion. *a*) The electrotonic effects on the miniature e.p.p.'s are absent in muscle fibers where the nerve supply is cut close to the muscle and thereby made inaccessible to the electrotonic currents. This rules out the possibility that the current flow in the muscle fibers themselves caused the changed rate of miniature e.p.p.'s. *b*) The effect of the electrotonus was absent in endplates that were more than a few millimeters from the site of applying the stimulus to the nerve. Since the decay of electrotonically spread potentials must be rapid in the terminal nerve fibers, this result indicates that the change in rate is initiated by effects in the presynaptic terminals. These experiments show that when the depolarization produced by a nerve impulse arrives at or near the presynaptic terminals, their secretory activity can be initiated or augmented. A mechanism coupling the presynaptic impulse and transmission is thus provided.

Some additional conclusions may be deduced from data on miniature e.p.p.'s. These activities increase in frequency approximately 10-fold for 15 mv depolarization (137). Therefore a spike, though lasting only a brief time, could mobilize the rapid release of a considerable number of transmitter packets since 100 mv depolarization might increase the rate of 'spontaneous' releases some 10^4 to 10^6 times. The number of packets involved in an e.p.p. during neuromuscular transmission is probably about 10^2 to 10^3 times the 'quantal' units that cause the miniature e.p.p.'s (52).

Increase in the rate of release or secretion of the transmitter at the presynaptic terminals is obviously an electrically activated event. However, the response at the effector terminals probably differs basically from the processes that generate the spike of the conductile membrane. The data of figure 17 were obtained with prolonged applications of electrotonic currents. The sustained increase of miniature e.p.p.'s during sustained depolarization therefore indicates that the processes leading to release of transmitter packets are not subject to inactivation as is the sodium conductance of the spike generator.

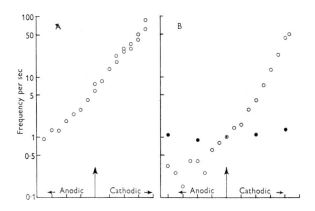

FIG. 17. Effects upon the frequency of miniature e.p.p.'s in rat diaphragm muscle fibers of electrotonus applied to the phrenic nerve. Abscissae show the intensity of applied electrotonic current in relative units; ordinates, the frequency of miniature e.p.p.'s scaled logarithmically. Arrows point to frequencies of the latter observed when no electrotonic currents were applied. 'Cathodic' current is depolarizing for the nerve terminals, 'anodic' is hyperpolarizing. *A:* The effects of the change in potential were essentially symmetrical on the logarithmic scale, increased frequency of miniature e.p.p.'s with cathodic and decreased frequency with anodic current. This was the most frequently encountered result. *B: open circles,* terminal depolarization was much more effective than hyperpolarization in changing the frequency in this experiment; *filled circles,* the same muscle was exposed to 12 mmole magnesium (normal concentration is 1 mmole). The frequency of miniature e.p.p.'s became essentially independent of the membrane potential of the nerve fibers. [From Liley (137).]

Gradation of Postsynaptic Potentials

Probably the miniature p.s.p.'s are small only because the area involved in their electrogenic activity is small in comparison with the total area over which the emf is electrotonically distributed. Suppose that we could measure the change in potential occurring at a single isolated site which valves sodium ions. In the resting state the emf across that site will be the resting potential, approximately the value of the potassium potential, E_K (91, 112, 113). When the valve 'opens' the emf must suddenly change from the resting value towards that of the sodium potential, E_{Na}, a change to internal positivity (113). The hypothetical 'valve', however, is located in a physical structure, the membrane, with finite resistance and capacity and with both its surfaces bathed in saline media. The step-like emf of the generator 'valve' must therefore distribute itself electrotonically over an area having definite electrical properties, becoming a potential change reduced in magnitude and distorted in form (fig. 2). The simultaneous activity of a number of valves' would lead to an increased potential, thus permitting gradation of the response from the minimal observable to the full value of the electrochemical potential. Since several species of ions are involved, the maximum p.s.p. strikes a balance between the different electrochemical potentials (cf. 52, 60).

Mechanisms of Graded Responsiveness

The most detailed data are available on graded responses of electrically excitable membrane and, although the theory of their production is still rudimentary, the same general process will probably be found to apply also to the graded responses of synaptic and sensory membrane (94–96). Graded local response is usually considered to be merely a stage in the events leading to the regenerative explosive activity which results in the spike (113). This view has been invalidated by the finding (4, 6, 92) that under various conditions all-or-none responsiveness can be converted to a fully graded one. Only graded responses occur in dually-responsive insect muscle fibers (37, 38) and probably in other electrically excitable membranes as well (97). The activity may vary from the minimal observable to a maximal response closely approximating the spike in amplitude and form (fig. 18; cf. fig. 21). The degree of graded responsiveness is not controlled by the membrane potential as it is considered to be in current theory (113).

Figure 18 also illustrates how an altered local excitatory state need not be caused by, nor reflected in, a changed membrane potential. Whether untreated or poisoned with a drug, the single cell showed subliminally enhanced excitability which was evidenced during an interval at least 0.2 sec. after each subthreshold stimulus. The cumulative growth of this 'excited' state in the untreated cell led to an explosive manifestation, the spike. After the cell was poisoned

the overt manifestation took the form of a progressively larger graded response, and this response approached the spike in amplitude.

A first approximation for revising theoretical concepts (94, 95) considers that the excitable membrane is composed of unit areas. Each has a population of electrogenic units (transducers, valves, etc.) which differ amongst themselves in the threshold for their excitation. In the explosively responsive population the thresholds for exciting the electrogenic elements of a given unit area are probably closely similar. Dispersion of that population distribution could result in conversion of all-or-none responsiveness to the graded type.

Transfer of Activity From Postsynaptic Potentials to Electrically Excitable Membrane

In the case of the skeletal muscle endplate or the squid giant fiber synapse a relatively well-defined 'patch' of electrically inexcitable synaptic membrane is surrounded by electrically excitable structure. In both cells, the p.s.p. is simple, only of the depolarizing variety, and initiated by impulses in a single presynaptic fiber (fig. 19). The p.s.p. then tends to be of a fixed amplitude and in these two systems usually causes sufficient depolarization of the contiguous electrically excitable membrane to generate a spike in the latter. Essentially, transmission then is one-to-one, each impulse of the prefiber generating a postjunctional spike.

Under various conditions, for example upon poisoning an endplate with d-tubocurarine, the p.s.p. decreases in amplitude and, when the depolarization falls below the critical firing level, no spike is generated (fig. 15). The transmission block may be overcome by a rapidly repetitive volley of neural stimuli which successively generate new p.s.p.'s or a local excitatory state before the previous have disappeared. The consequent augmentation of depolarizing electrogenesis may attain the critical level and transmission again occurs. This general phenomenon of increased effectiveness of repetitive stimuli is known as facilitation. The normally occurring p.s.p. produced by a given afferent neural stimulus may not be sufficiently large to evoke a spike. Repetitive stimuli in this case can summate the depolarizing p.s.p.'s and facilitation is then also manifested, the summed depolarization initiating a spike.

In the context of the electrophysiological mechanism, a facilitated overt response (e.g. of a muscle) may be produced by two fundamentally different

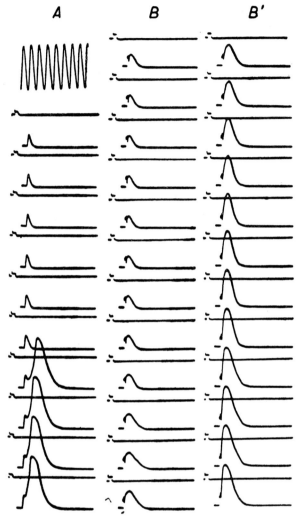

FIG. 18. All-or-none and graded responsiveness in an eel electroplaque. Two traces are recorded simultaneously, repeated at the rate of 5 per sec. The upper longer trace of each set is the zero base line for an internal microelectrode. It also carries the monitoring signal of a stimulus applied to the cell and shows that the stimulus strength remained constant in each of the two series. The lower trace of each set is that of the potential recorded with the microelectrode. The distances between the two represent the resting potential, about 70 mv. The weak stimulus in *A*, before the cell was treated with drug, at first produced only a subthreshold electrotonic depolarization. The seventh repetition of the stimulus is followed by a spike. The shorter latency at which successive spikes then develop indicates continued growth of excitability and its persistence through the 200 msec. intervals between stimuli. The resting potential remained unchanged. *B* and *B'*: The sequence of growth in response in the cell after 84 min. exposure to 500 μg per ml of physostigmine. The resting potential was not affected by the drug, which eliminated synaptic excitability and converted the all-or-none response of the electrically excitable membrane component to graded responsiveness. The testing stimulus was slightly stronger than before applying the drug, and the first trace seen (upper set of *B*) evoked a distinct,

synaptic processes. The one described just above is summation where each successive p.s.p. is no larger (cf. fig. 27*A*), and may indeed be smaller, than its predecessor. The excitatory action leading to the overt effect would be the increased total depolarization produced by the summed effects of the repeated p.s.p.'s. The overt effect would appear as a facilitation because of the profound functional difference between the local processes at the motoneuronal or neuromuscular synaptic junction and their production of an explosive propagated spike which triggers the contractile mechanism.

Essentially the same overt result, but an activity involving more complex synaptic processes, would occur if the successive p.s.p.'s augmented as a result of the repetitive stimulation. This synaptic facilitation will be discussed further in relation to heterosynaptic and homosynaptic excitatory phenomena (p. 184). It would seem to involve augmented responsiveness of the synaptic membrane to the transmitter agent, the converse to the decreased responsiveness in desensitization. As noted in that connection, defacilitation probably is ascribable to desensitization. Both facilitation and defacilitation, however, may be only apparent effects on the synaptic membrane, their real cause residing elsewhere. For example, facilitation could result from successively larger quantities of transmitter released from the presynaptic terminals. The converse, progressive exhaustion of the transmitter and decrease of the amount emitted at each impulse, would lead to defacilitation.

As is also the case with other electrical stimuli, the depolarizing p.s.p. first evokes a graded local response of the electrically excitable membrane (4) and the two depolarizations then sum to cause the explosive response of the spike (figs. 3, 7). The addition of hyperpolarizing p.s.p. to the depolarizing diminishes the magnitude of the latter and its excitatory effect. If the depolarizing p.s.p. then falls below the critical level, a spike is no longer elicited and the effect of hyperpolarizing p.s.p.'s is therefore inhibitory. It should be noted that inhibition may occur even though considerable depolarization is still generated. In other words, the countervailing inhibitory p.s.p.

though small, graded response. During the course of repetitive stimulation at 5 per sec. the response grew, at first gradually and then more rapidly, indicating that the rise of excitability is non-linear. The series illustrated ends before the response could grow to an amplitude as large as that of the spike, but in other experiments this was observed. [From Altamirano *et al.* (6).]

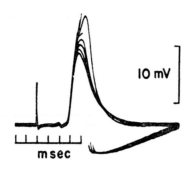

FIG. 19. Synaptic transfer in squid giant axons. The incoming presynaptic spike elicits only a small membrane potential change in the postsynaptic cell. The p.s.p. arises after a brief latency and, if it attains the critical firing level, elicits a spike. [From Bullock & Hagiwara (32).]

need not be as large as is the excitatory one. It must only be large enough to decrease the depolarizing p.s.p. below the critical firing level for the spike, but it can then produce dramatic effects since the absence of conductile activity eliminates further transfer to other cells and results in the disappearance of distant actions within the organism.

Synaptic Delay

Synaptic latency, which was discussed above, involves only the activity of the presynaptic terminals and the response of electrically inexcitable synaptic membrane. Synaptic delay includes not only the latency but also the utilization time of electrical excitability. This last involves the duration of the rise of the depolarizing p.s.p. and of whatever further depolarization this may develop in its excitatory action on electrically excitable sites, and the consequent time that is required for the p.s.p. (and the local response) to reach the critical level for evoking a spike. The rise time of the p.s.p. for this level may be brief, about 0.1 to 0.3 msec. (figs. 6, 12), but can be much longer (figs. 7, 9), particularly if the depolarizing p.s.p. is liminal for discharge of the spike. Temporal summation or facilitation, in which repetitively evoked depolarization becomes larger, may then decrease the utilization time and thereby shorten the synaptic delay (cf. 140). The shortening might also occur because of decreased synaptic latency or heightened synaptic excitability, effects which are discussed in the next section of this chapter.

The existence of synaptic delay has been ascribed chiefly to slowed conduction of the afferent impulse in the fine terminals of the presynaptic fibers (cf.

57, 140). That explanation is no longer tenable. Strong electrical stimuli directly applied to the innervated surface of the eel electroplaque, and therefore to the nerve terminals, nevertheless cause a neurally evoked response always after a considerable synaptic latency (fig. 6). Further evidence may be derived from figure 19 and other data of similar nature which show that the presynaptic spike arrives at the synaptic surface somewhat before the p.s.p. is elicited. Thus, synaptic latency and the utilization time involved in the rise of the p.s.p. to the critical firing level are probably the major factors in synaptic delay.

Superposition of Postsynaptic Potentials and Spikes

The electrically inexcitable generators of p.s.p.'s act independently of and in parallel with the electrically excitable membrane that produces the spike (4, 48, 71). Thus, a p.s.p. can be evoked during the spike, when a second response of the electrically excitable membrane is impossible due to its absolute refractoriness (figs. 6, 7). However, the combined response depends upon the prevailing electrochemical conditions of the cell. The p.s.p. may subtract from as well as add to the spike, the former occurring when the spike itself carries the membrane potential into the region at which the p.s.p. reverses as described above (48, 136; cf. 97). The conclusion that the spike under certain conditions wipes out the p.s.p. (cf. 60, p. 30 ff) may therefore require revision. A complicating factor that may explain these findings of Eccles and his colleagues is the distortion produced in the spike when the latter is elicited in a depolarized electrically excitable membrane (cf. 95). An 'undershoot' of apparently hyperpolarizing phase then terminates the spike, even though it is absent in the response evoked at the normal resting potential of the membrane (fig. 10; cf. 60, fig. 16). The distortion is probably due (95) to excess of potassium conductance over the sodium conductance as in squid giant axons (113). This excess would be caused by increased sodium inactivation produced by the depolarization.

The foregoing remarks indicate that electrical and physiological conditions of the soma membrane affect the recording of cellular potentials. The soma, however, is only one part of the cell, although it is the one most easily accessible to microelectrodes. Even in neurons without dendrites, as is the case in tissue-cultured dorsal root ganglion cells, the intracellularly recorded response to stimuli may take on complex forms (42). This indicates that activity in and the

---

properties of the axon contribute to the potential recorded from the soma.

The nature and degree of excitability may be different in various parts of the soma and dendrites. Thus the soma may be electrically inexcitable (17, 33, 80, 186, 189, 190). The depolarizing p.s.p.'s or generator potentials evoked at the soma excite spikes at electrically excitable regions some distance from the cell body. The superficial portions of apical dendrites in the cat cortex are not electrically excitable (107, 165), As mentioned earlier, the receptor portions of various sensory cells are electrically inexcitable and for this reason are capable of developing a sustained generator potential.[4]

Recent evidence (7, 17, 43, 82) also indicates that different portions of electrically excitable membranes of the cell body may have different thresholds. The 'initial segment' of the motoneuron (cf. 60) in the cat (82) and toad (7) responds first to an electrical stimulus and gives rise to the early part of the antidromic spike (fig. 12A'–F'). The spike of the rest of the cell body (if the latter is electrically excitable) occurs slightly later, the delay giving rise to a slight break in the recorded response.

In addition to these apparent inhomogeneities in the excitability of different parts of the soma and dendrites, slowed conductile spread, separate loci of origin for spike and p.s.p.'s and different loci for depolarizing and hyperpolarizing p.s.p.'s are all factors that may contribute to variations in the recorded response of the cell. Many variations can be theoretically deduced, but their analysis is beyond the present scope.

[4] Retinal receptors in fish (184) provide an interesting new example (102). Their electrical response is probably generated in cells other than the primary visual cells (cones). The response is a sustained electrogenesis. In some cells it is only hyperpolarizing, in others depolarization is also developed, depending upon the wavelength of the stimulating light. The amplitudes of the responses are graded, not only with the intensity of the light stimulus but also with its spectral composition. These characteristics of electrically inexcitable activity are produced apparently in the absence of spikes, but the electrogenesis, both hyperpolarizing and depolarizing, affects spike production in other conductile elements. It has been suggested (102) that these electrogenic cells (probably horizontal or bipolar cells or both) are excited by transmitter agents released by photochemically activated cones. The electrogenesis, in which an electrically excitable component is lacking, is in turn associated with secretory activity as in electrically inexcitable gland cells. The secretory products acting upon the retinal ganglion cells evoke neuronal activity of the latter, probably including excitatory and inhibitory p.s.p.'s which lead to patterns of spike activity seen in the optic nerve fibers.

GENERAL AND COMPARATIVE PHYSIOLOGY OF SYNAPSES

Forms and Magnitudes of Postsynaptic Potentials

Viewed as the nonregenerative responses of electrically inexcitable membrane, the forms and magnitudes of the p.s.p.'s may be expected to have rather simple relations to their excitants. The available experimental data are as yet rather scanty, but they do permit some general conclusions (cf. 60, 97).

As a first approximation, the degree of synaptic transducer action reflected in the rate and amount of electrogenesis may be considered to be roughly proportional to the quantity of excitant. A brief jet of labile transmitter or activating drug causes a brief response while the continued availability of the excitant causes a sustained electrogenesis. The duration of the p.s.p. in the first case will be determined by the time course of the transducer action initiated by the excitant (cf. also 53, 127, and papers cited there). However, the responses will be distorted by the electrical circuit properties of the membranes. Thus, the rising and falling phases of the p.s.p. may reflect this distortion which produces a slowing such as occurs in electrotonic propagation (fig. 2). The rise of the p.s.p. should be slowed less than its fall since the former occurs when the membrane resistance and time constant are relatively low. This is the case experimentally as numerous figures in this chapter indicate. The falling phase probably bears some relation to the time constant of the membrane (cf. 60), lasting longer when the time constant is larger, like the ballistic response of a slow galvanometer to a brief current. The relation, however, does not appear to be a simple one (95, 97), and the duration of the p.s.p. probably reflects importantly intrinsic time courses of transducer actions.

The duration of the p.s.p. caused by a single neural volley differs considerably in the various types of cells. The p.s.p.'s of squid giant axons and of eel electroplaques last only about 2 msec. (figs. 3, 19), those of *Aplysia* giant neurons (fig. 7) or cat salivary glands (fig. 20) may persist for nearly 1 sec. The e.p.p.'s and p.s.p.'s of other neurons have intermediate durations. In some cases, physostigmine and prostigmine both prolong the p.s.p., this effect probably involving the prolongation of the life of the transmitter, acetylcholine, by inactivation of cholinesterase (cf. 52, 53, 60, 68). Some of the quaternary ammonium compounds also prolong p.s.p.'s (cf. 52) and these actions may be caused by direct

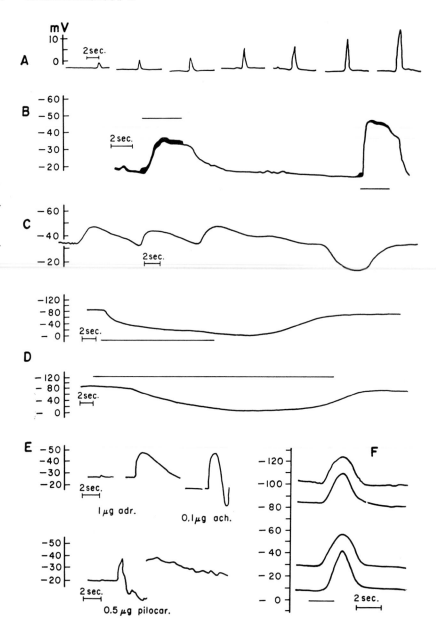

FIG. 20. Different types of electrical activity in cat salivary gland cells. Depolarization shown as downward deflection in these records. *A:* Type I cells produce hyperpolarizing p.s.p.'s which are graded with strength of the stimulus. Single shocks to chorda tympani evoke p.s.p.'s which last about 1 sec. *B:* Type I cells produce only hyperpolarizing p.s.p.'s to excitation of the sympathetic (*upper signal*) or parasympathetic (*lower signal*) nerves. However, the latencies and magnitudes of the p.s.p.'s differ somewhat. *C:* Type II cells develop hyperpolarizing p.s.p.'s on stimulating the chorda tympani and depolarizing p.s.p.'s through their sympathetic innervation. *D:* Type III cells (which may be myoepithelial elements of the ducts) respond only with depolarizing p.s.p.'s to parasympathetic (*above*) or sympathetic (*below*) stimulation. The resting potential, about −80 mv, is large in comparison with that of Type I or II cells and resembles that of muscle fibers. *E:* Type I cells respond with hyperpolarization to epinephrine, acetylcholine and pilocarpine. [From Lundberg (144).] *F:* The hyperpolarizing p.s.p. of the gland cell is remarkably insensitive to changes of the membrane potential. The resting potential was 30 mv. [From Lundberg (145).]

effects upon the kinetics of the ionic 'valving' of the transducer action.

The maximum attainable amplitudes of p.s.p.'s are probably determined by electrochemical conditions as described in a previous section of this chapter, but these need not be identical for different varieties of cells. Thus, most hyperpolarizing p.s.p.'s reach a limit set by the most negative electrochemical ionic species, but hyperpolarizing electrogenesis of glands can occur in the face of very high internal negativity (fig. 20). These differences reinforce the conclusion (91, 105) that electrical activity of bio-

logical membranes may involve a variety of mechanisms, some of which are not yet understood.

Postjunctional Cells with Depolarizing Postsynaptic Potentials

As noted above, some cells though not electrically excitable respond with depolarization to neural or chemical stimuli. Of general interest are electrically inexcitable invertebrate and vertebrate muscle fibers, such as the 'slow' muscle fibers of the frog (fig. 4A). They are diffusely innervated and neural stimuli give rise to graded summative depolarizations. These diffusely generated depolarizations can act as stimuli for the contractile mechanism, causing localized graded contractions (34, 35, 132).

Some salivary gland cells also generate only depolarizing p.s.p.'s (fig. 20) and these are produced by stimulation of either the sympathetic or parasympathetic nerves (144). Chemical stimulation by epinephrine, pilocarpine or acetylcholine then all cause the same type of electrogenesis, but it is not known whether all the excitants activate a single variety of electrogenic membrane or whether there are distinct, although similarly electrogenic, cholinoceptive and adrenoceptive components. As is the case with the electrically inexcitable muscle fibers, the synaptic electrogenesis of gland cells is also associated with and itself probably effects other cellular activity, in this case secretion.[5]

Torpedo and *Raia* electroplaques also generate only depolarizing p.s.p.'s but not to electrical stimuli (95). The cells which are derived from skeletal muscles therefore are in reality constituted from endplates. A specialization of these and other electroplaques permits series additions of the voltages produced by each cell; hence the electric organs generate considerable voltage. The discharges are under control of the nervous system and in some forms this may be useful for protection or aggression. The p.s.p.'s are brief in *Torpedo* but long-lasting in *Raia*.

Vertebrate skeletal muscle fibers of the 'twitch' system and autonomic ganglia combine depolarizing p.s.p.'s and spike-generating membrane (cf. figs. 9, 27), but the autonomic neuron may also produce hyperpolarizing p.s.p.'s since there are indications that inhibition may occur (64, 134). In both cases

---

[5] It was noted earlier (p. 154) that bioelectric responses of transmissional and conductile processes are essentially passive events resulting from the movement of ions in obedience to charged electrochemical equilibrium states. The change from one state to another is the active phenomenon, due to specific processes, transducer actions which are the responses of excitable membrane to appropriate stimuli. In gland cells, the secretory activity of the output component (fig. 16) probably occurs at membrane structures that are intimately mingled with those of the input component. Secretory electrogenesis thus is probably superimposed on the p.s.p.'s of the transducer input, and this is suggested also by the independence of the gland electrogenesis from electrochemical conditions (fig. 20 *E* and *F*). In some respects, therefore, electrogenesis of gland cells may differ from that of 'pure' p.s.p.'s of neurons or endplates. The details of these differences cannot now be specified since little is known about the nature of active transport mechanisms, such as are probably involved in secretion.

the p.s.p.'s have much longer durations than do the spikes. In muscle fibers the spike energizes the processes of contraction by a mechanism that is not yet known (cf. 121). Eel electroplaques also generate both depolarizing p.s.p.'s and spikes (cf. figs. 3, 6, 13), but the contractile machinery is missing in these modified muscle fibers. Eel electroplaques, like neurons, are diffusely innervated by many nerve fibers. Since the area of their innervated surface is more than 10 mm², their study has provided some data that are not readily obtained with the much smaller nerve cells. The results, however, very probably apply to the general case of synaptic transmission as will be described below (cf. 95).

Postjunctional Cells with Hyperpolarizing Postsynaptic Potentials

If cells capable of generating spikes were endowed only with hyperpolarizing p.s.p.'s, transmissional excitation of the electrically excitable responses would not occur, for in all cases known the spike is triggered by depolarization. Thus, it may be expected that cells in which solely hyperpolarizing synaptic electrogenesis occurs would be of restricted functional significance. From intracellular recordings two cases are known and in neither are spikes generated. These are salivary gland cells (144, 146; cf. fig. 20) and L-cells of the fish retina (102, 184, 191; cf. also footnote 4, above). As noted earlier, the membrane transducer actions and electrochemical effects of hyperpolarization are consistent with secretory activity; hence neurally evoked hyperpolarizing p.s.p.'s of glands have functional validity.

Postjunctional Cells with Both Types of Postsynaptic Potentials

Two varieties may be expected and both types occur: *1)* electrically inexcitable cells which do not generate spikes and *2)* cells which produce spikes as well as the p.s.p.'s. A clear case of the former is found in some salivary gland cells (fig. 20) in which each type of synaptic electrogenesis is probably associated with a different form of secretory activity. The different p.s.p.'s are specifically produced by stimulation of the two autonomic nerve supplies. Stimulation by cholinomimetic and adrenomimetic substances evokes oppositely signed electrogenesis. The R-G and Y-B cells of fish retina also produce depolarizing and hyperpolarizing potentials without spikes (184).

Some invertebrate muscle fibers possess dual synaptic activity (72, 73) and it has been suggested (96) that vertebrate smooth muscle may also belong to this category. If the fibers are not electrically excitable, the contractions caused by their depolarizing p.s.p.'s would be local, as in frog 'slow' muscle fibers (34, 35, 132). The hyperpolarizing p.s.p.'s would serve the function of diminishing or regulating the degree of the mechanical response by decreasing the depolarizations of the 'excitatory' p.s.p.'s.

By far the most prominent class are the cells in which spikes as well as the two kinds of p.s.p.'s are generated. Most, and perhaps all, neurons of the vertebrate central nervous system probably belong to this group (cf. 59, 60, 158, 159, 161–167). The hyperpolarizing and depolarizing p.s.p.'s appear to have nearly identical durations and the superposition of the two p.s.p.'s may decrease membrane depolarization sufficiently to eliminate spike production by an orthodromic excitatory pathway. This interaction of depolarizing and hyperpolarizing p.s.p.'s adds to the variety and flexibility of integrative activity within the central nervous system. The effects are achieved not only by relatively simple algebraic summation of the potentials but also by the interplay of more subtle factors which will be described in the next section of this chapter.

Fast and Slow Responses of Invertebrate Muscles

The muscle fibers of some insects and crustacea (cf. 116, 117) are known to be electrically excitable, but they also respond differently to stimulation of different excitatory nerves (fig. 21). Their 'fast' innervation, which may be constituted of one or several nerve fibers, produces large depolarizing p.s.p.'s upon which is superimposed a spike-like response, often showing a small overshoot. Stimulation of the 'slow' nerve fiber leads to a small depolarizing p.s.p. Upon this there may develop various gradations of the electrically excitable response. The mechanical activities are also different. The fast nerve fiber

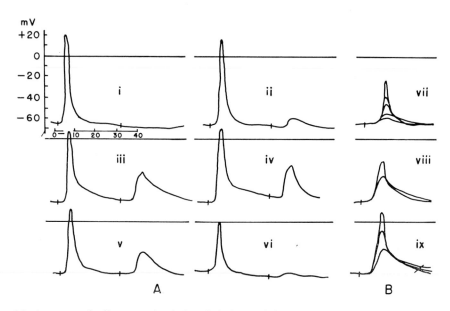

FIG. 21. Different responses produced in insect muscle fibers on stimulating their fast and slow innervation. Intracellular recording from extensor tibiae of the mesothoracic leg of *Schistocerca gregaria. A:* The responses of six different muscle fibers, first to stimulation of the fast nerve fiber and then the slow. In all but one muscle fiber, the fast response developed an overshoot. A notch on the response of fiber *ii* indicates the level on the p.s.p. out of which the spike-like activity developed. In fiber *i*, as in about 50 per cent of the muscle fibers, no response resulted on stimulating the slow nerve fiber. Various grades of activity are shown in the other examples. In three of these (*iii, iv, v*) the p.s.p. was large enough to evoke some local response of the electrically excitable membrane. *B:* Three examples of facilitation of the p.s.p.'s by repetitive stimulation of the slow nerve at about 30 per sec. The augmented p.s.p.'s evoked larger pulsatile local responses, and in one case (*ix*) an overshoot was obtained. Time and amplitude calibration in (*i*) apply to all records. [From Hoyle (116).]

evokes a brisk twitch or a maximal tetanus. The slow fiber calls forth small contractions which may grow slowly during repetitive stimulation.

The apparent paradox that depolarization, an electrical and unspecific stimulus, can evoke different forms of response in electrically excitable membrane has been resolved by the finding (37, 38) that the membrane of the muscle fibers of the grasshopper, *Romalea microptera*, though electrically excitable, responds only with graded activity. Other physiological and anatomical circumstances cooperate with this normally occurring graded responsiveness. The different nerve fibers evoke two degrees of depolarizing p.s.p.'s in the electrically inexcitable synaptic membrane. The p.s.p.'s evoked by the fast nerve fiber may be larger because of greater synaptic potency of the 'fast' transmitter system than in that of the slow fiber (e.g. a different agent, a higher concentration of transmitter, closer approximation of the pre- and postsynaptic membrane or larger area of synaptic contact). However, another alternative is that the membrane sites engaged by the terminals of the different fibers are different. The combination of graded p.s.p.'s and electrically excitable local responses is abetted by the closeness of synaptic terminations. The terminals of the fast nerve fiber, spaced as close as 40μ apart, can each evoke large local responses of the electrically excitable membrane. This graded activity, summing its depolarizing actions, can then evoke maximal responses which have the appearance of spikes. The associated contraction is a twitch. The smaller p.s.p.'s of the slow response can be graded in various proportions and can evoke local response of various degrees. The resulting contractions are also graded.

The mechanisms involved in the dual responses of muscle fibers are instructive for several reasons. Dual responsiveness is probably present in muscles of animals quite low in the evolutionary scale (117), and this suggests that electrically excitable membrane, like the sensory or synaptic, was originally gradedly responsive. The ability to develop spikes then would have been a later evolutionary stage (21, 103). Dual responsiveness also represents an exceedingly useful mode of activity for arthropods for their muscles are limited in number. The size of the muscles and therefore also the number of their fibers are limited by the exigencies of the exoskeleton. The number of nerve fibers is also rather small. Despite these limitations arthropods can manipulate their joints intricately and with precision and carry out locomotion with great dispatch and vigor. These different aspects of movement are all achieved with an economy of means because of special responsive mechanisms and anatomical conditions.

PHARMACOLOGICAL PROPERTIES OF SYNAPSES AND THEIR PHYSIOLOGICAL CONSEQUENCES

The discussion in this part of the present chapter will be limited to vertebrate synapses, concerning which information is more extensive than on invertebrate structures. However, the pharmacology of the electrically inexcitable sensory membrane of the crayfish stretch receptor probably parallels that of synapses in the cat brain (96). This suggests that in their general aspects the pharmacological properties of vertebrate and invertebrate synapses will be similar in principle, although, perhaps, involving different chemical substances. In crustacean neuromuscular synapses and in the inhibitory synapses of the stretch receptors the actions of amino acid drugs parallel to a degree the effects of these substances in cat brain (cf. 99, 163, and below). However, other invertebrate synapses appear to have no pharmacological relation to vertebrate synapses (cf. 99).

Classification of Drug Actions

Depending upon the theoretical approach and the experimental emphasis, several varieties of classification have arisen. Thus, drugs have been grouped as 'mimetics' or 'lytics', graded according to the degree to which they mimic or block the action of nerve impulses, or sometimes of a standard comparison substance (cf. 8). Particularly in describing effects of drugs on the more complex synaptic systems (chiefly of the central nervous system but also those of smooth muscle) substances have been classified as 'excitants' (or 'stimulants') and 'inhibitors' (or 'depressants'). For example, since both pentylenetetrazol (Metrazol) and strychnine are convulsant agents, both are classified as stimulants of the central nervous system (cf. 85). Recently (cf. 156) the drugs acting upon the peripheral cholinoceptive synapses of skeletal muscle and autonomic ganglia have been classified as 'depolarizing' or as 'nondepolarizing, competitive, antagonistic inhibitors' of the latter. This classification also applies to the simple depolarizing synapses of the eel electroplaques (table 2).

An extension of this classification (table 3) has proved experimentally and analytically more useful

TABLE 2. *Range of Effectiveness on Single Eel Electroplaques of Some Synapse Inactivating and Synapse Activating Drugs*

Substance	Minimum effective concentration in μg per ml
a) Compounds which inactivate the postsynaptic membrane of eel electroplaques, do not depolarize, but convert the all-or-nothing response of the electrically excitable membrane to the gradedly responsive	
Physostigmine	25
d-Tubocurarine	50
DFP*	100
Procaine	200
Tertiary analog of prostigmine	1000
Flaxedil†	
b) Compounds which activate synapses of eel electroplaques. The resultant depolarization secondarily inactivates the electrically excitable membrane. Synaptic electrogenesis still occurs	
Acetylcholine‡	5
Carbamylcholine	10
Decamethonium	10
Dimethylaminoethyl acetate (DMEA)‡	50
Prostigmine	50
Succinylcholine¶	

* This substance causes a secondary depolarization with consequent inactivation of the electrically excitable membrane.

† Included on the basis of the data of Chagas & Albe-Fessard (39) that the action of Flaxedil is similar to that of curare. These workers did not study membrane potentials or graded responsiveness. Chemically Flaxedil is tri-(diethyl-aminoethoxy) benzene triethyliodide.

‡ In the presence of 25 μg per ml physostigmine.

¶ On the basis of the data of Chagas & Albe-Fessard (39), who found a similarity of action with acetylcholine (see note †).

TABLE 3. *Possible Combinations of Actions of Synaptic Drugs*

Agent	Effect	Synapses Affected		Overt Action	Type Compound
		Depola-rizing (Excita-tory)	Hyper-polar-izing (Inhibi-tory)		
Activators	1	+	+	Excitation	Acetylcholine
	2	+	o	Excitation	Metrazol
	3	o	+	Inhibition	?
Inactivators	4	+	+	Inhibition	Curare
	5	+	o	Inhibition	GABA
	6	o	+	Excitation	Strychnine

\+ indicates an effect; o, none. Diphasic actions omitted.

TABLE 4. *Cortical Synaptic Actions of Aliphatic Amino Acids*

Car-bon No.	α-amino acids	ω-amino acids	α,ω-diamino acids
2	— —		X
	Glycine		
3	o (α-alanine)	— — — — (β-alanine)	X
4	o (α-aminobu-tyric)	— — — — (γ-aminobutyric)	— (2,4 diamino-butyric)
5	o (Norvaline)	— — (α-amino η-valeric)	o (Ornithine)
6	o (Norleucine)	+++ (ε-amino caproic)	+ (Lysine)
8	X	++++ (ω-amino caprylic)	X

Symbols: — to — — — — indicate increasing blockade of excitatory synapses which leads to overt 'inhibitory' action; + to ++++ represent increasing blockade of inhibitory synapses leading to 'excitatory' effects; o, compound not active; X, not available or not tried.

since it applies as well to hyperpolarizing synapses and to systems containing both electrogenic types (96, 97). The two major varieties of drugs are in this case classified as activators or inactivators of synaptic electrogenesis. The nature of the latter, depolarizing or hyperpolarizing, is determined only by the type of synapse not by the activator substance. Each major group is subdivided into drugs which act nonselec-tively or selectively upon either the depolarizing or hyperpolarizing synapses. The interactions of drugs and synapses disclose many subsidiary classifications, both in the drugs and in synaptic membranes (99, 100, 108), but these need not be considered here.

The overt manifestations of 'excitation' and 'in-hibition' of the six classes of drugs in table 3 need not correspond to the basic mode of achieving this effect at the synaptic level. Thus, the 'excitant' ac-

tions of the two convulsant agents, strychnine and pentylentetrazol, are produced by entirely different fundamental processes (166). The similarities in overt effects arise from the conditions that prevail in systems which contain many synapses and of both types. It is then likely that an activity is a mixture involving both excitatory and inhibitory synaptic actions, and the study of the central nervous system has revealed many examples of this. Blockade of synaptic activity thus becomes a positive act, en-hancing or diminishing overt manifestations such as motor activity, depending upon which type of

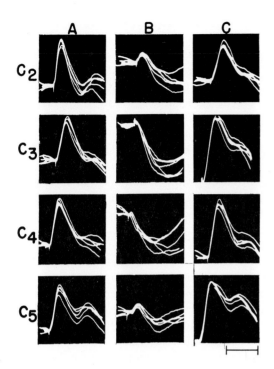

FIG. 22. Synaptic actions of shorter-chain ω-amino acids. Column *A* shows the response evoked in the cat cerebral cortex by a local electrical stimulus (five superimposed traces indicate the degree of variability). The surface negative potential (upward deflection) is the p.s.p. of superficial dendrites. *B* shows the effects of applying 0.2 cc of a 1 per cent buffered ω-amino acid. The substances are identified by the letters on the left which correspond to those in table 4. All the compounds inverted the surface negativity to a surface positivity by blocking production of depolarizing p.s.p.'s and thereby disclosing hyperpolarizing p.s.p.'s which are recorded as surface positivity (downward deflection). The action of all four substances was similar but differed in magnitude and rate of onset, both factors being largest with C_4 (GABA). Column *C* shows that recovery from the action of the compounds is seen 3 min. after rinsing the cortical surface several times with Ringer's solution. Time at bottom, 20 msec. [From Purpura *et al.* (163).]

synapse is inactivated. It is for this reason that selective blockade of inhibitory synapses by strychnine leads to 'excitatory' actions, augmented electrical activity or convulsions.

The selective action of many drugs on either hyperpolarizing or depolarizing synapses introduces an important factor. A substance may act powerfully on one synaptic system and yet be inert with respect to another which lacks the appropriate synaptic substrate for the drug. This has been experimentally verified with strychnine which is a highly selective inactivator of hyperpolarizing inhibitory synapses (fig. 14). Strychnine is inert, except in very high concentrations, on structures like the muscle end-

plate or the vermian cerebellar cortex of cat. However, when given in high concentration it does act to blockade the depolarizing excitatory synapses (166).

In view of the foregoing, tests on relatively simple synapses (table 2; figs. 11, 13, 15) may not be adequate for analyzing drug actions. This fact is illustrated by the recent demonstration and analysis of the synaptic actions of various amino acids (162, 163). The ω-amino acids tested (table 4), substances in which the amino group is on the terminal carbon farthest from the carboxyl radical, are selective inactivators of cortical synapses. The shorter chain compounds (C_2 to C_5, fig. 22) block depolarizing activity of the dendrites while compounds C_6 and C_8 (fig. 23) inactivate hyperpolarizing synapses.

One of these substances, γ-aminobutyric acid (GABA), occurs naturally in the brain (12, 173) and has been identified (16) as a component of the 'inhibitory factor' which can be extracted from mammalian brain and which diminishes the discharge of impulses in the mechanically excited crayfish stretch receptor. As a selective blockader of depolarizing receptor and synaptic membrane, GABA can only act as an ostensible 'inhibitor' when confronted with the simple depolarizing electrogenic membrane. Thus it acts on the cerebellar cortex as

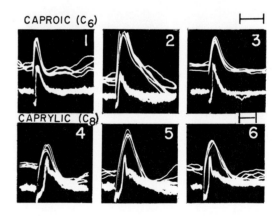

FIG. 23. The qualitatively different effects produced by ω-amino acids with longer carbon chains. In each experiment, responses were simultaneously evoked from the surface of the cerebral cortex (upper trace) and cerebellar cortex (lower trace). *1* and *4* show the responses in different experiments before applying the amino acids; *2* and *5*, the cerebral p.s.p.'s increased on applying C_6 or C_8. The cerebellar activity was not affected indicating that these ω-amino acids are inert toward the cerebellum. *3* and *6*, responses after rinsing the cortical surfaces with Ringer's solution. Time, 20 msec., is different in the two experiments. Four traces superimposed in each record. [From Purpura *et al.* (162).]

it does on crayfish stretch receptor membrane by eliminating the depolarizing electrogenesis (fig. 24). However, when GABA is applied to the cerebral cortex, its selective elimination of depolarizing surface-negative p.s.p.'s discloses the previously masked hyperpolarizing surface-positive p.s.p.'s. Acting in the cerebral cortex (figs. 22, 24) GABA and its congeners invert the electrocortical activity evoked by a stimulus.

The effects of the selective inactivators of hyperpolarizing synapses, C_6 and C_8 (fig. 23), also differ depending upon the type of electrogenic structure

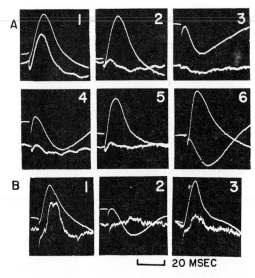

FIG. 24. Different effects of the selective inactivator of depolarizing p.s.p.'s at different sites. *A*, *1 to 5*: Simultaneous recordings from the cerebral cortex with a large surface electrode (upper trace) and a fine wire electrode (lower trace). *1*, both electrodes were on the surface and recorded nearly identically the evoked surface negative p.s.p.'s of the superficial cerebral dendrites. *2*, the fine electrode was inserted about 0.4 mm below the surface into an essentially isoelectric region. *3* and *4*, application of GABA to the cortical surface reversed the surface response into positivity, but this change did not appear in the subsurface recording. This indicates that the effect produced by the amino acid was on superficial p.s.p.'s only. *5*, rinsing the cortical surface restored the original activity at the surface. The subsurface recording was still unchanged. *6*, superimposed responses before and during the action of GABA. *B*: The simultaneous recordings in this experiment were from the cerebral cortex (upper trace) and the cerebellar (lower trace). *1*, before applying GABA; *2*, five drops of 0.1 per cent GABA were applied to each site. In the cerebral cortex the result was a reversal of surface potential. In the cerebellar cortex the surface negativity was eliminated by blockade of the depolarizing p.s.p.'s, but no positivity developed because of the paucity of hyperpolarizing synapses in this structure. *3*, recovery was rapid in the cerebral and slower in the cerebellar cortex. Time, 20 msec. [From Purpura *et al*. (163).]

that is used as a test object. Neither the crayfish stretch receptor nor the cerebellar cortex is affected by application of ω-aminocaprylic acid (C_8). However, the surface negativity evoked in the cerebral cortex is augmented by the blockade which C_6 and C_8 cause amongst the surface-positive p.s.p.'s of the hyperpolarizing synapses.

Recent work (Grundfest *et al.*, in preparation; cf. 99, 163) indicates that the axodendritic synaptic membrane in the cat brain stands in a doubly inverted pharmacological relation with some crustacean synapses. GABA and other inactivators of the cat depolarizing synapses activate crustacean inhibitory synapses. Picrotoxin, an activator of cat excitatory synapses, inactivates the crustacean inhibitory synapses. One of the selective inactivators of cat inhibitory synapses, carnitine (cf. 163), activates the excitatory synapses of lobster muscle fibers. However, these inverted parallels are not complete. The C_6 and C_8 ω-amino acids do not affect the crustacean synapses. Likewise, acetylcholine, *d*-tubocurarine and strychnine are without effect.

In sum, it may be concluded from the foregoing discussion that determination of the mode of action of a drug depends not only on the degree of intimate knowledge which may be obtained of its synaptic effects but also upon the type of information that may be provided by the test object. The synaptic structure used for the tests may be too complex to yield the details required, but also it may be too simple and provide only misleadingly partial information.

Identification and Characterization of Transmitter Agents

The preceding section sets the theoretical and methodological background for the problems treated in this. The quantity of transmitters released during activity of presynaptic terminals is probably exceedingly small (cf. 52, 59, 60, 68). The problem of their identification therefore is strongly conditioned by methodology. For example, norepinephrine has been known, since its laboratory synthesis in 1904 (cf. 193), to have properties similar to those of its homologue, epinephrine. Also, the work of Cannon and his associates (cf. 177) had indicated very clearly that there must be at least several sympathetic transmitters which were designated as sympathins E (excitatory) and I (inhibitory). Nevertheless, norepinephrine was not accepted as a possible sympathetic transmitter until it was shown in 1946 (cf. 193) that it is a natural constitutent of the body. Likewise, interest in GABA stems from the demonstration of its occurrence in the brain in an important pathway of synthesis (12, 172). Thus, the candidate for a transmitter agent must meet a number of requirements (cf. also 65): *a*) it must mimic closely the actions produced by the natural, neural stimulus; *b*) its actions must be affected by the same drugs and in the same ways as neural excitation is modified; *c*) it must be a naturally occurring constitutent, found in close proximity to the relevant synaptic structures; and *d*) it is desirable to demonstrate that it is formed by an appropriate metabolic pathway, that it is released at the time, place and in the degree suitable to transmitter action and that its accumulation to excess is prevented by another metabolic pathway.

Characterized by the foregoing criteria, acetylcholine and the catechol amines of the epinephrine group are still the only substances commonly agreed upon and accepted as peripheral transmitter agents. Most conspicuously, these substances derive their claim to transmitter agents by their actions as synapse activators. Thus, acetylcholine is probably the excitatory transmitter at electroplaques, muscle fibers, autonomic ganglia and some gland cells. At the effector junctions of the cardiac pacemaker and probably also in many smooth muscle systems (96), acetylcholine activates hyperpolarizing synapses and is inhibitory. The epinephrine group of transmitters acts similarly at other synapses. However, these transmitters also appear to have an accessory function (cf. 36). Thus epinephrine may antagonize the action of decamethonium (47) or relieve 'fatigue' of neuromuscular transmission upon repetitive stimulation (119).[6]

In complex synaptic systems, one may assign transmitter action to substances which do inactivate synapses. For example, GABA is a synapse inactivator, but if it is released by specific nerve fibers its effects would be essentially inhibitory—with the important exception that there would be no accompaniment of hyperpolarizing p.s.p. Likewise there might be transmitters, analogous to C_8, whose overt

action, excitation, might be produced by inactivating hyperpolarizing inhibitory synapses.

These considerations indicate the difficulty of identifying transmitters in a complexly organized synaptic structure. The difficulty is enormously compounded in the central nervous system, where even a small volume of tissue contains a huge number of synapses. In such a case all the criteria for categorizing transmitters cannot be fulfilled at present and therefore identification is always tentative, based as it must be on incomplete evidence.

Nevertheless, there is evidence from various sources that acetylcholine and the adrenergic agents do affect central nervous activity. Thus, circulatory injections of epinephrine (22) or acetylcholine (cf. 111) bring about EEG activation as does stimulation of the peripheral stump of the cat splanchnic nerve (22). The electrical activity of a cortical slab, isolated from its neural connections but surviving with intact blood supply, is altered upon electrical stimulation of the brain stem reticular formation (122). Thus, brain stem activity releases some transmitter agents which can then affect the isolated cortex. This finding has been extended to cross-perfused preparations (160). From that work it may be concluded that what is released during brain stem activity enters the systemic circulation and that it must be a substance (or several) more stable than is acetylcholine. The latter probably would have been destroyed completely or almost so during the time required for an exchange of circulating blood between donor and host. Many workers have shown that acetylcholine is found in the central nervous system as well as its synthesizing acetylating enzyme (for references to the recent literature cf. 65). The distributions of these substances in the brain and of sympathetic transmitters (192) have also been mapped. Lesions in some regions of the reticular formation augment or depress the sensitivity of the cortical electrical activity to epinephrine (178). Intraventricular application of cholinomimetic and adrenomimetic substances or of blockaders of the two types of synapses produce a variety of central nervous symptoms (cf. 75, and literature cited there). Intravenous injections of *d*-tubocurarine block central nervous synapses (cf. 165).

Evidence with respect to other agents is still inconclusive. Although 5-hydroxytryptamine (serotonin) and metabolically related substances are believed by some to be implicated in transmission, whether they act directly or not is still in question (cf. 26, 128, 148). As stressed earlier in this part,

[6] Neuromuscular blockade by decamethonium is a manifestation of Wedensky inhibition discussed earlier. Antagonism by epinephrine suggests that this transmitter agent acts as a competitive antagonist, or synapse inactivator, of cholinoceptive synaptic membrane. This type of action is apparently contradicted by the effect of epinephrine in lifting the blockade produced by repetitive activity. However, there need be no real contradiction for synaptic membrane may change its properties under different experimental circumstances, an indication of the complexity as well as lability of the active structure (cf. 96).

the difficulties are largely methodological because central synapses are so intricately interrelated and may present many varieties. Stemming from this is the difficulty of determining whether or not various synaptic sites are affected, and if they are what results are to be looked for. Thus it has been shown (162, 163) that the synaptically active amino acids affect primarily only axodendritic synapses of the cortex and only secondarily the axosomatic. Some consequences are seen in figure 25. Blockade of excitatory synapses of the dendrites by C_4 (GABA) or of inhibitory synapses by C_6 (ε-aminocaproic acid) does not affect the corticospinal discharge of the pyramidal cells. However, the convulsive electro-cortical activity induced by C_8 (ω-aminocaprylic acid) leads to prolonged discharge in the tract.

A further difficulty is the problem of accessibility of the central synapses to testing drugs. The blood-brain barrier apparently is highly effective for some

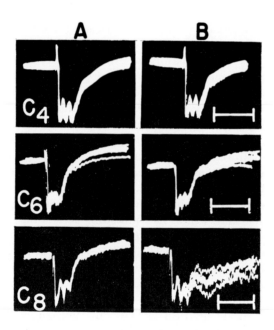

FIG. 25. Pyramidal tract activity when dendritic responses in cerebral cortex are affected by ω-amino acids. *Column A*, the discharge recorded from the pyramidal tracts to stimulation of the cerebral cortex in cats. Then, 0.2 cc of 1 per cent ω-amino acid had been applied for 10 min. The substances were C_4 and C_8 as noted in each row of records. The responses of *column B* were obtained when the cortical potentials had been altered as shown in figs. 22 and 24. Despite these changes, the pyramidal tract responses, generated by direct electrical stimuli and by axosomatic synaptic excitations, were not affected (C_4, C_6) except when as in the case of C_8, the drug caused convulsions. Then a long after-discharge, associated with the convulsions, developed. Ten superimposed traces in the upper records, five in the middle and lower set. Time 10 msec. [From Purpura *et al.* (163).]

substances, e.g. GABA [Roberts & Baxter (172)]. Recent experiments (164) demonstrate that local abolition of the blood-brain barrier permits the local action of systemically injected ω-amino acids. These results indicate that if the substances are elaborated within the brain they might act as transmitters (using the term for both synapse activators and inactivators; cf. above), although the usual experimental criteria would not disclose such action.

Modes of Action of Transmitter Agents and Synaptic Drugs

Since transmitters must be formed and, after their release, metabolized in the body, enzymes for these activities are components more or less related to the appropriate synaptic systems. In the search for mechanisms of drug action, interference with enzymatic or other metabolic processes has been frequently stressed (cf. 2, 13, 14, 26, 65, and literature cited in these papers). Undoubtedly, interference with these metabolic systems must cause synaptic disturbance; but it is likely that such actions are relatively slow, manifesting themselves, as in the case of vitamin deficiencies, only after depletion of reserves. This is not the case with drugs that have primary action on synapses (108). This may be seen in figures 22 to 24 in which the synaptic effects of some of the ω-amino acids were obtained within a second after they were applied and were rapidly reversed by dilution.

Furthermore, substances of the same type of action on enzymatic systems may have entirely different synaptic actions. Thus physostigmine, DFP and prostigmine are powerful inhibitors of cholinesterase. By that effect all three, in very high dilution, enhance neural action in eel electroplaques (5). This is merely the indication that they prolong the life of the labile transmitter agent. However, the synaptic actions of the three drugs on the eel electroplaque are diverse (table 2). In that capacity prostigmine is a synapse activator like acetylcholine itself. Physostigmine is an inactivator like *d*-tubocurarine and about as potent in that effect. DFP appears to have dual actions such as are to be found in the many other situations (cf. 95, 96, 127).

The conclusion reached from these considerations leads back to the view first proposed by Ehrlich (cf. 2, 14, 40) that drugs exert their action by affecting, perhaps by some form of chemical or electrostatic combination, the performance of specific molecular structures of the cell membrane. This receptor theory has had many vicissitudes, apparently largely because of static conceptions of such functional units.

Recently the models examined have been endowed with dynamic properties (cf. 2, 9, and literature cited in the papers). These current theoretical formulations have had some success in accounting for relations between structures of drugs and their functions. They do not, as yet, consider the implications of the recent findings concerning specificity of drug action on one or the other type of synaptic membrane. Thus the addition of one carbon link to an ω-amino acid converts a substance which is predominantly an inactivator of depolarizing synapses (C_5) to another (C_6) which inactivates chiefly, or perhaps exclusively, the hyperpolarizing type (table 4; figs. 22, 23). In other relations of drugs, similar abrupt transitions depending upon number of carbons (the transformation occurring at about five carbons) have also been noted (cf. 14, p. 147).

The occurrence of distinct varieties of synaptically acting chemotherapeutic agents, e.g. analgesics, antipyretics, etc., bespeaks relatively sharp, though not absolute, differences between synaptic membranes in differently acting regions of the central nervous system. Similar distinctions, both peripheral and central, derive from the relatively specific actions of other drugs. Thus, whether synaptic transmission is blockaded by atropine or by d-tubocurarine forms part of the differentiation between muscarinic and nicotinic cholinoceptive synapses.

Physiological Implications

Only a few selected aspects can be discussed here of the relations between the modes of action of transmitter agents and their physiological consequences.

A) TOPOGRAPHIC DISTINCTIONS. In many cases the action of a transmitter must be rather strictly localized. This is due to a number of factors which differ in importance for different transmitters and synaptic sites. The small quantity of transmitter released by a presynaptic nerve fiber would rapidly lose effectiveness upon diffusion and dilution in the volume away from the synaptic site. It may be destroyed by enzymes or fixed in various chemical combinations. Its effectiveness at other synaptic sites may be small or absent. The rate at which it moves from the region in which it was liberated may be very slow.

These, and other factors that may be postulated, tend to restrict transmitter action to limited sites, although under special experimental conditions diffusion is easily demonstrated (cf. 177). Electrical inexcitability of synaptic membrane and its chemical

specificities promote restriction of transmitter action which is desirable in intricate synaptic relations. The specificities of different, perhaps of alternating synapses in a synaptic sequence, as suggested by Feldberg (cf. 157), would be one means of achieving this result. In the spinal cord, interneurons and motoneurons appear to have somewhat different pharmacological properties (cf. 60).

Different parts of the same neuron might also have differently sensitive synaptic membranes. Thus, the ω-amino acids appear to be chiefly effective as synapse inactivators at the superficial axodendritic synapses of cortical neurons (fig. 25). In the context of electrically inexcitable activity of these dendrites (165) the function of dendritic electrogenesis is probably that of modulating somatic responsiveness, a consequence which cannot be discussed here (cf. 101).

B) SYNAPTIC SPECIFICITY AND TRANSMITTERS. Eccles (cf. 60) has emphasized the implication of Dale's suggestion (46) that one neuron at all its profuse terminals probably generates only one type of transmitter. This 'principle' is reasonable but is not at all an obligatory condition. Furthermore, a neuron secreting the same transmitter at different synaptic sites may produce depolarization and be an 'excitant' at one, or cause hyperpolarization and be an 'inhibitor' at another variety of synaptic membrane. Likewise, the same neuron might produce at its different terminals several varieties of transmitters which might all have the same effect, excitatory or inhibitory, or opposite actions, depending entirely upon the variety of postsynaptic membrane which is in synaptic relation with the transmitters. This emphasizes that the nature of the transmitter can determine synaptic potency and the kinetics of the synaptic activity (cf. 97). The type of electrogenic action is determined by the postsynaptic membrane.[7]

C) RECIPROCAL INTERACTIONS OF NEURAL PATHWAYS. The mechanisms of dual action discussed above have bearing upon the interpretation of reciprocal innervation. Sherington discovered in spinal reflexes (44) that the development of reflex activity in one muscle is associated with concurrent inhibition of antagonistic muscular activity. These interactions extend to

---

[7] Interactions of some drugs evoke apparently dual actions at the muscle endplate (cf. 53). These may be cases of the situation commented upon earlier, in which a drug activates some components and inactivates others in the same synaptic membrane. This implies that the membrane of a single synapse is not homogeneous.

other muscle groups that participate in an organized movement (cf. 140). These effects frequently are fully reciprocal, excitation in either path being associated with inhibition in the other, and thus they involve processes of reciprocal inhibition as well as primary excitation.

A mechanism, discovered by Lloyd (cf. 138) and termed direct inhibition, was believed to be mediated monosynaptically, the collaterals of the same afferent nerve fiber at one motoneuron evoking excitation, those to another producing inhibition. This mechanism would imply that the same transmitter evokes depolarizing p.s.p.'s in one neuron and hyperpolarizing p.s.p.'s in another cell. From the point of view of theoretical considerations this means of achieving reciprocal actions is perfectly feasible, as is the possibility that different transmitters are released at the different terminals of the same primary afferent nerve fiber. In the lobster cardiac ganglion (33, 186) one presynaptic nerve causes excitation in one neuron and inhibition in another.

The reality of monosynaptic direct inhibition of this type in the cat spinal cord is at present in dispute. Lloyd and his colleagues (cf. 194) maintain that a monosynaptic pathway exists while Eccles and his associates (cf. 60) consider that 'direct' inhibition is a disynaptic event. Whether the particular reflex pathways under discussion are monosynaptic or disynaptic is probably a matter of the specific structures involved and perhaps of the methodological details.[8] In principle, direct inhibition by monosynaptic reciprocal innervation can occur. Since it is theoretically feasible it seems unlikely that among the many types of connections elaborated in the nervous system one possible and rather simple variety has been omitted.

ROLE OF ELEMENTARY SYNAPTIC PROPERTIES IN INTEGRATIVE ACTIVITY

Spatial Interrelations of Synaptic and Conductile Membrane

Since p.s.p.'s are 'standing' nonpropagated potentials, their effect upon the electrically excitable

[8] Drugs such as pentobarbital, for example, can alter profoundly the pathways that produce pyramidal tract activity through thalamocortical relays. This is disclosed by changes in latency of several msec. when 4 to 10 mg per kg of pentobarbital are administered (99, 101, 161 and unpublished work).

membrane of the same cell depends upon the spatial arrangement of these differently excitable structures. Assuming as a first approximation that the electrically excitable membrane everywhere in a cell is triggered to discharge a spike by the same level of critical depolarization, and that the depolarizing p.s.p.'s are everywhere equal in amplitude, the intensity of excitation of the former by the latter will depend upon the distance between the synaptic focus and the nearest conductile membrane. The more closely the two electrogenic membrane sites approximate each other the more intense will be the excitation for triggering a spike. The apical dendrites of the cerebral cortex are not electrically excitable (107) and the p.s.p.'s of the axodendritic synapses generated at some distance from electrically excitable membrane therefore would not be expected to be as effective as the axosomatic p.s.p.'s generated in close contiguity with electrically excitable membrane. Thus, the apical dendrites of cortical neurons, although they generate intense synaptic activity (165) are not as effective in triggering spikes as are the depolarizing synaptic loci at the soma (27, 101).

Spatial considerations may also be applied to the effects of hyperpolarizing p.s.p.'s. The latter would be most intensely inhibitory if they are interposed between sites of excitatory p.s.p.'s and electrically excitable membrane. The depolarizing p.s.p., in that case, would be diminished not only by electrotonic averaging between the opposed electrogenic actions. The interposed hyperpolarizing site would receive more outward current flow than resting membrane since its resistance would be lower, and the potential gradient steeper. Consequently this bypass would result in less current flow from the depolarizing synaptic site to the electrically excitable but as yet inactive membrane. Thus, the loci at which depolarizing and hyperpolarizing p.s.p.'s are generated, both relative to each other and to electrically excitable membrane, must play an important role in determining the effectiveness of transmission from a given afferent volley. The simplifying assumption that all synaptic sites are electrogenically equivalent is probably not justified (see below). It is also likely that the conductile membrane in different parts of a cell varies with respect to its electrical threshold (79) or that it is differently electrogenic (69), and these factors may reinforce the transmissional inhomogeneity of different synaptic sites.

*Physiological Factors Determining
Transmissional Effectiveness*

A) SYNAPTIC POTENCY AND DRIVE. Just as different parts of the same cell exhibit variations with respect to electrical threshold so also do different cells in a population, that is, the critical firing level may be lower for one cell than for another. In that case, an afferent volley equally effective in generating p.s.p.'s in all the cells may discharge some of these but not others. It is unlikely, however, that the synaptic potency of a given influx is identical for all cells. Even in single multiply-innervated cells, such as the eel electroplaque (4), the p.s.p.'s generated over the large surface are of different amplitudes and always largest at a definite region of the cell surface. Thus, the p.s.p.'s generated in a population of motoneurons would vary in magnitude depending upon the synaptic potency of the afferents to each cell. This variation, added to that of the distribution of electrical thresholds, results in a population spread with respect to excitatory effects or synaptic drives. It is obvious that the degree to which the given synaptic inflow also excites hyperpolarizing p.s.p.'s as well as depolarizing, and the relative spatial distributions of the two electrogenic activities will affect the magnitude of the synaptic drive.

The differences in synaptic drive deduced above adequately account for a mass of experimental data. The cells in a population of neurons impinged upon by a sample from a population of innervating nerve fibers will respond with different degrees of depolarizing p.s.p.'s. Some of the cells will discharge spikes which can be recorded directly (e.g. fig. 12) or by means of other effects, as for example by their reflex activation of muscle in the case of motoneurons. In other cells excited by the afferent volley the p.s.p.'s alone are generated.

B) EXCITED AND DISCHARGED ZONES. Thus, an excitatory volley causing quantitatively different amounts of synaptic activity also divides the population of postjunctional cells qualitatively. One group, frequently by far the smaller, falls in the discharged zone, the other in the excited zone (fig. 26). In this distribution the occurrence and influence of hyperpolarizing inhibitory p.s.p.'s may also be considerable but need not be discussed in detail, except in the extreme case when the neural volley generates predominantly or entirely hyperpolarizing p.s.p.'s. In that case spike electrogenesis would not occur and the volley in isolation may produce no overt effects, although direct recording from the cells would dis-

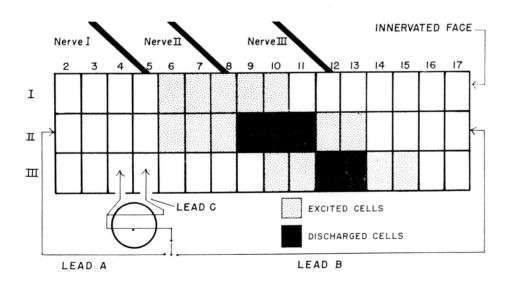

FIG. 26. Discharged and excited zones in a row of eel electroplaques on maximal stimulation of their three different nerve supplies. Cells 6 to 10 were excited by Nerve I as evidenced by their p.s.p.'s and long-lasting homosynaptic facilitation, but did not develop spikes to a single testing stimulus. Nerve II caused discharge of spikes in cells 9 to 11, but in addition excited cells 6 to 8 and 12 and 13. Nerve III discharged cells 12 and 13, exciting also cells 10, 11, 14 and 15. The diagrammatic representation of the recording leads shows the method that was used to test this population of cells. [From Altamirano *et al.* (5).]

close the p.s.p.'s. These, like the excitatory p.s.p.'s, should vary in amplitude in the population of post-junctional cells. An overt manifestation of the inhibitory p.s.p.'s would occur if the cells are at the same time producing excitatory p.s.p.'s and spikes or causing reflex activity in muscles. More or less selective afferent activation of inhibition, and its role in spinal reflex activity, was demonstrated by Sherrington (44, 182; cf. 140). Relatively specific descending pathways were found by Sechenov (180) in the frog and by Magoun and his colleagues (cf. 147) in the mammal.

c) FACILITATION. Study of spinal cord reflexes also demonstrated the existence of the excited zone by the effects of temporal and spatial facilitation, the excited cells being then termed the subliminal fringe. Both types of facilitation depend essentially upon the properties of summation and sustained response of p.s.p.'s described above. However, subsidiary effects also participate which will be discussed later. The unitary p.s.p.'s are relatively long lasting, in the cat central nervous system having a duration of about 15 msec. (figs. 12, 27). For that time at least, thforeere, an excited cell is somewhat depolarized, at first to a large degree, but not to that of the critical level for discharge, and then to a smaller amount, decreasing with time.

The presence of the excited cells can be tested by applying a second volley either through the pathway which delivered the first conditioning stimulus (homosynaptic testing) or through another innervating path (heterosynaptic testing).

d) HOMOSYNAPTIC FACILITATION. In this case, there will be no second response, neither an electrical activity nor a reflex contraction of muscles, if the stimulus interval is very short. Because of absolute

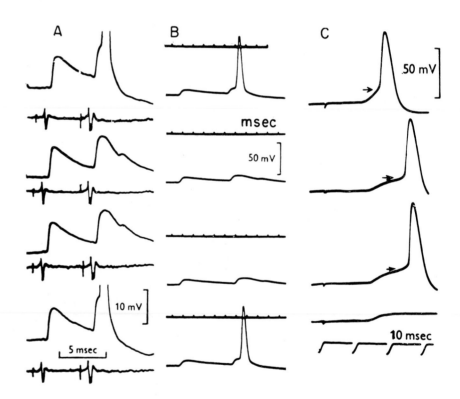

FIG. 27. Temporal facilitation and shortening of synaptic delays in neurons. *A, B:* From a cat motoneuron at high and low amplification. Two orthodromic stimuli, neither capable of discharging the cell, can evoke a spike by summation of the p.s.p.'s produced by each stimulus. Since the spike occurs only when the critical level of depolarization is attained, the summation interval may be sharply delineated as shown in this example. [From Brock *et al.* (24).] *C:* From a rabbit cervical sympathetic neuron. Progressively stronger stimuli to the preganglionic nerve increased the p.s.p. of the neuron and evoked its spike earlier as the critical firing level (shown by arrows) was attained earlier. [From Eccles (64).]

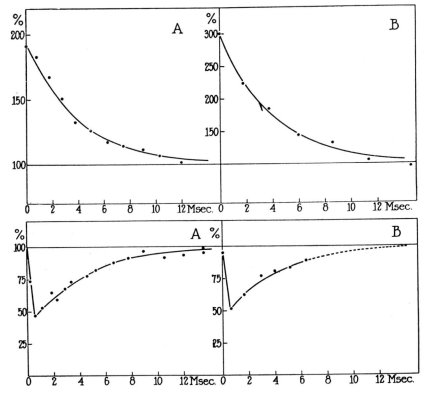

FIG. 28. The time courses of facilitation and direct inhibition (magnitude of response as percent of control value) tested on monosynaptic reflexes are nearly symmetrical. Facilitation (*upper curves*), *A* in an extensor and *B* in a flexor muscle. Inhibition (*lower curves*), *A* in a flexor and *B* in an extensor muscle. [From Lloyd (140).]

refractoriness of the presynaptic fibers, no impulses arrive at the synapses. At slightly longer intervals, relative refractoriness or persistent absolute refractoriness of the previously discharged postjunctional cells causes a depressed testing response, but then an interval is reached when the testing response can become many times higher than it would have been without the preceding conditioning activity. As noted above, the facilitation in the simplest cases lasts about 15 msec. (fig. 28), decreasing continuously from its peak value during this interval. It is likely, although this has not as yet been generally established, that the synaptic drive of the testing volley is also increased by antecedent activity of the nerve fibers. This enhancement may take place in the presynaptic fibers themselves. For example, invasion of the terminal branches by the conductile activity may be partial for a single volley and larger for a subsequent. Also, the amount of transmitter released by the second activity may be larger. In many junctional systems, the prolonged stimulation of the presynaptic nerve at relatively high frequencies for some time thereafter increases the effects produced by a subsequent single testing stimulus (76, 87, 124, 135, 139). This phenomenon, post-tetanic (cf. 118)

or postactivating (59) potentiation, may likewise depend upon the mechanisms just described. Increased synaptic drive may also involve the postsynaptic membrane as, for instance, by a temporary change in the excitability of the membrane to the transmitter agent. These residual presynaptic and postsynaptic effects may alter synaptic drive in either direction and act without relation to the residual p.s.p. from the first volley. Thus, the homosynaptic facilitation which occurs in the eel electroplaque (fig. 29) lasts for about 1 sec., whereas the p.s.p. lasts only 2 to 3 msec. (4, 5, 6).

E) HETEROSYNAPTIC FACILITATION. Heterosynaptic testing eliminates the complications introduced in homosynaptic facilitation except the refractoriness of the discharged postjunctional cells. The facilitation now may start at very brief intervals between the stimuli. Strictly speaking, however, heterosynaptic testing involves spatial factors for the terminations of one pathway may activate different synaptic sites than do those of the other. The facilitation is therefore likely to take place by electrotonic additions of the depolarization produced by the testing stimulus onto the residual level of general de-

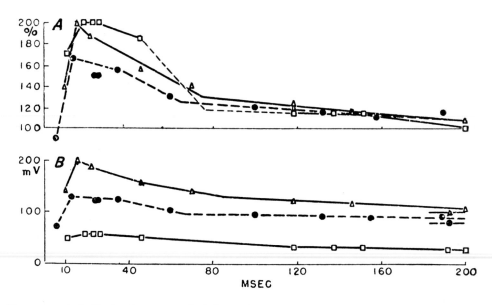

FIG. 29. The time course of homosynaptic facilitation in a group of eel electroplaques. The testing stimulus alone evoked responses shown by the horizontal lines at the end of the graph in *B*. At various intervals after a conditioning stimulus, the response to the test stimulus became larger than this control value and gradually returned toward it. ● : Facilitation without treatment with drug. △ : 12 min. after adding 50 μg per ml physostigmine the cells became somewhat more excitable, the whole curve of facilitation being lifted on the baseline of the larger response to the testing stimulus in isolation. This effect presumably developed because of the anticholinesterase action of physostigmine; it is also produced by prostigmine. The two substances, however, have opposite synaptic action, physostigmine being an inactivator of synaptic electrogenesis and prostigmine an excitant. □ : 64 min. later, the physostigmine had depressed synaptic excitability and the whole curve had fallen. Expressed in percentile values of the response to the testing stimulus alone in each condition, the three curves had essentially the same magnitudes and time courses (*A*). [From Altamirano *et al.* (6).]

polarization remaining from the prior stimulus. This is, indeed, the condition found experimentally (fig. 30*A*) in the electroplaques from the Sachs organ of the eel. Both depolarizing p.s.p.'s being short, facilitation occurs only during the first 2 msec. In cells of the main organ, however, heterosynaptic facilitation lasts some 50 to 75 msec. (fig. 30*B*) and in this case the effect must be due to alteration of the excitability of the synaptic membrane since presynaptic interactions are ruled out. The different behavior of the electroplaques in the two organs is probably ascribable to different spatial relations of their synapses. If those in the electroplaques of the main organ are closely spaced, diffusion of transmitter from the sites activated by the conditioning volley might affect the excitability of the synaptic loci innervated by the second neural pathway (95).

The data presented above derive from a particularly favorable structural configuration, a large postsynaptic cell with an extensive responsive membrane (about 15 mm² in area) diffusely innervated by several easily isolated nerve trunks. The experimental conditions that obtain in nerve cells do not usually permit as clear a delineation between different spatial interactions. However, in the case of cells with long dendrites, as in the cortex, it may be expected that interaction between different axosomatic synapses will be greater than that between these and the axodendritic.

F) SPATIAL SUMMATION OF CONVERGING PATHWAYS. Another variety of spatial summation is more frequently noted in the central nervous system. This is the case in which two widely separated neuronal complexes eventually converge upon one or more common paths. In that final common path the situation then reduces to a variant of the case discussed above. These convergent types of interaction are further complicated in the central nervous system by the involvement of inhibitory p.s.p.'s. Spatial

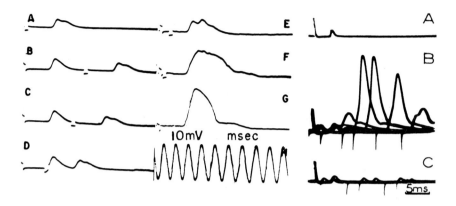

FIG. 30. Heterosynaptic facilitatory actions in eel electroplaques from different electric organs. *Left:* Absence of heterosynaptic facilitation in cells from the Sachs organ. Activity of one nerve evoked the response seen in *A.* This response was preceded by that evoked through another nerve in *B* to *G.* Only when the two stimuli (shock artifacts on the left of the records) were less than 1 msec. apart (*F, G*) was there a significant amount of facilitation caused by electrotonic summation of the brief p.s.p. [From Altamirano *et al.* (5).] *Right:* Heterosynaptic facilitation in cells of the main organ. *A:* The response to stimulating one nerve trunk. *B:* This nerve trunk is used to deliver the conditioning stimulus (artifact at the left, upward); the testing stimulus is applied at various intervals later to another nerve trunk (artifact down, superimposed traces). Marked facilitation reached a peak at 10 to 15 msec. and persisted through the end of the record at 25 msec. *C:* Nerve 2 was cut, and a third nerve trunk was used for the testing stimuli. No facilitation occurred. [From Albe-Fessard & Chagas (1).]

inhibition or facilitation may develop particularly in the more complex varieties of synaptic organization. The precise effects would depend on the specific pathways and electrical responses involved and cannot be discussed in this chapter (cf. 99–101, 161).

Integrative Utility of Electrical Inexcitability

The foregoing group of integrative activities depends essentially upon graded, algebraically summative potentials of opposite signs which are made available in synaptic transmission by electrical inexcitability. In some neurons, relatively large scale areas of membrane are not electrically excitable and this would appear to aid integrative functions. The superficial cortical dendritic surfaces, richly supplied with synaptic inflows, are an example of this. The synaptic activity that goes on at these dendrites result in algebraically summated potentials. Since these dendrites are not electrically excitable, the potentials must be transmitted electrotonically to the electrically excitable membrane of the pyramidal neurons. In each of these the potential can serve to modulate responsiveness to other, more potent synaptic inflows. The soma of lobster cardiac ganglion cells also are not electrically excitable (33, 109,

186). Thus, they can provide sites at which synaptic potentials of both signs may be generated and this electrical summation propagated electrotonically to act upon an electrically excitable membrane distal to the cell body.

Synaptic Determinants of Different Types of Reflexes

In the general context of principles, the precise structural and functional complexity of a reflex pathway is of little moment. Therefore, the specific properties of monosynaptic or multisynaptic reflexes need not be dwelt upon since they are finally referable to the intensity of synaptic drives upon the final common path. The analysis of synaptic mechanisms in many varieties of reflex response can likewise be simplified by merging all interneuronal activities with that of the final common path, essentially involving a reduction to the monosynaptic case.

Synaptic organizations involving very strong synaptic drive for depolarizing p.s.p.'s will manifest themselves by large synchronized efferent electrical activity or a twitch-like contraction in response to a single afferent volley. The amplitude of the response will depend upon the proportion of neurons that lie in the discharged zone. The lower the proportion of cells with depolarizing p.s.p.'s above the critical level, the greater will be the degree of facilitation on repetitive stimulation. If the majority of the cells in the excited zone develop p.s.p.'s only slightly below the level of critical depolarization, a few repetitive stimuli will rapidly evoke a maximal response. This gives rise to the general class of *d'emblée* reflexes (cf. 44). Augmentation of p.s.p.'s (synaptic facilitation) discussed earlier (p. 168) also will favor production of *d'emblée* reflexes.

When the p.s.p.'s of the excited zone are small, the responses may recruit very gradually with repetitive stimuli. Particularly when the synaptic organization is complex and the synaptic drives are weak will the latency of the response be long. Under these conditions it may also be expected that more frequent stimuli will shorten the latency markedly and increase the rate of growth of the response and perhaps its maximum value. In other words, the more weakly effective synaptic drives, including multisynaptic pathways, will show a greater frequency-dependence. Since the production of hyperpolarizing p.s.p.'s also involves excitation of synapses, the development of inhibitory activity will depend similarly upon the stimulus parameters.

Another effect in which the complexity of the synaptic organization plays a role is that of after-discharge. The involvement of multisynaptic pathways carries the likelihood that additional side paths will also be brought into activity and thus give rise to a circulating activity (78) or a series of delayed reverberations which may cause discharges of the final common path long after the initial stimulus is ended. This reverberation may take place by one-to-one excitation, but it is likely that another phenomenon plays an even greater role. This is the summation and persistence of p.s.p.'s associated with accumulation of a persistent transmitter agent. As individual Renshaw cells are capable of persistent repetitive discharge by a single stimulus (61), so some of the interneurons mediating excitatory p.s.p.'s can also remain active for a long time. The interplay of excitatory and inhibitory synaptic activity may produce complex patterns of waxing and waning after discharge. In individual cells this patterning would be reflected by a greater or lower frequency of discharge. Complex interactions of excitatory and inhibitory types occur even in the relatively simple nuclear structures like that of Clarke's column in the spinal cord (104, 115). The involvement of a widespread network of neuron complexes in after-discharge is indicated also by the fact that increasing the strength of the initiating stimulus may lead to no increase in the maximal amplitude of the reflex response but only in the duration of its after-discharge (182).

Role of Inhibition in Central Nervous System

The interrelations of depolarizing and hyperpolarizing p.s.p.'s in these various manifestations, insofar as they are dependent upon the specific organization of synapses, are beyond the scope of this chapter, but some general discussion is appropriate (cf. 101, 161). As was described earlier, hyperpolarizing p.s.p.'s need attain only relatively small amplitudes to produce inhibition. The effect, a sudden cutting off of conductile activity, may block the synaptic transfer to many systems which would normally participate in an activity. The results of a given excitatory and inhibitory interaction will differ depending upon the site at which an index of the effect is obtained. In a specific example let us assume that a single cell is acted upon by the synaptic interplay. Whether or not it is excited to produce a spike will have important consequences for the activity of other downstream neurons for which the cell chosen as an example serves as a valve. However, when recording from the interior of the cell, depolarizing and hyperpolarizing activities may be observed even in the absence of a spike. Thus, different criteria apply to activity in different parts of a complex pathway. The relations between activity in one part and another may even be dimmed or may disappear.

The activity set into motion by a synaptically complex pathway thus may be undetected in the overt response. For example, a single stimulus to the head of the caudate nucleus in the cat gives rise to a relatively simple, brief electrical response in a restricted cortical region. Analyses with paired or repetitive stimuli disclose (167) that many excitatory and inhibitory influences are activated, some for long periods of time. It is worth noting that anatomical data can rarely give information as to the presence of such intricate synaptic linkages and, of course, cannot distinguish those that are excitatory from the inhibitory.

It is most likely that in its normal functioning the central nervous system utilizes inhibitory activity as a means for braking excitatory activity which might otherwise be unduly prolonged or inclined to reverberation. In that sense, therefore, inhibitory synaptic electrogenesis would aid the precision of nervous activity. The removal of inhibitory electrogenesis either by drugs which specifically blockade hyperpolarizing synapses, or by pathological conditions, would then remove these brakes upon excitatory activity and abnormal function would result. This would be apparently caused by 'excitation' although its fundamental mechanism would in reality be the block of another, opposed type of synaptic activity, the inhibitory electrogenesis. The pharmacological classification of strychnine as a 'stimulant of the central nervous system', already discussed, illustrates the basic difference between a descriptive, phenomenological classification and that based on analysis of its mode of action.

Physiological Effects of Different Proportions of Depolarizing and Hyperpolarizing Postsynaptic Potentials

Apparently different physiological and pharmacological properties may result from different proportions of the two kinds of synaptic activity. Thus, the electrical activity of the cat cerebral cortex differs profoundly from that of the cerebellar, but these differences may be accounted for by the relatively small degree of inhibitory electrogenesis of the cerebellar cortex (161–166). Pharmacological differences, such as the insensitivity of the cerebellar cortex to local applications of strychnine, are equally ascribable to this quantitative factor.

However, the response of the cerebellar electrocortical activity to different drugs depends upon the mode of exciting that activity (Purpura, Girado & Grundfest, in preparation; cf. also 99–101, 163). Different cerebellopetal afferents may evoke potentials of different forms at a single cortical site. These potentials are composed of different proportions of excitatory and inhibitory synaptic activities as demonstrated by their different reactions to the various specifically acting drugs.

Synaptic Activity and Electrical Concomitants

The matters discussed under this heading relate physiological activity in the central nervous system to the methodology of its study by electrophysiological means. They are also considered by Frank in Chapter X of this work.

A) INTERPRETATIONS OF CHANGES IN AMPLITUDES OF POSTSYNAPTIC POTENTIALS. Since p.s.p.'s are not subject to refractoriness but are capable of summation and of being sustained, decrease in amplitudes of p.s.p.'s cannot be ascribed to their refractoriness or

'occlusion'. A depolarizing p.s.p. therefore can diminish only by virtue of the following factors.

1) The conductile process of the preceding unit is blocked by refractoriness. This is probably a minor element since profound alterations in synaptic responses occur at frequencies of repetitive activity so low that refractoriness of electrically excitable responses does not occur.

2) The transmitter of the presynaptic terminals may become exhausted or the receptor of the postsynaptic membrane may become altered. The latter factor has been discussed in connection with desensitization (p. 157).

3) Stimulation at high frequencies may, however, produce fused sustained p.s.p.'s that show little or no fluctuation from the steady level (fig. 9B, C). This effect probably develops when the synaptic membrane is maximally excited by the frequently released packets of transmitter agent. The steady depolarization (or hyperpolarization) can be recorded in the cerebral cortex (cf. 176, fig. 10).

4) Simultaneous and countervailing development of hyperpolarizing p.s.p.'s may mask the depolarizing. There is now considerable experimental evidence that this factor is most important in the complex synaptic organization of the central nervous system (165–167). Indeed, the overt electrogenesis observable in the cerebral cortex after a single stimulus may be only a small part of the total electrogenic activity. The major part is not recorded because depolarizing and hyperpolarizing p.s.p.'s are simultaneously produced and tend to cancel each other.

B) INTERPRETATION OF ELECTROTONIC EFFECTS OF STANDING POSTSYNAPTIC POTENTIALS. It has been frequently assumed that the surface negativity of the cerebral cortex caused by dendritic p.s.p.'s produces anodal polarization of their cell bodies (cf. 176, pp. 56 and 57). This conclusion is drawn from analogy with the effects of externally applied currents, a cathode on the surface depressing and a surface anode augmenting excitability of the cell bodies. This analogy is not valid in the physiological case. Externally recorded negativity means that the interior of the generating site is depolarized (i.e. more positive than the resting potential). Surface negative p.s.p.'s of apical dendrites therefore must always act as an excitatory (cathodal) stimulus for the electrically excitable membrane of their cells (cf. 97, 101).

C) SYNAPTIC TRANSDUCER ACTION AND ELECTROGENESIS. The recorded electrical activity might even

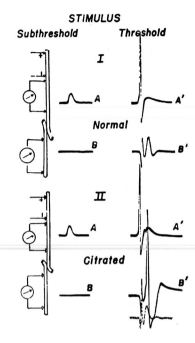

FIG. 31. Ephaptic excitation of squid giant axon. Two nerves are arranged as shown in diagram. I. Contact between nerves in sea water. A weak stimulus (*left*) evokes a local response of the pre-ephaptic fiber (seen in trace *A*). This is not propagated to the ephapse and has no effect on the latter (trace *B*). When a pre-ephaptic spike was evoked by a stronger stimulus (*A'*), the post-ephaptic nerve generated a local response (*B'*). Ahead of it is seen the electrotonic pick-up of the pre-ephaptic spike. II. Excitability of the axons was increased by removing calcium ions from the medium. The weak stimulus still could not evoke activity in the post-ephaptic fiber (*B*), since conductile activity was lacking in the pre-ephaptic unit (*A*). When a stronger stimulus evoked a spike (*A'*) the postephaptic fiber also produced a spike (*B'*). This arose on a step which is the local response of the postephaptic fiber (seen in isolation on the lowest trace). [From Arvanitaki (10).]

be absent if ionic processes leading to hyperpolarizing and depolarizing p.s.p.'s were equally balanced. Despite this, however, the transducer actions initiated by the excitants of depolarizing and hyperpolarizing synaptic membrane would still take place, and the ionic transports of the transducer action would still occur. Thus, ionic, metabolic and other biochemical effects might be produced in the apparent absence of electrical activity (96, 97).

EPHAPTIC EXCITATION

Electrical Modes of Transmission

In the course of efforts to validate the theory of electrical transmission many attempts were made

to confirm Kühne's dictum that "a nerve only throws a muscle into contraction by means of its currents of action." In 1882, Hering (110) found that a nerve volley initiated in one distal branch of the frog sciatic nerve and coursing centrally in the whole nerve trunk could set up activity in another branch when the impulses arrived at the centrally transected stump of the nerve. The current flow generated by the active fibers must have stimulated the previously inactive fibers. The effect has been confirmed many times (cf. 149) but nowhere more clearly than in a preparation involving two squid giant axons (10). It must be emphasized that specially favorable experimental conditions are required to produce this 'model' of transmission which is termed an 'ephapse' (false synapse). In the squid giant fiber (fig. 31) the electrical excitability of the ephaptic region is heightened by depriving the medium of calcium. The extrinsic current of the spike in the pre-ephaptic terminal is then capable of acting as a sufficiently strong electrical stimulus to evoke a postephaptic spike. As a weaker stimulus, it can elicit a graded local response. In more complex geometrical conditions between active and inactive cells, the directions of the extrinsic or field currents may produce hyperpolarizations as well as depolarizations (figs. 1, 32). The activity travelling in one fiber generates extrinsic current fields in contiguous parallel fibers which have a triphasic sequence (126) that successively produces hyperpolarization and depressed excitability, then depolarization and heightened excitability, followed again by hyperpolarization and depression (fig. 32).

A weakness of ephaptic transmission as a model of synaptic activity lies in the fact that basically it does not offer a mechanism for polarized transmission. Thus, in figure 31 the ephaptic excitation might very well have taken the opposite direction, from nerve B to nerve A. Special geometric properties were invoked by du Bois-Reymond and by Eccles (figs. 1, 32), and the latter also introduced the special electrophysiological rectifying effects of anodal and cathodal currents (fig. 32). These conditions might account for polarized transmission with an electrical mechanism; and, as will be described below, a high degree of rectification recently discovered in one kind of junction (83) does polarize conduction. However, the crucial distinction is whether or not current flow in a presynaptic terminal, or current flow imposed through the synaptic junction, can excite the activity of the latter. The answer, illustrated in this chapter with a number of examples (e.g. figs. 6, 19),

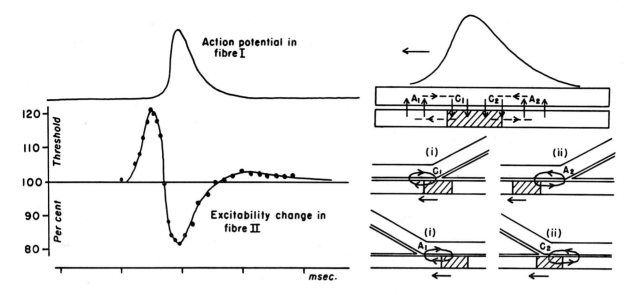

FIG. 32. Excitability changes caused by field currents. *Upper left:* A spike was produced by a stimulus to one of a pair of crab nerve fibers as in diagram *upper right.* The electrical excitability of the second fiber is shown (*lower left*) in relation to the time at which the spike passed the testing region. In the interval before the spike had reached that site, the excitability of the fiber was depressed. During the time that activity resided at the tested level, the excitability was augmented. This was followed by a second depressed phase as the activity propagated out of the tested site. [From Katz & Schmitt (126).] *Right:* Diagrams of the anodal, cathodal and anodal polarizing sequence generated in the inactive fiber by the spike in an adjoining fiber (*top*) and of different field current conditions produced by different geometrical arrangements (*bottom*). [From Eccles (57).]

seems to be clear. The current flowing across an active presynaptic terminal and across the postsynaptic membrane appears to be far too small to excite the postsynaptic cell. Furthermore, the processes associated with synaptic activity cannot be initiated by very strong applied currents.

Role of Field Currents in Central Nervous System

The activity of masses of cells or fibers in the central nervous system is particularly conducive to development of field currents within the volume of this structure (15). This fact suggested (88, 90) that field effects might play a role in determining the peculiarities of central nervous properties. The hypothesis appeared to have been confirmed by antidromic stimulations of motoneurons which altered the responses of contiguous motoneurons to a testing afferent volley (170). That conclusion, however, is invalidated by the subsequent finding (171; cf. 60) that the antidromic stimuli evoked synaptic activity within the spinal cord by means of the recurrent collaterals of the motoneurons.

Although field currents undoubtedly play some role (cf. 106), their wide significance must now be questioned in the light of the evidence that synaptic transmission is not effected by electrical stimuli. Changes in membrane potential produced in one cell by activity of contiguous elements appear to be small (33, 59, 125), although effects may be revealed by tests on electrically excitable membrane (106, 126, 185). However, the effects exerted electrochemically on p.s.p.'s (as described in the section in this chapter on the nature of postsynaptic potentials) are probably insignificant. Thus, electrical inexcitability renders the transmissional process insensitive to fields of current in the central nervous system (93). Teleologically considered, this is probably an advantage. The fields must shift from moment to moment as the loci of activity shift in the cellular mass of the volume conductor. The effects of these fields must therefore be highly unspecific, now producing increase, now depression of electrical excitability, actions that probably would disturb the precision of organized orderly synaptic transfer. Thus, electrical inexcitability of synaptic membrane removes a major hazard, that irregular effects of electric fields might disrupt the patterned activity of the central nervous system.

Dorsal Root Reflex

Acting upon electrically excitable components, however, field currents might still affect central nervous functioning. For example, small depolarization of a cell by field current might facilitate its discharge by an otherwise subliminal depolarizing p.s.p. Likewise, presynaptic terminals close to an active synaptic focus might be subjected to considerable potential change (51), an action which may account for the dorsal root reflex (188). This prolonged centrifugal discharge of dorsal root fibers is evoked with a latency of some milliseconds after the same or other dorsal root fibers carry a volley centripetally. The dorsal root reflex is enchanced by low temperatures as is the motor root reflex (29, 89). The latency, temperature effect and prolonged discharge of the dorsal root reflex indicate that it is produced by a synaptic activity in the spinal cord, and yet there is no histological evidence of synaptic inflows to the dorsal root collaterals. In the absence of the latter, ephaptic excitation may be invoked, but will involve synaptic pathways also. This could result from the field effects generated in the dorsal root terminals by the activity of some interneuronal pools. The activity of these cells, being evoked by synaptic transfer, would account for the apparent synaptic properties of the dorsal root reflex, but its final development would be by ephaptic excitation.

Ephaptic Transmission in Annelid and Crustacean Nerve Cords

In many species of these invertebrates there occur junctions (septa) between anatomically distinct elements, the segments of the septate giant axons. Across the septa considerable electrotonic current flow can take place and ephaptic electrical transmission is then possible (125; Kao, C. Y. & H. Grundfest, manuscript in preparation). The junctional membranes of these functional ephapses must therefore be fundamentally different from those of synapses, across which only insignificant electrotonic current flow occurs. However, the anatomical data to account for this difference are still unsatisfactory. The transverse sheaths which separate abutting segments of the septate giant axons appear to be identical with the sheaths that invest the axis cylinders (cf. 125). On the other hand, the junction between the medial giant axon and the motor giant fiber of crayfish seems to be formed by processes from the postjunctional motor nerve which penetrate the Schwann sheaths to make intimate contact with the

cell membrane of the prejunctional fibers (174). The junctions between two motor giant axons are also similar.

A) UNPOLARIZED EPHAPTIC JUNCTIONS. These have been studied with intracellular recordings in the septate giant axons of earthworm (125) and crayfish (Kao, C. Y. & H. Grundfest, manuscript in preparation). The septa, sometimes called 'unpolarized macrosynapses' (cf. 30, 125), appear to be merely the boundaries demarcating the multiple origins of the septate giant axons from a number of segments of the animal. Activity in one segment of the axon causes electrotonic potentials in the neighboring segments large enough to excite the latter. Thus, transmission is by local circuit excitation, essentially as in other axons. As in the latter, the ephaptic transmission of the septate axons is unpolarized, capable of propagating an impulse in either direction.

B) POLARIZED EPHAPTIC TRANSMISSION. One system recently described (83), the junction between cord giant fibers and efferent motor giant axons of crayfish, may be classified in this category. Current flowing outward from the depolarized prefiber can enter the junctional membrane of the postfiber, causing large depolarization in the latter (fig. 33A) and its ephaptic excitation. However, when the postfiber is depolarized (fig. 33B) the electrotonic effects in the prefiber are small. Likewise when the prefiber is hyperpolarized current flow in the postfiber is hindered (fig. 33A), while hyperpolarizing the postfiber causes large electrotonic changes in the prefiber (fig. 33B). The junctions thus exhibit rectification, with conductance in one direction (that tending to depolarize the postfiber) about 20 times greater than in the opposite direction. Thus, in the case of the motor giant fiber ephapse, the low electrical resistance in one direction and high resistance in the other makes for polarized ephaptic transmission.

Since the junction meets the criteria of anatomical discontinuity and transmissional polarization, it fits the definition of synapse extant since Ramón y Cajal and Sherrington. However, though it may be called an 'electrically excitable synapse' (83), it probably differs profoundly from the electrically inexcitable synapses discussed in this chapter. The distinction between ephaptic junctions which have low electrical resistance and synapses which have high resistance helps to make the classification more precise. Thus, experiments similar to those shown in

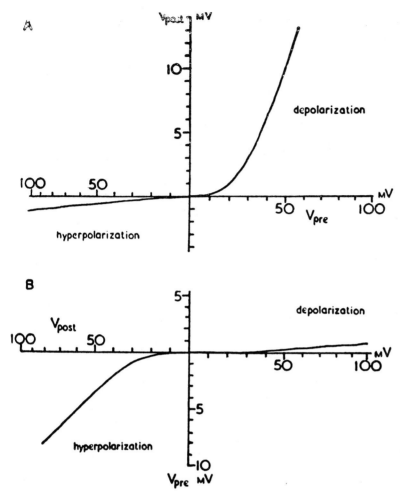

A

B

FIG. 33. Rectification at the junction between a cord giant fiber and a motor giant axon in crayfish results in polarized ephaptic transmission. *A:* Current was allowed to flow through a microelectrode in the prejunctional cord giant axon. The changes in the membrane of the same fiber were recorded with another microelectrode and are shown on the abscissa. The ordinate indicates the membrane voltage recorded at the same time with a microelectrode in the postjunctional fiber. When the prefiber was depolarized, a steeply rising depolarizing change also took place in the postfiber. As an extrinsic local circuit change was produced by a spike in the prefiber, it would lead to an electrically excited response of the postfiber. When the prefiber is hyperpolarized (left side of *A*), only small changes in potential develop in the postfiber. The ratio of current flowing in the two directions is about 20:1. *B:* In this experiment current was applied to the postfiber, the abscissa shows the change in membrane potential of this fiber and the ordinate the change in membrane potential of the prefiber. When the postfiber is hyperpolarized, there is a considerable current flow into it from the prefiber, causing some electrotonic hyperpolarization of the latter. When the postfiber is depolarized, little current flows into the prefiber and it therefore cannot be stimulated by a spike in the postfiber. Electrical excitation across the junction is thus transmitted only from the pre- to the postfiber. [From Furshpan & Potter (83).]

figure 33 were done on the squid giant axon synapse by Tasaki. He "could not detect any recognizable spread of electrotonic effects across the synapse in either direction" (personal communication). It is likely that pharmacological data and various other criteria of the constellations listed in table 1 will distinguish the two types of transmission systems further.

Several properties of the polarized ephaptic junction may be deduced from the available data and from general considerations. Rectification is exhibited by the membranes of many, though not all, cells, although not to the same large degree (cf. Tasaki, Chapter III). Where found, it is manifested by a higher membrane resistance to inward current than to outward flow. In the present case two membranes are involved and, if both are rectifiers, then they must each act in opposite polarity to the other. On the other hand, only one of the two membranes need show rectification and this situation is the more

probable. It also seems most likely that this property resides in the surface of the prefiber for in that case the membrane would permit outward current flow and restrict inward as in other cells. The membrane of the postfiber would then need have no rectifier properties but would resemble that of the septa in its low nondirectional resistivity.

As may be seen from figure 34, current probably flows outward across the prejunctional membrane during the ephaptic transmissional process whereas in the rest of the active region the membrane current is inward. Furthermore, excitation of the postfiber must occur at membrane sites where the local circuit current flows outward, not at the ephaptic region where it flows inward. Therefore, neither junctional membrane of this polarized ephapse takes part in the active responses of the junction. Like the membranes at the septa they therefore need not be excitable.

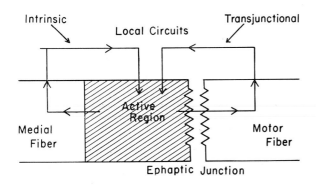

FIG. 34. Diagram showing the current flows that probably take place at a polarized ephaptic junction. In the prejunctional fiber membrane current flow is inward in the region of activity. Longitudinal current flow takes place behind this region as part of the intrinsic local circuit within this fiber. Current flows outward through the membrane recovering from previous activity. Outward current also flows in the prejunctional membrane of the ephapse. This enters the postephaptic cell at its junctional membrane and flows out through adjacent regions of membrane, exciting the latter. Note the profound difference between the current flows postulated for ephaptic transmission in this diagram and the hypothetical situation at synaptic junctions shown in fig. 1.

Evolutionary Aspects of Ephaptic Transmission

In their transverse divisions the septate axons bear the sign of their segmental origin. The processes of a number of neurons at a nerve cord segment fuse to produce a short length of giant axon. End-to-end apposition of the segmental fibers then forms a long axonal pathway. To the extent that the septa disappear or that their resistance is low the segmented axons approach the nonsegmented giant axons in efficiency as through conduction pathways, excited by local circuit action.

The septate axons, however, combine with through conduction, another feature which is absent in the nonsegmented giant fibers (Kao, C. Y. & H. Grundfest, manuscript in preparation). They make elaborate local synaptic connections, both efferent and afferent, with other fibers of the nerve cord. Although the anatomy of these connections is not as yet clear, the synaptic properties of the septate axons probably derive from their segmental origin of the fibers. The septate giant axons therefore play a much greater role in the integrative activity of the nervous system than can the nonseptate axon which lack these synaptic connections (103, 125).

On the basis of the interpretation given in the previous paragraphs, the polarized, electrically excitable ephaptic junction may be derived from the septal junctions by the addition of rectifier property to one of the junctional membranes. Two other features further strengthen the resemblance between septate and motor giant fibers. The two motor axons of a segment make unpolarized connections with each other. In this case, too, electron microscopy has not as yet revealed essential details (cf. 174). Also, like the septate axons, the motor giant fiber combines 'chemically mediated synapses' with an ephaptic junction (83). The former presumably are electrically inexcitable.

Thus, it appears likely that motor giant fibers of the crayfish bear a close functional similarity to the septate axons but with a significant modification away from the latter. It remains to be seen whether ephaptic polarized transmission made possible by rectification is a fairly common evolutionary variant. Another interesting correlation, whether or not this transmission scheme developed only in those animals that have septate unpolarized ephapses, might give further clues to their evolutionary origin.

Quasiartificial Synapses

The excitation of giant nerve fibers in annelid nerve cords by activity in other giant axons is well documented (31) and may be an ephaptic phenomenon In *Protula* the sites of transfer vary from one occasion to another and have been termed quasiartificial synapses. These systems have not yet been studied with intracellular recording. The latter could help to determine whether the transmission is ephaptic or whether it is associated with complex synaptic phenomena such as have been found in earthworms (125).

REFERENCES

1. ALBE-FESSARD, D. AND C. CHAGAS. *J. physiol.*, Paris 46: 823, 1954.
2. ALBERT, A. *Ergebn. Physiol.* 49: 425, 1957.
3. ALTAMIRANO, M. AND C. W. COATES. *J. Cell. & Comp. Physiol.* 49: 69, 1957.
4. ALTAMIRANO, M., C. W. COATES AND H. GRUNDFEST. *J. Gen. Physiol.* 38: 319, 1955.
5. ALTAMIRANO, M., C. W. COATES, H. GRUNDFEST AND D. NACHMANSOHN. *J. Gen. Physiol.* 37: 91, 1953.
6. ALTAMIRANO, M., C. W. COATES, H. GRUNDFEST AND D. NACHMANSOHN. *Biochim. et biophys. acta* 16: 449, 1955.

7. ARAKI, T. AND T. OTANI. *J. Neurophysiol.* 18: 472, 1955.

8. ARIËNS, E. J. *Experientia* 13: 161, 1957.

9. ARIËNS, E. J. AND J. M. VAN ROSSUM. *Arch. internat. pharmacodyn.* 110: 275, 1957.

10. ARVANITAKI, A. *J. Neurophysiol.* 5: 89, 1942.

11. ARVANITAKI, A. AND N. CHALAZONITES. *Arch. sc. physiol.* 10: 95, 1956.

12. AWAPARA, J., A. J. LANDUA, R. FUERST AND B. SEALE. *J. Biol. Chem.* 187: 35, 1950.

13. BAIN, J. A. In: *Ultrastructure and Cellular Chemistry of Neural Tissue,* edited by H. Waelsch. New York: Hoeber-Harper, 1957, p. 139.

14. BARLOW, R. B. *Introduction to Chemical Pharmacology.* New York: Wiley, 1955.

15. BARRON, D. H. AND B. H. C. MATTHEWS. *J. Physiol.* 92: 276, 1938.

16. BAZEMORE, A., K. A. C. ELLIOTT AND E. FLOREY. *Nature, London* 178: 1052, 1956.

17. BENNETT, M. V. L., S. M CRAIN AND H. GRUNDFEST. *J. Gen. Physiol.* 113: 325, 1957.

18. BERNARD, C. *Compt. rend. Soc. de biol.* 1: 90, 1849.

19. BERNSTEIN, J. *Untersuchungen uber den Errengungsvorgang im Nerven- und Muskelsysteme.* Heidelberg, 1871.

20. BERNSTEIN, J. *Arch. Physiol.* Leipzig, 1882, p. 329.

21. BISHOP, G. H. *Physiol. Rev.* 36: 376, 1956.

22. BONVALLET, M., P. DELL AND G. HIEBEL. *Electroencephalog. & Clin. Neurophysiol.* 6: 119, 1954.

23. BOYD, I. A. AND A. R. MARTIN, *J. Physiol.* 132: 74, 1956.

24. BROCK, L. G., J. S. COOMBS AND J. C. ECCLES. *J. Physiol.* 117: 431, 1952.

25. BROCK, L. G., J. S., COOMBS AND J. C. ECCLES. *J. Physiol.* 122: 429, 1953.

26. BRODIE, B. B. In: *Third Conference on Neuropharmacology,* edited by H. A. Abramson. New York: Macy, 1957, p. 323.

27. BROOKHART, J. M. AND A. ZANCHETTI. *Electroencephalog. & Clin. Neurophysiol.* 8: 427, 1956.

28. BROOKS, C. McC., J. C. ECCLES AND J. L. MALCOLM. *J. Neurophysiol.* 11: 417, 1948.

29. BROOKS, C. McC., K. KOIZUMI AND J. L. MALCOLM. *J. Neurophysiol.* 18: 205, 1955.

30. BULLOCK, T. H. *Cold Spring Harbor Symp. Quant. Biol.* 17: 267, 1952.

31. BULLOCK, T. H. *J. Comp. Neurol.* 98: 37, 1953.

32. BULLOCK, T. H. AND S. HAGIWARA. *J. Gen. Physiol.* 40: 565, 1957.

33. BULLOCK, T. H. AND C. A. TERZUOLO. *J. Physiol.* 138: 341, 1957.

34. BURKE, W. AND B. L. GINSBORG. *J. Physiol.* 132: 586, 1956.

35. BURKE, W. AND B. L. GINSBORG. *J. Physiol.* 132: 599, 1956.

36. BURN, J. H. *Functions of Autonomic Transmitters.* Baltimore: Williams & Wilkins, 1956.

37. CERF, J., H. GRUNDFEST, G. HOYLE AND F. McCANN. *Biol. Bull.* 113: 337, 1957.

38. CERF, J., H. GRUNDFEST, G. HOYLE AND F. McCANN. *Biol. Bull.* 113: 338, 1957.

39. CHAGAS, C. AND D. ALBE-FESSARD. *Acta physiol. latinoam.* 4: 49, 1954.

40. CLARK, A. J. *The Mode of Action of Drugs on Cells.* London: Arnold, 1933.

41. COUTEAUX, R. In: *International Review of Cytology.* New York: Acad. Press, 1955, vol. IV.

42. CRAIN, S. M. *J. Comp. Neurol.* 104: 285, 1956.

43. CRAIN, S. M., M. V. L. BENNETT AND H. GRUNDFEST. *Biol. Bull.* 113: 342, 1957.

44. CREED, R. S., D. DENNY-BROWN, J. C. ECCLES, E. G. T. LIDDELL AND C. S. SHERRINGTON. *Reflex Activity of the Spinal Cord.* Oxford: Clarendon Press, 1932.

45. CURTIS, H. J. In: *Medical Physiology* (10th ed.), edited by P. Bard. St. Louis: Mosby, 1956, p. 944.

46. DALE, H. H. *Proc. Roy. Soc. Med.* 28: 319, 1935.

47. DALLEMAGNE, J. AND E. PHILIPPOT. *Acta anaesth. belg.* 3: 125, 1952.

48. DEL CASTILLO, J. AND B. KATZ. *J. Physiol.* 125: 546, 1954.

49. DEL CASTILLO, J. AND B. KATZ. *Nature, London* 175: 1035, 1955.

50. DEL CASTILLO, J. AND B. KATZ. *J. Physiol.* 128: 396, 1955.

51. DEL CASTILLO, J. AND B. KATZ. *J. Physiol.* 132: 630, 1956.

52. DEL CASTILLO, J. AND B. KATZ. In: *Progress in Biophysics.* London: Pergamon, 1956, vol. 6, p. 121.

53. DEL CASTILLO, J. AND B. KATZ. *Proc. Roy. Soc. London. ser. B* 146: 339, 1957.

54. DE ROBERTIS, E. D. P. AND H. S. BENNETT. *J. Biophys. & Biochem. Cytol.* 1: 47, 1955.

55. DU BOIS-REYMOND, E. *Gesammelte Abhandlungen zur allgemeinen Muskel- und Nervenphysik.* Leipzig: Veit, 1877, vol. 2.

56. ECCLES, J. C. *J. Physiol.* 101: 465, 1943.

57. ECCLES, J. C. *Ann. New York Acad. Sc.* 47: 429, 1946.

58. ECCLES, J. C. *J. Neurophysiol.* 9: 87, 1946.

59. ECCLES, J. C. *The Neurophysiological Basis of Mind.* Oxford: Clarendon Press, 1953.

60. ECCLES, J. C. *The Physiology of Nerve Cells.* Baltimore: Johns Hopkins Press, 1957.

61. ECCLES, J. C., P. FATT AND K. KOKETSU. *J. Physiol.* 126: 524, 1954.

62. ECCLES, J. C., B. KATZ AND S. W. KUFFLER. *J. Neurophysiol.* 4: 362, 1941.

63. ECCLES, J. C. AND W. J. O'CONNOR. *J. Physiol.* 94: 9(P), 1938.

64. ECCLES, R. M. *J. Physiol.* 130: 572, 1955.

65. ELKES, J. In: *Third Conference on Neuropharmacology,* edited by H. A. Abramson. New York: Macy, 1957, p. 205.

66. EYZAGUIRRE, C. AND S. W. KUFFLER. *J. Gen. Physiol.* 39: 87, 1955.

67. EYZAGUIRRE, C. AND S. W. KUFFLER. *J. Gen. Physiol.* 39: 121, 1955.

68. FATT, P. *Physiol. Rev.* 34: 674, 1954.

69. FATT, P. *J. Neurophysiol.* 20: 27, 1957.

70. FATT, P. *J. Neurophysiol.* 20: 61, 1957.

71. FATT, P. AND B. KATZ. *J. Physiol.* 115: 320, 1951.

72. FATT, P. AND B. KATZ. *J. Exper. Biol.* 30: 433, 1953.

73. FATT, P. AND B. KATZ. *J. Physiol.* 121: 374, 1953.

74. FELDBERG, W. AND A. FESSARD. *J. Physiol.* 101: 200, 1942.

75. FELDBERG, W., J. L. MALCOLM AND S. L. SHERWOOD. *J. Physiol.* 132: 130, 1956.

76. FENG, T. P. *Chinese J. Physiol.* 16: 341, 1941.

77. FESSARD, A. AND B. H. C. MATTHEWS. *J. Physiol.* 95: P9, 1939.

78. FORBES, A. *Physiol. Rev.* 2: 361, 1922.

79. FRANK, K. AND M. G. F. FUORTES. *J. Physiol.* 134: 451, 1956.

80. FREYGANG, W. H., JR. *J. Gen. Physiol.* 41: 543, 1958.

81. FULTON, J. F. *Physiology of the Nervous System* (3rd ed.). New York: Oxford, 1949.

82. FUORTES, M. G. F., K. FRANK AND M. C. BECKER. *J. Gen. Physiol.* 40: 735, 1957.
83. FURSHPAN, E. J. AND D. D. POTTER. *Nature, London* 180: 342, 1957.
84. GALVANI, L. *De viribus electricitatis in motu musculari Commentarius*, 1791. English translation by R. M. Green. Cambridge: Licht, 1953.
85. GOODMAN, L. S. AND A. GILMAN. *The Pharmacological Basis of Therapeutics* (2nd ed.). New York: Macmillan, 1955.
86. GÖPFERT, H. AND H. SCHAEFER. *Arch. ges. Physiol.* 239: 597, 1938.
87. GRANIT, R. *J. Physiol.* 131: 32, 1956.
88. GRUNDFEST, H. *Ann. Rev. Physiol.* 2: 213, 1940.
89. GRUNDFEST, H. *Am. J. Physiol.* 133: 307, 1941.
90. GRUNDFEST, H. *Ann. Rev. Physiol.* 9: 477, 1947.
91. GRUNDFEST, H. In: *Electrochemistry in Biology and Medicine*, edited by T. Shedlovsky. New York: Wiley, 1955, chapt. 8.
92. GRUNDFEST, H. In: *Fifth Conference on the Nerve Impulse.* New York: Macy, 1956, p. 177.
93. GRUNDFEST, H. In: *Problems of Modern Physiology of the Nerve and Muscle System.* Tiflis: Publ. House, Acad. of Sciences, Georgian S.S.R., 1956, p. 81.
94. GRUNDFEST, H. In: *Physiological Triggers.* Washington: Am. Physiol. Soc., 1957, p. 119.
95. GRUNDFEST, H. In: *Progress in Biophysics.* London: Pergamon, 1957, vol. 7, p. 1.
96. GRUNDFEST, H. *Ann. New York Acad. Sc.* 66: 537, 1957.
97. GRUNDFEST, H. *Physiol. Rev.* 37: 337, 1957.
98. GRUNDFEST, H. *J. Neurophysiol.* 20: 316, 1957.
99. GRUNDFEST, H. *Fed. Proc.* 17: 1006, 1958.
100. GRUNDFEST, H. *Electroencephalog. & Clin. Neurophysiol.* In press.
101. GRUNDFEST, H. In: *Symposium on Reticular Formation of the Brain*, edited by L. D. Proctor, R. S. Knighton, H. H. Jasper, W. C. Noshay and R. T. Costello. Boston: Little, 1958, p. 473.
102. GRUNDFEST, H. *Arch. ital. biol.* 96: 135, 1958.
103. GRUNDFEST, H. In: *Evolution of Nervous Control from Primitive Organisms to Man.* AAAS Symposium, Section on Medical Science, Dec. 29, 1956. To be published.
104. GRUNDFEST, H. AND B. CAMPBELL. *J. Neurophysiol.* 5: 275, 1942.
105. GRUNDFEST, H., C. Y. KAO AND M. ALTAMIRANO. *J. Gen. Physiol.* 38: 245, 1954.
106. GRUNDFEST, H. AND J. MAGNES. *Am. J. Physiol.* 164: 502, 1951.
107. GRUNDFEST, H. AND D. P. PURPURA. *Nature, London* 178: 416, 1956.
108. GRUNDFEST, H. AND D. P. PURPURA. In: *Symposium on Curare and Curarizing Substances.* Amsterdam: Elseviers, 1959.
109. HAGIWARA, S. AND T. H. BULLOCK. *J. Cell & Comp. Physiol.* 50: 25, 1957.
110. HERING, E. *Sitzber. Akad. Wiss. Wien (Abt. III)* 88: 237, 1882.
111. HIMWICH, H. E. AND F. RINALDI. In: *Brain Mechanisms and Drug Action*, edited by W. S. Fields. Springfield: Thomas, 1957, p. 15.
112. HODGKIN, A. L. *Proc. Roy. Soc., London. ser. B* 148: 1, 1958.
113. HODGKIN, A. L. AND A. F. HUXLEY. *J. Physiol.* 117: 500, 1952.
114. HODGKIN, A. L. AND W. A. H. RUSHTON. *Proc. Roy. Soc., London. ser. B* 133: 444, 1946.

115. HOLMQVIST, B., A. LUNDBERG AND O. OSCARSSON. *Acta physiol. scandinav.* 38: 76, 1956.
116. HOYLE, G. In: *Recent Advances in Invertebrate Physiology.* Eugene: Univ. Oregon Press, 1957.
117. HOYLE, G. *The Nervous Control of Muscular Contraction.* London: Cambridge, 1957.
118. HUGHES, J. R. *Physiol. Rev.* 38: 91, 1958.
119. HUTTER, O. F. AND W. R. LOWENSTEIN. *J. Physiol.* 130: 559, 1955.
120. HUTTER, O. F. AND W. TRAUTWEIN. *J. Gen. Physiol.* 39: 715, 1956.
121. HUXLEY, A. F. In: *Progress in Biophysics.* London: Pergamon, 1957, vol. 7, p. 255.
122. INGVAR, D. H. *Acta physiol. scandinav.* 33: 169, 1955.
123. JENDEN, D. J., K. KAMIJO AND D. B. TAYLOR. *J. Pharmacol. & Exper. Therap.* 111: 229, 1954.
124. JOB, C. AND A. LUNDBERG. *Acta physiol. scandinav.* 28: 14, 1953.
125. KAO, C. Y. AND H. GRUNDFEST. *J. Neurophysiol.* 20: 494, 1957.
126. KATZ, B. AND O. H. SCHMITT. *J. Physiol.* 100: 369, 1942.
127. KATZ, B. AND S. THESLEFF. *J. Physiol.* 138: 63, 1957.
128. KILLAM, E. K. AND K. F. KILLAM. In: *Brain Mechanisms and Drug Action*, edited by W. S. Fields. Springfield: Thomas, 1957, p. 71.
129. KRIVOY, W. A. AND J. H. WILLS. *J. Pharmacol. & Exper. Therap.* 116: 220, 1956.
130. KUFFLER, S. W. AND C. EYZAGUIRRE. *J. Gen Physiol.* 39: 155, 1955.
131. KUFFLER, S. W. AND B. KATZ. *J. Neurophysiol.* 9: 337, 1946.
132. KUFFLER, S. W. AND E. M. VAUGHAN-WILLIAMS. *J. Physiol.* 121: 319, 1953.
133. KÜHNE, W. *Proc. Roy. Soc., London. ser. B* 44: 427, 1888.
134. LAPORTE, Y. AND R. LORENTE DE NÓ. *J. Cell. & Comp. Physiol.* Suppl. 2, 35: 61, 1950.
135. LARRABEE, M. G. AND D. W. BRONK. *J. Neurophysiol.* 10: 139, 1947.
136. LETTVIN, J. Y., W. S. MCCULLOCH AND W. PITTS. *Am. J. Physiol.* 187: 614, 1956.
137. LILEY, A. W. *J. Physiol.* 134: 427, 1956.
138. LLOYD, D. P. C. *J. Neurophysiol.* 4: 525, 1941.
139. LLOYD, D. P. C. *J. Gen. Physiol.* 33: 147, 1949.
140. LLOYD, D. P. C. In: *Textbook of Physiology* (17th ed.), edited by J. F. Fulton. Philadelphia. Saunders, 1955, p. 1.
141. LORENTE DE NÓ, R. *A Study of Nerve Physiology.* New York: Rockefeller Inst. for Med. Res., 1947, vols. 131 and 132.
142. LORENTE DE NÓ, R. In: *The Spinal Cord.* Boston: Little. 1953, p. 13.
143. LUFT, J. H. *J. Biophys. & Biochem. Cytol.* 2: 229, 1956.
144. LUNDBERG, A. *Acta physiol. scandinav.* 35: 1, 1955.
145. LUNDBERG, A. *Nature, London* 177: 1080, 1956.
146. LUNDBERG, A. *Physiol. Rev.* 38: 21, 1958.
147. MAGOUN, H. W. *The Waking Brain.* Springfield: Thomas, 1958.
148. MARRAZZI, A. S. In: *Brain Mechanisms and Drug Action*, edited by W. S. Fields. Springfield: Thomas, 1957, p. 45.
149. MARRAZZI, A. S. AND R. LORENTE DE NÓ. *J. Neurophysiol.* 7: 83, 1944.
150. MINZ, B. *The Role of Humoral Agents in Nervous Activity.* Springfield: Thomas, 1955.
151. MOUNTCASTLE, V. B., P. W. DAVIS AND A. L. BERMAN. *J. Neurophysiol.* 20: 374, 1957.

152. PALAY, S. L. *J. Biophys. & Biochem. Cytol.* 2: Suppl. 193, 1956.

153. PALAY, S. L. AND G. E. PALADE. *J. Biophys. & Biochem. Cytol.* 1: 69, 1955.

154. PARKER, G. H. *The Elementary Nervous System.* Philadelphia: Lippincott, 1919.

155. PATON, W. D. M. *Ann. New York Acad. Sc.* 54: 347, 1951.

156. PATON, W. D. M. AND W. L. M. PERRY. *J. Physiol.* 119: 43, 1953.

157. PERRY, W. L. M. *Ann. Rev. Physiol.* 18: 279, 1956.

158. PHILLIPS, C. G. *Quart. J. Exper. Physiol.* 41: 58, 1955.

159. PHILLIPS, C. G. *Quart. J. Exper. Physiol.* 41: 70, 1955.

160. PURPURA, D. P. *Am. J. Physiol.* 186: 250, 1956.

161. PURPURA, D. P. In: *Symposium on Reticular Formation of the Brain*, edited by L. D. Proctor, R. S. Knighton, H. H. Jasper, W. C. Noshay, R. T. Costello. Boston: Little, 1958, p. 435.

162. PURPURA, D. P., M. GIRADO AND H. GRUNDFEST. *Science* 125: 1200, 1957.

163. PURPURA, D. P., M. GIRADO T. G. SMITH, D. A. CALLAN AND H. GRUNDFEST. *J. Neurochem.* 1958. In press.

164. PURPURA, D. P., M. GIRADO, T. G. SMITH AND J. A. GOMEZ. *Proc. Soc. Exper. Biol. & Med.* 97: 348, 1958.

165. PURPURA, D. P. AND H. GRUNDFEST. *J. Neurophysiol.* 19: 573, 1956.

166. PURPURA, D. P. AND H. GRUNDFEST. *J. Neurophysiol.* 20: 494, 1957.

167. PURPURA, D. P., E. M. HOUSEPIAN AND H. GRUNDFEST. *Arch. ital biol.* 96: 145, 1958.

168. RAMÓN Y CAJAL, S. *Histologie du Système Nerveux de l'homme et des vertébrés.* Madrid: Consejo Superior de Investigaciones Científicas Instituto "Ramón y Cajal", 1952, 2 vols.

169. RAMÓN Y CAJAL, S. *Neuron Theory or Reticular Theory? Objective Evidence of the Anatomical Unity of Nerve Cells*, translated by M. U. Purkiss and C. A. Fox. Madrid: Consejo Superior de Investigationes Científicas Instituto "Ramón y Cajal", 1954.

170. RENSHAW, B. *J. Neurophysiol.* 4: 167, 1941.

171. RENSHAW, B. *J. Neurophysiol.* 9: 191, 1946.

172. ROBERTS, E. AND C. BAXTER. *Proc. 9th Ann. Mtg. Am. Acad. Neurol.*, 1957.

173. ROBERTS, E. AND S. FRANKEL. *J. Biol. Chem.* 187: 55, 1950.

174. ROBERTSON, J. D. *J. Biophys. & Biochem. Cytol.* 2: 381, 1956.

175. ROBERTSON, J. D. In: *Ultrastructure and Cellular Chemistry of Neural Tissue*, edited by H. Waelsch. New York: Hoeber-Harper, 1957.

176. ROITBAK, A. I. *Bioelectric Phenomena of the Cerebral Cortex* (in Russian). Tiflis: Publ. House, Acad. of Sciences, Georgian S.S.R., 1955.

177. ROSENBLUETH, A. *The Transmission of Nerve Impulses at Neuroeffector Junctions and Peripheral Synapses.* Cambridge: Technology Press and New York: Wiley, 1950.

178. ROTHBALLER, A. B. *Electroencephalog. & Clin. Neurophysiol.* 8: 603, 1956.

179. SCHARRER, E. AND B. SCHARRER. In: *Handbuch der mikroskopischen Anatomie des Menschen.* Berlin: Springer, 1954.

180. SECHENOV, I. In: *Selected Works XV International Physiological Congress, Moscow.* State Publ. House, 1935.

181. SHERRINGTON, C. S. In: *A Textbook of Physiology* (7th ed.), edited by M. Foster. London: Macmillan, 1897.

182. SHERRINGTON, C. S. *The Integrative Action of the Nervous System*, 1906. Reprinted, London: Cambridge, 1947.

183. SHERRINGTON, C. S. *Proc. Roy. Soc., London. ser. B* 97: 519, 1925.

184. SVAETICHIN, G. *Acta physiol. scandinav.* suppl. 134, 39: 17, 1956.

185. TERZUOLO, C. A. AND T. H. BULLOCK. *Proc. Nat. Acad. Sc.* 42: 687, 1956.

186. TERZUOLO, C. A. AND T. H. BULLOCK. *Arch. ital. biol.* In press.

187. THESLEFF, S. *Acta physiol. scandinav.* 34: 218, 1955.

188. TOENNIES, J. F. *J. Neurophysiol.* 1: 378, 1938.

189. TOMITA, T. *Jap. J. Physiol.* 6: 327, 1956.

190. TOMITA, T. *J. Neurophysiol.* 20: 245, 1957.

191. TOMITA, T. *Jap. J. Physiol.* 7: 80, 1957.

192. VOGT, M. *J. Physiol.* 123: 451, 1954.

193. VON EULER, U. S. *Noradrenaline.* Springfield: Thomas, 1956.

194. WILSON, V. J. AND D. P. C. LLOYD. *Am. J. Physiol.* 187: 641, 1956.

CHAPTER VI

Skeletal neuromuscular transmission

PAUL FATT | *Biophysics Department, University College, London, England*

THE EXISTENCE OF A REGION between motor nerve and voluntary muscle which has special properties emerged from experiments on the action of the South American Indian arrow poison, curare, performed by Claude Bernard about 1850 (2). Bernard's aim in the first place was to show that muscle was excitable independently of its nerve supply. Having previously paralyzed a frog with curare, he isolated a nerve-muscle preparation and showed that, while an electrical stimulus applied to the nerve was ineffective, a contraction resulted if it were applied directly to the muscle. Inferring that curare interfered with the functioning of the nerve but not of the muscle, he carried the investigation a step further by preparing a frog with a ligature which interrupted the blood supply to the hind legs but not the nervous connections. When curare was introduced above the ligature, a paralysis developed which affected only the anterior part of the body. Most significant was the observation that pinching the skin above the ligature did not elicit movement in that region but caused the normal reflex thrust of the hind legs. It was concluded from this that curare did not cause a loss of sensation, and its effect was therefore ascribed to a poisoning of the motor nerve, for, as was already seen, in the presence of curare the muscle could still be excited directly. But since curare apparently did not affect the motor nerve in its more central course from the spinal cord to the level of the ligature either, it was maintained that the poison acted on the motor nerve only in its most peripheral part, where contact was made with the muscle.

Following this penetrating study, investigations were carried out over a number of years by other workers into the method of action of substances that affect nerve-muscle transmission more or less specifically. Besides curare, one of the chief of these was nicotine. When a small amount of this drug was injected into an animal or added to the solution bathing an isolated muscle, a contraction occurred which was abolished by curare at the same time as was the contraction produced by nerve stimulation. It was further found that chronic denervation did not eliminate the capacity of the muscle for responding to nicotine, which was still antagonized by curare, although the nerve terminals underwent severe deterioration (34, 46, 57, 59). From this it was concluded that the site of action of curare, as well as nicotine, was not in the nerve endings, as had previously been supposed, but in the muscle fiber.

A quantitative investigation of the effects of these substances was made by Langley about 1910 (58, 60, 61). By the application of small droplets of nicotine solution along a muscle fiber, he found that nicotine in low concentration initiated a contraction only when applied in the region of the nerve endings. A concentration one thousand times greater than the minimum effective dose was required to produce a contraction elsewhere along the muscle fiber. Furthermore, curare interfered with the action of nicotine in low concentration but had no effect on the contraction produced by the high concentration that did not act exclusively in the innervated region. The manner in which curare and nicotine acted was inferred from the observation that increasing concentrations of curare were able to antagonize increasing concentrations of nicotine over a wide range of such concentrations, and that the effects of the two substances were to some extent reversible, the same result being achieved irrespective of the order of their application. This led to the suggestion that nicotine and curare competed with each other in forming a loose combination with a 'receptor substance,' which was thought to occur in the muscle fiber immediately around the nerve endings where it could be acted upon by the nerve impulse. Nicotine or the nerve impulse when acting on this receptor would lead to a contraction, while its combination with curare would prevent either of them being effective.

In 1936 the concept of a distinctive chemical process in neuromuscular transmission was given a secure foundation by the work of Dale and his followers. They succeeded in showing that a nerve impulse on reaching the terminals in a muscle caused the release of a pharmacologically active substance (18). On the repetitive stimulation of the motor nerve fibers, to the exclusion of other types of nerve fibers, a substance appeared in the fluid perfusing the muscle that was capable of causing a contraction of muscle from the leech and a fall in arterial pressure of the cat. From the relative effectiveness of the substance on these two test preparations and the modification in their response produced by drugs, as well as from the chemical stability of the substance under various conditions, it was concluded to be acetylcholine, the pharmacological action of which was already known. Its release was found to be undiminished when transmission was abolished by curare. Further experiments showed that the rapid injection of acetylcholine into a muscle by its blood vessels caused the excitation of muscle fibers and a contraction (7, 8, 9). This occurred in the chronically denervated muscle as well as in the normal one, and, as in the case of nicotine, this excitatory action could be abolished by curare. The effect of physostigmine was also examined. It was found to prolong and intensify the response to injected acetylcholine and to cause repetitive muscle discharges to a single nerve impulse. From earlier studies it was known that physostigmine has the specific action of inhibiting the enzyme that destroys acetylcholine.

All these findings are compatible with the chemical theory of transmission, according to which transmission is accomplished by the nerve impulse causing the release of a small quantity of acetylcholine from the nerve endings. This substance combines with a special receptor substance in the junctional region of the muscle fiber and, by so doing, alters the properties of the fiber in such a way as to lead to excitation and contraction. This mediation of transmission by a specific chemical is fundamentally different from the process occurring when an impulse is conducted along a continuous structure, in which case an essential factor for the spread of excitation is a flow of electric current between adjacent parts. An alternative explanation of neuromuscular transmission is expressed in the electrical theory, according to which transmission is affected by the action currents generated by the impulse in the prejunctional nerve terminals passing through the adjacent muscle fiber in the appropriate direction and in sufficient magnitude to cause excitation. This theory was formulated when the electrical events associated with the conducted impulse were first studied, and the attempt was made to account for both processes by a common mechanism. The selective sensitivity of transmission to various treatments was ascribed to secondary effects, in particular to the alteration of the electrical excitability of the postjunctional structure.

The results of experiments in which chemicals are involved, either the collection of acetylcholine after nerve stimulation or the application of various chemicals to evoke or modify the response of the postjunctional structure, are consistent with the chemical theory. A decisive result which excludes the possibility of electrical transmission comes from the study of the alteration of properties of the postjunctional region during transmission. It is found that the characteristic alteration responsible for excitation of the muscle fiber cannot be brought about by a current generated externally to the fiber. On the other hand an alteration of precisely this type is produced by the application of acetylcholine to the junctional region of the muscle fiber. Accepting the correctness of the chemical theory of transmission, one is able to give an integrated account of a wide range of experimental observation, distinguishing between those events which occur prejunctionally and involve the release of acetylcholine, and those which occur postjunctionally and involve the reaction of acetylcholine with the receptor and the resultant change in the properties of the muscle fiber membrane.

MORPHOLOGY

The detailed morphological description which follows applies to junctions on skeletal muscle in vertebrates where the normal response to a single nerve impulse is a propagated action potential and a twitch. These are the junctions of which both the morphology and physiology have been most intensively studied. There are other junctions, in the amphibian at least, where the normal mechanical response of the muscle fibers is a slow tonic contraction which can only be elicited in appreciable tension by a train of nerve impulses (53, 55). These fibers are innervated by a special class of small diameter nerve fibers which form numerous, widely distributed terminations of the *en grappe* type on them.

The twitch muscle fibers are innervated by coarse motor nerve fibers. On issuing from the central nervous system, each nerve fiber branches repeatedly both before and after reaching the muscle it supplies. By this branching the nerve fiber forms junctions on many muscle fibers, the number varying greatly for muscles in different parts of the body in a given animal. Conversely, muscle fibers have been found to be supplied each with a few nerve endings at widely separated positions along their length (47, 50). These multiple junctions are in some cases made by separate nerve fibers and in others by branches of a single fiber. The variations in the distribution of nerve fibers to muscle fibers in different preparations and their probable relation to differences in function have been discussed by Tiegs (73).

In the morphology of the single junction, the pattern made by the nerve fiber in terminating also shows marked differences from species to species and from muscle to muscle. This field was early thoroughly explored by Kühne (56). Confining consideration to the more familiar objects of investigation, he drew a distinction between the plate type of ending in the mammal and reptile and the bush type in the frog. In both types the nerve comes into contact with the muscle fiber immediately after losing its myelin sheath and branches repeatedly on its surface to form the terminal apparatus. In the former type, the extent of this apparatus is limited to a roughly circular space (the endplate) which has a diameter of 25 to 70 μ. Viewed in a section at right angles to the muscle fiber surface this region is marked by a rounded eminence. Within the confines of the endplate the terminal branches cover a large fraction of the included muscle fiber surface. In the case of the other type of ending (the endbush) the nerve terminal branches range over a much wider area. The terminal apparatus here consists mainly of several large, straight branches 100 to 300 μ in length, running parallel to the axis of the muscle fiber and connected

into a continuous system by shorter lengths at right angles.

As a result of careful cytological examination, it is recognized that there are three sharply defined components of different cellular origin at the junction (14). The first of these is the terminal apparatus of the nerve. The second is the specialized region of muscle fiber surface contacted by the nerve endings. A characteristic of this region is an increased density of muscle nuclei (fundamental nuclei of the junction), the presence of which is suggestive of a higher degree of synthetic activity here than elsewhere in the muscle fiber. The third component is a layer of neuroglia which in this position is referred to as the teloglia and which appear to be continuous with the Schwann cell envelope of the myelinated fiber. It contributes about half the nuclei seen in the junctional region (the sole nuclei), the remainder being the fundamental nuclei in the muscle. It is dispersed over the entire endplate where it forms the rounded eminence and accompanies the terminal nerve filaments along their extended course in the endbush. In spite of the gross differences that exist between the two types of ending, the detailed relationships between these three cellular components are fundamentally the same. From the use of cytological and histochemical staining methods it appears that the nerve terminal branches lie sunk in grooves in the muscle fiber surface (14, 16). Only a small part of the circumference of the nerve is not in close proximity to the surface of the muscle lining the groove. The sides of the groove appear to be marked with a set of parallel lines 0.3 to 1 μ apart which are oriented more or less normal to the axis of the groove and extend a short distance into the muscle beyond the clearly defined edges of the nerve cylinder. In the case of the endbush, where there are long stretches of unbranched nerve fiber, the ruling is highly regular, the lines running from one edge of the groove to the other without deviating from this geometrical relation. In the endplate where the nerve filaments usually extend for no more than a few diameters before terminating or branching, the arrangement of the lines is less regular, adjacent lines frequently fuse with one another, while their spacing is maintained relatively constant. Examination of the junction with the electron microscope reveals regularly spaced narrow infoldings of the membrane of the muscle fiber lining the groove (71). These fine junctional folds very probably correspond to the lines seen under the light microscope. Figures 1 and 2 show the relation between nerve and muscle over a wide range of magnification. The width of the folds is

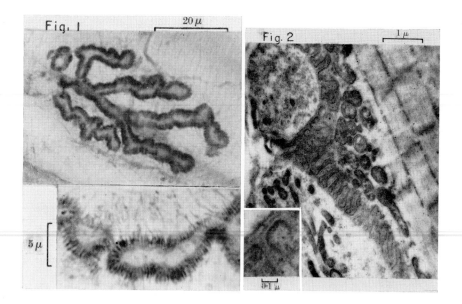

FIG. 1. Surface view of neuromuscular junction of lizard stained with Janus green. The only parts to have taken up the stain are the regions of muscle bordering the nerve terminals (the subneural apparatus) and a short piece of nerve at the termination of the myelin. The final part of the myelinated nerve fiber appears in the extreme left of the upper picture. In the lower picture a portion of the junction is shown at higher magnification revealing the lines in the subneural apparatus, which are oriented at right angles to the edge of the nerve and which are uniformly spaced about 0.4 μ apart. [From Couteaux (15).]

FIG. 2. Electronmicrograph of lizard neuromuscular junction. Two nerve terminal branches are seen in the left side of the main picture with the muscle to the right. The dark oval bodies in the nerve and muscle are mitochondria. The surface of the muscle at the junction is thrown into a series of folds, which correspond in their repetition interval and depth to the lines in fig. 1. From the appearance where the surface membrane of the nerve can be clearly seen, it is established that it does not enter the folds. The inset gives an enlarged view of the situation at the junction. The surface membranes of nerve and muscle probably correspond to the two dense lines separated by about 0.07 μ. [From Robertson (71).]

about 0.05 μ and their depth about 0.5 μ. This infolding considerably increases the area of postjunctional membrane which may have an important bearing on the magnitude of the alteration produced in the junctional region during transmission. The teloglia does not occur within the grooves but appears to remain in contact with the exposed part of the nerve cylinder. This suggests that it plays no direct role in the transmission process.

LOCAL ELECTRICAL RESPONSE

The study of neuromuscular transmission received a great impetus with the application of electrical recording techniques to the junctional region. It was observed by a number of workers that after a muscle had been treated with just sufficient curare to prevent contraction from nerve stimulation, there still occurred an electrical change in the muscle, though this was different from the action potential type of response (13, 30, 33, 43, 45, 72). The response was not propagated, being recorded in monophasic form between different positions along the muscle. In the sartorius muscle of the frog, with one electrode kept on the nerve-free pelvic end and the other moved from place to place, the magnitude of the recorded potential change was found to be correlated with the density of nerve endings under the moving electrode. The potential change arising at a focus of nerve endings (recorded with respect to a distant nerve-free point on the muscle) consists of a transient negative deflection having a relatively brief rising phase and a slower return, the later part of which follows an approximately exponential time course. This response has been generally referred to as the endplate potential, notwithstanding that in the amphibian muscle, where it has been studied most, the nerve ending is not of the morphological form described as an endplate.

On increasing the concentration of curare in the fluid bathing the muscle, the amplitude of the response is reduced. When, on the other hand, the concentration is decreased from that required to block transmission, action potentials in individual muscle fibers appear as more rapid and complex deflections superimposed on the endplate potential. With further reduction of curare, the action potential component increases and obscures the endplate potential. The endplate potential was early inferred to be developed across the surface membrane of the muscle fiber, although confined to its junctional region, because of the similarity of this potential with that which could be evoked by a brief pulse of current applied anywhere along the muscle. More compelling evidence came from the study of the interaction of the junctional response and the muscle action potential, the latter elicited by direct stimulation and propagated into the junctional region. It was found by this method that the action potential and the endplate potential did not sum with each other, and that the action potential was capable of abolishing the later part of the endplate potential when timed to coincide with its summit.

The most accurate basis for an analysis of the potential changes in the muscle fiber to determine the manner of their generation is the results from intracellular recording (40). This involves inserting a very fine electrode through the surface membrane of individual muscle fibers and recording potentials between it and another electrode in the surrounding fluid. Intracellular recording not only makes more accurate measurements of the electrical response possible but also greatly simplifies its interpretation. After minor corrections for extracellular gradients of potential when current is flowing, the potentials observed by this method are those obtaining across the surface membrane of the muscle fiber at the position of insertion of the electrode. The frog muscle fiber is found to have a resting membrane potential of about 90 mv (inside negative with respect to outside), which is the same in the junctional region as elsewhere along the fiber. The addition of curare to the solution bathing the muscle in a concentration sufficient to block transmission has no effect on this resting potential. With the intracellular electrode situated in the junctional region of the fiber, an endplate potential is recorded in response to nerve stimulation.

It appears as a transient positive deflection, i.e. as a transient reduction of membrane potential from its resting level. Its amplitude varies from fiber to fiber and depends upon the concentration of curare. In a frog sartorius muscle, critically curarized to abolish contraction, different fibers have been found to display endplate potentials ranging from 1 mv to more than 20 mv. The response would be expected under these conditions to range in size up to the threshold depolarization for initiating an action potential which would be about 40 mv. Immediately at the junction the endplate potential has a rising phase lasting 1.5 msec. Following the attainment of the summit, the potential declines to one half in another 2 msec. The rate of fractional decay decreases beyond this, the time required to fall from one half to one quarter being about 5 msec. A potential change can be detected at points on the fiber up to a few millimeters distant from the nerve ending, becoming progressively more attenuated and slowed with increasing distance (fig. 3).

This potential wave has been analyzed to determine the movement of charge underlying it. The amplitude of the potential at various instants is plotted against distance along the fiber. Assuming that the membrane capacity remains constant during the response, the curves thus formed indicate the spatial distribution of charge displaced from the membrane capacity (relative to its initial condition of charge). The area beneath each curve is a measure of the total charge displaced at the given instant. The plot of these areas against time shows that the charge is built up to a maximum in about 2 msec., and after this it decays exponentially with a time constant of about 25 msec. A determination of the passive electrical characteristics of the muscle fiber shows that this latter value corresponds to the electric time constant of the membrane. This result is consistent with the idea that there is a brief phase of transmitter action, confined to about the initial 2 msec. of the response, during which charge is transferred inward across the membrane, and that this is followed by a gradual dissipation of the displaced charge at a rate determined by the electrical characteristics of the inactive fiber membrane. It agrees with the results of the interaction between the endplate potential and action potential from which it appears that the charge displacement built up by junctional activity can be removed by the high conductance of the spike at a time shortly following the summit of the endplate potential.

From a knowledge of the membrane capacity for a unit length of fiber, the displacement of charge may be calculated. For an endplate potential of 20 mv peak amplitude the maximum displacement of charge is found to be about 10^{-9} coulombs. Given information on the complete electrical characteristics of the fiber, i.e. of the separate values of membrane capacity and membrane and core conductances, it is possible to analyze more completely the potential wave in the fiber. An approximate treatment, in which the observed response of the fiber is compared with a theoretically derived potential wave for charge placed instantaneously at a point along the fiber, confirms the above interpretation of the generation of the endplate response by a brief transfer of charge in a small area of membrane.

In a normal uncurarized muscle, the rate of rise of the endplate potential is about three times as fast as in the above case, due evidently to a proportionately more intense transfer of charge. On the endplate potential reaching a level of depolarization of about 40 mv, an action potential is initiated, indicated by a sudden increase in the rate of change of potential. The threshold for the initiation of an action potential has been examined by the direct application of a current pulse, both at the junction and away from it, and has been found to occur at all points at this same level. The spike which follows the initial depolarization produced by the endplate potential is however characteristically different at the junction where it is evoked from elsewhere in the course of its propagation (40, 69; cf. fig. 4). After rising from the level of threshold to zero membrane potential at a rate which

is not noticeably different in the two cases, the junctional spike produces a smaller reversal of membrane potential than the normal muscle spike away from the junction. Thus, at the summit of the junctional spike the membrane potential is reversed to the extent of about 20 mv (total spike height of 110 mv), compared to a reversal of about 35 mv for the normal spike (total height, 125 mv). The summit of the junctional spike occurs earlier and is sharper than that of the normal spike. After reaching the summit the potential falls to the level of zero membrane potential where it remains nearly steady for about 1.5 msec. before declining further. In contrast, the normal spike declines rather slowly for about 2 msec. after its summit, but then falls more rapidly past zero membrane potential.

It can be shown that these features, which distinguish the junctional spike, do not depend on some special characteristic of the action potential process in the region where it occurs. When an action potential is propagated into the junctional region without the nerve having been active, the response is the normal muscle action potential similar to that which is elicited elsewhere along the fiber. Moreover, these features cannot be attributed to the response having originated in the region of observation rather than having propagated into it, since the propagated action potential and the one which is initiated in the region of recording by a brief pulse of current show little difference beyond the attainment of threshold. It is concluded therefore that these features arise from a

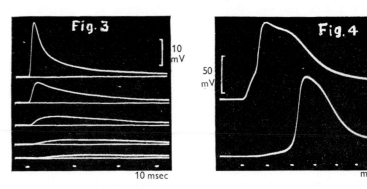

FIG. 3. Endplate potentials recorded intracellularly from a single curarized muscle fiber of a frog. The series of five records were taken at intervals of 1 mm along the fiber. The top record shows the response at the junction as inferred from the fact that the response was maximum at this position. [From Fatt & Katz (38).]

FIG. 4. Action potentials recorded in a muscle fiber in response to a nerve impulse. The upper record was taken at the junction, the location of which had earlier been determined by the response in the presence of curare. The lower record was taken 2.5 mm away in the same fiber. A trace of the endplate potential can still be seen in the lower record, appearing as a gradual rise of potential which precedes the foot of the spike. [From Fatt & Katz (38).]

modification of the action potential response by junctional activity. The effect of this activity is consistently to cause a deviation toward a level near zero membrane potential. This accounts for the reduction in peak amplitude of the spike and the delay on the falling phase. As a first approximation it may be assumed that the fundamental changes effected in the membrane by the two types of activity which are superimposed at the junction (i.e. spike and junctional activity) do not interact. The effect of transmitter action on the spike, as well as the initial development of the endplate potential, can then be satisfactorily accounted for by an increase in membrane conductance in series with an emf set near the level of zero membrane potential. However during the action potential the situation is complicated by the presence in the membrane of two important components of conductance, one due to the passage of sodium ions and the other to potassium ions, which follow different time courses and are dependent on the level of membrane potential. In order to determine the effect of transmitter action more accurately, the spike has been set up independently of the nerve response by direct stimulation of the muscle fiber (24). In this way, using a suitably timed nerve impulse, transmitter action was made to begin at any chosen stage of the action potential process, and the resultant deviation of the potential observed. It was thus shown that the equilibrium potential for junctional activity lies between 10 and 20 mv, with the interior of the fiber negative.

The generation of the endplate potential has also been studied in the absence of an action potential by applying a steady current to the muscle fiber and thereby altering the membrane potential at which the transmitter operates. Significant results have been obtained only with currents directed inwardly across the membrane and causing a hyperpolarization, since with currents in the opposite directions complications arise owing to the initiation of muscle action potentials. The endplate potential was found to vary in such a manner as to maintain its rate of rise nearly directly proportional to the level of membrane potential at which it occurred. An equally good fit of the data could be obtained with a straight line for which zero response would occur at a membrane potential of 15 mv, internally negative. There is thus complete agreement, as far as the equilibrium value is concerned, between the results obtained from the effect of junctional activity on the membrane at rest and on the membrane undergoing an action potential.

In the case of the endplate potential arising in the otherwise resting membrane, an analysis has been made to determine what size the added conductance would have to be to produce the observed rising phase of the response. The muscle fiber has been treated as a cable with known distributive characteristics, and the conductance has been considered as applied suddenly at a point along this cable. From the change of potential occurring in the uncurarized muscle up to the level at which the spike is initiated, the conductance is calculated to correspond to a resistance of about 20,000 ohms. This may be considered in relation to the resting resistance of about 500,000 ohms, which is shunted as a result of junctional activity, and which is in effect the resistance of the membrane over a length of about 4 mm of fiber (twice the space constant of the fiber). An analysis has also been made of the effect of junctional activity to reduce the reversal of membrane potential at the summit of the spike, together with any additional displacement produced by an applied current. The added conductance calculated from this information is roughly in agreement with the value obtained from the rising phase of the endplate potential.

There appears thus to be a convergence of evidence to show that the effect of junctional activity on the muscle fiber membrane can be represented as the addition of a conductance in series with a fixed emf. This may further be interpreted as the creation of a new path for the diffusion of ions across the membrane. The equilibrium value (15 mv, internally negative) toward which the membrane potential is displaced is the same as the emf that would be expected to occur for the unrestricted diffusion of ions between two solutions, having the ionic composition of the intra- and extracellular media. It is therefore concluded that in the new diffusion path created by transmitter action, no selectivity is exerted in the passage of different ion species other than that already existing in the aqueous media on the two sides of the membrane.

The investigations on neuromuscular transmission considered so far in this section have concerned the amphibian muscle fibers that under normal conditions respond to a nerve impulse with a twitch. The conclusions reached, as to the fundamental alteration in the postjunctional membrane produced by the action of the transmitter, seem likely to be valid generally for junctions on vertebrate skeletal muscle fibers. However, marked variations in the overall electrical response have been found to occur in different preparations, and these are adduced to stem mainly from differences in the electrical characteristics of the muscle fiber membrane in parallel with the junctionally responding region.

In the mammalian muscle fiber under normal conditions, the endplate potential does not form a conspicuous step on the rising phase of the spike as it does in the amphibian (4). The explanation for this lies in the fact that the threshold depolarization for initiating an action potential is here much lower (about 10 mv compared with 40 mv in the frog), and at this level the transition between endplate potential and spike does not involve an appreciable change in rate of rise of potential. In the curarized preparation the response differs from that seen in the frog in having a shorter decaying phase and in becoming attenuated more rapidly with increasing distance from the junction. These differences are attributable entirely to a higher conductance of the muscle fiber membrane with a consequent reduction in the electric time and space constants.

The tonic muscle fibers of the frog, supplied by the small diameter motor nerve fibers, display differences in their electrical response from the twitch fibers of the same animal which are again mainly attributable to the electrical properties of the fiber membrane, though the disposition of the nerve endings also plays an important part (10, 11, 54). The tonic muscle fiber is unable to develop an action potential, due apparently to the absence of the mechanism by which the sodium permeability of the membrane is increased by depolarization. The entire time course of the junctional response can therefore be observed under all conditions without the complication of a superimposed spike. In addition the amplitude of the junctional response can be varied by stimulation of different nerve fibers. Owing to a wide and relatively uniform distribution of their endings along the muscle fiber, the potential wave does not show a marked attenuation with distance, and at no position does it have the initially rapid and later relatively slow decline of the endplate potential recorded at the junction of a twitch fiber. Another distinctive feature of the response in these fibers is that the membrane potential goes through a phase of hyperpolarization after recovering from the depolarization. A similar phase of hyperpolarization is found to follow a wave of depolarization elicited by a current pulse applied directly to the muscle fiber, from which it is inferred that this feature is not due to some peculiar characteristic of the transmission process but depends rather on the electrical behavior of the membrane.

ACTIVITY OF THE NERVE TERMINALS

In the preceding section, the local electrical changes brought about in the normal and in the curarized muscle fiber by the arrival of an impulse in the prejunctional nerve terminals have been described. In this section the behavior of the terminals will be considered under various conditions, in so far as this throws light on their specialized properties. Almost all the information to be presented is derived from recording potential changes in the muscle fiber. According to the chemical theory of transmission, activity in the nerve terminals causes a release of acetylcholine which then reacts with the muscle to produce an alteration in it. Hence, when recording from the muscle, an indication of activity at the terminals is obtained, provided that allowance is made for possible effects in the later stages of the transmission process. An example of such an effect is the reduction of the responsiveness of the muscle fiber by curare through its competition with acetylcholine.

When the membrane potential is recorded in the junctional region of a muscle fiber, a sequence of small transient changes of potential (as shown in fig. 5) is observed even in the absence of a nerve impulse (3, 41, 62). Although their peak amplitude is only of the order of 0.5 mv, these potential changes have

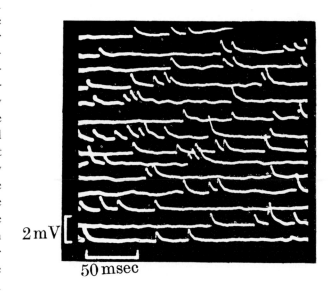

2 mV

50 msec

FIG. 5. Spontaneously occurring miniature endplate potentials recorded at the junctional region of a muscle fiber of a frog. The location of the recording position was confirmed by the form of the response elicited by a nerve impulse. [From Fatt & Katz (39).]

many of the characteristics of a response to a nerve impulse. Their time course is similar to the endplate potential in a curarized muscle. They appear largest at the same place along the muscle fiber and become attenuated by changes in the position of the recording electrode in the same way. Furthermore, they are diminished in amplitude by curare and increased and prolonged by anticholinesterases. All these features may be accounted for by the properties of the postjunctional element and its reaction with acetylcholine. That the nerve terminals are responsible for the release of acetylcholine producing these discharges—called miniature endplate potentials—is shown by the fact that they are abolished on nerve degeneration and their frequency of occurrence is modified by various treatments applied to the nerve. In addition there is strong evidence that the endplate potential evoked by a nerve impulse is itself resolvable into units of the size of miniature potentials.

The miniature discharges occur in a random time sequence, the probability of occurrence in any given interval of time remaining constant irrespective of previous discharges. The distribution of intervals between successive discharges is accordingly found to follow a simple exponential function, decaying with increasing interval, and can be described by a single parameter, the mean frequency of discharge. Exceptions to this are occasional bursts which consist of a number of miniature endplate potentials occurring within a short period of time. They are the only indication of a possible coupling between discharges, and can be readily recognized and excluded from a statistical analysis. In the frog under normal conditions the mean frequency of spontaneous discharges varies greatly at different junctions, extending at least over the range 0.1 per sec. to 100 per sec. In mammalian muscle the frequency is more nearly constant around 1 per sec.

The distribution of amplitudes of the miniature endplate potentials at a junction can be fitted approximately by a Gaussian curve with a standard deviation equal to about 30 per cent of the mean. With this relatively small variation, the amplitudes effectively do not grade down to zero, and hence under suitable recording conditions there is no uncertainty in counting the discharges. By a variation in recording technique, placing the microelectrode in contact with the muscle fiber membrane without penetrating it, it is possible to restrict the recording of miniature discharges to those arising in a small fraction of the junctional region contacted by the

nerve terminals. In this way, one tenth or so of the miniature discharges occurring within the fiber are recorded selectively while the remainder appear greatly attenuated and are in effect rejected (27). Even under these conditions the amplitude of the miniature potentials appears to be continuously distributed, there being no clear indication of a number of discrete sizes which are repeated.

A notable feature of the miniature discharge is that the release of acetylcholine which produces it does not appear to change under various treatments which have an important influence on the generation of an electrical response (28). Even in the situation where the nerve and muscle membranes have been completely depolarized by a high concentration of potassium ions, it can be shown by repolarizing the muscle fiber with an applied current that the intermittent release of small quantities of acetylcholine, capable of producing miniature potentials, still occurs (26). It is therefore concluded that the release of acetylcholine forming these discharges does not depend upon the occurrence of electrical activity of the action potential type in any structural unit within the nerve terminal.

Unlike the amplitude (considered as a quantity of acetylcholine released from the terminal), the frequency of the spontaneous discharges is highly sensitive to changes in the condition of the preparation. Changes in the osmotic pressure of the surrounding fluid, for example, have a strong effect, the frequency increasing reversibly as this is raised (41, 44, 62). A finding which is important in indicating a possible relation between electrical events in the nerve and these spontaneous discharges is that their frequency can be altered by the application of a current to the nerve which, by spreading into the terminal portion, will alter the membrane polarization there (23, 64). The frequency is found to vary approximately exponentially with changes in the polarizing current in the nerve, being increased by depolarization of the terminals. The frequency of discharge is also increased when the concentration of potassium ions in the bathing fluid is raised above the normal level, this probably operating in the same way as current by causing a reduction of membrane potential.

The rate of rise of the endplate potential, up to the level at which an action potential is initiated, is about one hundred times greater than the mean rate of rise of the miniature endplate potential. A decrease in the calcium ion concentration of the solution bathing the preparation causes a reduction in the endplate potential, while the amplitude of the spontaneous discharge is left unchanged; the same effect is produced by the addition of magnesium ions (4, 19, 20, 21, 41, 63). Calcium appears to exert a specific facilitatory action on the release of acetylcholine by a nerve impulse, and the action of magnesium may then be accounted for by a competition with calcium for the reactive site. This antagonistic relation between calcium and magnesium at the terminals is in contrast to their common action in raising the threshold depolarization for the initiation of an action potential in a nerve or muscle fiber. By the withdrawal of calcium or addition of magnesium or both, the endplate potential can be reduced to a small fraction of its normal size and can be made to approach in amplitude the spontaneous miniature potential. When this is done, the amplitude of the response to successive nerve impulses is seen to fluctuate widely, in contrast to its constancy under normal conditions or when the response is reduced to any degree by treatment with curare. With the junction sufficiently deprived of calcium, the response occurs intermittently. When the proportion of failures is large, the responses to a series of nerve impulses have a distribution of amplitudes similar to that of the spontaneous discharge. At a somewhat lower level of depression, the distribution shows several peaks, corresponding to small integral multiples of the mean of the spontaneous potentials. It is evident that the endplate potential under these conditions is composed of a variable whole number of miniature endplate potentials, the fluctuation being due to variation in number and in size of units. The result of an analysis of this fluctuation for the probability of occurrence of different numbers of units can be accurately fitted by a Poisson distribution. This implies that there is no interaction between units, the probability of occurrence of each being unaffected by the number of units composing the response.

With the distribution in this form, relatively large fluctuations in response would occur only when the number of contributing units is small. As the number increases, the amplitude of fluctuation relative to the mean amplitude of response will vary in inverse proportion to the square root of the number of units, while the additional dispersion due to variation in amplitude of individual units will become progressively less significant. Fluctuations occur in the curarized endplate potential, evoked under conditions in which the release of acetylcholine from the nerve terminals is normal, and these can be attributed to a variation in the number of units around such a magnitude as would be predicted roughly from the size of the normal response (68). The probability that the normal endplate potential is composed of these units is greatly strengthened by the observation that an increase in the calcium ion concentration beyond that normally present in the bathing fluid produces a further increase in the size of the response, which is entirely attributable to an increase in the release of acetylcholine from the nerve terminals, and which is presumably due to an increase in the probability of release of individual units of acetylcholine (13, 29, 43, 52). The curarized endplate potential can in this way be increased two or three times in size.

In contrast with the effect on the response to a nerve impulse, changes in the calcium concentration in either direction from normal are usually found to have no effect on the frequency of spontaneous miniature potentials. Calcium withdrawal (or magnesium addition) does, however, reduce the frequency when this has first been raised by the presence of a high concentration of potassium ions or by a current applied to depolarize the nerve terminals. It thus appears that the depletion of calcium ions has a similar action in preventing an increase in the probability of a unit of acetylcholine being released during a given time interval by a maintained depolarization, as in reducing the probability of its release by a nerve impulse.

Another procedure which modifies the number of units responding to a nerve impulse is the previous activation of the nerve. In the curarized amphibian muscle, the second of two closely spaced nerve impulses elicits a larger endplate potential than does the first (30, 43, 72). With continued repetitive stimulation of the nerve, the individual responses increase progressively until a steady condition is attained. By this means the size of the response may be increased to two or three times that elicited by an isolated impulse. (This increase is in addition to the summation of electrical changes in the postjunctional structure, the later responses adding to the potential change remaining from previous responses.) In the case where two impulses are set up in the nerve the potentiation of the response to the second is found to be greatest at the shortest interval of time at which the nerve will conduct. The effect falls gradually as the interval between the nerve impulses is increased, the response having returned to its unpotentiated size at an interval of about 100 msec. That this potentiation is a prejunctional phenomenon and moreover that it involves a change in the number of units of acetylcholine released is revealed by studying the effect under conditions in which the number of units responding to a nerve impulse is small. For this purpose the calcium concentration is reduced (or magnesium added) until the response to a single nerve impulse has a mean amplitude of one or a few units. With two nerve impulses at a short interval apart the response to the second is found to be statistically larger, as in the curarized preparation. Examination of the distribution of amplitudes for the first and second responses in a number of trials reveals that the increase in the second is accompanied by a reduction in its fluctuation, indicating that the change is entirely the result of an increase in the number of units responding (22). It is further found that the number of units responding to the first nerve impulse in a particular trial has no effect on the number responding to the second in that trial. This leads to the conclusion that the potentiation of the second response depends solely on the previous presence of an impulse in the nerve and not on the number of units of acetylcholine released by the impulse.

Whereas in the amphibian the second of two nerve impulses elicits an endplate potential which is larger than the first, in the curarized mammalian preparation the response to the second is smaller up to an interval of a few seconds (30, 65, 66). Evidence of potentiation by previous activity of the nerve is procured where the conditioning treatment is a large number of nerve impulses. When between a few hundred and a few thousand impulses are set up in the nerve within 5 to 20 sec., the later impulses in the train elicit a considerably reduced response owing to the depressant effect of preceding volleys. The time course of subsequent changes in the effectiveness of transmission is revealed by testing with a single impulse at a variable time after the termination of the conditioning train of impulses. It is thus found that the effectiveness of transmission gradually increases from the depressed state to beyond that occurring in the absence of previous activity (5, 48, 65). The magnitude and time course of this potentiation depends on the number of conditioning nerve impulses; it is larger, arises later and is more prolonged, the greater the number of impulses. Following a few thousand impulses, the maximum is not reached until about 0.5 min. after conditioning, when the response as measured by the size of the endplate potential may be 50 per cent greater than the normal and the total duration of the potentiated state may be 10 min.

When the curare-free mammalian preparation is subjected to calcium depletion, a behavior is observed which is similar to that in the frog. The second of two closely spaced nerve impulses now elicits a greater response than the first (67). The effect of conditioning with a train of impulses is to cause a summation of the potentiation left behind by individual nerve impulses. It is apparent that the potentiation in the wake of a nerve impulse has a very prolonged phase of low level effectiveness, which, while hardly noticeable after a single impulse, is able to sum over a large number of impulses to produce an appreciable potentiation of very great duration. When the calcium concentration is normal, the earlier part of this potentiation is outweighed by the depression which follows each nerve impulse but does not sum over as long a period of time. The fact that the depression does not occur in the calcium depleted preparation when the number of units of acetylcholine released by each impulse is small makes it appear highly probable that this effect, unlike the potentiation, depends on the amount of acetylcholine released by previous impulses.

In the mammalian muscle under normal conditions, the frequency of spontaneous discharges is found to be increased immediately following the response to a conditioning nerve impulse at which time the response to a second impulse is diminished. After conditioning with a large number of impulses, the frequency is increased many times and returns only very slowly to normal (6, 62). The final part of its return parallels the time course of the subsidence of the potentiation of transmission, as observed in the curarized muscle. The effect of previous activity of the nerve is apparently to increase the potentiality of the terminals for releasing units of acetylcholine, both spontaneously and in response to a nerve impulse.

PROPERTIES OF THE JUNCTIONAL RECEPTOR

The most direct method for investigating the receptive properties of the muscle fiber is to add acetylcholine to the surrounding fluid without involving the nerve terminals. Two techniques have been used: the acetylcholine has been applied either uniformly to the whole muscle fiber, or in a highly localized manner to the region contacted by the nerve endings. The effect is a depolarization of the muscle fiber in the junctional region (12, 17, 36, 51). After preliminary treatment with an anticholinesterase, which prevents the enzymatic destruction of acetylcholine, the technique of uniform application allows quantitative information to be obtained on the reactivity of the receptor with varying concentrations of acetylcholine. When the acetylcholine concentration is as high as 1 μmole per liter, muscle fibers are depolarized sufficiently for spikes to be initiated. For low concentrations, not exceeding that required to elicit spikes, the depolarization is nearly proportional to the acetylcholine concentration. With high concentrations the depolarization elicited by acetylcholine can be measured in the wake of an initial burst of spikes, when the muscle fiber in the region of the junction is refractory to the initiation of further spikes. At the lower concentrations the depolarization is maintained for many minutes while the acetylcholine remains in the surrounding fluid; at the higher concentrations a perceptible decline is observed within a few minutes, the rate of decline being greater the higher the concentration of acetylcholine. This effect is apparently the result of a gradual desensitization of the receptor by its forming a different and less readily reversible combination with acetylcholine than that which results in depolarization.

More accurate information on the spatial distribution of the receptor and the time course of its reaction may be obtained by applying brief pulses of acetylcholine with a micropipette (25, 70). It is found that the high sensitivity to acetylcholine does not extend beyond very limited regions in the neighborhood of the nerve terminal branches, for in the frog, where the terminals are spread over about a 200 μ length of fiber, it is necessary to position the micropipette to within 10 or 20 μ in order to obtain a high sensitivity. It is further observed that acetylcholine exerts its powerful action only when applied externally; it has no specific effect when released within the muscle fiber, even though the pipette is situated immediately beneath a region of the fiber surface that is found to be sensitive to external application. With the micropipette critically placed over the junction so as to obtain maximum sensitivity, the depolarization evoked by a brief pulse of acetylcholine rises to a peak in about 15 msec. This order of time would no doubt be required for the diffusion of acetylcholine from its point of release to the receptor some microns away.

Among agents that affect neuromuscular transmission, the one that has received most attention is curare. This term applies to a group of related substances which act by competing with acetylcholine for the receptor. Combination of curare with the receptor does not itself affect the electrical properties of the membrane, but it prevents acetylcholine combining and thereby exerting a depolarizing action. Among the common inorganic ions, sodium appears to have the most marked effect on the combination of acetyl-

choline with the receptor (36, 42). After the complete withdrawal of sodium ions from the bathing solution, the application of acetylcholine elicits a small depolarization, which is augmented considerably by the presence of only a small concentration of sodium. This effect is not produced by the addition of calcium or potassium ions. It is inferred to be due to a change in the reaction between the receptor and acetylcholine, rather than in a later stage of the process leading to depolarization, from the fact that sodium ions also increase the ability of acetylcholine to compete with curare for the receptor. A facilitation of the reaction between the receptor and acetylcholine in muscles of the frog is also produced by the addition to the bathing medium of very small concentrations of epinephrine and norepinephrine, the substances released by impulses at the terminals of sympathetic postganglionic nerve fibers (49).

The anticholinesterases are a group of substances that affect transmission by competitively inhibiting the enzyme cholinesterase, which is concentrated in the junctional region of the muscle fiber and normally hydrolyzes acetylcholine soon after its liberation from the nerve terminals. Unlike the reaction between the receptor and acetylcholine or curare, which must be very rapid in reaching an equilibrium, that between the enzyme and a reversible anticholinesterase takes many minutes. With the anticholinesterase exerting its maximum effect and presumably completely inhibiting the enzyme, the time course of transmitter action is in two stages (31, 40). The 2 msec. phase of high intensity transmitter action is virtually unchanged and accounts for the early rapid rise of the endplate potential. This is succeeded by a prolonged phase of low level transmitter action which heightens and prolongs the endplate potential.

Other organic compounds besides acetylcholine exert a depolarizing action at the junction. Some of the substances that have been examined combine in various degrees the properties of acetylcholine, curare and anticholinesterases (32, 74). In the case where the first two actions are combined, the agent in a concentration which produces a small depolarization prevents acetylcholine from adding to this to the extent obtaining when the former is absent. Different substances are found to follow various time courses in their action, and where the same one exerts multiple types of action, each may develop along a different time course. Furthermore the relative effectiveness for each type of action may vary between different preparations.

Transmission would be expected to be influenced at

various stages by changes of temperature. The most conspicuous result of lowering it is a prolongation of the phase of transmitter action. This appears to be due largely to a reduction in the activity of cholinesterase since at low temperatures treatment with an anticholinesterase produces little additional change (4, 31). It is found, however, that, while the time course of the curarized endplate potential is lengthened, the peak amplitude is not significantly increased as it should be if the early phase of transmitter action were unaltered. In the mammalian muscle this appears to be the result of curare competing more effectively with acetylcholine at the reduced temperature and thus offsetting the effect of the reduction in cholinesterase activity on the peak potential change.

An experiment, highly relevant to the conclusion that the alteration of the properties of the muscle fiber produced by a nerve impulse is consistent with the operation of a chemical mediator, is the demonstration that the depolarization elicited by acetylcholine has its origin in the same conductance change that has been shown to occur during transmission (26). For this purpose the muscle has first been nearly completely depolarized by immersing it in a solution with a high concentration of potassium ions. In this condition the application of acetylcholine produces no discernible change in membrane potential. When the membrane is now polarized in either direction by the passage of current across it, acetylcholine produces a potential change that partly compensates for the displacement from the unpolarized state, and this is attributable to an increase in membrane conductance similar to that observed for the preparation initially in its normal environment.

CONCLUSION: MECHANISM OF TRANSMISSION

From the rate at which acetylcholine appears in the effluent from a perfused muscle during repetitive stimulation of the motor nerve fibers, it has been estimated that the quantity released from the nerve endings at a single junction in response to a single nerve impulse is about 10^{-18} moles (1, 35). Although the value obtained in this way is liable to be too small because of losses in the collection procedure and because of a depression in the release mechanism by previous activity, it is not likely to be in error in its order of magnitude. It may be compared with the minimum quantity of about 5×10^{-16} moles of acetylcholine which is required to evoke a muscle action potential when applied to the junctional region by a

micropipette (25, 70). The factor of 200 between these two quantities can be satisfactorily accounted for by the geometry of the junction. The nerve endings from which the acetylcholine is released are probably everywhere in very close proximity to the receptive region of the postjunctional surface with a consequent high efficiency for its reaching the receptor. On the other hand, when acetylcholine is applied by a micropipette, it would have to diffuse over a greater distance and be considerably dispersed before reacting with the receptor, and a larger quantity would therefore be required to produce a comparable effect. Even if the micropipette were placed directly on a sensitive region, the application of a moderate amount of acetylcholine would no doubt lead to a rapid saturation and inactivation of the receptor there because of its high local concentration, and the initiation of an action potential would require the action of acetylcholine over a greater part of the receptive area.

From the concentration of acetylcholine required to produce an action potential when applied uniformly to the preparation and from the quantity that is released by a nerve impulse, it is possible to calculate the volume in which the acetylcholine released from the nerve terminals would be present when reacting with the receptor (37). The result shows that the acetylcholine must exert its maximum effect before diffusing more than 1μ, a distance which is consistent with morphological findings on the minute separation of the pre- and postjunctional surfaces. Furthermore, assuming that diffusion occurs away from the immediate neighborhood of the junction, the time during which the acetylcholine will remain in an effective concentration is shown to be less than 1 msec. The brief duration of transmitter action may reflect the operation of this diffusion, though the possibility remains that the reaction between the receptor and acetylcholine does not reach an equilibrium in such a short period of time and the kinetics of this reaction may then influence the time course of transmitter action. At least it is clear that the enzymatic destruction of acetylcholine is not involved in the early, high intensity phase of transmitter action, as it is not affected by the presence of an anticholinesterase. The failure of the destruction of acetylcholine adds a later low level phase of transmitter action which probably occurs after the acetylcholine has diffused away from the immediate neighborhood of the terminals where it is released and is dispersed over the entire junctional region.

The high degree of chemical specificity of the receptor and the competition for it of different substances with different final effects is suggestive of the behavior of an enzyme. It is highly relevant to this that substances which are able to displace acetylcholine from the enzyme cholinesterase are also able to displace it from the receptor. The receptor appears almost certainly to be a protein constituent of the muscle fiber membrane with its reactive sites exposed on the outer surface. As a result of the combination of these sites with acetylcholine, the physical properties of the membrane alter and a new path appears for the diffusion of ions of various species through it. In electrical terms transmitter action may be approximately described as the placing of an additional conductance across the membrane which short-circuits any previously existing potential difference. In that the experimental findings are in agreement with this interpretation, they exclude the possibility of electrical transmission by which the junctional response is considered to be produced by an externally

generated current impressed upon the muscle fiber. At the same time they eliminate the possibility that the response may be of the nature of a local response, a specific increase in membrane permeability to sodium ions boosting an initially small potential change, such as may occur when the membrane is depolarized to near the threshold for setting up an action potential. It appears that the junctional response cannot be brought about by any means of electrical stimulation of the postjunctional structure but only by a specific chemical reaction of the receptor. The presence at the junction of a region capable of responding in this way does not appear to affect the action potential developed there, except by an addition of the independent actions of the two types of activity. The probable significance of this is that the area occupied by the receptor is small and does not detract appreciably from the area engaged in producing the action potential.

REFERENCES

1. ACHESON, G. H. *Fed. Proc.* 7: 447, 1948.
2. BERNARD, C. *Leçons sur les effets de substances toxiques et médicamenteuses.* Paris: Baillière, 1857, p. 267.
3. BOYD, I. A. AND A. R. MARTIN. *J. Physiol.* 132: 61, 1956.
4. BOYD, I. A. AND A. R. MARTIN. *J. Physiol.* 132: 74, 1956.
5. BOYD, T. E. *Am. J. Physiol.* 100: 569, 1932.
6. BROOKS, V. B. *J. Physiol.* 134: 264, 1956.
7. BROWN, G. L. *J. Physiol.* 89: 220, 1937.
8. BROWN, G. L. *J. Physiol.* 89: 438, 1937.
9. BROWN, G. L., H. H. DALE AND W. FELDBERG. *J. Physiol.* 87: 394, 1936.
10. BURKE, W. AND B. L. GINSBORG. *J. Physiol.* 132: 586, 1956.
11. BURKE, W., AND B. L. GINSBORG. *J. Physiol.* 132: 599, 1956.
12. BURNS, B. D. AND W. D. M. PATON. *J. Physiol.* 115:41, 1951.
13. COPPÉE, G. *Arch. internat. physiol.* 53: 327, 1943.
14. COUTEAUX, R. *Rev. Canad. Biol.* 6: 563, 1947.
15. COUTEAUX, R. *Internat. Rev. Cytol.* 4: 335, 1955.
16. COUTEAUX, R. AND J. TAXI. *Arch. Microsc. Morphol.* 41: 352, 1952.
17. COWAN, S. L. *J. Physiol.* 88: 3P, 1936.
18. DALE, H. H., W. FELDBERG AND M. VOGT. *J. Physiol.* 86: 353, 1936.
19. DEL CASTILLO, J. AND L. ENGBAEK. *J. Physiol.* 124: 370, 1954.
20. DEL CASTILLO, J. AND B. KATZ. *J. Physiol.* 124: 553, 1954.
21. DEL CASTILLO, J. AND B. KATZ. *J. Physiol.* 124: 560, 1954.
22. DEL CASTILLO, J. AND B. KATZ. *J. Physiol.* 124: 574, 1954.
23. DEL CASTILLO, J. AND B. KATZ. *J. Physiol.* 124: 586, 1954.
24. DEL CASTILLO, J. AND B. KATZ. *J. Physiol.* 125: 546, 1954.
25. DEL CASTILLO, J. AND B. KATZ. *J. Physiol.* 128: 157, 1955.
26. DEL CASTILLO, J. AND B. KATZ. *J. Physiol.* 128: 396, 1955.
27. DEL CASTILLO, J. AND B. KATZ. *J. Physiol.* 132: 630, 1956.
28. DEL CASTILLO, J. AND B. KATZ. *Prog. Biophys. & Biophys. Chem.* 6: 121, 1956.
29. DEL CASTILLO, J. AND L. STARK. *J. Physiol.* 116: 507, 1952.
30. ECCLES, J. C., B. KATZ AND S. W. KUFFLER. *J. Neurophysiol.* 4: 362, 1941.
31. ECCLES, J. C., B. KATZ AND S. W. KUFFLER. *J. Neurophysiol.* 5: 211, 1942.
32. ECCLES, J. C. AND W. V. MACFARLANE. *J. Neurophysiol.* 12: 59, 1949.
33. ECCLES, J. C. AND W. J. O'CONNOR. *J. Physiol.* 94: 9P, 1938.
34. EDMUNDS, C. W. AND G. B. ROTH. *Am. J. Physiol.* 23: 28, 1908.
35. EMMELIN, N. AND F. C. MACINTOSH. *J. Physiol.* 131: 477, 1956.
36. FATT, P. *J. Physiol.* 111: 408, 1950.
37. FATT, P. *Physiol. Rev.* 34: 674, 1954.
38. FATT, P. AND B. KATZ. *J. Physiol.* 111: 46P, 1950.
39. FATT, P. AND B. KATZ. *Nature, London* 166: 597, 1950.
40. FATT, P. AND B. KATZ. *J. Physiol.* 115: 320, 1951.
41. FATT, P. AND B. KATZ. *J. Physiol.* 117: 109, 1952.
42. FATT, P. AND B. KATZ. *J. Physiol.* 118: 73, 1952.
43. FENG, T. P. *Chinese J. Physiol.* 15: 367, 1940.
44. FURSHPAN, E. J. *J. Physiol.* 134: 689, 1956.
45. GÖPERT, H. AND H. SCHAEFER. *Arch. ges. Physiol.* 239: 597, 1938.
46. HEIDENHAIN, R. *Arch. Anat. Physiol., Physiol. Abt.* Suppl., 7: 133, 1883.
47. HUNT, C. C. AND S. W. KUFFLER. *J. Physiol.* 126: 293, 1954.
48. HUTTER, O. F. *J. Physiol.* 118: 216, 1952.
49. HUTTER, O. F. AND W. R. LOEWENSTEIN. *J. Physiol.* 130: 559, 1955.
50. KATZ, B. AND S. W. KUFFLER. *J. Neurophysiol.* 4: 209, 1941.
51. KUFFLER, S. W. *J. Neurophysiol.* 6: 99, 1943.
52. KUFFLER, S. W. *J. Neurophysiol.* 7: 17, 1944.
53. KUFFLER, S. W. AND R. W. GERARD. *J. Neurophysiol.* 10: 383, 1947.
54. KUFFLER, S. W. AND E. M. VAUGHAN WILLIAMS. *J. Physiol.* 121: 289, 1953.

55. KUFFLER, S. W. AND E. M. VAUGHAN WILLIAMS. *J. Physiol.* 121: 318, 1953.
56. KÜHNE, W. *Ztschr. Biol.* 23: 1, 1887.
57. LANGLEY, J. N. *J. Physiol.* 33: 374, 1905.
58. LANGLEY, J. N. *J. Physiol.* 36: 347, 1907.
59. LANGLEY, J. N. *J. Physiol.* 37: 285, 1908.
60. LANGLEY, J. N. *J. Physiol.* 39: 235, 1909.
61. LANGLEY, J. N. *J. Physiol.* 48: 73, 1914.
62. LILEY, A. W. *J. Physiol.* 132: 650, 1956.
63. LILEY, A. W. *J. Physiol.* 133: 571, 1956.
64. LILEY, A. W. *J. Physiol.* 134: 427, 1956.
65. LILEY, A. W. AND K. A. K. NORTH. *J. Neurophysiol.* 16: 509, 1953.
66. LUNDBERG, A. AND H. QUILISCH. *Acta physiol. scandinav.* Suppl. 111, 30: 111, 1953.
67. LUNDBERG, A. AND H. QUILISCH. *Acta physiol. scandinav.* Suppl. 111, 30: 121, 1953.
68. MARTIN, A. R. *J. Physiol.* 130: 114, 1955.
69. NASTUK, W. L. *J. Cell. & Comp. Physiol.* 42: 249, 1953.
70. NASTUK, W. L. *Fed. Proc.* 12: 102, 1953.
71. ROBERTSON, J. D. *J. Biophys. & Biochem. Cytol.* 2: 381, 1956.
72. SCHAEFER, H. AND P. HAASS. *Arch. ges. Physiol.* 242: 364, 1939.
73. TIEGS, O. W. *Physiol. Rev.* 33: 90, 1953.
74. ZAIMIS, E. J. *J. Physiol.* 122: 238, 1953.

CHAPTER VII

Autonomic neuroeffector transmission

U. S. VON EULER | *Department of Physiology, Faculty of Medicine, Stockholm, Sweden*

CHAPTER CONTENTS

DEVELOPMENT OF THE CONCEPT

THE IDEA OF CHEMICAL TRANSMISSION of nerve impulses was apparently first expressed by Elliott (41) who in 1904 suggested the possibility that when the sympathetic nerve impulse reached the target cell it caused an action by liberating epinephrine "on each occasion when the impulse arrives at the periphery." This hypothesis was based on the similarities in action of epinephrine and sympathetic nerve activity, irrespective of whether the action was activation or inhibition.

Elliott's idea, although representing an entirely new concept, must have struck many as plausible, and it was not surprising that thinking should proceed along similar lines. Thus Dixon & Hamill (36) applied the idea to parasympathetic nerves, comparing their action with that of muscarine, and after this time it became primarily a matter of skillful experimentation to prove the correctness of the theory and to carry the new concept to general acceptance. This task proved more difficult than was perhaps anticipated. It was chiefly due to the precision of observation and judgment of Dale (25) and the ingenious experimentation of Loewi (83) that the postulate of chemical transmission became transformed into an accepted concept. Acetylcholine gradually moved into the center of interest as a possible candidate for parasympathetic nerve transmission. In Dale's paper concerning the action of injected acetylcholine, he stated that it caused "pronounced vagus-like inhibition of the heart, and various other effects of stimulating nerves of the cranial and sacral divisions of the autonomic system—secretion of saliva, contraction of the oesophagus, stomach and intestine and of the urinary bladder."

The direct experimental proof was provided by Loewi (83) who showed that the fluid collected from an isolated frog's heart during vagus stimulation inhibited a second heart (fig. 1). The effect of the "Vagusstoff" was annulled by atropine and in a large series of experiments it could be shown that the liberated substance behaved in every respect, pharmacologically and chemically, like a choline ester. It is generally assumed that it is acetylcholine.

Stimulation of the sympathetic nerves in Loewi's experiments caused the release of a factor which accelerated the heart and had properties similar to those of epinephrine. Chemical transmission of sympathetic nerve impulses was independently demonstrated by Cannon & Uridil (21) who found that the stimulation of hepatic nerves increased the rate of the denervated heart and raised the arterial pres-

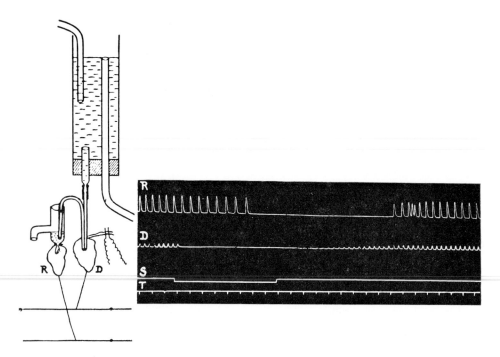

FIG. 1. Bain's modification of the original experiment performed by Loewi in 1921. The diagram represents a reservoir of salt solution from which there is a passage to the donor heart (D); pressure from the reservoir assures a continuous flow of the solution through that heart to the recipient heart (R). The donor heart still has its proper nerves. Each heart is attached to a writing lever. The record is that of the two hearts, donor and recipient. When the vagal fibers of the donor were stimulated (S), there was a prompt arrest of that heart (D), and later a slowing and arrest of the recipient heart (R), with gradual recovery. Time (T) is recorded in 5-sec. intervals. [From Bain (7).]

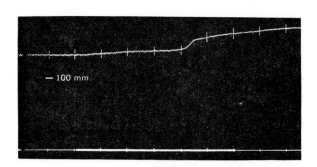

FIG. 2. Rise of arterial pressure and increase of heart rate from 196 to 220 beats per min. following stimulation of the hepatic nerves in the cat. Time, 5 sec. [From Cannon & Uridil (21).]

sure (fig. 2). It did not dilate the pupil, however, which would have been expected if the substance carried by the blood were epinephrine.

The principle of chemical transmission was later greatly developed chiefly by the work of Cannon & Rosenblueth and their associates, and by Dale, Feldberg, Minz and their co-workers. A very useful distinction was introduced by Dale (27) when the terms adrenergic and cholinergic nerves were coined (fig. 3). While acetylcholine still holds the position allotted to it since 1914 as the cholinergic chemotransmitter, the concept of epinephrine as adrenergic transmitter has had to yield to its nonmethylated homologue norepinephrine (124). The "curiously anomalous" effect on the iris observed by Cannon & Uridil in 1921 (21) became readily explained by the recognition that norepinephrine and not epinephrine was the mediator of adrenergic nerve action.

For a detailed account of the problem of autonomic neuroeffector transmission the reader is referred to the monographs of Gaddum (50), Cannon & Rosenblueth (20), Muralt (133), Rosenblueth (113) Minz (96, 97), Euler (129) and the recent survey of neurochemistry (101).

ANATOMICAL CONSIDERATIONS

As in other fields of physiology, valuable hints may be gained by studying the microarchitecture of the region in question, in this case the structural relationships between the autonomic postganglionic nerve endings and the target cells. These cells in principle include the heart muscle cells and the secretory cells of the glands in addition to those of smooth muscle. Much conflicting evidence has been presented with regard to the innervation of smooth muscle cells by autonomic nerve fibers. It may suffice to mention that an histologist as experienced as Stöhr (121) found that less than one cell in a hundred was innervated. The numerous reports on intracellular nerve endings in smooth muscle cells seem to require reconsideration since an ingrowth of axonal endings into a cell appears for many reasons unlikely, and even unnecessary, especially in view of the probable distribution of the transmitter in the terminal parts of the axons, to be discussed later. It must therefore be seriously considered whether the alleged findings are not due to misinterpretation of the histological pictures. It is well known that smooth muscle cells may serve their proper function without innervation, and unless it can be shown that each smooth muscle cell receives intracellular nerve twigs there is every reason to regard the few exceptions known at present as interesting special cases of unknown functional significance. The finding of numerous endings in the ciliary muscle of the eye does not alter the general picture. There is nothing known so far to indicate any kind of 'motor end plate' on the smooth muscle cell. Knoblike thickenings ending at or near the cell surface have been described, however, both by older histologists and more recently. Similar structures, sometimes assuming the picture of bead-strings, have been repeatedly found at autonomic nerve endings (54, 62, 72). Garven & Gairns suggest "that the small beads on the course of the finest fibrils represent the actual release points of the humoral agents within the cytoplasmic continuum provided by cells other than the neurones."

As will be discussed in the following section the results of studies of electrical phenomena in the smooth muscles do not suggest direct innervation of such cells.

Cannon & Rosenblueth (20) have regarded the few innervated cells as having special functions and have named them 'key cells.' Their contention was that by chemical transmission concentrated to these, the neighboring cells will be affected by the diffusing neurotransmitter. There is little evidence to support this hypothesis, however. Moreover, since it is known that the autonomic nerve transmitters are present

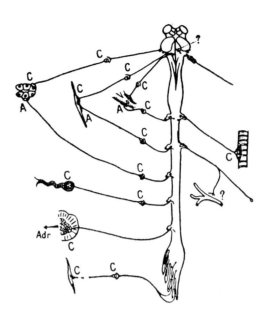

FIG. 3. Dale's schematic representation of the autonomic nervous system. A, adrenergic; C, cholinergic elements. [From Dale (28).]

all along the axons, it is unlikely that they should be released only at one point of the axon in a small number of special cells.

The question of the innervation of the smooth muscle cell cannot be answered with complete certainty but the best evidence points at a peripheral branching system of the postganglionic autonomic nerve fibers extending to the immediate neighborhood of each smooth muscle cell (62). By release of the chemical transmitter during nerve stimulation, the cells will be reached by the active chemical substance through diffusion. The proportion of cells activated in an organ and the degree of activation will clearly depend upon the amount of transmitter set free, which in its turn is a function of the frequency and strength of the stimulus applied to the nerve.

HUMORAL VERSUS ELECTRICAL TRANSMISSION

The bulk of evidence points to the conclusion that denervated smooth muscle is electrically inexcitable (100, 114). Even if direct stimulation of denervated smooth muscle may lead to contraction, this is weak and differs in several respects from that produced by the chemical stimuli. It appears likely that the direct stimulation effect is unspecific and due to a direct gross action on the contractile material. An important argument is further that single stimuli are not capable of eliciting contractions. Whether the negative results of stimulating the denervated adrenal medulla (114) can be used as support for the thesis of inexcitability of denervated target cells is open to doubt.

The inexcitability of autonomic effectors has also been studied by 'chemical denervation,' by use of drugs which block the action of the autonomic nerves on the target cells. Such experiments have been made on the piloerectors after ergotoxin (20) and on the salivary gland cells after chlorpromazine (42).

It may therefore be concluded that the smooth muscle cell lacks the ability to respond to direct electrical stimulation. Since there is ample evidence to show that these cells respond readily to the chemical stimuli which are known to be released from the terminal parts of the autonomic postganglionic nerves, there seems to be no need to postulate electrical transmission for functional reasons.

For a detailed discussion of the dual theory of chemical and electrical transmission advocated by Monnier & Bacq (100) see Cannon & Rosenblueth (20). While there is no evidence for electrical transmission from the postganglionic autonomic nerve fiber to the effector cell, the situation may be different in the case of autonomic synapses (101).

Smooth muscle thus differs fundamentally from skeletal muscle in that the latter is rapidly activated by a trigger mechanism requiring direct contact between the nerve fiber and the effector and working on the all-or-none principle. The sustained activity of the smooth muscle appears to operate on the entirely different principle of graded responses (115). More data are required, however, before the activity of the single smooth muscle cell in response to physiological stimuli can be ascertained.

THE ADRENERGIC NERVE TRANSMITTER

Identification

As outlined in the introductory section, Loewi's experiments in 1921 supported the idea that the sympathetic (adrenergic) transmitter was epinephrine-like. The suggestions by Barger & Dale (9), Bacq (4) and Greer, Pinkston, Baxter & Brannon (58) that norepinephrine conformed better with the actions of the sympathetic transmitter than did epinephrine received little attention until it was shown by von Euler (124) that the adrenergic nerves contained not epinephrine but norepinephrine. The identification of the transmitter with levo-norepinephrine was proved

by biological tests and by colorimetric methods (129). For the identification of the transmitter the differentiation from epinephrine became of primary importance. On most target cells the actions of epinephrine and norepinephrine are qualitatively similar, but the relative activity varies from one organ to another. Thus the action of epinephrine may be over one hundred times that of norepinephrine on the rat's uterus and on the fowl's rectal cecum while the two amines have about the same activity on the isolated heart. By comparing the actions of the purified extracts containing the neurotransmitter on a series of test preparations it is possible to ascertain whether the relative actions of the unknown compound go parallel with one or the other of the standard substances. Though norepinephrine passed unnoticed by chemical tests in the so-called pure crystalline epinephrine prepared from suprarenals for nearly 50 years, the amines are now readily separated by chromatography (73).

Generally a single pair of test objects showing sufficiently large differences in the activity ratio between epinephrine and norepinephrine suffice for differentiation between the two amines. Suitable pairs are for instance the cat's arterial pressure and the fowl's rectal cecum. On the former preparation norepinephrine is from 1 to 5 times more active as a pressor agent than epinephrine, while it has only $\frac{1}{4}$ to $\frac{1}{200}$ of the activity of epinephrine on the fowl's rectal cecum (fig. 4).

The virgin uterus of the cat, and the iris are 5 to 10 times more sensitive to epinephrine than to norepinephrine and may be used for differentiating purposes. The rat's uterus under certain conditions is stimulated by norepinephrine and relaxed by epinephrine (fig. 5).

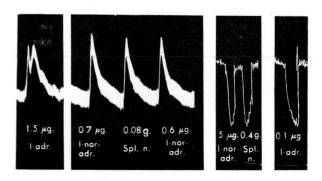

FIG. 4. Effect of epinephrine (l-adr), norepinephrine (l-nor-adr) and extract of beef splenic nerves (Spl. n.) on the arterial pressure of the cat and on the isolated rectal cecum of the fowl. [From von Euler (128).]

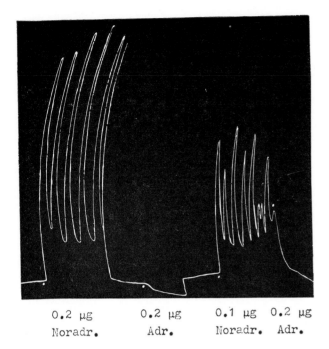

0.2 µg   0.2 µg   0.1 µg   0.2 µg
Noradr.   Adr.   Noradr.   Adr.

FIG. 5. Rat uterus, 3 hours post partum. 0.1 and 0.2 µg norepinephrine stimulates, 0.2 µg epinephrine inhibits the uterus. [From Greeff & Holtz (56).]

It has been observed for some time that although the actions of epinephrine on the arterial pressure of the cat may be reversed by antisympathomimetic substances (ergotoxine, yohimbine, benzodioxane, dibenamine, phentolamine), the effects of sympathetic nerve stimulation are at the most weakened or annulled but never reversed. The explanation was obtained when it was observed that the action of norepinephrine on the arterial pressure is not reversed but only diminished by doses which reverse the action of epinephrine. This difference has been utilized for the classification of the adrenergic neurotransmittor both *in vitro* (124, 129) and *in vivo* (20, 48).

The identification has subsequently been confirmed by other methods, notably by paper and column chromatography, allowing separation from other catechol amines and characterization by specific color or fluorescence reactions. Extracts of heart yield fractions on column chromatography which show the same R-value as pure norepinephrine and the same biological actions (55). A particularly good source of the adrenergic transmitter is the splenic nerves, from which norepinephrine can be separated by column chromatography and identified by location and by analysis of the active fractions (fig. 6). Venous blood from the spleen collected dur-

ing stimulation of the adrenergic nerves contains practically pure norepinephrine (98, 108).

The effects of reflex activation of sympathetic nerves as well as the effects of direct nerve stimulation show all the characteristics of norepinephrine actions (9, 48, 52, 58).

The release of an active substance on stimulation of the nerves to an organ does not necessarily mean that this substance is the corresponding chemotransmitter. In the experiments of Loewi in 1921 it is likely that the effects observed were due to released epinephrine, for which good evidence was obtained later (84, 124). There is no evidence, however, that epinephrine serves as adrenergic nerve transmitter in any animal. In the frog the spleen contains chiefly norepinephrine (105), and it can not be excluded that the epinephrine released on sympathetic nerve stimulation originates from chromaffin cells and not from adrenergic nerve endings. In such a case the substance released from the heart (which lacks coronary vessels in the frog) is not a neurotransmitter proper and the mechanism involved would be analogous to the release of epinephrine from the suprarenals on stimulation of its preganglionic nerves.

Although the theory of Cannon and Rosenblueth concerning the two sympathins is chiefly of historical interest is may be briefly outlined here. [For a detailed discussion see Cannon & Rosenblueth (20), and Rosenblueth (113).] According to this theory epinephrine is the adrenergic nerve transmitter, which on reaching the target cells combines with some

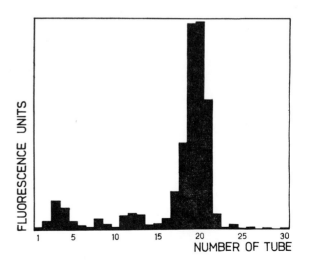

FIG. 6. Column chromatogram of extract of beef splenic nerves after adsorption on aluminium oxide and elution, showing a maximum for norepinephrine. [From von Euler & Lishajko (132).]

TABLE 1. *Norepinephrine Content of Beef Nervous Tissue*

in μg per gm (129)

Splenic nerve	8.5–18.5
Splanchnic nerve	4
Sympathetic chain, thoracic	2.5–4.9
Sympathetic chain, cervical	0.6
Mesenteric nerve	1.5–3
Superior cervical ganglion	1
Saphenous nerve	0.2–1
Phrenic nerve	0.15–0.25
Vagus nerve	0.1
Spinal cord	0.1
Brain	0.04–0.20

cell constituent to form what was termed inhibitory (I) or excitatory (E) sympathin or both. These findings are readily explained on the assumption that the actions observed were either due to the true adrenergic neurotransmitter, norepinephrine, or to epinephrine released from other sources, presumably chromaffin cells, or a mixture of both, as suggested by Bacq in 1934 and subsequently proved by the demonstration of both amines in autonomically innervated organs (126). The term sympathin should preferably be abandoned in the physiological literature since it does not discriminate between the neurotransmitter and the hormones released as a result of preganglionic stimulation of chromaffin cells.

Occurrence, Biosynthesis and Storage of Adrenergic Nerve Transmitter

Unless it is assumed that the chemical transmitters are being formed and released at the moment of nervous excitation it must be concluded that they are present in the axon and released from some kind of store. Systematic studies of the content of transmitter substances in postganglionic nerves have been made both for the cholinergic and for the adrenergic system. Such experiments have shown that the content of norepinephrine in a nerve correlates well with the number of unmyelinated fibers of autonomic origin (111). As seen in table 1 the amount of norepinephrine varies greatly and is highest in the splenic nerves which are known to contain practically only postganglionic sympathetic fibers. In other nerves, such as the vagus, the amount is quite small and this is true also for most motor nerves and the majority of sensory nerves. For technical reasons it is impossible to prepare nerves in their most peripheral parts, hence it has not been possible to study directly the content of the transmitters in the immediate vicinity

of the target cell, which for many reasons would have been desirable. On the other hand it has been possible partly to overcome this difficulty by making extracts of whole organs and estimating their transmitter content, thus measuring the total amount present in the tissue including the finest nerve ramifications (110, 129). Proof that the transmitter substances so found are actually due to the presence of postganglionic nerve fibers has been obtained by studying the effect of denervation. If the postganglionic nerves are severed and allowed to degenerate, the amount of norepinephrine in the peripheral tissue falls to very low figures or disappears completely. This indicates that the tissue is not able to store the transmitter by itself but does so by means of its autonomic nerve fibers. Further support for this opinion is provided by experiments showing that some 4 to 8 weeks after degeneration of the cardiac nerves the content of adrenergic transmitter in the sheep heart increases again and after the lapse of a few months reaches the original value (fig. 7) (55). Similar results have been obtained for other organs

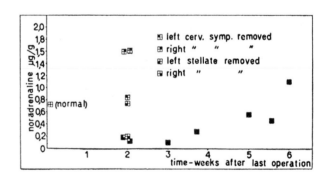

FIG. 7. Norepinephrine content of sheep hearts before and various times after sympathetic denervation. [From Goodall (55).]

TABLE 2. *Norepinephrine Content in Beef Organs*

in μg per gm (129)

Spleen	1.5–3.5
Lymph glands	0.5–0.8
Heart	0.3–0.6
Ciliary body and iris	0.4
Liver	0.25
Arteries and veins	0.1–1
Lung	0.15
Intestine	0.15
Uterus	0.15
Testicle	0.04
Skeletal muscle	0.04
Bone marrow	0.0

such as the spleen and the kidney of the sheep (129). The stores of the transmitter substance can thus be estimated by extracting the tissue and subjecting it to chemical or biological analysis. The content of adrenergic transmitter in an organ (table 2) provides a measure of the relative supply of adrenergic nerves.

Norepinephrine was first suggested as a link in the biosynthesis chain leading to epinephrine by Blaschko (11). The basis for this was given by Holtz, Heise & Lüdtke (68) who discovered an enzyme capable of decarboxylating levo-dihydroxyphenylalanine (dopa) to its corresponding amine, hydroxytyramine (dopamine). This enzyme was present in liver and kidney and has also been demonstrated in the adrenals and in adrenergic nerves (69). While it has been shown experimentally that homogenates of the adrenal gland synthesize norepinephrine from tyrosine (74), via dopa (33) and dopamine (59), this sequence has not been shown for adrenergic nerves although there can be little doubt that this is the case. At any rate it has been found that extracts of the spleen or splenic nerves contain relatively large amounts of dopamine (117, 132). The biosynthesis may therefore be depicted by the following scheme:

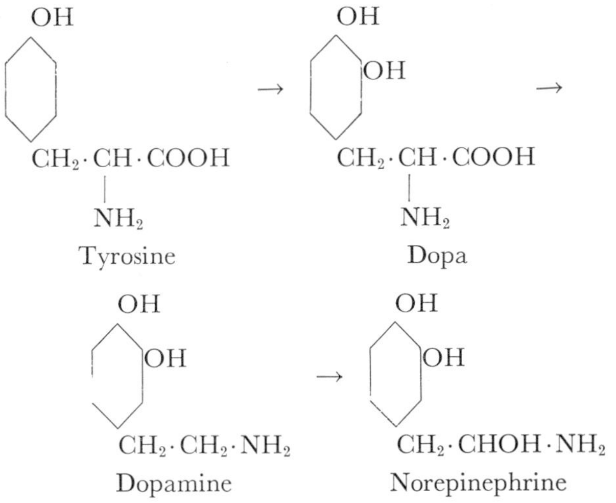

OH   OH

$CH_2 \cdot CH \cdot COOH$ $\rightarrow$ (OH) $CH_2 \cdot CH \cdot COOH$ $\rightarrow$

NH_2 NH_2

Tyrosine   Dopa

OH   OH

(OH) $CH_2 \cdot CH_2 \cdot NH_2$ $\rightarrow$ (OH) $CH_2 \cdot CHOH \cdot NH_2$

Dopamine   Norepinephrine

It appears likely that the biosynthesis is located in the place of storage (see below). Analysis of extracts of autonomic nerves have shown that the norepinephrine content is a function of the proportion of adrenergic fibers. These contain the transmitter along their whole length and also in the cell soma. A very marked accumulation in the terminal parts must be assumed for the following reasons. Splenic nerves of the beef contain about 15 μg norepinephrine per gm fresh tissue after removal of the sheath, while the content of the whole organ is about 3 μg per gm. Since

all of the splenic norepinephrine disappears on section and degeneration of the adrenergic nerves to the organ it is assumed that the norepinephrine found in the organ is bound to its nerves. On the other hand it is inconceivable that 20 per cent of the splenic tissue consists of nerves, and it follows from this that some parts of the nerves, presumably the endings, contain much more of the transmitter than the main nerve trunks.

Even after removal from the body, organs retain their adrenergic transmitter substance for a considerable time. A beef spleen may thus be stored at room temperature for 24 hours without any detectable loss of norepinephrine. This indicates that it is not present in a freely diffusible form and strongly suggests that it is bound in such a way as to prevent contact with inactivating enzymes.

Evidence has been obtained for the storage of the hormones of chromaffin cells in specific granules (12, 63). By increasing the acidity of the surrounding solution to pH5 or lower, the chromaffin cell hormones are released from the granules (63). When the same principle was applied to the isolated spleen by perfusing it with a solution containing acids such as ascorbic, citric or lactic acid, the transmitter substance was released and could be demonstrated in the perfusion fluid (40). Also other substances which have been found effective in releasing the hormones from isolated granules had a similar action on the perfused spleen, such as detergents, digitonin and lecithinase from snake venom.

These experiments add support to the hypothesis (127) that the neurotransmitter is stored, and probably manufactured, in specific structures in the adrenergic axon. Experiments by Euler & Hillarp (131) have demonstrated that a microgranular fraction rich in norepinephrine can be separated by high speed centrifugation from a homogenate of beef splenic nerves. The chemotransmitter is apparently stored in elements surrounded by a membrane since a suspension of the sediment in Ringer's solution does not give off norepinephrine to the surrounding fluid. If acid is added to pH4 in the suspension, the norepinephrine is instantaneously released, however, and can be demonstrated by biological and chemical methods in the suspension fluid. The microgranular stores are apparently specific for the chemotransmitter since the histamine which is abundant in the beef splenic nerves (about 100 μg per gm nerve) is not present in the same structural elements. Certain cellular fractions have been found to contain more than 1.5 μg norepinephrine per mg dry weight or around 20 times the amount per mg dry weight found in the whole nerve before homogenization.

The theory may then be advanced that the adrenergic nerve transmitter is bound to elements which in principle are of a kind similar to those found in the chromaffin cells. Since these can be regarded as homologues of the postganglionic neurons it might be expected that their constituents with specific activity are stored in a similar way. The structural elements serving as stores may also well be the units for biosynthesis. Apparently this takes place very rapidly so as to maintain a practically constant store. Continuous and prolonged stimulation of nerves *in vitro* (88) or *in vivo* (129) does not deplete the stores. There is no evidence that the granules of the chromaffin cells leave the cell body in connection with the release of the hormones; this may be assumed also for the storing elements of the postganglionic adrenergic neurons. It may be postulated that the microstructures elaborating and containing the neurotransmitter are formed in the cell soma and transported along the axon towards the periphery by the axoplasm flow (135). These assumptions would provide a satisfactory explanation for the findings that *a)* the chemotransmitter is accumulated in the terminal parts of the neuron, and that *b)* continuous stimulation does not deplete the nerves of its chemotransmitter. The theory involving the assumption of intra-axonal microstructural elements thus seems to explain several phenomena encountered in the field of neurotransmission.

Release

Stimulation of the adrenergic nerves, either directly or reflexly, immediately releases norepinephrine which is then allowed to diffuse to the adjacent target cells. From the above section it may be inferred that the transmitter is released from microstructures and accumulated at the terminal parts of the nerves, presumably in a way similar to that operating in the chromaffin cells. The large number of discrete terminal ramifications offer only short diffusion distances, enabling each cell to be reached by the chemical transmitter in a very short time. While under normal conditions the adrenergic chemotransmitter is released chiefly, if not entirely, as a result of reflex stimulation, various experimental approaches have been made in order to study the release in more detail, such as *a)* observation of the effects of direct nerve stimulation on the innervated organ, *b)* recording of the effects of stimulation of adrenergic nerves on remote organs, *c)* quantitative estimation of the content of the neurotransmitter in the venous effluent from the stimulated organ, and *d)* measuring the release of transmitter from isolated nerves stimulated *in vitro*, or from organs perfused *in vitro*.

INFLUENCE OF STIMULATION FREQUENCY. The effect of stimulation of the adrenergic nerves—or usually mixed nerves containing adrenergic fibers—provides the basis for most of our knowledge of the action of the adrenergic system on various target organs. A study of these effects not only permits qualitative information on the type of effect on the organ but also offers opportunities for gaining quantitative information, for instance about the influence of stimulus strength and frequency on the effect. In this way the release mechanism can be studied at least on a semi-quantitative basis which can hardly be accomplished by reflex stimulation.

While the technique of studying the response of an organ to variation in the intensity of the stimulus gives an idea of the excitability of the nerve fibers, information about the release mechanism is better obtained by varying the stimulus frequency. Such experiments are preferably performed using stimulation intensities which will allow participation of all fibers. As shown in figure 8, the curves obtained by Rosenblueth (112) showing the relationship of stimulus frequency and effect on various autonomic effectors have the general shape of rectangular hyperbolas. The results show the noteworthy feature that considerable effects are achieved even at very low frequencies. As can be seen from figure 8, even frequencies of less than 1 per sec. are capable of causing marked effects. Nearly maximal actions have been recorded with frequencies of the order of 5 per sec., for instance on the piloerectors and the nictitating membrane. The results imply that even very low frequencies are sufficient to release considerable amounts of the transmitter. In table 3 the optimum frequencies for a number of effectors are given. Maximal effects are obtained with frequencies varying from 20 to 30 per sec. in most effector systems. Even a frequency of 10 per sec. generally elicits more than 80 per cent of the maximal response.

An interesting difference is noted between the ratio of the effects of single stimuli and those of maximal tetanic stimuli on smooth and skeletal muscles, no doubt depending on the trigger mechanism in the latter. Thus the ratio between the effects is much higher for the smooth muscle than for the skeletal muscle.

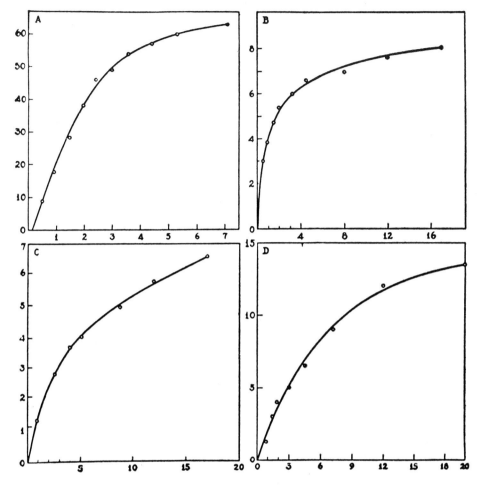

FIG. 8. Frequency-response curves of sympathetic effectors. *A: abscissae*, frequencies of stimulation of the lumbar sympathetics; *ordinates*, angles of erection of a hair in the tail of a cat. *B: abscissae*, frequencies of stimulation of the cervical sympathetic; *ordinates*, heights of the records of isotonic contractions of the nictitating membrane 15 sec. after the beginning of stimulation. *C*: as in *B*, but isometric contractions of the nictitating membrane. *D: abscissae*, frequencies of stimulation of the right cardioaccelerator nerves; *ordinates*, maximal increases of heart rate per 15 sec. [From Rosenblueth (112).]

Even after cutting a considerable portion of the nerve the maximal effect may be approached, provided the frequency of stimulation is increased sufficiently. The effect of low frequencies on a partially severed nerve is smaller than in the intact nerve, however, which might be expected.

The conclusion drawn from these experiments is that the neurotransmitter diffuses to the neighboring cells as its concentration is raised by increasing the stimulation frequency. The principle of activation of smooth muscle cells may therefore be a general release of transmitter within the mass of these cells, making individual innervation as for the skeletal muscle fibers unnecessary.

TABLE 3. *Frequencies of Preganglionic Stimulation, Giving Maximal Response of Effectors* (20)

Effectors	Frequency Stim. per sec.
Sympathetic	
Pilomotors	15
Nictitating membrane	20
Pregnant uterus	20
Intestine	20
Adrenal medulla	25
Heart (postgangl.)	25
Parasympathetic	
Heart	30
Submaxillary gland	35
Stomach	25

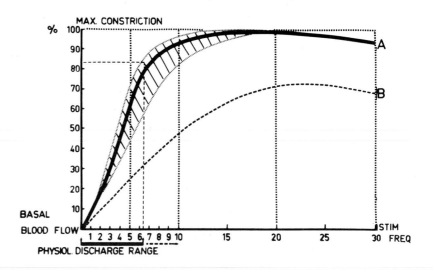

FIG. 9. Vasoconstrictor effect of electric stimulation of lumbar sympathetics at varying frequencies in the cat. Striped area indicates the variations observed in 40 experiments. *A* represents average of 10 experiments with the biggest response; *B*, average response after vasodilator drugs. [From Folkow (46).]

The effect of stimulation at various frequencies of sympathetic nerves to the muscular blood vessels in the lower part of the hind limb of the cat has been measured by recording the outflow (46).

Figure 9 shows the correlation between stimulation rate and the constrictor response. It is clearly seen that low stimulation frequencies are very effective. This applies also to cutaneous blood vessels (22).

A detailed analysis of the mechanism of the release has been made by Brown & Gillespie (14) using the cat's spleen. Samples of venous blood were collected and the norepinephrine content assayed on the arterial pressure of the pithed rat. Supramaximal stimuli were applied to the splenic nerve, the total number of stimuli being 200, irrespective of the frequency. Both adrenal glands were removed and the splanchnic nerves cut. The output of norepinephrine was expressed as amount released per stimulus.

As illustrated in figure 10*A* the norepinephrine output per stimulus was low at low frequencies, but as the frequency increased the amount found in venous blood rose sharply to a maximum at about 30 stimulations per sec. Since the output per stimulus was the same before and after addition of isopropyl isonicotinyl hydrazine (Marsilid), an effect of amine oxidase on the transmitter liberated at lower frequencies could be excluded. The possibility was also discussed that, although the amount of transmitter released by each nerve volley might be constant, more was 'utilized' by tissue receptors at a low rate of stim-

ulation. After blocking tissue receptors with N-N-dibenzyl-β-chloroethylamine (dibenamine), it was found that the output per impulse reaching the blood was greatly increased at the lower frequencies and maintained a constant value at different frequencies. From these observations it was concluded that the norepinephrine release per nerve volley is constant and that the fraction removed by the tissues is greater at the lower frequencies of stimulation (cf. section on removal of transmitter, p. 227).

The experiments quoted above may have an interesting implication in that the small or absent overflow at low stimulation frequency (or adrenergic nerve activity) and the larger overflow at higher activity may cause an excretion pattern in the urine which 'amplifies' the actual release and makes differences more pronounced than would be expected from the activity of the effector.

EFFECTS ON REMOTE ORGANS. This method of studying the release of the adrenergic transmitter is the one which led to the discovery and demonstration of such a mechanism. The first experiments of this kind were made by Cannon & Uridil in 1921 (21) who observed the effect of stimulating the liver nerves on the heart and iris sensitized by denervation. They ascribed the effect to a "special and unknown substance" apparently being set free by the stimulation. This kind of experiment was developed further by Cannon and Rosenblueth and their co-workers in the

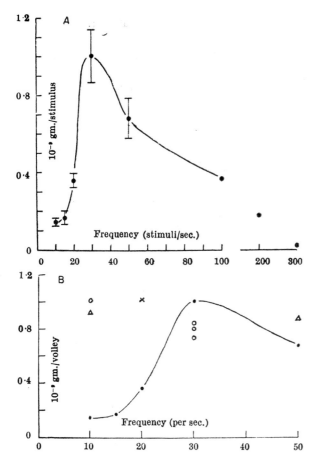

FIG. 10. *A*: Mean output per stimulus of 'sympathin' plotted against the frequency of stimulation. At all frequencies of stimulation the total number of pulses was 200. The vertical lines represent the standard errors of the means. Figures for 100, 200 and 300 pulses per sec. are single observations. *B*: First part of the graph in *A* with an extended scale for frequency. The individual results from three animals previously given dibenamine are shown. The output per stimulus at 10 pulses per sec. has increased and equals the maximum in the untreated animal. There is no obvious variation with frequency. [From Brown & Gillespie (14).]

work on 'sympathin'. While the study of the transmitter release in this manner, by recording the effect on sensitized remote target organs, was valuable in the elucidation of the transmission mechanism as such, its physiological significance is doubtful. Even though Cannon and Rosenblueth and their co-workers obtained increases in heart rate, dilatation of the pupil and contraction of the nictitating membrane in denervated organs after stimulation of sympathetic nerves in other parts of the body, the appearance of remote effects caused by transportation of the released transmitter by the blood is by no means a constant phenomenon.

The failure of some authors (22) to observe remote effects even on the highly sensitized denervated nictitating membrane in spite of intense stimulation of sympathetic nerves has been taken to indicate the presence of peripheral inactivation mechanisms which largely eliminate an overflow of transmitter. However, a physiologically occurring overflow in the meaning of Cannon and Rosenblueth cannot be denied for the following reason. If the catechol amines are estimated in urine from adrenalectomized patients the amounts of epinephrine are very low while the norepinephrine content tends to be even higher than in normal subjects (129). The only possibility for norepinephrine to occur in the urine then is a release from some source in the body other than the adrenals. Since the adrenergic nerves are known to contain large amounts of this transmitter, it appears legitimate to assume that during the incessant activity of the adrenergic system a certain overflow of transmitter takes place continuously.

As to the value of the remote effects studied by Cannon and Rosenblueth as a proof of chemotransmission from nerves, it should be borne in mind that nervous stimulation might also cause a release from chromaffin cells present in the tissues. This criticism does not invalidate their conclusions in principle since there is good evidence in some of Cannon and Rosenblueth's experiments that at least some of the effects are due to the release of norepinephrine.

It is interesting to note that the so-called inhibitory sympathin is obtained when the splanchnics are stimulated but not when the hepatic nerves are stimulated (fig. 11). It is known that the splanchnic nerves may innervate groups of chromaffin cells at various sites. Their secretory products may then be carried by the blood stream to excite the denervated organ. In case of the hepatic nerves there was only a stimulating effect but no inhibitory effect on the denervated uterus of the cat, indicating that practically only norepinephrine was released in this case. As far as can be ascertained at the present time this norepinephrine is released from adrenergic nerve endings.

The question whether reflex liberation of the adrenergic transmitter could be large enough to cause actions on remote organs has also been studied (80). As a result of afferent sciatic or brachial nerve stimulation it was possible to demonstrate a contraction of the denervated nictitating membrane in the adrenalectomized cat. It has also been possible to show a reflex liberation of the adrenergic transmitter by action on remote organs, for instance after excitement and struggle (103). The slower development of

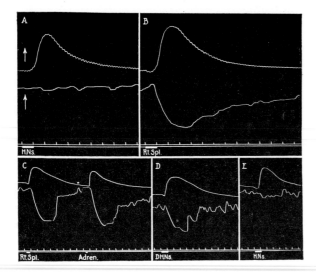

FIG. 11. *Upper curves*, decentralized nictitating membrane *lower curves*, denervated nonpregnant uterus of the cat. Contraction upwards. Time, 30 sec. *A*: hepatic nerves stimulated. *B*: right splanchnic nerves stimulated after exclusion of adrenals. *C*: same as in *B* and injection of 1.5 µg epinephrine. *D*: duodenohepatic nerves stimulated. *E*: same as in *D* after severance of duodenal nerves. [From Cannon & Rosenblueth (19).]

the blood-borne action on the denervated heart after reflex excitation, resulting from struggle, as compared with the rapid and large effect in cases where the adrenals were active may be explained by the gradual and prolonged release of moderate amounts of transmitter in the former case. The activation of the adrenals has a tendency to cause an 'explosive' release. A continuous liberation into the blood stream during 'sham rage' has also been noted (136) in decorticate cats showing a quasiemotional state as evidenced by the reduction in the rate of the denervated heart after section of the hepatic nerves. Even as a consequence of normal emotions a release of transmitter into the blood has been observed.

On exposure to cold no sign of continuous effect on the denervated nictitating membrane of the cat was found, however (107). The persistent erection of hairs when the animal is in cold surroundings is apparently not accompanied by a liberation of enough transmitter to affect remote organs even if these are sensitized.

During hypoglycemia there is no evidence for activation of the sympathetic system as a whole. Only a selective release of epinephrine from the suprarenal has been demonstrated by direct analysis of the venous blood (38). The contention expressed by Cannon and Rosenblueth that "it is characteristic of the sympathetic system, when specially excited, to act as a whole; thus adrenine is secreted by splanchnic impulses at the same time that sympathetic impulses elsewhere in the body are liberating sympathin" has not been corroborated by later experiments and experience. It is now reasonably certain that the secretion of epinephrine is a process which occurs independently and often during quite other conditions than the activation of other parts of the sympathetic system. It would also appear peculiar if the action of epinephrine in maintaining blood sugar homeostasis should be obligatorily linked with, for instance, a rise of arterial pressure as a result of generalized adrenergic activity. The statement of Cannon and Rosenblueth that "adrenine and sympathin collaborate in affecting structures innervated by sympathetic nerves" is only true in a restricted sense and its biological significance is too limited to be set forth as a general rule. The statement also illustrates the hazards of using the term 'sympathin' since this may represent either epinephrine or norepinephrine. It may be recalled that the two amines have opposite effects for instance on the vessels of the skeletal muscles (1, 8, 37). Even if the leakage of transmitter into the blood stream is negligible from the point of view of physiological action, this phenomenon has been of great heuristic value as in Cannon and Rosenblueth's work and also in the extensive work dealing with the excretion of the neurotransmitter in urine (67, 129).

Information about the nerve transmitter may also be gained by collecting blood or perfusing fluid from an organ during stimulation of the sympathetic nerves, and by recording the effects of this fluid on suitable test organs. Studies of this kind are in principle similar to the pioneer experiments by Loewi. Active substances in the effluent have been demonstrated in many instances, such as from the frog's stomach (13), the aqueous humour (3), the rabbit's intestine (45) and the dog's tongue (6).

By the use of an appropriate testing technique it could be shown later that the active substance released by adrenergic nerve stimulation conformed in its properties with norepinephrine (14, 93, 98, 106, 108). In these studies the venous plasma of the stimulated organ was tested. Most investigators have also stated that smaller amounts of epinephrine were sometimes also liberated. The significance of the simultaneous appearance of small amounts of epinephrine will be considered below.

The release of epinephrine-like materials on stimulation of the vagus nerve to the atropinized heart has also been reported (65, 94). The former authors concluded that the epinephrine-like substance was released from intracardiac adrenergic neurons controlled by preganglionic fibers in the vagus. Whether the substance was released from neurons proper or from chromaffin cells is not clear, however.

STIMULATION OF ISOLATED NERVES. Attempts have been made to study the release of the adrenergic transmitter by stimulating isolated nerves, thus avoiding the possibility of interaction of the innervated tissues. In unpublished experiments Gaddum & Khayyal (50) stimulated an isolated sympathetic nerve suspended in salt solution and found that a sympathomimetic substance was released into the solution. This effect was later attributed to damage to the nerve by the stimulating electrodes (53). However, the original finding was later confirmed (79). This is in agreement with the fact that the whole nerve trunk contains norepinephrine.

EXHAUSTIBILITY. Studies on the exhaustibility of the transmitter sources have shown that even prolonged stimulation, reflex or direct, does not seem to lessen the release. Orias (104) stimulated the preganglionic fibers of the cervical sympathetic 10 times a sec. for 1 hour and found no signs of fatigue in the responses of the nictitating membrane. These experiments were repeated by Dye (39) who applied not less than 108,000 stimuli during 3 hours to the preganglionic nerves without evidence of exhaustion. Luco & Goñi (88) found that stimulation of sympathetic nerves for 1 hour did not diminish the content of transmitter in the nerve. It may therefore be assumed that release of the transmitter can continue for an unlimited time. This is an indication in the first place that the transmitter is readily resynthesized but also that the release mechanism is built to render continuous service.

Removal of Transmitter

Although it is apparent from the observations of remote effects of adrenergic nerve stimulation and from the excretion of norepinephrine in urine that a certain proportion of the released neurotransmitter is transferred into the circulating blood, it is generally assumed that most of the transmitter is being inactivated at or near the site of release (16, 47).

The experiments of Brown & Gillespie (14) indicate that the removal of the transmitter is more efficient when it is released at a slow rate. As to the mechanism of removal, their experiments suggest that the trans-

mitter is being attached to a certain extent to the effector cells and presumably inactivated at this site.

Our knowledge about the mechanism of inactivation is still very incomplete. The inability of isopropyl isonicotinyl hydrazine (Marsilid) to affect to any noticeable extent the amount of transmitter recovered in the effluent blood after stimulation of the splenic nerves does not support the common opinion that amine oxidase plays an important part in this respect.

In experiments in which the transmitter was released from a perfused spleen by various chemical means, the amount of norepinephrine found in the effluent was not greatly influenced by adding amine oxidase inhibitors to the perfusion fluid (129). Moreover, administration of Marsilid to an animal does not augment the degree or duration of adrenergic reflex actions in the cat, such as the pressor effect of carotid occlusion, indicating that amine oxidase, at any rate, does not attack the transmitter between the moment of release and the action on the effector cell.

The problem of the removal of the transmitter after its release may be regarded from two aspects. One part of the transmitter apparently is directly attached to the effector cells [or 'utilized' (14)] while another portion is leaking into the blood vessels, or by-passing the target cells as it were. It is conceivable that after saturation of the target cells the remainder of the released transmitter diffuses through the capillary wall and enters the blood stream. The situation might be regarded as analogous to that prevailing during reabsorption of a threshold substance by the renal tubules where an excess causes an 'overflow' into the urine. If the amount of the transmitter which is caught by the effector cells is considered first, it appears probable that it is being inactivated by some process so far unknown. It may well be that on many occasions this part represents the greatest part of the released transmitter. The second part which is not taken up by the cells may theoretically be attacked by enzymes on its diffusion way to the blood or lymph capillaries. Apparently this is not the case since amine oxidase inhibitors did not appreciably alter the yield in the effluent blood (14). Not even after having reached the blood stream is the inactivation complete as seen by the excretion in urine of neurotransmitter which undoubtedly originates in adrenergic nerves, as indicated by the excretion in adrenalectomized patients. Knowing the proportion of norepinephrine excreted in urine after intravenous infusion at a constant rate, it seems possible to obtain an idea of the 'overflow' of adrenergic transmitter per unit of time. From infusion experiments in man it has been found that the proportion of norepinephrine excreted in urine is 1.5 to 4 per cent of that infused during the same time (129). If the total excretion of norepinephrine (free and conjugated) in man during 24 hours, when the subject is performing daily routine work but no severe muscular work, can be estimated at 60 μg (109, 129), the amount of neurotransmitter overflow may be estimated at approximately 2 to 3 mg per 24 hours.

The careful study of the distribution of monoamine oxidase (MAO) in various nerve cells by Koelle & Valk (76) does not support the opinion that MAO is specifically occurring in adrenergic nerves, since no significant differences were found in the MAO activity in nerve cell bodies and fibers of the stellate, superior cervical, nodose, dorsal root and ciliary ganglia of the cat. The enzyme is localized in smooth muscle cells of blood vessels. It is absent in cardiac muscle, but high activity is found in renal tubule cells and hepatic cells. Since the removal of the transmitter by inactivating enzymes is more likely to occur in the target cells than in the neurons producing the transmitter this result is not unexpected.

Small amounts of the transmitter are successfully removed during the passage of blood through the tissue, up to 90 per cent during a single passage through muscle and skin. This is in harmony with the findings that after infusion of norepinephrine and epinephrine in man only a small percentage appears in the urine, the rest being inactivated.

Mechanisms of inactivation other than by MAO are conceivable, such as by catechol oxidases and peroxidases and by conjugation. The relative unimportance of the inactivation of circulating catechol amines by MAO is further borne out by the observation that cobefrine (α-methyl-*dl*-norepinephrine) is excreted in a similar small proportion as epinephrine and norepinephrine after injection in man (129), although it is not attacked by this enzyme. It must therefore have been inactivated (to more than 90 per cent) by some other mechanism which presumably would have been similarly active on the catechol hormones.

POSSIBLE ADRENERGIC NERVE TRANSMITTERS OTHER THAN NOREPINEPHRINE

It may well be asked whether there is any way of distinguishing between the release of the chemotransmitter from the nerve terminals and the secretory products from chromaffin cells in the tissues. Since very little is known about the mass and distribution of such scattered chromaffin cells or whether they secrete epinephrine or norepinephrine or both (and in the latter case the relative proportions), it is hard to evaluate the amount of neurotransmitter *sensu strictiori* which is released upon stimulation of sympathetic nerves. Assuming that chromaffin cells are present in an organ, they would be made to release their secretory products by stimulation of the preganglionic fibers in the sympathetic nerve.

A partial answer to this problem has been afforded by studies on the content of the active catechol amines in tissues and organs. There is good evidence that the catechol amines found in extracts of organs and tissues are derived from their adrenergic nerves and chromaffin cells. This is shown by *a)* the large reduction or disappearance of the catechol amines after postganglionic denervation (18, 55, 129), *b)* the absence of these substances in the nerve-free placenta (116, 124) and *c)* the reappearance of such substances upon regeneration of the postganglionic nerves (55, 129). It is known that section and degeneration of the preganglionic fibers that innervate the chromaffin cells do not cause depletion of the secretory products of these cells, while section of the postganglionic fibers causes disappearance of their transmitter substance. It is thus possible by analysis of the catechol amine content of an organ after preganglionic and postganglionic denervation to obtain information on the occurrence of chromaffin cells. The results of such experiments have been that 'postganglionic' nerve section usually leaves a small remnant of activity. It is typical of this that the proportion of epinephrine is higher than it is in the organ with its nerves intact (55, 129). Sometimes the epinephrine content is unchanged. The conclusion has been drawn from these experiments that practically all of the norepinephrine is present in the postganglionic nerves while the epinephrine must have been located outside the adrenergic neurons, in all likelihood in chromaffin cells. Such cells have been described in the heart by Trinci (123).

Further evidence along the same line has been obtained from experiments on the isolated perfused rabbit heart either beating spontaneously or driven electrically at a faster rate (32). By recirculation of the perfusing fluid it is possible to concentrate the active substances released from the heart. After separation by chromatography and biological estimation on the rat's arterial pressure the following results (expressed as micrograms per heart in 40 min.) were obtained.

	Electrically driven	
	Norepinephrine	Epinephrine
Mean:	0.01 ± 0.01	0.08 ± 0.02
	Spontaneously beating	
Mean:	0.02 ± 0.01	0.08 ± 0.02

These results are of interest since they clearly show that the proportion of epinephrine is far higher than that occurring in extracts of hearts or in the coronary blood plasma after stimulation of cardiac sympathetic nerves (129). The reason for the large release of epinephrine in the spontaneously beating heart is obscure, however. It therefore appears justified to conclude that the epinephrine released probably originates from chromaffin cells. On the other hand the norepinephrine left in an organ after postganglionic denervation constitutes such a small part of the total amount found in the organ with its nerves intact that the amount normally released on sympathetic nerve stimulation must come from the adrenergic nerves. Analysis of the urine from adrenalectomized patients has also shown that the amount of epinephrine is exceedingly small compared with that of norepinephrine (129). Moreover, no increase in the epinephrine output was observed in the adrenalectomized patients subjected to tilting head-up which doubled the norepinephrine output. This speaks strongly against the assumption that epinephrine is released from adrenergic nerves in man. Moreover, the epinephrine content of splenic nerves is as a rule extremely low, a fact suggesting that the small epinephrine amounts found in spleen extracts (129) or sometimes in the effluent blood from the spleen after stimulation of its nerves (108) is not part of the neurotransmitter. For a discussion of the adrenoxine theory of Bacq & Heirman (5) the reader is referred to the survey on this subject by the same authors.

It is clearly a matter of choice whether the epinephrine released from chromaffin cells in the tissue upon sympathetic nerve stimulation should be regarded as a chemical transmitter. If one agrees to that terminology, the release of suprarenal medullary hormones should likewise be called chemical transmission. This, however, is apt to cause confusion of the concepts. It must still be left an open question whether the epinephrine-like actions observed upon stimulation of sympathetic fibers to the skin (57) are due to a release from chromaffin cells.

The possibility of dopamine serving as a neurotransmitter requires further study. Holtz, Credner & Koepp (66) showed that it occurred normally in urine. Its formation was explained as an action of l-dopadecarboxylase on dopa. Later dopamine was demonstrated by Goodall (55) in extracts of the suprarenal gland and in extracts of mammalian heart.

Since the presence of catechol amines in organs is correlated with their adrenergic nerves or chromaffin cells, it might be expected that the former also contain dopamine. This has been shown to be the case; dopamine was found in comparatively large amounts in extracts of splenic nerves (117). It seems reasonable to assume that the dopamine found in organs is present in their adrenergic nerves. If this assumption is correct the question arises as to how dopamine is stored and whether it is released upon nerve stimulation. Generally the amount of dopamine in an organ is hardly large enough to cause biological effects comparable to those caused by the norepinephrine. However, the bovine lung contains large amounts of dopamine in comparison with norepinephrine (132), and it cannot be ruled out that dopamine exerts biological actions in this case. After chromatographic separation the amount of dopamine was found by biological and chemical methods to be 0.5 to 1 µg per gm tissue while the norepinephrine was 0.01 to 0.03 µg per gm. Since the biological activity of the two substances is approximately in the proportion 50 to 100:1, it is obvious that dopamine may be biologically significant in the lung.

It has been claimed that isopropylnorepinephrine occurs in small amounts in extracts of the adrenal gland (81). Apparently the amounts are too small to permit detection with the usual colorimetric and biological methods, since these give very good agreement with the figures for epinephrine and norepinephrine. However, it has been reported that it can be separated by chromatographic technic, a certain fraction showing the characteristic biological action of the isopropyl compound.

It has been reported that, after stimulation of the sympathetic nerves to the lungs, the isopropyl compound appears in the effluent blood (82). Chromatographic separation of catechol compounds in extracts of up to 1000 gm bovine lungs have failed to detect this fraction, although catechol acetic acid, dopamine and norepinephrine are readily identified (132).

THE CHOLINERGIC NERVE TRANSMITTER

Identification

Dixon & Hamill (36) pointed out as early as 1909 that there was very little inherent difference between the action of muscarine on the heart and electrical excitation of the vagus. They continue: "If it is permissible to argue from analogy there is reason in the suggestion that excitation of a nerve induces the local liberation of a hormone which causes specific activity by combination with some constituent by the end organ muscle or gland." Only a few years later Dale (25) and Dale & Ewins (30) related the phenomena observed on stimulation of parasympathetic nerves to some earlier research by Hunt & Taveau (71). Among a large series of choline esters prepared by them, acetylcholine was shown to be the most biologically active, on an average about 1000 times more active than choline. During studies on ergot extracts, Dale (26) found a substance which produced actions similar to muscarine and identified this substance with acetylcholine. In his further work Dale was able to state that the actions of vagus stimulation and also other actions of the cranial and sacral divisions of the autonomic system were mimicked very faithfully by acetylcholine. The effects were remarkably evanescent and were always abolished by a small dose of atropine. On the basis of these observations by Dale it became extremely likely that acetylcholine actually was the substance which causes the effect of parasympathetic nerve impulses on the target cells. Further support for the idea that the substance released at the parasympathetic nerve endings was acetylcholine was supplied by Dale & Dudley (29) who showed in 1929 that it was present in the spleen of the horse and the ox. They prepared the substance and isolated it as chloroplatinate.

The identification of the parasympathetic cholinergic nerve transmitter is based upon biological tests. The amounts of acetylcholine which are liberated and occur in the organism are generally too small to be determined by chemical methods. Some of the biological methods are very sensitive, but on the other hand the specificity is not always above doubt. The methods most widely used are the negative inotropic action of acetylcholine on the heart of the frog, the hypotensive effect in the cat and the contracting effect on the intestine of the guinea pig or other animals. Other preparations which may yield more specific results are the leech muscle, the rectus abdominis muscle and the isolated lung of the frog. The isolated heart of the clam *Venus mercenaria* has also been used. For the identification of acetylcholine, the finding of Fühner (49) that the dorsal muscle of the leech was greatly sensitized to acetylcholine by addition of physostigmine was one of the more important. The preparation was introduced as a specific and quantitative biologic test for acetylcholine in 1932 by Minz (95). After preparation the muscle is suspended in Ringer's solution from one-half to several hours to relax it, and physostigmine is added to the solution in a concentration of 1–200,000 to 1–2,000,000. After about 20 min., the muscle is highly sensitized to acetylcholine so as to detect and measure acetylcholine in concentrations as low as 10^{-9}. The frog rectus is less sensitive but fairly specific for acetylcholine. The isolated frog lung has also been used and may have an even higher sensitivity than the leech muscle; it is claimed to contract in an acetylcholine solution of 10^{-16} (34). The heart of *Venus mercenaria* has also been reported to have high sensitivity to acetylcholine, up to 10^{-12}, although it varies at different times of the year.

In order to allow the conclusion that the actions observed on these test preparations actually have been due to acetylcholine, certain other conditions must be fulfilled. The action has to be increased by drugs inhibiting the acetylcholine esterase such as physostigmine, the activity should disappear after incubation with blood and the active principle should be inactivated when exposed to 1N alkali for 10 min. at room temperature, which is typical of choline esters. As a general rule different kinds of tests have to be consistent, i.e. when compared with a standard of acetylcholine the unknown extracts should elicit the same quantitative action in relation to acetylcholine (fig. 12).

One of the chief difficulties in demonstrating the neurochemical transmission from cholinergic nerves arises from the fact that in most cases the parasympathetic nerves have their autonomic synapses very close to the target organ. Therefore, stimulation of the nerves also releases acetylcholine from the preganglionic nerve. The acetylcholine released by stimulation of vagus nerve in the frog's heart may actually be due partly to the release of the substance from the synapses.

The introduction of physostigmine in experimental work made it possible to demonstrate the mediated effect with greater certainty since the substance was not immediately destroyed. Loewi's original experiments were later confirmed by many others. Among the sources of transmitter which have been tried may

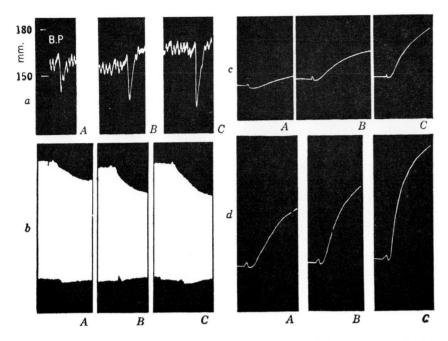

FIG. 12. Tests of a perfusate of physostigminized Locke's solution passing through the vessels of the stomach of a dog during vagal stimulation. The samples collected before stimulation were slightly, if at all, active. *A*: effects on the arterial pressure of a physostigminized cat under chloralose. *B*: isolated frog heart (Straub). *C*: physostigminized rectus abdominis of the frog. *D*: physostigminized leech muscle. In each series, *B* shows the effect of the perfusate collected during vagal stimulation; *A* and *C* correspond to two strengths of acetylcholine (*C* is double *A*). [From Dale & Feldberg (31).]

be mentioned the heart and the salivary glands (61, 134) in physostigminized animals. Particularly illuminating were the experiments by Feldberg & Krayer (44) who showed that blood from the coronary veins of physostigminized animals produced a contraction of the leech muscle shortly after vagal stimulation. This effect was abolished by atropine and the active substance was destroyed by blood. Even reflexly released transmitter was demonstrated in this way.

Although the cholinergic transmitter has not been identified with the same certainty as the adrenergic one, the sum of evidence obtained by indirect methods leaves no serious doubt that it is either acetylcholine or some other choline ester with very similar action (15).

In the autonomic neurotransmission to the salivary glands both adrenergic and cholinergic fibers seem to take part. By studying the distribution of cholinesterase Koelle (75) found in the cat, rabbit and rhesus monkey that the concentration of the true cholinesterase was higher in cholinergic neurons than in adrenergic and sensory neurons. Cholinesterase was also found to form a fine network around the outside of the acini while it was not found in the acinar cells (118). The network is united with the nerve trunk and is considered to be cholinergic in the submaxillary gland and adrenergic in the sublingual gland.

Occurrence, Biosynthesis and Storage

It may be assumed that, if the postganglionic nerve endings release acetylcholine during nerve stimulation, this has been synthesized and stored in the axon. For this reason acetylcholine would be expected to occur as a natural constituent of cholinergic nerves. In this connection only the postganglionic fibers are being considered. Analysis of the acetylcholine content of such fibers has shown large amounts in the short ciliary nerves, 3 to 8 μg per gm, which is only a little less than the amounts found in motor nerve fibers or in preganglionic fibers (92, 125). The figures are much higher than the acetylcholine content in postganglionic sympathetic fibers, such as the splenic nerve where the acetylcholine-like action only corresponds to 0.2 to 0.5 μg per gm. The difference in content suggests a specific function of the excess acetylcholine in the postganglionic parasympathetic fibers. The high content in these may be regarded as strong support of the idea that these fibers act by releasing acetylcholine. [For further details concerning the occurrence and biosynthesis of acetylcholine in cholinergic nerves see Burgen & MacIntosh (15), Gaddum (50) and Rosenblueth (113).]

The method of estimating the amount of acetylcholine directly in the tissue cannot be used, however, to estimate the amount of the cholinergic postganglionic transmitter, since this will also occur in preganglionic autonomic fibers and in motor nerves and possibly also in small amounts in all kinds of nerves.

The biosynthesis of the cholinergic transmitter has been largely elucidated by the studies of Nachmansohn & Machado (102). These authors were able to show that an extract from rat brain contained an enzyme system which could synthesize acetylcholine in the presence of ATP as the source of energy. This enzyme was called choline acetylase. It was shown later that the acetylcholine synthesis occurs in two steps. In a first reaction acetate is transformed into active acetate, and in a second the active acetate combines with choline to form acetylcholine (78). The research work of Stern & Ochoa (120) and others indicates that choline acetylase catalyzes the last step in the acetylcholine formation and that the active acetate is an acetyl coenzyme (coenzyme A). The acetate used for the synthesis has to be activated by means of ATP, coenzyme and a transacetylase. The active acetate thus formed is used for the final synthesis of the acetylcholine. Choline acetylase has been extracted from brain and from electric organs but is also present in all nerve tissues. It has even been demonstrated in tissues from various invertebrates, such as annelids and flatworms. The presence of choline acetylase in mitochondrial fractions in homogenates of brain (60) suggests that this may be the case also in the postganglionic neurons.

As to the storage of the cholinergic transmitter it appears likely that it is confined to structural elements as demonstrated for adrenergic nerves. Some indirect support for the opinion that acetylcholine is also inclosed in separate particles may be found in the early experiment by Loewi & Hellauer (86). Loewi (85) points to the finding that when nerve tissue is extracted with Ringer's solution, the bulk of acetylcholine is found in the insoluble residue but that the use of hypotonic solution causes the greater part of the acetylcholine to be released. This suggests that the acetylcholine is located in particles surrounded by a membrane similar to mitochondria. When Ringer's solution is used for extracting the acetylcholine in a cholinergic nerve, such as the vagus, most of the acetylcholine goes into solution, however. It is also noteworthy that when acidified solutions are used, the total amount of acetylcholine is extracted as is also the case when extraction is made with acidified alcohol. Some of the acetylcholine may be bound to some lipid complex soluble in ether, which acetylcholine in itself is not (86).

An analogous behavior is shown by epinephrine and norepinephrine and histamine. It therefore seems possible that these amines form ether-soluble but water-insoluble compounds in the particles. It is of interest in this connection that Hillarp & Nilson (64) found a high content of phosphatides in the suprarenal medullary granules.

Release in Organs

Very little is known concerning the mechanism of release of the cholinergic transmitter in the autonomic neuromuscular junctions. By studying the release of acetylcholine from the spontaneously beating or electrically driven rabbit's heart, it has been possible to show that the release is significantly higher at a faster heart rate. Thus a spontaneously beating heart with a mean rate of 56 per min. released 0.26 ± 0.08 μg per heart in 40 min. while electrically driven hearts with a mean rate of 210 per min. released 0.97 ± 0.36 μg per heart in 40 min. (32).

The release of acetylcholine from an organ does not necessarily mean that this substance originates from nervous tissue since it is known that even nerve-free tissue is able to synthesize and release acetylcholine (17).

Most of the knowledge on the action of acetylcholine and its release refers to the motor endplate which has been studied in detail from a chemical point of view as well as by electrophysiological techniques. There is hardly any doubt, however, that the mechanism of release of the cholinergic transmitter from the postganglionic cholinergic nerves is similar in kind to that already outlined for the adrenergic transmitter. We may thus assume that the active transmitter is released at a terminal portion of the nerve and acts directly in a chemical manner on the smooth muscle fibers. There is no reason to believe that the smooth muscle cells are directly innervated by cholinergic postganglionic fibers any more than they are by adrenergic fibers.

RELEASE FROM ISOLATED NERVES. Although no experiments seem to have been made with stimulation of postganglionic cholinergic nerves, several authors have reported that stimulation of cholinergic preganglionic nerves causes a release of acetylcholine (2, 10, 23, 79). It may be assumed that similar events take place during stimulation of postganglionic cholinergic nerves.

The inhibitory action of atropine on the effect of cholinergic nerve stimulation has been shown to depend on blocking of the target cell to the released transmitter. It was demonstrated by Feldberg & Krayer (44) that atropine does not interfere with the release as such.

The failure of atropine to block the effect of stimulating the vagus nerve on the intestine may be due to an action of a transmitter different from acetylcholine, released from the enteric nerve system. The nature of this postulated transmitter is not known, but it should be recalled that substance P (51) occurs in the intestine and is insensitive to atropine.

Rosenblueth (113) has advanced the idea that the cholinergic nerve transmission proceeds in two stages of which the first is a release of acetylcholine followed by a second in which the nerve transmitter subsequently forms 'parasympathin' which then acts directly on the target cell.

Stimulation experiments on postganglionic cholinergic nerves (short ciliary nerves) have shown that the optimum frequency is about 25 per sec. (89). As in the case of adrenergic nerves, prolonged stimulation caused only slight signs of exhaustibility. Thus stimulation for 1 to 2 hours caused a sustained contraction of the iris; thereafter the effect gradually declined.

Removal of Transmitter

As early as 1914 Dale (25) had assumed that acetylcholine was destroyed rapidly in the organism by some hydrolyzing enzyme. Such an enzyme was actually discovered by Loewi & Navratil (87) in extracts of frog's heart. They also found that this enzyme could be inhibited by physostigmine. This was in agreement with the results of earlier experiments of Dixon & Brodie (35) and others who found that this drug increased some of the effects of parasympathetic nerve stimulation. Moreover, Loewi & Navratil were able to show that it increased the effect of the substance liberated from the frog's heart upon stimulation. The 'Vagusstoff' thus behaved like a choline ester since it was a) inhibited by atropine which is a specific inhibitor, at least in small doses, and b) protected by physostigmine which is known to inhibit choline esterase. It is generally assumed that the cholinergic transmitter is being inactivated locally to a great extent. Information about the distribution of cholinesterase in the peripheral tissue is accumulating rapidly as a result of the development of suitable methods. This includes important findings about the distribution of cholinesterase at the motor endplates and in the central nervous system (43, 77). It may be assumed that part of the transmitter released in peripheral organs, such as the smooth muscle organs and glands, is diffusing out in the blood stream where it is rapidly inactivated by the cholinesterase present. It is also possible that cholinesterase is present in the target cells in amounts large enough to destroy any amount of the transmitter diffusing into the cell.

MECHANISM OF ACTION OF NEUROTRANSMITTERS

The neurotransmitters exert direct action on target cells independently of whether or not the cells are autonomically innervated. This is shown by the pronounced action of the transmitter substances on nerve-free organs, like the placenta, or on denervated structures.

The mode of action of the neurotransmitters on the target cells has been much discussed. Clark (24) related the minimal effective doses of acetylcholine and epinephrine on the frog's heart and the frog's stomach to the total surface of the cells affected and arrived at the conclusion that while the effective dose of 0.02 μg per gm covered a surface of about 1 cm² the total area of the cells was 6000 to 20000 cm². For this reason it was obvious that the active substance only needed to attack a minute part of the cell in order to elicit its action.

It is generally assumed that the active substance, be it a neurotransmitter or a pharmacologically active drug of a different kind, has to unite in some way with the target cell before exerting its action. Often the sites of binding between the cell and the active molecule are referred to as receptors. According to Clark these postulated receptors, in or on the cell, occupy only a very small portion of the cell volume or surface. Morphological evidence for specific receptor patches on the cell surface is still lacking, however.

A discussion of the number of molecules of a transmitter required to activate a single cell depends obviously on the type of administration and on the sensitivity of the cell. If 0.02 μg acetylcholine is necessary to inhibit one gram of frog's heart, as in Clark's example, the minimal effective amount per gm of tissue is about 10^6 molecules per cell. In isolated organs entirely different results may be obtained. Thus 0.05 mμg epinephrine per ml suspension fluid is sometimes enough to elicit an inhibitory effect on the fowl's isolated rectal cecum. In this case obviously a much smaller number of molecules are capable of producing the action, since most of them are in the suspension fluid without contact with the organ. If it is assumed that 10 per cent of the molecules are acting on 1 gm of organ containing 10^{10} cells, then the number of molecules per cell will be only 10, provided that the active substance is distributed on all cells. This is probably not the case. All calculations of this kind therefore appear very dubious.

It is conceivable that the neurotransmitter takes part in a chemical reaction sequence which is influenced thereby in a quantitative or even qualitative manner. Whether this action is initiated at specific receptor patches at the surface or at specific metabolic structure elements in the interior of the cell is not known. It may be recalled that there is good evidence for the permeation of neurotransmitters through cell membranes, since this is the basis for most of our information regarding their release.

Elaborate schemes of receptor mechanisms have been presented by several authors and terms suggested for the postulated receptors. Since these efforts primarily represent an attempt to put the known facts in a formal system but hardly contribute to our actual knowledge, these systems will not be dealt with here. Recent contributions to the discussion have been given by Zupančič (137) and Stephenson (119).

How the neurotransmittor elicits a relaxation or a contraction of the target cell is still obscure. It can be assumed that the active substance initiates or reinforces some process which eventually causes physicochemical changes in the contractile material conducive to such effects.

Attempts have been made to correlate the inhibitory actions of epinephrine with the formation of lactic acid (99), which is believed to be the metabolic product directly responsible for the inhibitory action. The hypothesis obviously requires that the widely varying activity ratios of epinephrine and norepinephrine for an organ like the fowl's rectal cecum (from 4 to 200) are associated with corresponding variations in the formation of lactic acid in the reacting target cells, a demonstration which has not been made.

On account of the large differences in action between the levo- and dextroisomers of epinephrine, for instance, it has been inferred that the active substance combines with an optically active constituent of the cell (122). Recent careful studies on the biological activity of optical isomers of sympathomimetic amines have shown that the difference in action between the isomers is even greater than has been hitherto recognized (90).

These results suggest that the neurotransmitter is involved in enzymatic reactions, a conclusion which also appears most likely for other reasons.

Another approach to the study of the mode of action of neurotransmitters on the target cell is based on the quantitative relationships between dose and action. Such quantitation of the effects has been used for the elaboration of formulae of various kinds. It is outside the scope of this article to discuss these studies. It may be said generally, however, that by applying this principle to single cells more information may be gained. In most cases the relationship between dose and action is approximately expressed by a rectangular hyperbola. Its precise biological significance is not as yet clear.

Summarizing, it may be concluded that not much more knowledge about the mode of action of the neurotransmitters on target cells has been gained since Langley's time when he ascribed the differentiating effect of the transmitter, relaxation or contraction, to a receptor substance in the cell.

A relevant question is whether two neurotransmitters released in the same organ act on the same or different cells and to what extent they interfere with one another's actions. Morison & Acheson (20) found similar hyperbolic concentration-action curves for epinephrine and acetylcholine on the nictitating membrane of the cat. When the two substances were injected together, their actions added up along the same curve. These results would seem to allow the important conclusion that the two neurotransmitters act independently by exerting separate actions. Whether or not these are on the same or different cells cannot be decided from these experiments.

NEUROTRANSMITTERS IN BLOOD AND URINE

It has been discussed above that some of the neurotransmitter released at the autonomic postganglionic nerve endings passes beyond the target cells and reaches the blood stream. If this occurs to any considerable extent it should be possible to demonstrate the neurotransmitters in the blood. Such attempts have been made and there is some evidence for the opinion that the neurotransmitter of the adrenergic system normally occurs in small quantities in the blood. However, since the methods of demonstrating norepinephrine in blood require fairly large quantities of blood and are rather laborious (70, 91), they have not been widely used. Some indirect information has been obtained by studying the excretion in urine (67, 130). Even if norepinephrine occurs in peripheral blood it remains to be shown that it is derived from postganglionic nerves and not from the suprarenal medulla or from chromaffin cells. Proof of its overflow and passage into the blood has been given, however, by studies on the excretion in urine in adrenalectomized patients. In these patients the only important sources of norepinephrine can be the postganglionic nerves. For the same reasons as outlined above the excretion of acetylcholine, after treatment of the organism with physostigmine, will not allow any conclusions as to the release at the postganglionic nerve endings since acetylcholine is also released at many other sites.

REFERENCES

1. ALLEN, W. J., H. BARCROFT AND O. G. EDHOLM. *J. Physiol.* 105: 255, 1946.
2. BABSKY, E. B. *Bull. Biol. Med. Exper. USSR* 5: 51, 1938.
3. BACQ, Z. M. *Arch. internat. physiol.* 36: 167, 1933.
4. BACQ, Z. M. *Ann. Physiol.* 10: 467, 1934.
5. BACQ, Z. M. AND P. HEIRMAN. *Arch. internat. physiol.* 50: 153, 1940.
6. BAIN, W. A. *Quart. J. Exper. Physiol.* 23: 381, 1933.
7. BAIN, W. A. *Quart. J. Exper. Physiol.* 22: 269, 1932.
8. BARCROFT, H. AND H. J. C. SWAN. *Sympathetic Control of Human Blood Vessels.* London: Arnold, 1953.
9. BARGER, G. AND H. H. DALE. *J. Physiol.* 41: 19, 1910–11.
10. BERGAMI, G. *Boll. Soc. ital. biol. sper.* 11: 275, 1936.
11. BLASCHKO, H. *J. Physiol.* 101: 337, 1942.
12. BLASCHKO, H. AND A. D. WELCH. *Arch. exper. Path. u. Pharmakol.* 219: 17, 1953.
13. BRINKMAN, R. AND E. VAN DAM. *Arch. ges. Physiol.* 196: 66, 1922.
14. BROWN, G. L. AND J. S. GILLESPIE. *Nature, London.* 178: 980, 1956.
15. BURGEN, A. S. V. AND F. C. MACINTOSH. In: *Neurochemistry*, edited by K. A. C. Elliott, I. H. Page and J. H. Quastel. Springfield: Thomas, 1955, p. 311.
16. BURN, J. H. AND J. ROBINSON. *Brit. J. Pharmacol.* 6: 101, 1951.
17. BURN, J. H., E. M. VAUGHAN WILLIAMS AND J. M. WALKER. *J. Physiol.* 131: 317, 1956.
18. CANNON, W. B. AND K. LISSÁK. *Am. J. Physiol.* 125: 765, 1939.
19. CANNON, W. B. AND A. ROSENBLUETH. *Am. J. Physiol.* 104: 557, 1933.
20. CANNON, W. B. AND A. ROSENBLUETH. *Autonomic Neuro-Effector Systems.* New York: Macmillan, 1937.
21. CANNON, W. B. AND J. E. URIDIL. *Am. J. Physiol.* 58: 353, 1921.
22. CELANDER, O. *Acta physiol. scandinav.* suppl. 116, 32: 1, 1954.
23. CHANG, H. C., W. M. HSIEH, T. H. LI AND R. K. S. LIM. *Chinese J. Physiol.* 14: 19, 1939.
24. CLARK, A. J. *The Mode of Action of Drugs on Cells.* London: Arnold, 1933.
25. DALE, H. H. *J. Pharmacol. & Exper. Therap.* 6: 147, 1914.
26. DALE, H. H. *J. Physiol.* 48: iii, 1914.
27. DALE, H. H. *J. Physiol.* 80: 10P, 1933.
28. DALE, H. H. *Brit. M. J.* I: 835, 1934.
29. DALE, H. H. AND H. W. DUDLEY. *J. Physiol.* 68: 97, 1929.
30. DALE, H. H. AND A. J. EWINS. *J. Physiol.* 48: xxiv, 1914.
31. DALE, H. H. AND W. FELDBERG. *J. Physiol.* 81: 320, 1934.
32. DAY, M. *J. Physiol.* 134: 558, 1956.
33. DEMIS, D. J., H. BLASCHKO AND A. D. WELCH. *J. Pharmacol. & Exper. Therap.* 117: 208, 1956.
34. DIJKSTRA, C. AND A. K. M. NOYONS. *Arch. internat. physiol.* 49: 257, 1939.
35. DIXON, W. E. AND T. G. BRODIE. *J. Physiol.*, 29: 97, 1903.
36. DIXON, W. E. AND P. HAMILL. *J. Physiol.* 38: 314, 1909.
37. DUNCANSON, D., T. STEWART AND O. G. EDHOLM. *Fed. Proc.* 8: 37, 1949.
38. DUNÉR, H. *Acta physiol. scandinav.* 32: 63, 1954.
39. DYE, J. A. *Am. J. Physiol.* 113: 265, 1935.
40. ELIASSON, R., U. S. v. EULER AND L. STJÄRNE. *Acta physiol. scandinav.* Suppl. 118, 33: 63, 1955.
41. ELLIOTT, T. R. *J. Physiol.* 32: 401, 1905.
42. EMMELIN, N. *Acta physiol. scandinav.* 34: 29, 1955.
43. FELDBERG, W. S. *Pharmacol. Rev.* 6: 85, 1954.
44. FELDBERG, W. AND O. KRAYER. *Arch. exper. Path. u. Pharmakol.* 172: 170, 1933.
45. FINKLEMAN, B. *J. Physiol.* 70: 145, 1930.
46. FOLKOW, B. *Acta physiol. scandinav.* 25: 49, 1952.
47. FOLKOW, B. *Physiol. Rev.* 35: 629, 1955.
48. FOLKOW, B. AND B. UVNÄS. *Acta physiol. scandinav.* 15: 365, 1948.
49. FÜHNER, H. *Arch. exper. Path. u. Pharmakol.* 82: 57, 1918.
50. GADDUM, J. H. *Gefässerweiternde Stoffe der Gewebe.* Leipzig: Thieme, 1936.
51. GADDUM, J. H. *Polypeptides Which Stimulate Plain Muscle.* Edinburgh: Livingstone, 1955.
52. GADDUM, J. H. AND L. G. GOODWIN. *J. Physiol.* 105: 357, 1947.
53. GADDUM, J. H., M. A. KHAYYAL AND H. RYDIN. *J. Physiol.* 89: 9, 1937.
54. GARVEN, H. S. D. AND F. W. GAIRNS. *Quart. J. Exper. Physiol.* 37: 131, 1952.

55. GOODALL, McCH. *Acta physiol. scandinav.* 24: suppl. 85, 1951.

56. GREEF, K. AND P. HOLTZ. *Arch. internat. pharmacodyn.* 88: 228, 1951.

57. GREEN, H. D., J. A. MACLEOD, D. A. ANDERSON AND A. B. DENISON, JR. *J. Pharmacol. & Exper. Therap.* 112: 218, 1954.

58. GREER, C. M., J. O. PINKSTON, J. H. BAXTER AND E. S. BRANNON. *J. Pharmacol. & Exper. Therap.* 62: 189, 1938.

59. HAGEN, P. *J. Pharmacol. & Exper. Therap.* 116: 26, 1956.

60. HEBB, C. O. AND B. N. SMALLMAN. *J. Physiol.* 134: 385, 1956.

61. HENDERSON, V. E. AND M. H. ROEPKE. *Arch. exper. Path. u. Pharmakol.* 172: 314, 1933.

62. HILLARP, N.-Å. *Acta anat.* 2: suppl. 4, 1946.

63. HILLARP, N.-Å. AND B. NILSON. *Acta physiol. scandinav.* 31: suppl. 113, 79, 1954.

64. HILLARP, N.-Å. AND B. NILSON. *Acta physiol. scandinav.* 32: 11, 1954.

65. HOFFMANN, F., E. J. HOFFMANN, S. MIDDLETON AND J. TALESNIK. *Am. J. Physiol.* 144: 189, 1945.

66. HOLTZ, P., K. CREDNER AND W. KOEPP. *Arch. exper. Path. u. Pharmakol.* 200: 356, 1942.

67. HOLTZ, P., K. CREDNER AND G. KRONEBERG. *Arch. exper. Path. u. Pharmakol.* 204: 228, 1947.

68. HOLTZ, P., R. HEISE AND K. LÜDTKE. *Arch. exper. Path. u. Pharmakol.* 191: 87, 1938–39.

69. HOLTZ, P. AND E. WESTERMANN. *Arch. exper. Path. u. Pharmakol.* 227: 538, 1956.

70. HOLZBAUER, M. AND M. VOGT. *Brit. J. Pharmacol.* 9: 249, 1954.

71. HUNT, R. AND R. DE M. TAVEAU. *Brit. M. J.* 2: 1788, 1906.

72. JABONERO, V. *Acta neuroveg.* Suppl. 6, 1955.

73. JAMES, W. O. *Nature, London* 161: 851, 1948.

74. KIRSHNER, N. AND McCH. GOODALL. *Fed. Proc.* 15: 110, 1956.

75. KOELLE, G. B. *J. Pharmacol. & Exper. Therap.* 114: 167, 1955.

76. KOELLE, G. B. AND A. DE T. VALK, JR. *J. Physiol.* 126: 434, 1954.

77. KUFFLER, S. W. *Arch. sc. physiol.* 3: 585, 1949.

78. LIPTON, M. A. AND E. S. G. BARRON. *J. Biol. Chem.* 166: 367, 1946.

79. LISSÁK, K. *Am. J. Physiol.* 127: 263, 1939.

80. LIU, A. C. AND A. ROSENBLUETH. *Am. J. Physiol.* 113: 555, 1935.

81. LOCKETT, M. F. *Brit. J. Pharmacol.* 9: 498, 1954.

82. LOCKETT, M. F. *J. Physiol.* 133: 73P, 1956.

83. LOEWI, O. *Arch. ges. Physiol.* 189: 239, 1921.

84. LOEWI, O. *Arch. ges. Physiol.* 237: 504, 1936.

85. LOEWI, O. *Experientia* 12: 331, 1956.

86. LOEWI, O. AND H. HELLAUER. *Arch. ges. Physiol.* 240: 449, 1938.

87. LOEWI, O. AND E. NAVRATIL. *Arch. ges. Physiol.* 214: 689, 1926.

88. LUCO, J. V. AND F. GOÑI. *J. Neurophysiol.* 11: 497, 1948.

89. LUCO, J. V. AND H. SALVESTRINI. *J. Neurophysiol.* 5: 27, 1942.

90. LUDUENA, F. P., B. F. TULLAR, L. V. EULER AND A. M. LANDS. *XX Internat. Physiol. Congr., Abstr. of Communic.:* 30, 1956.

91. LUND, A. *Acta pharmacol. et toxicol.* 6: 137, 1950.

92. MACINTOSH, F. C. *J. Physiol.* 99: 436, 1940.

93. MANN, M. AND G. B. WEST. *Brit. J. Pharmacol.* 5: 173, 1950.

94. MCDOWALL, R. J. S. *J. Physiol.* 104: 41P, 1945.

95. MINZ, B. *Arch. exper. Path. u. Pharmakol.* 168: 292, 1932.

96. MINZ, B. *La Transmission Chimique de l'Influx Nerveux.* Paris: Flammarion, 1947.

97. MINZ, B. *The Role of Humoral Agents in Nervous Activity.* Springfield: Thomas, 1955.

98. MIRKIN, B. L. AND D. D. BONNYCASTLE. *Am. J. Physiol.* 178: 529, 1954.

99. MOHME-LUNDHOLM, E. *Acta physiol. scandinav.* 29: suppl. 108, 1953.

100. MONNIER, A. M. AND Z. M. BACQ. *Arch. internat. physiol.* 40: 485, 1935.

101. NACHMANSOHN, D. In: *Neurochemistry*, edited by K. A. C. Elliott, I. H. Page and J. H. Quastel. Springfield: Thomas, 1955, p. 390.

102. NACHMANSOHN, D. AND A. L. MACHADO. *J. Neurophysiol.* 6: 397, 1943.

103. NEWTON, H. F., R. L. ZWEMER AND W. B. CANNON. *Am. J. Physiol.* 96: 377, 1931.

104. ORIAS, O. *Am. J. Physiol.* 102: 87, 1932.

105. ÖSTLUND, E. *Acta physiol. scandinav.* 31: suppl. 112, 1954.

106. OUTSCHOORN, A. S. AND M. VOGT. *Brit. J. Pharmacol.* 7: 319, 1952.

107. PARTINGTON, P. P. *Am. J. Physiol.* 117: 55, 1936.

108. PEART, W. S. *J. Physiol.* 108: 491, 1949.

109. PITKÄNEN, E. *Acta physiol. scandinav.* 38: suppl. 129, 1956.

110. RAAB, W. *Biochem. J.* 37: 470, 1943.

111. REXED, B. AND U. S. VON EULER. *Acta psychiat. et neur. scandinav.* 26: 61, 1951.

112. ROSENBLUETH, A. *Am. J. Physiol.* 102: 12, 1932.

113. ROSENBLUETH, A. *The Transmission of Nerve Impulses at Neuroeffector Junctions and Peripheral Synapses.* New York: Technol. Press, Mass. Inst. Technol. and Wiley, 1950.

114. ROSENBLUETH, A. AND W. B. CANNON. *Am. J. Physiol.* 108: 384, 1934.

115. ROSENBLUETH, A. AND D McK. RIOCH. *Am. J. Physiol.* 106: 365, 1933.

116. SCHMITERLÖW, C. G. *Acta physiol. scandinav.* 16: suppl. 56, 1948.

117. SCHÜMANN, H. J. *Arch. exper. Path. u. Pharmakol.* 227: 566, 1956.

118. SNELL, R. S. AND J. R. GARRETT. *Nature, London* 178: 1177, 1956.

119. STEPHENSON, R. P. *Brit. J. Pharm.* 11: 379, 1956.

120. STERN, J. R. AND S. OCHOA. *J. Biol. Chem.* 179: 491, 1949.

121. STÖHR, P. *Mikroskopische Anatomie des Vegetativen Nervensystems.* Berlin: Springer, 1928.

122. TIFFENEAU, M. *Ann. Physiol.* 10: 535, 1934.

123. TRINCI, G. *Mem. R. Accad. Sc. Bologna* 4: 295, 1907.

124. VON EULER, U. S. *Acta physiol. scandinav.* 12: 73, 1946.

125. VON EULER, U. S. *J. Physiol.* 107: 10P, 1947.

126. VON EULER, U. S. *Pharmacol. Rev.* 3: 247, 1951.

127. VON EULER, U. S. *Pharmacol. Rev.* 6: 15, 1954.

128. VON EULER, U. S. In: *Neurochemistry*, edited by K. A. C. Elliott, I. H. Page and H. J. Quastel. Springfield: Thomas, 1955.

129. VON EULER, U. S. *Noradrenaline; Chemistry, Physiology, Pharmacology and Clinical Aspects*. Springfield: Thomas, 1956.

130. VON EULER, U. S. AND I. FLODING. *Scandinav. J. Clin. & Lab. Invest*. In press.

131. VON EULER, U. S. AND N.-Å. HILLARP. *Nature, London* 177: 44, 1956.

132. VON EULER, U. S. AND F. LISHAJKO. *Acta physiol. et pharmacol. neerl*. 6: 295, 1957.

133. VON MURALT, A. *Die Signalübermittlung in Nerven*. Basel: Birkhäuser, 1946.

134. VON SAALFELD, E. *Arch. ges. Physiol*. 235: 15, 1934.

135. WEISS, P. AND H. B. HISCOE. *J. exper. Zool*. 107: 315, 1948.

136. WHITELAW, G. P. AND J. C. SNYDER. *Am. J. Physiol*. 110: 247, 1934.

137. ZUPANČIČ, A. O. *Acta physiol. scandinav*. 29: 63, 1953.

CHAPTER VIII

Neuromuscular transmission in invertebrates

E. J. FURSHPAN | *Biophysics Department, University College, London, England*

CHAPTER CONTENTS

TO PRODUCE THE MOST EFFICIENT CONTRACTION, a muscle fiber must be activated along its entire length almost simultaneously; otherwise, the contracting portions of the fiber must lengthen inactive regions before communicating their tension to the tendon. That is, the active parts of the fiber will operate in a less effective range of the length-tension curve. At least two mechanisms are known which can achieve this relatively synchronous excitation of the fiber: *a*) a comparatively rapidly conducting muscle action potential, and *b*) numerous motor nerve endings along the length of the muscle fiber. The term 'multiterminal innervation' (61) will be used to describe this second situation. The first device (conducted muscle action potential) is most commonly found in the skeletal muscle of vertebrates. The most notable exception is the case of the slow muscle fibers of the frog [see Kuffler & Vaughan Williams (45)] in which there is multiterminal innervation and a lack of a conducted muscle spike. It should be pointed out that vertebrate twitch muscle fibers which exhibit such a spike may have more than one motor endplate (38). These cases should probably not be included within the definition of multiterminal innervation, however, for in the absence of the propagated muscle spike, the density of the nerve endings is not sufficient to allow an appreciable contraction.

The second mechanism (many nerve endings) seems to predominate in the somatic musculature of the invertebrates. An examination of the evidence for this type of innervation will serve as one of the themes of this chapter. It will also be interesting to consider what differences in function between the two systems seem to follow from the dissimilarity in the means of spreading the muscular excitation. A related question will also be examined—the other anatomical specializations associated with multiterminal innervation. One such feature commonly found is polyneuronal innervation or the receipt by one muscle fiber of more than one motor axon, and of particular interest, of motor axons which elicit from the same fiber responses of different strength and time course. In most vertebrate muscles, by contrast, the conducted action potential is all-or-nothing and produces a stereotyped twitch. Thus different types of contraction evoked by different nerve fibers do not occur. Peripheral inhibition, as found in certain invertebrate muscles, offers another example of polyneuronal innervation and this topic will be considered as well. Another question that will be discussed concerns the number of motor neurons which innervate whole muscles. Here, too, a contrast with vertebrate muscle will be seen in many cases and again the dissimilarity between the ways in which the excitation is spread throughout the muscle fiber can be thought to underlie these differences. That is, in spite of the all-or-nothing contractions, fine gradations of tension are possible in most vertebrate twitch muscles because of the large number of motor units. Where conducted muscle potentials are absent, however, gradation of contraction can be effected by variations in the degree of excitation within each muscle fiber. In some of these cases, therefore, one need not be surprised if only a few motor axons are found to innervate whole muscles. The general scheme of presentation will be to consider together studies on the same group of animals.

ARTHROPODS

Crustaceans

Some of the elementary features of crustacean nerve-muscle systems were known in the nineteenth century, chiefly from the work of Biedermann. In a histological study (7) he observed that the nerve fibers ramifying on the surface of the opener-muscle (abductor of the dactylopodite) of the crayfish claw were apparently all branches of only two axons. These two fibers ran very close to one another and both divided at each branch point in approximately the same place. The axons remained in juxtaposition even into the very fine ramifications on the surface of single muscle fibers. Thus both axons seemed to innervate the same muscle fibers. Mangold (51) corroborated these findings and introduced the term 'diplotomic' branching for this type of concomitant division of two nerve fibers. He also corroborated the double innervation of single muscle fibers. Mangold saw that as a fine nerve twig, consisting of two efferent axons within a single sheath, approached the surface of the muscle fiber the nerve sheath joined and became continuous with the sarcolemma. Then the axons would continue to ramify beneath the sarcolemma and thus come into close contact with the striated elements. He also saw that more than two axons might divide together in a manner analogous with diplotomic splitting, and he figures three axons doing so on the surface of the closer-muscle (adductor of the dactylopodite) of the crayfish claw. Hoffman (29) examined the gross anatomy of the innervation of the four most distal muscles of the claw. One of his unusual observations was that a single nerve fiber innervated two muscles: an axon going to the extensor of the carpopodite (stretcher-muscle) continued into the next segment to end in the opener-muscle. He showed diplotomic branching for the opener-, stretcher-, and bender- (flexor of the carpopodite) muscles, and found three or more axons going to the closer-muscle. Hoffman also studied the distribution

of these various axons within the two nerves which run through the length of the claw.

Knowledge of the differences in function of the two or several axons innervating a single muscle also goes back to Biedermann. Richet (60) had observed that with weak stimulation of the crayfish limb nerve the claw opened, and with stronger shocks it closed. Biedermann (8) extended these observations. In experiments in which he eliminated one or the other of the two muscles (opener- or closer-muscle) operating the dactyl, he was still able to obtain opening or closing depending on the strength of nerve stimulation; and if electrodes placed at the muscle evoked contraction, excitation of the nerve could inhibit this contraction. Biedermann correctly concluded that there must have been separate nerve fibers to mediate the inhibitory process; and since the opener-muscle, for example, received only two axons, one of these was designated the excitor and the other the inhibitor.

Lucas provided information on the function of the additional axon in a muscle with a triple innervation. He observed (49) both slow and twitch contractions in the closer-muscle of the lobster claw; and further found that the strength-duration curve for indirect stimulation (by way of the nerve) showed a sharp discontinuity at the point at which one type of contraction was replaced by the other. From these, and additional experiments on the crayfish claw (50), Lucas concluded that the two contraction types were evoked by stimulation of different 'substances' (types of nerve elements).

This conclusion has been amply confirmed and it is now known that more than one type of motor axon can innervate a single crustacean muscle and that the electrical and mechanical responses evoked by each can differ with respect to amplitude, time course, facilitation and fatigue. The most convincing demonstration of this was provided by van Harreveld & Wiersma (74) who succeeded in isolating and stimulating single functioning motor axons from crayfish limb nerves. In particular they studied nerve fibers evoking contraction of the closer-muscle. In normal preparations (but not in regenerated claws) two such axons were always found and stimulation of the remainder of the nerve did not result in contraction of this muscle. A single impulse in the thicker of the two axons evoked a rapid twitch, while a train of impulses was needed in the thinner fiber to produce even a small contraction. About 30 sec. were required to attain maximal tension during stimulation of the thin axon at 40 shocks per sec. This time for the thick nerve fiber was only about 1 sec. and the terms 'slow' and 'fast' were therefore used to describe the two contractions. These same terms were then extended to the concomitant muscle potentials and to the axons themselves (e.g. 'slow axon'). The muscle potentials showed even greater differences, the slow potentials being very small but augmenting with repetitive stimulation. Despite this increase (facilitation) they remained smaller than a single fast muscle-potential. In the crayfish closer muscle, which is perhaps not typical in this respect, the fast potential normally exhibited no facilitation.

SIZE OF THE EFFERENT NERVE SUPPLY. One of the questions considered subsequently by these same authors and their collaborators concerned the numbers of excitatory and inhibitory axons supplying the seven most distal limb muscles in different species of decapod crustaceans. The latter included crayfish, lobsters, rock lobsters, crabs, hermit crabs and various other anomurans. The techniques involved isolation and stimulation, separately, of as many of the axons having an excitatory or inhibitory effect upon a particular muscle as could be found, and an additional estimate of the minimum number of efferent axons using methylene-blue staining. All limb muscles that were examined received at least two axons and at most five, and of these at least one was always an inhibitor. The different groups of decapods showed diversity in the numbers of inhibitory nerve fibers supplying a particular muscle, but the numbers of excitatory axons were constant from species to species. The following table summarizes the findings for motor decapod axons only (74, 75, 76).

Note that Hoffman's histological observation that one axon supplied two muscles was confirmed by physiological methods. In addition to the nerve fibers listed in table 1, each muscle receives at least one inhibitory axon and in some species there are muscles receiving two (78). Further, it is typical for an inhibitory axon to supply more than one muscle (up to seven), and variations in the particular muscles supplied by a common inhibitor were also found. Wiersma & Ripley (85) have summarized the inhibitory innervation of these muscles.

POLYNEURONAL INNERVATION. From the early histological work and the fact that inhibition can counteract excitation, it was apparent that motor and inhibitory axons both innervate the same muscle fibers. Can a muscle fiber also receive more than one excitatory axon? There is now convincing evidence, both

TABLE 1. *Number of Excitatory Axons Supplying the Seven Most Distal Limb Muscles of Decapod Crustaceans*

Muscle (common name)	Segment Moved	Type of Movement	No. of Motor Axons
Opener	Dactylopodite	Abduction (or extension)	1*
Closer	Dactylopodite	Adduction (or flexion)	2
Stretcher	Propodite	Extension	1*
Bender	Propodite	Flexion	2
Main flexor	Carpopodite	Flexion	4
Accesory flexor	Carpopodite	Flexion	1
Extensor	Carpopodite	Extension	2

* This same axon innervates both muscles.

histological (73) and physiological, that this is indeed possible. Although the observation is attended by some difficulties, the fibers of the closer-muscle have been seen to contract following stimulation of either the fast or slow axon (72). Wiersma & van Harreveld (84) showed that stimulation of one of the motor axons to the closer-muscle augmented a contraction evoked shortly afterwards by stimulation of the other (heterofacilitation). No mutual influence with respect to fatigue or facilitation of the muscle action potentials, however, could be demonstrated. These results suggested the presence of a pathway susceptible to mutual influence somewhere between muscle action potential and contraction; and the conclusion was drawn that at least some of the contractile substance was activated by both axons. More recently Fatt & Katz (22) used intracellular electrodes to demonstrate that muscle potentials were evoked in the same fibers by both fast and slow axons, and it was shown that the potentials could summate. There is no good quantitative determination of what percentage of the fibers in a muscle receiving two excitatory axons are innervated by both axons.

van Harreveld & Wiersma (76) have also considered the question of polyneuronal innervation in a muscle with four motor axons (and one inhibitor). Here, too, they found that a test contraction set up by stimulation of one of the four axons was slightly augmented by previous stimulation of any of the other three motor axons (heterofacilitation). Their experiments did not provide direct evidence, however, concerning the numbers of axons supplying each muscle fiber. More recently, Furshpan (26) has studied the same muscle (main flexor of the carpopodite in the

California rock lobster), recording from the muscle fibers with intracellular electrodes while stimulating the four motor axons separately. In this way 20 or 30 fibers in each preparation were sampled and if, upon stimulation of a particular axon, a monophasic muscle potential in the direction of depolarization was recorded at the microelectrode, it was concluded that the impaled fiber was innervated by the axon in question. While reasons were presented for believing that the sampling was not entirely random, the following results were recognized. Some of the muscle fibers did receive all four of the motor axons (and presumably the inhibitor as well); these were, however, a small minority comprising about 5 to 10 per cent of those tested. The remaining fibers were approximately equally distributed among those innervated by one, two, or three of the motor axons, and different combinations of two and three axons were found. Further, the size of the muscle potential which stimulation of a nerve fiber evoked could vary considerably from muscle fiber to muscle fiber. Thus this muscle shows remarkable heterogeneity with respect to the number, combination and effectiveness of the motor axons which supply its individual fibers. This is a factor which it is important to consider in attempting to correlate muscle potentials and contraction and emphasizes the desirability of performing such experiments on single muscle fibers.

It is not known to what extent this analysis applies to the simpler case of a muscle receiving only two motor axons, but from experiments cited above, and from some incomplete work with intracellular electrodes (unpublished observations), it seems as if most fibers receive both axons. Here, too, there is heterogeneity with respect to the size of the muscle potentials evoked and some fibers have been found in which the 'slow' axon elicited much larger responses than did the 'fast'; more work is needed, however.

MULTITERMINAL INNERVATION. In a histological study d'Ancona (14) encountered considerable variation among different crustaceans, but in extreme cases he observed numerous nerve terminals on single muscle fibers, at times to the extent of an ending for each sarcomere (cf. 41). van Harreveld (73) has also described numerous axon terminations on single fibers. In one particularly good preparation (from the opener-muscle of crayfish) he observed 28 nerve endings on one muscle fiber, the latter being 3.5 mm long; it is not known whether this density of endings is typical. Because of the numerous terminations on

each muscle fiber and the fact that even small nerve branches may run for considerable distances on the fiber surfaces, a dense tree of intramuscular nerve elements was observed. van Harreveld (72) described this as a 'feltwork'. Holmes (30), however, contested these observations and showed that connective tissue around the muscle fibers could be made to stain to give the appearance of a 'feltwork'. While this is undoubtedly so, it is very unlikely that the structures which van Harreveld observed were not terminals since he was able to follow them back to larger axon branches, and since in the opener-muscle with its double innervation, he saw two fibers terminating together at each ending.

Another controversial point which became associated with the question of multiterminal innervation concerned the presence of conducted muscle action potentials of the type found in the vertebrates. Because the potentials which were usually recorded with external electrodes summated and were monophasic, Wiersma & van Harreveld generally propounded the view that such propagated potentials would not be found in crustacean muscle and that the spread of excitation would be effected solely by the numerous nerve endings (79, 82). In 1946, Katz & Kuffler (42) were able, however, to record in crayfish and crabs diphasic muscle action potentials which were propagated at a velocity of about 20 cm per sec. The conducted spikes were seen to arise from summating potentials resembling the vertebrate endplate potential. The summating potentials were recorded from only circumscribed regions of the muscle fibers, thus providing physiological evidence against multiterminal innervation. Twitches were seen to accompany spikes, while with the local-type potentials slower smoother contractions were observed. Thus they viewed crustacean muscle as essentially similar to that of the vertebrates, but with some quantitative differences: namely, that in the crustaceans the safety factor for transmission would be lower so that facilitation and recruitment would be more important and the efficacy of local endplate potentials in evoking contraction would be enhanced.

These two views were subsequently reconciled by Fatt & Katz who clearly showed, using intracellular recording electrodes, the presence of conducted muscle spikes (20) but, on the other hand, also gave a physiological demonstration of multiterminal innervation (22). In the latter paper they reported that, wherever a microelectrode entered a muscle fiber, an 'endplate potential' (e.p.p.[1]) could be recorded following nerve stimulation. Further, they were able to enter a given muscle fiber at a number of points along several millimeters of its length and to measure the amount of variation in the amplitudes of the e.p.p.'s. This variation was comparatively small and the duration of the rising phase of the e.p.p.'s was practically constant along the length of the fiber. These findings should be compared with the situation in, for example, frog twitch muscle fibers (19). The earlier results (42) which indicated the presence of only localized e.p.p.'s were probably due to partial denervation of the fibers in dissecting the 'strip' preparations that were used.

Despite this clarification, major problems of crustacean neuromuscular transmission remain. Little is known about the relative effectiveness of the different e.p.p.'s which can be set up in one muscle fiber, or of the spike, in evoking contraction. The mechanism whereby the nerve impulse leads to an e.p.p. is very incompletely understood. The spike, too, has some curious attributes which warrant further study. Each of these problems will be considered in turn.

ELECTROMECHANICAL COUPLING. This topic is perhaps outside of the subject of neuromuscular transmission in the usual sense of that phrase. In many of the experiments which have been performed, however, both the electrical and mechanical responses to nerve stimulation were recorded and some of the observations concerning the latter will be considered briefly. It has been found by Wiersma & van Harreveld (83) that in certain muscles (e.g. the claw-closer of *Blepharipoda occidentalis*) low-frequency stimulation (10 to 15 shocks per sec.) applied to the fast axon could elicit large muscle potentials unaccompanied by any visible contraction; while a stimulus of the same frequency delivered to the slow axon evoked much smaller muscle potentials which, nevertheless, set up a contraction. Reasons were presented for believing that this seemingly paradoxical behavior could occur within a single muscle fiber. Inasmuch, however, as the electrical recording was made with external electrodes and the contraction observed was that of the whole muscle, it is not possible to conclude definitely that this was the case. The unequivocal

demonstration of this phenomenon will probably have to be made on single muscle fibers. The possible presence of such a phenomenon is interesting because it would seem to suggest that the transmitter has some other effect aside from that which is manifested in the change in muscle membrane potential. A related observation has been made by Kuffler (43) on the muscles of the fast and slow stretch receptors of the crayfish abdomen. This preparation has the advantage that the muscle bundle is very small and can be isolated, with its nerve supply, and observed under a microscope with transmitted light, and that at the same time a fiber can be impaled with a microelectrode for intracellular recording of membrane potential. In the fast muscle bundle he observed that if a nerve impulse evoked only an e.p.p. (which was usually 10 to 25 mv in amplitude) no contraction was visible. Only if the e.p.p. gave rise to a spike was there visible contraction, and then a rapid twitch was the result. In the slow muscle bundle, however, only e.p.p.'s (5 to 15 mv) were observed and these were accompanied by contraction. The failure of the fast e.p.p.'s to bring about any visible muscle shortening is puzzling in view of the fact that they are distributed along the length of this muscle by numerous nerve endings and attain a size which may be a considerable fraction of the spike amplitude. Wiersma (80) has also recently published observations made on lobster closer-muscles which indicate that fast e.p.p.'s may fail to bring about contraction, while spikes succeed in doing so.

THE TRANSMISSION PROCESS. It seems very likely that the transfer of excitation across the crustacean neuromuscular junction is effected by a chemical transmitter, rather than by the passive flow of the nerve action current. While the total number of nerve endings may be large (73), in any given section of muscle fiber the ratio of areas of axon membrane to muscle fiber membrane is probably always quite small. Thus there is little current from the nerve terminals available for charging the capacitance of the muscle fiber, which is particularly large (approximately 40 μf per cm^2) in crustacea (20). There are some analogies with the vertebrate neuromuscular mechanism which are only suggestive; during repetitive stimulation of the nerve, random, often large, variations in the size of the e.p.p. can be seen (22). These fluctuations might be caused by intermittent failure of conduction in some of the terminal nerve branches; but it is also possible that they represent a quantal release mecha-

[1] There is some disadvantage in using the term 'e.p.p.' since it suggests the presence of a particular anatomical structure, which is probably absent in the crustaceans, and suggests a functional similarity with the vertebrate neuromuscular junction, the actual extent of which is unknown.

nism for the transmitter. Spontaneous miniature e.p.p.'s have not, however, been observed (see Chapter VII). Facilitation, which at the vertebrate endplate is also a property of the transmitter-release mechanism (16), is usually present and often striking at crustacean nerve-muscle junctions (42, 83).

The chemical identity of the crustacean neuromuscular transmitter(s) is unknown. That it is not acetylcholine or a closely related compound seems very likely from a number of experiments (3, 17, 40). Wright (88) was able to obtain blocking in the crayfish closer-muscle with curare and dihydroerythroidin, but perfusion with solutions containing approximately 10^{-3} and 5×10^{-4} gm per ml, respectively, was necessary. Other physiologically active compounds that have been found to have little or no effect on crustacean neuromuscular junctions are trimethylamine, trimethylaminoxide, tyramine (40), choline (see, however, 20 and below), mecholyl, carbachol, muscarine, strychnine, pilocarpine, digitalin, epinephrine, nicotine, caffeine and rotenone (17). Although a number of drugs, such as local anesthetics and veratrine, were found to affect the response of the nerve-muscle system, their action was probably on the nerves for the most part.

THE MUSCLE SPIKE. As mentioned above, an e.p.p. of sufficient size will, at least in some fibers, evoke an additional membrane response, the spike potential. This spike differs in several aspects from, for example, the conducted action potential of frog twitch muscle fibers. Although it may overshoot the resting potential, the inside of the muscle fiber becoming relatively positive during its peak, often this overshoot is absent. The spike is commonly not all-or-nothing, its height varying continuously with the size of the depolarization (20) or e.p.p. (26) evoking it. It may be nonpropagated and, when conduction occurs, the velocity is low (25 to 40 cm per sec.). A striking property of the spike was discovered (20) during an attempt to replace the sodium ions of the external fluid by an 'inert' cation. Substitution of choline for the sodium unexpectedly resulted in an increase in the size and duration of the spike. Fibers which had previously shown only local spikes exhibited large conducted ones in the choline medium. Even more striking increases were obtained with other quarternary ammonium compounds (e.g. tetraethyl- and tetrabutylammonium). With the latter (TBA) increases in spike duration of several hundred times were common and action potentials lasting up to 18 sec. were observed. The TBA effect was irreversible and,

surprisingly, even after a preparation which had been exposed to this drug was washed with a solution containing no sodium and no TBA (but with sucrose and excess magnesium) large long-lasting spikes were still observed. Experiments to determine if it were the ammonium compounds themselves which were carrying the current during the spike were inconclusive. It was noticed that during prolonged exposures to TBA the resting potential decreased, accompanied, however, by an increase in membrane resistance. The possibility was therefore considered that TBA reduces potassium conductance. Although such an assumption could help to explain the enormous prolongation of the spike, the identity of the ion carrying the inward current during the action potential is still unknown.[2]

PERIPHERAL INHIBITION. It is now known that the inhibition described above is mediated by separate peripheral axons which run and branch with the motor axons. A direct demonstration of this was provided by van Harreveld & Wiersma (75) who were able to isolate, as single functioning axons, the motor and inhibitory nerve fibers to several muscles in the crayfish cheliped. It was found that contraction evoked by the first type of axon could be reduced or abolished by concomitant stimulation of the second. The inhibitor was more effective in suppressing slow than fast contractions, and in some muscles the latter were unaffected by inhibitory stimulation (53). A study of the comparative effectiveness of the inhibitors to various muscles in a number of species was made (81). The results were expressed in terms of the ratio of the frequency of inhibitory-axon to that of excitatory-axon stimulation when the former was just sufficient to suppress all contraction. The most effectively inhibited motor system found was the slow contraction of the bender-muscle of *Pachygrapsis crassipes* in which this ratio was about one-third. Fast systems most usually had values of this ratio above, slow systems below, unity.

A surprising result was obtained when the electrical, as well as the mechanical, events were recorded during inhibition. It was found (44, 53) that contraction could be completely suppressed, while the muscle potentials might be reduced by a variable amount or apparently not at all. The extent to which the e.p.p.'s were affected depended upon the relative

[2] Evidence that calcium ions carry this current has recently been obtained by P. Fatt & B. Ginsborg (*J. Physiol.* 142: 516, 1958).

times of arrival of the inhibitory and motor nerve impulses. Maximum reduction (to about 20 per cent) occurred when the former slightly preceded the latter; and no effect on the e.p.p.'s was seen if the inhibitory impulse arrived much after the excitatory. Thus, it was suggested that inhibition could act in two places: on some process *a*) between nerve impulse and muscle potential, and *b*) between muscle potential and contraction.

More recently, changes in the muscle membrane during inhibition have been studied by Fatt & Katz (21) using intracellular electrodes. They confirmed previous results that the e.p.p. can be greatly reduced during inhibition and that the extent of the reduction depends upon the relative timing of the inhibitory and motor nerve impulses. In order to test for other postjunctional effects of inhibitory impulses, two microelectrodes were inserted into the same muscle fiber, one in a recording circuit for measuring membrane potential and the other connected to a current generator for the purpose of altering the level of the membrane potential. Then it was found that inhibitory nerve impulses did not result in any detectable postjunctional potential changes if the membrane potential was at a certain level, usually at or near the resting potential; but if the membrane potential were displaced, by passing current through the other intracellular electrode, inhibitory nerve impulses were followed by transient muscle potentials, similar to, but slower than, e.p.p.'s. They were referred to as I-potentials and could appear either as transient hyperpolarizations or depolarizations depending upon whether the resting membrane potential had been decreased or increased, respectively, by the current passed through the second microelectrode. That is, the I-potentials were seen as reductions of any displacement of the membrane potential from some equilibrium level, usually close to the resting potential. These are the effects which would be expected if the event underlying the I-potentials was a transient increase in some fraction of membrane conductance and, in particular, the conductance of some species of ions having an equilibrium potential equal to the membrane potential at which no I-potential appears. K^+ or Cl^- might, therefore, be the ions involved. Although the conductance change underlying the I-potential does tend to reduce any deviation of the membrane potential (including an e.p.p.) from an equilibrium potential near to the resting potential and would thus serve as an inhibitory mechanism, the effect was found to be insufficient to account quantitatively for all of the inhibition actually observed.

Another mechanism was therefore suggested in which the inhibitory and excitatory transmitter substances would specifically antagonize one another at the receptor sites on the muscle membrane. The original observation that contraction can be abolished without any reduction in the size of the e.p.p.'s still awaits confirmation using intracellular recording of potential while observing contraction of the same fiber (cf. 18).

Insects

There have been fewer physiological studies of insect than of crustacean motor systems, but there seem to be many resemblances between the neuromuscular mechanisms of these two groups, as well as some interesting differences. Among the latter, one should note the apparent lack of peripheral inhibitory axons in the insects. Also, the histological appearance of the motor nerve endings can be, at least superficially, different from that in the crustaceans; for in many insect species, rather than continuously tapering to submicroscopic dimensions, the nerve terminals present an enlarged bulbous or conical appearance. According to Marcu (52), however, these structures, referred to as Doyere's cones (cf. 25), may only represent a sudden and profuse branching of the nerve ending in which the individual twiglets are not always seen. Marcu also studied a species of orthopteran in which the manner of branching of the nerve was more similar to the situation in crustaceans. Hoyle (35), working with the locust, has observed what may have been the terminal apparatus still attached to the final nerve branch after pulling the latter free from the muscle fiber. The axons, probably beyond the place at which they had entered the sarcolemma, were continuous with a branched claw-shaped structure which spread over an area 20 to 30 μ in diameter.

The insects also show a difference from the crustaceans in the gross organization of the muscle. For example, Hoyle (35) observed that the muscle fibers of the locust were organized into muscle bundles each of which received separate nerve and tracheal branches. He referred to these bundles as 'muscle units'. In some muscles this type of arrangement did not seem to signify any fundamental difference from the crustacean situation. For example, the extensor tibia is innervated by three efferent axons and the branches from two or all three of the axons supply each muscle unit. But in the flexor tibia, each of the five or six muscle units was supplied by separate neurons. The fibers of a unit may receive, however, more than one axon. Working with the same muscle in another orthopteran (*Romalea*), Ripley (61) found at least six steps of contraction strength as he increased the intensity of the stimulus applied to the motor nerve. Of these, four represented twitches and two, slow contractions. It seems likely that at least the four twitch contractions involved different sets of muscle fibers.

The points of similarity between these two groups of arthropods include the small number of motor nerve fibers (35, 51, 58, 61, 62), multiterminal (15, 25, 36) and polyneuronal (36, 51, 58) innervation of single muscle fibers, and different contraction types (fast and slow) evoked from the same muscle by stimulation of different axons (36, 58, 61). The above references are to both histological and physiological studies, and the evidence derived from the latter will be considered in greater detail. For example, Pringle (58) was able to distinguish twitch and slow contractions in the flexor tibia of the cockroach and observed visually that the same muscle fibers could be involved in either type of contraction. There have been different explanations offered for these two contraction types. Pringle, on the one hand, has suggested that the distinction between twitch and slow contraction would lie in the number of muscle fibers activated by the two types of motor axons. Thus, he attributed the facilitation observable in the slow system to a progressive recruitment of additional muscle fibers, each fiber giving an all-or-nothing response. Wilson (86), on the other hand, has recently studied the same muscle, using intracellular electrodes, and suggested that the two contraction types occur in two different groups of muscle fibers, much as in the slow and twitch systems of the frog. His evidence, however, was indirect inasmuch as the contraction of the impaled fibers was not recorded, and the motor axons were not separately stimulated. There is yet a third possible explanation for the two contraction types in insect muscle. According to this explanation, the fast axon would give rise to a fast muscle action potential (spike) which would evoke a twitch; while the slow axon, innervating many of the same muscle fibers, would give rise to a slower, smaller, facilitating muscle potential, the mechanical response to which would be a slow smooth contraction. This is the mechanism which seems largely to explain the fast and slow systems in the crustaceans (see above). It is known that this mechanism must be present to some extent, and is probably the most important of the three, although the other two may operate as well. Both in crustaceans and in insects, however, there is the possibility of slow potentials evoking spikes and thereby twitches so that recruitment may occur in the slow as well as in the fast systems, and further there may be muscle fibers innervated solely by either fast or slow axons.

Evidence for fast and slow potentials occurring in the same fibers of insect muscle has recently been provided by Hoyle (36). He worked mostly with the extensor of the tibia of the migratory locust and showed that it received three motor axons. One of them, which ran in a separate nerve, seemed to innervate all the fibers of the muscle and evoked in them an action potential consisting of a spike arising from an e.p.p. The accompanying contraction was a rapid twitch. This nerve fiber was designated by the letter F, as an abbreviation for fast. A second axon was referred to as S_1 (signifying a slow response), even though its stimulation resulted in fast action potentials and contractions in some of the muscle fibers. That is, S_1 seemed to have two different types of endings and could produce markedly different effects in two classes of muscle fibers. In about two-thirds of the S_1-innervated fibers, stimulation of that axon evoked small, remarkably slow potentials, longer than 1 sec. in duration. They were capable of summating to plateaus of depolarization of 50 mv (during repetitive nerve stimulation) without giving rise to spikes. The other one-third of the fibers supplied by S_1 showed very much more rapid e.p.p.'s which could give rise to spikes. The size and speed of these latter e.p.p.'s were similar to, but somewhat less than those following stimulation of F. The slow responses were designated as S_{1a} and were accompanied by slow contractions, while the faster potentials, which gave rise to twitches, were referred to as S_{1b}. Of the total number of fibers in the muscle, only about 30 per cent were supplied with S_1 endings of either type (20 per cent S_{1a}; 10 per cent S_{1b}). The third axon, S_2, which was smaller than either F or S_1, produced an electrical response in only a few of the fibers but a contraction in apparently none of them. The muscle potential consisted of a brief depolarization followed by a more prolonged hyperpolarization (up to several hundred msec.). Although both phases were small (less than 1 mv) the hyperpolarizations could summate during repetitive activity and thus raise the resting potential of the muscle fiber. The S_2 response was most clearly seen in fibers with low resting potentials and could not raise the membrane potential above the level of about 70 mv. Hoyle has not been able to demonstrate that S_2 causes any inhibition of either contraction or action potentials evoked by the other two axons. In fact, stimulation of S_2 sometimes seemed to augment the contraction elicited by F, and Hoyle ascribes to S_2 the function of raising the membrane potential briefly before a maximum effort is required by the animal. The unusual features of the S_{1a} and S_2 responses would certainly warrant further study of the mechanism of their generation. Concerning the various combinations of the responses which were found in a single muscle fiber, F could apparently occur with any of the others since that axon innervated all of the fibers. Responses S_2 and S_{1a} were seen together in one fiber, but none was found which showed both S_{1b} and S_2 effects.

Aside from this demonstration of polyneuronal innervation, the use of intracellular electrodes has also provided evidence for multiterminal innervation. Working with the flexor of the tibia, del Castillo et al. (15) found that cooling the muscle reduced the size of the e.p.p. so that it did not give rise to a spike. They then found that the height of the e.p.p. did not vary by more than 10 to 15 per cent when the recording was made from different points along the muscle fiber. The spikes recorded in these experiments overshot zero potential (i.e. the inside of the fiber became relatively positive) in good preparations, but the magnitude of the overshoot was always less than 20 mv (cf. 27). Information was also obtained concerning the mechanism of neuromuscular transmission. It was found that the amplitude of the e.p.p. was proportional to the size of the resting potential as experimentally altered by passing current with a second microelectrode. This is the result which had previously been obtained from work with frog muscle (19) where it was found that the transmitter released by the nerve impulse seemed to act by causing an increase in the conductance of the endplate membrane.[3] There is no evidence that the presumed transmitter in insects is acetylcholine. Roeder & Weiant (62) were unable to affect neuromuscular transmission with curarine in a dilution of 10^{-3}.

MOLLUSCS

Much of the preceding information on the neuromuscular mechanism of arthropods was obtainable because of several fortunate characteristics of those

[3] Such evidence is not conclusive by itself, however. It has recently been shown by E. Furshpan & D. D. Potter (J. Physiol., in press) that even at an 'electrical' synapse the amplitude of the postsynaptic response can vary with the level of membrane potential.

systems. The few large motor axons, which run in comparatively long nerves, can often be dissected free and stimulated separately, and the muscle fibers are most often large and can be impaled with microelectrodes. The absence of these features from most other invertebrates makes experiments with them considerably more difficult to perform. Thus, one finds interesting phenomena which are difficult to interpret because it is not known whether they reflect properties of the nerves, muscles, neuromuscular junctions or neural synapses.

A good example of these difficulties is provided by a number of studies on the anterior byssus retractor muscle (ABRM) of Mytilus edulis. One of the more interesting properties of this and many other lamellibranch muscles is the ability to maintain considerable tension for very long periods of time. Some muscles may remain contracted for more than ten days (46) while durations of a few hours are common (4, 37). Several explanations of this ability have been put forward. On the one hand there is the idea of a molecular 'catch-mechanism' (71, 77). According to this hypothesis, one set of nerves would bring about a change in the contractile mechanism so that, following contraction, the muscle could remain shortened without expending additional energy. Another set of nerves would bring about an active reversal of this state and relax the muscle. On the other hand, an explanation has been sought in terms of already known properties of nerve-muscle systems. According to the tetanus hypothesis, the muscle would remain contracted only as long as there were periodic depolarizations of the muscle fiber membranes, relaxation ensuing at the cessation of such activity (12, 37, 46, 48). It has also been pointed out by proponents of this hypothesis that the passive tension decay in these muscles, following activation, is very slow and that this factor would contribute considerably to the economy of contraction (2). Molluscan muscle would then differ from other muscles only in the slowness of its relaxation.

Intermediate between the 'catch-mechanism' and tetanus hypothesis is one in which the 'viscosity' (and thus the rate of passive tension decay) of the muscle would be variable, depending upon the way in which the muscle had been activated. When prolonged contraction was required the muscle could be put into the 'high viscosity' state and then infrequent activation would suffice to maintain a tetanus (39, 87). This idea was suggested by Winton (87) following a study of the Mytilus ABRM. He found that the muscle responded differently to alternating and to direct current stimulation. Following the cessation of an a.c. stimulus the muscle relaxed comparatively rapidly, but after d.c. stimulation would do so very much more slowly. In this slowly relaxing state the muscle would support considerable tensions for long periods and seemed to be less susceptible to fatigue. In one example, when a d.c. stimulus was applied to the muscle for 14 sec. of every minute, a continuous gradually increasing contraction was observed during the experimental period (15 min.). When, however, a.c. was used, also for 14 sec. per min., each burst of stimulation gave rise to a discrete contraction, the strength of which decreased during successive minutes. It was also found that the maintained tension following a d.c. shock could be abolished by a.c. stimulation. That is, following this a.c.-induced contraction, the rate of relaxation was rapid even though the muscle had been in the slowly-relaxing state immediately previously. These effects have since been confirmed by a number of authors (see below). In a recent paper, however, Hoyle & Lowy (37) report that while they commonly found similar results, they often did not. In some case both types of stimuli gave rise to contractions of equal duration and sometimes a.c. evoked more prolonged shortening than did d.c. Nevertheless, since the two types of stimulation are not likely to occur naturally, interest lies mainly in their use as experimental tools, and the different responses, although not invariable, might still reflect two types of mechanisms within the muscle.

Fletcher (24) confirmed Winton's observations as part of a general study of the ABRM in which he also recorded the muscle action potentials. In most experiments he found no muscle potentials (after the initial one) during a d.c.-induced tonus. This observation laid the ground for the 'catch-mechanism' hypothesis. van Nieuwenhoven (77) also confirmed Winton's main findings but was able, as well, to duplicate some of these effects with indirect stimulation. Relatively strong faradic stimulation of the pedal ganglion, from which the muscle appeared to receive its innervation, gave rise to the familiar prolonged contraction. Subsequent ganglionic stimulation of lower intensity abolished the remaining tension. Thus he suggested that one set of nerves from the ganglion would set the 'catch-mechanism' while another would reverse this action. Twarog (71) has recently made some pharmacological observations which she interprets in terms of this same scheme. She found, for example, that relatively small concentrations of acetylcholine (ACh) sufficed to give rise to prolonged contractions of the ABRM which were accompanied by steady depolarization. Washing out the ACh restored the resting potential of the muscle without, however, reducing its tension. This maintained contraction was then found to be abolished by the addition of very small concentrations of 5-hydroxytryptamine (5-HT). Then subsequent additions of ACh gave rise only to transient shortening (which could, nevertheless, be of larger amplitude than that following the initial application of ACh). Twarog has also demonstrated the presence of ACh, a choline esterase and 5-HT in this muscle. She suggests that ACh is the chemical mediator evoking contraction (and setting the 'catch-mechanism') and that 5-HT would be the transmitter responsible for active relaxation. That these substances are released during activity has not been shown. Hoyle & Lowy (37) have confirmed this inhibiting or relaxing effect of 5-HT on this muscle but conclude that it is not the natural transmitter. In their experiments the contractions were evoked by electrical stimulation rather than by the application of ACh. Before considering further their observations on 5-HT, it will be convenient to describe another effect which they obtained. If the muscle was in a tonic state, subthreshold stimulation would often bring about relaxation. It is likely that in their experiments excitation was effected by way of the nerve and this observation is therefore very similar to that made by van Nieuwenhoven (see above) with 'weak' shocks applied to the ganglion. These authors, however, refer to the phenomenon as inhibition. Returning now to the effects of 5-HT, they found that once this drug had been added to the bath the prolonged, tonic contractions could no longer be evoked by d.c. stimulation, although the phasic contractions were still readily obtainable. The effect still persisted, however, after several hours, despite periodic washing with sea water. Inasmuch as the inhibition (or relaxation) following subthreshold nerve stimulation was rapidly reversible, they suggested that 5-HT could not be the normal mediator of this effect.

Lowy (46, 47, 48) and Hoyle & Lowy (37) have made a number of other observations, all of which they interpret in terms of the tetanus hypothesis. For example, they have almost always been able, by using large amplifications, to record small irregular electrical activity, presumably muscle potentials, throughout the duration of a prolonged contraction in disagreement with Fletcher's findings. The potentials were localized and different patterns of activity were recorded simultaneously from different regions of the muscle. These potentials were considerably smaller than those found by other authors in this muscle (23,

59, 70). The difference would seem to lie in the fact that on the one hand (Fletcher and others) the synchronized response of a large part of the muscle fibers was recorded immediately following the stimulus; while on the other hand (Hoyle & Lowy) recording, at much higher gain, was made from two asynchronously active regions of the muscle some time after cessation of the stimulus. (The potentials recorded by Fletcher were more prolonged than those seen by other workers; but this might have been due to his recording apparatus.) Nevertheless, the significant point would seem to be that there is electrical activity in the muscle during the prolonged tonic contractions; and this was found to be true whether shortening was brought about by d.c. stimulation or addition of ACh. (The origin of these potentials, which persist for so long after a stimulus, will be considered below.) Since these muscles do seem, therefore, to require periodic activation during tonic contractions, the main support for the 'catch-mechanism' hypothesis is removed. It will be recalled that Twarog (71) had found that the muscle could repolarize during the tonic contractions induced by ACh. Her recording apparatus would not, however, have detected the potentials observed by Lowy and others. It was also found by these latter authors that when the muscle relaxed, following subthreshold stimulation or the application of 5-HT, the electrical activity ceased. Further, it has been found by Abbott & Lowy (1) that the heat production of the ABRM measured during either an ACh-induced tonus or during a tetanus (stimulating at 2 per sec.) is the same, although the value obtained in both cases is very small compared, for example, to that of frog muscle. Thus, the most attractive interpretation of the ability of molluscan muscles to maintain tensions for prolonged times would seem to be the one given by Abbott & Lowy (2). It is based on the observation that once the contractile elements of these muscles shorten, they return to the rest length only very slowly, and thus infrequent activation suffices for the maintenance of tension. During a d.c.-induced tonus this repeated activation is being supplied by some means, as evidenced by the recorded electrical activity. What then is the source of these potentials, inasmuch as they are present in muscles which are isolated from the central nervous system for long times after the cessation of a stimulus and often in the apparent absence of stimulation? To study this Bowden & Lowy (9) have examined histologically the intramuscular nerve supply of a number of lamellibranch muscles, including the ABRM. Histochemical methods for the

detection of the presence of cholinesterase revealed a dense plexus of nerve fibers and structures which they interpreted to be nerve cell bodies. These findings provide a possible explanation of the 'spontaneous' potentials and disclose an additional factor which must be considered in interpreting experiments on these muscles, namely the possible presence of peripheral interneuronal synapses. For example, Schmandt & Sleator (70) found that the large synchronous muscle potentials which they observed in the ABRM were conducted decrementally (at a rate of about 20 cm per sec.). One possible interpretation of their results is that the muscle fibers show no conducted response and that the apparent conduction is carried out by synapsing intramuscular nerve elements. The decrement could then arise from the failure of transmission at some of these synapses.

The finding of electrical activity during the d.c.-induced tonus also complicates the interpretation of most of Winton's results and diminishes the necessity for an hypothesis of the type that he proposed. Nevertheless it is still possible that the muscle can relax at different rates depending upon the means by which it was activated (possibly by different motor nerves).

COELENTERATES

As experimental objects for the study of neuromuscular transmission, the coelenterates present some of the same difficulties as those found in the molluscs. The motor axons are supplied by a net of synapsing neurons. The muscle fibers are very fine, usually being several to less than one micron in diameter when extended. They are arranged in sheets or 'fields,' although there are places where the arrangement is more compact and discrete muscles can be distinguished.

Actinozoans

Pantin was the first to have stimulated these animals electrically rather than mechanically and thus had some idea of the number of impulses set up in the nerve net. Much of the work has been devoted to the properties of this net, but there are a number of phenomena which are pertinent here. Most of the earlier work was done with the sea anemone *Calliactis parasitica*, and one of the responses studied was the contraction of the sphincter muscle (at the top of the column) following stimuli applied to the side of the column (54). A single electric shock evoked no visible contraction. Two shocks, however, above a certain low threshold did elicit a response. The size of the latter was dependent upon the interval between the two stimuli, provided that this was greater than about 50 msec. (refractory period) but not larger than about 3 secs. (facilitation interval).

These phenomena were interpreted by Pantin as follows. The first of the two stimuli applied to the side of the column would result in a nerve impulse arriving at each 'endplate' (57) of the sphincter but would be unable to activate the muscle. It would, however, facilitate the neuromuscular transmission process so that a second impulse arriving soon after might affect activation. The increase of contraction size with shorter intervals would then be due to the success of the nerve impulse at a greater number of junctions. This idea implies an all-or-nothing contraction of the muscle fibers. The advantage of such an hypothesis is that the introduction of a threshold for successful neuromuscular transmission helps to explain the sharp differences between the effects of one and two stimuli.

The evidence that the facilitation is a property of the neuromuscular junction is that it did not seem to reside in either the nerve net or the muscle by itself. For example, a single impulse traversed the whole column nerve net, for a contraction could be evoked by applying a second shock with another pair of electrodes at some other point on the column, and a single shock could similarly be shown to make the entire column nerve net refractory. That the muscle did not require facilitation was shown by applying the stimuli directly to the sphincter. Then a single shock of intensity several times the two-shock threshold gave rise to a contraction localized in the region of the electrodes (56). It seems likely that stimulation of the muscle was direct, since the shortening which followed two weaker shocks, and which was mediated by the nerve net, involved the whole muscle.

The above hypothesis suggests an analogy with the partially curarized nerve-muscle preparation of the frog in which the endplate potentials (e.p.p.'s) following the first nerve impulse would all be subthreshold. 'Facilitation' would then represent the summation of successive e.p.p.'s to a supraliminal level. This model must be modified, however, to account for some later observations made by Ross & Pantin (68). They found that if the interval between two stimuli was adjusted so that the second shock just did not give rise to a contraction, then a third shock separated from the second by this same interval

also just failed to cause a contraction. On the basis of the above scheme, however, one would have expected that the second shock would have brought the local excitatory state to a level immediately below threshold. The excitation following the third stimulus would then have added to that level and threshold would have been exceeded in some fibers. To explain these observations the authors invoked an extra process of sensitization of the neuromuscular junction which would be necessary, in addition to the excitation process. Alternatively, it seems possible to account for these observations in terms of a known phenomenon. This is the facilitation, as distinct from the summation of e.p.p.'s, which occurs at frog neuromuscular junctions and which is a property of the nerve endings (16). That is, an e.p.p. is not only added to what remains from a preceding one but can be, by itself, larger. Thus in the experiment described above, with the long intervals used, summation of local responses might have no longer been present, and only the facilitation process would have been operating. It must be remembered, however, that any electrical concomitants of transmission which may be present have not yet been recorded, and such attempted explanations are only speculative.

The responses of the sphincter of *Calliactis* described above are very similar to those recorded from the longitudinal retractors of the mesenteries of *Metridium senile* (28). In both species these muscles bring about withdrawal responses and provide the quickest contractions of which the animal is capable. They may be likened to the escape reactions of some of the higher invertebrates (earthworm, squid and crayfish) which are mediated by giant nerve fibers. It is apparent, however, that all the other activities of the anemone, such as locomotion and feeding, are built up from very slow contractions (5, 28, 55). The latter include the slowest contraction known, and are so leisurely that usually no movement can be seen on casual observation, despite the fact that very considerable changes in the shape of the animal are almost continuously taking place (as shown by time-lapse photography, etc.).

Although the fundamental difference between the fast and slow contractions is not known, an operational definition of the two is supplied by the following criteria assembled from Batham & Pantin (6) and Ross (67). It seems particularly useful to distinguish two separate contraction types since both occur in the same muscles. *a*) The slow contractions are evoked by lower frequencies of stimulation. Whereas one shock every three seconds is usually about the lowest frequency for evoking fast contractions, slow ones persist with shock intervals up to about 15 sec. Apparently, frequencies above one or two stimuli per second do not succeed, and there is an optimal frequency which may be considerably lower than this. For example, in one experiment (67) a small slow contraction superimposed on the quick one followed five shocks separated by intervals of 1.2 sec. The maximal slow contraction, however, in response to this number of stimuli was not obtained until the intervals between them were increased to 13.6 sec. *b)* Whereas the fast contraction ensues within less than 0.1 sec. after the first effective stimulus (usually the second shock), the slow contraction may not begin until 30 to 150 sec. after the beginning of a train of stimuli. *c)* Five or six stimuli, rather than two, are often the fewest that will evoke a visible slow response. The size of the contraction increases with additional shocks up to a maximum. *d)* The rising phase of a summated fast contraction has the appearance of an incomplete tetanus. The rise time for each step usually occupies less than 1 sec. The slow contraction, however, is entirely smooth, and the rising phase may extend over 0.5 to 1 min. The initial rate of rise is extremely slow.

The fast and slow contractions have been shown to occur in some of the same muscles, such as the sphincters of *Calliactis* and *Metridium*, the longitudinal retractors of *Metridium*, etc. Can, then, a single muscle fiber contract in both ways? There is some indirect evidence that this can happen. When the slow contraction of muscles, capable of also giving strong fast responses, is observed under the microscope, all regions of the muscle can be seen to be shortening and no local buckling occurs (6). If the recovery of tension following a quick release is compared during the two types of response in the same muscle, it is found that the time course is rapid in both cases and similar to the original rate of tension development for the fast contraction (67). Thus, there is some reason to believe that the same contractile material gives rise to both contractions, and that the rate and extent of activation of the contractile substance is the distinguishing feature. One is then faced with the problem of how the two different types of activation are brought about. The fact that the slow shortening exhibits a longer refractory period (i.e. has a higher minimum effective stimulation frequency) than the fast contraction suggests that different excitable elements are involved. But if the same muscle fibers give both types of shortening, these elements must be the nerve fibers, and thus one might expect to find more than one nerve net innervating such muscles. While there is good histological evidence in the scyphozoans (see below) for distinct nerve nets mediating different contractions, no such observations have been made in the actinians, and there is, as yet, too little information to resolve this question.

Scyphozoans

Associated with their more free-living existence, the behavior patterns of the medusae may differ considerably from those of the anemones. Their most conspicuous activity is a comparatively rapid, more or less rhythmical, contraction of the circular musculature of the bell. These contractions provide the basic swimming movement. Bullock (13) has studied them using strip preparations (63) from three species of scyphozoans and has compared them with the contractions of anemone muscles. They differ from the quick contractions of the mesenteric retractors of *Metridium* (see above) in several respects. *a)* A single threshold shock usually evokes some contraction of the bell. *b)* The duration of the facilitation interval in the bell is longer than in the retractor. In the former muscle, a contraction following a previous one by about seven seconds is usually still augmented. *c)* The duration of a single contraction is a fraction of that in the medusa preparation. *d)* The absolute refractory period of the bell musculature is several times longer (about 700 msec. in the medusae as compared with probably less than 200 msec. in the anemones).

Because of the long refractory period and the relatively short duration of the mechanical event, there can be very little summation of tension during a series of contractions of the bell; and facilitation appears as an increase in the strength of separate successive 'twitches.' In the anemone mesenteric retractor, on the other hand, the facilitation interval is shorter than the duration of the contraction and facilitation and summation are always seen together. These differences can be related to the differences in function of the two types of muscles. The anemone retractors are involved in withdrawal responses and, with summation of successive contractions, can bring about a striking decrease in the height of the animal. These muscles can shorten to less than 20 per cent of their extended length. The musculature of the medusan bell, by contrast, provides a pumping action and resembles the vertebrate heart in having a relatively long refractory period.

The site of the facilitation is probably, by analogy with the actinians, the neuromuscular junction. It is not a property of the nerve net, for, following a single shock, the excitation spreads over the entire bell (13); Horridge (31) has shown that this excitation consists of a single all-or-nothing nerve impulse. It has not been proved, however, that the facilitation is not a property of the excitation-contraction coupling within the muscle fibers.

There have been several histological studies of the nerve net which presumably distributes the excitation of the swimming movement. Schäfer (69) described large bipolar neurons in the subumbrellar epithelium. The nerve fibers were more or less straight, were usually unbranched and were comparatively thick (15 μ). This description has recently been confirmed by Horridge (32) who found that the nerve fibers were in the range 6 to 12 μ. Both authors described tapering of the nerve fibers towards their ends, but there was no consistently observed structure which would constitute a motor nerve ending [see, however, the illustrations in Schäfer (69)]. Bozler (11) also described the large bipolar neurons, and observed smaller ones, as well as numerous multipolar neurons with branching axons. One might then wonder if the different types of neurons form physiologically distinct nerve nets which would underlie different behavioral responses (i.e. types of contraction). This question will be considered next.

Aside from the swimming movements described above, localized and more prolonged contractions of regions of the bell can also be observed (10, 13, 33). Since it has been shown that the excitation underlying the swimming movement is spread over the entire bell by a single impulse traversing a nerve net (31), the presence of local contractions does suggest the existence of another nerve net in which the spread of excitation is limited. Further, Romanes (63) showed that a wave of excitation, distinct from the wave of contraction, could cross the bell. In one demonstration of this, he removed seven of the eight marginal ganglia (in which the excitation for the rhythmical swimming movements arise) and applied to some point on the bell a stimulus too weak to evoke a contraction wave (swimming movement) directly. Then after some delay, a contraction wave would spread out from the intact ganglion. Additional examples suggesting the presence of more than one nerve net can be found in Horridge (33).

One more case, however, will be considered for here there is good correlation between histological and physiological observations. Horridge (34) has studied the ephyra larva of *Aurellia* which shows two types of contractions. There are a) the generalized, rapid, rhythmic swimming movements and b) prolonged contractions involving a variable fraction of the animal and normally associated with feeding. Following strong mechanical stimulation, the prolonged contraction may involve the whole animal. In histological preparations, two types of nerve net can be distinguished. The first is composed of bipolar neurons which are confined almost entirely to the epithelium overlying the radial and circular musculature. The fibers of these neurons are highly oriented, running in the same direction as the muscle fibers. The second net consists mainly of multipolar cells, with some bipolars, and is present throughout the entire epithelium. The fibers of this net are not particularly oriented except in the region around the mouth. Some of the neurons of this diffuse net send fibers to the surface of the epithelium and would appear to be sensory cells. This observation alone suggests that the diffuse net is associated with the local, prolonged contractions since these latter are evoked by tactile stimuli. Experiments designed to test this hypothesis yielded affirmative results and also provided evidence that the swimming movements are mediated by the other net of bipolar oriented neurons. For example, eight radial cuts were made through the disc so that the band of circular muscle, with its overlying net of bipolar cells, was sectioned into eight separate arcs. The cuts were not continued all the way to the center of the disc and the animal thus remained in one piece. It was then found that each arm, with its arc of circular muscle, still produced the rhythmical swimming movements but that the beat of each was independent of all the others. A strong tactile stimulus, however, could still produce a co-ordinated contraction of the whole animal.

The Mechanism of Transmission in Coelenterates

Practically nothing is known of the actual mechanism by which nerve-net excitation crosses the junction to the muscle fibers. Tissue extracts have been made and tested on neuromuscular transmission but without success (65, 66). Numerous drugs have been tested on the responses of the sphincter muscle of intact *Calliactis*. Acetylcholine, curare, nicotine, epinephrine, histamine and a number of other drugs are without apparent effect (64). Several drugs, however, were effective in high concentrations and after prolonged exposure. Tyramine, tryptamine and 933F, after immersion of the animal in solutions of 10^{-4} gm per ml for one- and one-half to several hours, brought about several-fold increases in the muscular response, and contractions following single shocks were then commonly seen. These drugs did not evoke any contraction in the absence of other stimuli. Depressant drugs were also found. Ergotoxin (10^{-5}) and trimethylamine oxide (10^{-3}), respectively, reduced and abolished sphincter contraction. The fact that such high concentrations and long application times were required need not argue against the significance of these results, since there are probably considerable barriers to diffusion in the intact animal, and all effects observed were fully reversible. Magne-

sium chloride also depresses neuromuscular transmission both in anemones (68) and in medusae (13) and in these cases high concentrations and prolonged exposures are also necessary.

While the above experiments may provide interesting clues, they do not allow any specific conclusions about the mechanism of transmission, and there would not seem to be any *a priori* basis on which to decide whether this process occurs in these animals by local circuit action ('electrically') or by means of some mediator ('chemically').

REFERENCES

1. ABBOTT, B. C. AND J. LOWY. *J. Phsyiol.* 130: 25P, 1955.
2. ABBOTT, B. C. AND J. LOWY. *J. mar. biol. A. U. K.* 35: 521, 1956.
3. BACQ, Z. M. *Arch. internat. physiol.* 42: 47, 1935.
4. BARNES, G. E. *J. Exper. Biol.* 32: 158, 1955.
5. BATHAM, E. J. AND C. F. A. PANTIN. *J. Exper. Biol.* 27: 290, 1950.
6. BATHAM, E. J. AND C. F. A. PANTIN. *J. Exper. Biol.* 31: 84, 1954.
7. BIEDERMANN, W. *Sitzber. Akad. Wiss. Wien. (Abt. III.)* 96: 8, 1887.
8. BIEDERMANN, W. *Electrophysiology.* London: Macmillan, 1898, vol. II.
9. BOWDEN, J. AND J. LOWY. *Nature, London* 176: 346, 1955.
10. BOZLER, E. *Ztschr. vergleich. Physiol.* 4: 797, 1926.
11. BOZLER, E. *Ztschr. Zellforsch. u. mikroskop. Anat.* 5: 244, 1927.
12. BOZLER, E. *Experientia* 4: 213, 1948.
13. BULLOCK, T. H. *J. Cell. & Comp. Physiol.* 22: 251, 1943.
14. D'ANCONA, U. *Trab. Lab. Invest. Biol. Univ. Madrid.* 23: 393, 1925.
15. DEL CASTILLO, J., G. HOYLE AND X. MACHNE. *J. Physiol.* 121: 539, 1953.
16. DEL CASTILLO, J. AND B. KATZ. *J. Physiol.* 124: 574, 1954.
17. ELLIS, C. H., C. H. THIENES AND C. A. G. WIERSMA. *Biol. Bull.* 83: 334, 1942.
18. FATT, P. *Physiol. Rev.* 34: 674, 1954.
19. FATT, P. AND B. KATZ. *J. Physiol.* 115: 320, 1951.
20. FATT, P. AND B. KATZ. *J. Physiol.* 120: 171, 1953.
21. FATT, P. AND B. KATZ. *J. Physiol.* 121: 374, 1953.
22. FATT, P. AND B. KATZ. *J. Exper. Biol.* 30: 433, 1953.
23. FLETCHER, C. M. *J. Physiol.* 90: 233, 1937.
24. FLETCHER, C. M. *J. Physiol.* 90: 415, 1937.
25. FOETTINGER, A. *Arch. Biol. Paris* 1: 279, 1880.
26. FURSHPAN, E. J. Doctor's Thesis. Pasadena, Calif.: California Inst. of Technology, 1955.
27. HAGIWARA, S. AND A. WATANABE. *Jap. J. Physiol.* 4: 65, 1954.
28. HALL, D. M. AND C. F. A. PANTIN. *J. Exper. Biol.* 14: 71, 1937.
29. HOFFMANN, P. *Ztschr. Biol.* 63: 411, 1914.
30. HOLMES, W. *Nature, London* 151: 531, 1943.
31. HORRIDGE, G. A. *J. Exper. Biol.* 31: 594, 1954.
32. HORRIDGE, G. A. *Quart. J. Microsc. Sc.* 95: 85, 1954.
33. HORRIDGE, G. A. *J. Exper. Biol.* 33: 366, 1956.
34. HORRIDGE, G. A. *Quart. J. Microsc. Sc.* 97: 59, 1956.
35. HOYLE, G. *Proc. Roy. Soc., London. ser. B* 143: 281, 1955.
36. HOYLE, G. *Proc. Roy. Soc., London. ser. B* 143: 343, 1955.
37. HOYLE, G. AND J. LOWY. *J. Exper. Biol.* 33: 295, 1956.
38. HUNT, C. C. AND S. W. KUFFLER. *J. Physiol.* 126: 293, 195?.
39. JOHNSON, W. H. *Biol. Bull.* 107: 326, 1955.
40. KATZ, B. *J. Physiol.* 87: 199, 1936.
41. KATZ, B. *Biol. Rev.* 24: 1, 1949.
42. KATZ, B. AND S. W. KUFFLER. *Proc. Roy. Soc., London. ser. B* 133: 374, 1946.
43. KUFFLER, S. W. *J. Neurophysiol.* 17: 558, 1954.
44. KUFFLER, S. W. AND B. KATZ. *J. Neurophysiol.* 9: 337, 1946.
45. KUFFLER, S. W. AND E. M. VAUGHAN WILLIAMS. *J. Physiol.* 121: 289, 1953.
46. LOWY, J. *J. Physiol.* 120: 129, 1953.
47. LOWY, J. *J. Physiol.* 124: 100, 1954.
48. LOWY, J. *Nature, London* 176: 345, 1955.
49. LUCAS, K. *J. Physiol.* 35: 326, 1907.
50. LUCAS, K. *J. Physiol.* 51: 1, 1917.
51. MANGOLD, E. *Ztschr. allg. Physiol.* 5: 135, 1905.
52. MARCU, O. *Anat. Anz.* 67: 369, 1929.
53. MARMONT, G. AND C. A. G. WIERSMA. *J. Physiol.* 93: 173, 1938.
54. PANTIN, C. F. A. *J. Exper. Biol.* 12: 119, 1935.
55. PANTIN, C. F. A. *J. Exper. Biol.* 12: 139, 1935.
56. PANTIN, C. F. A. *J. Exper. Biol.* 12: 389, 1935.
57. PANTIN, C. F. A. *Proc. Roy. Soc., London. ser. B* 140: 147, 1952.
58. PRINGLE, J. W. S. *J. Exper. Biol.* 16: 220, 1939.
59. PROSSER, C. L., H. J. CURTIS AND D. M. TRAVIS. *J. Cell. & Comp. Physiol.* 38: 299, 1951.
60. RICHET, C. *Physiologie des Muscles et des Nerfs.* Paris: Ballière, 1882.
61. RIPLEY, S. H. Doctor's Thesis. Pasadena, Calif.: California Inst. of Technology, 1953.
62. ROEDER, K. D. AND E. A. WEIANT. *J. Exper. Biol.* 27: 1, 1950.
63. ROMANES, G. J. *Philos. Trans.* 167(I): 659, 1878.
64. ROSS, D. M. *J. Exper. Biol.* 22: 21, 1945.
65. ROSS, D. M. *J. Exper. Biol.* 22: 32, 1945.
66. ROSS, D. M. *J. Exper. Biol.* 29: 235, 1952.
67. ROSS, D. M. *J. Exper. Biol.* 34: 11, 1957.
68. ROSS, D. M. AND C. F. A. PANTIN. *J. Exper. Biol.* 17: 61, 1940.
69. SCHÄFER, E. A. *Philos. Trans.* 169(II): 563, 1879.
70. SCHMANDT, W. AND W. SLEATOR, JR. *J. Cell. & Comp. Physiol.* 46: 439, 1955.

71. TWAROG, B. M. *J. Cell. & Comp. Physiol.* 44: 141, 1954.
72. VAN HARREVELD, A. *J. Exper. Biol.* 16: 398, 1939.
73. VAN HARREVELD, A. *J. Comp. Neurol.* 70: 267, 1939.
74. VAN HARREVELD, A. AND C. A. G. WIERSMA. *J. Physiol.* 88: 78, 1936.
75. VAN HARREVELD, A. AND C. A. G. WIERSMA. *J. Exper. Biol.* 14: 448, 1937.
76. VAN HARREVELD, A. AND C. A. G. WIERSMA. *J. Exper. Biol.* 16: 121, 1939.
77. VAN NIEUWENHOVEN, L. M. Doctor's Thesis. Utrecht: State Univ. Utrecht, 1947.
78. WIERSMA, C. A. G. *J. Comp. Neurol.* 74: 63, 1941.
79. WIERSMA, C. A. G. *Biol. Symp.* 3: 259, 1941.
80. WIERSMA, C. A. G. *Arch. neerl. Zool.* 11: 1, 1955.
81. WIERSMA, C. A. G. AND C. H. ELLIS. *J. Exper. Biol.* 18: 223, 1942.
82. WIERSMA, C. A. G. AND A. VAN HARREVELD. *J. Exper. Biol.* 15: 18, 1938.
83. WIERSMA, C. A. G. AND A. VAN HERREVELD. *Physiol. Zool.* 11: 75, 1938.
84. WIERSMA, C. A. G. AND A. VAN HERREVELD. *Physiol. Zool.* 12: 43, 1939.
85. WIERSMA, C. A. G. AND S. H. RIPLEY. *Physiol. comparata et Oecol.* 2: 391, 1952.
86. WILSON, V. J. *J. Exper. Biol.* 31: 280, 1954.
87. WINTON, F. R. *J. Physiol.* 88: 492, 1937.
88. WRIGHT, E. B. *J. Cell. & Comp. Physiol.* 33: 301, 1949.

CHAPTER IX

Brain potentials and rhythms—introduction

A. FESSARD | *Collège de France, Paris, France*

CHAPTER CONTENTS

FOR OBVIOUS REASONS, the study of brain potentials and of their rhythms is by far the most complicated task that has ever been proposed to electrophysiologists. It is therefore not surprising that its development has been relatively slow. In the period from 1875 to 1913, the names of Caton (16), Fleischl von Marxow (25), Danilewski (19), Beck & Cybulski (7) and Prawdicz-Neminsky (44, 45) stand out among the few pioneers who experimented on animals, preceding the epoch-making discovery of brain waves in man by Hans Berger in 1924 [first published in 1929 (8)]. As a matter of fact, not before the end of the first third of this century did cerebral electrophysiology truly enter the regular scope of neurophysiological research with the first works of Fischer (24), Kornmüller (35, 36), Bartley (6), Bishop (9), Adrian & Matthews (2), Gerard *et al.* (26, 27), Wang (50), Bremer (10), Gozzano (29), Adrian (1) and Jasper (31). During this same period, clinical electroencephalography was developing vigorously and furnishing itself results important for the comprehension of cerebral mechanisms. Perhaps in no other field of neurophysiology is there such a reciprocity of relations between the findings of investigation on experimental animals and those of clinical observations. This circumstance has contributed to the particular character of cerebral electrophysiology today;

but an introduction to this chapter may better take into account more fundamental features of this field of research by considering broadly the three questions of the general nature, the special characteristics and the functional significance of brain potentials and rhythms, each special aspect being dealt with in detail in subsequent chapters.

GENERAL NATURE OF BRAIN POTENTIALS

The question of the nature of brain potentials leads us back to the preceding chapters on neuron physiology, for there is nothing essentially new appearing in the brain of a bioelectrical nature, nothing not having a physicochemical basis common to all neurons. The fundamental phenomena of neuronal activity, i.e. brief all-or-nothing spikes, graded slow waves, potential gradients of ill-defined duration, have been well recognized as the sole components of brain potentials. On the other hand, conduction of impulses along fibers, transmission of excitation or inhibition across synapses, electrotonic spread and 'ephaptic' interactions, and finally rhythmic generation of potentials are the general kinetic operations from which all attempts to explain the integrated activities of the brain must start.

Detection of these elementary processes within the brain and description of their quantitative parameters as compared to those of neurons belonging to other structures (such as the spinal cord, ganglia in vertebrates or invertebrates, peripheral sensory neurons) are the tasks that have been and are still being carried out by electrophysiologists since the pioneer work of Renshaw *et al.* (46) who introduced the highly rewarding microelectrode technique in brain physiology.

Among those who early worked along this line, let us mention Moruzzi and several collaborators of his school (42 and many subsequent papers), Jung *et al.* (34), Amassian (5), Li & Jasper (38), Albe-Fessard & Buser (3, 4), Tasaki and colleagues (49), Rose & Mountcastle (48) and Phillips (43). These workers have started a probably long-lasting and fruitful era of intensive microexploration of cerebral structures. For the identification and analysis of single unit activities within the brain, knowledge already acquired from more accessible structures, particularly from spinal motoneurons, can be of great help (see Chapters III and X of this work).

In another direction, leading down to the molecular level, are the investigations of those interested in biophysical and biochemical mechanisms, as well as drug actions, that are related to, or interfere with, electrical activities of brain tissue. The way in which these activities depend upon metabolic factors, circulatory and respiratory conditions, ionic and hormonal content of the *milieu intérieur*, is far from being exactly known. An alteration of the resting potentials is assumed to be the basis of some ionic and drug actions.

SPECIAL CHARACTERISTICS OF BRAIN POTENTIALS

Brain potentials, apart from the common aspects they share with other biopotentials, have special characteristics which are related to the structure and specific properties of the tissue within which they are engendered. How these relations can explain the different modalities of potentials encountered is the central theme of the chapters constituting the present subsection of this volume. A broad survey of the factors involved may help to grasp the wonderful complexity and diversity of electrical manifestations offered by a mammalian brain, either in its so-called spontaneous activity or under experimental conditions including controlled stimulation. Thus we come to the classical distinction between evoked potentials (considered by Chang in Chapter XII) and autogenic rhythms (discussed by Walter in Chapter XI) to which a transitional modality must be added, that of induced rhythmical activities of temporary character or after-discharges (also appearing in the chapter by Chang).

Other general distinctions within the field of brain potentials will be considered below, together with some of the problems confronted by the modern neurophysiologist.

FUNCTIONAL SIGNIFICANCE OF BRAIN POTENTIALS

The third aspect is the functional significance of brain potentials and their rhythms. We are not directly concerned here with this functional aspect which will be examined in later chapters of this volume. However, it is difficult and to a certain extent artificial, once a potential has been described, not to speak of the link it appears to have with an actual operation of the nervous system of which it thus becomes a sign: projection of an afferent message, interactions between central activities or emission of efferent impulses. This most often involves simple questions of functional topography or chronology but may also go so far as to relate to highly integrated psychological processes (as will appear in Walter's chapter) or to the well-defined symptoms of pathological behavior such as those of epileptic seizures (described by Gastaut in Chapter XIV) once it has been recognized that reliable correlations exist between these phenomena and some parameter or parameters of brain potentials or rhythms that have initially been studied for themselves. New specific aspects of brain potentials are often discovered as a consequence of functional explorations of this kind.

Let us return to the special characteristics of potentials arising within the brain. These appear either in the form of more or less durable states—potential gradients and regular periodic changes—or in the form of responses to direct or indirect stimuli. In both cases, one must clearly distinguish the microphysiological approach applying to single units from the record of potentials arising within more or less numerous neuronal populations.

MICROPHYSIOLOGICAL STUDIES

The microphysiological approach reveals not only the most common processes of neural electrogenesis but also important differences between the electrical behavior of single units. Among the various types of neurons, some are more accessible than others to microelectrode study. The pyramidal cells of the cerebral cortex, the Purkinje cells of the cerebellum, the neurons of the main sensory relay nuclei and those in the midbrain reticular formation and the centrum medianum of the thalamus have been the most carefully studied. The general shape of the neuron, the distribution of synapses along its surface and the differential properties of its successive segments—the dendrites, cell body, axon hillock, myelinated axon, naked branches and endings—are determining factors of its electrical behavior. One of the more important contributions of contemporary research is the unveiling of the distinctive electrogenic properties of dendrites at least in certain specialized neurons by studies such as those of Buser (15), Chang (17), Clare & Bishop (18), Grundfest & Purpura (30), Lorente de Nó (41) and Roitbak (47). Dependency of recorded potentials upon morphological characteristics of the neurons was initially recognized by Lorente de Nó (40) when he made a distinction between neurons generating open fields and those generating closed or semiclosed fields.

The problems attacked by the microphysiological technique involve the most fundamental operations taking place in the brain, the neuron being considered as a relay, as a focus of integration or as a source of rhythmic activity. All three cases pose the common question of the way in which slow waves—i.e. postsynaptic potentials, after-potentials, autogenic local variations of the resting potential—and spikes or trains of spikes interact with each other.

Bombardment by afferent impulses leads to the build-up of slow variations, negative in the case of excitation and positive with inhibition. These slow waves in turn produce, accelerate, slow or suppress efferent impulses. Through these two closely allied reciprocal processes, the neuron performs its elementary functions. From this rather monotonous theme of action, almost infinite varieties of neural behavior arise, determined partly by the intrinsic properties of the neuron and partly by those of its environment, including its connections with other neurons.

This last consideration draws attention to the notion that in the central nervous system, and especially in the brain, unit activity described in isolation would be nonsense. Simultaneous recordings from single units in different parts of the brain with a multitude of microelectrodes is a technical achievement that cannot go very far relatively to the number of neurons involved in the simplest operations carried out by the cerebral structures. This brings us to examine the resources of the macrophysiological approach.

MACROPHYSIOLOGICAL STUDIES

A priori, the macrophysiological approach can give significant results only when a large mass of neurons working in approximate synchrony is activated. Fortunately this can be experimentally induced by application of brief stimuli to nerves and central tracts leading to the brain, or by local stimulation of the cerebral structure themselves. On the other hand, spontaneous synchronizations often occur, which are imperfect and of limited extent in normal conditions but exaggerated and widespread in convulsive states. In any case, synchrony is essentially a feature of the slow components of neuronal activity. Spikes usually appear in complete asynchrony and remain practically undetectable with macroelectrodes, whereas the microelectrode technique is well fitted for spike recording. Thus these two approaches are more or less complementary.

In addition to the basic factors which determine the course of elementary electrogenic processes at the neuronal level, many others come into play and combine in various ways to generate the different forms of complex brain potentials, transitory evoked potentials, periodic waves, or steady gradients. All the characteristics of a multiplicity of elements—number, density, internal organization and extrinsic relations—take part in the final result but cannot always safely be inferred from it.

Chance distribution of elementary properties, such as latencies, excitability levels, is the familiar statistical aspect first to be considered here. Then come the problems related to the physical conditions of reception: recording may be superficial or deep; electrodes are of various types, numbers and placements; distribution of potentials in a volume conductor of limited extent has its intangible laws which can be applied here only with very crude approximation.

A further step considers the role of architectonic organization, a factor of primary importance here, for physical as well as for physiological reasons. Laminar, nuclear or reticular structures cannot produce similar electric fields, and the field configuration in each particular case depends upon the way in which neurons of different kinds are distributed and oriented within the structure. For instance, surface potentials derived from the cerebral cortex can be thought of as engendered by polarized leaflets, the unit components of which are parallel dipoles formed by the long pyramidal neurons. Synchrony itself is favored by such regularity of internal organization, as a result of a certain congruence between the spatial order existing in the neural structures and that displayed by the total electric field produced by the active elements of these structures. However, this assumption of a field effect, although very likely in closely packed and orderly arranged populations of neurons, has not been universally accepted. Interactions can of course also occur through synaptic connections at short distance and these must be taken into account. Most frequently, synchrony in a population of neurons can be explained by the triggering action of a common pacemaker to which these neurons are linked; it thus depends on the gross connections within the brain or 'tractology'. But the problem remains of how the units in a pacemaker are themselves synchronized.

This leads us to a major aspect of brain potentials, their frequent appearance in regularly rhythmic sequences. The origin of these periodic activities has been the object of discussions and controversies. A pluralistic attitude seems to be the wisest, the rhythmic state being only a formal appearance that may be produced by diverse causes.

It may first be nothing else than the amplified expression of an elementary autorhythmic property of some neurons whereby they emit pulses or become the site of local oscillatory states. This is so commonly encountered in microphysiological experiments with isolated elements that one can hardly doubt that this mechanism operates at times in the central nervous system. But neurons in the brain never work in isolation and the factors, synaptic, electrotonic or ephaptic, intervening in synchronization must affect the properties of the autorhythmic generators. It may even be that rhythmicity owes its existence, in many cases, to some particular arrangement of the neuronal connections in the grey matter. Several mechanisms have been proposed which are possible but not definitively demonstrated. For instance, alternating states of excitation and inhibition, with their corresponding opposite electric signs, may appear by virtue of reciprocal connections between the generating neurons, as proposed by Jung (33); or closed chains of neurons, which have been traced through central structures by Lorente de Nó (41), may open the way to recurring pulses activating a homogeneous pool of neurons.

It seems more sound to many neurophysiologists to replace these postulated effects of a rigid circuitry by others attributable to the properties of diffuse networks. Neural nets finely woven with short, inter-

connected neurons are present almost everywhere in the grey matter. A certain average level of intrinsic activity may be maintained within these structures by an incessant and random circular reactivation of their elements. This results in an asynchronous bombardment of the neurons responsible for recordable potentials. The determining factor of periodicity is then the recovery cycle of these neurons. This mechanism, first postulated by Eccles (22, 23), has received strong support from the experiments of Burns on isolated slabs of cortex (11, 12).

Finally, steady potential gradients within large assemblies of neurons and their slow modifications under certain conditions appear to be correlated with spontaneous or evoked activities in the grey matter, according to the views of O'Leary and his collaborators (28; see Chaper XIII). The correlations may express cause-effect relationships in either direction. For instance, long-lasting after-bursts in isolated slabs of cerebral cortex have been related by Burns (13, 14) to gradients that appear as the consequence of different recovery rates of the resting membrane potentials at the two ends of particular neurons. One more factor capable of inducing rhythmic states has thus been revealed. But, since the pioneer studies of Dusser de Barenne et al. (20, 21), Libet & Gerard (39), Jasper & Erickson (32), Leão (37) and the recent investigators just mentioned, very few workers have been tempted by the delicate techniques involved in direct current recordings. These may however represent the next fruitful advance of brain electrophysiology.

Brain potentials and their rhythms are the net result of a conjunction of many heterogeneous factors —physical conditions, anatomical organization, statistical effects and the differential properties of the neuron segments—implicated in different ways. Consequently, brain potentials are able only to reveal a limited aspect of cerebral activity and must always be suspected of giving a distorted picture of the real events. This is why it is so important to arrive at a better understanding of their elaboration, for, correctly interpreted, they remain the unrivalled signs of what occurs in the intimacy of cerebral tissue and the main basis for explaining brain functions.

REFERENCES

1. ADRIAN, E. D. *J. Physiol.* 88: 127, 1936.
2. ADRIAN, E. D. AND B. H. C. MATTHEWS. *J. Physiol.* 30: 1, 1933.
3. ALBE-FESSARD, D. AND P. BUSER. *J. physiol., Paris* 45: 14, 1953.
4. ALBE-FESSARD, D. AND P. BUSER. *J. physiol., Paris* 47: 67, 1955.
5. AMASSIAN, V. E. *Electroencephalog. & Clin. Neurophysiol.* 5: 415, 1953.
6. BARTLEY, S. H. *Psychol. Monogr.* 94: 30, 1933.

7. BECK, A. AND N. CYBULSKI. *Zentralbl. Physiol.* 6: 1, 1892.

8. BERGER, H. *Arch. Psychiat.* 87: 527, 1929.

9. BISHOP, G. H. *Am. J. Physiol.* 103: 213, 1933.

10. BREMER, F. *Compt. rend. Soc. de biol.* 118: 1241, 1935.

11. BURNS, B. D. *J. Physiol.* 111: 50, 1950.

12. BURNS, B. D. *J. Physiol.* 112: 156, 1951.

13. BURNS, B. D. *J. Physiol.* 125: 427, 1954.

14. BURNS, B. D. *J. Physiol.* 127: 168, 1955.

15. BUSER, P. *J. physiol., Paris* 48: 49, 1956.

16. CATON, R. *43d Annual Meeting Brit. Med. Assoc. Edinburgh,* Aug. 3–6, 1875.

17. CHANG, H. T. *Cold Spring Harbor Symp. Quant. Biol.* 17: 189, 1952.

18. CLARE, M. H. AND G. H. BISHOP. *Electroencephalog. & Clin. Neurophysiol.* 7: 85, 1955.

19. DANILEWSKI, V. J. *Physiol. Sbornike* 2: 77, 1891.

20. DUSSER DE BARENNE, J. G., W. S. McCULLOCH AND L. F. NIMS. *J. Cell. & Comp. Physiol.* 10: 277, 1937.

21. DUSSER DE BARENNE, J. G., C. S. MARSHALL, W. S. McCULLOCH AND L. F. NIMS. *Am. J. Physiol.* 124: 631, 1938.

22. ECCLES, J. C. *Electroencephalog. & Clin. Neurophysiol.* 3: 449, 1951.

23. ECCLES, J. C. *The Neurophysiological Basis of Mind.* Oxford: Clarendon Press 1953.

24. FISCHER, M. H. *Arch. ges. Physiol.* 120: 161, 1932.

25. FLEISCHL VON MARXOW, E. *Zentralbl. Physiol.* 4: 537, 1890.

26. GERARD, R. W. AND B. LIBET, *Am. J. Psychiat.* 96: 1127, 1940.

27. GERARD, R. W., W. H. MARSHALL AND L. J. SAÜL. *Am. J. Physiol.* 109: 38, 1934.

28. GOLDRING, S. AND J. L. O'LEARY. *Electroencephalog. & Clin. Neurophysiol.* 6: 189, 1954.

29. GOZZANO, M. *Riv. neurol.* 8: 212, 1935.

30. GRUNDFEST, H. AND D. P. PURPURA. *Nature, London* 8: 416, 1956.

31. JASPER, H. H. *Psychol. Bull.* 34: 411, 1937.

32. JASPER, H. H. AND T. C. ERICKSON. *J. Neurophysiol.* 4: 333, 1941.

33. JUNG, R. *Electroencephalog. & Clin. Neurophysiol.* 4: 57, 1954.

34. JUNG, R., R. VON BAUMGARTEN AND G. BAUMGARTNER. *Arch. Psychiat.* 189: 521, 1952.

35. KORNMÜLLER, A. E. *Fortschr. Neurol., Psychiat.* 5: 419, 1933.

36. KORNMÜLLER, A. E. *Die Bioelektrischen Erscheinungen der Hirnrindenfelder.* Leipzig: Thieme, 1937.

37. LEÃO, A. P. *J. Neurophysiol.* 10: 409, 1947.

38. LI, C. L. AND H. H. JASPER. *J. Physiol.* 121: 117, 1953.

39. LIBET, B. AND R. W. GERARD. *J. Neurophysiol.* 4: 438, 1941.

40. LORENTE DE NÓ, R. *J. Neurophysiol.* 1: 207, 1938.

41. LORENTE DE NÓ, R. *J. Cell. & Comp. Physiol.* 29: 207, 1947.

42. MORUZZI, G., J. M. BROOKHART AND R. S. SNIDER. *Fed. Proc.* 8: 113, 1949.

43. PHILLIPS, C. G. *Quart. J. Exper. Physiol.* 41: 58, 1956.

44. PRAWDICZ-NEMINSKY, W. W. *Zentralbl. Physiol.* 27: 951, 1913.

45. PRAWDICZ-NEMINSKY, W. W. *Arch. ges. Physiol.* 209: 363, 1925.

46. RENSHAW, B., A. FORBES AND B. R. MORISON. *J. Neurophysiol.* 3: 74, 1940.

47. ROITBAK, A. I. *Bioelectric Phenomena of the Cerebral Cortex* (in Russian). Tiflis: Publ. House, Acad. of Sciences, Georgian S. S. R., 1955.

48. ROSE, J. E. AND V. B. MOUNTCASTLE. *Bull. Johns Hopkins Hosp.* 94: 238, 1954.

49. TASAKI, I., E. H. POLLEY AND F. ORREGO. *J. Neurophysiol.* 17: 454, 1954.

50. WANG, G. H. *Chinese J. Physiol.* 8: 121, 1934.

CHAPTER X

Identification and analysis of single unit activity in the central nervous system

KARL FRANK | *National Institute of Neurological Diseases and Blindness,*
National Institutes of Health, Bethesda, Maryland

CHAPTER CONTENTS

SOMEWHERE IN THE MIDDLE of the wide range of approaches to neurophysiology is the study of the physiological properties of the individual neurons in the central nervous system. In order to put this approach in its proper perspective, it should be emphasized that the functioning of the central nervous system as a whole is as difficult to predict from the known properties of each of its cellular components as are the properties of the units from the behavior of the whole. While it is not sufficient for understanding the nervous system, it is necessary to study the individual nerve cells, their various structures, their different patterns of activity and the mechanisms operating to yield and to limit such activity.

A great body of knowledge has been built up about the nature of neurons in the peripheral nervous system. One of the most fruitful approaches to the study of single units in the central nervous system is through the extension and elaboration of these peripheral findings. Properties of peripheral nerve fibers, of sensory and motor end organs and of ganglion cells are continually being discovered within the spinal cord and brain, and these properties must be carefully checked lest differences or totally new mechanisms be thereby overlooked.

Neurons show a variety of changes which can be observed in a study of their activity. Optical, thermal and mechanical changes have all been observed to accompany activity in nerve, but chemical and especially electrical changes have been used most extensively to acquire our present knowledge of single cell neurophysiology.

SINGLE UNIT TECHNIQUES

Techniques for single unit studies all require some means of isolating the unit to be studied. Cells which cannot be isolated anatomically due to their many connections with other cells may sometimes be isolated electrically. This may be done either by limiting nervous activity at a particular time to the unit under study or by restricting the sensitivity of the recording device to the electrical activity of that unit alone.

Single Fiber Isolation

By carefully dissecting trunks of peripheral nerve fibers or spinal roots into smaller and smaller bundles, it is often possible to reach a size of filament within which only a few or even only one nerve fiber remains functional (see Chapter III). Such a fiber can then be stimulated or its action potential recorded in isolation. This technique has been used to study the patterns of activity of individual motoneurons in response to various types of excitation and inhibition (1, 6, 21, 31, 37, 38, 44). Essentially the same technique has been used by Fessard & Matthews (24), by Kato *et al.* (40) and by others to limit afferent impulses to those carried by a single fiber. Such single unit afferent impulses have been shown to produce long-lasting potential changes on nearby afferent fibers (the dorsal root potential) and reflex excitation, provided other excitatory pathways had previously brought the reflex nearly to threshold. The same technique has enabled Adrian & Zotterman (2) and Cohen *et al.* (13) to study activity patterns of single sensory receptors. Finally, Fatt (22) has similarly isolated a single motor fiber from its peripheral nerve. A nerve impulse was conducted antidromically by this fiber, and its invasion of the motoneuron cell body and dendrites was followed by mapping the electrical potential field produced in the surrounding volume conductor of the spinal cord.

MICROELECTRODES. In the experiment just described, isolation of the unit was achieved by the peripheral nerve dissection which permitted only one fiber to be stimulated. An alternative method of isolating responses from single units is to use a microelectrode which is small enough to be selectively sensitive to the activity of a single cell. With such a method it is not necessary to interfere with the patterns of activity of other cells in the nervous system since the potentials they generate in the microelectrode are small compared with the signals being studied. This method of isolation requires that the microelectrode be of small enough dimensions to permit it to be placed closer to the unit to be studied than to other active units. A wire or needle sharpened to a diameter of about 0.01 mm ($10\ \mu$) and insulated except at its tip satisfies this requirement for many nerve cells in the spinal cord and brain (7). Much larger electrodes (50 to 100 μ) appear to damage individual units (50) while still far

enough away from them so that their potential fields are masked by the background activity of other cells. Smaller metal recording electrodes require special techniques. A number of these have been developed and are described below.

METAL ELECTRODES. Svaetichin (52) describes a technique for filling fine glass pipettes with silver solder (fig. 1*A*), thus providing a very small metallic recording surface down to less than 1 μ, well insulated by a smooth tapering glass shaft. The tips of these electrodes are plated with rhodium and then coated with platinum black to prevent oxidation and to increase the surface area.

Howland *et al.* (35) has also used a glass insulated metal wire prepared by drawing a glass pipette down onto a 12 μ nichrome wire which had previously been passed through the tube. While single unit activity has been recorded with these electrodes in the cat's spinal cord, they are not very satisfactory for this purpose and have been used mostly to record the composite responses of fiber tracts and cell groups.

Dowben & Rose (16) have devised a more satisfactory metal microelectrode which they have used with considerable success in studying unitary activity of the thalamus. These workers have made use of the low melting point of the metal indium which permits them to fill predrawn glass pipettes of 3 to 5 μ tip diameter with the metal (fig. 1*B*). The metal surface at the tip is coated with gold and then platinum black which probably reduces the electrical resistance of the metal-to-electrolyte surface due to the porous nature of the platinum black and reduces the rate at which the surface becomes polarized during the passage of electrical currents.

Perhaps the ultimate in fine tipped metal microelectrodes is produced by the electroetching and polishing technique (32). Hubel (36), applying this technique to a tungsten wire which he then insulates with a clear lacquer down to the tip, has produced an electrode of 0.4 μ tip diameter with which he has recorded the intracellular potentials of motor horn cells in the spinal cord of the cat (fig. 1*C*).

A metal-electrolyte interface or junction behaves somewhat like a condenser due to polarization effects. In general the greater the current density at the junction the more rapidly it becomes polarized. Thus, as the tip of a metal electrode becomes smaller the difficulty with polarization increases. Successful attempts have been made to reduce polarization by coating the microelectrode tip with platinum black (16, 52) and by using amplifiers which draw very small currents (Bak, A. F., manuscript in preparation; and 36). Electrode polarization causes a variation in sensitivity of the electrode-recording device combination with the frequency of the recorded potential. Lower frequencies are more attenuated than higher frequencies, and slow changes in potential tend to be lost. In addition there is sometimes a fluctuation in contact potential between metals and electrolytes. Because of these shortcomings, metal microelectrodes have been used more for recording extracellular transient potential changes and patterns of unitary

activity than for studying the exact form of the potential waves or lasting potential changes.

MICROPIPETTES. The problems inherent in recording from a metal surface of very small area are in part avoided by using a glass pipette filled with an electrolyte. With such an electrode the electrolyte-metal boundary is moved back from the tip to the shank where a long wire provides a large surface area (fig. 2A). This electrode, while not suffering from a limited

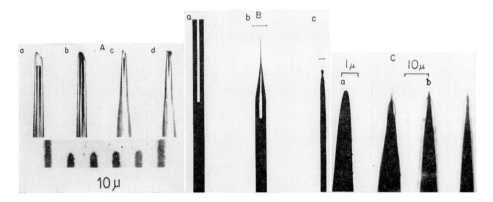

FIG. 1.*A*. Silver-filled glass micropipettes *a* and *c* show glass-insulated microelectrodes with tip containing no metal. *b* and *d* are the same electrodes after electrolytic filling with rhodium. Scale: 10 *μ* [From Svaetichin (52).] *B*. Stages in preparation of an indium-filled micropipette: *a*, capillary tubing half filled with low melting point metal; *b*, the capillary after tip is drawn but before metal is pushed to fill it completely; *c*, electrode tip showing platinum black deposit. Calibrations: 1 mm for *a* and *b*; 10 *μ* for *c*. [From Dowben & Rose (16).] *C* Lacquered tungsten microelectrodes sharpened by electropolishing: *a*, electronmicrograph of uncoated wire; *b*, optical photograph of three coated electrodes immersed in water to show normal variation in coating. [From Hubel (36).]

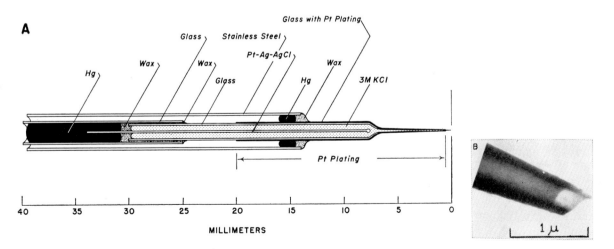

FIG. 2.*A*. (*left*) KCl filled microelectrode used for intracellular recording showing one method of mounting. Platinum lead from amplifier contacts inner mercury droplet as outer shield is clamped. If shield is driven electrically by negative capacity amplifier, platinum coating is usually omitted. [From Frank & Fuortes (26).] *B*. (*right*) Electronmicrograph of the tip of a similar pipette. [From Nastuk & Hodgkin (47).]

metal-electrolyte surface area, has plenty of problems of its own. But in addition to the important role it has played in peripheral nerve (see Chapter III), muscle and ganglion studies, the micropipette has provided most of our present detailed knowledge of the physiology of single nerve cells in the central nervous system. This is partly because these electrodes have been made small enough to penetrate single nerve cells without destroying them, thus permitting measurement of the potential across the cell membrane (figs. 2B and 6B). For this reason and because the use of this type of electrode appears to hold much promise for future investigations, more space will be devoted to its description.

Ling & Gerard (42) are commonly given credit for introducing micropipettes, probably because they were the first to record action potentials from inside single muscle fibers with these electrodes. However, Graham & Gerard (30) had previously recorded the resting membrane potential of frog muscle fibers with similar fine electrodes filled with saline, and many workers before them have used coarse pipettes for recording electrical potentials as in the use of small calomel half-cells and agar bridges [references to this work are listed by Svaetichin (52)].

CONSTRUCTION. Ling & Gerard (42) made micropipettes by hand, drawing 1 to 2 mm glass tubing down to a fine tip in an oxygen-gas microflame. Alexander & Nastuk (4), Livingston & Duggar (43) and others have devised machines for pulling pipettes similar to that shown in figure 3. This machine heats the glass tube over a short length until it is soft enough to be drawn out by the pull of the electromagnet. Increasing the heater temperature or the length of the heater coil produces a longer, gentler tapered section on the pipette. Figures 2A and B show the size and one way of mounting glass micropipettes. Another method of mounting supports the tip of a glass micropipette on a 1 mil tungsten wire (59). This method has been used to permit recording of intracellular potentials from muscle where movement would dislodge a rigidly mounted pipette.

FILLING. The size of the tips of such micropipettes ranges upward from a few tenths of a micron (fig. 2B). The problem of filling them with an electrolyte becomes more difficult as the size of the tip is reduced. Above about 5 μ the pipettes can be filled with a syringe by expelling the air from the tip. Boiling for several hours submerged in the electrolyte is satisfactory for all but the smallest tips although it appears

FIG. 3. Vertical micropipette puller. Upper clamp fixed; lower clamp pulled down by solenoid, gently at first when glass begins to soften, hard just before pipettes separate. Tips are drawn down out of heater coil which is turned off any time after pull is completed. (Developed at National Institutes of Health, Instrument Section.)

to enlarge them somewhat. N. Tasaki (55) has devised the most satisfactory method of filling. The pipettes are immersed in methyl alcohol in a chamber which is gradually evacuated until the alcohol boils vigorously for a few minutes. The low viscosity and low boiling point of the alcohol permit the finest tips to be filled quickly and without damage. The alcohol can then be replaced by the desired electrolyte by diffusion in about two days. Preboiling and filtering the electrolyte reduces the formation of air bubbles and clogging by foreign particles. The micropipettes are best stored in alcohol or water and are transferred to the desired electrolyte a few days before they are needed.

A micropipette can be filled with a variety of different electrolytes. Considerations to be taken into account are electrical conductivity, similarity of cation and anion mobilities, the possibility of damage to cells through the diffusion of the electrolyte out of the pipette and the purpose for which the pipette is used.

The conductivities of several electrolytes which have been used are given in table 1. The rate of diffusion from the tips varies widely, of course, but the magnitude of this effect can be seen from an example given by Nastuk & Hodgkin (47). They report a diffusion of KCl from a 0.5 μ micropipette filled with 3 M KCl of 6×10^{-14} M per sec. If a micropipette maintaining this flow is introduced into an infinite liquid space, the concentration of KCl at equilibrium can be determined from the relation

$$C_x = \frac{F}{4\pi x D} + C_\infty$$

where C_∞ is the uniform concentration of KCl in the space before introducing the pipette, x is the distance from the pipette tip, F is the rate of flow of KCl from the tip and D is the diffusion coefficient. Applying reasonable values for the electrode described above indicates that the order of magnitude of the increase in concentration of KCl at a distance of 10 μ from the tip is 3×10^{-4} M per l. This may be compared to the figure 1.5×10^{-4} M per l. taken by Coombs et al. (15) as the concentration of K^+ in the intercellular spaces of the cat's spinal cord.

When a micropipette carries an electric current, there is a selective migration of ions through the tip superimposed on the movement by diffusion just discussed. If the ionic concentration in the pipette is much greater than that outside the tip then, regardless of its direction, the current will be carried largely by movement of ions from inside to outside the tip, by anions if the electrode is negative and by cations if it is positive. When the mobilities of the ion species are different, the electrical conductivity of the pipette will change with the direction of current carried, and the electrode will show rectification. These properties of micropipettes have been used to advantage both for excitation of membranes and for determining the effects of specific ions on the behavior of single cells (15).

ELECTRICAL PROPERTIES OF MICROPIPETTES. *Resistance.* The electrical resistance of a micropipette may be thought of as the sum of the resistance of a truncated cone of the inside electrolyte and the resistance of the volume conductor around the tip. If the tip diameter is less than 1 μ, more than 90 per cent of the resistance lies in the last 10 μ of the tip. In actual practice these electrodes generally range from a few to several hundred MΩ.

The resistance of a pipette is also dependent on the direction, amplitude and sometimes on the duration of the current it is carrying. For very small currents of brief duration, the electrode usually behaves either like a pure resistance or a simple rectifier. The rectifier action of pipettes has not been studied systematically for a large number of electrolytes. When even small currents are maintained for a long time, the resistance may increase. This has been interpreted by Taylor in the Appendix to Jenerick & Gerard (39) as a movement of low-conductivity external electrolyte into the tip due to bound surface charges on the glass, and is a reversible phenomenon. Larger currents delivered in pulses at constant voltage may cause sudden erratic changes in resistance, and the amplitude of current pulses at which these changes begin generally differs with polarity. Sustained application of several volts across a micropipette will often increase its resistance irreversibly to more than $10^9\Omega$. Some form of clogging in the extreme tip is suggested, and it is usually possible to break the fine tip by gently bumping the pipette under a microscope, thus reducing its resistance to a usable value. A pipette of the dimensions described above might have a resistance of 20 MΩ for a current of up to about 10^{-7} amp. in either direction and pass this current without markedly departing from a pure resistance. Tasaki (personal communication) has been able to select equally fine, hand-drawn micropipettes carrying up to 10^{-6} amp. provided the external volume conductor was sufficiently acid.

When used with a good preamplifier (see page 267), the ability of a micropipette to carry current is relatively unimportant if it is to be used only for measur-

TABLE 1. *Conductivity of Solutions Used in Microelectrodes**

Solution	23.5°C	38°C
KCl (3 M)	0.26	0.27
NaCl (1%)	0.018	0.02
NaCl (2 M)	0.14	0.17
K$_2$SO$_4$ (0.6 M)	0.08	0.10
AgNO$_3$ (sat.)	0.20	0.23
CuCl$_2$ (sat.)	0.08	0.10
FeCl$_3$ (20%)	0.075	0.12
Trypan Red (sat.)	0.03	0.03

* In reciprocal ohms (mhos) per cm.

Composition of solutions: KCl 3 M solution: 224 gm KCl dissolved and diluted to 1 liter. NaCl 1%: 0.5 gm NaCl dissolved and diluted to 50 cc. NaCl 2 M: 5.85 gm NaCl dissolved and diluted to 50 cc. K$_2$SO$_4$ 0.6 M: 5.2 gm K$_2$SO$_4$ dissolved and diluted to 50 cc. AgNO$_3$ saturated: 122 gm AgNo$_3$ dissolved in 100 cc water. CuCl$_2$ saturated: 110 gm CuCl$_2$ dissolved in 100 cc water. FeCl$_3$ 20%: 20 gm FeCl$_3$ dissolved and diluted to 100 cc. Trypan Red saturated: about 1 gm/100 cc; excess filtered off.

ing potentials. But when stimulating or polarizing currents are to be delivered to the penetrated cell (see page 274) or when ions are to be delivered through the tip by iontophoresis then pipettes must be selected for their current-carrying ability.

Capacitance. The ability of a micropipette to follow rapid changes in the electrical potential at its tip varies inversely with the electrical capacitance across its walls (see below). The capacitance across the glass wall of a micropipette between inside and outside electrolytes depends upon the thickness of the wall and on the length of that portion of the pipette which is immersed in the external volume conductor. Since in a drawn glass pipette the ratio of wall thickness to diameter remains approximately constant the capacity is proportional to the immersed length. Freygang (28) calculates the capacity across a pipette drawn from Pyrex tubing No. 7740 having a ratio OD/ID of 2 as 0.4 $\mu\mu$f per mm. This is close to the measured value for an actual pipette of 0.37 $\mu\mu$f per mm of immersion. The total capacity is linear with immersion depth except for a minor change occurring as the shoulder of the pipette enters the external conductor. Nastuk's figure of 1 $\mu\mu$f per mm would indicate a smaller ratio of OD/ID (47).

Tip potential. Nastuk & Hodgkin (47), who used micropipettes filled with 3 M KCl, assumed provisionally that measurements of potential made with such pipettes are not altered by a junction potential at the electrode tip. However, Nastuk (46), del Castillo & Katz (17) and Adrian (3) showed that with many such fine tipped pipettes there is a potential difference across the tip which may be as large as 70 mv, inside negative, and that this tip potential may change suddenly with movement of the pipette in muscle or nervous tissue. Thus measurements of steady potential differences, e.g. the membrane potential of a cell, will be in error if the tip potential of the micropipette differs at two points. Such a difference can arise in two ways. The tip potential of the pipette may be changed by clogging or unclogging the tip as it moves through the nervous tissue. In this case alternate measurements at two points would not generally be expected to repeat the error. A more consistent error will be encountered if the two points whose potential difference is to be measured are in regions of different ionic composition, and if the tip potential of the micropipette is different in the two regions. Adrian (3), attempting to clarify this point, measured the tip potential of a series of pipettes in both 100 mmole KCl and 100 mmole NaCl. He found that the difference in tip potential in the two solutions

was proportional to the tip potential in 100 mmole KCl. Adrian considers the mechanism of the tip potential to be a selective reduction in mobility of some of the ions, particularly that of the anion and probably due to some form of blocking. He argues that if a pipette has a small tip potential it is less likely to show a change or introduce an error due to tip potential. On this basis he measures the resting potential of muscle membrane by selecting only those pipettes whose tip potentials are less than 5 mv, inside negative. While it is true that such a pipette would be expected to introduce only a small error of 1 or 2 mv in the measurement of potential difference between two test solutions (100 mmole KCl and 100 mmole NaCl), there seems to be less certainty that a pipette having an initially small tip potential will not increase its tip potential during its movement through tissue. In the particular case of the resting potential across a cell membrane, errors introduced by variation of tip potential cannot be eliminated by repeated comparisons since the cell membrane is generally damaged by repeated penetration. For this reason, micropipette measurements of steady potential difference between different points in the nervous system are subject to considerable uncertainty at the present time.

Frequency response. Metal microelectrodes are generally poor for measurement of d.c. or of very slowly varying potentials as described above, but at higher frequencies their impedance drops to relatively low values. The resistance of a glass micropipette on the other hand is quite independent of frequency at low frequencies. This does not mean that an ordinary amplifier connected to a micropipette necessarily records biological potentials with a good frequency response. Indeed, this is one of the failings of these electrodes.

A micropipette must generally pass through a region of grounded volume conductor before reaching the highly localized region whose potential is to be recorded. The capacity across the glass wall between the inside electrolyte and this external volume conductor (see above) tends to reduce the high-frequency response of the electrode. Since most of the resistance of the pipette is located very near its tip, it can be well represented in such an application by the equivalent circuit of figure 4. If the input impedance of the amplifier is high enough to be neglected in comparison to R_E and C_E, a sudden change in voltage E will be recorded as an exponential rise having a time constant $\tau = R_E C_E$; that is, the recorded voltage V will rise to about 63 per cent of E in the time τ. For any form of voltage signal E fed in, the

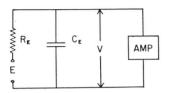

FIG. 4. Approximate equivalent circuit for an intracellular micropipette. E, cell potential to be recorded; R_E, resistance of microelectrode tip plus preparation; C_E, capacity between electrolyte inside micropipette and grounded volume conductor in which it is immersed; V, potential recorded by amplifier.

recorded voltage will be

$$V = E - \tau \frac{dV}{dt}.$$

The error in recorded voltage is thus proportional to the electrode resistance, to its capacity to ground and to the first derivative of the recorded voltage. When the input voltage is a sine wave, the frequency at which the recorded voltage is reduced to 0.7 E is given by

$$f = \frac{1}{2\pi R_E C_E}$$

Amplifiers. Amplifiers used for recording from micropipettes must have special features to minimize the effects of the inherent shortcomings of the electrodes described above. Ideally, the amplifier must have an input resistance which is high in comparison with the electrode resistance, a low enough input grid current so that its effects at the tip of the electrode can be neglected and a negligible effective capacity between input and ground. These requirements of the amplifier do not include voltage gain which can be accomplished in a following amplifier. Thus the preamplifier, as it is usually called, is actually an impedance transformer intended to isolate the source of potential being measured from the loading effects of the conventional voltage amplifier.

A number of practical preamplifiers have been designed to meet these special requirements with varying degrees of success. The simplest is the cathode follower circuit of which a good example is that described by Nastuk & Hodgkin (47). This circuit gave an overall recording time constant of 70 μ sec. when tested with a 22 MΩ pipette, showing an effective input capacitance of 3.2 $\mu\mu$f. An improved circuit called a negative capacity amplifier has been used in various forms by several authors: Solms *et al.* (51); Woodbury (58); Wagner & MacNichol (57); Moore,

J. W., & K. S. Cole, manuscript in preparation; Lettvin, J. Y., & B. Howland, manuscript in preparation; Bak, A. F., manuscript in preparation. This type of preamplifier, by utilizing positive feedback to the input grid, in effect adds a controlled negative capacitance in parallel with the positive input capacitance. By minimizing the sum of these capacities, a considerable improvement can be made in the recording time constant. Used with micropipettes like those described above, these circuits can reach an effective input capacitance of 0.5 $\mu\mu$f or less.

IDENTIFICATION OF SINGLE UNITS

Position

One of the more difficult problems in the use of micropipettes is the determination of their positions. Identification of the structure or structures generating the various potentials recorded by the micropipette requires some knowledge of the relative positions of the pipette and the structures which might be responsible for the potentials. Knowledge of which neuron the pipette is in or near is of less interest than the kind of neuron and the position of the pipette relative to the various parts of such a neuron. Information of this kind has been obtained by direct microscopic observation, by marking techniques and by inferences drawn mostly from the nature of the potentials recorded.

Direct observation of the microelectrode position is limited to those structures which can be dissected free of opaque or translucent surrounding tissues. This technique has been used in recording from muscle fibers [see bibliography in Jenerick & Gerard (39)]; peripheral nerve fibers (Chapter III, 54); invertebrate heart ganglion cells (12); eel electroplaques (5); dorsal root ganglion cells (53); photoreceptor cells (33); and stretch receptor cells (41). Even in structures where this technique is possible, there are severe limitations. The tips of micropipettes are often submicroscopic or close to the limit of resolution with visible light, thus requiring ideal conditions of lighting, numerical aperture, color contrast and contrast of indices of refraction. Pressure from the pipette often distorts the tissue, and even under the best conditions it may be difficult for example to determine optically whether the pipette is inside or outside of a particular cell wall. However, a large part of the present body of knowledge of the electrophysiology of single cells has been acquired by studies using this technique.

A new technique has been proposed for extending direct vision to structures within the central nervous system. This is accomplished by the use of a long thin solid cone of glass mounted in front of the microscope objective which extends to the focal plane. Incident illumination is supplied through the objective, and the cone is moved through the tissue until the desired object appears in the small field of view bounded by the flat end of the cone. Using this technique, motoneurons have been seen in unfixed tissue, and their nuclei and dendrites are clearly visible. It is hoped that this technique can be used for determining microelectrode position.

Marking techniques have been used extensively for locating gross microelectrodes. One method produces a lesion by passing radio-frequency current through an insulated metal electrode bared at its tip. The lesion is subsequently made visible by staining the fixed and sectioned material. Another method using steel electrodes plates off iron by passing a current through the electrode. The region where the iron has been deposited is then stained blue by ferrocyanide and prepared by frozen section technique, Marshall's modification of Hess' method (45). The resolution of about half a millimeter made possible by these two techniques is not yet great enough to permit identification of single cells or parts of cells. Success in marking a single cortical pyramidal cell has been claimed recently by Rayport (48) who passed a current through a micropipette filled with a 3 N FeNH$_4$SO$_4$ solution. Iron ions moved by electrophoresis into the penetrated cell were later stained blue by the ferrocyanide reaction of Hess (34). This is the only case known to the author of a single nerve cell penetrated blindly and subsequently identified visually.

The identification of nervous structures by inferences made from the potentials recorded from microelectrodes is uncertain and subject to revision whenever further information modifies the assumptions on which such inferences are based. However, pending the development of a more direct method, the study of single unit activity in the central nervous system is limited to such inferences as can be made based on comparisons of potentials recorded from microelectrodes in the central nervous system with those recorded from cells under direct vision or otherwise identified.

Axons

The potentials to be expected from axons in the central nervous system can be predicted from meas-

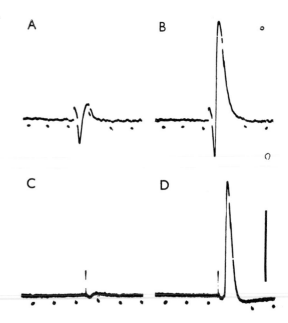

FIG. 5. Effect of volume conductor on potentials recorded by intracellular electrodes. The microelectrode is inserted in a fiber of a ventral root. In *A* and *B* the root is surrounded by paraffin oil; in *C* and *D* the oil is replaced by Ringer's fluid. *A* and *C*, stimulus just subthreshold for penetrated fiber; *B* and *D*, maximal stimulus. Calibration: 50 mv. Time: 1 msec. [From Frank & Fuortes (26).]

urements made on peripheral nerve (see Chapter III). If a nerve surrounded by an insulating medium is made to conduct a synchronous volley of impulses, a fairly large action potential can be recorded monopolarly from a gross electrode in contact with the nerve. As seen in figure 5*A*, a microelectrode similarly situated records the same large external action potential with respect to a distant electrode on inactive tissue. If the microelectrode then passes through the membrane of a fiber participating in the volley, the action potential it records will be the algebraic sum of the outside potential previously recorded and the action potential produced across the fiber membrane (fig. 5*B*). The effect of a volume conductor, such as the spinal cord or brain surrounding the active fibers, can be simulated by replacing the insulating medium with a conductor such as saline. Figure 5*C* shows that the external recording is then markedly reduced and the action potential developed across the penetrated fiber membrane is recorded by an internal microelectrode with little distortion (fig. 5*D*). When the impulses in the fibers are not synchronous, the already small external potential field becomes negligible; but, whatever the external field may be, it will be approximately recorded by an electrode inside or outside a resting fiber. Thus it can be anticipated that extrinsic potentials inside a volume conductor such as the spinal cord or brain are small and do not appreciably distort the potentials recorded by microelectrodes inserted in active neural elements except in the presence of large synchronous volleys in a limited volume conductor.

Figure 6A is a section of the lumbar region of a cat's spinal cord showing cell bodies of neurons as black dots. A line drawn across such a section indicates the structures which may be encountered by a microelectrode as it is advanced through the tissue. A very few motoneuron somata but many small cells and innumerable fibers will be in the path of the electrode. Apparently penetration of fibers occurs only when very fine micropipettes are used. With coarser electrodes the majority of the elements which can be impaled behave as if they were cell somata. Figure 6B shows the relative sizes of a cat's motoneuron and a typical glass micropipette.

The potentials recorded from a microelectrode as it is moved through a cat's spinal cord are indicated

in figure 7. The upper extreme of this potential is repeatedly recorded and is taken to indicate the potential in the extracellular spaces since it is close to the potential recorded from the fluid conductor on the cord surface. The negative deflections are presumed to indicate penetration or destruction of cellular membranes, on analogy with peripheral findings. While some of the negative potentials recorded must be from neural elements since they are correlated with spikes like action potentials, others may be from nonneural elements such as glia cells.

If the electrode is allowed to remain in a position where it records a steady negative potential, spikes or action potentials can generally be seen occurring either spontaneously or in response to stimulation (figs. 7A and B). The amplitude of these action po-

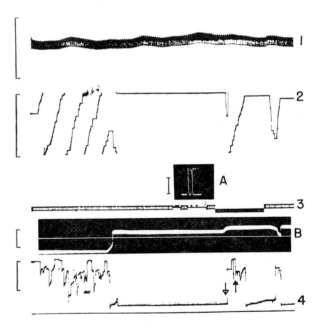

FIG. 7. Simultaneous records taken during penetration of a cat's spinal cord with a KCl filled micropipette. 1: Carotid blood pressure. 2: Movement of the electrode. The limit of deflection of the instrument was reached by a movement of 200 μ. After this the pen jumped back and began recording further movement in the same way. Upward deflection indicates increased penetration. 3: Signals from shutters of the cameras used for making records of inserts A and B. 4: Record of electrode potential relative to reference electrode on vertebral column. Note potential fluctuations when electrode is moved and steady negativity when it is, presumably, inside the membrane of a unit. Insert A shows responses of the penetrated unit to stimulation of a ventral root, as photographed by a single frame camera. Insert B shows a strip of record taken by a moving film camera at the time indicated by the two arrows in 4. Calibrations: 1, 50 to 150 mm Hg; 2, 200 μ; inserts A and B and 4, 50 mv. Time: 60 sec. for 1, 2, 3 and 4; 1 msec. for A. [From Frank & Fuortes (26).]

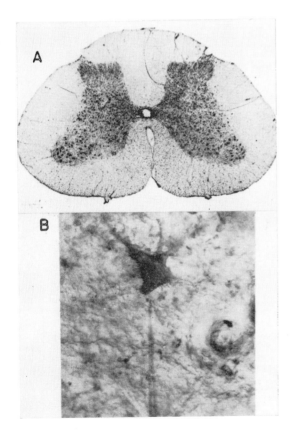

FIG. 6. A. Section of cat's spinal cord at L6. Thionin stain to show cell bodies. B. Methylene-blue stain of unfixed slice of spinal cord showing KCl filled micropipette penetrating a motoneuron near the surface of the slice. [From Frank & Fuortes (26).]

tentials is related to the more or less steady resting potential as shown in figure 8. The majority of units penetrated show spikes larger than the corresponding resting potentials. Occasionally, small or large spikes are recorded with negligible resting potential, and many of these have a diphasic positive-negative shape as shown in 9A. Spikes accompanying large steady resting potentials may be either brief like those recorded from dorsal or ventral root fibers, as in figure 9B, or of longer duration, as in figure 9C.

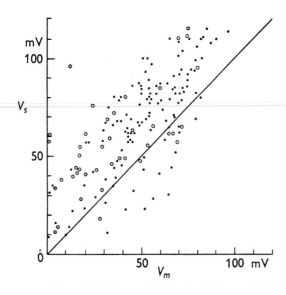

FIG. 8. Plot of spike amplitude against steady voltage as measured from presumed extracellular potential level. One hundred and sixty-seven units from penetrations of cats' spinal cords. Open circles from units identified as primary afferent fibers; filled circles from other units. [From Frank & Fuortes (26).]

Damage to Penetrated Units

A unit may be considered to have been seriously damaged when the potentials recorded from it decrease rapidly and are small and drawn out; and when the pattern of activity recorded differs from that obtained before penetration. Minor damage cannot be recognized, and the degree of abnormality due to insertion of the microelectrode can only be postulated in a number of cases.

The assumption that small spikes are recorded from damaged structures seems to be contradicted by the observation that elements producing small spikes may respond with normal patterns to orthodromic stimulation. However, this is probably due to the fact that damage can occur at the place of recording (axon) without involving the structures responsible for the generation of the response (soma and dendrites).

Primary Sensory Fibers

When the microelectrode penetrates a primary afferent fiber after it has entered the central nervous system, the unit can still be provisionally identified as sensory by several features. a) The action potential should have about the same shape, size and duration as those recorded with microelectrodes in peripheral nerves or dorsal roots. Of course, fine afferent branches may not meet this requirement and other axons may not be excluded. b) If conduction latency is less than about 0.5 msec., it may be presumed that no synapse is traversed. This criterion cannot be used if long conduction paths are involved. Also this presumption excludes the possibility of very fast synapses, such as

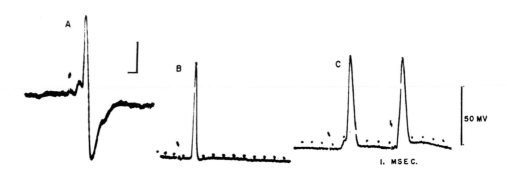

FIG. 9.A. Diphasic potential recorded from a cat's motoneuron just prior to penetration as indicated by subsequent sudden development of negative resting potential. Artifact indicates shock to dorsal root. Calibration: 20 mv. Time: 1 msec. B. Brief spike presumably from inside an axon in the cat's spinal cord. Calibration: 20 mv. Time 1 msec. C. Action potential from a cat's motoneuron following first dorsal and then ventral root stimuli. Calibration: 50 mv. Time: 1 msec.

might be required for the inhibitory interneurons proposed by Eccles *et al.* (20). *c*) The unit in question should follow trains of stimuli up to a rate of at least 500 impulses per sec. This figure may eliminate some small afferent fibers and may let in some synapses of very high safety factor but probably separates the vast majority of postsynaptic from presynaptic elements. *d*) If the unit responds to stimulation of a dorsal root or peripheral nerve which is cut distal to the point of stimulation, then there should be only one response for each stimulus. This last criterion eliminates afferent fibers carrying dorsal root reflex responses (10, 25, 56), but these have never been observed at shorter latencies than 2.5 msec. and cannot follow at high frequencies (26). *e*) Primary afferent fibers not separated from their sensory receptor cells can often be made to fire repetitively by natural stimuli such as touch, pinch or stretch. These trains of impulses are characterized by their extremely regular rhythms under sustained excitation and can readily be distinguished from most postsynaptic elements in this regarded. Again this type of criterion tends to prevent the discovery of regularly firing postsynaptic elements should these exist. While none of the above criteria is definitive alone, together they form a rather satisfactory method for identifying primary afferents penetrated by microelectrodes in the central nervous system. Using these criteria, primary afferents have been identified as deep as 4.5 mm below the dorsal surface of the cat's spinal cord (26).

Motoneurons

Responses from motoneurons may be identified by their correlation with antidromic stimulation with the adoption of only very reasonable assumptions. Microelectrodes in ventral root fibers of the spinal cord give responses to ventral root shocks which are similar to those recorded from dorsal root fibers. When the electrode is in the spinal cord, similar short-latency spikes are recorded following ventral root stimulation (fig. 10B). These are presumably the axons of motoneurons.

However, another type of short-latency response may be recorded following ventral root stimuli as shown in figure 10A. Brock *et al.* (11), Frank & Fuortes (26) and Woodbury & Patton (60) showed that these responses are of longer duration than axon spikes (figs. 10A and B), are followed by a long-lasting hyperpolarization (fig. 15) and when elicited within a critical interval following a previous spike, break at the inflection point on the rising phase as shown in

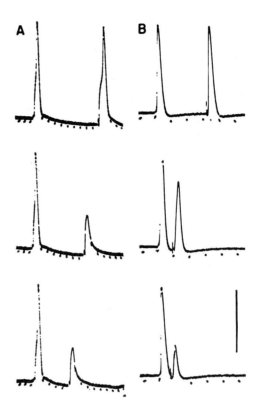

FIG. 10. Antidromic conduction block in cat's motoneurons. Electrodes inserted in the cord may pick up two types of short latency responses to pairs of ventral root shocks. In unit of column *A* the response to the second of a pair of shocks suddenly drops to 30 to 40 per cent when the shock interval is reduced below a critical stimulus interval (about 10 msec. here, but often much shorter or longer). Conduction block must occur near microelectrode since blocked impulse is visible there. Unit of column *B* shows instead a smooth decrease in height o second response as stimulus interval is decreased. Calibration: 50 mv. Time in both columns: 1 msec. (Note different sweep speeds in *A* and *B*.) Only units like that in *B* are found in ventral roots. [From Frank & Fuortes (26).]

figure 10A. The short latency of these responses identifies them as from motoneurons, and the inflection in the rising phase has been interpreted as due to a loss in safety factor for conduction for axon hillock to soma (11, 26). If one accepts that the block in conduction at the critical stimulus interval occurs at the axon hillock then, since only elements with long-duration spikes show evidence of conduction block, it may be concluded that long spikes originate upstream from the axon hillock, i.e. in the cell bodies or dendrites, and short spikes originate in axons.

The role of motoneuron dendrites in the generation of potentials following antidromic stimulation has not yet been settled. Fatt (22) has recorded poten-

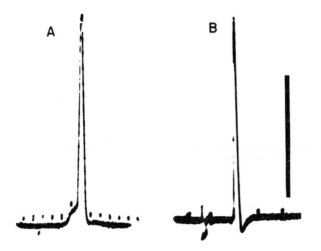

FIG. 11. Responses obtained in cat's spinal cord and identified as from interneurons by criteria discussed in text. *A.* Spike duration about 1 msec. after prespike potential, presumably a soma response. *B.* Spike duration about 0.3 msec. with no prespike potential, presumably from an axon. Brief postspike hyperpolarization is a frequent but not a constant finding and may indicate damage done to a fiber by the microelectrode. Calibration: 50 mv. Time: 1 msec. [From Frank & Fuortes (26).]

tials which he interprets as indicating antidromic conduction along the dendrites for a distance in excess of 1 mm. But the diphasic responses of figure 9*A* can be interpreted as due to the sum of conductive and reactive currents outside some inactive membrane, according to Freygang (28). If this interpretation is correct, then at least some of the dendrites of motoneurons probably do not participate in the actively conducted action potential.

Interneurons

It is convenient, for the gross identifications possible in the spinal cord with these techniques, to define an interneuron as a postsynaptic unit which does not send its axon to ventral roots. The criteria for deciding if a unit is postsynaptic are the latency of its response and whether it responds with more than one impulse to a single afferent volley. There is no doubt that if we accept spontaneously firing units which cannot be driven by the electrical stimuli available we may include some primary afferents from distant receptors as interneurons, but most of these can be eliminated by the regularity of their firing.[1] Figure 11 shows two

[1] For a discussion of possible confusion between interneurons and primary afferents conducting dorsal root reflexes see Frank & Fuortes (26).

typical units satisfying the above criteria. Many workers have studied patterns of activity of single cells with extracellular electrodes and some have reported patterns of intracellular potentials. For references to these, see especially Chapters II and IV of this volume and their bibliographies.

One class of interneurons deserves mention in a discussion of neuron identification. Occasionally units are penetrated which respond to a single ventral root volley with a very high frequency train of spikes instead of the single action potential shown by motoneurons. Eccles *et al.* (19) have named these Renshaw cells in honor of Birdsey Renshaw (49) who predicted the existance of such cells making synapses with the axon collaterals of motoneurons. The function of these cells has not been established, but Eccles *et al.* (19) be-

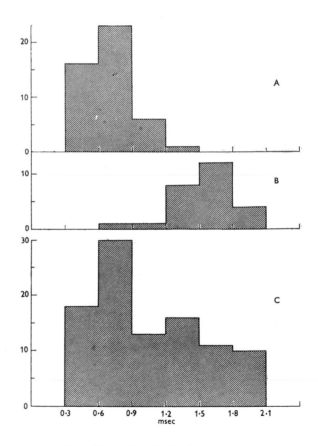

FIG. 12. Charts illustrating distribution of duration of spikes recorded from different structures in the cat's spinal cord. *Abscissa:* spike duration in msec.; *ordinates:* number of spikes within 0.3 msec. groups. *A.* Spikes recorded from dorsal and ventral root fibers. *B.* Spikes recorded from motoneuron somata or dendrites identified by criteria given in text. *C.* Spikes recorded from postsynaptic elements of the cord other than those of *A* and *B.* [From Frank & Fuortes (26).]

lieve that they supply inhibition to the motoneurons, the activity of which excites them.

That both fibers and somata of interneurons are penetrated is indicated by figure 12 which shows that, after known primary afferents (*A*) and motoneuron somata (*B*) are eliminated, the remaining spikes from interneurons are distributed in duration of action potentials as though they were made up of many fibers and fewer somata.

Slow Potentials

As has been shown above it has not been possible yet to distinguish clearly between cell somata and dendrites with intracellular electrodes. But grouping these two structures together a fairly clear-cut distinction is possible between soma-dendrites and fibers on the basis of the slow potentials recorded from within them. As seen in figure 13, a unit classified as a motoneuron soma shows a long lasting graded response to subthreshold excitatory afferent stimulation which is commonly called a synaptic potential. If this potential reaches a critical level of depolarization, as shown in figure 14, a spike is initiated and this spike is followed

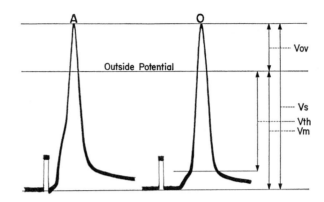

FIG. 14. Diagram illustrating terminology used to describe antidromic (*a*) and orthodromic (*o*) spikes from cat's motoneurons and the level of polarization, Vth, which must be achieved if a propagated spike is initiated. All potentials are measured from the outside potential taken as 0. Vm, resting membrane potential, inside negative; Vs, total spike height; Vov, spike overshoot, amount inside goes positive at peak of spike. [From Frank & Fuortes (27).]

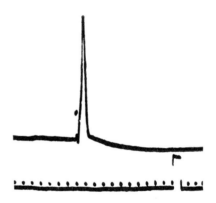

FIG. 15. Spike and slow potential recorded from cat's motoneuron following antidromic stimulation. Calibration: 20 mv. Time: 1 msec.

by an even longer lasting period of hyperpolarization, such as those in figures 15 and 13*C*. These slow potentials are apparently attenuated in the axon so that, at the gains employed with intracellular recording, no slow potentials are recorded from fibers unless they are penetrated close to the soma (18, 26). This finding, which is based upon identifications made using the criteria just discussed, itself becomes a method of identifying long duration spikes as from somata or dendrites and short spikes as from fibers.

Steps in Development of Cell Spikes

Once the identification of the various units penetrated in the central nervous system has been accepted,

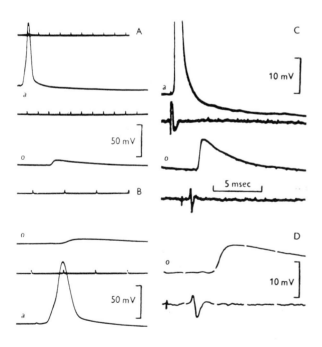

FIG. 13. Spikes and slow potentials recorded from a cat's motoneuron following antidromic (*a*) and orthodromic (*o*) stimulation. All records made from same motoneuron at different sweep speeds and amplifications. Note respective time and potential scales, msec. marks shown in *A*, *B* and *D*. Note dorsal root spike records in *C* and *D* which are recorded with negativity downward. [From Brock *et al.* (11).]

a further study can be made of the details of their behavior. The most definitive of these studies has been made on the large motoneurons of the cat by Eccles (18), Fuortes *et al.* (29) and Fatt (23), and in the toad by Araki *et al.* (9), and Araki & Otani (8). While these studies are too detailed to report in full, it would seem pertinent to this discussion of the identification of single unit activity to describe briefly the model which has been developed to account for the activity of certain nerve cells (fig. 16). All nerve cells certainly do not behave according to this model, but some features of the electrical activity of cells are so general that they justify some generalizations from a model built for a particular cell.

A neuron in the central nervous system might be

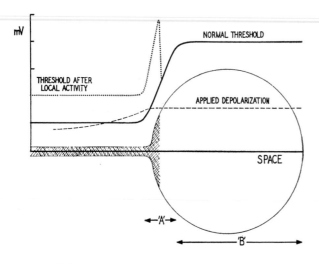

FIG. 16. Diagram to illustrate initiation of impulses in a motoneuron. A spherical soma is indicated and its axis passing through the center of the axon is used as *abscissa* for the plot. *Ordinate:* membrane depolarization measured from resting membrane potential. The dashed line indicates relative potential changes evoked in various positions of neuron by synaptic activity in soma and dendrites (not differentiated) or by currents applied through a microelectrode in the sphere. The solid line represents the depolarization level required to evoke firing of different parts of the membrane. 'B' designates that part of the neuron having a high threshold, and 'A' the transitional region between this area and the low threshold axon. In normal conditions threshold stimuli, either synaptic or applied through microelectrode, will initiate an impulse in a region where the dashed line first crosses above the solid line. (If depolarization is sudden, attenuation along the axon will be steeper than that for steady depolarization due to capacity of the membrane.) The dotted line is intended to indicate the depolarization required to elicit firing shortly after activity which has involved only the cross-hatched areas of the neuron, e.g. after a blocked antidromic impulse. [From Fuortes *et al.* (29).]

considered to consist of its soma and dendrites which are connected to its axon by a thin unmyelinated segment arising from the axon hillock. Presynaptic fibers make synaptic connections with this cell through terminal knobs which end on its soma and dendrites. Some of these specialized endings are excitatory and others inhibit activity of the cell. Probably through a mechanism of secretion of excitor or inhibitor transmitter substances by the presynaptic terminals, the membrane of the postsynaptic cell is made selectively permeable to certain inorganic ions (16). Normally these transient changes in ion permeability alter the equilibrium potential of the membrane and either depolarize it (excitation) or hyperpolarize it (inhibition). The sum of these synaptic potentials in the soma and dendrites spreads electrotonically with decrement to a sensitive target area, probably the thin initial segment of the axon and part of the axon hillock. The threshold of this region, that is the magnitude of the depolarization necessary to start an action potential in it, is lower here than in the soma and dendrites (normally perhaps one third). Thus, in spite of the fact that the synaptic potential is larger in the soma and dendrites than in the thin segment, the lower threshold of this region permits it to be the site of origin of the propagated action potential. The action potential is then propagated out the axon and may or may not spread backwards over the soma and dendrites. Following activity the soma-dendritic region remains refractory longer than the target area so that a second spike elicited during this period may be conducted in the axon without spreading to the soma or dendrites as seen in figure 10*A* and in the paper by Fuortes *et al.* (29). It is probable that the safety factor for propagation from target area to soma-dendritic region varies, not only with the condition of the cell, but also from one type of cell to another so that normal behavior in cells may differ in this respect. But cells in so many different parts of the nervous system show similar electrical properties that the main features of the model just described may well be of general application.

Stimulation Through Microelectrodes

Electric currents delivered through intracellular microelectrodes produce excitation similar to that caused by conducted impulses. Such direct stimulation plays a role in the identification of penetrated units, and is so generally useful in studying the properties of cells that some reference should be made to the

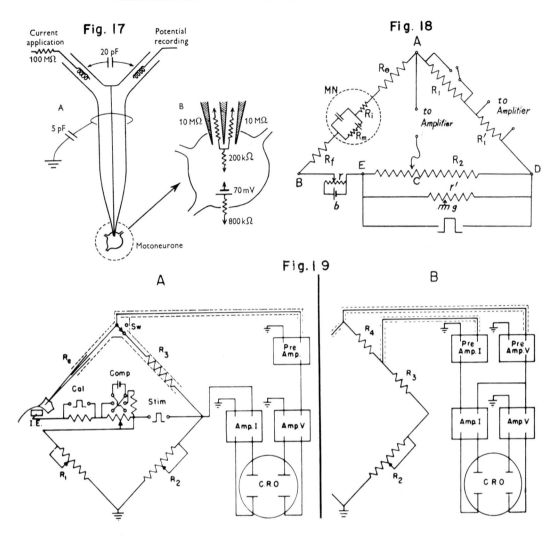

FIG. 17.*A.* A double-barrelled microelectrode and its immediate connections. Typical values are given of the several electrical characteristics which are significant in the use of the electrode. *B.* Enlarged view showing approximate equivalent circuit with motoneuron ignoring reactance. [From Coombs *et al.* (14).]

FIG. 18. Diagram of arrangement for recording the response of a motoneuron to rectangular current pulse delivered through an intracellular electrode. MN, motoneuron; R_e, microelectrode resistance; R_f, resistance of spinal cord and bath; b, unit dry cell; r, 500Ω (b and r compensate for membrane and electrode potentials); R_2, 2 kΩ; r', 200Ω; R_1, 98.3 MΩ; R_1', 0.92 MΩ. Rectangular pulses applied between E and D. Spike potentials recorded from A and C. Current through electrode was monitored by recording potential across R_1'. [From Araki & Otani (8).]

FIG. 19. Two arrangements used for stimulating and recording through a single micropipette electrode. R_1: 1 kΩ; R_2: 10 kΩ; R_3: 44MΩ. Electrode resistance R_e usually between 10 and 100 MΩ. The resistor of the calibrator (Cal) and the variable resistor of the compensator (Comp), 100Ω each. The fixed resistor of the compensator 300Ω and the battery supplies 1.5 v. Stimulating and calibrating pulses are applied through radio-frequency stimulus isolation units. The indifferent electrode, I.E., is a silver-silverchloride wire and is usually placed in the cat's mouth. Sw is a switch used for d.c. compensation and for measurement of R_e. In *A* stimulating current is measured by the voltage drop across R_2, which is equal to the drop across R_3 when the bridge is balanced. *B* shows an alternative method for measuring current. R_2 and R_3 are same as in *A*. R_4 has a value of 5 MΩ, and two preamplifiers of balanced gain are used for differential recording of the voltage drop across R_4. CRO is a double-beam oscilloscope indicating electrode current and voltage. [From Frank & Fuortes (27).]

two main techniques which have been used. Coombs *et al.* (14) used a double-barrelled micropipette (fig. 17) passing stimulating or polarizing currents through one barrel while recording the intracellular potential with the other barrel. Araki & Otani (8) (fig. 18) and Frank & Fuortes (27) (fig. 19) used a bridge circuit to permit simultaneous stimulation and recording through the same microelectrode tip. These articles should be consulted for details and limitations of the two techniques.

By means of these techniques it has been possible to study the excitabilities of penetrated units. Differentiation of axons from somata is often possible on the basis of their excitabilities. For example large axons in the cat's spinal cord have a rheobasic current of about 1.7×10^{-9} amp., while units identified as motoneuron somata or dendrites require an average of

about 7×10^{-9} amp. through the micropipette to reach threshold.

Cells firing with regular trains of impulses appear to generate their own impulses at some particular site of origin. When depolarizing currents are applied through the micropipette placed near such a locus the rate of firing is increased in proportion to the applied current. Since the applied current decrements rapidly along an axon and presumably also along a dendrite, current through the pipette will not affect the firing rate when the micropipette is at a distance from this site of origin. It is therefore possible to tell whether the locus of recurrent firing in a cell is near to or far from the tip of the micropipette. If it is accepted that such a locus is normally situated near the axon hillock, then the response of a repetitively firing unit to applied polarizing currents can be used to infer whether it is an axon or a soma.

REFERENCES

1. Adrian, E. D. and D. W. Bronk. *J. Physiol.* 67: 119, 1929.
2. Adrian, E. D. and Y. Zotterman. *J. Physiol.* 61: 151, 1926.
3. Adrian, R. H. *J. Physiol.* 133: 631, 1956.
4. Alexander, J. T. and W. L. Nastuk. *Rev. Scient. Instruments* 24: 528, 1953.
5. Altamirano, M., C. W. Coates and H. Grundfest. *J. Gen. Physiol.* 38: 319, 1955.
6. Alvord, E. C., Jr. and M. G. F. Fuortes. *J. Physiol.* 122: 302, 1953.
7. Amassian, V. E. *Electroencephalog. & Clin. Neurophysiol.* 5: 415, 1953.
8. Araki, T. and T. Otani. *J. Neurophysiol.* 18: 472, 1955.
9. Araki, T., T. Otani and T. Furukawa. *Jap. J. Physiol.* 3: 254, 1953.
10. Barron, D. H. and B. H. C. Matthews. *J. Physiol.* 94: 26, 1938.
11. Brock, L. G., J. S. Coombs and J. C. Eccles. *J. Physiol.* 117: 431, 1952.
12. Bullock, T. H. and C. Terzuolo. *J. Physiol.* 138: 341, 1957.
13. Cohen, J. J., S. Hagiwara and Y. Zotterman. *Acta physiol. scandinav.* 33: 316, 1955.
14. Coombs, J. S., J. C. Eccles and P. Fatt. *J. Physiol.* 130: 291, 1955.
15. Coombs, J. S., J. C. Eccles and P. Fatt. *J. Physiol.* 130: 326, 1955.
16. Dowben, M. and J. E. Rose. *Science* 118: 22, 1953.
17. del Castillo, J. and B. Katz. *J. Physiol.* 128: 396, 1955.
18. Eccles, J. C. *J. Physiol.* 139: 198, 1957.
19. Eccles, J. C., P. Fatt and K. Koketsu. *J. Physiol.* 126: 524, 1954.
20. Eccles, J. C., P. Fatt and S. Landgren. *J. Neurophysiol.* 19: 75, 1957.
21. Eccles, J. C. and H. E. Hoff. *Proc. Roy. Soc., London. ser. B* 110: 483, 1932.
22. Fatt, P. *J. Neurophysiol.* 20: 27, 1957.
23. Fatt, P. *J. Neurophysiol.* 20: 61, 1957.
24. Fessard, A. and B. H. C. Matthews. *J. Physiol.* 95: 39, 1939.
25. Frank, K. *XIX Internat. Physiol. Congr.*: 362, 1953.
26. Frank, K. and M. G. F. Fuortes. *J. Physiol.* 130: 625, 1955.
27. Frank, K. and M. G. F. Fuortes, *J. Physiol.* 134: 451, 1956.
28. Freygang, W. H., Jr. *J. Gen. Physiol.* 41: 543, 1958.
29. Fuortes, M. G. F., K. Frank and M. C. Becker. *J. Gen. Physiol.* 40: 735, 1957.
30. Graham, J. and R. W. Gerard. *J. Cell. & Comp. Physiol.* 28: 99, 1946.
31. Granit, R. and G. Strom. *J. Neurophysiol.* 14: 113, 1951.
32. Grundfest, H., R. W. Sengtaken, W. H. Oettinger and R. W. Gurry. *Rev. Scient. Instruments* 21: 360, 1950.
33. Hartline, H. K., H. G. Wagner and E. F. MacNichol, Jr. *Cold Spring Harbor Symp. Quant. Biol.* 17: 125, 1952.
34. Hess, W. R. *Beitrage zur Physiologie des Hirnstammes.* Liepzig: Thieme, 1932.
35. Howland, B., J. Y. Lettvin, W. S. McCulloch, W. Pitts and P. D. Wall. *J. Physiol.* 122: 24P, 1953.
36. Hubel, D. H. *Science* 125: 549, 1957.
37. Hunt, C. C. *J. Physiol.* 117: 359, 1952.
38. Hunt, C. C. *J. Gen. Physiol.* 38: 813, 1955.
39. Jenerick, H. P. and R. W. Gerard. *J. Cell. & Comp. Physiol.* 42: 79, 1953.
40. Kato, G., Z. Kaku and I. Tasaki. *XV Internat. Physiol. Congr.*: 95, 1935.
41. Kuffler, S. W. *J. Neurophysiol.* 17: 558, 1954.
42. Ling, G. and R. W. Gerard. *J. Cell. & Comp. Physiol.* 34: 383, 1949.
43. Livingston, L. G. and B. M. Duggar. *Biol. Bull.* 67: 504, 1934.
44. Lloyd, D. P. C. and A. K. McIntyre. *J. Gen. Physiol.* 38: 771, 1955.
45. Marshall, W. H. *Stain Technol.* 15: 133, 1940.
46. Nastuk, W. L. *J. Cell. & Comp. Physiol.* 42: 249, 1953.
47. Nastuk, W. L. and A. L. Hodgkin. *J. Cell. & Comp. Physiol.* 35: 39, 1950.
48. Rayport, M. *Fed. Proc.* 16: 104, 1957.

49. RENSHAW, B. *J. Neurophysiol.* 9: 191, 1946.
50. ROSE, J. E. AND V. B. MOUNTCASTLE. *Bull. Johns Hopkins Hosp.* 94: 238, 1954.
51. SOLMS, S. J., W. L. NASTUK AND J. T. ALEXANDER. *Rev. Scient. Instruments* 24: 960, 1953.
52. SVAETICHIN, G. *Acta physiol. scandinav.* suppl. 86, 24: 5, 1951.
53. SVAETICHIN, G. *Acta physiol. scandinav.* suppl. 86, 24: 278, 1951.
54. TASAKI, I. *Jap. J. Physiol.* 3: 73, 1952.
55. TASAKI, I., E. H. POLLEY AHD F. ORREGO. *J. Neurophysiol.* 17: 454, 1954.
56. TOENNIES, J. F. *J. Neurophysiol.* 1: 378, 1938.
57. WAGNER, H. G. AND E. F. MacNICHOL, JR. *Navy Med. Res. Inst. Project Report* 12: 97, 1954.
58. WOODBURY, J. W. *Fed. Proc.* 12: 159, 1953.
59. WOODBURY, J. W. AND A. J. BRADY. *Science* 123: 100, 1956.
60. WOODBURY, J. W. AND H. D. PATTON. *Cold Spring Harbor Symp. Quant. Biol.* 17: 185, 1952.

CHAPTER XI

Intrinsic rhythms of the brain

W. GREY WALTER | *Burden Neurological Institute, Bristol, England*

CHAPTER CONTENTS

GENERATION OF SPONTANEOUS OSCILLATION

Prevalence of Spontaneous Rhythms

DURING THE 30 YEARS that have elapsed since Berger first began to record electrical activity from human brains, many suggestions have been made to account for the unexpected spontaneity and regularity of these rhythmic potential changes which resemble so little the familiar action potentials of the peripheral nerve. Rhythmic electrochemical activity is not in itself a rare phenomenon; it is common in primitive organisms and can appear even in simple inorganic chemical reactions such as that between iron and nitric acid or between mercury and hydrogen peroxide (39). Such reactions, of course, involve more than a simple combination of forces or reagents; for the generation of rhythmic activity there must always be present in the system some sort of circular or feed-back pathway through which the effect of products of the reaction can influence the state of the original reagents.

Origin of Spontaneous Activity

In such a system where action and reaction are intercoupled, activity once initiated will tend to persist, but the first cause may be obscure. 'Spontaneous' activity is in fact a difficult conception to define or illustrate in practice and the situation is not simplified by substituting the terms 'endogenous', 'autogenous' or 'autochthonous', for in all these words there is implicit the assumption that the behavior of the system depends not on its previous state but in some way on itself, as if there were an element of choice or free will. This implication is verbal rather than philosophical and need not be taken very seriously; the difficulty is mainly that man-made machines are designed for obedience rather than for originality and it is difficult to define the use of function of a mechanism that seems to act independently of outside influences. Clearly, if the electrical rhythms of the brain were entirely spontaneous and independent they would be very hard to fit into any hypothesis of neurophysiology, but, as is well known, these rhythmic discharges are generally greatly affected by external signals and need be considered as spontaneous only in the sense that the energy required for their maintenance is freely available in the brain and that their existence implies some sort of regenerative, retroactive or feed-back loop. Even if, as several observers have suggested (13, 21), the source of the rhythmicity may be in the nerve cells themselves rather than in the manner of their interconnection, there must still exist, even within this intimate microcosm, a re-entrant loop of energy transfer around which two sets of variables can mutually control one another. The physiological nature of the retroactive pathway is hard to identify and around this point controversy has raged for many years, involving many experiments and strong feelings. Viewed without rancor, the dispute seems academic; most of the claims and assertions on both sides can be justified, few of the denials can be confirmed. There seems little doubt that in certain circumstances single nerve cells can discharge spontaneously at a steady rate (3, 51). On the other hand, large populations of healthy isolated brain cells may remain quite inactive for long periods (17) yet respond rhythmically when stimulated.

Conditions for Oscillation

SIMPLE HARMONIC MOTION. It can be shown that, whenever and wherever an oscillation appears, there must be a retroactive mechanism of some kind. The most familiar—though not perhaps most strictly relevant—form of oscillation is the simple harmonic motion of a pendulum. Even in the case of the simple pendulum, sustained vibration depends on the regular transmutations of position and velocity as shown in the basic equations.

$$\frac{dS}{dt} = V,$$

$$\frac{dV}{dt} = \frac{-g}{L} \sin S$$

where S is angular position; V, velocity; g, constant of gravitation; and L, length of pendulum

From these it is seen that changes in S depend on the value of V while changes in V depend on the value of S. This is the basic condition for feedback, and wherever two variables are thus interdependent oscillatory behavior is likely to occur. From the dynamic standpoint a swinging pendulum is not a single object but a system of two variables. Whether the system will be 'spontaneously' active or stable is another question and depends upon the sign of the constants that determine the feed-back ratio. In the case of the pendulum, the sign is negative, so the system is stable near its resting state. An 'ideal' frictionless pendulum however would be unstable because the random Brownian movement of its molecules would inevitably set up an oscillation at its natural frequency which, in the absence of damping, would continue indefinitely. This effect can be observed in the case of the very small light suspensions of sensitive galvanometers.

A large pendulum, however, is stable in the sense that the frictional losses limit the extent and duration of any oscillation. In the 'ideal' case the feed-back factor is unity; in any practical case it is less than unity, so to sustain an oscillation energy must be supplied from outside the system. Furthermore, the more massive the system, the more precisely must the energy be distributed in time so as to reinforce the movement of the pendulum; it must be phase-locked to the oscillatory element.

This example of simple harmonic motion illustrates two ways in which rhythmic activity may be generated: first by interaction between a 'noisy' or random energy source and a small-scale or loss-free retroactive system, second by interaction between a phase-controlled energy source and a normally damped retroactive system. Obviously intermediate conditions between these extremes exist and many of them can give the impression of 'spontaneity' because the relation between the time-distribution of energy and the degree of damping of the oscillatory system may not be obvious without careful experiment. In such a system, activity once initiated will tend to persist, but the first cause may be obscure.

RELAXATION OSCILLATORS. Lest it should be thought that some sort of simple harmonic motion is the only possible source of rhythmic activity, another mechanical illustration should be considered. This is in the class of 'relaxation oscillation'; a simple example is the autosiphon in which one end of an inverted U tube is connected to the outlet of a water tank with the top of the ∩ below the top of the tank and the open end of the ∩ near the bottom of the tank. If the tank be now filled from a steady source, the level will rise in a linear fashion until the water level reaches the top of the ∩. At this point a siphon will be formed and the water tank will empty through the siphon, if the rate of flow through the ∩ is greater than that from the source. When the water level falls below the open end of the pipe, the siphon will be broken and the whole process will be repeated. The rate of change of water level with respect to time over the cycle will approximate to two intersecting straight lines, the slope of which will depend upon the rate of filling and the rate of emptying respectively. An interesting case is when the rate at which the siphon empties is exactly equal to the rate of filling; in these circumstances the water level will rise linearly to a maximum and remain there indefinitely. The system is stable, but the flow of water is continuous. Obviously, in such conditions, a slight change in flow rate at input or output will engender relaxation oscillations of level. Instability in this system will result from a rise or fall in input or output, and only very careful examination of the rate chart would disclose which, in any particular occasion, was the most likely cause.

Another interesting feature of this system is that a transient change in, say, the rate of water input can act as a 'stimulus' to initiate a complete cycle of operation provided the rate of change exceeds a certain threshold. The value, form and scale of the response to such a 'stimulus' will be independent of the nature of the stimulus and will be all-or-none. It will also have an absolute and a relative refractory period. In fact, a system of this type is closely analogous to the schema generally proposed for nervous action. The steady filling and emptying of the tank corresponds with the metabolism of an excitable structure, and the excitability-stability relation is similarly dependent on the maintenance of a dynamic equilibrium. Furthermore, there is illustrated a relation between excitability and homeostasis. If the constancy of water level in the tank—or potential difference in a nerve cell—is regarded as an important condition, then the system is evidently an admirable device for autoregulation within certain limits of external variation. The standard unit 'response' of discharge—and replenishment—is a signal that the limits of self control have been exceeded. Continued rhythmic activity is a signal of sustained excess or deficiency.

DISTINCTION BETWEEN SIMPLE HARMONIC AND RELAXATION OSCILLATORS. The behavior of this elementary hydraulic model may be contrasted with the simple harmonic motion of a pendulum; the wave form in the first case is a series of asymmetric transients while in the second it is of course strictly sinusoidal. The autosiphon shows no tendency to oscillate after a disturbance is over whereas the pendulum exhibits a damped train of vibrations. Similarly, the autosiphon,

when stable, can be triggered to give a full cycle of activity by a minimal but supraliminal stimulus, whereas the pendulum requires either full scale transient deflection or repeated stimulation at its natural frequency to evoke a maximal discharge. The resonance of the pendulum is typical of such systems; the strict relation between sharpness of resonance and length of build-up and die-away time is important. The autosiphon exhibits no true resonance; its response is all-or-none. However, it can display the phenomenon of pararesonance; the maximum rate of discharge is produced most economically when stimuli are given at the same rate as the natural period of the operation cycle.

ELECTRIC EQUIVALENT OF HYDRAULIC MODEL. This detailed analogy is presented because appreciation of the differences between the two main classes of rhythmic activity is essential for understanding the difficulties which still surround interpretation of the rhythmic electrical phenomena in the nervous system.

The character of the relaxation oscillator which is most instructive physiologically is that it is a nonlinear system; its operation depends upon the sharp threshold which separates one regime from another.

If the hydraulic model seems too trivial, the components may be replaced with electrical ones, potential difference for water-level, current for flow, capacitors for the tank, resistors for the pipes, discharge tubes with their nonlinear voltage-current characteristics for the siphon. This produces a circuit arrangement familiar to electronic designers as a time-base or sawtooth oscillator. In fact, such an electric model has been built and is in regular use for teaching and demonstration to illustrate the behavior of a system containing several such circuits in a chain or cascade (56). In this embodiment of the analogue, a series of such systems, coupled together, can be seen to provide for propagation, inhibition, unidirectional synaptic transmission and other basic properties of axonic and neuronic action. When more elaborate forms of interconnection and switching are provided, properties such as homeostasis and ultrastability appear, as demonstrated by the machines constructed by Ashby (4) and Uttley (52).

The working hypothesis embodied in the simple model of nervous action is that every element of a nerve cell from soma to terminal dendrite is, in effect, a miniature relaxation oscillator. Each element thus considered is connected to those on both sides of it so as to facilitate by its own activity their tendency to discharge. A crude hydraulic counterpart would be a series of autosiphons, each emptying into the one beside it so that should any one element operate, the whole chain would be initiated. This model would not work, however, for it requires that each element be above all the others which is absurd. In the electric model this difficulty is overcome by providing capacitors which direct a proportion of the discharge current of each element to the trigger tubes of the adjacent ones so as momentarily to raise the potential differences across them to their discharge threshold. This is an important feature, since it suggests that in a living nerve the current generated at any active region, the action current, may produce fields of potential difference great enough to initiate at a distance the electrochemical process responsible for the characteristic depolarization and discharge. This effect is of course demonstrated by the circumvention of a blocked region in a nerve by leading the action current through an inert conducting bridge (30).

SPONTANEOUS RHYTHMIC ACTIVITY IN
EXCITABLE TISSUES

Rhythmic Activity in Single Units

With these properties in mind we may revert to the question of spontaneous rhythmicity. In a single nerve cell, as in a single element of the nerve model, spontaneous rhythmic activity will tend to occur whenever the discharge threshold is at or below the polarization potential. As is well known, depression of the threshold of excitation, or lengthening of the accommodation constant by the action of drugs, does induce spontaneous rhythmic activity, even in normally passive peripheral nerve fibers (19). In general, the amplitude and rate of such a discharge depends on two factors: the rate of charge or polarization, and the rate of discharge or depolarization. These two time constants are independent variables to a first order of approximation and may be analogous to the two resistors in a sawtooth relaxation oscillator which control the sweep speed and fly-back speed, respectively. In this comparison the flyback is equivalent to the action potential or spike discharge, which need not be numerically equal to the total available polarization potential.

Rhythmic Activity in Networks

Now, when several such elements can interact with one another by their electric fields, the aggregate

system will tend to exhibit generalized rhythmic activity at a frequency very much lower than that suggested by the time constants of the single elements. The repolarization time of neurons in the central nervous system is probably equivalent to their refractory period and lasts about 1 msec. The maximum frequency of spontaneous discharge for such a neuron is therefore of the order of 1000 pulses per sec., but the lowest rate depends on the relation of the degree of depolarization to the threshold. In effect this implies that there should be an inverse relation between the amplitude and the frequency of a spontaneous rhythm.

The basic waveform of a discharge determined in this way should be of an asymmetrical sawtooth variety, the asymmetry being more apparent at higher amplitude, though the proportions are actually constant. It can be shown, however, that in the case of a large population of mutually interacting unstable elements the waveform of the aggregate discharge may be so smoothed as to lose all traces of its angularity and come to be indistinguishable from a sinusoidal rhythm. This principle is actually applied in electronic circuit design to obtain a sine wave signal from a square or triangular source which can be activated or synchronized without the inertia of a conventional sine wave oscillator.

The conclusion to be drawn is that the wave form of a spontaneous rhythm originating in a population of active elements is of limited assistance in determining the mechanism of its source; a pure sine wave may originate in an assembly of relaxation oscillators, but a relaxation wave form is less likely to be the output of a single harmonic source.

Rhythmic Activity in Primitive Organs

Having now considered the basic properties of rhythmic generators in general, we may turn to the specific features of this class of activity in the brain. At the very outset it must be admitted that no convenient generalization is possible. Rhythmic discharges are common in the nervous and muscular systems of nearly all animals, but there is as yet no proof that they can all be attributed to the same mechanism.

For example, details of the intrinsic rhythms of the cardiac ganglion cells in crustacea have been described by Hagiwara & Bullock (26) and Bullock & Terzuolo (14). The wave form of these rhythms seems to be typical of the relaxation oscillator type, as shown in figure 1. Harris & Whiting (27) have

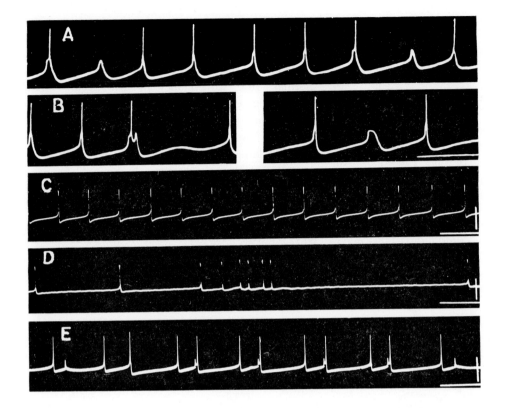

FIG. 1. Spontaneous electrical discharges in single cells of lobster cardiac ganglion. The wave form is suggestive of a relaxation oscillation with two separate time constants. *A* and *B* are from the same cell in the lobster. It shows a large pacemaker potential, presumably arising nearby, and another prepotential before the spike. This can fail to elicit a spike, can continue (end of *A*) or redevelop (third spike of *B*) after the spike, and can initiate repolarization almost as complete as a spike can. Note the failure of the prepotential to arise following the third spike in *B*, with instead an undulation leading to a new cycle. *C*, *D* and *E* are three different crab cells of type *D*, showing different forms and permutations of pacemaker potential and repolarization. Scales: *A*, *B*, 500 msec.; *C*, *D* and *E*, 50 mv, 200 msec. [From Bullock & Terzuolo (14).]

confirmed the early observations of Paton (45) and Wintrebert (68) that in embryonic elasmobranchs spontaneous rhythmic activity of the musculature is entirely myogenic in origin. A tendency to repetitive activity seems to be intrinsic in many excitable structures and, indeed, absence of spontaneous discharges may be a special case of control or inhibition. In primitive or embryonic organisms the intrinsic rhythms are generally little affected by external stimuli, whereas in more highly developed structures, such as the human brain, responsiveness to stimulation is the general rule.

This difference suggests that, as in other living structures and functions, a basic mechanism which survived the first stages of evolution because of its simple utility may, as it were, be exploited in the later stages of specialization to fulfill a much more

elaborate function. As a crude working hypothesis, we may consider that the rhythmic properties of primitive creatures and rudimentary organs, which at first provided a simple means of propulsion, have in our own brains assumed an essential role in the systematic timing and distribution of information within the neuronic network.

Intrinsic Rhythms in the Human Brain

For the purpose of this chapter, attention will be directed mainly to the rhythmic activity of the human brain. This has received the greatest attention since the discovery of Hans Berger of the human electroencephalogram (9); the observation and measurement of the rhythmic features of the human EEG have been practised on an increasing scale for 20 years in several hundred laboratories. There is the further advantage that such correlation with function as may be established can be followed more closely in human subjects whose mentality and behavior are more familiar and comprehensible than are those of other animals.

The rhythmic wave-like potential changes designated as 'alpha rhythms' by Berger are the most prominent and peculiar feature of human brain activity, and these rhythms will be taken as representative of rhythmic activity in normal conditions. An example appears in figure 2. Since Berger's original discoveries, brain rhythms have been subclassified, not only on the basis of their frequency and amplitude but also on their provenance and functional correlation. Employing these criteria, three other main classes of rhythm have been identified in human subjects: 'theta rhythms' with a frequency of 4 to 7 cycles per sec., occupying typically the parietal and tem-

poral regions of the brain and associated with childhood, and emotional stress in some adults (fig. 3); 'delta rhythms' with frequencies from less than 1 up to 3½ cycles per sec., associated with deep sleep in normal adults, with infancy and with organic brain disease (fig. 4); and 'beta rhythms' with frequencies higher than 14 cycles per sec., generally associated with activation and tension. In considering the nature and correlations of the alpha rhythms, it should always be recalled that these other rhythmic phenomena exist and that their mechanisms may be as different from those of alpha rhythms as are their functional associations. Moreover, in the realm of brain pathology, relatively enormous rhythmic discharges are associated with certain types of epileptic seizures, and these again may originate in a manner quite different from that of the normal alpha rhythms.

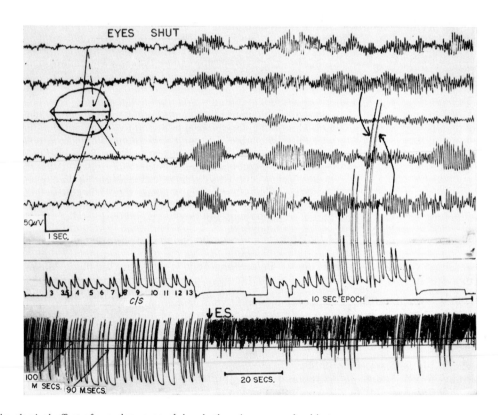

FIG. 2. An example of the classical effect of eye closure on alpha rhythms in a normal subject. Upper five traces were recorded from electrode sites shown in the diagram in the upper left corner. These five primary records show the typical burst of alpha activity as the eyes are closed, followed by marked amplitude modulation, the alpha rhythms being most prominent in the posterior occipital derivations. The sixth trace representing the frequency analysis, indicates the presence of two components at 9 and 10 cycles per sec. The seventh trace, that showing the period analysis, indicates the presence of wave intervals varying from 90 to 110 msec. The three methods of display are essentially complementary since each system emphasizes certain characters at the expense of others; all the information is present in the primary records but is not easily extracted from them visually.

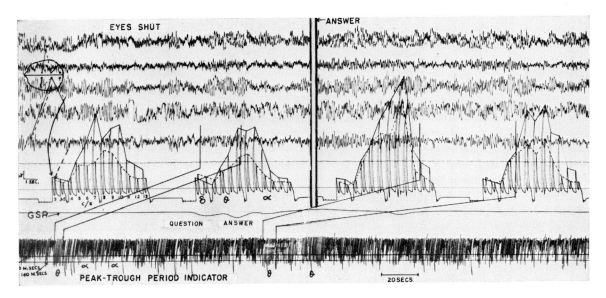

FIG. 3. Alpha and theta activity in a normal young subject. Records as described for figure 2. The primary records are particularly complex. In the frequency analysis records, the solid lines connect the peaks related to channel 3, while the dotted lines connect the peaks related to channel 5. This analysis reveals components in the theta and alpha bands which fluctuate independently in the two hemispheres. During the first half of the record the subject was at rest and the second half was replying to an annoying question. During this phase the theta content increased in the transverse derivation (channel 5) after a period of activation and fluctuation in skin resistance (G.S.R.). The period analysis shows fluctuations in wave intervals between about 100 and 140 msec. corresponding to periods of relative alpha and theta activity. The prolonged theta activity is a characteristic of this response to annoyance.

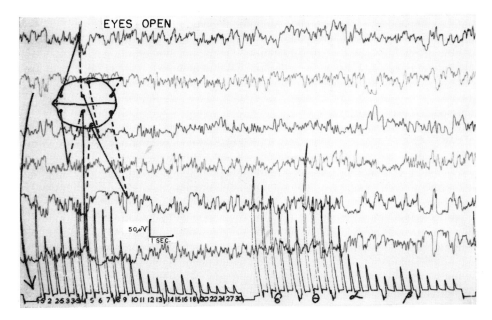

FIG. 4. Delta and theta activity recorded from a normal child aged 3. Six primary records (above) and frequency analysis record (below). In early youth these rhythms are characteristically diffuse and complex; the frequency analysis shows almost equal abundance in the range from 1.5 to 9 cycles per sec. with a peak in the theta band at 5 cycles per sec. These rhythms are almost unaffected by stimulation.

PROPERTIES OF ALPHA ACTIVITY AS TYPICAL
OF INTRINSIC RHYTHMS

Early Reports

The early studies of alpha rhythms in human beings
were made with straightforward recording devices—
mirror oscillographs, cathode ray oscillographs and,
later, ink writing recorders. These provide simple
graphs of voltage changes with respect to time; it is
unfortunate that the human eye is severely limited in
its capacity to analyze a curve of this sort, being attracted to the most prominent features and tending to
ignore or misrepresent the minor ones. Berger's early
studies, original and detailed though they were, provided only limited information about the distribution and complexity of the alpha rhythms because he
employed only one or two separate recording chan-

nels; his impression that the alpha rhythms were developed by the whole brain was due to this limitation.
During the last 20 years however, the technical trend
has been toward multiplication of channels and
elaboration of analyzing devices. There is no doubt
that in consequence the picture of alpha activity has
become progressively more and more involved and
controversial. Adrian & Matthews (1), and Adrian
& Yamagiwa (2) were the first to prove that the
alpha rhythms usually arose in the posterior regions of
the brain, and they were able to demonstrate in some
subjects an abrupt change in the sign of the potential
gradient of the alpha waves over the scalp, an effect
which has since become known as a 'phase-reversal
focus'. In the simplest case, a potential distribution
of this sort could be produced by an equivalent generator within the head oriented radially with its
axis projecting toward the surface at the 'focus', and

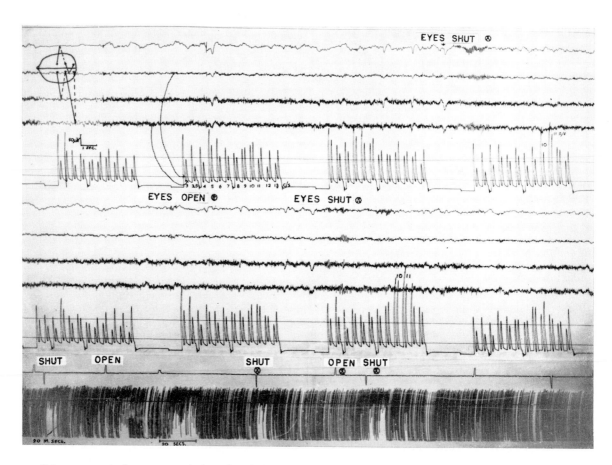

FIG. 5. Primary records, frequency analysis and period display from a subject of the alpha M
type. Upper portion contains four primary records and a frequency analysis which is continued in
the middle portion; the lowermost record is the period display. Immediately on eye closure there
is a brief burst of alpha activity at 10 to 11 cycles per sec., but even this is sometimes lacking. The
spectrum of brain rhythms is almost 'white,' although the absence of regular rhythms makes the
faster activity seem more obvious.

this was the schema tentatively suggested for the origin of the alpha rhythms in the human brain.

Individuality of Alpha Rhythms and their Variation

During the last 10 years several experiments have expanded and modified the methods introduced by Adrian & Matthews and have also widened their survey to the study of a large number of subjects. These observations have shown clearly that, unlike most physiological phenomena, the alpha rhythms must be considered in relation to each individual of a given species and not merely as a specific or generic character. In other words the alpha rhythm patterns, in terms both of spatial distribution, frequency and relation to function, are highly characteristic of every individual. The variation is so wide that classification of alpha type must include a class of normal person in whom no alpha activity whatever is visible (fig. 5), even in those conditions which are most favorable to the appearance of these rhythms in other people. At the other extreme there are people in whom alpha rhythms persist even in circumstances which are most inclined in other subjects to interrupt or suppress this activity. A distribution of this sort is extremely difficult to reconcile with any simple theory of spontaneous activity, and any general scheme to account for these phenomena must include considerations of mental and even social character—aspects of human existence which are in general far removed from the domain of neurophysiology.

Accepting the need for considerable reserve, it is generally true that the amplitude of spontaneous rhythms in the alpha category is inversely correlated with visual attention. Empirically the frequency range acceptable for alpha rhythms is from 8 to 13 cycles per sec., and the distribution of frequency in a large population follows a more or less normal Gaussian curve, the mode falling at about 10 cycles per sec. The tails of the curve should extend to about 6 and 15 cycles per sec.; about one in 5,000 individuals does in fact show rhythms at these limits which comply with the arbitrary definition of alpha rhythms.

Complexity of Alpha Rhythms

The appearance of alpha rhythms in normal people is usually suggestive of intrinsic complexity and various methods of analysis have been applied to the study of this possibility. Whatever method is used the great majority of alpha rhythms are compound in the sense that there are usually several components within the alpha band (65). The superposition of these vari-

ous components in a record produces an appearance of continuous but irregular modulation; sometimes the amplitudes and frequencies are so constant over a period of time that a regular pattern of 'beats' is produced. The identification of the various alpha components can also be accomplished geometrically by recording from electrode patterns in which derivations may be made from orthogonal electrode chains. With this arrangement one component may be found to be more prominent in records from anteroposterior electrodes and another from traverse ones. Furthermore, the components may be distinguished by their functional activity or responsiveness. For example, in those people with persistent alpha rhythms, one component may continue when the eyes are open while another is more prominent when the eyes are shut during mental activity. The geometrical and functional separation of alpha components is perhaps more convincing than their display by instrumental analysis, but the three methods can be employed together to construct a dynamic picture of spontaneous activity in relation to function and behavior. Other methods of analysis of alpha rhythms have been proposed by Sato (47), Krakau (35), Burch (15), Kozhevnikov (34) and Bekkering (8). These have not so far been applied to a very wide range of subjects and situations but their trials have been promising (15, 16, 24, 25, 36, 66).

In experiments designed to exploit the three principal methods of analysis, simultaneous observations of changes in the autonomic nervous system and the behavior of the subject are of considerable value. These techniques have not yet been fully developed so the information is still inadequate to give a clear indication of alpha significance in terms of somatic change. A further difficulty is that such experiments involve some selection of 'suitable' subjects and this has caused considerable difficulty in comparing results from different laboratories. For example, there is a natural inclination to choose for study people with large regular alpha rhythms since they seem likely to provide records which are easier to measure and interpret. Selection of people in this group inevitably limits the scope of investigation, and there is even some evidence that subjects with extremely prominent and persistent rhythms may display mental characters bordering on the pathological.

Identification of Alpha Components

When allowance is made for these limitations, there remain certain general features which seem incontestable. First, the attenuation and constriction of alpha activity during visual attention and mental vigilance is almost invariable. When means are available for instrumental analysis, a convenient form for the measure of alpha activity is 'abundance'. This includes dimensions both of amplitude and of persistence. It is comparable with a measure of energy, but this term is undesirable because of its precise connota-

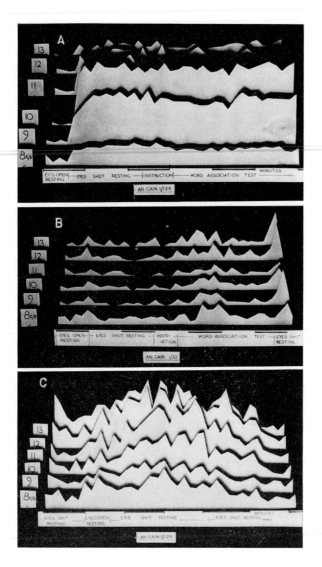

FIG. 6. An assembly of cut-outs showing fluctuations in abundance of alpha components over long periods during the performance of various tasks: (*A*) in a subject of the alpha-responsive type showing an immediate and sustained rise in all alpha components on eye closing and a lack of response to mental activity with the eyes shut; (*B*) with greatly increased analyser gain the alpha components are barely perceptible in an alpha-M type subject; (*C*) in a responsive versatile subject the various components fluctuate over a wide range during the performance of a psychological task.

tion in physical systems. When analyzed in terms of the abundance of its various components, the changes of alpha activity during spontaneous or induced variations of behavior can be plotted as abundance with respect to time (fig. 6). Necessarily, each component is arbitrarily identified by its frequency, usually as a whole number of cycles per second, but a composite plot of these arbitrary components reveals the nature and extent of the complexity previously referred to. Often the various components exhibit some degree of independence, particularly during the performance of an exacting task, and the individuality of the spontaneous rhythms is considerably emphasized by this procedure. The classical responsive types of alpha rhythm rise and fall inversely according to the intensity of concentration of the subject, but during a period of tranquillity the pattern of frequency and distribution may remain almost constant so that even short samples of record are similar to one another.

At the other extreme, subjects showing little alpha activity display an extremely varied pattern, even during rest. Those alpha components which are present in such records fluctuate in abundance from moment to moment, so that extremely long samples of record must be taken if the samples are to resemble one another.

This observation has suggested that a useful measure of alpha character would be the length of sample necessary for all of a set of such samples to fall within a specified range of variation. This computation is performed automatically with a wave analyzer fitted with an electronic averaging device. This measure provides an estimate of the repertory of a person's alpha activity and has been found to be related to the scope and variety of interests in a population of normal young adults. The aspect of cerebral mentality defined in this way has been termed versatility (50). Detailed analysis of alpha responses has suggested that, in some people at least, relative abundance of the slower alpha components may be associated with rest or inactivity of the mechanisms of internal imagination, while abundance of the faster components is more closely linked with the lack of significant afferent signals from the receptors. Thus with the eyes closed and the subject relaxed, the most abundant rhythm may be at 9 cycles per sec.; but when the subject is given a mental task to perform with the eyes shut, the frequency of the dominant rhythm may seem to rise to, say, 11 cycles per sec. In some cases, however, the apparent acceleration is due to attenuation of the lower frequency components during concentration, leaving the higher frequency ones unmasked. In this condition the subject is attending to imaginary or endogenous signals and is ignoring external ones.

The intricate and elusive relations between the various brain rhythms and mental functions have been explored also by Mundy-Castle (43) who has identified three types of theta thythm and two of beta rhythm, as well as various categories of activity in the alpha range of frequencies. The statistical relations between types of brain rhythm and psychological character have been analyzed in detail by Werre (66) who concludes that, although no unique associations can be established between any single EEG variable and any specific psychological parameter, none the less certain electrical patterns are contingent on psychological grouping. For example, alpha frequency is related to the performance of psychotechnical tests, since subjects with low frequencies perform slowly but steadily, those with high frequencies fast and regularly and those with complex alpha rhythms erratically.

Although the alpha-blocking effect is seen most clearly in response to visual stimuli, it can also be produced in some subjects by nonvisual stimuli which are novel and startling. The effect of nonvisual stimuli usually wears off quite rapidly, but if an ineffective stimulus is then accompanied or followed by an effective visual one the neutral stimulus may become 'conditioned'. Conditioning of alpha blocking was first studied intensively by Jasper & Shagass (31) and has recently been extensively employed in the experimental analysis of learning by Gastaut et al. (24). They attribute generalized desynchronization of intrinsic rhythms by a novel stimulus to activation of the brain stem reticular system, and local desynchronization by a specific stimulus to activation of the thalamic reticular system.

Degree of Constancy and Range of Variation in Alpha Frequency

Although the frequency and distribution of alpha rhythms in any particular subject are characteristic and individual, the rate of an alpha rhythm can sometimes be shifted slightly. The range of normal variation is limited to a fraction of a cycle per second, however, and such changes cannot be identified and measured easily in conventional records. The effect is easily demonstrated with a toposcope display system (56, 57, 61, 64) designed to emphasize and correlate rhythmic activity in many regions. An example taken from a normal subject is shown in figure 7. The frequency of the major alpha rhythms is here 8.80 cycles per sec. over a wide area at rest. During mental activity the rhythm disappears in all but two derivations in the right centroparietal region where the frequency rises to 9.45 cycles per sec. and then gradually subsides to its original frequency in about 90 sec. (fig. 8). This example illustrates two very important features of alpha activity: first, the extreme constancy in frequency in tranquil conditions; second, the degree of independence of the two hemispheres and even of adjacent regions during activity. As can be seen in figure 9, one minute after the start of the experiment when the right centroparietal region is showing alpha rhythm at 9.1 cycles per sec., the left temporoparietal derivation has resumed alpha activity but at 9.35 cycles per sec. Nevertheless, when the period of attention is over, all regions return precisely to their original rate of 8.80 cycles per sec.

This degree of constancy is by no means unusual and has been reported also by Brazier & Casby (12) and Barlow & Brazier (5) using an entirely different method of analysis and correlation. The pattern of frequency fluctuation, however, is an individual character and is related to the complexity of the resting alpha activity; if there are several rhythms, the apparent changes in frequency are usually abrupt and extensive and may be in the direction of acceleration or deceleration. Changes of this type are attributable to the substitution of one process for another rather than to changes of rate in the same process. In general, a particular alpha rhythm seems to be capable of about ±0.5 cycles per sec. variation within the physiological range; a greater change can be induced by the administration of drugs but such alterations are associated with signs of intoxication. For example, ingestion of 100 ml of alcohol in 1½ hr. in one subject reduced the alpha frequency from 10 to 9 cycles per sec., but the subject was seriously inebriated and relapsed into a prolonged stupor 40 min. later. Conversely, activating drugs such as amphetamine or pipradrol compounds in sufficient doses may raise the frequency of an alpha rhythm by as much as 1 cycle per sec., but this is associated with marked mental stimulation and agitation (fig. 10). The effects of hallucinogenic drugs such as LSD 25 are also related to mental change; doses sufficient to raise the apparent alpha frequency, from e. g. 10 to 12 cycles per sec., induce characteristic transformations in mood and character.

FIG. 7. Toposcope display system record of the effect of mental activity on alpha frequency and distribution in a normal subject. Each of the 22 circular areas is the face of a cathode ray tube connected to an electrode pair over the brain. There are thus 22 channels. In each circuit there has been introduced a spiral scanning time-base upon which are projected the variations in brilliance proportional to the rhythmic changes of voltage resulting from brain activity. In this case the rotation speed of the signals was one-third of the frequency of the resting alpha rhythm, which was 8.8 cycles per sec. The duration of each exposure was 8 sec. The intrinsic rhythms are seen as white smudges in each indicator tube. The first exposure (A) shows the alpha distribution and frequency at rest; during the next exposure (B) the subject was asked to begin a series of mental tasks; the immediate effect of the instructions was to suppress the alpha activity in all but two channels in the right hemisphere where the frequency rose to 9.4 cycles per sec. The subsequent exposures were taken during performance of the task and show a gradual return to the resting state. During this period the alpha activity decelerated slowly and returned to the left hemisphere where it remained accelerated for a longer period than on the right side. The return to the original condition took nearly 100 sec., but the final frequency was exactly the same as before the activation. [From Walter (61).]

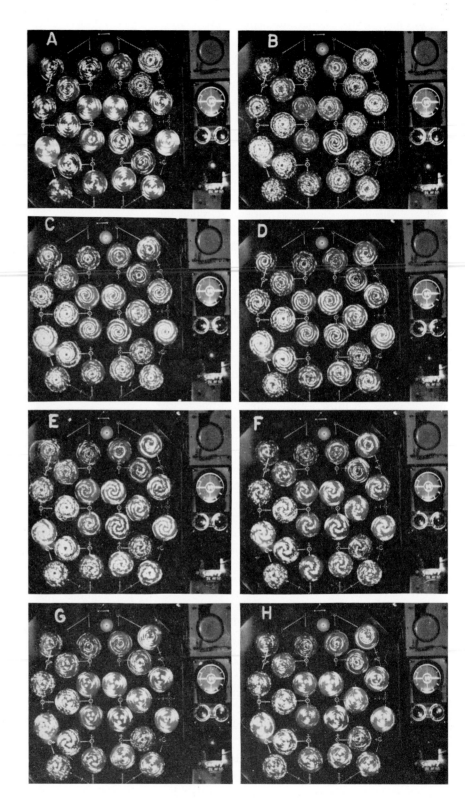

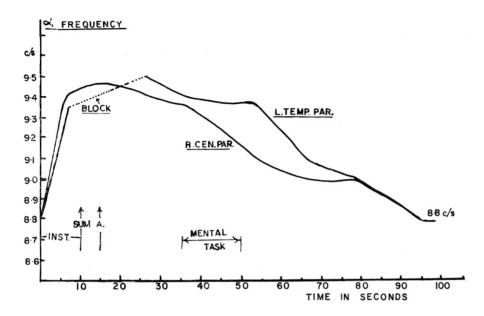

FIG. 8. A plot of the alpha frequencies in the right centroparietal and left temporoparietal regions derived from the experiment represented in figure 7. Independent fluctuations of the two hemispheres are far outside the error of observation and are characteristic of the subject. [From Walter (61).]

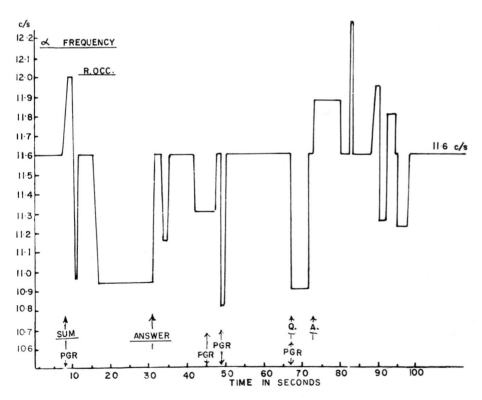

FIG. 9. Fluctuations in alpha frequency of another normal subject studied in the same way as in figure 7, exhibiting complex alpha analysis. The resting frequency of 11.6 cycles per sec. is replaced by others at 12 and 10.95 cycles per sec. which alternate in dominance, but the original rate is returned to at the end of the activation period. [From Walter (61).]

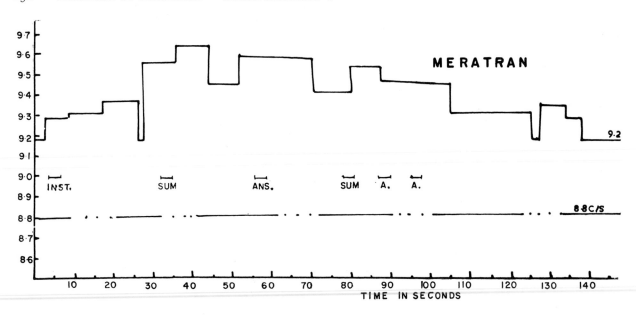

FIG. 10. Alpha frequency changes in the same subject as in figures 7 and 8 under the influence of pipradrol (Meratran). The steady frequency has risen by 0.4 cycles per sec. and the rate of change during attention is abrupt and discontinuous, but again the frequency returns to precisely its original value. [From Walter (61).]

Effects of Activation and Stimulation

The effects of generalized or nonspecific activation on the spontaneous alpha rhythms are slight but characteristic; of equal interest are the relations between responses to specific physiologicfal stimuli and the distribution and time relations of the intrinsic rhythms. The most dramatic and effective changes are of course those produced by visual stimulation. In one of the early reports on the effect of flicker, Adrian & Matthews (1) described these as 'driving the alpha rhythm', but more detailed study (42, 53) has shown that, except in certain circumstances, responses to photic stimulation are distinct from alpha waves. Those circumstances in which alpha rhythms are involved in evoked responses are of particular interest in the study of spontaneous activity since the interaction between rhythmic external stimuli and intrinsic brain rhythms indicates a possible function of the latter. Bishop (10, 11) reported cyclic changes in the excitability of the visual system of the rabbit and the relation of such changes to intrinsic alpha rhythms has been studied by several other experimenters, Bartley & Bishop (6), Gastaut et al. (23), Lindsley (40) and Lansing (37). In some animals there seems to be good evidence for periodic fluctuations in the excitability of the visual system, but in human subjects the observations are inconclusive because of the

wide variation between individuals. The properties of the retina interfere seriously with attempts to measure the time relations between visual stimulus times and evoked responses; in effect, the retina acts as an integrator for brief flashes of light so that the volley of impulses in the visual pathways is a very ragged one, spread over a period of over 50 msec. even when the stimulus is a flash of light lasting only a few microseconds. This means that even if the central visual structures were totally 'blind' for half of every alpha wave, they could still receive signals that fell in the blind phase because the afferent volley would outlast the critical period.

Synchronization of Alpha Rhythms

There is a further complication to be considered; the alpha rhythms can only be 'driven' over a narrow range of frequencies, but this range is enough to allow them to be synchronized or locked in phase by afferent visual signals. This is demonstrated clearly in toposcope records; this device can be arranged to deliver brief flashes of light in a time-sequence of doublets or triplets at any chosen repetition rate. In this way the pattern of true evoked responses can be distinguished from the superficially similar but functionally distinct pattern of synchronized alpha rhythms. When the repetition rate of the flash groups is set at about the alpha frequency or a submultiple of this, many subjects show no signs of the stimulus pattern but only a sharp synchronization of the alpha rhythm. This effect can also exist together with an evoked pattern and the two modes of response may appear in adjacent regions which may exchange modes from time to time. The effects of alpha driving and alpha synchronization can combine to corrupt an evoked response by interpolation of the 'missing' component in a triplet pattern, or by omission of one of the responses.

The distinction between rhythm synchronization and true evocation is important in the interpretation of the results of such experiments; it is not always easy to achieve because the identity of a cerebral process can be inferred only indirectly from its electrical characters. However, with the toposcopic display system the peculiar phase or time relations of the alpha rhythms in different parts of the brain can be used to supplement identification by frequency, distribution and responsiveness. Records taken with electrodes on the scalp almost always reveal clear differences in the time of appearance of alpha waves in various regions. In general, the maximum potential change is earlier in the anterior regions than in the occiput, and besides this anteroposterior sweep there is evidence of an even greater discrepancy in phase between the longitudinal and transverse derivations covering the same region. The commonest appearance is for the alpha waves in the transverse derivations to lead those in the longitudinal ones by 90°; for example, the peak of the waves seen in the parietotemporal channel occurs at the instant of zero potential in the parieto-occipital one. These phase relations are so clear and consistent that they can be used as a diagnostic sign of alpha activity; when the effect of a stimulus is merely to synchronize this activity, the characteristic phase relations are usually maintained. On the other hand, where there is a true evoked response, this shows the expected latency, which varies slightly from region to region, but the phase relations are not those of the alpha activity.

Even before these details of alpha activity were known the possibility had been considered that such rhythms represented a more elaborate process than a simple time cycle of excitability. It may be supposed that the regular rise and fall of threshold in the brain resembles the ebb and flow of a tide round the globe. The time of high tide, so to say, varying from port to port will not merely control the accessibility of the various relay stations but will also act as a clock,

transforming time into space patterns and contrariwise. From this conjecture have been derived a number of variations on the theme of scanning, elaborated by McCulloch (41), Wiener (67), Walter (56) and others. The nearest to conclusive evidence of such a process is the phenomenon described by Walter (58) as 'abscission'; the elements of a visual time pattern are cut off and projected in a spatial pattern in the visual association regions of the brain. The time relations and distribution of this effect suggest that the sweep of alpha waves through the cortex may provide the time-space transformation. Auxiliary subjective evidence is provided by the illusions of mottled moving patterns of colored light seen when gazing at a featureless flickering field. The illusions are powerful enough to produce aberrations of color vision as indicated by the Ishihara test when viewed by a flickering light (59) and they are attributed to the same cause as the complex electric patterns evoked by flicker—interaction between rhythmic volleys of impulses in the visual pathways with the intrinsic scanning rhythms.

Evidence from Intracerebral Electrodes

The spontaneous brain rhythms as seen in scalp records seem to have a characteristic geometry as well as a proper frequency and relation to function. Such records are open to the obvious criticism that being derived from electrodes on the surface of the head, they can represent only the average field of vast aggregations of neural units, all remote from the electrodes in terms of neuronic dimensions. Additional information is now available from investigations with microelectrodes placed in or near to individual neurons and their processes (38) and also from electrodes implanted in the brains of human subjects for clinical study (20, 48, 49).

These methods are still in the early stages of development, but they have nevertheless already indicated that even in the intimate details of brain mechanisms spontaneous rhythmic activity is a distinct phenomenon; it cannot be considered as an aggregate or envelope of unitary neuronic spike discharges. Nor is there any invariable relation between the spontaneous wave-like potential changes near a neuron and its all-or-none action potentials. When the probability of a cortical unit discharging is low, then its rate of firing may be governed to some extent by the field of the spontaneous rhythms; unit spikes are seen more commonly in the phase when

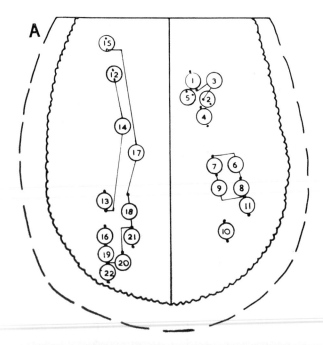

FIG. 11. Records taken with the toposcope in the laboratory of Dr. Sem-Jacobsen in Oslo from a psychopathic patient in whom electrodes had been implanted intracerebrally three days earlier. *A*. The approximate position of the electrodes for the 22 indicator tubes, derived from X-ray projection drawings. The anterior channels were connected to electrodes deep in the medial structures; the posterior ones were in the middle of the parietal and occipital lobes. *B*. The distribution of the intrinsic alpha rhythms with the eyes shut. There are three distinct components, one at 8.8 cycles per sec. in channel 14, another at 8.5 cycles per sec. in channels 16 and 18 through 22, and a third at 9.15 cycles per sec. in channel 17. There is also a theta rhythm at 7 cycles per sec. in channel 5. The alpha rhythms in the posterior regions show the characteristic phase differences suggesting a moving source. The signals in channel 8 are artefacts arising at a high-resistance electrode. *C*. Record made a few seconds later during flicker stimulation at 8.8 flickers per sec. The only regions showing clear fundamental synchronization are those corresponding to channels 11 and 17 and 19. Channel 14 shows deceleration to 8.6 cycles per sec., channel 20 is unaffected and channels 21 and 22 show a response at twice the stimulus rate. *D*. Flicker stimulation with triplet groups of flashes at 4.2 groups per sec. evokes a replica of the stimulus pattern only in channels 18 and 20. Channels 14,

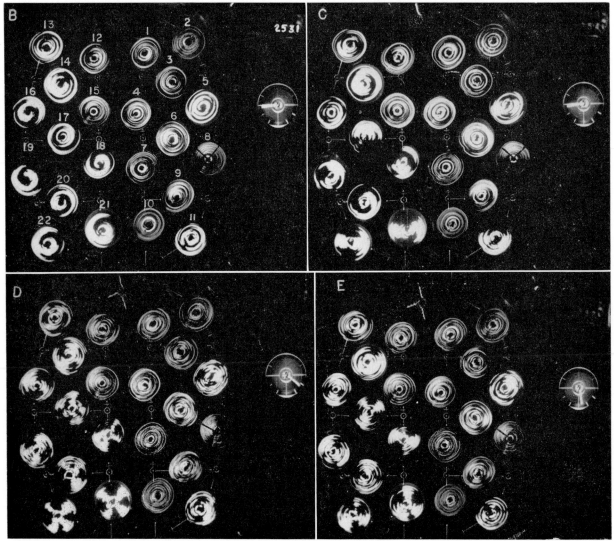

the region of the neuron concerned is electronegative with respect to the surrounding tissue. Li *et al.* (38) have suggested that the microlocation of spontaneous rhythms in the layers II to V of cat cortex may be similar to that of the recruiting responses evoked by thalamic stimulation. Stimulation of this type is effective only when its frequency is close to that of the spontaneous cortical rhythms, that is at 5 to 8 cycles per sec., and this relation is reflected in a correspondence between the phase of the recruiting response, the spontaneous rhythms and the unit discharges. It is not clear, however, whether the spontaneous activity in these preparations is functionally homologous with the alpha rhythms in human subjects.

In some cases, therefore, the spontaneous rhythms can act as electrotonic escapements, but there are many occasions when the spontaneous rhythms and unit discharges are quite unrelated. This variability is manifest even in conditions of normal adaptation; Ricci *et al.* (46) have described the complexities of the relations between unit firing and surface rhythms in the occipital cortex of monkey during the establishment of conditioned responses to sounds associated with light flashes at 7 per sec. They conclude that such a response "is a complex pattern of interwoven inhibitory and excitatory processes", in which the electric fields of relatively slow wave-like spontaneous rhythms are interlaced with the rapid all-or-none discharges of individual cells. A similar image was employed by Walter (58) to describe the topologic details of evoked and spontaneous activity in human subjects engaged in learning: "an interweaving of reciprocal electric filaments to generate an intricate and durable texture of significant association."

Such observations suggest that an important factor in cerebral mechanisms must be the geometry of the electric fields in the region of neurons and their processes. It is often forgotten that these fields have vectorial as well as scalar aspects—they have direction as well as magnitude. As already mentioned, the geometric and time relations of alpha rhythms as seen on the scalp might be due to the adventitious effect of remoteness from the source in a volume conductor. Walter & Dovey (63) reported observations of alpha rhythms in the depths of the occipital lobe in

patients investigated for the delimitation of cerebral tumors, but they could not study the details of this activity. Recently Cooper *et al.* (18) have been able to obtain toposcopic records of alpha rhythms derived from electrodes implanted in the brains of patients with no organic brain disease. In these experiments the subjects were provided with up to 70 fine wire electrodes in various regions of the brain as described by Dodge *et al.* (20) and Sem-Jacobsen *et al.* (48). In one subject it was possible to record from intracerebral electrodes connected to the amplifiers in the network pattern customary for toposcope studies of scalp potentials. These records (fig. 11) of alpha activity from the depths of the brain show phase—and space—relations quite similar to those found in the superficial fields. The effects of synchronization by photic stimulation and of blocking by attention were also similar. As reported by Sem-Jacobsen *et al.* (49), the greatest amplitude of the alpha rhythms was found about 2 cm below the surface of the brain, but the rhythm existed also between pairs of electrodes 4 to 5 cm deeper. This extension of the alpha activity could not be due to purely electric conduction, since the phase of the waves was not always identical in the various regions and bursts of activity sometimes occurred in one region and not in others.

The conclusion from these studies is that some alpha rhythms involve deep structures as well as cortex and the time relations of the alpha waves indicate some sort of spread from front to back and depth to surface. The tendency of the transverse components of the rhythm to be phase-shifted by 90° with respect to the longitudinal ones suggests that there may be two interlocked processes, one generated by a corticobasal mechanism, the other, essentially corticocortical with peaks corresponding in phase to the moment of most rapid potential change—that is, zero potential—of the corticobasal process.

Relation Between Alpha Rhythms and Effector Function

The possibility that the alpha cycle may act as a gating mechanism for afferent signals has suggested that a similar relationship might be found for efferent ones. Kibbler *et al.* (32), Kibbler & Richter (33) and

---

16 and 19 are synchronized at twice the group rate (8.4 cycles per sec.) and channels 21 and 22 respond at 4 × 4.2 = 16.8 cycles per sec. *E.* Flicker stimulation with triplets at 5.6 groups per sec. evokes true replica in channel 17, rhythms at 11.2 cycles per sec. in channels 16, 18, 19 and 20, and at 3 × 5.6 = 16.8 in channels 21 and 22. All these patterns were associated con-

sistently with specific frequencies and modes of stimulation and were similar to those derived from scalp records. The arithmetic and geometric relations of the various features in such records suggest the presence of a number of mechanisms, each with its own domain, intrinsic rhythmicity and responsiveness to stimulation.

Bates (7) reported a tendency for the voluntary movements of human subjects to be synchronized in phase with their alpha rhythms, and this effect has been observed in several ways. The experiments of Lansing (37) indicate that the shortest and longest visuomotor reaction times in some human subjects tend to fall at points about 50 msec. apart in opposite phases of the alpha cycle. There was also some relation between motor response and spontaneous tremor, a fact suggesting that cyclic changes in excitability were operating also at the level of the spinal motoneuron pool. This is perhaps to be expected since the control of voluntary movement is not believed to depend upon complex activation of reflex circuits through high central structures. Observations of these relations have so far yielded only statistical information; there is no clear indication of how the timing and gating mechanism operates, and there are many exceptions to any rule that can be formulated. Experiments with auditory rather than visual stimuli have given even less conclusive results (44). In planning and interpreting such experiments it is important to allow for the tendency of some intrinsic rhythms to be pulled in to synchrony by the signals which they or other rhythms may in turn control. This interaction, together with integration by receptors, may be responsible for the discrepancies in the reports by different observers.

Effect of Temperature Changes

The ease with which alpha frequency can be measured and its constancy in normal conditions has encouraged the study of the effects of metabolic change. Hoagland (28) induced fever artificially and reported a rise in alpha frequency with temperature of nearly 0.5 cycles per sec. per degree C in normal subjects and an even higher temperature coefficient in syphilitic patients. Krakau (36), using an optical method of frequency analysis, was unable to confirm this effect in all his subjects and suggested that whatever changes may occur during artificial fever might be due to the general arousal by the situation as much as to the rise in temperature. This seems likely, since measurement of alpha frequency in a few subjects with the toposcope has shown no regular variation of alpha frequency with the normal diurnal changes of body temperature which would be expected to result in fluctuations of about 0.25 cycles per sec. It would seem that the alpha mechanisms are to some extent protected from the primary effects of temperature change.

DELTA, THETA AND BETA RHYTHMS

Relation of Delta and Theta Rhythms to Age

As a representative of the class of intrinsic rhythms, alpha activity is unique in its close and clear relation to sensory function. The other forms of rhythmic activity in the human brain, designated by Greek letters for convenience rather than clarity, are more familiar in clinical than in physiological studies, but, apart from the paroxysmal discharges associated uniquely with epilepsy, all are found in normal conditions. Delta and theta rhythms are characteristic of infancy and childhood, accompanying the maturation of normal children in a highly variable but significant manner (60). They precede, but in later years are often mingled with, adult alpha rhythms and their rate of subsidence is a common measure of development.

Delta Rhythms

When delta rhythms persist appreciably beyond the age of 10 or 12, the character of the child is usually suggestive of immaturity in a particular fashion to which Hodge *et al.* (29) have given the name ductility, the tendency to be led easily. In the extreme this is associated with minor recidivist delinquency combined with an appealing personality. In such cases the delta rhythms are often most prominent in the right temporo-occipital region and show little responsiveness to stimulation. Another type of delta rhythm is seen in some children with immature but not necessarily defective personalities. This is bilateral, monorhythmic and strikingly responsive to stimulation, acting almost as an alpha rhythm, particularly when it is localized to the occipital lobes. In otherwise normal people there is no obvious explanation of this effect, but a similarly responsive rhythmic slow activity is seen also in patients with organic disturbance of deep midline structures, and it is possible, therefore, that this type of slow responsive rhythm is an expression of inadequacy of the diffuse arousal systems. Corroboration of this can sometimes be obtained from suppression of the delta rhythms by administration of activating drugs, such as amphetamine, which are believed to act on the diffuse ascending reticular formation.

The association of delta activity with disease, dystrophy, damage and deep sleep—from which alliteration the phenomenon was accorded its designation—has suggested that it may have some sort of limiting or protective function (54, 56). This notion has been called by Walter the phylactic hypothesis. Since the brain is poorly endowed with certain of the protective devices conducive to the preservation of other organs—such as pain and repair—it is reasonable to conjecture that some mechanism may exist to constrain or restrict the influence of conditions likely to initiate excessive and persistent activity. The relatively great size and wide extent of delta rhythms—which may reach potential differences of 1 mv on the scalp—suggest that as electrotonic inhibitors they may in times of distress give the brain a chance to survive through inactivation of its cells.

Theta Rhythms

The class of theta rhythms—which were at first confused with slow alpha rhythms and later identified as related to thalamic lesions (62)—is most characteristically associated in normal young people with feelings of disappointment and frustration. They are evoked most easily by the termination or withdrawal of an authentic agreeable stimulus and often show a markedly stereotyped pattern of growth and decline over a period of about 20 sec. or so following such an experience. Clinically their persistence is linked with psychopathic character traits. It has been suggested (55) that, if the alpha rhythms be considered as scanning for visual pattern, then theta rhythms may represent a scanning for visceral pleasure. Such an analogy of analogies is notoriously meretricious, but if comprehension is to grow, some working hypothesis must be formulated, and at least experiments can be planned to discover why, just as the alpha rhythms wax great at the moment when patterns are excluded by closing the eyes, so theta rhythms tend to arise at the conclusion of pleasure.

Beta Rhythms

The beta rhythms, which were the second class of brain activity to be identified by Berger, are still uncertain in their significance and even in their definition. Mundy-Castle (43) has proposed that beta rhythms be considered in two classes, beta I and beta II. Beta I is suppressed during cortical activity and is often, though not invariably, harmonically related to a component of the alpha rhythms; this relationship is responsible for the wave form of the *rythme en arceau* of Gastaut (22). In order to avoid further confusion in this already disordered domain, it might be convenient to designate his particular combination of rhythms the ' μ ' rhythm because of its resemblance to the outline of the Greek letter. The beta II of Mundy-Castle is augmented during cortical activity and may represent an acceleration or concentration of efferent activity arising from the scansion of cortical regions engaged in the analysis of endogenous or exogenous patterns. Precise classification of these rhythms—which are particularly elusive because of their rate and the restriction of their domains—must await further study of their location and functional correlates.

ORIGIN OF INTRINSIC RHYTHMS

The various intrinsic, apparently spontaneous, yet often responsive, electrical rhythms of the brain are clearly in a different class of phenomenon from the unitary propagated spike potentials which act as the main operational code elements in the nervous system. The slower rhythmic oscillations seem more likely to be involved, as it were, in the administrative departments of central neurophysiology. If their rate of discharge were less constant or their wave form less pure, they might be considered as trivial projections of spatially asymmetric postsynaptic potentials in large populations of pyramidal cells with particularly long dendritic processes. It is indeed conceivable that the degree of asymmetry and the electric moment of the dendritic potentials might be large enough in some circumstances to generate the fields observed on the scalp. Even if this is the mechanism of generation, however, the gross variations from person to person and the delicate relations between the frequencies, time relations and geometric properties of the rhythms with the character and actions of the organism suggest that the intrinsic rhythms are more than the resultant of adventitious topography. The processes of evolution are too parsimonious to allow such entities to be multiplied beyond necessity. The refinements of modern techniques should enable schools of investigators trained in complementary disciplines to solve this enigma which so impedes our understanding of brain function.

REFERENCES

1. ADRIAN, E. D. AND B. H. C. MATTHEWS. *Brain* 57: 355, 1934.
2. ADRIAN, E. D. AND K. YAMAGIWA. *Brain* 58: 323, 1935.
3. ARVANITAKI, A. *Arch. internat. physiol.* 52: 381, 1942.
4. ASHBY, W. R. *Design for a Brain.* London: Chapman, 1952.

5. BARLOW, J. S. AND M. A. B. BRAZIER. *Electroencephalog. & Clin. Neurophysiol.* 6: 231, 1954.

6. BARTLEY, S. H. AND G. H. BISHOP. *Am. J. Physiol.* 103: 173, 1933.

7. BATES, J. A. V. *Electroencephalog. & Clin. Neurophysiol.* 2: 227, 1950.

8. BEKKERING, D. H. *Electroencephalog. & Clin. Neurophysiol.* 8: 721, 1956.

9. BERGER, H. *Arch. Psychiat.* 87: 527, 1929.

10. BISHOP, G. H. *Am. J. Physiol.* 103: 213, 1933.

11. BISHOP, G. H. *Arch. Ophth., Chicago* 14: 992, 1935.

12. BRAZIER, M. A. B. AND J. U. CASBY. *Electroencephalog. & Clin. Neurophysiol.* 4: 210, 1952.

13. BREMER, F. *Electroencephalog. & Clin. Neurophysiol.* 1: 177, 1949.

14. BULLOCK, T. H. AND C. A. TERZUOLO. *J. Physiol.* 138: 341, 1957.

15. BURCH, N. R., T. H. GREINER AND E. G. CORRELL. *Fed. Proc.* 14: 23, 1955.

16. BURCH, N. R., A. J. SILVERMAN AND T. H. GREINER. *Electroencephalog. & Clin. Neurophysiol.* 8: 157, 1956.

17. BURNS, B. D. *J. Physiol.* 112: 156, 1951.

18. COOPER, R., G. ØHRN, C. PATTEN, C. W. SEM-JACOBSEN AND W. G. WALTER. *Electroencephalog. & Clin. Neurophysiol.* In press.

19. COWAN, S. L. AND W. G. WALTER. *J. Physiol.* 91: 101, 1937.

20. DODGE, H. W., A. A. BAILEY, C. B. HOLMAN, M. C. PETERSEN AND C. W. SEM-JACOBSEN. *Electroencephalog. & Clin. Neurophysiol.* 6: 599, 1954.

21. FESSARD, A. In: *Brain Mechanisms and Consciousness*, edited by E. D. Adrian, F. Bremer, H. H. Jasper and J. F. Delafresnaye. Oxford: Blackwell, 1954.

22. GASTAUT, H. *Rev. neurol.* 87: 176, 1952.

23. GASTAUT, H., Y. GASTAUT, A. ROGER, J. CORRIOL AND R. NAQUET. *Electroencephalog. & Clin. Neurophysiol.* 3: 401, 1951.

24. GASTAUT, H., A. C. JUS, F. MORREL, W. STORM VAN LEEUWEN, S. DONIGER, R. NAQUET, H. REGIS, A. ROGER, D. BEKKERING, A. KAMP AND J. WERRE. *Electroencephalog. & Clin. Neurophysiol.* 9: 1, 1957.

25. GERSHUNI, G. AND V. A. KOZHEVNIKOV. *Problems of the Modern Physiology of the Nervous System.* Tiflis: Publ. House, Acad. of Sciences, Georgian SSR, 1956, p. 53.

26. HAGIWARA, S. AND T. H. BULLOCK. *Biol. Bull.* 109: 341, 1955.

27. HARRIS, J. E. AND H. P. WHITING. *J. Exper. Biol.* 31: 501, 1954.

28. HOAGLAND, H. *Am. J. Physiol.* 116: 604, 1936.

29. HODGE, R. S., V. J. WALTER AND W. G. WALTER. *Brit. J. Delinq.* 3: 1, 1953.

30. HODGKIN, A. L. *J. Physiol.* 90: 183, 1937.

31. JASPER, H. H. AND C. SHAGASS. *J. Exper. Psychol.* 28: 373, 1941.

32. KIBBLER, G. O., J. L. BOREHAM AND D. RICHTER. *Nature, London* 164: 371, 1949.

33. KIBBLER, G. O. AND D. RICHTER. *Electroencephalog. & Clin. Neurophysiol.* 2: 227, 1950.

34. KOZHEVNIKOV, V. A. *Physiol. J., USSR* 43: 983, 1957.

35. KRAKAU, C. E. T. *Electroencephalog. & Clin. Neurophysiol.* 3: 97, 1951.

36. KRAKAU, C. E. T. AND G. E. NYMAN. *Acta physiol. scandinav.* 29: 281, 1953.

37. LANSING, R. W. *Electroencephalog. & Clin. Neurophysiol.* 9: 497, 1957.

38. LI, C. L., C. CULLEN AND H. H. JASPER. *J. Neurophysiol.* 19: 131, 1956.

39. LILLIE, R. S. *Protoplasmic Action and Nervous Action.* Chicago: Univ. Chicago Press, 1923.

40. LINDSLEY, D. B. *Electroencephalog. & Clin. Neurophysiol.* 4: 443, 1952.

41. McCULLOCH, W. S. *Electroencephalog. & Clin. Neurophysiol.* Suppl. 2, 1949.

42. MUNDY-CASTLE, A. C. *Electroencephalog. & Clin. Neurophysiol.* 5: 187, 1953.

43. MUNDY-CASTLE, A. C. *Electroencephalog. & Clin. Neurophysiol.* 9: 643, 1957.

44. O'HARE, J. J. *Factorial Study of EEG and Auditory Functions.* Washington: Catholic Univ. Am., 1957.

45. PATON, S. *J. Comp. Neurol.* 21: 345, 1911.

46. RICCI, G., B. DOANE AND H. H. JASPER. *IV Congr. Internat. Electro-encephalog. et Neurophysiol., Rapp., Discus. et Document.* Acta med. belg., 1957, p. 401.

47. SATO, K. *Folia psychiat. neurol., Japan* 5: 198, 1952.

48. SEM-JACOBSEN, C. W., R. G. BICKFORD, M. C. PETERSEN AND H. W. DODGE. *Proc. Staff Meet., Mayo Clin.* 28: 156, 1953.

49. SEM-JACOBSEN, C. W., M. C. PETERSEN, H. W. DODGE, J. A. LAZARTE AND C. HOLMAN. *Electroencephalog. & Clin. Neurophysiol.* 8: 263, 1956.

50. SHIPTON, J. AND W. G. WALTER. In: *Conditionnment et Reactivite en Electroencephalographie*, edited by H. Fischgold and H. Gastaut. Paris: Masson, 1957, p. 185.

51. TAUC, L. *J. physiol., Paris* 47: 769, 1955.

52. UTTLEY, A. M. *Electroencephalog. & Clin. Neurophysiol.* 6: 479, 1954.

53. WALTER, V. J. AND W. G. WALTER. *Electroencephalog. & Clin. Neurophysiol.* 1: 57, 1949.

54. WALTER, W. G. *J. Neurol. Neurosurg. & Psychiat.* 1: 359, 1938.

55. WALTER, W. G. *J. Ment. Sc.* 96: 1, 1950.

56. WALTER, W. G. *The Living Brain.* London: Duckworth, 1953.

57. WALTER, W. G. *Electroencephalog. & Clin. Neurophysiol* Suppl. 4: 7, 1953.

58. WALTER, W. G. In: *Brain Mechanisms and Consciousness*, edited by E. D. Adrian, F. Bremer, H. H. Jasper and J. F. Delafresnaye. Oxford: Blackwell, 1954.

59. WALTER, W. G. *Nature, London* 177: 710, 1956.

60. WALTER, W. G. In: *Child Development*, edited by J. M. Tanner and B. Inhelder. London: Tavistock Press, 1956.

61. WALTER, W. G. *Proc. Roy. Soc. Med.* 50: 799, 1957.

62. WALTER, W. G. AND V. J. DOVEY. *J. Neurol. Neurosurg. & Psychiat.* 7: 57, 1944.

63. WALTER, W. G. AND V. J. DOVEY. *Lancet* 2: 5, 1946.

64. WALTER, W. G. AND H. W. SHIPTON. *Brit. Inst. Radio Engin.* 2: 260, 1951.

65. WALTER, W. G. AND J. SHIPTON. In: *Conditionnment et Reactivite en Electroencephalographie*, edited by H. Fischgold and H. Gastaut. Paris: Masson, 1957, p. 177.

66. WERRE, P. F. *Relations between EEG and Psychological Data in Normal Adults.* Leiden: Leiden Univ. Press, 1957.

67. WIENER, N. *Cybernetics.* New York: Wiley, 1948.

68. WINTREBERT, P. *Arch. Zool. Exper. Gen.* 60: 221, 1920.

CHAPTER XII

The evoked potentials

HSIANG-TUNG CHANG[1] | *Rockefeller Institute, New York City, and the Institute of Neurophysiology, University of Copenhagen, Denmark*

CHAPTER CONTENTS

INTRODUCTION

Definition

BY AN EVOKED POTENTIAL is meant the detectable electrical change of any part of the brain in response to

[1] Present address: Academia Sinica, Shanghai, China.

deliberate stimulation of a peripheral sense organ, a sensory nerve, a point on the sensory pathway or any related structure of the sensory system. Although observations of evoked potentials have most frequently been made in the sensory system, potentials produced by other means such as by direct electrical stimulation or antidromic stimulation of the neuron fall into the same category.

In physiology the term 'potential' is often very loosely used as signifying merely the electrical change. Strictly speaking, the potential at a point of the tissue implies the same meaning as in physics and thus denotes the work necessary to bring a unit charge from infinity up to the point in question which is located in an electrostatic field. Its absolute value can be measured only with one electrode placed on the active tissue and the other grounded. It would be necessary to record the current rather than the potential if the two recording electrodes were placed on the same active tissue. However, it is possible to obtain a close approximation of the potential value by means of Laplacian placement of electrodes in which one active electrode is surrounded by a number of similar electrodes combined together as a single pole. This method of recording seems to have certain advantages, especially when precise localization and determination of the distribution of the action potential are desired (58). The evoked potential differs from the so-called spontaneous electrical changes in many respects, notably the following. *a*) It bears definite temporal relationship to the onset of the stimulus. In other words, it has a definite latent period determined by the conduction velocity of the nerve impulses, the conduction distance between the point of stimulation and the point of recording, the synaptic delay and the number of synapses involved. In a given system the latency is generally fixed and consistent under similar experimental conditions. *b*) It has a definite pattern of response characteristic of a specific system which is more or less predictable and reproducible under similar conditions. *c*) It usually appears in a circumscribed area of the central nervous system where the active tissue is located.

Identification of the evoked potential requires knowledge of anatomical connections between the site of stimulation and the point of recording. As distinct from spontaneous electrical activity, potentials evoked by deliberate stimulation of peripheral sensory nerves are sharply localized in the central nervous system. The procedure of evoked potential registration thus becomes a useful tool for the investigation of sensory pathways. It has been particularly fruitful when applied to the study of cortical representation of the auditory, visual and various cutaneous sense organs.

Limitations of Evoked Potentials as Tools for Anatomical Study

It is not intended at present to discuss in detail sensory localization demonstrated by the evoked potential technique. This is discussed in the chapters of this handbook dealing with the various sensory mechanisms. However, in order to caution against the misuse of the technique it may be pertinent to mention briefly here some fundamental aspects of the evoked potential, especially those which limit its usefulness in anatomicophysiological study. First, the method is valuable in determining the area of sensory projection on the cerebral cortex only when the observation is made under such conditions that the cerebral cortex is not in an exalted state of excitation, if the true sensory projection area is to be determined. It is an obvious fact that in so complex an organization as the cerebral cortex each neuron is potentially related to any other neuron through a vast number of chains of synaptic connections. When a given neuron is activated by an afferent impulse, almost any other neuron may become excited unless some restrictive influence is exerted to curb the spread of the evoked potential to remote regions where no afferent fibers terminate directly. Second, the appearance of an electrical change in a given area of the cerebral cortex does not necessarily indicate the presence of neuronal activity underlying that area. As pointed out long ago by Helmholtz, measurement of the external field of electrical current on the surface of a living tissue is not adequate to ascertain the location of the internal electromotive force. The electrical changes detected from the surface of the brain may be derived from a purely physical process such as the

potential field created by the passage of electrical current along a nerve bathed in a conducting medium. According to the volume conductor principle (47, 49), when a synchronous volley of impulses passes along a nerve embedded in a volume of conducting medium, there will appear in the medium a travelling electric field around the nerve. Such a field is caused by the flow of electric current from the inactive region to the depolarized region of the nerve. The region occupied by the nerve impulse serves as a fictitious sink of current flow and the regions lying ahead and behind the impulse as fictitious sources. Thus, the sign of the action current recorded from the active elements in the brain is negative-positive diphasic at the point where the nerve impulse is initiated, positive-negative diphasic at the point where the conducting path ends and positive-negative-positive triphasic at the middle of the conducting path. At points away from the active element the sign of the detectable action potential will depend on the position of the electrode relative to the direction and the pattern of the isopotential lines of the traveling electric field.

COMPONENTS OF EVOKED POTENTIALS AND THEIR IDENTIFICATION

The action potential in the brain evoked either by electrical stimulation of the ascending pathways or by adequate stimulation of the sense organs consists of two components, the presynaptic and the postsynaptic. The former indicates the arrival of impulses passing along the axon and their terminals, and the latter the activities of the cell body and dendrites. For the purpose of illustration, the evoked potential of the sensory cortex may be taken as an example. Following the arrival of a volley of afferent impulses from the thalamus, the projection area of the cerebral cortex gives rise to a surface-positive primary response followed sometimes by a series of rhythmic afterdischarges. The primary response is made up of the presynaptic potential produced by the activity of thalamocortical fibers and the postsynaptic potential produced by the discharge of intracortical neurons.

The incoming impulses from the thalamus are often blended with, and obscured by, the powerful postsynaptic discharge of the cortical neurons. This is especially true when the afferent impulses are initiated by stimulation of the peripheral sense organs or of the pathway far away from the cerebral cortex. In that event, the afferent impulses usually arrive at the cortex asynchronously due to temporal dispersion.

In the visual system, however, the radiation potential is discernible in the cortical response to stimulation of the optic nerve for two reasons: first, distinct groups of fibers according to size are present throughout the pathway from the optic nerve to the optic radiation; and, second, there are no intercalated neurons in the lateral geniculate body which, if present, would destroy the synchrony of conduction of optic impulses and thus obliterate the characteristic triple-spike radiation potential. In the auditory system as well as in the somesthetic system the presynaptic component of the evoked potential can also be demonstrated, though less prominently than in the visual system, if the corresponding thalamic nucleus is directly stimulated with a brief electric shock.

In spite of the composite nature of the primary response, the two components can be readily differentiated from each other by various experimental procedures as described below.

The Latent Period

The presynaptic component of the evoked potential, being the initial sign of activity, has the shortest latency with a value contingent upon the fiber diameter and the conduction distance of a given system. It is readily identifiable in a system composed of fibers of uniform size. The temporal dispersion of the presynaptic impulses passing along a bundle of fibers of different sizes may make the time of arrival at the point of recording vary over a wide range so that the last impulses may overlap with the postsynaptic discharge set up by the fast fibers. Under such circumstances it is impossible to distinguish presynaptic from postsynaptic activity merely by the latency; only the activity of the fastest fibers of the group can be ascertained. In fact, such is always the case in the cortical and subcortical potentials evoked by adequate stimulation of peripheral sense organs.

Another factor which may seriously limit the applicability and the value of latency measurement is the possible reduction in conduction velocity of impulses at nerve terminals resulting from the diminution of fiber diameter. It is not known whether the impulses vanish instantly at the specialized presynaptic endings. According to Barron & Matthews (4), and Lloyd & McIntyre (46) a prolonged negativity persists at the afferent terminals of spinal dorsal root fibers and is detectable at a considerable distance from the active fibers as the dorsal root potential DR-IV in Lloyd's terminology. The prolonged depolarization of a dorsal root fiber following a single shock stimulation can be recorded with an intracellular microelectrode (41).

Effect of Repetitive Stimulation

It has long been known that synaptic transmission can be blocked by stimuli delivered in quick succession. At certain rates of stimulation the amplitude of the electrical response involving synapses decreases with each response, becoming successively smaller than the preceding one until finally the response disappears entirely. The repolarization process of the membrane of the neuron soma which receives the presynaptic excitation apparently requires a longer time than the axon. The postsynaptic neuron is not able to respond to successively arriving impulses until the recovery of its excitability becomes complete. The effect of synaptic block by repetitive stimulation is especially pronounced in subjects under deep anesthesia by barbiturates. The method has been successfully used in differentiation of the presynaptic from the postsynaptic components of the evoked potential in the lateral geniculate body by Bishop & McLeod (8). As another example to illustrate the differential effect of repetitive stimulation on the pre- and the postsynaptic potentials, the electrical response of the pyramidal tract to electrical stimulation of the motor cortex may be taken. According to the study by Patton & Amassian (57) the pyramidal response to cortical stimulation consists of an early wave resulting from direct stimulation of the motor neurons and a later wave resulting from the activity of cortical internuncial neurons, which is elicited indirectly or synaptically. The former can follow repetitive stimulation at frequencies as high as 340 per sec. with only slight reduction in amplitude, whereas the latter disappears from the response when stimulus frequency is increased from 44.7 per sec. to 127 per sec.

The presynaptic response or the response of an axon to direct electrical stimulation is usually able to follow faithfully the stimuli at a high rate limited only by the refractory period. The degree of the blocking effect of repetitive stimulation seems to increase with the increase in number of synapses involved. For instance, in the first relay station of the dorsal root fibers, i.e. the cuneate nucleus, the postsynaptic discharge of a single neuron to repetitive stimulation of peripheral sense organs or of its nerve can follow the rate of stimulation as high as 100 per sec. without substantial modification of either the response amplitude or the latency. Increase in rate of stimulation reduces the number of spikes of the responding neuron. It has been observed, though very infrequently, that the cuneate neuron may respond to peripheral stimulation at a rate as high as 500 per sec. (2). Evoked potentials of the thalamic neurons, which receive afferent impulses after a number of synaptic relays at lower levels of the neural axis, cannot follow rates of stimulation even as low as 20 per sec. The somatic sensory cortex is known to be unable to respond fully to peripheral stimulation at a rate higher than 7 per sec. in animals under barbiturate anesthesia (33); in other conditions the rate may be as high as 14 per sec. (40).

Effect of Changes in Internal and External Milieu

The axon is generally known to withstand adverse changes of the internal or external milieu better than the cell body and dendrites. In accordance with this tenet, the postsynaptic potential which involves the activity of the latter structures has been found to be more susceptible to the lack of oxygen than the presynaptic potential. In complete anoxia produced by asphyxiation or by inhaling pure nitrogen, for instance, the postsynaptic potential can be abolished in about 90 sec. while the activity of the presynaptic fibers may last for a considerably longer period of time. The greatest difference between the pre- and the postsynaptic potentials, however, lies in the rate of recovery from anoxia. Experimental evidence shows that the axonal component of the cortical response to stimulation of the medullary pyramid begins to recover from the effect of anoxia in about 1 min. after the readmission of oxygen and resumes its original size in about 5 min. The postsynaptic component of the response, on the other hand, will not reappear until 5 or 6 min. later. A complete recovery may require even 10 or 20 min., depending on how soon oxygen was readmitted (21, 22). Similarly, the synaptically elicited wave (I-wave) of the pyramidal response to cortical stimulation is reduced in size after 70 sec. of asphyxia and virtually abolished after 130 sec., while the directly elicited discharges (D-wave) persist (57).

Like anoxia, mechanical pressure, traumatic injury and low temperature all depress the postsynaptic function sooner and more severely than the presynaptic activity. There are some chemicals such as strychnine and tubocurarine which may enhance specifically the postsynaptic activity without markedly affecting the presynaptic potentials (20, 25).

It has been observed that when the cortical surface was cooled by controlled refrigeration, the functional activity of dendrites of cortical neurons was partially blocked at temperatures below 28°C and was completely abolished at 22°C, while the functional activity of axon remained without adverse changes. From this fact it may be inferred that the postsynaptic potential which involves the process of depolarization of dendrites must be affected by low temperature more severely than the potentials derived from the directly excited axons (21).

Anatomical Considerations

In determining whether or not a potential component is pre- or postsynaptic, the anatomical situation must be considered as a decisive factor. Obviously one cannot assign a potential as postsynaptic if there are only directly excited fibers present in the system involved. In the case of antidromic action potential in the optic nerve elicited by stimulation of the optic tract, for instance, it is obviously not possible to have a postsynaptic component in the potentials obtained (24). However, it would not be so easy to be certain in a central structure which is embedded among a complicated mass of various neural elements. In that circumstance, the characteristics of the recorded potential must be taken into consideration together with the related anatomical organization of the system concerned. An approach of this kind has been adopted frequently in analysis of evoked cortical potentials. We may take as an example the microelectrode study of the cortical potential evoked by stimulation of the ventrolateral nucleus of the thalamus (43). Recordings taken from different depths of the cerebral cortex invariably show the presence of positive-negative diphasic spikes in the early phase of the potential. These spikes which have comparatively low voltage are frequently seen at all levels below 0.7 mm. The negative phase of the spike increases as the electrode is pushed deeper into the cortex. They can easily be distinguished from the high voltage spikes derived from the cell bodies. The short latency and the brief duration of the spikes makes it certain that they are from the presynaptic thalamocortical fibers which are known to terminate mainly in the fourth layer of the cortex located about 0.7 mm beneath the cortical surface in the cat. Alignment of simultaneous recordings from the cortical surface with a gross electrode and those from the depth when a microelectrode shows a temporal coincidence of the small diphasic spikes and the usual elevations of the potential of surface recordings which have often been designated as radiation potentials.

The cell body discharges are usually spikes of high voltage and are of quite long duration. The difference in duration between the potentials of a single axon and of a single cell body has been established through the microelectrode studies on spinal ganglia (65), on the spinal cord (68), on the lateral geniculate body and on the cerebral cortex (66). According to Woodbury & Patton (68) the duration of the spike is about 0.6 msec. for the axon and 1 msec. for the cell body. Tasaki *et al.* (66) put the values as 1 msec. or less for axonal response and 1.5 to 3 msec. for the cell body response. Frank & Fuortes found the respective values for dorsal root fibers and cell body of the spinal motoneurons to be 0.6 msec. and 1.6 msec., respectively (35).

NEURAL MECHANISMS FOR THE ELABORATION OF
EVOKED CORTICAL POTENTIALS

The generation of the radiation spikes of the evoked potential is a relatively simple problem. It is a generally accepted opinion that the initial sharp spikes with short latency represent the arrival of afferent impulses which are purely presynaptic in nature. Sufficient evidence is available that the main part of the surface positive wave of the primary response on which the presynaptic spikes may be superimposed is made up of the discharges of the cortical neurons.

*Types of Neural Elements Involved and
Their Mode of Action*

As to exactly what cortical elements are responsible for the production of this potential and what is the mechanism by which an afferent volley initiates the discharge of those elements, remain points to be elucidated. Since there are few available data concerning the roles played by different types of cortical elements, the postulation of a mechanism for the genesis of the evoked cortical potential must be made on the basis of the histological organization of the cerebral cortex and the established principles of electrophysiology. In view of the fact that the basic pattern of the cortical response to afferent impulses appears remarkably constant throughout the sensory cortex and that the sensory cortex invariably receives specific thalamic afferent fibers and possesses a very well developed granular layer, these latter two struc-

tural characteristics must be taken into consideration in offering any explanation of the evoked cortical potential.

The specific afferent fibers arising from the thalamus are known to terminate mainly in the fourth layer by a rich plexus of repeatedly arborized endings. Afferent impulses coming along these fibers make their first synaptic contact with Golgi type II cells in the fourth layer. Golgi type II cells are characterized by the presence of short axons terminating in profuse arborizations in a localized region surrounding the parent cell body. Their dendrites are rather few and poorly developed. By virtue of their anatomical characteristics they are not able to transmit impulses to distant regions but serve as amplifiers by which the afferent impulses are reinforced. They are undoubtedly indispensable for the elaboration of the evoked cortical potentials. However, since there is no definite orientation of the conducting structure of these cells and the electric field created by the discharge of these cells is a closed type (48), their activity cannot be recorded as any sizable potential from the cortical surface. The consequence of the discharge of Golgi type II cells in layer IV is probably to activate the star pyramids and the star cells in the same layer which in turn activate the numerous medium and small pyramids which eventually depolarize the large pyramids in the fifth and sixth layers. The large pyramids send out efferent axons to some other parts of the central nervous system.

*The Initiation of Postsynaptic Impulses
in Pyramidal Neurons*

The detectable surface-positive potential can be reasonably assigned to the propagation of nerve impulses along the vertically oriented apical dendrites of different sized cortical pyramids. Under normal conditions the depolarization process of cortical pyramids resulting from a supraliminal synaptic excitation is apt to start at the somatic membrane around the cell body rather than at the terminal portion of the dendrites. According to a recent postulation (17, 23) the pericorpuscular synaptic knobs constitute the most effective apparatus for the initiation of a postsynaptic discharge, whereas the subliminal excitation of paradendritic synapses can produce only electrotonic changes and so modify the state of excitability of the neuron. The paradendritic synapses, because of their lower density of distribution and their special manner of contact with the next neuron, are believed to be inadequate to effect a postsynaptic neuronal discharge under ordinary conditions. It is well known that the dendritic shafts of the large pyramidal neurons in the fifth and sixth layers of the sensory cortex do not give off branches in the fourth layer where the terminals of the thalamo-cortical fibers and the aggregations of Golgi type II cells are located. The only contact between the large pyramidal cells and the afferent elements is made through the comparatively few paradendritic synapses which are not sufficient to bring about a postsynaptic discharge. It is most unlikely that the afferent fibers from the thalamus and Golgi type II cells in layer IV can ever directly activate the large pyramidal cells. The discharge of the large pyramidal cells on arrival of an afferent volley of impulses must be achieved through the action of pericorpuscular synapses supplied by small and medium pyramidal cells.

Apical Dendrites and Electrical Signs of the Evoked Potential

From the point of view set forth above, the surface-positivity of the primary response of the evoked cortical potential can be reasonably explained. When the pyramidal cells are indirectly activated by afferent impulses through chains of internuncial neurons including Golgi type II cells, star pyramids and small and medium pyramidal cells which make pericorpuscular synapsis with the large pyramids, the post-synaptic impulses initiated at the cell body will serve as a sink and the apical dendrites as a source of the current flow. The record of such electrical change taken from the cortical surface will be a positive wave. As soon as the impulses arrive at the apical dendritic plexus at the cortical surface, the electrical sign of the potential will be reversed. The surface-negative wave following the positive deflection of the primary response may be accounted for, at least in part, on this basis. As pointed out previously (14) this interpretation does not exclude the possibility that other cortical elements participate in the elaboration of the surface negative deflection. In fact, the neurons situated in the upper layers of the cortex must also be involved.

The conduction velocity of impulses passing along dendrites is less than 2 m per sec., which is many times slower than that of impulses passing along axons. There is also a decremental reduction in velocity as the impulses are propagated from the proximal part to the terminal regions of the dendrites (21). The long duration of the surface-positive wave of the evoked potential gives every indication of being a

manifestation of dendritic activity. It is more than probable that the process underlying the surface-positive wave and the following negativity lie mainly in the apical dendrites of different groups of cortical pyramids. The deeply situated basal dendrites of the pyramidal cells are mostly oriented toward the sub-cortical white matter or more or less horizontally. In other words, they are arranged in a direction roughly opposite to that taken by the apical dendrites. Thus, during the discharge of the pyramidal cells the potential changes originating from the basal dendrites must be greatly neutralized by the divergently propagating potentials along the overwhelmingly dominant apical dendrites, if the potentials are recorded from a lead on the cortical surface.

Microelectrode Findings Concerning the Mechanism of Impulse Initiation in Single Neurons

Without going into a detailed discussion of the fundamental mechanism by which the propagated impulse is initiated by electrical or synaptic excitation, it may be relevant to mention here a few experimental facts which seem to characterize the synaptically evoked potentials as contrasted with the antidromically produced potentials. As revealed by intracellular microelectrode recordings, the discharge of a neuron elicited by synaptic excitation of the cell body or dendrites is characteristically different from that elicited by stimulation of its axon. The synaptically produced discharge as well as the spontaneous firing of a neuron is usually preceded by a slowly rising positive deflection upon which the sharp spike rides when the discharge threshold is reached. On subliminal stimulation only the small deflection will be present. Such preliminary potentials have been observed in spinal motoneurons (11), in the thalamus (60) and in Betz cells of the motor cortex (59). It has sometimes been called the 'synaptic potential'. Since it may be present without necessarily involving synaptic transfer of impulses and since the term also describes the potentials recorded by other means, it has been suggested to adopt the noncommittal term 'prepotential' in its place (68).

The fact that the prepotential is present mostly in the evoked or spontaneously occurring responses which involve the activity of cell body and dendrites but not in the antidromic responses seems to suggest that activity of the dendrites plays an important role in initiation of the spike discharge. In this respect Eyzaguirre & Kuffler's study on single neurons of the lobster and crayfish has thrown much light on the mechanism of impulse initiation in a neuron (30–32). Eyzaguirre & Kuffler found that subliminal excitation of the dendrite by mechanical stretch of the muscle in which the dendrites are imbedded produces a reduction of the membrane potential of the cell body through the electrotonic effect. A propagated discharge takes place only when the membrane potential is reduced to a certain level. From this it appears that the prepotential of the evoked response may represent nothing but a partial depolarization of the resting membrane potential resulting from subliminal excitation of dendrites by bombardments of presynaptic nerve endings. Antidromic discharge of a neuron apparently calls for no such build-up of the excitability level as a prerequisite and is therefore devoid of the characteristic small prepotential often seen in responses produced by synaptic action.

AFTER-DISCHARGES

The term 'after-discharge' has been conventionally employed to describe the epileptiform discharges of neurons following strong tetanic stimulation which persist long after the cessation of stimulation. Since accumulated experimental data show that repetitive bursts occur not only after tetanic stimulation but also after a single shock applied to the system, we will designate all the discharges which outlast the duration of stimulation, tetanic or single shock, as after-discharges, in the very loose sense of the terminology.

For the sake of convenience in discussion, after-discharges can be classified into three types: *1)* repetitive firings of single elements which are self-maintained without the participation of other elements in their production; *2)* persistent local after-discharges involving the activity of closely situated intrinsic neurons which form short neuronal circuits; and *3)* periodic discharges involving reverberating activities of a closed neuronal circuit formed by long chains of neurons connecting remotely separated structures.

Repetitive Firing of Individual Neurons

Microelectrode recordings from the thalamic and the cortical neurons show that a single neuron fires several times in response to an afferent volley. To a stimulus at threshold strength a neuron generally responds by giving rise to a single spike. As the stimulus increases in strength, the number of the spikes increases correspondingly. It has been reported that a thalamic unit may fire seven times in quick succession

in response to optimal stimulation of the skin receptors (60). A single neuron in the reticular formation, for instance, may give rise to a train of as many as 20 spikes in response to a single stimulus (3). In so far as the length of the train is concerned, natural adequate stimulation of the sense organs seems to be more effective than electrical stimulation of the nerve. In electrical stimulation, once the threshold is reached further increase in intensity seems to be rather ineffective in inducing any greater responses. On the contrary, strong stimulation may inhibit the successive spikes. This is true for somesthetic, auditory, visual and olfactory systems.

In a long train of repetitive discharges at high frequency, the first spike is usually the largest in amplitude and the second the smallest. The rest of the spikes following the second gradually increase in size until they approach, but rarely become as large as, the first one. The deficit of the successive spikes is probably caused either by the incomplete repolarization of the neuron membrane following a forceful discharge, or by the postexcitatory depression associated with the process of hyperpolarization of the membrane.

The repetitive discharge of a single neuron is believed to be a self-sustained process which is initiated only by the afferent volley but is not the result of repeated bombardments by presynaptic impulses. This belief is based on the observation that a small deflection immediately preceding the first spike of a train, which can be interpreted as a presynaptic potential, is present only once at the beginning of the train. No similar potential has ever been observed preceding the successive spikes. The individual spikes in a train do not correspond to the successive arrivals of presynaptic volleys of impulses. Therefore, the repetitive firing cannot be regarded as resulting from the repetitive arrival of presynaptic impulses. Single nerve elements are endowed with the capacity to discharge repetitively in response to a stimulus. It has been repeatedly demonstrated that following a single shock applied to the dorsal root a burst of four or five unit spikes can be recorded in the dorsal column where, due to the absence of intercalated neurons, synapses are not involved.

The intimate nature of the self-generating mechanism of after-discharge inside the neuron is not known. Burns (13) suggests that the repetitive firing of a cortical neuron following stimulation is due to the difference in recovery rates of resting membrane potentials at the two ends of a neuron such that one end is repolarized more slowly than the other. By virtue of the differential rates of depolarization a neuron is able to fire repetitively, resembling the oscillatory discharge and recharge of two thyratron tubes with two different-valued condensers in the circuit. This concept of Burns is apparently derived from his observation that after-discharge of skeletal muscle fibers may be caused by treatment with decamethonium iodide, which is believed to prevent the end plate membrane from repolarizing as rapidly as the neighboring membrane of the muscle fiber.

Local After-Discharges Involving Intrinsic Neuronal Circuits

Although individual neurons are capable of discharging repetitively in response to a single stimulus, long lasting activities in the central nervous system are mostly manifestations of neuronal discharges resulting from a self-re-exciting mechanism involving numerous neurons arranged in closed circuits in the same structure.

As demonstrated by Burns (12), an isolated slab of cerebral cortex is able to discharge following a single shock applied to the cortical surface. Such discharges may last for many minutes or even hours in some instances and are detectable not only in the circumscribed area directly under stimulation but also in regions at some distance from it. They are evidently not the repetitive firings of the directly stimulated neurons but the responses of neurons synaptically excited through neuronal circuits. After-discharges of this kind usually develop increasing intensity and then suddenly stop altogether at the climax. They may resume the activity after a brief pause. In such a case, the activity of individual neurons apparently depends on the arrival of impulses from some other neurons in the circuit for re-excitation. To perpetuate the activity, the circulating impulses must be maintained above the liminal strength and arrive at the next neuron at an opportune moment when the excitability of the neuron is favorable. The abrupt cessation or suspension of the after-discharge at its climax is probably due to the postexcitatory depression of some neurons in the circuit which fail to respond to the arriving impulses so that the circuit is broken. The self-re-exciting circuits are present in every part of the central nervous system where internuncial neurons exist. Many neurons, especially those whose axons are short but have numerous collaterals, constitute the main source for the elaboration of local after-discharges.

The activation of the internuncial neurons through collaterals has been demonstrated in the cerebral cortex. The action potential of the motor cortex produced by a single shock stimulation of the medullary pyramid consists of the initial deflections with short latency and in addition a rather prolonged discharge which has a latency of 14 to 16 msec. It cannot be interpreted as antidromic activity of the directly stimulated large pyramidal neurons. Such later components of the antidromic cortical potential are variable, labile and more susceptible to the action of anoxia, specific drugs (strychnine for instance) and tetanic stimulation—showing characteristics of the responses involving synapses. When two successive stimuli are applied to the medullary pyramid at short intervals, the cortical response to the second is usually blocked. The temporal course of the recovery process is similar to that of orthodromically evoked potentials. Unit activity of the internuncial neurons participating in the development of such activity can be recorded from different strata of the cortex with a microelectrode. Perhaps the most interesting is the fact that the large pyramidal neurons whose axons have been stimulated originally can be re-excited synaptically by their own collaterals. The discharge of the same pyramidal neuron resulting from the internuncial activity is detectable from the point on the medullary pyramid where the single shock stimulus has been first applied. Thus, the action of the self-re-exciting circuit is completed. The particular significance of the collateral activity of the pyramidal fibers lies in the fact that they constitute a part of the feed-back mechanism in the cerebral cortex by which a message is sent back to the original dispatcher for modification of the subsequent responses. If the feed-back impulses are sufficiently strong and arrive when the brain excitability is in the most favorable condition, it is even possible to initiate a rhythmic after-discharge of the efferent neurons. It is believed that the prolonged epileptiform after-discharges following strong stimulation of the motor cortex and the seizures in pathological cases are produced, at least in part, by a feed-back mechanism through the collaterals in the closed chains of neurons.

Rhythmic After-Discharges Involving Long Neuronal Circuits: Corticothalamic Reverberatory Activity

The primary response of the sensory cortex to an afferent volley is often followed by a train of regularly spaced surface-positive waves with intervals ranging from 50 to 150 msec. (14). The frequency of the repetitive waves seems to be independent of the stimulus strength but varies with the state of anesthesia and the area from which the observations are made. The repetitive discharges evoked by afferent impulses differ from the spontaneous waves in many respects, though they may happen to have the same frequency. The evoked repetitive discharges are always surface-positive waves whereas the spontaneous activity of cortical neurons is not necessarily so. The latter appears to be regulated to some extent by the intralaminar nuclear groups of the thalamus (39); but the evoked periodic after-discharges are not affected by surgical removal or electrical stimulation of the massa intermedia (14).

The presence of the evoked periodic discharges is dependent upon the integrity of the pathways between the cerebral cortex and the thalamic nucleus concerned. The periodic waves recorded from the corresponding thalamic nucleus are similar in pattern to those observed from the sensory cortex and can be abolished by removal of the cortex. Likewise, repetitive discharge of the same kind can be evoked by direct stimulation of the cortical surface and abolished by the destruction of the corresponding thalamic structure or by interruption of the thalamocortical connections. From these experimental facts it is suggested therefore that the specific periodic after-discharges following afferent stimulation represent the activity of the reverberating circuit between the sensory cortex and the thalamus. It is assumed that a volley of afferent impulses from the thalamus, after arriving at the cortex, will return to the thalamic nucleus and ascend again to the cortex to start another cycle of activity along a closed chain of neurons.

It is believed that the general periodic waves observed in the central nervous system can be due to many causes. The activity of reverberating circuits is only one of many possible mechanisms underlying the periodic waves. It would be a mistake to regard all kinds of rhythmic discharges as being due to the activity of reverberating circuits. The evoked repetitive discharge in the sensory cortex must be distinguished from the spontaneous rhythmic waves which sometimes present themselves in such a manner as to confuse or mislead the observer. It is true that in unanesthetized animals or in animals anesthetized with chloralose the rhythmic discharges following a single sound stimulus do occur in the medial geniculate body after decortication (36). However, as pointed out by Galambos, rhythmic waves also occur spontaneously without deliberate stimulation. It is obviously a mechanism entirely different from that

underlying the specific corticothalamic reverberating waves which, under experimental conditions, can be evoked only by an afferent volley from the thalamus or by direct cortical stimulation. So specific is this response that corticothalamic waves have never been obtained by stimulation of a symmetrical point on the opposite cortex although the callosal response itself may be a very intense one (18, 19). The failure of a callosal volley to initiate the repetitive discharges of the sensory cortex at the same cortical locus where the thalamic volley can do so very well seems to provide strong evidence that the appearance of the repetitive waves is dependent on the presence of a specific neuronal circuit rather than being representative of mere local after-discharge of an unorganized aggregate of neurons having autorhythmic properties.

One of the main difficulties in interpretation of the specific periodic after-discharges according to the hypothesis of corticothalamic reverberation is perhaps the long interval (45 to 150 msec.) between the consecutive waves which appears to be of too great a duration to be accounted for solely by the time necessary for the impulses to travel along the neuronal circuit between the thalamus and the cortex. A possible explanation is that the surface-positive reverberating waves, like the positive component of the primary response, presumably consist of synchronous discharges of cortical neurons triggered by the recurrent thalamic volleys but not the afferent impulses themselves. The latter may not be detectable from the cortical surface. Because of the variation in size of fibers interconnecting the thalamus and the cortex and the variation in number of synapses interposed in the circuit, the degree of temporal dispersion of the circulation of the reverberating impulses along the circuit must result in a continuous train instead of intermittent waves. It is probable that among the returning impulses only those which arrive at certain phases of the excitability cycle of the cortical neurons are capable of initiating synchronous discharges of these neurons, and the others which arrive at the cortex during the period of postexcitatory depression rendered by the previous wave will not cause excitation. Therefore, the interval between the reverberating waves is probably determined by the state of excitability of the cortical neurons at the time of action, rather than by the conduction time and the number of synapses in the circuit. Thus, it becomes evident that the activity of the corticothalamic reverberating circuit cannot be taken as a simple circulating of impulses along a closed chain of neurons.

According to Bremer (9) the initiation and maintenance of the periodic waves in the cerebral cortex, although considered by him to be fundamentally a manifestation of autorhythmicity of neurons, necessitate a minimal influx of corticipetal impulses. The requirement of this minimal number of afferent impulses for the production of periodic cortical waves is in some respects close to the essential concept underlying the proposed mechanism of corticothalamic reverberation. The dependence of the so-called spontaneous activity of cortical neurons on activation by afferent impulses has been convincingly proved by Burns (12). He demonstrated that the spontaneous activity of isolated slabs of the cerebral cortex did not ensue unless a bridge was left connected with the rest of the brain. However, such slabs may exhibit periodic activity if kept normally oxygenated (42).

EXCITABILITY CHANGES ACCOMPANYING AND
FOLLOWING THE EVOKED POTENTIAL

Like peripheral nerves or other excitable tissues the aggregate of neurons in the central nervous system, after being activated either by direct or synaptic stimulation, undergoes a cycle of excitability change consisting of a refractory phase and a recovery phase. After recovery, it may go into another period of secondary depression during which the neurons fail to respond or respond with less vigor. Uniquely in the sensory cortex, a periodic variation in excitability may develop as a result of the corticothalamic reverberating activity.

Refractory Periods

The absolute refractory period following the response of the somesthetic cortex to an afferent stimulus was about 8 msec. and the total recovery time was 17 msec., as determined in monkeys under ether anesthesia. Barbiturates have the effect of lengthening the recovery time. For example, under pentobarbital anesthesia the absolute and the relative refractory periods were found to be of the order of 25 to 50 msec. and 87 to 144 msec., respectively (52, 55). Forbes & Morison (33) found that the amplitude of the primary response of the somesthetic cortex was reduced to 50 to 70 per cent of its initial value when the sciatic nerve of a cat was stimulated at a frequency of 5 to 7 per sec., implying that the relative refractory period was much longer than the value obtained by Marshall *et al.* (55). Forbes *et al.* (34) later reported that stimulation of the sciatic nerve at a frequency of 60 per sec.

produced no detectable cortical response after the response to the first stimulus of the series. They also reported the decrease in size of the primary response to repetitive stimuli at a frequency of 5.5 per sec. and the phenomenon of alternative response to repetitive stimuli delivered at the rate of 14 per sec.

The values of the absolute and relative refractory periods in the visual cortex of man and animals as determined by Gastaut *et al.* (37) were 20 and 40 msec., respectively. According to Tunturi (67), the absolute refractory period in the auditory cortex to a click lasts 20 to 100 msec. and the duration of the relative refractory period is 100 to 250 msec. A glance at the figures obtained by various investigators makes one immediately realize the impossibility of finding standard values for these events since the experimental conditions which determine the results are extremely variable. Among the more important factors affecting the excitability of the brain are the anesthetics used in the experiment (40), the depth of anesthesia during which the observations are made (29, 33, 62), the arterial pressure (6), the moisture (54), the temperature, etc. The level of tonic reticular activity is also a factor of major importance (40).

The effect of barbiturates on the excitability of the nervous system is particularly interesting. It has been suggested that barbiturates act selectively on internuncial neurons in the cortex rather than on the afferent pathway. The suggestion remains to be reconciled with the fact that under barbiturate anesthesia the primary response of the evoked potential is little affected as compared with the marked suppression of the spontaneous cortical waves. As is known, the primary response of the evoked cortical potential consists largely of the activity of cortical internuncial neurons.

The total period of refractoriness of the auditory cortex following a direct electric shock was about 44 msec. The absolute refractory period was estimated as about 7 or 8 msec. This value as compared with that of the peripheral nerve or with that of the individual neurons in the central nervous system is indeed very large. The absolute refractory period of a nerve fiber is known to occupy about the same time as the rising phase of the action potential, which usually does not exceed 1 msec. It has been frequently observed that the minimal interval between successive spikes in a train of unit discharges may be as brief as 1 msec. or less, implying that the refractory period of single neurons following a discharge is substantially shorter than that of the potential recorded from the aggregates of neurons. The reason for this difference between single neurons and neuronal aggregates is not entirely understood. Perhaps in the case of neuronal aggregates the processes of postexcitatory depression have superseded the phase of true refractoriness and therefore make it appear that the refractory period is prolonged. The true refractory period is believed to be the same as the period during which the repolarization process of the membrane potential of the active neurons is taking place. Its value is determined by the rate of the repolarization process.

Postexcitatory Depression

The phase of postexcitatory depression may be defined as the period immediately following the initial recovery from refractoriness during which the nervous tissue undergoes various degrees of lowered excitability. The basic pattern of the event exists in the excitability cycle of any kind of nervous tissue including the cerebral cortex, the spinal cord, peripheral nerves and sympathetic ganglia.

The degree and duration of the postexcitatory depression vary more or less proportionately with the stimulus strength and the number of neurons previously activated by the conditioning stimulus. There may be no obvious secondary depression following the refractory period if the previous response is weak. After an intense response of the cortex the postexcitatory depression may last for several hundred milliseconds. Extremely severe depression lasting for a second or more has been observed following the response of the cortex treated with strychnine. This is true for cortical responses to topical stimulation as well as for those to afferent impulses (15). By using paired electric shocks applied to the optic nerve, both Marshall (53) and Clare & Bishop (26) demonstrated the existence, in the visual cortex and in the lateral geniculate body, of a typical excitability cycle with the supernormal phase followed by a long period of postexcitatory depression. When the retina is continuously illuminated, not only the onset but also the cessation of the photic stimulus produce the phenomenon of postexcitatory depression of the cerebral cortex. The visual cortex undergoes a period of severe depression immediately after the recovery of the cortex from the refractoriness caused by retina excitation. In extreme cases this period of temporary depression may last for as long as several seconds. A similar phenomenon is present in the auditory system. Rosenblith *et al.* (61) observed that the neural response to a click as recorded from the round window and from the auditory cortex of the cat were depressed within the first 40 sec.

after sudden exposure to continuous tones. The postexcitatory inactivation of the cortex discussed here may constitute a physiological basis for the temporary blindness and deafness following a sudden exposure to strong light and loud sound. The diminished excitability of neurons during the period of postexcitatory depression is believed to be associated with the membrane potential changes of the neuron following the discharge. From recent microelectrode studies of the electrical properties of single neurons it has been observed that the repolarization of the membrane potential may develop into a phase of hyperpolarization which reaches a maximum at 5 to 10 msec. and may last for as long as 100 msec. During the period of hyperpolarization the action potential of the neuron is inhibited (27, 28). The time courses of the repolarization and the hyperpolarization processes bear a close relationship to the refractoriness and the postexcitatory depression of the neuron.

Periodic Variation in Cortical Excitability

Unique to the sensory area, the excitability state of the cortex does not always return to the normal level following the completion of a usual excitability cycle but undergoes a further cyclic waxing and waning with regular intervals. The periodic excitability change of the visual cortex was described by Bishop in 1933 (5). However, he believed it was an indication of the excitability change of the optic pathways rather than of the cortical neurons themselves. The periodic variation in excitability of the auditory cortex beyond the unresponsive period caused by a sound stimulus was observed by Jarcho (38). He noticed the periodic depression of the cortex at a frequency coincidental with the repetitive corticothalamic after-discharges. No increased excitability was seen at any time, however. Jarcho's finding was soon confirmed with the further disclosure that in company with the rising and falling of the corticothalamic reverberating waves, there are concomitant increase and decrease of cortical excitability (14, 15). The temporal relation between the repetitive waves and the excitability change of the cerebral cortex resulting from the corticothalamic reverberating activity was found to be such that the cortical excitability is increased during the developing phase of the reverberating wave and decreased during the returning phase of the reverberating wave. An alignment of the excitability curve and the contour of the reverberating waves on the same time scale show that the maximum of the increased excitability is reached in the middle of the developing phase, that the maximum of decreased excitability is reached in the middle of the returning phase and that the excitability remains unchanged both at the peak and at the valley of the reverberating waves. Mathematically speaking, the sinusoidal curves representing the reverberating waves and the excitability changes are 90° out of phase, the maximum of cortical excitability being one quarter of a period ahead of the peak of the reverberating waves (15).

Though intimately related with the corticothalamic reverberating waves, the periodic variation of cortical excitability following an afferent stimulation may be manifested in the absence of detectable repetitive waves. At the onset of continuous illumination of the retina, for instance, the waxing and waning of the cortical excitability can be demonstrated even within the prolonged period of postexcitatory depression during which the reverberating waves are not distinctly visible (16). The significance of the periodic excitability change of this kind is not known. Its relation with the spontaneous brain waves has been discussed by Gastaut (37) and Lindsley (44). The periodic variation in excitability of spinal neurons has been described by Bernhard (7), but the mechanism involved in this case is believed to be different. The relation of the reticular formation to cortical excitability has been studied by King *et al.* (40).

Interaction of Afferent Impulses in the Cerebral Cortex

Information concerning the excitability change of the cortex on which the present discussion is based is obtained mainly from experiments in which the cortical excitability is determined by a testing volley having the same source as the conditioning one. When two afferent volleys of different origin, an auditory and a callosal, for instance, are sent to the same locus of the cortex, the evoked responses to the combined stimuli are characteristically different. The cause of the difference seems to lie in the fact that the callosal and thalamic afferent volleys arrive at different strata of the cortex and activate different sets of neurons, among which a certain number of common elements are involved in the responses to both volleys (19). Probably for the same reason the cortical response to acoustic stimuli can be inhibited or facilitated by simultaneous or successive stimulation of a symmetrical point on the opposite cortex (10).

In an extensive study of the interaction at different levels of the variously evoked afferent impulses, Amassian (1) observed that both the cortical and the thalamic responses to the second of two successive stimuli, delivered at certain intervals to the same nerve or to two separate branches of a peripheral nerve, were always defective. The blocking of the cortical or subcortical response by an antecedent volley was interpreted as inhibition as distinguished from occlusion. Occlusion, by definition, denotes the phenomenon in which the total effect of two processes when activated simultaneously is smaller than when activated separately due to partial overlapping or sharing of common elements. In real occlusion one process should not be completely abolished, though it may be greatly lessened, by another simultaneously occurring process. If it is, it would merely indicate that the common elements can be totally activated by either of the two processes. Thus, the complete blocking of the cortical or subcortical response to stimulation of the volar branch of the ulnar nerve by previous stimulation of the dorsal branch of the same nerve described by Amassian may be regarded as a phenomenon of inhibition, and the defect of cortical response to splanchnic stimulation preceded by a shock to the tibial nerve a phenomenon of occlusion, since the splanchnic nerve and the tibial nerve do have separate focal areas of projection with overlapping fringes in the thalamus and the cortex.

This argument about occlusion is perhaps also applicable to Marshall's investigation of the interaction between the ipsilateral and contralateral visual pathways which converge with overlapping terminal branches on some common neurons in the visual cortex (53). It is significant that bilateral interaction does not occur at the geniculate level, since the optic fibers from the two retinae do not mingle but terminate in separate laminae of the lateral geniculate body. There are no common neurons available at that level for the impulses from both sides to act on each other, although the impulses reach the same nucleus. However, if two stimuli of equal strength are applied to the same optic nerve at proper intervals the geniculate response to the second stimulus is greater than that to one stimulus alone. Apparently, the neurons in the subliminal fringe are recruited into action due to temporal summation.

Modification of Cortical Excitability by Constant Inflow of Afferent Impulses

It has long been known that the proper excitability level in an animal when awake is maintained by an incessant action of afferent impulses. It has frequently been reported clinically that patients completely deprived of sensory abilities fall asleep immediately and can be aroused only by stimulation of some sense organs. Experimental evidence shows that afferent impulses necessary for keeping the cerebral cortex in a state of vigilance reach it from the reticular formation. Impulses in the main ascending sensory pathways apparently travel in collaterals entering the reticular formation, since they cannot maintain wakefulness after destruction of the reticular formation (45, 63, 64).

Perhaps one of the more illustrative examples showing the effect of constant afferent inflow on cortical excitability is the phenomenon of photic potentiation (16). The electrical response to stimulation of the lateral geniculate body was found to be many times greater when the retina was illuminated than when it was in the dark. Not only was the size of the cortical response to geniculate stimulation greater but also the threshold of the response was lower during retinal illumination than in the dark. The effect of photic potentiation on cortical responses developed progressively after the onset of retinal illumination and reached its maximum in about 5 sec. Once the maximal effect was attained, it was sustained at that level as long as the retinal illumination persisted. The enhanced cortical response was promptly reduced to the preillumination magnitude as soon as the light stimulus was withdrawn. The mechanism underlying this potentiation phenomenon is believed to lie mainly in the lateral geniculate body. As is well known, some retinal elements discharge steadily at low frequency in the absence of light which is apparently not strong enough to set up a discharge of the postsynaptic neurons in the lateral geniculate body. Nevertheless, the summated effect of the incessant bombardment of these subliminal impulses will raise the excitability of the geniculate neurons. If meanwhile an electric shock is applied directly to the geniculate body, the neurons which are normally in the subliminal fringe will discharge because of the summation of the existing presynaptic impulses induced by retinal illumination and the electric stimulus directly applied to the geniculate body. The gradual development of the photic potentiation effect in the case of repetitive stimulation of the geniculate body seems to constitute a good example of recruitment in the truly physiological sense of the term.

A similar process is present, though much less pronounced, in the auditory system. Rosenblith *et al.* (61) described the enhancement, by exposure to continuous tones, of potentials evoked in the cortex by a click. Their results suggest that tones of certain frequencies, especially tones at frequencies between 100 and 500 cycles per sec., show a very effective potentiation effect following the initial period of depression, while those of high frequencies are not as effective.

Preliminary observations have been reported on the potentiation effect of continuous retinal illumination on the cortical response to stimulation of the auditory pathway (16). The interaction between the visual and auditory impulses appears to take place not only in the cerebral cortex through the association neurons but also in subcortical structures, since the removal of the visual cortex cannot completely abolish the photic potentiation effect on the auditory response. The explanation for the interaction between the visual and auditory impulses at the subcortical level is rendered difficult by the lack of direct fiber connections between the medial and the lateral geniculate bodies. The pulvinar is considered a possible site of subcortical correlation for the two great special sensory systems. Since the importance of the core structures of the brain stem in the activation of the cerebral cortex has been recognized (50, 51, 56), it is possible that the interaction at the cortical level between the afferent impulses from different sources may be executed indirectly through the system of the diencephalic and mesencephalic reticular formation where collaterals of ascending fibers from different kinds of sense organs converge. The centrally located area in the brain stem comprising the midbrain's tegmentum, the subthalamus, the hypothalamus and the intralaminar portion of the thalamus, has been found to be able to desynchronize the electrocortical activity when it is stimulated repetitively at a rapid rate. It can also exert various effects on the cortical potentials evoked by single shock stimulation of a particular sensory system when it is stimulated singly in close approximation to the eliciting shock. Stimulation of this area in the brainstem has also been described as having a catholic activating effect on the entire cerebral cortex and especially the frontal lobe of the brain. This activating system receives afferent impulses from various sensory sources through the collaterals of ascending tract fibers and transmits them to the cerebral cortex, probably both by the thalamic and the capsular corticipetal routes.

SUMMARY

An evoked potential may be defined as the detectable electrical change in the brain in response to deliberate stimulation of any part of the nervous system.

Such potentials differ from the spontaneous electrical activity in that they have a definite temporal relationship to the onset of the stimulus, a constant pattern of response and a focus of maximal response in the brain. The technique of evoked potential registration has been widely used as a tool for anatomical studies of the central nervous system. However, the conclusions drawn from the results of such studies are justified only when the limitations of this technique are duly considered.

The primary response of the evoked cortical potential consists of a presynaptic component produced by the impulses from the afferent fibers and a postsynaptic component produced by the discharge of intracortical neurons. These two components can be differentiated from each other by various experimental procedures, such as by study of a) latency, b) the effect of repetitive stimulation, c) the relative tolerance to changes in internal and external milieu and above all d) the anatomical considerations.

The neural mechanism for elaboration of the evoked cortical potential is formulated on the basis of the histological organization of the cerebral cortex and the general principles of neurophysiology. In a proposed scheme it is suggested that the afferent impulses from the thalamocortical fibers first excite the Golgi type II cells in the fourth cortical stratum which in turn transmit the postsynaptic impulses to star pyramids and the star cells in the same layer, then to small and medium pyramidal neurons in the supragranular layers and finally to the large pyramidal neurons in the deep layers. The surface-positive deflection of the evoked potential is attributed to the synchronized propagation of impulses along the apical dendrites from the cell body of pyramidal neurons inward to the cortical surface. The depolarization process of the cortical pyramidal neurons is believed to start always at the cell body due to the effective excitatory action of the pericorpuscular synapses. The subliminal excitation of the paradendritic synapses has the effect only of modifying the excitability state of the neuron. This hypothesis is supported by the results of microelectrode findings of single neurons.

After-discharges can be classified into three kinds: 1) the self-sustained repetitive firing of single elements, 2) persistent local after-discharges involving the activity of closely situated intrinsic neurons and 3) the periodic after-discharges involving the activity of reverberating circuits interconnecting distant structures. Of these three, the most frequently observed in the central nervous system is the local after-discharge, maintained by a mechanism of self-re-excitation through collaterals and numerous closed neuronal circuits within the cortex. The activities of the long reverberating circuit are not to be confused with other kinds of periodic waves which may happen to have similar frequency and similar wave form.

The brain undergoes a cycle of excitability changes accompanying and following the evoked potential. The true refractory period which lasts for less than a millisecond is thought to be related to the repolarization process of the neuron. The postexcitatory depression which may last for as long as 100 msec. is probably a functional manifestation of the hyperpolarization process. Because of the supersession of the refractory phase by the process of postexcitatory depression, the value of the true refractory period of the neuronal aggregate cannot be accurately determined. In addition to the regular excitability cycle there is a periodic variation of excitability accompanying the reverberating activity of the sensory cortex.

Although the evoked potentials in different systems are independent processes, they do show interaction probably due to the overlapping of their fiber distribution or the convergence of the afferent impulses on the common neurons, or through the integration in a general activating system such as the reticular formation. Such interaction of afferent impulses in the cerebral cortex makes it possible for the constant afferent inflow in any particular sensory system to modify the level of cortical excitability as a whole.

REFERENCES

1. AMASSIAN, V. E. A. Res. Nerv. & Ment. Dis., Proc. 30: 371, 1952.
2. AMASSIAN, V. E. AND J. L. DEVITO. Fed. Proc. 13: 3, 1954.
3. AMASSIAN, V. E. AND R. V. DEVITO. J. Neurophysiol. 17: 575, 1954.
4. BARRON, D. H. AND B. H. C. MATTHEWS. J. Physiol. 92: 276, 1938.
5. BARTLEY, S. H. AND G. H. BISHOP. Am. J. Physiol. 103: 159, 1933.
6. BEECHER, H. K., F. K. McDONOUGH AND A. FORBES. J. Neurophysiol. 1: 324, 1938.
7. BERNHARD, C. G. J. Neurophysiol. 7: 397, 1944.
8. BISHOP, P. O. AND J. G. McLEOD. J. Neurophysiol. 17: 387, 1954.

9. BREMER, F. *IVe Congr. Neurol. Internat., Rapp.* 1 : 7, 1949.
10. BREMER, F. *Rev. neurol.* 87 : 162, 1952.
11. BROCK, L. G., J. S. COOMBS AND J. C. ECCLES. *J. Physiol.* 117 : 431, 1952.
12. BURNS, D. B. *J. Physiol.* 112, 156, 1951.
13. BURNS, D. B. *J. Physiol.* 127 : 168, 1955.
14. CHANG, H.-T. *J. Neurophysiol.* 13 : 236, 1950.
15. CHANG, H.-T. *J. Neurophysiol.* 14 : 95, 1951.
16. CHANG, H.-T. *J. Neurophysiol.* 15 : 5, 1952.
17. CHANG, H.-T. *Cold Spring Harbor Symp. Quant. Biol.* 17 : 189, 1952.
18. CHANG, H.-T. *J. Neurophysiol.* 16 : 117, 1953.
19. CHANG, H.-T. *J. Neurophysiol.* 16 : 133, 1953.
20. CHANG, H.-T. *J. Neurophysiol.* 16 : 221, 1953.
21. CHANG, H.-T. *J. Neurophysiol.* 18 : 332, 1955.
22. CHANG, H.-T. *J. Neurophysiol.* 18 : 452, 1955.
23. CHANG, H.-T. In: *Problems of the Modern Physiology of the Nervous and Muscle Systems.* Tiflis: Publ. House, Acad. of Sciences, Georgian SSR, 1956.
24. CHANG, H.-T. *J. Neurophysiol.* 19 : 224, 1956.
25. CHANG, H.-T. AND B. KAADA. *J. Neurophysiol.* 13 : 305, 1950.
26. CLARE, M. H. AND G. H. BISHOP. *Electroencephalog. & Clin. Neurophysiol.* 4 : 311, 1952.
27. COOMBS, J. S., J. C. ECCLES AND P. FATT. *J. Physiol.* 130 : 291, 1955.
28. COOMBS, J. S., J. C. ECCLES AND P. FATT. *J. Physiol.* 130 : 326, 1955.
29. DERBYSHIRE, A. J., B. REMPEL, A. FORBES AND E. F. LAMBERT. *Am. J. Physiol.* 116 : 577, 1936.
30. EYZAGUIRRE, C. AND S. W. KUFFLER. *J. Gen. Physiol.* 39 : 87, 1955.
31. EYZAGUIRRE, C. AND S. W. KUFFLER. *J. Gen. Physiol.* 39 : 120, 1955.
32. EYZAGUIRRE, C. AND S. W. KUFFLER. *J. Gen. Physiol.* 39 : 155, 1955.
33. FORBES, A. AND B. R. MORISON. *J. Neurophysiol.* 2 : 112, 1939.
34. FORBES, A., A. F. BATTISTA, P. O. CHATFIELD AND J. P. GARCIA. *Electroencephalog. & Clin. Neurophysiol.* 1 : 141, 1949.
35. FRANK, K. AND M. G. F. FUORTES. *J. Physiol.* 130 : 625, 1955.
36. GALAMBOS, R., J. E. ROSE, R. B. BROMILEY AND J. R. HUGHES. *J. Neurophysiol.* 15 : 359, 1952.
37. GASTAUT, H., Y. GASTAUT, A. ROGER, J. CARRIOL AND R. NAQUET. *Electroencephalog. & Clin. Neurophysiol.* 3 : 401, 1951.
38. JARCHO, L. W. *J. Neurophysiol.* 12 : 447, 1949.
39. JASPER, H. AND J. DROOGLEEVER-FORTUYN. *A. Res. Nerv. & Ment. Dis., Proc.* 26 : 272, 1947.
40. KING, E., R. NAQUET AND H. W. MAGOUN. *J. Pharmacol. & Exper. Therap.* 119 : 48, 1957.
41. KOKETSU, K. *Am. J. Physiol.* 184 : 338, 1956.
42. KRISTINNSEN, K. AND G. COURTOIS. *Electroencephalog. & Clin. Neurophysiol.* 1 : 265, 1949.
43. LI, C. L. AND H. JASPER. *J. Physiol.* 121 : 117, 1953.
44. LINDSLEY, D. B. *Electroencephalog. & Clin. Neurophysiol.* 4 : 443, 1952.
45. LINDSLEY, D. B., L. H. SCHREINER, W. B. KNOWLES AND H. W. MAGOUN. *Electroencephalog. & Clin. Neurophysiol.* 2 : 483, 1950.
46. LLOYD, D. P. C. AND A. K. MCINTYRE. *J. Gen. Physiol.* 32 : 409, 1949.
47. LORENTE DE NÓ, R. *A Study of Nerve Physiology.* New York: Studies from The Rockefeller Institute for Medical Research 131–132, 1947.
48. LORENTE DE NÓ, R. *J. Cell. & Comp. Physiol.* 29 : 207, 1947.
49. LORENTE DE NÓ, R. In: *The Spinal Cord,* edited by J. L. Malcolm and J. A. B. Gray. Boston: Little, 1953, p. 132.
50. MAGOUN, H. W. *Physiol. Rev.* 30 : 455, 1950.
51. MAGOUN, H. W. *Arch. Neurol. & Psychiat.* 67 : 145, 1952.
52. MARSHALL, W. H. *J. Neurophysiol.* 4 : 25, 1941.
53. MARSHALL, W. H. *J. Neurophysiol.* 12 : 277, 1949.
54. MARSHALL, W. H. *Electroencephalog. & Clin. Neurophysiol.* 2 : 177, 1950.
55. MARSHALL, W., C. N. WOOLSEY AND P. BARD. *J. Neurophysiol.* 4 : 1, 1941.
56. MORUZZI, G. AND H. W. MAGOUN. *Electroencephalog. & Clin. Neurophysiol.* 1 : 455, 1949.
57. PATTON, H. D. AND V. E. AMASSIAN. *J. Neurophysiol.* 17 : 345, 1954.
58. PERL, E. R. AND J. U. CASBY. *J. Neurophysiol.* 17 : 429, 1954.
59. PHILLIPS, C. G. *Quart. J. Exper. Physiol.* 41 : 58, 1956.
60. ROSE, J. E. AND V. B. MOUNTCASTLE. *Bull. Johns Hopkins Hosp.* 94 : 238, 1954.
61. ROSENBLITH, W. A., R. GALAMBOS AND I. J. HIRSH. *Science* 111 : 569, 1950.
62. ROSENZWEIG, M. R. *Am. J. Physiol.* 163 : 746, 1950.
63. STARZL, T. E., C. W. TAYLOR AND H. W. MAGOUN. *J. Neurophysiol.* 14 : 461, 1951.
64. STARZL, T. E., C. W. TAYLOR AND H. W. MAGOUN. *J. Neurophysiol.* 14 : 479, 1951.
65. SVAETICHIN, G. *Acta physiol. scandinav.* Suppl. 86, 24 : 23, 1951.
66. TASAKI, I., E. H. POLLEY AND F. ORREGO. *J. Neurophysiol.* 17 : 454, 1954.
67. TUNTURI, A. R. *Am. J. Physiol.* 147 : 311, 1946.
68. WOODBURY, J. W. AND H. D. PATTON. *Cold Spring Harbor Symp. Quant. Biol.* 17 : 185, 1952.

CHAPTER XIII

Changes associated with forebrain

excitation processes: d.c. potentials

of the cerebral cortex[1]

JAMES L. O'LEARY

SIDNEY GOLDRING

Divisions of Neurology and Neurosurgery, and the Beaumont May Institute of Neurology, Washington University School of Medicine, St. Louis, Missouri

CHAPTER CONTENTS

BESIDES THE SPONTANEOUS and evoked potentials conventionally recorded from the cerebral cortex, the exposed brain in a resting state ordinarily shows a voltage difference between cortical surface and ventricle (d.c. potential). If the brain is not disturbed following its preparation for recording, this pia-ventricular potential may remain relatively steady, and for that reason we have referred to it as steady potential (SP).

Aided by grants from the Allen P. and Josephine B. Green Foundation and the Public Health Service (B-882).

The role SP plays in neuronal functioning can be assayed only after taking account of the nonneuronal sources which complicate its interpretation. It is also necessary to differentiate such d.c. potentials from those of pH and oxygen electrode recording. The latter, although employing a d.c. method, depend upon the change which occurs in a critical electrode as a result of a tissue change in its milieu. By contrast, the d.c. recording described hereafter employs very stable electrodes to register changes in the distribution of electrical charge in the intervening tissue.

Reduced oxygen tension incident to systemic deterioration, or intracellular poisoning of respiratory enzyme systems (e.g. by cyanide ions) can produce predictable changes in it. Injury effects and anesthesia are unavoidable complications of any experimental neurophysiological procedure and can also result in SP alterations. Control of these and possibly other factors which limit the applicability of the method is necessary if we are to reach an understanding of the relation between spontaneous and evoked potentials of the usual electrocorticogram and SP changes which may develop coincidentally or subsequently.

Several early studies of d.c. potential are relevant to the approach outlined here. Libet & Gerard (30) first showed that a pia-ventricular potential exists in the frog brain, postulating that a change in such potential can alter spontaneous cortical activity. Jasper & Erickson (22) at about the same time observed a d.c. voltage component associated with high voltage convulsoid discharge. Later Leão (26, 27) proved that a marked d.c. change also accompanies a wave of spreading depression as it propagates across the cortex. This phenomenon will be discussed in detail under experimental findings.

One may assume with Libet & Gerard (30) that a significant component of the pia-ventricular potential arises from an end-to-end polarization of the cortical pyramids, and that the transcortical potential over an area of cortex represents chiefly the average of the polar charges of the contained neurons. However, the potential difference along an individual pyramidal neuron has relative rather than absolute pertinence, for it can be recorded not only when one end of the cell is depolarized, but when, for any reason, the two ends become unequally depolarized. The polarization of both ends might, for example, be lowered unequally, raised unequally, or one raised and one lowered. With externally applied polarization as studied by Bishop & O'Leary (2) it is almost certainly the latter which occurs. Surface-positive polarization applied to an area of cortex accentuates the surface-negative component of evoked potential transients recorded therefrom; accentuation of the surface-positive component occurs during applied surface-negative polarization.

Reviewed herein are: a) the requisites for reliable d.c. recording together with an assay of difficulties which, if unrecognized, may render experimental data unreliable; b) the transient d.c. alterations which have been shown to accompany or follow spontaneous or induced changes in the pattern of the usual ECG, such as changes in spontaneous activity, evoked responses, recruiting waves, barbiturate spindles, strychnine and veratrine spikes; c) changes associated with the occurrence of high voltage convulsoid activity; d) d.c. change accompanying spreading depression; e) evidence linking the polarity of usually recorded evoked potential phenomena with those of accompanying d.c. change; f) d.c. cortical changes produced by repetitive stimulation at sites distant from the recording electrodes and requiring transmission along paths containing intervening synapses; and g) injury potential effects.

SUGGESTED TECHNIQUE FOR CORTICAL D.C. RECORDING

For many experimental studies it is important to monitor the potential continuously. Minor displacements of the recording electrodes or injury (either of which may be due to movement of the animal), an

obstruction in the airway, or periodic excesses of stimulation, can unstabilize a preparation temporarily or permanently. Then, swings of several millivolts from one polarity to the other may occur. Movement of the electrodes alone may occasion swings in potential in either direction, whereas with the other conditions mentioned the changes are characteristic; these will be discussed later. In the rabbit (less often in our experience in the cat) SP swings occur which accompany either spreading depression (Leão) or the appearance of high voltage convulsoid activity. In the rabbit the latter is a common enough accompaniment of excesses of electrical stimulation. Unidirectional drifts may also occur during systemic deterioration, or with oxygen lack or deepening anesthesia. These necessitate quick recognition if the preparation is to continue to provide reliable data.

To measure SP one needs nonpolarizable electrodes. Continuous monitoring during experiments lasting for several hours indicates the need for stable electrodes. We have used calomel half-cells having a difference of potential in Tyrode's of 0.5 to 1.0 mv. A flexible pipette may be led from one member of a pair to the cortical surface of the selected region; that from the other can be introduced either into the ventricle or the subcortical white matter. In the rabbit the former (ventricular) position to the surface gives an individual difference of potential of surface-positive polarity amounting to 1 to 4 mv. If the deep electrode tip is introduced into the subcortical white matter the potential difference may be larger due to the addition of injury potential. Monopolar recording from surface cortex to a point upon the periosteum gives a change of the same polarity as that evident with transcortical recording. The difference of potential is greater than the pia-ventricular potential but less than that led between surface and white matter. Transcortical (or pia-ventricular) d.c. recording is believed to offer greater promise for establishing correlates with spontaneous and evoked activity of the usual ECG because of the more localized leading.

A conventional condensor-coupled electroencephalograph as well as a d.c. amplifier may be used both for monitoring and for the study of d.c. changes. It is only necessary to short-circuit the input 4 to 8 times per sec. Each short circuit discharges such potentials as have accumulated upon the input condensors because their time course has been too long to permit passage into the amplifier. The discharge causes the pens to return momentarily to the baseline of the amplifier. When a chopper is used, if the recording apparatus is set so that a negative ECG transient registers as an upward deflection, a correlated negative SP change appears as a series of down-going pips, the amplitude of which determines the voltage of the change. Vice versa, positive SP changes are recorded as up-going pips. The deflection of the pips then is opposite to the direction in which ECG transients are recorded, although each has the same polarity. The reason is that each interruption of the input returns the pens from a positive or a negative potential value to the zero baseline of the amplifier (fig. 1). The conventional ECG can be recorded upon other channels of the same electroencephalograph, using neighboring pairs of polarizable electrodes for the pickup.

The recording system must be flexible enough to detect microvolt changes at the same time that it is prepared to register a change of several millivolts. To accomplish this two devices are used: a) several channels of amplification record from the same lead combination at different sensitivities; b) a balancing potentiometer is placed in series with one of the calomel half-cells to oppose the electrical effect of any sizeable shift through the application of a countervoltage. The amplitude of an SP change can then be read directly from the potentiometer. During swings of several millivolts the more sensitive channels are first turned off while the least sensitive one is balanced. Thereafter, the others are balanced in order toward the most sensitive one. That one is used continuously to record SP concomitants of evoked and spontaneous activity, and the d.c. changes it records are the ones which can be correlated most directly with ECG manifestations of neuronal activity. From the calomel half-cells, records of the quicker d.c. changes which are registered upon the most sensitive channel of the electroencephalograph can also be led through a d.c. amplifier to a cathode-ray oscillograph. During

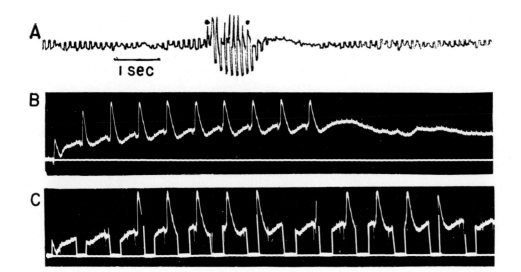

FIG. 1. Steady potential change accompanying cortical recruiting in the rabbit. Light ether anesthesia. Stimulation in medial thalamus. Recording from frontal cortex. A. Recorded by conventional condensor-coupled electroencephalograph the input of which is short-circuited 8 times per sec. Negative polarity recruiting responses are recorded as upward deflections, and black dots indicate the first and last responses of a series. The SP change is recorded as a series of downward deflections, each indicating a short circuit of the input. Although opposite in direction from the deflections representing the recruiting transients each represents a d.c. change of negative polarity. Records B and C serve to clarify the situation. For each the base line from which the d.c. change is a departure is indicated by a straight white line. B. The same recruiting response recorded upon an oscilloscope with use of a direct-coupled amplifier. Note negative steady potential change accompanying recruiting series. Surface of the cortex remained negative with respect to the underlying white matter for approximately 750 msec. following the last recruiting response. C. Another recruiting response series recorded under similar conditions to that of B. Input is again short-circuited 8 times per sec. as in A. Note that each short circuit returns the beam to the base line of the amplifier. Had this series been recorded by means of the same amplifier using condensor coupling, the d.c. shift should have been eliminated and the oscilloscope record would have been the counterpart of A. The chopper signals on C have been retouched due to printing difficulties.

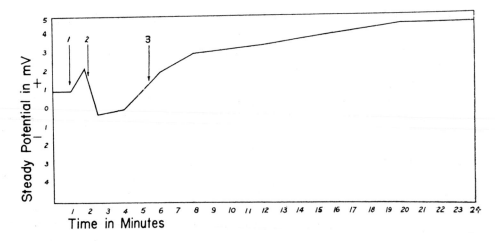

FIG. 2. Graph of change in SP during asphyxia which resulted from clamping airway. *1*, tracheal airway clamped; *2*, ECG completely suppressed; *3*, heart stops. [From Goldring & O'Leary (11).]

oscillographic recording upon strips of film, the chopper is temporarily disconnected. By convention, shifts in potential from the base line will be referred to as positive or negative with respect to the surface electrode.

Under optimal conditions the initial determination of pia-ventricular SP has varied usually between 0.5 and 5.0 mv positive (11). These data include measurements upon 20 rabbits which were anesthetized with ether for only the brief time required to procainize the skin and paravertebral muscles over the C_5 cord segment and divide the cord there. Anesthesia could then be discontinued, and the scalp similarly infiltrated with procaine as a prelude to exposing the brain for recording. With insertion of the deep lead into the subcortical white matter (in the cat), negative injury potential about the deep electrode tip contributes to the positivity at the surface, and larger voltage discrepancies may be recorded. In human subjects under nitrous oxide and thiopental anesthesia in whom the pia-ventricular potential has been recorded, the measurement in the majority of cases has been 0.3 to 0.5 mv positive (17). Here injury potential was not believed to be a significant complicating factor. Returning to the animal experiments, we note that SP may not fluctuate more than 0.5 mv during several hours of continuous recording if no procedure is undertaken after the preparation of the animal. With the high cord section (at C_1), necessitating artificial respiration, systemic failure has often developed in rabbits; under this circumstance SP may show a continuous negative drift terminating with the death of the animal. Clamping the trachea in an animal in

good condition, in which SP has not undergone significant alterations during several hours of continuous recording, will result in a significant SP change (11). While variable and somewhat complex, this consists principally of an initial positive shift (2 mv) followed by an even more prominent negative one (4 mv). The major change which follows clamping of the airway usually ends in 8 min. The heart ceases to beat between the maximum and the end of the negative deflection (fig. 2).

Leão (26) demonstrated a similar negative shift incident to cortical anemia and van Harreveld *et al.* have also shown a negative SP shift with asphyxia (41, 43). Other investigators, leading from the cortex and using the sciatic nerve as reference point, have also recorded SP shifts with anoxia and asphyxia (4, 10).

The injection of malononitrile, which liberates cyanide ions, evokes an analagous picture (18). This has been followed during the intravenous injection of between 10 and 20 ml of a freshly prepared 1 per cent solution delivered by Murphy drip. As the injection proceeds the animal becomes hyperpneic, and at about that time the ECG commences to slow, with the appearance of random components showing higher voltage than previously. As the ECG changes, SP commences to shift positively. With further deterioration in the preparation the ECG becomes isoelectric, and SP continues to shift positively to a total of 2.5 mv. Clonic convulsive movements may appear during the positive phase. These electrical events can be reversed if 5 per cent sodium thiosulfate is injected at the beginning of the positive SP change.

Then the ECG and SP will revert to the preinjection status. Unless the thiosulfate is injected the change continues for 3 to 8 min.; respiration stops and shortly thereafter the heart also. Meanwhile SP undergoes an opposite shift which carries it 3 to 4 mv more negative than it was at the start of the experiment (fig. 3).

We have followed SP under ether anesthesia more carefully than under any other. Commencing at a light level of anesthesia and deepening it gradually, SP may remain relatively steady although occasionally a positive shift may occur. If inhalation anesthesia is carried too deep, SP may shift negatively by comparison with the preceding light anesthesia baseline. However, as long as anesthesia is maintained at a relatively light level, the changes it occasions in SP are relatively insignificant, and induced physiological variations are much like those encountered in a relatively unanesthetized state. Finally, solutions added to the cortical surface which are not isotonic may disturb SP for several minutes. These are diffusion potential artifacts.

Summarizing, one must emphasize that to provide a stable base for measuring induced SP changes there should be careful control of injury, anesthesia and oxygen tension.

EXPERIMENTAL STUDIES

Spontaneous SP Changes Correlated with Interruption in Usual Resting Cortical Rhythm

It often is not possible to demonstrate SP alterations which coincide with a change in the ECG rhythm of the lightly anesthetized animal. However, in the rabbit (12) we have noted repeated brief negative shifts amounting to 0.6 mv which coincide with low voltage ECG intervals between runs of regular frequency activity. Furthermore, a relatively rapid increase in ECG amplitude with substitution of slower for usual frequencies may show an accompanying positive SP shift. In the pentobarbitalized cat a significant negative shift can be recorded during and succeeding barbiturate spindles, sometimes outlasting the spindle by several seconds.

After-effects of Evoked Responses

Since singly evoked responses are quick transients, the only SP change which could be expected to occur would appear as an aftermath. We have studied such after-effects in the visual cortex of the rabbit (11, 12) together with the conditions leading to their summa-

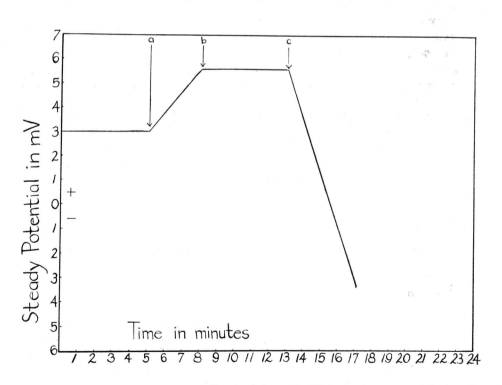

FIG. 3. Graph of change in SP during intravenous injection of 20 ml of 1 per cent solution of malononitrile. *a*, start of injection; *b*, ECG commences to become isoelectric; *c*, respiration stops.

tion during repetitive stimulation. The after-effects of singly evoked responses may not be evident at the beginning of an experiment but appear as the experiment proceeds. They may be positive, negative or diphasic when evoked by stimuli applied to the opposite optic nerve or the corresponding lateral geniculate nucleus. The positive SP component follows the evoked response transient immediately and may reach a voltage of 0.4 mv and persist for 1.5 sec. (fig. 4). In diphasic after-effects the positive component is usually of briefer duration (0.5 sec.) and is followed by a negative one of similar voltage lasting for 1.5 sec. When a negative after-effect alone is encountered its start is delayed for 0.3 to 0.5 sec. after the evoked response is over.

When repetitive stimulation of the optic nerve (submaximal for cortical evoked responses) with frequencies of 20 to 30 per sec. continued for 2 to 10 sec. is used, negative after-effects are observed to sum, and positive after-effect is minimal (12, fig. 5). However, a positive change may replace the negative one if cortical excitability had been significantly changed by a preceding major paroxysm (fig. 5F, G). Near-threshold stimulation of the lateral geniculate nucleus also gives chiefly summation of negative after-effect (12). At one half maximum to maximum stimulus strength, positivity usually develops early in the course of stimulation, to be replaced later by a negative SP change which persists past the end of stimulation. From this and other evidence we have concluded that in the response to repetitive stimulation, positive and negative after-effects sum algebraically, different effects predominating at different strengths of stimulation. This indication of the existence of processes of opposite electrical sign, the electrical manifestations of which can cancel completely, may relate to the

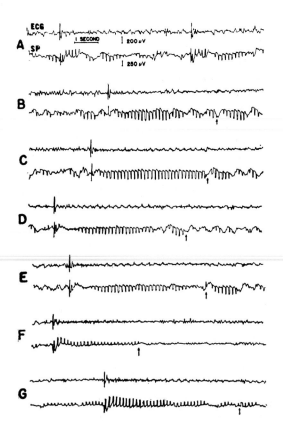

FIG. 5. SP change resulting from repetitive stimulation of the optic nerve at different strengths. *A*. Diphasic after-effect of a single evoked visual response for comparison. Stimulus frequency for subsequent records of figure was 25 per sec. For each strip the initial evoked response in ECG marks the beginning of stimulation and the arrow its cessation. *B*. Negative SP change during repetitive stimulation at threshold. *C*. Stimulus strength one-third maximal; here negativity is most prominent. *D*. Stimulus strength half maximal; the negativity develops somewhat later. *E*. Stimulus strength maximal; the negativity appears later and is not as marked as in *C* and *D*. Initial positivity in SP is seen to occur at the start of stimulation. *F*. Similar repetitive stimulation 5 min. following a major lasting shift in SP; stimulus strength as in *C*. The SP change is now surface-positive. *G*. Same as *F* except that stimulus strength is that of *E*. [From Goldring & O'Leary (12).]

difficulty of demonstrating SP after-effects early in the course of some experiments.

SP Changes Associated with Recruiting Responses

With repetitive stimulation (6 to 20 per sec., 30 v, 0.1 msec. duration) in the midline thalamus of the rabbit under light ether anesthesia, a negative cortical SP change amounting to 0.2 to 0.6 mv ordinarily develops during the rise in amplitude of the conventional ECG transients of negative polarity as shown

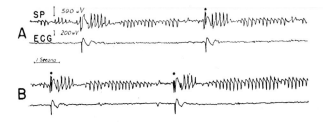

FIG. 4. After-effects which follow primary visual response in rabbit. After each evoked response there is a diphasic (positive-negative) after-effect. Black dots indicate position of first short-circuiting signal to occur after each response. [From Goldring & O'Leary (11).]

in figure 1 (15, 16). It also persists significantly after the period of stimulation. Oscillographic recording shows that there is a significant SP negative change after even the first spike of a series, and that this change is summated with the after-effects of succeeding higher amplitude spikes as the recruiting series continues. The persistence of the SP negativity after the stimulus is turned off indicates that it is truly an after-effect disturbance comparable to that which follows single evoked responses. Increasing the stimulus frequency to between 6 and 20 per sec. (the voltage and shock duration remaining constant) increases the amplitude and duration of the negative SP change. At 20 per sec. a further increase in amplitude and duration of SP negatively occurs if the stimulus duration is increased from 0.1 to 1.0 msec.

SP After-effects of Strychnine and Veratrine Spikes

The effect of strychnine has been studied in the rabbit and the cat (12, 13, 14). In the rabbit a 0.05 per cent strychnine solution applied to the cortex may be of sufficient strength to suppress the spontaneous component of the ECG; a minor 0.3 to 0.4 mv negative SP shift appears within 10 min. following the application of the drug to the cortical surface. The strychnine spikes which occur sporadically at this time show no detectable after-effect. However, a solution sufficiently strong to occasion intermittent repetitive spike paroxysms (0.5 per cent) causes a positive after-effect to appear following each

random spike which appears between the paroxysms. With application of a crystal of strychnine, negative after-effects follow each instead. A 0.1 per cent strychnine sulfate solution applied to the cortex of the cat also occasions a minor negative SP shift, and here after-effects of strychnine spikes have a negative polarity. When the single spikes occur in rapid succession the negativities associated with individual spikes summate (fig. 6). The SP change which occurs during a strychnine activated paroxysm will be referred to later.

Veratrine hydrochloride (10^{-4}) applied to the cortex of the pentobarbitalized cat unstabilizes SP almost immediately, resulting in one or more 5 to 15 mv negative shifts from each of which SP may recover significantly (13, 14). A plot of several such shifts following veratrine application shows a downward negative drift, and the SP does not again reach its value at the start of the experiment. Finally, however, it stabilizes upon a plateau. At that time the initial positive phase of the evoked response becomes significantly prolonged and spikes of dominantly positive polarity appear spontaneously, or may be initiated (as in the visual cortex) by turning the room lights on or off. Each evoked response and each such spike is accompanied by a positive after-effect which may endure for 5 to 10 sec. (fig. 7). Barbiturate spindles also come to show a principally positive polarity in the ECG, and they, too, show a positive polarity SP change which persists significantly after the end of the spindle (13, fig. 8). If strychnine is

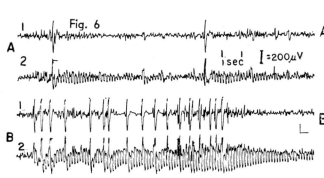

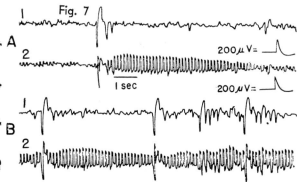

FIG. 6. Effect of 0.1 per cent strychnine sulfate solution applied to cortical surface of cat under pentobarbital anesthesia. *1* and *2* indicate ECG and SP records, respectively. *A*. Individual spontaneous strychnine spikes with negative after-effects. *B*. Occurrence of a cluster of spontaneous strychnine spikes with summation of the negative after-effects. [From Goldring & O'Leary (14).]

FIG. 7. Effect of application of veratrine hydrochloride (10^{-4}) to surface of the cortex of the cat under pentobarbital anesthesia. *1* and *2* indicate ECG and SP records, respectively. *A*. Single spontaneous positive veratrine spike with a long positive after-effect. *B*. A series of such spikes with positive after-effects. [From Goldring & O'Leary (13).]

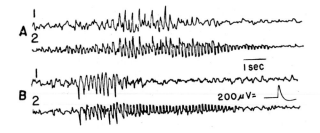

FIG. 8. SP change accompanying barbiturate spindles in a pentobarbitalized cat. *1* and *2* indicate ECG and SP records, respectively. *A.* Spontaneous barbiturate spindles with transients which are chiefly negative accompanied by a negative shift in SP which outlasts the spindle. *B.* Same cat shortly after the application of veratrine (10^{-4}) to cortical surface. The transients in the spindles are now chiefly positive and the SP change accompanying the spindle has also become positive. [From Goldring & O'Leary (13).]

applied before veratrine the barbiturate spindles may at first show an accentuation of their negative components accompanied by negative after-effect; when veratrine takes effect the principal polarity of the spindle changes from negative to positive and the after-effect also comes to have a positive polarity.

SP Concomitants of Convulsoid Discharge

These have been studied in detail in the rabbit (11, 12). Such a cortical discharge can be initiated locally by surface-positive polarization across the cortex, by repetitive stimulation (10 to 16 per sec.) in the related thalamic relay nucleus, or by strychnine applied locally in sufficient concentration. In animals stimulated repeatedly and vigorously such paroxysms may commence to appear intermittently without preceding activation. The latter situation is analogous to the abrupt appearance of convulsive discharge in man.

With few exceptions the course of SP change during convulsoid activity has been a positive shift of 1.0 to 1.5 mv correlated with the build-up of the discharge in the ECG tracing. As the tonic discharge becomes clonic the SP commences to return toward the preparoxysmal balance; as the discharge ceases SP continues to shift negatively, sometimes reaching a value of 5 mv negative to the preparoxysmal balance (fig. 9). When paroxysms follow each other in quick succession, a positive SP shift occurs with each, and a negative one coincides with the interseizure silent period.

The initiation of a paroxysm by polarization applied across the cortex from surface to white matter has particular interest in view of the polarization

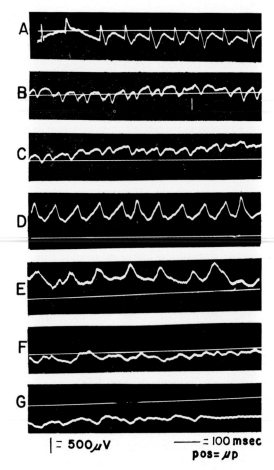

| = 500μV   ——— = 100 msec
                              pos = μp

FIG. 9. Steady potential change during paroxysm in rabbit. Light ether anesthesia. Paroxysm induced by repetitive 10 per sec. stimulation of the lateral geniculate nucleus with bipolar electrodes. Straight white line of each trace indicates the base line of the amplifier from which the d.c. change is a departure. Record from optic cortex with transcortical leading, positive up. *A.* Start of stimulation of lateral geniculate nucleus indicated by an evoked response following each stimulus. No consistent change in SP was observed during this period. *B.* 12 sec. after start of stimulation. In this strip the positive phase of evoked response has dropped out and the later negative component of evoked response has commenced to double, indicating the start of the paroxysm which persists into the poststimulatory period. Vertical white lines indicate end of period of stimulation. As paroxysm commences SP commences to shift positively. *C.* 15 sec. after start of stimulation. SP has continued to shift positively. *D.* 20 sec. after the start of stimulation. Further positive shift as the poststimulatory paroxysm reaches its maximum. *E.* 25 sec. after start of stimulation. Paroxysm diminishing in intensity and SP is now commencing to shift negatively. *F* and *G.* 35 and 40 sec. after start of stimulation. The paroxysm disappears as SP shifts further negatively.

theory advanced by Libet & Gerard (30) and supported by Bishop & O'Leary (2). Such applied polarization may be expected to shift the charges along the pyramidal neurons, perhaps increasing or decreasing the excitability of the substrate. By use of surface-positive applied polarization, a paroxysm can be initiated in the rabbit at a significantly lower intensity than is required to produce a paroxysm with surface-negative polarization. Such a paroxysm is also accompanied by a positive SP change. This, likewise, is supplanted by a negative one after the paroxysm disappears. If a paroxysm is initiated by sufficiently strong surface-negative polarization, that paroxysm is also related to a surface-positive SP shift which develops in reaction to the immediately preceding surface-negative applied polarization.

More recent studies (16) have revealed an SP change accompanying a cortical paroxysm induced by ventroanterior thalamic stimulation opposite to the one initiated by the methods cited above (stimulation of relay nucleus and polarization). In this instance the SP shifts negatively during the high voltage discharge and then positively in the postparoxysmal depression period (fig. 10). A cortical

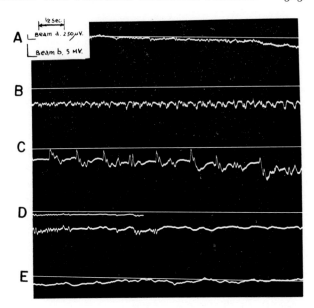

FIG. 11. SP shift accompanying cortical paroxysm induced by thiocarbohydrazide in rabbit. Straight white lines are base lines from which shifts in SP are read. Positive is up. *A.* 15 min. after intravenous injection of 30 mg of thiocarbohydrazide. SP commences to shift negatively. *B.* 10 sec. later SP shifts more negatively and paroxysmal activity begins. *C.* 6 sec. later paroxysmal activity continues and SP remains shifted negatively. *D* and *E.* As high voltage discharge breaks up and stops, SP shifts back to the base line. The tracing nearest the base line in *D* is the same paroxysm recorded at lower amplification on the *b* beam of the oscilloscope. This beam is set at lower gain in order to record the full excursions of larger SP shifts. In the 10 sec. interval between *C* and *D*, the *a* beam threatened to move off the tube face and therefore the *b* beam was turned on. In all other strips only the *a* beam is shown. There is a 10 sec. interval between *D* and *E.*

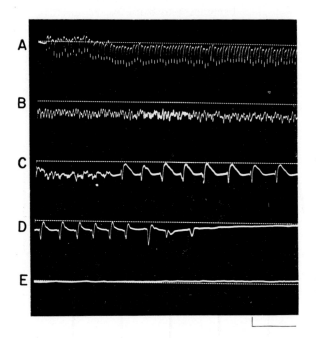

FIG. 10. D.C. change accompanying a cortical paroxysm induced by repetitive stimulation of ventroanterior thalamic nucleus in the cat. *A.* Negative d.c. shift with 20 per sec. stimulation. A 3 sec. strip of record has been omitted between *A* and *B*; with continuation of stimulation there is an increase in negative d.c. change. *C.* Upon cessation of stimulation (white dot) high voltage paroxysmal activity is in evidence and the steady potential remains shifted negatively. *D.* Return of steady potential to the prestimulatory base line with termination of paroxysm. *E.* Positive shift of steady potential in the poststimulatory isoelectric period. Vertical line of right angle in right lower corner represents 500 μv; horizontal line, 1 sec. Positive is up.

paroxysm initiated by the intravenous injection of convulsive drugs such as thiocarbohydrazide and pentylenetetrazol (Metrazol) is accompanied by a similar d.c. change as shown in figure 11 (Goldring, S., P. Vanasupa & J. L. O'Leary, manuscript in preparation). Other workers have also demonstrated SP shifts accompanying paroxysmal activity. van Harreveld & Stamm (43) found a negative SP shift with cortical paroxysm produced by faradic stimulation of the cortical surface or intravenous injection of pentylenetetrazol, and Liberson, using the guinea pig, found SP shifts accompanying induced paroxysmal discharge in the hippocampus (29, 44).

D.C. Changes Which Accompany Spreading Depression (SD)

In 1944 Leão (24) discovered a depression of the usual cortical rhythms of the rabbit which spreads slowly outwards from the site of a weak mechanical, electrical or chemical stimulus to the cortex. This reaction was elicited more readily from the rostral pole of the hemisphere, and from there a wave of depression could envelop almost the whole of the convexity, propagating at a velocity of only 2 to 5 mm per min. Neither evoked potentials nor motor responses to cortical stimulation could be observed when the front of the depression reached the sensorimotor cortex. Leão also observed that the propagation of the SD was accompanied by dilation of pial vessels (25), an observation confirmed by van Harreveld & Ochs (42) who also held that in the rabbit the vasodilatation is preceded by a smaller wave of vasoconstriction. Species differences in cortical susceptibility to SD have been noted. It is produced more easily in the rabbit than in the cat and is seen only occasionally in the monkey (33, 36, 45). Cortical maturity may also play a role: Bures (3) was unable to obtain SD during the first days of life in the rat, although he could elicit it readily in the newborn guinea pig.

There is substantial evidence indicating that SD is an abnormal reaction which results from exposure of the brain to unphysiological conditions. Marshall and co-workers (32, 34, 35, 36) have shown that SD appears consistently only if the brain has been dehydrated, exposed to the atmosphere for long periods, cooled, or bathed in Ringer's solution having ten times the usual concentration of potassium. In the absence of one or another of the above conditions they were unable to elicit SD in the cat or monkey at all, although occasionally it could still be developed in the rabbit. Because they were able to record SD through the intact dura of the rabbit, van Harreveld et al. (45) disagreed with the view that SD is an abnormal reaction. However, later, utilizing the various conditions described by Marshall and co-workers, van Harreveld & Bogen (40) obtained SD in the area retrosplenialis granularis dorsalis, a region into which SD does not propagate under usual recording conditions in the rabbit.

The d.c. variation which accompanies SD has a duration of 4 to 6 min. (26). With the critical recording electrode placed upon the pial surface an involved cortical region becomes negative for 1 to 2 min. with respect to a subcortical or an extracortical reference electrode. Within that time the surface-negativity reaches a maximum of 8 to 15 mv, thereafter decreasing with somewhat greater rapidity. The involved region then becomes 3 to 8 mv surface-positive but returns to the predepression base line in 3 to 5 min. (fig. 12). As the d.c. potential changes from surface-negative to positive, large amplitude (2 to 3 mv) negative slow waves or the repetitive spikes of convulsive discharge may occur. The occurrence of these transients or repetitive spikes led Leão to the con-

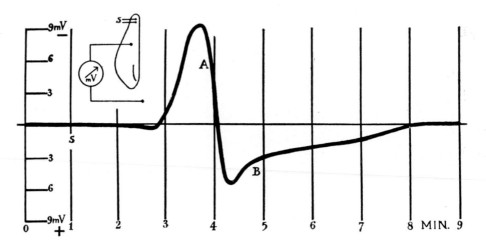

FIG. 12. A representative experiment on the slow voltage variation accompanying the spreading depression of activity. The curve was drawn from voltage readings taken with five sec. intervals. In this and the other two figures, an upward deflection denotes negativity of the cortex with respect to the extracortical reference electrode. Electrodes arranged as shown in the inset (s: stimulating electrodes). Stimulation, 5 sec. of 'tetanizing' current from an induction coil, delivered at the time marked S. In this representative curve there is indicated the time of occurrence (from A to B) of the specific electrical activity which often develops during the depression of the 'spontaneous patterns.' [From Leão (26).]

clusion that SD and the spread of convulsive discharge may be closely related.

By recording the d.c. change at successive cortical depths Leão (27) was able to show that the negative shift appeared later at an intracortical electrode than at one directly above it on the surface. Also, when an electrode upon the pial surface or in the superficial cortex recorded a significant negative variation, a deeper cortical electrode showed a positive variation. From these observations Leão concluded that SD starts in the superficial cortex and is propagated downward to involve the entire cortical thickness. Freygang & Landau (9) reached the same conclusion.

A negative voltage variation similar to the one which accompanies SD has been observed with cortical anemia, anoxia and asphyxia (11, 17, 26, 43), a fact suggesting neuronal depolarization as an important contributory factor in all. Extrapolating from results obtained during depolarization in peripheral nerve (6, 7), one would expect decreased cortical impedance to result from both SD and cortical anoxia. However, several workers (9, 28, 41) have reported the opposite occurrence. Freygang & Landau (9) have suggested that swelling of the neuronal and glial elements of cortex may account for the increased cortical impedance which accompanies SD and cortical anoxia, arguing that cellular swelling would increase the resistance of the extracellular current shunt and thus the tissue resistance. van Harreveld & Ochs (41) have agreed with this view. However, recent studies of nervous tissue with the electron microscope (31) have failed to reveal the existence of an extracellular space in the cortex, thus suggesting that other explanations need also be entertained. On the other hand van Harreveld (39) has reported direct confirmation of swelling in the superficial dendritic plexus during SD, using histological sections prepared after freezing.

Grafstein's (21) recent observations with microelectrodes are also important. She noted increased firing of single units at the start of SD, suggesting some other explanation for the depression of ECG conventionally recorded with macroelectrodes. Asynchronous firing of single units leading to cancellation of opposing effects could, however, reconcile macro- and microelectrode results. Grafstein's observations have also led her to implicate depolarization resulting from the liberation of potassium as the cause of SD. Thus, the increased neuronal discharge shown by microelectrode studies could result in decreased cell permeability (depolarization) and the liberation of potassium. The latter could chemically stimulate adjoining cells, the process spreading to involve the entire cortex.

Relation of Polarity of Evoked Transient to Polarity of SP Change Also Consequent to Stimulation

Much indirect evidence has been presented here indicating that the same neuronal activity occasions both the transient of the conventional ECG and the SP changes described. Direct proof is also needed and is possible to obtain in an experimental situation which provides a layer of neurons synaptically activated from one surface with impulses conducted away from the other. The lateral geniculate nucleus of the cat was studied by Bishop & O'Leary (2) who showed that the postsynaptic spike recorded from a critical electrode in the optic radiation over the geniculate cell layers has a positive polarity, and that, as the critical electrode enters the cell layers, the polarity reverses to negative. They concluded that, with regard to evoked potentials of the lateral geniculate, the cell body during activity becomes negative to its own conducting axon. Vastola (46) undertook to repeat this experiment, determining the reversal point of the evoked transient from the same electrode used to record the summated SP shift which accompanies rapid repetitive stimulation. For this purpose he used glass capillary tube electrodes having a tip diameter of $250\ \mu$ and led from calomel cells. The critical electrode was passed from the optic radiation through the cell layers, the reference electrode being situated in the central white matter anterior to the lateral geniculate body. He determined the maximal evoked response transient obtainable from a single shock applied to the contralateral optic nerve, and then proceeded to study, at different strengths of stimulation between threshold and maximum, the SP shift which occurs concurrently with stimulation to 150 per sec. Dorsal to the cell layers SP became positively shifted during repetitive stimulation; at 0.5 mm dorsal to the cell layers the SP shift accompanying repetitive stimulation reversed polarity; with increasing depth of the critical electrode the negative shift increased further until the electrode tip was in the middle of the first layer of the nucleus. Then it gradually decreased as the electrode passed through the remaining cell layers and into the thalamus ventral to the nucleus. The polarity of the SP shift coincided with the polarity of the postsynaptic wave which he recorded by the conventional single shock method. As an added precaution Vastola used the chopper technique at a fast rate of interruption to prove that the SP between the individual transients also shifted negatively.

Effects of Stimulation at a Distance Along a Multisynaptic Path Upon Transcortical SP

Dondey & Snider (8) recorded SP from the cerebral cortex in much the same fashion as outlined herein, using animals prepared under ether anesthesia and maintained under *d*-tubocurarine (15 mg per kg). Besides confirming the findings reported previously concerning the relation between the appearance of cortical paroxysm and of positive SP shift, and between the postictal silent period and negative shift, they studied the effect of fast frequency cerebellar stimulation (200 and 300 per sec., 10 to 30 v.). Such stimulation induced a positive shift in cortical SP lasting for as long as 50 sec. and becoming as large as 5 mv. Suppression of cortical spindles occurred during the shift and was the principal criterion for the efficacy of the cerebellar stimulation. Under the same circumstances slow frequency stimulation, ranging between 10 and 20 per sec., induced a negative SP shift in the cortex which might last as long as 70 sec. and reach 4 mv in amplitude. With the lower frequency stimulation the ECG did not change as significantly and spindles might occur throughout the recording. In both the instances of fast and of slow stimulation, SP recording from the nucleus ventralis lateralis of the thalamus showed oppositely polarized effects. Dondey & Snider found in addition that fast frequency stimulation of the cerebellum might prevent the expected negative shift which occurs at the end of cortically induced paroxysmal discharge; instead positivity continued much beyond the cessation of the paroxysm.

Injury Potential Components

D.C. changes with injury were reported by Walker *et al.* (47) and Meyer & Denny-Brown (37, 38). Kempinsky's (23) study of the distribution of SP change associated with experimental vascular occlusion of the middle cerebral artery in the cat conclusively demonstrates that a significant component of such injury effect is a demarcation potential across the zone of injury in the white matter. He used pia-ventricular, subcortical-ventricular and transcortical leads simultaneously. The prompt, sustained negative shift which he obtained in the center of the cortical area of distribution of the vessel could be recorded in the subcortical-ventricular and the pia-ventricular combinations but not in the cortex-subcortex one. When recorded simultaneously at different cortical loci, the magnitude of the shift decremented toward the periphery of the ischemic region.

Human Studies Using Scalp Recording

In a study by Goldring *et al.* (19) it was shown that d.c. changes can also be recorded from the human scalp during electroconvulsive therapy. The difficulty which arises in the interpretation of these and other d.c. changes recorded from the scalp with non-polarizable electrodes is the complication introduced by d.c. changes which occur in the skin. Of the results reported in the literature the negative shift with 3 per sec. spike and dome discharges (5) seems most free of this criticism.

DISCUSSION OF ORIGIN OF STEADY POTENTIALS

Starting from a base of transcortical voltage measurement called steady potential (SP), evidence thus far accumulated supports the existence of d.c. concomitants of conventionally recorded cortical excitation processes. The d.c. changes which correspond have also been obtained from some subcortical centers. In one such nucleus (the lateral geniculate) it seems clear that there is a close association between d.c. change and the neural excitation process (46). In the cortex d.c. changes occur subsequent to brief transients such as evoked responses, strychnine and veratrine spikes, and during and after repetitive ones like barbiturate spindles or recruiting responses. Thus, by means of a d.c. amplifier the electrical sign of excitation at a cortical point can be recorded transcortically significantly after the activity obtained with a condensor-coupled amplifier has disappeared.

The evidence is yet insufficient to decide whether such d.c. changes are simply a prolongation of the same neural process which occasions a neuron's discharge or are analogous to the after-potentials of peripheral nerve. If the latter, evidence for metabolic causation needs to be considered. There are also indications, but no proof, for excitability change occurring simultaneously with certain after-effects, and this also needs close investigation. If excitability change does occur, the analogy with peripheral nerve after-potentials becomes much closer.

After-effects appear to sum algebraically, giving different polarity under different conditions of excitation. As used here the term algebraic summation implies something more than the simple cancellation of opposing equal forces. Such an explanation might suffice for the absence of detectable after-effect early in the course of some experiments, but a somewhat more complicated interpretation is needed to explain all of the observed phenomena of after-effect summation during repetitive processes. An increasingly negative after-effect during summation might thus be due either to exaggeration of a negatively directed tendency, or to suppression of a positively directed one and vice versa. The plasticity of interaction between the two forces is exemplified in the summation of cortical evoked response after-effects induced by repetitive stimulation of the opposite optic nerve, as compared to that of the lateral geniculate nucleus. Optic nerve stimulation in our experience can cause only a summation of positive after-effect when applied at maximum, if at all; most usually the summation is that of negative after-effect. Geniculate stimulation produces summated after-effect consistently at stimulus values below maximum. Another indication that the same neuronal firing can produce negative after-effect in one situation and positive in another lies in the comparison between the summed negative after-effect of clusters of strychnine spikes, and the positive summation which accompanies the high voltage paroxysm that develops intermittently in the same strychninized cortex.

The unifying concept which promises the most aid in harmonizing knowledge of the electrical signs of the quicker transients with those of the slower d.c. concomitants of neural excitation is that of Libet & Gerard (30). These writers postulated a polarization gradient along the vertically oriented cortical neurons. For each neuron this gradient would extend from the surface dendritic expansions in the plexiform layer to a deeper level, even to layer VI, where the soma-axon junction is situated. Further evidence relating polarization gradients to neural excitation is obtained by the simple expedient of changing the charge distribution along the pyramidal cells artificially. This affects significantly the positive and negative components of evoked potential, surface-negative polarization accentuating the positive phase, surface-positive polarization the negative phase.

Other support for Libet & Gerard's view is to be found in the change in visual evoked response during the cycles of intense negative d.c. shift which char-acterizes the veratrinized cortex. The effect of veratrine applied to the cortical surface is to depolarize the terminal dendritic brushes of the cortical neurons (13, 14), and from this depolarized superficial region intense waves of depolarization appear to spread downwards over the cortical dendrites, progressively engulfing the cortical neurons from above. The initial positive phase of evoked response is due to the successive activation of groups of neurons, each excited after synaptic conduction. The summation produced is signified by the four fast spikes which appear successively higher upon the rising phase of the evoked potential. During the intense negative veratrine shift these spikes are removed successively from above downwards, and the order of their removal corresponds with the expectancy from their positions in the cortical depth as obtained by the null point of measurements of Bishop & Clare (1).

The changes in charge distribution may actually be more complicated than is suggested by the results of these experimental studies. Besides the situation in which the charge at the two ends might change in opposite direction to produce an SP effect, a d.c. change might also ensue if both ends changed in the same direction unequally. Such a concept is now susceptible to experimental proof only from the limited aspect of charge distribution along the neuron's exterior. If interior differences of potential exist between the superficial dendrites and the cell soma, it will require microelectrode recording to reveal them.

SUMMARY

Present methods of recording the d.c. potential across the cerebral cortex are presented. These require detailed attention to oxygen tension, anesthesia and injury, and necessitate stable electrodes for recording purposes. The SP across the cortex remains relatively steady under good experimental conditions and serves as a base line for examining slower concomitants of neural excitation. In several situations it has been shown that such SP concomitants do relate to the quick transient phenomena conventionally recorded from the cortex. Significant summation of d.c. change associated with single transients can appear during repetitive phenomena. The best promise of relating d.c. and transient phenomena is in terms of the polarization theory of Libet & Gerard (30).

REFERENCES

1. BISHOP, G. H. AND M. H. CLARE. *J. Neurophysiol.* 16: 1, 1953.
2. BISHOP, G. H. AND J. L. O'LEARY. *Electroencephalog. & Clin. Neurophysiol.* 2: 401, 1950.
3. BURES, J. *Electroencephalog. & Clin. Neurophysiol.* 9: 121, 1957.
4. BURGE, W. E., G. C. WICKWIRE, O. S. ORTH, H. W. NEILD AND W. P. ELHARDT. *Am. J. Physiol.* 116: 19, 1936.
5. COHN, R. *Arch. Neurol. & Psychiat.* 71: 699, 1954.
6. COLE, K. S. AND R. F. BAKER. *J. Gen. Physiol.* 24: 535, 1941.
7. COLE, K. S. AND H. J. CURTIS. *J. Gen. Physiol.* 24: 551, 1941.
8. DONDEY, M. AND R. S. SNIDER. *Electroencephalog. & Clin. Neurophysiol.* 7: 243, 1955.
9. FREYGANG, W. H., JR. AND W. M. LANDAU. *J. Cell. & Comp. Physiol.* 45: 377, 1955.
10. GOLDENSOHN, E. S., M. D. SHOENFELD AND P. F. HOEFER. *Electroencephalog. & Clin. Neurophysiol.* 3: 231, 1951.
11. GOLDRING, S. AND J. L. O'LEARY. *J. Neurophysiol.* 14: 275, 1951.
12. GOLDRING, S. AND J. L. O'LEARY. *Electroencephalog. & Clin. Neurophysiol.* 3: 329, 1951.
13. GOLDRING, S. AND J. L. O'LEARY. *Electroencephalog. & Clin. Neurophysiol.* 6: 189, 1954.
14. GOLDRING, S. AND J. L. O'LEARY. *Electroencephalog. & Clin. Neurophysiol.* 6: 201, 1954.
15. GOLDRING, S. AND J. L. O'LEARY. *Electroencephalog. & Clin. Neurophysiol.* 9: 381, 1957.
16. GOLDRING, S. AND J. L. O'LEARY. *Electroencephalog. & Clin. Neurophysiol.* 9: 577, 1957.
17. GOLDRING, S., J. L. O'LEARY AND R. B. KING. *Electroencephalog. & Clin. Neurophysiol.* 10: 233, 1958.
18. GOLDRING, S., J. L. O'LEARY AND R. L. LAM. *Electroencephalog. & Clin. Neurophysiol.* 5: 395, 1953.
19. GOLDRING, S., G. ULETT, J. L. O'LEARY AND A. GREDITZER. *Electroencephalog. & Clin. Neurophysiol.* 2: 297, 1950.
21. GRAFSTEIN, B. *J. Neurophysiol.* 19: 154, 1956.
22. JASPER, H. AND T. C. ERICKSON. *J. Neurophysiol.* 7: 333, 1944.
23. KEMPINSKY, W. H. *Electroencephalog. & Clin. Neurophysiol.* 6: 375, 1954.

24. LEÃO, A. A. P. *J. Neurophysiol.* 7: 359, 1944.
25. LEÃO, A. A. P. *J. Neurophysiol.* 7: 391, 1944.
26. LEÃO, A. A. P. *J. Neurophysiol.* 10: 409, 1947.
27. LEÃO, A. A. P. *Electroencephalog. & Clin. Neurophysiol.* 3: 315, 1951.
28. LEÃO, A. A. P. AND H. M. FERRIERA. *An. Acad. Brasileira Cien.* 25: 259, 1953.
29. LIBERSON, W. T. *Am. J. Psychiat.* 112: 91, 1955.
30. LIBET, B. AND R. W. GERARD. *J. Neurophysiol.* 4: 438, 1941.
31. LUSE, S. A. *J. Biophys. & Biochem. Cytol.* 2: 531, 1956.
32. MARSHALL, W. H. *Electroencephalog. & Clin. Neurophysiol.* 2: 177, 1950.
33. MARSHALL, W. H. *Electroencephalog. & Clin. Neurophysiol.* 4: 223, 1952.
34. MARSHALL, W. H. *Electroencephalog. & Clin. Neurophysiol.* Suppl. 4: 82, 1953.
35. MARSHALL, W. H. AND C. F. ESSIG. *J. Neurophysiol.* 14: 265, 1951.
36. MARSHALL, W. H., C. F. ESSIG AND S. J. DUBROFF. *J. Neurophysiol.* 14: 153, 1951.
37. MEYER, J. S. AND D. DENNY-BROWN. *Electroencephalog. & Clin. Neurophysiol.* 7: 511, 1955.
38. MEYER, J. S. AND D. DENNY-BROWN. *Electroencephalog. & Clin. Neurophysiol.* 7: 529, 1955.
39. VAN HARREVELD, A. *Fed. Proc.* 16: 131, 1957.
40. VAN HARREVELD, A. AND J. E. BOGEN. *Proc. Soc. Exper. Biol. & Med.* 91: 297, 1956.
41. VAN HARREVELD, A. AND S. OCHS. *Am. J. Physiol.* 187: 180, 1956.
42. VAN HARREVELD, A. AND S. OCHS. *Am. J. Physiol.* 189: 159, 1957.
43. VAN HARREVELD, A. AND J. S. STAMM. *Am. J. Physiol.* 173: 171, 1953.
44. VAN HARREVELD, A. AND J. S. STAMM. *J. Neurophysiol.* 17: 505, 1954.
45. VAN HARREVELD, A., J. S. STAMM AND E. CHRISTENSEN. *Am. J. Physiol.* 184: 312, 1956.
46. VASTOLA, E. F. *Electroencephalog. & Clin. Neurophysiol.* 7: 557, 1955.
47. WALKER, A. E., J. J. KELLROSS AND T. J. CASE. *J. Neurosurg.* 1: 103, 1944.

CHAPTER XIV

The physiopathology of epileptic seizures

HENRI GASTAUT | *Faculté de Médecine, Marseille, France*

M. FISCHER-WILLIAMS | *London Hospital, London, England*

CHAPTER CONTENTS

BECAUSE OF THE IMPORTANT medical application of this chapter, it seems useful to preface it with a short summary of the clinical and electroencephalographic events accompanying epileptic seizures in man.

SYMPTOMATOLOGY

There are two types of epilepsy, from both the clinical and the electroencephalographic point of view: *a*) generalized epilepsy, in which the clinical manifestations involve the entire individual and the EEG discharges can be recorded all over the scalp; and *b*) partial epilepsy, in which only a part of the individual is involved clinically and the electrical disturbance can be recorded from a part of the scalp only.

Types of Generalized Epilepsy

It is clear that the different types of generalized epilepsy are similar in their electrical and clinical manifestations; they constitute a remarkably homogeneous group in symptomatology. From the clinical point of view, the two important features which they have in common are loss of consciousness and convulsions involving the whole skeletal musculature to a greater or lesser extent. These phenomena are so spectacular that the other manifestations, notably those in the autonomic sphere, are relegated to second place. From the EEG point of view, their common manifestation is a seizure discharge of convulsive waves which are bilateral, synchronous, symmetrical and generalized over the scalp. The following three varieties of generalized epilepsy are distinguished according to the duration of the attack, to the relative importance of motor or mental symptoms and to the characteristics of the EEG discharge.

GRAND MAL. This is characterized by: *a*) duration of more than 1 min.; *b*) initial total loss of consciousness with postictal coma; *c*) generalized tonic contraction at first continuous and later interrupted by periods of relaxation which causes the so-called 'clonic' phase; *d*) a discharge of rhythmical, bilateral, synchronous and symmetrical spikes at 10 ± 2 cps, the amplitude of which increases while the frequency diminishes and in which the terminal elements, separated by intervals of electrical silence, constitute groups, each corresponding to a jerk in the clonic phase.

PETIT MAL OF 'ABSENCE' VARIETY. This is characterized by: *a*) a shorter duration (5 to 20 sec.); *b*) more or less complete loss of consciousness which is never followed by postictal coma; *c*) abortive muscular contractions, which are hardly discernible and occur three times a second, involving the eyelids and sometimes the muscles of the head and upper limbs; and *d*) a rhythmical, bilateral, synchronous and symmetrical discharge of a complex pattern, comprising a spike followed by a slow wave and repeated three times a second.

PETIT MAL OF MYOCLONIC TYPE. This is characterized by: *a*) an exceedingly brief duration (a fraction of a second); *b*) a single violent jerk which, though generalized, predominantly involves the muscles of the arms or head and sometimes appears on one side only; and *c*) a short burst of spikes, with or without one or several slow waves, and constituting, as the case may be, multiple spikes, multiple spikes and waves, or even a spike and wave.

The 'spikes' of grand and petit mal are in reality waves whose form and period differ only slightly from those which characterize the waves of the alpha rhythm and have nothing to do with the spikes, correctly so-termed, of interictal discharges in partial epilepsy.

Types of Partial Epilepsy

These forms of epilepsy, by contrast, constitute an essentially heterogeneous group.

CLINICAL ASPECTS. From the clinical point of view, the seizures are manifested by mental, sensory or motor symptoms involving the autonomic or cerebrospinal systems. *a*) The sensory symptoms may be classified as somesthetic, visual, auditory, vertiginous, olfactory or gustatory. *b*) Mental symptoms include all degrees of clouded consciousness and also positive phenomena affecting perception, ideation or mood—illusions or hallucinations, 'forced thinking' or conversely a blotting out of thought, and feelings of anxiety, fear or anger. *c*) Visceral symptoms are characterized by abnormal sensations or activities involving the alimentary system (abdominal or epigastric sensations, chewing with salivation, borborygmi, defecation, etc.), the cardiovascular or respiratory systems (precordial pain, tachycardia, vasomotor phenomena, cough, apnea, etc.), and in addition but less frequently, symptoms involving the glands, erectores pilorum, sphincters, pupils, etc. *d*) Somatomotor symptoms include abnormal tonic or clonic movements, the commonest being deviation and contraversion. Apart from these, there are numerous abnormal gestures which are responses to hallucinations (gesture of fear during a terrifying vision) or to sensations (for example, the gesture of placing the hand on the abdomen associated with a painful epigastric sensation), or which merely represent the release of automatisms during an ictal or postictal confusional episode. Gibbs *et al.* (88) proposed the term 'psychomotor' for seizures in which there are gestures such as these but especially for attacks with confusional automatisms.

An enumeration of symptoms cannot serve as the basis for a classification of the partial epilepsies; it is even less satisfactory relative to physiopathological interpretation. It is indeed exceptional for an attack of partial epilepsy to be manifested by a single symptom; quite the contrary, most of the seizures simultaneously involve various sensory, mental and motor phenomena. In addition, it is impossible to locate a precise region of the brain to which the origin of each of the above-mentioned symptoms might be assigned. The conception of 'representation' is misleading (91) when motor and sensory 'representations' are said to be contralateral, homolateral or bilateral, or primary, secondary or supplementary, and to occupy different cortical and subcortical regions. It thus becomes impossible to relate salivation, for example, exclusively to the opercular region, or deviation of the head and eyes simply to the 'premotor' region.

ELECTROENCEPHALOGRAPHIC ASPECTS. Partial epileptic seizures differ from generalized seizures in that their discharges can be recorded from a part of the scalp only, and they show a great diversity of expression. Without attempting to give a full description, we may divide them into two main topographical groups: *a)* localized partial discharges, consisting of rhythmic spikes, occasionally from the frontal or central regions, but much more frequently from the temporal or parieto-occipital regions and *b)* diffuse partial discharges, showing as desynchronization or slow hypersynchronization and arising from all or a part of one or both hemispheres (usually the temporofrontal regions).

In addition there are numerous cases in which localized and diffuse discharges both appear during the same seizure with a variety of temporospatial relations. The discharges appear either independently or concomitantly, and either in or out of phase; they usually involve the anterior temporal and frontal or the posterior temporal and parieto-occipital regions.

It is of course well recognized that any partial seizure may become generalized and then present the electrical and clinical characteristics of a grand mal fit, whether or not it is preceded by myoclonic jerks. One must therefore carefully distinguish between fits which are generalized from the start and those which become generalized after a partial onset.

ETIOLOGY

It is generally recognized that epileptic seizures may be divided into two main categories, according to whether or not there is a demonstrable brain lesion. One category comprises the so-called secondary or symptomatic epilepsies arising from a lesion which is infective, degenerative, traumatic, neoplastic or vascular; these constitute a well-recognized and undisputed entity. The etiology in the other category has always been controversial; some authors regard these epileptic fits as the result of brain lesions which are undemonstrable and consider that they should be called collectively cryptogenic epilepsy; others believe that they represent disordered metabolism or a fault in cerebral function, unassociated with any organic abnormality. They should therefore be qualified as 'functional', 'metabolic' or 'primitive' as opposed to those that are 'organic' or 'secondary'. This termi-

nology unfortunately has not been adhered to, and it has become customary to call functional epilepsies either 'idiopathic' or 'essential'. This has given rise to a discussion the etymological origin of which has gone unrecognized but which has caused divergence of opinion which was more apparent than real. However this may be, the existence of two types of epilepsy is now accepted.

Functional Epilepsy

This disorder is encountered in only 5 per cent of all cases, according to Bicard *et al.* (17). It is also known as primitive, essential, genuine, idiopathic, metabolic, genetic, etc. It results from a fault in the functioning of the brain manifested by an epileptic 'predisposition', fairly often hereditary. It is not associated with any anatomically detectable lesion of the brain and it is not accompanied by any interictal neurological or psychiatric manifestations; and it is always manifested by seizures (grand mal or petit mal) which are generalized from the start of the attack.

Organic Epilepsy

This type is very common (95 per cent of all cases). It is also known as symptomatic or secondary. It is caused by an anatomically recognizable cerebral lesion and for this reason it may be associated with neurological or psychiatric abnormalities between fits; it may develop on a 'soil' already predisposed to convulsions and thus a mildly irritative lesion may be markedly epileptogenic; and only rarely is it manifested as a primarily generalized seizure, rather usually appearing as partial epilepsy which may or may not become secondarily generalized.

PHYSIOPATHOLOGY OF SEIZURES
GENERALIZED FROM START

This presentation will be divided into two parts. The first will be an impartial review with some description of the experimental results accumulated over nearly two centuries of effort to explain the mechanism of generalized seizures, particularly those of grand mal. The second will furnish a personal interpretation of these experimental results, based on modern neurophysiological data.

Experimental Results

The various types of primarily generalized epilepsy have been reproduced experimentally in animals and man.

GRAND MAL. It is easy to produce a grand mal seizure in animals by any measure acting as a diffuse assault on the brain and causing a sufficiently widespread disorder of cerebral metabolism: by applying a strong electric current to the whole of the brain (transcranial electroshock), by injecting analeptic drugs such as pentylenetetrazol (Metrazol), megimide, picrotoxin, absinthol, by oxygen intoxication, or by sudden withdrawal of sedatives in chronic experimental barbiturate poisoning.

On the contrary, it is very difficult in these same animals, to cause by means of minimal and localized measures seizures which are generalized from the onset. Thus limited electrical stimulation and minimal glial scars developed around the site of injection of aluminum hydroxide never cause generalized epileptic fits, although they regularly produce seizures of partial epilepsy which may become generalized (84). In order to produce a grand mal seizure from the onset, one needs to increase the severity and particularly the extent of the local disturbance in these experiments, to involve mid-line structures or to administer an agent with a generalized subliminal action.

In man one obviously cannot produce focal experimental cerebral lesions, but it is well established that, as in other animals, various measures with a widespread cerebral action will cause grand mal seizures: electroshock treatment, pentylenetetrazol, oxygen poisoning, rapid withdrawal of barbiturates (particularly in addicts of short-acting barbiturates), etc. All these forms of experimental or accidental epilepsy in man and animals are indeed comparable to spontaneous seizures of grand mal generalized from the start, for they always include an immediate loss of consciousness, tonic and clonic convulsions, and a bilateral, synchronous and symmetrical seizure discharge in the EEG.

We have not regarded as grand mal seizures those which are precipitated in man and animals by various types of cerebral anoxia. These seizures are tonic, lacking the clonic phase, and are accompanied by depression of cerebral electrical activity and not by a bisynchronous discharge. They are none the less of fundamental interest for the understanding of grand mal epilepsy and we shall return to the subject later.

THEORIES OF GENERALIZED CONVULSIONS. *a) Subcortical theory.* The idea that generalized convulsions have a subcortical origin has been held by physicians ever since ancient times for logical reasons which are easily understood (187). In the second century A.D., Galen attributed grand mal epilepsy to a 'thick humor' in the middle and posterior part of the ventricles. Willis in 1682 had a similar conception when he related the fit to "a strong spasmodic copula distilled from the blood into the brain, affecting the animal spirits which lie in the middle of the brain, and causing an explosion." This idea persists to our day since Högner [quoted by Marinesco *et al.* (135)] recently defended the view that the epileptic discharge depends on distension of the third ventricle by excess formation of cerebrospinal fluid, producing an excitation of the centers around the ventricle.

Experimental study of this subcortical theory was begun in the middle of the eighteenth century when Haller showed that generalized convulsions could be provoked by irritation of the white matter in the depths of the brain. At the beginning of the next century Flourens (1823) performed his famous experiments on the medulla oblongata. This allowed Hall (96) to formulate his theory of the medullary origin of reflex epilepsy, which was taken up by Schroeder van der Kolk in 1859 (174) who concluded that "an exalted sensibility and excitability of the medulla oblongata is the just cause of epilepsy." As early as 1838 Nothnagel provoked generalized convulsions by mechanical stimulation of the medulla oblongata, and much later Binswanger (18) and Bechterew (16) repeated these experiments using an electric current or a needle prick.

Stimulation experiments were not, however, the only ones supporting the subcortical mechanism of generalized seizures. Toward the beginning of the twentieth century, a large number of ablation experiments showed that the cerebral cortex, and the greater part of the telencephalon, diencephalon and mesencephalon, were not necessary for the experimental production of generalized epilepsy. Various measures were used in these experiments: transcranial application of an electric current (89, 130, 166, 171, 191); cooling of the brain (44); and injections of pentylenetetrazol (Metrazol) (14, 95, 130, 173), of insulin (126, 153), of picrotoxin (36) or of a mixture of chloralose and strychnine (144). Thus generalized convulsions are seen in the diencephalic, the mesencephalic and even in the rhombencephalic animal which possesses nothing but the medulla and pons, but they no longer occur in the spinal animal. One has therefore to postulate the existence of an anatomical structure in the brain stem, which extends to its most caudal part, and which is connected with the spinal motor neurons and able to transmit to them convulsant impulses. Such a structure, suspected by Lucciani under the name of 'common motor center' may, perhaps, be identified as the brain stem reticular formation, the most caudal part of which furnishes crossed and direct descending pathways to the motor neurons in the spinal cord.

b) Cortical theory. The famous experiments of Fritsch & Hitzig in 1870 (51) led to the theory of the cortical origin of generalized epilepsy. These authors demonstrated that weak electrical stimulation applied to the sigmoid gyrus in the dog provoked focal movements, whereas more intense or more prolonged stimulation of this region provoked generalized convulsions more or less rapidly. Today we would consider this phenomenon as a secondary (subsequent) generalization and consider it entirely separate from seizures generalized from the start (see below). At that date, however, these experiments led to doubts concerning the subcortical mechanism of epileptogenesis. Thus Ferrier in 1873 (47) concluded, "It is not necessary to assume that the medulla oblongata is the primary seat of the motor disturbance in fits."

Only 13 years after the famous experiments of Fritsch & Hitzig, Franck & Pitres (49) showed that it was impossible to localize an 'epileptogenic center' in the motor cortex only, since ablation of this region did not stop convulsions provoked by its stimulation. Thus it became necessary to postulate the propagation of epileptogenic activity from the point stimulated to the whole of the cerebral cortex or to subcortical structures able to maintain convulsions. To this end, Unverricht (1889) announced his 'law of irradiation', conceiving an 'intracortical' conduction of the epileptic seizure which, starting from a point on one hemisphere, is propagated superficially to the whole cortex. Lewandoski in 1907 (131) defended the theory of transcallosal propagation, as did Erickson (43) much later, although he regularly obtained generalized seizures after section of the corpus callosum. Since these fits were clonic on the side opposite to the stimulated hemisphere and tonic on the same side, Erickson concluded that subcortical structures play an accessory part in the propagation of the epileptic discharge, at least as far as the clonic component is concerned. Karplus (123) on the contrary supposed

that the spread of a discharge localized in the cortex takes place mainly by subcortical pathways. He thus prepared the way for later research which confirmed this view, as we shall show in the section on seizures of partial epilepsy secondarily generalized.

In these theories of the cortical origin of generalized epilepsy the authors assumed that convulsive seizures depended on a discharge transmitted from the motor cortex of both hemispheres to the spinal neurons by way of the pyramidal tracts. This concept was vigorously attacked by Prus in 1898 (162) who showed that these tracts were not essential for seizure production. von Economo & Karplus confirmed this work in 1910, demonstrating the persistence of tonic-clonic seizures in animals after bilateral destruction of the pyramidal tracts and the pes pedunculi. The same kind of experiments were undertaken by Mettler & Mettler in 1940 (141) who wrote, "epileptiform seizures cannot be evoked from the cortex if only the pyramids are intact, but can be evoked if they alone are severed," a conclusion which leaves one to suppose that extrapyramidal structures and pathways play a predominant part in the mechanism of generalized convulsions.

Electrophysiological experiments soon came to confirm the results of these ablation experiments. Hoefer & Pool (99) showed that, during a seizure, spike-discharges of cortical origin are intermittent in pyramidal pathways but continuous in extrapyramidal pathways situated in the reticular formation. Recently, Zanchetti & Brookhart (199) have demonstrated that there is no modification in pyramidal responsiveness after pentylenetetrazol has been administered in doses large enough to induce "spontaneous convulsive discharges". Schlag (172) obtained similar results after injections of physostigmine or acetylcholine. The two authors suggest that these convulsants do not directly affect pyramidal neurons and cortical interneurons but act through other neuronal structures, notably those in the reticular formation.

All these experiments indicate that, although cortical seizures may be secondarily generalized, it is unlikely that in fits that are generalized from the start the primary origin is cortical with corticospinal propagation.

c) Eclectic theory of cortical-subcortical mechanism of generalized convulsions. Although there is agreement that generalized convulsions do not necessarily depend on the cerebral cortex, some authors consider that this applies only to the tonic phase. Among these one must mention Binswanger (18) and Wortis & Klenke (198) who obtained only tonic seizures by mechanical or electric stimulation of the pons and the hypothalamus, and Ziehen (201) who was unable to obtain clonic convulsions after cortical ablation. These results have been confirmed by Samaja (171), Prevost (161) and Bouché (19). This difference between the sites of origin of clonic and tonic convulsions was elevated into a law by Bechterew (16). Horsley offered an even more eclectic opinion when he wrote in 1886 (100), "tonic and clonic spasms may be produced by any motor center, but the combination and sequence of tonic-clonic could originate only from the cerebral motor cortex." Such an interpretation however is not universally accepted. Bubnoff & Heidenhain (23), Pollock & Davis (159), Pike et al. (157), Spiegel (180), and Marinesco et al. (135) insist upon the fact that clonic as well as tonic convulsions may originate exclusively in subcortical structures.

MECHANISM OF THE BIOELECTRIC DISCHARGES IN GENERALIZED EPILEPSY. Certainly the most striking aspect of generalized seizures recorded from the cortex is the excessive synchrony of the elements responsible for each wave of activity. For this reason the epileptic seizure has sometimes been called a 'paroxysmal hypersynchrony'. Actually, the synchrony of the components is always imperfect and what mainly characterizes them is isorhythmicity (48). This isorhythmicity, as well as the approximate synchrony, is partly explained by the fact that different cortical regions, primarily passive, are connected with one or several subcortical foci of activity which act as their common pace maker or pace makers. We know that when several pace makers compete, only one is dominant, although changeover from one to another may take place.

This community and this unity of control represent what one might call the external factors of isorhythmicity; there is a synchrony or at least a grouping of elements when the controls are mediated by fast conducting pathways.

On the other hand, the mechanism of internal synchronization, which engenders and organizes the convulsive subcortical pace makers of the passive cortical areas, is much more complicated, depending on many intricate factors. Here interactions between neighboring neurons of the same type may arise either from synaptic connections or from reciprocal field effects at a short distance. The seizure occurs when these interactions become unusually important and especially when they thus create the conditions

for explosive autorecruitment. This may come from different causes, according to Fessard (48): lowering of the excitability threshold of neurons, failure of inhibitory mechanisms, structural arrangements favorable to synaptic or ephaptic interactions, alterations of the recovery cycles so that those of a whole population of neurons come to have more similar periodicities, etc. Even chance can be invoked, for if the other conditions are favorable, a fortuitous and initially restricted synchrony may bring on synchronization of excitable elements of a larger population of neurons as a result of intense interactions which will be powerful in proportion to the number of units already recruited. The fact that the synchrony, whatever its cause, results in wider synchronization is the basic principle of the paroxysmal character of seizures.

The generalized nature of the seizure discharge which accompanies tonic-clonic convulsions was demonstrated by workers who studied its distribution in the brain of animals. Thus Jung (116) by using electroshock, and Gastaut & Hunter (66) and Starzl et al. (184) by injecting pentylenetetrazol recorded such a discharge from the whole of the cerebellar and cerebral cortex (iso- and allocortex) and all the subcortical structures from the caudate nucleus to the mesencephalon. Jung observed that electrical stimulation, which was insufficient to provoke a generalized fit, caused the discharge to appear in subcortical (thalamic and subthalamic) structures and the allocortex (Ammon's horn) and spared only the isocortex. These results agree well with those of Gastaut & Hunter (66) who observed that following an injection of pentylenetetrazol, bisynchronous discharges appear first in the diencephalon.[1]

Thus one may suppose that generalized discharges originate in diencephalic structures, whence they irradiate to the whole of the brain, a hypothesis which is confirmed by direct stimulation of the median diencephalon.

Electrical stimulation of the nonspecific thalamic structures at low frequency provokes a 'recruiting' response (38-40, 106, 109, 183). Such responses, when

---

[1] These results do not however agree with those of Starzl et al. (184) who found that a convulsant dose of pentylenetetrazol provoked first a cortical discharge which was secondarily 'driven' to the subcortical structures by projection fibers. Starzl et al. even concluded that, in the animal with an 'entirely' isolated cortex, the convulsant dose of pentylenetetrazol caused a generalized cortical discharge without any response in the diencephalon. These are obviously disturbing differences which are difficult to reconcile, but may be due to differences in technique.

evoked by mid-line stimulation, are widely distributed over the two hemispheres and are synchronous and symmetrical on the two sides; their generalized distribution thus resembles that of a grand mal seizure.

Chemical stimulation of the diencephalic brain stem produces generalized electrical discharges. Murphy & Gellhorn (148) obtained generalized discharges by injecting strychnine into the hypothalamus, and recently Ralston & Ajmone-Marsan (163) provoked bursts of bisynchronous convulsant waves, predominantly frontal, by injecting penicillin into the thalamic reticular formation in the mid-line. These bursts could be precipitated by electrical stimulation of the thalamus and appear in the same territory as the 'recruiting' response. The authors indeed believe that propagation takes place along the non-specific thalamocortical pathways responsible for the recruiting response.

It is remarkable that generalized cortical discharges provoked by stimulation of the thalamic reticular formation do not persist after cessation of stimulation and are never accompanied by convulsions, and it is even more remarkable that generalized convulsions may be observed in the absence of all cortical electrical discharge. This is the case notably in the tonic seizures which are seen in certain forms of syncope and which appear in the EEG as total electrical silence instead of a generalized seizure discharge, as shown by Gastaut & Fischer-Williams (63).

It is interesting to note that techniques as unlike each other as those which have been applied to the study of the mechanism of generalized convulsions and of the accompanying bioelectric discharges should lead to similar conclusions: the incrimination of the brain stem reticular formation in the origin of these phenomena, the caudal part for the convulsions and the rostral part for the bioelectric discharges.

These conclusions obviously invalidate postulation of direct relationships between the discharge of cortical neurons and the muscular contractions, since both of these depend upon a third event, namely the reticular discharge. For the same reason, no significant relationships between the convulsive brain waves recorded from the scalp and the convulsive movements observed at the periphery are to be expected; they are separate both causally and temporally. These considerations are further emphasized by the following three observations.

a) The onset of the EEG discharge and that of the tonic phase of the grand mal fit may be separated by a relatively long time interval.

b) The electrical seizure discharge may occur in-

dependently of any tonic-clonic manifestations of grand mal, and vice versa. Thus EEG discharges of the grand mal type may appear alone in sleep (87), whereas tonic seizures secondary to acute cerebral ischemia are not accompanied by any electrical discharge whatsoever.

c) The EEG discharge and the convulsions, even when they begin together, do not necessarily evolve in a way which is, so to speak, superimposable. Thus, simultaneous EEG and electromyographic recording show some correlation during the clonic phase but none during the tonic phase (5, 168).

PETIT MAL OF MYOCLONIC TYPE. This has been induced in man and animals by all the measures capable of provoking grand mal. Myoclonic jerks[2] occur before the convulsive seizure when widespread interference with cerebral function acts in a sufficiently slow and progressive manner (anoxia, oxygen intoxication, hypoglycemia, injection of pentylenetetrazol, picrotoxin, chloralose, bromide of camphor, etc.). One has but to increase the interference and metabolic disturbance slightly in order to witness the appearance of a grand mal seizure, following the myoclonic jerks.

However, as in grand mal, focal cerebral lesions do not produce the bilateral myoclonic jerks of petit mal unless they are near the mid-line or unless their action is facilitated by the addition of a mild widespread activator, for example a subconvulsant dose of pentylenetetrazol.

When the disturbance is severe enough to provoke spontaneous myoclonus with its accompanying multiple spikes, any moderately intense sensory stimulation, such as a sound, touch or flash of light, precipitates myoclonus after a very brief latent period. Examples include the myoclonus provoked by sound after sodium santonin poisoning (189), myoclonus evoked by touch and sound after ingestion of bromide of camphor (149), and the multiple spikes and waves and myoclonus produced by flicker, sound and touch after pentylenetetrazol (52). There is here a further analogy between experimental myoclonic jerks and

[2] Jerks in myoclonic petit mal must not be confused with the clonic phase of generalized convulsive epilepsy. The confusion arises mainly out of etymology, but we consider it a source of grave error and the subject is later treated in greater detail. Suffice it to say here that these jerks are positive phenomena, related to an actual neuronal discharge in the central nervous system, whereas the clonic phase in a generalized fit is a negative phenomenon and represents the momentary interruption of the prolonged tonic discharge of grand mal.

those of clinical petit mal which are well known to be precipitated by sensory stimulation, especially those that are unexpected or repeated, for example the intermittent photic stimulation at 15 flickers per sec. used by Walter *et al.* (193).

The possibility of producing myoclonus at will, in either animals or man, by the combination of camphor and touch, or of pentylenetetrazol and photic stimulation enabled Muskens and later Gastaut to study its mechanism and describe the following characteristics.

a) Myoclonic jerks occur, as do the convulsions of grand mal, even in the rhombencephalic animal. (Similarly, bilateral myoclonic jerks, either spontaneous or provoked by noise or touch, are characteristically seen in pontine anencephalics.)

b) The multiple spike and wave of myoclonus, far from being limited to the rolandic cortex or even to the whole of the cortex, is recorded in all the grey matter of the brain, right into the mesencephalon.

c) In myoclonus provoked by sensory stimulation, the electrical discharge appears in the mesencephalic formation and the thalamus before being projected to the cortex.

d) A discharge with the same cerebral distribution and in every other way comparable to myoclonic multiple spikes is provoked by electrical stimulation of the anterior part of the thalamic nuclei in the midline.

e) The clinical and electrical phenomena of myoclonus, as in the case of grand mal, may be entirely independent in their time relationships; thus multiple spikes and waves may occur without jerks and vice versa.

With reference to propagation of the discharge, it has been shown that photic stimulation in an animal given pentylenetetrazol provokes, quite apart from the specific geniculostriate response, a discharge in the reticular formation of the brain stem together with an ascending thalamocortical discharge and a descending reticulocerebellar and reticulospinal discharge (55, 65, 68). The existence of reticulospinal irradiation is also implicated in the work of De Hass *et al.* (37) who showed that clonic responses evoked by afferent stimulation persist in the decorticate cat given pentylenetetrazol. Muskens (149) in 1926 already had a presentiment of this kind of irradiation when he related the sensoclonic phenomenon to "an influx produced in a reflex way in the region of the reticular substance in the pons and medulla."

Thalamocortical and reticulocortical irradiation, observed by Gastaut & Hunter (66) and confirmed by Hunter & Ingvar (101), was further demonstrated in an indirect way by the results of De Hass *et al.* (37). They showed that the presence of the specific sensory cortex was not necessary for obtaining an irradiated frontal response to photic or auditory stimulation in the cat after pentylenetetrazol administration; this obviously excludes the hypothesis of purely corticocortical conduction. Reticulocortical propagation was also demonstrated by Jasper *et al.* (108) who showed electrographically *a)* that the postdischarges from the visual cortex do not irradiate to other cortical regions by corticocortical pathways and certainly not to the frontocentral region where the multiple spikes, irradiated under the effect of photic stimulation, are recorded; and *b)* that a parastriate postdischarge projects directly to the intralaminar nuclei which project in turn to the frontal cortex. It seems therefore that the concept of the subcortical origin of petit mal of myoclonic type is well founded.

PETIT MAL OF 'ABSENCE' TYPE. This is the only variety of generalized epilepsy which has not been satisfactorily reproduced experimentally. The various measures causing generalized cerebral disturbance, which so effectively reproduce grand mal and myoclonus, have never provoked in the nonanesthetized animal transient loss of 'consciousness' comparable to the 'absence' of petit mal.

It is very easy to induce brief loss of consciousness by means of focal cerebral disturbances and particularly by limited electrical stimulation of many different structures with indwelling electrodes (thalamus, hypothalamus, subthalamus, the basal and limbic rhinencephalon, etc.). Loss of consciousness in these cases, however, is accompanied by an 'arrest' and 'orientation' reaction with postural readjustment and various types of gesture, which are much more suggestive of psychomotor attacks than the 'absence' of petit mal. One must therefore conclude that, despite the attempts of various authors and notably of Hunter & Jasper (102), of Kaada (119) and of Ingvar (103), petit mal 'absence' has not yet been definitely reproduced in animals. The same holds true of man according to Gastaut & Roger (77).

On the other hand the bilateral synchronous 3 cps spike-and-wave discharge has been reproduced in animals under special conditions. All the authors, having injected pentylenetetrazol or other convulsants systemically in the anesthetized and craniotomized animal, have provoked at will long-lasting, self-perpetuating discharges of spike and wave which are generalized, bilateral, synchronous and symmetrical. This spike-and-wave pattern, however, repeats itself at intervals which are very variable and only exceptionally around 3 cps. At best, it can not be related to any modification in alertness of the anesthetized animal. If the effect of rhythmical sensory stimuli is added to that of pentylenetetrazol, it is also easy to induce a spike-and-wave discharge maintained at the frequency of stimulation, for example at 3 cps continuing for as long as desired (66). However, the fact that the rhythm has to be maintained actively and ceases as soon as stimulation is stopped completely disqualifies the phenomenon from being considered as a form of experimental epilepsy. The same criticism may be levelled at the spike-and-wave in the isocortex or allocortex which can be evoked with great difficulty by rhythmical electrical stimulation of the mid-line nuclei of the thalamus (12, 103, 109, 118).

Recently Ralston & Ajmone-Marsan (163) have produced in the cat EEG patterns which are very close to the bilateral synchronous spike-and-wave discharge of petit mal. They produced a discrete irritative lesion in the nonspecific thalamic system by stereotaxic injection of penicillin. As a result, fusiform bursts of slow waves developed at a frequency of 3.5 to 5 cps, were of great amplitude and tended to appear synchronously over the ipsilateral hemisphere when the lesion involved the intralaminar nuclei but over the two hemispheres when the lesion was in the mid-line. On the basis of the topography of these thalamic lesions and cortical discharges, and of the identity between these discharges and those produced by thalamic stimulation (either single-shock stimulation provoking 'triggered' spindles, or repetitive stimulation provoking a recruiting response), the authors conclude that these discharges are 'transmitted' by the nonspecific thalamocortical projection system. With a sufficiently severe lesion spikes also appear, at first in the thalamus and later projected to the cortex where they may be grouped with the bursts of hypersynchronous waves; they may thus sometimes constitute rhythmical spike-and-wave complexes. From these observations the authors have come to believe that the discharges of petit mal depend on stimulation of the nonspecific thalamic system near the mid-line, but that different systems are involved in the production of the spikes and of the slow waves.

The fact that it has not been possible to reproduce petit mal 'absences' in animals has not prevented experimental studies on man. Thus Spiegel et al. (182), Williams (197) and Kirikae et al. (125) have recorded numerous episodes of 'absences' simultaneously in the cortex and in the thalamus. All these authors admit that spike-and-wave discharge takes place in the two structures at the same time, unless it occurs first in the thalamus; the British and Japanese authors even feel that the slow wave in the complex is essentially thalamic whereas the spike represents the cortical element. Thus Williams suggests that the paroxysm begins in the thalamus with a rhythm of slow sinusoidal waves of which each element propagates itself to the cortex, there to fire off a spike which, in its turn transmitted to the thalamus, provokes there another slow wave and so on. Hayne et al. (98) report contradictory results, for they do not believe that there is any discharge in the thalamus during petit mal 'absences' with bilateral and synchronous spike-and-wave in the cortex.

Petit mal 'absence' also differs from the other types of generalized epilepsy in its electroclinical correlations. Loss of consciousness is undoubtedly associated with the spike-and-wave discharge, since no clinical petit mal seizure occurs without this particular discharge. The reverse is quite possible, however, and discharges are frequently recorded without clinical manifestations.

Although electroclinically allied to the other varieties of generalized epilepsy, it must be admitted that, from the experimental point of view, the findings relating to petit mal 'absences' are not analogous to those in grand mal and myoclonus. Perhaps for this reason, there is no agreement on the mechanism of 'absence' and its accompanying EEG pattern. Shimizu et al. (177) believe, indeed, that the petit mal spike-and-wave discharge has a localized cortical origin and that it is rapidly transmitted to the whole of the cortex of both hemispheres by means of corticocortical association pathways, chiefly via the corpus callosum. They base this view on their electrothalamographic findings in man, and especially on the following results of animal experiments: a) intracarotid injection of pentylenetetrazol, which carries it to the ipsilateral cortex, provokes a bisynchronous spike-and-wave pattern more easily and more often than does injection via a vertebral artery, which would take it to the central grey matter; b) intracarotid injection provoked only unilateral spike-and-wave complexes when pentothal had been injected into the other carotid. However this may be, it must be admitted that this view is peculiar to the Chicago school and that the majority of electroencephalographers accept the theory of a diencephalic pacemaker mechanism in petit mal 'absences' as in the other types of generalized epilepsy (105). Ingvar (103) does not fully support either theory, believing the matter unsettled.

Cohn (30) pointed out that the spike component of the spike-wave (spike-dome) complex in man is not exactly synchronous over the whole of the scalp, since its beginning, measured at two homologous points on the two hemispheres, could show an asynchrony of the magnitude of about 5 to 20 msec. Such a finding appears to lead to conflict with the theory of Jasper & Droogleever-Fortuyn (109) who argued that the cortical discharge in petit mal depends on the activity of a single mid-line pacemaker which projects synchronously to the two hemispheres at once. Despite their discordance, one may reconcile the observations of Cohn and of Jasper by taking into account the anatomical relations demonstrated by Nauta & Whitlock (151). These authors showed that in the anteromedial part of the thalamus, which was the region stimulated by the Montreal workers, there is a band of compact fibers from the brain stem reticular formation going, on the one hand, to the subcortical grey matter and, on the other hand, to the nucleus reticularis of the thalamus which in turn projects diffusely over the isocortex. These anatomical facts may explain how Jasper & Droogleever-Fortuyn, stimulating in the mid-line a tract of fibers with bilateral distribution, were able to obtain a bilateral and synchronous cortical discharge, whereas the spontaneous spike-and-wave discharge recorded by Cohn, arising in a central but bilateral and diffuse pace maker in the thalamus, may give the asynchrony which he observed. It is relevant at this point to recall that it was in the lateral part of the thalamus that Williams (197) recorded the start of the petit mal discharge.

Interpretation of Experimental Results

In the previous section we have limited ourselves to a presentation of experimental results with a minimum of interpretation. In this section we shall be expressing personal views in an attempt to present a more general unifying conception of the physiopathology of generalized seizures. In the first part we consider the nature and origin of the neuronal discharge responsible for a generalized seizure, taking grand mal as an example. In the second we shall envisage the causes of this discharge. Finally, a third part will be devoted to a study of the mechanisms by which this discharge is prematurely interrupted or rhythmically inhibited, and which are responsible for the two varieties of petit mal (myoclonic and 'absence' types). The final aim of this section will be achieved when we

have demonstrated the existence of a similar mechanism in all three main varieties of generalized epilepsy.

ORIGIN, NATURE AND PROPAGATION OF NERVOUS ACTIVITY RESPONSIBLE FOR GENERALIZED GRAND MAL SEIZURE. If we envisage generalized grand mal epilepsy as a group of clinical and electrical phenomena, necessarily involving convulsions, associated with an EEG discharge of generalized hypersynchronous waves, the results which we have reviewed in the preceding section lead us to relate it to a reticular discharge propagated toward the cortex, resulting in the EEG manifestations, and toward the periphery, inducing the convulsions.

This conception of generalized epilepsy is however disputable in so far as it regards the two phenomena as necessarily associated, and affords them equal importance, whereas the two can be dissociated and only one of them corresponds to the clinical definition of epilepsy. One may try to explain grand mal epilepsy in terms of a hypersynchronous discharge, but one can not postulate the existence of hypersynchronous discharge in an affection which (until we know more about it) is characterized only by convulsions and loss of consciousness.

If we admit that the clinical and EEG manifestations of generalized epilepsy are not necessarily linked and that the former are of greater 'medical' interest, we should first of all try to explain these clinical phenomena and afterward search for the factors that link them to the hypersynchronous discharges by which they are usually accompanied. We shall therefore examine the experimental conditions which provoke transient generalized convulsions, whether or not they are reputed to be 'epileptic', and seek to delineate their precise physiopathological mechanism. In the present state of knowledge, there are four convulsive conditions which throw light on the problem.

a) Convulsions with loss of consciousness, characterized by intense contractions resulting in opisthotonus, preceded or followed by one or two muscular jerks, are precipitated in man and in animals by all forms of cerebral anoxia (anoxemic anoxia from insufficient partial pressure of oxygen, toxic anoxia, and ischemic anoxia due to cardiac arrest and fall in arterial pressure). These phenomena have been studied electrophysiologically in animals by Noell & Dombrowsky (152), Ward (194), Ward & Wheatley (195), Ajmone-Marson & Fuortes (4) and Gastaut *et al.* (70). The concordant results of these authors may be summarized as follows.

1) During acute anoxia, depression of electrical

activity extends progressively from the telencephalon to the diencephalon, and then to the mesencephalon and the metencephalon, during which time the most caudal structures, notably the reticular formation (in the pons, medulla and the spinal cord) develop or continue to show considerable electrical activity.

2) Anoxic convulsions are no longer seen after the bulbar part of the reticular formation has been destroyed by diathermy (194). One must therefore conclude that anoxic seizures depend on the activity of the caudal reticular formation when no longer under the control of the higher nervous structures (fig. 1).

b) Convulsions without loss of consciousness, characterized by intense contractions in opisthotonus, preceded and followed by clonic jerks, are provoked in man and animals by the administration of strychnine or other poisons (e.g. nitrogen mustards, dichlorodiphenyltrichloroethane). These convulsions have been studied from the electrophysiological point of view in animals by Bremer (21), Markham et al.

(136), Ruf (169), Marossero & Garrone (137), Bremer & Bonnet (22), Johnson (112) and Gastaut et al. (71). These studies give the following remarkably similar results.

1) Strychnine convulsions are accompanied by a hypersynchronous discharge in the whole of the reticular formation of the spinal cord and the brain stem but excluding the intralaminar and mid-line nuclei of the thalamus, stimulation of which provokes the recruiting response.

2) This reticular discharge secondarily extends to the cerebellum. Bremer has shown that the discharges recorded in the cerebellar cortex are evoked by those coming from the reticular formation which he considers the site of the autorhythmic tetanic activity. This reticular discharge also extends to the motor neurons of the spinal cord, the hypersynchronous activity of which is directly responsible for the convulsions. On the contrary, it does not extend to the cerebral cortex which reacts by desynchronization.

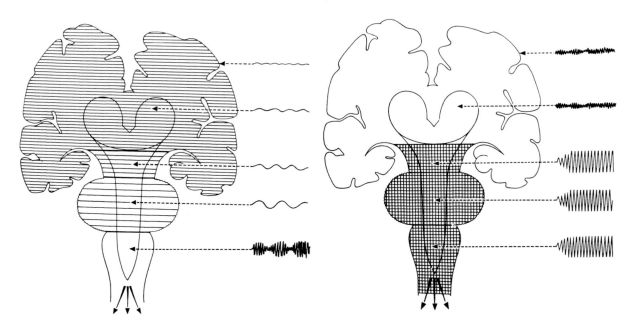

FIG. 1. Schematic representation of the mechanism of anoxic convulsions. The density of the horizontal lines is proportional to the damage to the neurons due to the anoxia. This damage is maximum at the corticothalamic level where the bioelectric rhythms are abolished also. It is diminished at the level of the hypothalamus and especially of the mesencephalon, where there are still slow rhythms. It is not present in the reticular formation of the bulb where the electrical activity is normal. It must thus be concluded that the anoxic convulsions (represented by the arrows) depend upon the normal activity of the caudal reticular formation when it is no longer subject to the control of the higher nervous centers

FIG. 2. Schematic representation of the mechanism of strychnine convulsions. The cross-ruled areas of the brainstem are those where the hypersynchronous discharge of the strychnine type occurs. The thalamocortical structures are completely spared by this discharge and show only a desynchronization which is normal when there is an intense excitation of the reticular formation. It must thus be concluded that strychnine convulsions result from a caudal reticular discharge without any participation of telencephalic structures or even of the thalamus.

3) The neuronal reactivity of this desynchronized cortex is normal or diminished, but never augmented (199). Chang (26) also found that strychnine decreased the excitability of the cortical neurons. One must therefore conclude that strychnine convulsions result in a caudal reticular discharge without any participation in the structures of the telencephalon or even of the thalamus (fig. 2).

c) Intense tonic contraction with loss of consciousness preceded by a few isolated clonic jerks and followed by a phase of rhythmical clonic convulsions are provoked by different convulsants (analeptics), notably by thujone, beta-ethylbetamethylglutarimide (Megimide) and pentamethylenetetrazol (Metrazol). An electrophysiological study of these convulsions in animals has been made by Gastaut & Hunter (65), Gastaut *et al.* (71), Ajmone-Marsan & Marossero (5) and Starzl *et al.* (184) with the following results.

1) During these convulsions[3] a hypersynchronous discharge replaces all normal activity in the di- and telencephalic formations, clearly predominating over the cortex and in the thalamus. This discharge decreases in importance in the midbrain tegmentum where it is not able to replace local spontaneous activity. It is practically absent from the rhombencephalon and the spinal cord where normal or increased spontaneous rhythms continue.

2) The responsiveness of the cortex to electrical stimulation (as shown by the threshold and sensitivity of the corticospinal neurons) remains unchanged even when pentylenetetrazol is used in sufficiently large quantities to induce 'spontaneous' convulsive discharges (199). Assessing neuronal excitability by the chronaxic method, Chauchard *et al.* (27) demonstrated that subconvulsant doses of pentylenetetrazol depressed excitability of the cortex while increasing that of the brain stem and spinal cord, an action comparable to that of anoxia.

One must therefore conclude that pentylenetetrazol-induced convulsions are evoked by a mechanism which is analogous to that of anoxic seizures, i.e. a 'liberation' of the activity of the caudal reticular formation because the overlying nervous structures are functionally excluded, having been invaded by a discharge (fig. 3).

d) Convulsions have been provoked in animals by the administration of pentylenetetrazol in strongly

[3] We will consider in this paragraph and the next only the tonic phase of convulsions provoked by analeptics. The rhythmic clonic phase which follows the tonic phase depends on the effect of a special inhibitory mechanism, which will be the object of a special study later.

strychninized animals (3, 5). These convulsions are expressed by:

1) hypersynchronous di- and telencephalic discharge of the pentylenetetrazol type and by a reticular discharge in the mesorhombencephalon of strychnine type, these discharges developing completely independently;

2) tonic spasm of purely strychnine type not bearing any resemblance to pentylenetetrazol convulsions or any relation to the cortical pentylenetetrazol discharge.

One must therefore conclude that these seizures result from a caudal reticular discharge of strychnine nature, without the participation of the di- and telencephalic structures activated by pentylenetetrazol (fig. 4).

Comparing these different mechanisms, it appears that generalized tonic spasm and isolated clonic convulsions depend exclusively on the caudal reticular formation which acts on the effector neurons, and particularly on the motor neurons of the spinal cord, by means of the various reticulospinal and vestibulospinal pathways and projections. These pathways, like the structures from which they come, are capable of inhibiting as well as reinforcing muscle tone, but not in the same proportion since only the medial part of the caudal reticular formation is inhibitory, whereas all the rest of the reticular formation and the vestibular formation is facilitatory (133). It may therefore be supposed that the inhibiting action is less efficacious than the facilitating one and that it is entirely masked when the reticular formation is activated as a whole. These views are consistent with the findings of the classical neurophysiologists of the Sherrington school for when the portion of the reticular system, inhibitory as well as facilitatory, lying caudal to a midbrain transection, is liberated from the influence of higher centers, a state of decerebrate rigidity results and not one of hypotonia. The mode of activation of this caudal reticular formation varies, however, for during the tonic spasms it may represent either a positive phenomenon, a hypersynchronous neuronal discharge or a negative phenomenon, a liberation by depression or functional exclusion of the overlying structures.

The loss of consciousness accompanying the convulsions would seem to depend exclusively on the rostral thalamic reticular formation and the cortex. In man anoxic seizures (in certain syncopes) and pentylenetetrazol seizures, as indeed all other generalized epileptic seizures, are accompanied by unconsciousness related to functional exclusion of the thalamocortical system which is either deprived of oxygen or occupied by a hypersynchronous discharge. Con-

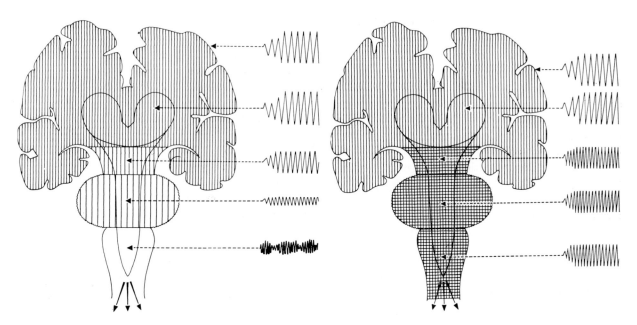

FIG. 3. Schematic representation of the mechanism of pentylenetetrazol (Metrazol) convulsions. The density of the vertical lines is proportional to the importance of the hypersynchronous discharge of the pentylenetetrazol type. This discharge is maximum at the thalamocortical level and it diminishes in the mesencephalon and the metencephalon to disappear in the caudal reticular formation where normal electrical activity persists. It must thus be concluded that the pentylenetetrazol convulsions are produced by the same mechanism as the anoxic, i.e. a 'liberation' of the activity of the neurons of the caudal reticular formation when the higher nervous centers are invaded by a discharge which results in their functional exclusion.

FIG. 4. Schematic representation of the effect provoked by pentylenetetrazol in an animal already heavily strychninized. The vertical lines represent the hypersynchronous pentylenetetrazol discharge at the thalamocortical level, while the squares represent the hypersynchronous strychnine discharge in the brain stem. It can be seen that the strychnine tetanus which is present at this time depends exclusively on the discharge of the caudal reticular formation without any involvement of the diencephalic structures activated by the pentylenetetrazol.

versely strychnine convulsions (tetanus or rabies spasms and tonic cerebellar fits probably depend on the same mechanism) do not involve the thalamocortical system and are characterized by preservation of consciousness.

We may now attempt to apply these hypotheses to the convulsions of grand mal epilepsy, believing that pentylenetetrazol-induced seizures are the only ones which faithfully reproduce spontaneous epilepsy in man with its hypersynchronous cortical discharge and its well differentiated tonic and clonic phases. A grand mal seizure seems to depend on a thalamic discharge which involves the nonspecific reticular structures and is projected to the cortex in what may be considered a generalized recruiting response transmitted along the diffuse cortical projection pathways. Since the system responsible for recruitment is also responsible for generalized epileptic discharges (66, 109, 163) and, since it also seems implicated in the production of bursts of barbiturate 'sleep' (107, 143),

one is tempted to compare the hypersynchronous discharge of generalized epilepsy with a sort of paroxysmal 'sleep' localized to the thalamocortical system and provoking a functional exclusion of this system. This functional elimination may be directly responsible for the loss of consciousness and indirectly responsible for the convulsions by liberating the underlying reticular structures. Given the antagonism which exists between the thalamic and the mesencephalorhombencephalic part of the reticular formation,[4] one may suppose that a momentary depression of the caudal reticular system can, under

[4] The recruiting as well as the augmenting responses evoked by thalamic stimulation are blocked by stimulation of the reticular formation (85, 147); the pyramidal discharge synchronous with the augmenting response is suppressed during reticular formation stimulation (155). Conversely, the recruiting response is enhanced by the destruction or the barbiturate depression of the reticular formation (111, 124), as well as many other responses induced by thalamic stimulation.

certain circumstances, favor a thalamocortical discharge indirectly responsible for the seizure, so explaining the part that sleep plays in inducing generalized seizures.

Finally, assuming the independence of these two systems, one may postulate that a factor which can precipitate thalamocortical hypersynchrony can equally (and independently) precipitate hypersynchrony of the reticular formation. In this way there may be a double reticular discharge of which one, the thalamic, may be responsible for the cortical manifestations of the seizure and the other, the mesencephalorhombencephalic, for its peripheral manifestations.

One therefore arrives at the following conclusions. Generalized grand mal epilepsy is related to a subcortical mechanism corresponding first to a paroxysmal discharge of the thalamic reticular system transmitted to the cortex by the diffuse thalamocortical projection pathways, which explains the loss of consciousness. This discharge results in functional exclusion of the thalamocortical formations, thus liberating 'normal' or reinforced activity of the caudal reticular system; this release, by putting into play the tonicogenic reticulospinal system, explains the peripheral convulsions.

It will be noticed that this conception is closely akin to that of Hughlings Jackson who related epileptic seizures not only to abnormal neuronal discharges but to consequent liberation of other parts of the brain.[5]

CAUSES OF RETICULAR DISCHARGES, THALAMIC AND MESENCEPHALORHOMBENCEPHALIC, RESPONSIBLE FOR GRAND MAL EPILEPSY. In only a very small number of

[5] In 1874 Hughlings Jackson wrote (104): "The principle that we get over-action of lower centres from the mere removal of the higher centres has very important applications. . . . Strong epileptic discharges paralyse the nervous centre (or much of it) in which they begin or through which they spread." He then applied this generalization "to the cases where the discharge begins in the highest series. There is loss of use of that series after a discharge beginning in it, where that discharge has been excessive. But obviously violent action (maniacal raving) could not result from this loss of use (a *paralytic* condition) of the highest centres. That accounts only for loss of consciousness. . . . That is only the patient's negative condition, and his condition is duplex. There is the positive element— the mania—to be accounted for. My opinion is that the mania is the result of over-action (morbidly increased discharge, but not epileptic discharge) of the processes just below those which have been put hors de combat." We realize that the above remarks do not refer primarily to generalized grand mal epilepsy, but they nevertheless exemplify some aspects of the unrivalled enlightenment of Hughlings Jackson.

epileptics has a focal or diffuse irritative lesion in the reticular formation been found to be the cause of generalized seizures. However, characteristic lesions in these regions have been found in certain familial degenerative epilepsies (of the Unverricht-Lunsborg type).

Since there are no demonstrable reticular lesions in the majority of subjects with grand mal seizures generalized from the start and since they are never present in cases of experimental generalized epilepsy, the discharge responsible for these seizures no doubt depends on a functional abnormality of these reticular neurons. It is possible that this functional abnormality depends on the unique anatomical arrangement that is found here; numerous afferent collaterals (183) arriving from many different parts of the peripheral and central nervous system (fibers from sensory lemnisci, the special senses, the cortex, subcortical regions and cerebellum) all converge toward common reticular elements and set up phenomena of summation (146). With this spatiotemporal summation on neighboring neurons and, provided that these are in a hyperexcitable state (either because of constitutional factors or acquired disorders), the normal inflow of nerve impulses in the reticular formation may cause sufficient synchronous cellular potentials to build up an effective electrical stimulus. This stimulus would entail a discharge of the surrounding hyperexcitable cell bodies by direct electrical spread independent of any process of synaptic transmission (ephaptic phenomenon). Once this process has been started, the discharge would spread like an avalanche throughout the reticular formation with a speed of the same order as that of the transmission of the nerve impulse from neuron to neuron. This theory, formulated by Gastaut (54), is only a particular application of the general hypothesis suggested by Moruzzi in 1950 (145): "A normal neuron, by the simple fact of being subjected to a bombardment of nervous activity at high frequency, can enter into convulsive state. . . . It is the ordinary inflow of nerve impulses which determine the fact that a neuron passes from normal activity to an 'epileptic' state. . . . Any neuron may become 'epileptic,' simply through the effect of bombardment of nervous activity."

In an unstable system (such as an organization of hyperexcitable neurons) it is usually an external force that upsets equilibrium. It is not surprising therefore that a volley of impulses, converging on a center whose state of tension is abnormally raised, supplies the energy necessary to build up a hypersynchronous discharge. This conception was held in the nineteenth century by pioneers of the modern study of epilepsy who from Hall (96) onwards elaborated the bulbar reflex theory of generalized epilepsy and believed that it depends on a "discharge produced in a reflex way in the region of reticular substance of the pons and medulla . . ." (149) under the effect of "an exalted sensibility and excitability of the medulla oblongata" (174). One should not conclude, however, that generalized epilepsy is merely a reflex phenomenon and speak of reflex epilepsy; this unphysiological term is not applicable today to any variety of epilepsy.

The hyperexcitable state of the neurons, which is a factor necessary to the production of the reticular discharge, may depend on the existence of an 'irritative' cerebral lesion lying in the neighborhood or even at a distance from the brain stem. Johnson & Walker (113–115) and Kopoloff et al. (127) have shown that epileptogenic lesions localized in one hemisphere are always accompanied by a diffuse hyperexcitable state of the neurons manifested by a general lowering of the convulsant threshold. It may depend equally well on a functional factor as yet undetermined, a 'humoral' or 'cerebral' factor acting at the level of the synapses, the axons or the cell bodies, and responsible for an 'epileptic predisposition' found both in man and in animals. This epileptic predisposition and hyperexcitable neuronic state may be quantitatively appreciated by determining the convulsant threshold with the photopentylenetetrazol method (52). The threshold is low in patients suffering from seizures generalized from the start and in those whose attacks of partial epilepsy pass very easily into secondary generalization.

DURATION AND TERMINATION OF DISCHARGE IN GENERALIZED EPILEPSY. The duration and ending of a grand mal seizure depend on a dual mechanism: a negative process of neuronal exhaustion, and a positive process of inhibition.

The first of these mechanisms which may bring about the cessation of the seizure, the progressive fatigue and final exhaustion of the neurons, is attributed either to the accumulation of acid metabolites or to the fact that the reserves necessary for cellular functioning have been used up, or to both processes at once. The first hypothesis, "Ermüdung" in the sense of Verworn (1900), has not been satisfactorily demonstrated, for although the pH of the motor cortex shows a tendency toward acidity during the fatigue stage of a faradic seizure (42), it changes toward alkaline values at the end of a pentylenetetrazol-induced seizure of generalized epilepsy (110).

On the other hand the second hypothesis, "Erschöpfung" in the sense of Verworn, has been largely demonstrated. Ruf prolonged a pentylenetetrazol seizure for 30 min. by administering oxygen to an experimental animal and for 1 hr. by giving epinephrine as well as oxygen. Davis & Remond (35), using a polarographic cathode method sensitive to oxygen concentration, demonstrated the existence of relative hypoxia in the cerebral cortex developing during convulsive activity. Whatever may be its intimate nature, the part played by neuronal exhaustion in the electroclinical manifestations of grand mal seizures is supported by the following considerations.

At the beginning of a grand mal fit the EEG discharge does not diminish in frequency, for there exists an initial indefatigability. This however may be apparent only if, as Rosenblueth & Cannon (168) believe, hypersynchrony is still incomplete at this moment and if different cortical elements are responsible for successive convulsive waves. It may, however, be real if the neurons enjoy oxygen pressures at the onset of the seizure distinctly higher than those which determine its extinction and if in addition their hyperexcitability is so intense at that time that they could discharge with very low oxygen pressures. Whatever the case may be, the EEG discharge of sustained frequency, characteristic of the beginning of the grand mal seizure, corresponds to a discharge of the peripheral motor units which is equally sustained but of much higher frequency and which provokes the tetanus at the beginning of the tonic phase.

Once the seizure has lasted some seconds, progressive slowing of the EEG discharge develops, indicating increasing length of the functional refractory period of the thalamocortical neurons as they fatigue. This increasing state of fatigue also affects the reticulospinal neurons and thereby converts the complete tetanus into an incomplete tetanus which imprints a vibratory character on the last part of the tonic phase.

At a certain point of fatigue, the functional refractory period has become so lengthened that the discharge is interrupted for a short time. This, the first period of extinction, appears in the EEG as an interval of electrical silence and at the periphery as relaxation of the tonic phase introducing the first clonus. This momentary rest permits partial recovery of energy, which entails a recrudescence of the discharge (first group of spikes) and of the muscular contraction (first clonic jerk). A further period of extinction then follows, longer than the first, and is itself followed by another discharge. The cycle continues in this way throughout the whole of the clonic phase until total exhaustion, which is characterized by lasting extinction of both electrical activity and convulsions.[6]

Postictal recovery is slow; it is manifested electrically by the appearance of abnormal rhythms, first delta then theta, and from the clinical point of view by coma and an episode of gradually clearing confusion.

This simplified picture of a grand mal seizure might lead one to believe that the fit is limited to a cortical discharge recorded on the EEG and the convulsions observed clinically. This is far from being the case, since all the cerebral neurons discharge at the same time as the cortical cells recorded on the EEG and all the peripheral effector structures are activated at the same time as the skeletal muscles. Thus the whole of the autonomic system is involved in a grand mal seizure, but its effects are masked by the spectacular nature of the generalized convulsions. We may recall, for example, the fact that the smooth musculature is brought into play, in the pupils, nipples and viscera; that salivary, sweat and vaginal glands are stimulated; and that there are alterations in cardiac rhythm, arterial pressure and vasomotor activity. This widespread action is easily understood since the diffuse projections, which radiate out from the brain stem reticular formation, go not only to the cortex but to all the grey matter of the brain, and because the reticulospinal pathways connect with the autonomic preganglionic centers in the brain stem and spinal cord just as they do with the somatomotor centers in these same regions.

The second mechanism involves active inhibition. It may be supposed that the rhythmical interruption of a grand mal seizure depends not only on neuronal exhaustion, but also on the development of intermittent inhibition in 'suppressor' structures.

Expounding this theory in 1949, Jung (116) suggested that the inhibitory structure was the caudate nucleus, for it was from there that he recorded large regular slow waves, coinciding with the episodes of relaxation in the clonic movements and interposed between the fast rhythms recorded from the cortex and the thalamus. This hypothesis agrees well with the

views of Dusser de Barenne et al. (41) who believed that inhibitory neurons situated in the caudate nucleus were acted upon by the various cortical 'suppressor' zones, and that they were effective through the thalamus and a corticocaudothalamo-cortical circuit. The close relationship between the theories of Jung and of Dusser de Barenne is further demonstrated by the fact that Gastaut & Hunter (66) and Starzl et al. (184) recorded these same slow waves in the intralaminar and mid-line nuclei of the thalamus.

From these experimental results one may postulate the existence of a thalamocaudate inhibitory system[7] 'branched-off in a side-chain' from the nonspecific thalamocortical projection system, a system which may actively inhibit the reticular formation of the thalamus as well as that of the caudal brain stem and thus prevent the discharge of cortical spikes at the same time as the peripheral contraction.

In other words, the thalamocortical discharge of grand mal responsible for cortical spikes and for reticular 'release' (with its consequent tonic phase) may be equally responsible for putting into action the inhibitory system, the slow waves from which rhythmically interrupt the discharge of spikes. The slow wave represents not a convulsion wave but a veritable state of neuronal depression linked to a phenomenon of active inhibition (the 'braking' wave of Jung, the phylactic wave of Walter, or the inhibitory wave of Gastaut).

This theory explains the absence of the true clonic phase in anoxic and strychnine seizures, for in these the telencephalon which incorporates the inhibitory system is functionally depressed or not actively brought into play. It explains why the tonic strychnine convulsions can be interrupted by a clonic phase when large doses of pentylenetetrazol are injected into a slightly strychninized animal (fig. 5). It also explains why the seizures induced by pentylenetetrazol or other analeptics in the diencephalic, mesencephalic

---

[6] However, fatigue is probably responsible only for the progressive slowing of the discharge and not for the rhythmical interruption which depends exclusively on the inhibitory mechanism described later.

[7] The existence of definite connections between the head of the caudate nucleus and the nonspecific formations of the thalamus has been demonstrated by physiological neuronography (176). Histological proof of these connections were given: a) by Ranson et al. (164, 165) and Papez (154) who showed direct connections (in both directions) between the pallidum and the anterior ventral nucleus of the thalamus (the former receiving fibers from the caudate and the latter now incorporated in the nonspecific system of the thalamus); and b) by Stefens & Droogleever-Fortuyn (185) and Nauta & Whitlock (151) who demonstrated projections between the head of the caudate and the intralaminar and mid-line thalamic nuclei.

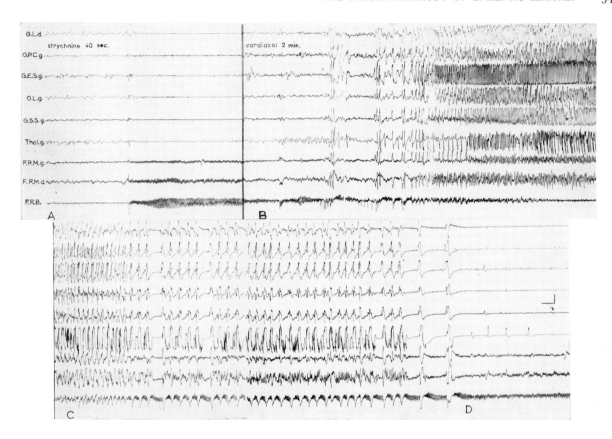

FIG. 5. Experimental evidence for a thalamic inhibitory system responsible for the interruption of the tonic convulsion of reticular origin and for the tonic-clonic course of generalized epileptic seizures. The first five tracings are cortical (right lateral gyrus, left precruciate gyrus, left ectosylvian gyrus, left lateral gyrus and left suprasylvian gyrus). The sixth tracing is from the left thalamus. The last three tracings are reticular (right and left mesencephalic reticular formation, below the plane of the red nucleus, and the bulbar reticular formation). A. The cat which has received a weak dose of strychnine 40 sec. previously begins a typical hypersynchronous discharge after an auditory stimulus which provokes an evoked potential in the ectosylvian gyrus, in the thalamus and especially in the bulbar reticular formation. Note the exclusively reticular level of the hypersynchronous strychnine discharge and its bulbar predominance, while all the rest of the brain shows merely desynchronization. B. When the action of the strychnine starts to show a decline, so that the reticular formation discharge is of decreased amplitude and regularity and the peripheral tetanus is less intense, a strong dose of pentylenetetrazol is given. This provokes first several spike discharges appearing independently in the bulbar reticular formation and in all the rest of the brain, and then an intense rhythmical discharge at the thalamocortical as well as the mesencephalic levels but sparing the bulbar reticular formation where the strychnine discharge persists. This episode evidently corresponds to a tonic seizure caused by excitation of the bulbar reticular formation by the strychnine and by 'liberation' of this structure under the influence of the pentylenetetrazol discharge which results in what may be a type of functional exclusion of the thalamocortical level. C. Eventually there develops in the thalamus a rhythm of slow waves of large amplitude and progressively slower frequency. During each of these slow waves there is electrical silence in all the leads, particularly in the bulbar reticular formation where each slow wave interferes with the hypersynchronous discharge of the strychnine type. This corresponds to active inhibition, since the tonic seizure stops for the same time during each interruption of the bulbar discharge, thus making possible the rhythmic relaxations which characterize the clonic phase of the seizure. D. Finally all parts of the thalamocortical system are exhausted (extinction), while the strychnine discharge continues unchanged in the bulbar and even the mesencephalic reticular formation.

or rhombencephalic animal should only be tonic; they may be accompanied by a few clonic jerks with brief seizure discharges, but there is never a clonic phase for this only represents the rhythmic inhibition of the tonic spasm. Finally, it explains the erroneous interpretation given by Ziehen (200) and Bechterew (16) who, on the basis of the results of decortication, related the tonic component in grand mal to brain stem structures and the clonic component to the cerebral cortex.

One may conclude therefore that neuronal fatigue and exhaustion are responsible for the progressive slowing of the cortical and muscular discharge in grand mal during its tonic phase, whereas the thalamocaudate inhibitory system is responsible for the periods of relaxation in the clonic phase and for the episodes of cortical electrical silence or slow 'braking' waves which are the EEG accompaniment of the relaxation periods.

MYOCLONUS OF PETIT MAL. This disorder may be considered as a miniature or extremely short grand mal seizure (54, 59, 149). Numerous arguments may be adduced in favor of this concept.

a) The etiology is often the same. Myoclonus is frequently associated with grand mal fits, and precedes the majority of spontaneous grand mal attacks (52, 149, 170) or of attacks precipitated by pentylenetetrazol (Feuillet). In most cases the myoclonic jerks which precede grand mal are repeated at shorter and shorter intervals until their fusion constitutes the beginning of the tonic phase (Ribot, Muskens).

b) Electrographically, the form, frequency and topography of the discharges are the same in grand mal as in myoclonic petit mal; the multiple spikes of myoclonus appear like a burst of spikes in the clonic phase of grand mal or, even more, like the discharge just at the onset of the tonic phase.

c) Clinically, the peripheral manifestations are similar in the two types, generalized increase in muscle tone masking the fact that other effectors are brought into play.[8]

d) Finally, experimental studies furnish the most important arguments. Myoclonus is provoked experimentally by the same procedures as grand mal fits and is accompanied by a similar thalamocortical discharge. This liberates the facilitating reticulospinal

[8] The myoclonic discharge is obviously too brief to cause glandular secretion, but it is however able to bring about a slight alteration in arterial pressure (Morin & Roger, unpublished observations).

system responsible for the momentary tonic reinforcement which we call 'myoclonus'.

The one feature that differentiates myoclonus from a grand mal seizure is its duration, and therefore only the abrupt and premature ending of the myoclonic discharge remains to be explained. The sustained frequency testifies to the fact that it is not terminated by exhaustion and that a process of active inhibition, like that already envisaged in regard to grand mal fits, is probably involved.

It may be concluded that patients suffering from myoclonic petit mal possess a more active inhibitory system than those with grand mal, and that this system is thrown into action from the start of the thalamocortical discharge, thus bringing about an almost immediate interruption of the seizure. This explains why the generalized muscular contraction is only momentary and why the EEG expression is limited to a few spikes which are isolated or followed by one or several 'braking' slow waves.

PETIT MAL 'ABSENCE'. Petit mal 'absence' may be interpreted on the basis of the same hypothesis as myoclonic petit mal. It may be considered as a thalamic discharge occurring in a subject with a very effective inhibitory mechanism. Because of this, the discharge is inhibited almost immediately after it has been fired and a slow 'braking' wave appears in the thalamus immediately after the development of a single spike. The rhythmic repetition of the phenomenon may be explained on the basis that the termination of each wave of inhibition allows the thalamic discharge to reappear, provoking a spike and a new inhibitory wave.

The spikes and slow waves are transmitted to the cortex by the system of diffuse projection and furnish the classical spike-and-wave recorded on the EEG during the 'absence'. Relative independence may exist between the two mechanisms generating the spike and the wave so that they function separately for a certain length of time; this may explain the numerous cases of atypical spike-and-wave, and particularly those cases in which the spike disappears and leaves only the slow waves at the end of a clinical 'absence'. This independence also helps to explain the observations made in man by Williams (197) and in animals by Ralston & Ajmone-Marsan (163) who dissociated the spike and the slow wave in the thalamus and on the cortex.

Most of the features of petit mal and notably those which distinguish it from, or even oppose it to, grand mal may be interpreted on the basis of the predominance in petit mal of the thalamocaudate system from which are generated the slow waves and a process of active inhibition.

a) The loss of consciousness can be related to the hypersynchronous discharge which is propagated from the thalamus to the whole of the brain and prevents normal cerebral functioning. The lack of convulsions may depend on the fact that the reticular activation is rhythmically inhibited and can express itself only by a slight muscular contraction with each spike of the spike-and-wave.

b) This hypothesis of the predominance of the inhibitory system from which are generated the slow waves may explain why petit mal is seen especially in patients with a well-marked tendency to ictal and interictal slow hypersynchronization. Certain 'absences' are characterized solely by a discharge of slow waves. There is also a prevalence of slow rhythms in between petit mal seizures (theta rhythms, delta rhythms in the frontal and occipital regions, and hypersynchronous bursts during overbreathing).

c) This same hypothesis may explain why the 'absences' are frequently precipitated by conditions which favor this slow hypersynchronization (hyperpnea, sleep, closure of the eyes, and administration of pentylenetetrazol, pentothal, chlorpromazine, etc.). These synchronizing measures depress the mesorhombencephalic reticular formation and thus 'release' the thalamocortical system of spindles, the hypersynchronous discharges which depend on this same thalamocortical system and the accompanying 'braking' slow waves.

d) The relative antagonism between the rostral and caudal parts of the reticular formation may throw light on the fact that certain physiological conditions (such as puberty) or therapeutic agents (such as the diones) can transform petit mal 'absences' into grand mal seizures. Petit mal is distinguished from grand mal by this functional predominance of thalamocaudate inhibition, so that the hypersynchronous thalamic discharge is prematurely inhibited and liberation of the caudal reticular formation is prevented. One has but to suppose that endocrine modifications or certain medications selectively depress the inhibitory system; this lessened inhibition may explain the prolongation of the hypersynchronous thalamic discharge, the bulbar 'release' and the transformation of petit mal into grand mal.

One common theoretical basis thus may explain the three varieties of generalized epilepsy which have been shown by empirical observation to be closely linked. Grand mal and petit mal in their pure forms are indeed exceptional, whereas the association, either temporary or permanent, of two or three forms is the general rule. This theory of common causality may help in understanding the characteristics of the EEG discharge and the somatic manifestations of the three types of generalized epilepsy; it may explain the loss of consciousness which is a feature of grand mal and the 'absence' of petit mal. Myoclonic petit mal is too brief to interrupt the chain of psychological events whose temporal dimensions are greater than the duration of the seizure. Indeed one cannot envisage the receipt and transmission of messages, their analysis and transformation into sensations, ideas or actions, and their storage in the form of memory, at a time when most of the cerebral neurons are collectively occupied in discharging simultaneously and when the source of this discharge is exactly the structure whose function is to regulate the whole of cerebral activity.

PHYSIOPATHOLOGY OF PARTIAL EPILEPSIES

Experimental Results

Seizures of partial epilepsy have been reproduced in animals only by provoking a localized cerebral disturbance. Since this necessitates opening the skull, the method cannot be applied to man. All experimental results have therefore been obtained in animals, but relevant information may be gathered from patients with a verified epileptogenic lesion.

A localized experimental cerebral disturbance can be epileptogenic either directly by acting on the neurons or indirectly by causing a lesion which is later epileptogenic. In the first case, no actual lesion is produced in the brain; the epileptogenic stimulation is either an electric current applied locally, a source of heat or cold, or a chemical irritant (strychnine, penicillin, carbachol, creatine, physostigmine, acetylcholine, nicotine, picrotoxin, etc.). On the contrary, in the second case, the cerebral assault does not directly precipitate a seizure but leads to localized cicatrization which is responsible for the irritation that later provokes seizures. Aluminum hydroxide, acting as a foreign body without immediate chemical action, is the substance commonly used to provoke this type of irritation. In both cases, the cerebral disorder may be produced in the cortex or in the depths of the brain in various subcortical structures; in both cases, it gives rise to seizures which may remain partial throughout their whole duration or which may become generalized only after a certain time.

EXPERIMENTAL PARTIAL EPILEPSY OF CORTICAL (ISO-CORTICAL) ORIGIN. *a*) *Local application of strychnine.* When strychnine or another convulsant is applied to the isocortex, it provokes clinical and electrical manifestations reminiscent of certain seizures of partial epilepsy in man. Only those clinical manifestations which involve discharges provoked in the motor, and notably the somatomotor, areas have been studied [(15) and numerous more recent authors], probably because they are the only ones which can be demonstrated in the anesthetized animal under the special experimental conditions required.

In the classical 'cortical strychnine clonus' of Baglioni & Magnini (15), convulsions appear in the contralateral musculature a few seconds after the application of strychnine. They are at first confined to the parts corresponding to the cortical region treated but they later spread to other muscular groups on that side of the body. Contrary to the generalized epilepsies already discussed, the impulses for these clonic movements are undoubtedly transmitted from the somatomotor cortex to the spinal motor neurons by way of the pyramidal tracts. This conclusion arises out of the following experimental results: *1*) convulsive discharges can be recorded from pyramidal fibers synchronously with the clonic twitches (2); *2*) both the movements and the pyramidal discharges continue when the brain stem is interrupted at midbrain levels, leaving only the pes pedunculi intact (196).

If the cutaneous zones corresponding to the strychninized region are stimulated, these convulsions appear sooner and are intensified and rapidly generalized. This 'reflex' reinforcement of the cortical epileptic process was discovered by Amantea (8) in 1921; it is lost when the strychninized cortical focus is destroyed.

The EEG manifestations of the local application of strychnine consist of a bioelectric oscillation of great magnitude (more than a millivolt), known as the 'strychnine spike', which is repeated at more or less regular intervals. This spike does not remain localized to the spot on which the strychnine is applied but spreads like a drop of oil to the whole of the corresponding area (for example to the whole of the somatomotor area). It is also propagated at a distance to the homologous structures of the opposite hemisphere and to the allied subcortical structures (for example to the ventrolateral nucleus of the thala-

mus when the strychnine is applied to the somatomotor region). The strychnine spike however can develop to its fullest and continue to be repeated even though it is not accompanied by these phenomena of propagation. Indeed, neuronal isolation of a cortical area (that is to say, its separation from neighboring cortical areas and from subcortical centers) does not prevent the appearance of strychnine spikes on local application.

The strychnine discharge has been very fully investigated by workers in basic neurophysiology [see bibliographies (145, 146)] because it is so easily provoked and so easily repeated. From these studies, and particularly those of Jung (117) and Moruzzi (146) one may draw the following conclusions. *1*) The strychnine spike results from a process of hypersynchrony, that is from the simultaneous discharge of the great majority of the neurons in the strychninized area, a hypersynchrony which probably is due to ephaptic (extrasynaptic) interactions between the different elements which are put into play by electric currents conducted through the intercellular spaces. *2*) Recorded with macroelectrodes, the strychnine spike only shows its slow triphasic (positive, negative, positive) envelope, which corresponds no doubt to slow potentials and to an electrotonic spread and decremental conduction in the dendritic plexuses. With microelectrode recording, however, one observes in addition a burst of very rapid spikes (400 to 1,000 cps) which begins with the first positive phase and ends with the second negative phase. It is this burst of rapid spikes, which is transmitted along the axons of the pyramidal cells (1) to the spinal motor neurons, which provokes the muscular twitch.

b) *Localized electrical stimulation.* The electroencephalographic effect of a single brief electric shock is seen as a variation of the local potential which differs little from the strychnine spike except that it is diphasic, at first negative and then positive. Using intracellular microelectrodes, Buser & Albe-Fessard (24) were able to record this slow variation of potential at actual neuronal level. In addition the microelectrodes record the burst of brief spikes (less than a millisecond) at high frequency (up to 1,000 cps) which accompanies the strychnine discharge and which is propagated along the length of the axons. (These spikes are obviously positive in the interior of the neurons and negative in their neighborhood.)

A series of electrical shocks results in repetition of the above phenomena so long as the frequency of stimuli is not too rapid. Above a certain frequency, the discharge appears only at the end of stimulation under the form of a self-sustained electrographic activity known as a postdischarge.

This postdischarge has most of the features characteristic of the evoked electrical or strychnine potential: *1)* diffusion to the whole of the area containing the stimulated spot; *2)* propagation to the contralateral homologous area; *3)* subcortical propagation to allied structures; and *4)* development on a strip of vascularized but neuronally isolated cortex. On the other hand, it differs in that it has the peculiar attribute of being self-sustained and of continuing rhythmically for a shorter or longer time after the end of the stimulation. It is no longer a single bioelectrical oscillation of great amplitude repeated at variable intervals, but a series of oscillations slowing progressively and soon interrupted by intervals of electrical silence of which the last represents a long phase of postictal extinction.

French *et al.* (50) have observed that all cortical regions can be made to show a postdischarge following supramaximal electrical stimulation, but that only some regions show a postdischarge from stimulation which is only just above threshold. On this basis they describe zones as 'epileptogenic' in the following descending scale: the motor and premotor cortex (motor area for the face and the hand), and the teletemporal and uncinate cortex being most susceptible; next the posterior insular and superior temporal cortex; and after that the parietal cortex. On the other hand the frontal and especially the occipital cortex are resistant to experimental epilepsy.

The clinical effects of electrical stimulation have been studied only in respect of the somatomotor region for the same reason as in the case of strychnine convulsions. The potential evoked by a single electric shock is accompanied by an isolated contralateral 'clonus' identical with the 'cortical strychnine clonus' of Baglioni & Magnini (15). The electrical after discharge is accompanied by a convulsive attack (which might be termed a motor after discharge) involving the appropriate contralateral part, each cortical oscillation corresponding to a clonic jerk and to a burst of high frequency activity in the corticospinal pathways.

As in the case of strychnine, one can facilitate or prolong the clinical and EEG effects of electrical stimulation of the cortex by stimulating the appropriate cutaneous reflexogenic areas or the parts of the brain that project to that particular cortical zone. In this way subthreshold stimulation of the sensorimotor region facilitates the provocation of a seizure from the homologous contralateral area. With supra-

maximal stimulation applied to the subcortical white matter after removal of the corresponding somatomotor area, it is even possible to provoke a seizure in the homologous opposite region (27).

c) Epileptogenic cortical lesions. These are caused by local application of aluminum hydroxide, according to the technique of Kopeloff *et al.* (127), and appear as fibroglial scars developing slowly around a foreign body. Attacks of partial epilepsy are seen 4 to 12 wk. after application and persist for several years.

The clinical effects of such lesions have been studied most frequently when they were located in the somatomotor area of the monkey. These take the form of Jacksonian seizures beginning in one limb or the face on the contralateral side and spreading progressively (with Jacksonian march) to include the rest of that half of the body. Between seizures, there may be isolated twitches of the muscles involved in the beginning of the paroxysm (epilepsia partialis continua). Peripheral stimulation of all kinds, chiefly of the special sense organs (e.g. a loud and continuous noise), may precipitate or reinforce isolated clonic jerks and may even fire off a Jacksonian fit.

Very few authors have had the curiosity to apply aluminum cream to cortical areas other than the somatomotor. Cure & Rasmussen (34), however, applied it to the insula of monkeys and they mention spontaneous seizures but unfortunately describe only one, characterized by a bilateral tonic-clonic spasm without any localized feature. Kopeloff *et al.* (127) applied aluminum cream to the occipital, frontal, middle and anteriortemporal cortex of the monkey without producing seizures in which there was any detectable motor phenomenon. Nor did Gastaut *et al.* (83) observe any paroxysmal motor effects after subpial injection of aluminum hydroxide in the cat in regions corresponding to the occipital lobe and to the tip of the temporal lobe and the temporal lobe proper. These negative findings are very important, chiefly in so far as they show that temporal and teletemporal scars, at least in the monkey and the cat, do not provoke 'psychomotor' seizures, sometimes attributed in man to similarly placed lesions.

The EEG manifestations resulting from experimental scars appear in the form of slow variations of local potential in a sporadic or in a rhythmical manner. The sporadic variations are analogous to those provoked by a single electric shock or the application of strychnine, since they appear as predominantly negative polyphasic variations in the form of a spike followed by a single slow wave or a spike-and-wave complex. The rhythmical variations are in every way comparable to postdischarges provoked by an electric current: that is to say, they appear as rhythmical discharges of localized spikes whose frequency diminishes progressively and which are often interrupted by slow waves or intervals of silence before they come to an end.

Recording with microelectrodes, Thomas *et al.* (188) observed in addition cellular discharges which were rather different from those provoked by strychnine or a single electric shock. The units often showed spontaneous prolonged bursts of activity, usually beginning with a high frequency train of impulses (approximately 1,000 cps) followed by longer bursts at somewhat lower frequencies (approximately 300 cps). Such a discharge may repeat its whole cycle intermittently or settle down to a steady train of impulses at about 150 to 200 cps which may be kept up indefinitely.

d) Propagation of experimental isocortical epileptic discharges. The use of recording electrodes at a distance from the stimulated region has shown that all epileptic discharges are propagated locally and to a greater or lesser distance. Local propagation proceeds very slowly (from 1 mm per sec. to 1 mm per min.) through a multitude of fine fibers and synapses, often arranged in reverberating circuits which constitute the fibrillary network of the cortex. Studying local propagation by means of vector recordings, Green & Naquet (93) came to the conclusion that it may represent extrasynaptic spread from cell to cell following dendritic depolarization. Sporadic and rhythmical discharges are propagated at a distance in different manners (160). The rhythmical discharges (the 'postdischarges') are propagated much more widely than are the sporadic discharges; it is the former type only that we shall be considering here, for it alone corresponds to the propagation of an epileptic seizure. (The sporadic discharges only represent the 'interseizure' irritative manifestations, and a knowledge of them is not indispensible for understanding the actual seizures.) Numerous authors have studied the propagation of postdischarges from different parts of the cerebral cortex. A complete bibliography of the numerous works devoted to these cortical postdischarges can be found in Green & Naquet (93). We shall give only a brief account[9] of subcortical propagation of postdischarges engendered in different parts of the cerebral cortex, neglecting corticocortical propagation which takes place mainly in the homologous contralateral region by means of commissural fibers.[10]

Frontal postdischarges are propagated chiefly to the brain stem reticular formation (tegmentum mesencephali, hypothalamus and intralaminar nuclei of the thalamus) and secondarily to the caudate nucleus, the amygdala and the hippocampus. Cingular postdischarges have a similar but less marked propagation, and orbital postdischarges propagate particularly to the amygdala and hippocampus.

Postdischarges in the motor region travel chiefly to the brain stem reticular formation, the septal region and the corpus striatum. Temporal postdischarges are mainly propagated to the amygdala, hippocampus, septal region, subthalamus, hypothalamus and the mesencephalic reticularis, and secondarily to the corpus striatum and the pulvinar. Occipital postdischarges go chiefly to the thalamus (pulvinar and lateral geniculate body, and neighboring intralaminar nuclei) and secondarily to the subthalamus and the reticular formation.

Thus the postdischarges localized in the cortex are characterized by remarkably important subcortical propagation which nearly always involves the brain stem reticular formation and the amygdalohippocampal system. This tendency for cortical epileptic discharges to invade subcortical nonspecific structures or the brain stem had already been evidenced by the interseizure sporadic discharges. Thus von Baumgarten *et al.* (190) demonstrated the reticular influence of strychnine spikes and potentials evoked by a single shock in the rolandic region; this was manifested by reinforcement, or conversely by inhibition of the spontaneous discharges of single reticular units recorded with microelectrodes.

EXPERIMENTAL PARTIAL EPILEPSY OF RHINENCEPHALIC (ALLOCORTICAL) ORIGIN. We shall study seizures caused by epileptogenic measures involving not only the allocortex but all the rhinencephalon, both its cortical and nuclear parts.

a) Implantation of in-dwelling electrodes. This method has permitted the study of seizures of partial epilepsy provoked by electrical stimulation of the rhinen-

---

[9] This summary takes account of the works of Walker & Johnson (192), Kaada (119), Ajmone-Marsan & Stoll (6), Stoll *et al.* (186), Gastaut *et al.* (72), Jasper *et al.* (108), Segundo *et al.* (175), French *et al.* (50), Poggio *et al.* (158), and Creutzfeld (31).

[10] Contralateral homologous conduction takes place via the corpus callosum or the anterior commissure according to the site of the lesion. This was demonstrated by physiological neuronography (140) and by study of experimental epileptogenic scars (127–129).

cephalic formations (56, 72, 80, 81, 83, 122, 132, 150). The clinical manifestations are of interest. Stimulation of the hippocampus or gyrus fornicatus provokes a simple reaction of 'attention' and contralateral 'orientation' of the head when the stimulus is of weak intensity. When a stronger stimulus is applied, it provokes more complex reactions suggestive of anxiety, fear or anger. In every case, the animal shows some lack of awareness and responds little or not at all to outside influences. This impaired responsiveness contrasts with the accompanying portrayal of 'arrest' and 'attention' and is paradoxical if one interprets it as the expression of clouded consciousness. The paradox, however, disappears if one thinks that it reflects extremely concentrated attention on an abnormal psychological event created by the stimulation, perhaps an illusion or a hallucination.

Stimulation of the piriform cortex, or the underlying amygdala, provokes complex phenomena in which are associated: 1) contraversive deviation which may or may not be accompanied by abnormal tonic or clonic movements; 2) complex gestures apparently reactive to abnormal sensations involving the buccofacial region or the extremities (licking the lips, clearing the throat as though to get rid of a foreign body, or lifting and shaking a paw); 3) actions with a feeding significance (lapping, mastication, salivation or deglutition); and 4) changes in the autonomic, respiratory and circulatory spheres, including pupillary changes, micturition and defecation.

The electroencephalographic effect of electrical stimulation of the rhinencephalon has been studied by Gastaut et al. (72, 80, 81, 84), Gloor (90), and Feindel & Gloor (46), who investigated chiefly the amygdala, and by Kaada (119, 121), Creutzfeldt & Meyer-Mickeleit (32), and Andy & Akert (10, 11) who studied the hippocampus particularly. In these studies postdischarges were produced which involved the structure stimulated (amygdala or Ammon's horn) and were transmitted to: 1) the homologous contralateral region; 2) allied structures such as the hypothalamus, the septum and the anterodorsal thalamus; 3) the corpus striatum and midbrain tegmentum; 4) the pyriform cortex, the orbito-insulotemporal cortex and secondarily the anterior part of the gyrus cinguli; and 5) sometimes even to the rest of the isocortex. There is considerable difference of opinion among authors as to propagation to the isocortex, which according to some is predominantly to the frontal regions and according to others to the occipital regions.

Propagation to these structures may be either simultaneous or successive, and Gastaut et al. (72, 80, 83) particularly stress the fact that the postdischarges are erratic, and that they may be transmitted, for example, from the amygdala to the temporal and septal regions, then to the posterior hypothalamus and from there to the frontal cortex, returning again to the temporal region.

b) *Local application or injection of aluminum cream.* Stereotaxic techniques have made it possible to produce epileptogenic scars in the same limbic or basal rhinencephalic structures. The experimental results closely resemble those of electrical stimulation (81, 83, 84).

The clinical manifestations are typically seizures which occur 2 or 3 mo. after injection of aluminum hydroxide into the amygdaloid nucleus. The following description of seizures in cats is given by Naquet (150): "The animal suddenly changes its attitude, sometimes tries to escape, becomes anxious, immobile, then sniffs violently, especially to the side of the amygdaloid scar; at the same time one notes pupillary dilatation, clonic movements of the homolateral eyelids, rapidly followed by facial hemispasm with deviation of the head to the opposite side, clonic masticatory movements and salivation. The seizure may stop at this stage, or else the cat lifts its anterior contralateral paw and there appear clonic movements of the whole of the contralateral side of the body followed by a generalized fit with urinary incontinence. A 'confusional' state with loud miaowing follows the seizure. In some cases, there are in addition various types of seizures which are predominantly 'psychological'. Suddenly the animal becomes immobile, its pupils dilate, its behavior changes, it lifts its contralateral paw as though to defend or attack, there is marked piloerection and it bites if one tries to touch it. This seizure lasts 20 to 40 sec. and suddenly the animal becomes affectionate again. Alternatively, the animal suddenly tries to escape, miaows fiercely, its pupils dilate and its behavior gives the impression that it sees or hears something alarming. This seizure terminates rapidly."

The electroencephalographic manifestations will now be described. Between seizures, one observes sporadic discharges of slow waves, of spikes or spike-and-wave complexes at the periphery of the amygdaloid, hippocampal or septal lesions, which are transmitted to one or several of the following regions: uncus, insula, tip of the temporal lobe, temporal lobe proper, posterior orbital region (78, 84, 167). These discharges may be on the same or the opposite side of the lesion and sometimes may even predominate on the contralateral side, but they are never bilateral and synchronous. Independent contralateral discharges may indicate a secondary vascular extension of the lesion to the other side (69) but may also indicate a functional 'unleashing' of these homologous contralateral structures which have acquired an epileptogenic potential through being bombarded. For these reasons, ablation of the epileptogenic focus on the side of the lesion does not necessarily lead to the disappearance of the contralateral discharges which may persist for several months after operation (84).

During seizures, the discharges show a great variety of forms: *1*) rhythmical discharges of spikes or slow waves observed around the lesion, propagated to the same cortical areas as the interictal discharges, chiefly to the orbitoinsuloteletemporal cortex; *2*) propagation of the discharge to subcortical structures, chiefly the septum, the hypothalamus and the tegmentum mesencephali, generally accompanied by diffuse cortical manifestations like desynchronization or slow hypersynchronization occupying all or part of one or both hemispheres (78, 84, 167). Sloan, Ransohoff & Pool emphasize the bisynchronous 4 to 6 cps ictal discharges which they recorded in monkeys with amygdaloid scars.

EXPERIMENTAL PARTIAL EPILEPSY OF SUBCORTICAL ORIGIN. If one excludes the amygdala and septum which have been linked to the rhinencephalon, few subcortical structures have been studied from the point of view of experimental epilepsy. Different parts of the thalamus, subthalamus and tegmentum mesencephali have, however, received indwelling electrodes or been injected with aluminum cream (72, 73).

The clinical manifestations produced by limited electrical stimulation include autonomic and deviational phenomena which bear only a distant and fragmentary resemblance to the seizures provoked by stimulation of the basal rhinencephalon. The scars from aluminum implantation have never given rise to spontaneous seizures, probably because the diencephalic structures have a high convulsant threshold. However, injection of subliminal doses of pentylenetetrazol in cats with diencephalic scars have always precipitated seizures very similar to those provoked from the basal rhinencephalon. This led Gastaut & Roger (78) to believe that at least some of the aspects of rhinencephalic seizures depend on the fact that allied diencephalic formations are brought into play.

The electroencephalographic manifestations are of several types. With hypothalamic, subthalamic and tegmental epileptogenic lesions there are sporadic and local interictal discharges, transmitted to the orbitoinsulouncotemporal region which, as we have already seen, is involved when the rhinencephalon discharges. This curious observation is explained by the findings of physiological neuronography and of histology which demonstrate a large number of connections between the orbitoinsuloteletemporal region on the one hand and the hypothalamus, subthalamus and tegmentum mesencephali on the other (67).

Irritative lesions of other subcortical structures cause discharges in other parts of the cerebral cortex. Thus lesions of the lateral (dorsal and posterior) and of the posterior nuclei of the thalamus produce their effects in the posterior temporal and the parietal cortex, whereas lesions of the pulvinar, the lateral geniculate and the corresponding region of the nucleus reticularis affect the occipital cortex. Lesions of the medial geniculate, the suprageniculate nucleus and the corresponding region of the nucleus reticularis act on the superior temporal cortex.

EXPERIMENTAL PARTIAL EPILEPSY, SECONDARILY GENERALIZED. All partial epilepsies may become generalized whether they are of cortical or subcortical origin, and whether caused by direct chemical or electrical stimulation or resulting indirectly from an epileptogenic scar. The partial epilepsy which has been best studied from the point of view of generalization is that caused by localized cortical electrical stimulation. Generalized convulsions develop when the strength of local stimulation passes a threshold value wherever this cortical stimulation may be, even after sagittal section of the telencephalon, diencephalon and mesencephalon (181); it is thus certain that the subcortical structures extending as far as the rhombencephalon are responsible for the generalization of the convulsions.

A study of epilepsy of the Openshowski-Speranski variety leads to the same conclusions. Here generalized seizures, so frequent that they constitute status epilepticus, are provoked by refrigeration of a small part of cerebral cortex on one side. This is a generalized epilepsy which is at first partial, for immediate ablation of the refrigerated zone abolishes it, but the generalization is of subcortical origin since convulsions (which are bilateral) still appear after ablation of the somatomotor region of both hemispheres (45) and after section of the corpus callosum (179).

Subcortical structures influence the generalization

of somatomotor or occipital strychnine epilepsy under the facilitating effect of a bombardment of afferent 'influx' coming from the corresponding sensory areas [the epilepsy of Amantea (8) and of Clementi (28, 29), described on p. 355]. This led Moruzzi to write: "When, in the photic epilepsy of Clementi, we illuminate the retina, we not only send nervous impulses into the striate area which has been strychninized, but at the same time we activate the whole of the cerebral cortex through the ascending reticular formation of the brain stem." The generalized seizure that follows is presumably subcortical since subsequent ablation of both somatomotor areas does not prevent the convulsions from developing (9). It is therefore most likely that any discharge of partial epilepsy, once it is of sufficient magnitude, can be transmitted to the centrencephalic structures from the thalamus to the medulla, and from there be generalized to the rest of the brain.

There is supporting EEG evidence for these conclusions. Jasper et al. (108) showed that the majority of cortical postdischarges are transmitted to the reticular formation of the thalamus and brain stem. French et al. (50) demonstrated a subcortical reticular mechanism in generalized postdischarges provoked by localized cortical stimulation. "Surface regions displaying the characteristic local response (persistent after discharge) seem to have the capacity secondarily to excite certain diffusely projecting subcortical structures (reticular formation, septal region and amygdala) which are capable of disseminating the induced discharge widely." Finally, in microphysiological studies in strychnine epilepsy, von Baumgarten et al. (190) have shown that each strychnine spike developed in the motor cortex alters the spontaneous activity of the neurons of the reticular formation so that their activity is momentarily reinforced; this effect must play a large part in the phenomenon of generalization.

EXPERIMENTAL PARTIAL EPILEPSY WITH ERRATIC DISCHARGES. In some cases, a seizure of partial epilepsy stops as suddenly as it starts, the postictal electrical silence appearing simultaneously in all the discharging structures. In other cases, however, the discharge comes to an end in one formation and is transmitted at the same time to another more or less distant part, thus prolonging the seizure. This phenomenon was first described by McCulloch & Dusser de Barenne in 1935 (139) with reference to electrical postdischarges in animals anesthetized with diallyl barbituric acid. Walker & Johnson (192), studying the

same phenomenon, showed that in the normal monkey localized postdischarges stop abruptly, whereas in the monkey with an experimental epileptogenic lesion they are transmitted from one cortical region to another and continue for several minutes. McCulloch (138) reinvestigated the question, with seizures provoked by chlorophenothane (DDT) and other poisons and particularly in a case of status epilepticus in a monkey with an experimental frontal epileptogenic lesion. He describes how the epileptic discharge would appear at one point on the cortex, disappear and suddenly reappear at an unforeseen spot, like a 'jack-in-the-box'. Gastaut & Roger (78) studied multiple and successive cortical seizures following stimulation of the amygdaloid nucleus. They showed that these 'surprise' discharges do not really arise independently in different parts of the cortex, but that they represent one and the same discharge transmitted from a certain point on the cortex to allied subcortical structures and from there to other cortical regions. It was only in 1953 that Gastaut et al. (75, 76) demonstrated in man the existence of multiple cortical discharges probably corresponding to this same mechanism of 'erratic' propagation. Since then, the Marseilles workers have constantly emphasized that these erratic discharges are frequent and especially significant in so-called 'psychomotor' epilepsy.

Anatomical Studies

Patients with partial epilepsy usually harbor conspicuous organic cerebral lesions, in contrast to those cases in which the seizure is generalized from the start. In cases of partial epilepsy with a single somatomotor or sensory symptom related to the pre- or postrolandic, occipital or superior temporal regions, a lesion in that particular area is usually demonstrable anatomically as well as electrographically. The most frequent lesion is a cicatrix or atrophy, and much more rarely a neoplasm. The lesion is usually superficial and involves only the cortex locally (a corticomeningeal scar or localized cortical atrophy), but sometimes it goes deeper and is not seen on inspection of the exterior of the brain.

In polysymptomatic partial epilepsy, however, with the sensory, mental and motor manifestations of psychomotor epilepsy, true focal lesions are usually not seen. The lesions on the contrary are remarkably diffuse in these patients. The most frequent lesion is corticosubcortical atrophy with more or less well-marked neuronal degeneration or necrosis, associated with reactional gliosis. The cerebral atrophy may involve the whole of one hemisphere and sometimes also the contralateral cerebellar hemisphere, but it generally predominates in the temporal lobe and may involve it alone. The lesion is maximal in most cases in the internal aspect of the temporal lobe and the inferior surface of the frontal lobe in the region which comprises the anterior part of the hippocampal gyrus—including the uncus and amygdala—Ammon's horn, the temporal tip, the insula and its opercula, the anterior perforated space and the posterior part of the orbital convolutions. This is a region which is furrowed from front to back by the rhinal fissure lined by the endorhinal fissure, and which Gastaut proposed to name the 'pararhinal region' for this has the advantage of connoting the alloperiallocortical (rhinencephalic) nature of the parts involved.

Physiopathogenesis of Partial Epilepsies

ORIGIN AND CAUSE OF NEURONAL DISCHARGE IN PARTIAL EPILEPSY. The discharge in the partial epilepsies generally starts in the immediate neighborhood of the epileptogenic lesion where the neurons show hyperexcitability, as demonstrated by Walker & Johnson (192). These workers found that around an aluminum-produced scar weaker electric stimulation produced a postdischarge, or smaller doses of pentylenetetrazol were required to evoke local spikes.

In certain cases, however, the discharge begins at a distance from the epileptogenic lesions, either in allied structures or even in structures which are entirely independent. We have already seen that an experimental epileptogenic lesion in the right amygdala in a cat can cause ictal discharges in the left amygdala, and in man a right-sided temporal epileptogenic lesion. This is seen in the experiments of Walker & or left temporal or in the occipital regions. These facts, emphasized by the Marseilles school, may be explained by the conception that neuronal excitability is heightened at a distance from the epileptogenic lesion. This is seen in the experiments of Walker & Johnson (192) and of Kopeloff et al. (127) who demonstrated a lowered convulsant threshold in cortical or allied subcortical structures, and even in the whole brain in animals with an epileptogenic scar.

It is a very important conception that neuronal excitability may be intensified remotely from the epileptogenic lesion in structures anatomically allied to the lesion but not themselves showing any organic alteration. The degree of excitability may indeed be so high that, under the influence of an afferent volley, the allied structure may discharge as well as, if not more intensely than, the epileptogenic focus itself (61). One concludes therefore (53–55, 57) that, although the existence of a sporadic spike or a rhythmic discharge in an EEG or a corticogram constitutes the most reliable proof of a local epileptic process, it in no way guarantees that the epileptogenic lesion is seated in the same place. Working on this general principle, Gastaut & Roger (78) demonstrated the following facts.

a) The epileptogenic lesion may or may not coincide with a given EEG focus; it may even be a long way off. Gastaut (82) showed that a large number of occipital seizure discharges appear in patients with an anterior temporalpararhinal lesion, while Segundo et al. (175) observed true electric occipital seizures in the monkey following postdischarges induced in the amygdala.

b) The existence of an EEG spike focus is always a valuable criterion for localization in partial epilepsy, but only as a physiological argument in relation to the clinical facts; it never permits one to incriminate a lesion of the underlying cortex directly and with certainty.

c) A spike focus in the electrocorticogram is always a useful finding for the neurosurgeon, allowing him to judge where the primary epileptogenic focus probably lies on the basis of anatomophysiological reasoning. It never unfailingly indicates the territory to be resected nor its boundaries; the surgeon has to remove the lesion or the structure involved and not just the spike-bearing area.

d) The existence of several, concomitant or independent spike foci does not necessarily signify a corresponding number of lesions. Also, the existence of a focus of bilateral and symmetrical spikes, concomitant or independent, does not necessarily signify a bilateral lesion.

e) The persistence of a spike focus after ablation of an epileptogenic focus does not necessarily mean that the whole or a part of the lesion persists nor that a new lesion has been created by the operation; it may be that the local perilesional hyperexcitability persists or is enhanced for a shorter or longer time. In the same way, the persistence or appearance of a contralateral spike focus after ablation of an apparently unilateral lesion does not necessarily imply that a previously unobserved contralateral lesion exists; it may be a matter again of local hyperexcitability which is transmitted to the other side. This was reproduced experimentally by Gastaut *et al.* (84). They provoked bilateral and symmetrical spike foci with a one-sided lesion resulting from aluminum scarring and then observed that the contralateral focus persisted after ablation of the single lesion.

This instability and variability of the epileptic discharge is seen even in patients who only show perilesional discharges. These discharges originate at some point on the periphery of the lesion; when the lesion is extensive and surrounded by a large 'halo' of neuronal hyperexcitability, the discharges may arise in different seizures at places far removed from each other. This was recorded experimentally by Roger (167) in whose experience the seizure discharges around a single but extensive lesion involving most of the amygdaloid nucleus sometimes began in the hippocampus and sometimes in the entopeduncular nucleus or the anterior amygdaloid zone or the lateral amygdaloid nucleus. Pathological hyperexcitability maintained around and at a distance from epileptogenic lesions thus plays an essential part in the development of the seizures of partial epilepsy.

Of equivalent or greater importance is the part played by the innate hyperexcitability of certain regions which show a low convulsant threshold and a striking epileptogenic predisposition. The various authors who have studied these local differences in the convulsant thresholds have come to the following conclusions. The hippocampus has the lowest threshold of excitability of all the cerebral structures so far explored (11, 25, 31, 86, 94, 119–121, 142). The motor cortex has the next lowest threshold (168), especially in the region corresponding to motor representation of the face and hand (50). In order of decreasing excitability there follows the cingular region, the tip of the temporal lobe and the uncinate region with the underlying amygdala, the first temporal convolution and, finally, the parietal region. The frontal region and particularly the occipital region have the highest epileptogenic threshold. It is hardly necessary to stress the importance of these findings which explain why the majority of partial epilepsies have a somatomotor or tempororhinencephalic symptomatology and why focal frontal or occipital epilepsies are so rare.

Spontaneous regional hyperexcitability and hyperexcitability developing around and remote from a cerebral lesion thus play a fundamental part in the development of seizures of partial epilepsy. It is similar to the part played by general neuronal hyper-

excitability in the development of generalized seizures, and which we have already termed a 'predisposing role'.[11]

The precipitating factor is also the same in the partial as in generalized epilepsies. This factor is a volley of afferent stimuli which, although without pathological effect under normal conditions, can provoke paroxysmal hypersynchrony when local hyperexcitability is present. The precipitating role of afferent stimuli was physiologically demonstrated once (and perhaps for all) by the remarkable experiments of Clementi (28), in which strychninization of the visual cortex is in no way detectable until visual stimulation is applied, whereupon it provokes myoclonic movements of the eyelids and sometimes even a generalized convulsive seizure. The experiments of Amantea (8) exemplify the same principle, showing that strychninization of the somatomotor area, is insufficient to produce strychnine clonus yet precipitates Jacksonian or even generalized seizures when the appropriate reflexogenic cutaneous territory is stimulated. It is indeed hardly necessary to remind clinicians of the numerous cases of parietal, temporal, amygdaloid or hippocampal partial epilepsy precipitated by an unexpected movement (7), a noise (13, 74), music (33, 97), rapid ingestion of a large quantity of water (20) or an emotion (62, 178).[12]

In most cases, however, the fact that afferent stimuli precipitate a seizure is not clinically apparent because local hyperexcitability increases at the approach of an attack and is finally so marked that any volley of nervous impulses resulting from an insignificant stimulus is sufficient to fire off a paroxysm.

PROPAGATION AND TERMINATION OF NEURONAL DISCHARGE IN PARTIAL EPILEPSY. We have already seen that a localized discharge may extend locally or be propagated concomitantly or successively to various

---

[11] An epileptogenic lesion may obviously develop in a patient with a predisposition for epilepsy expressed as generalized neuronal hyperexcitability, either constitutional or acquired. The two factors are then added together. For this reason a cerebral lesion will frequently provoke seizures of partial epilepsy in one subject and not in another. For the same reason, Lennox found a degree of familial predisposition in the parents of symptomatic epileptics, because partial epilepsy develops particularly in those who are already so predisposed.

[12] Conversely the continuous physiological bombardment of the discharging region may entail its desynchronization and abort a seizure; that is the reason why certain epileptics abort their somatomotor or psychomotor fits by forcible extension of the limb in which the jerks first appear or by concentrating their attention fixedly on an idea or a perception.

allied structures or even to the whole brain. Numerous authors have studied propagation of epileptic activity and we may summarize their work as follows. *a*) Local propagation of the discharge proceeds very slowly like a 'drop of oil' through the fibrillary network of grey matter. This explains the Jacksonian 'march' so characteristic of seizures provoked by the discharge of structures somatotopically arranged (for example the jerks which extend from the face to the hand while the cortical discharge travels from one representative part of the cortex to the next adjacent part). *b*) Remote propagation takes place very rapidly along fibers of large diameter. This explains the almost immediate bringing into play of the whole group of structures of a corticosubcortical 'sector' and the stereotyped symptomatology during one or subsequent seizures when the discharge remains localized to such a sector. On the contrary, when propagation takes place to various 'sectors' successively, a variety of disturbances appear during the course of one or subsequent seizures.

The discharge in partial epilepsy is propagated by means of normally functioning nerve fibers and synapses from an epileptogenic center which is anatomically altered to allied centers which are anatomically healthy. This implies that the discharge originates as a lesional (or more likely perilesional) phenomenon but that its propagation is an exclusively functional phenomenon. Moruzzi says: "It is ordinary nervous activity which determines that allied neurones pass from a state of normal activity to one of epileptic functioning."

Although involving only normal functions, this mode of propagation is nonetheless pathological since it does not exist in the normal subject. Indeed, the following two conditions are necessary for its production. *a*) Hyperexcitability of the neuronal population allied to the epileptic center, explaining the sensitivity which it acquires under epileptogenic bombardment. We have already shown that this is always the case in generalized epilepsy; and according to Johnson & Walker (114): "Not only the primary focus is hypersensitive, but this hypersensitivity is found in the other cortical and subcortical structures with which it is intimately connected. This hypersensitivity manifests itself by a lowered threshold for electrical and chemical stimulation and seems to result from functional disturbance at the level of the normal neurons, as a result of the influence of the epileptogenic focus."

b) The epileptic discharge cannot be propagated unless the bombardment from the epileptogenic cen-

ter is efficacious. For this, it requires the following properties: the bombardment discharges must be of high frequency (1,000 cps); these discharges must activate a sufficient number of terminals on the same cells in order to provoke spatial summation; these discharges must be rhythmically spaced so as to use the facilitation of supranormality provoked in each neuron by the previous discharge and thus to produce temporal summation; and the bombardment must continue long enough to produce a progressive effect.

Although hyperexcitability of allied centers is always required, all the conditions necessary to make bombardment effective are not necessarily present at one time. Certain ones, indeed, depend on the functional or anatomical characteristics of the bombarded or bombarding centers and of the pathways which unite them. The phenomena of spatial summation, for example, depend exclusively on the number of fibers transmitting the bombardment and on their mode of terminating on allied neurons. All of these conditions vary from one system to another and make certain epileptic propagations easier than others.

A center allied to an epileptogenic focus reacts differently, according to its degree of excitability and according to the efficacy of bombardment. *a*) It may remain indifferent. *b*) Its spontaneous activity may simply be increased. *c*) It may respond stroke for stroke to the bombarding discharges as they arrive; thus true evoked potentials are produced in answer to the convulsive waves of the primary focus, with a latency corresponding to the propagation along axons and across synapses. Under these conditions the allied center can be said to have become epileptic because of the primary focus. *d*) The allied center may become epileptic on its own account, that is, it may dissociate itself from the epileptogenic focus and show secondary autonomous convulsive activity. This may persist after the end of the primary discharge and be propagated to allied structures as a tertiary discharge (so-called 'erratic' discharge).

A 'center' secondarily made epileptic by bombardment from a primary epileptogenic focus thus modifies the seizure according to its own anatomical and functional characteristics. One of two things usually follows; either the seizure remains partial but is enriched by electroclinical symptoms consequent upon the new discharge and this discharge may lead to another, or the fit becomes generalized.

In the first case a seizure may begin with focal clinical and electroencephalographic signs and pass through a series of equally focal episodes. Many psychomotor attacks have this pattern, notably those in which an occipital EEG discharge accompanying a visual episode follows or precedes a temporal discharge with aphasia (60, 76).

The second eventuality explains the fact that any partial seizure may become generalized. Generalization takes place more readily when the partial seizure is more intense, when it occupies a region closely connected to the centrencephalic reticular formation, and when the patient has an epileptic predisposition or, in other words, generalized neuronal hyperexcitability. When all these conditions are present, the partial seizure becomes generalized almost immediately, and the localizing signs at the onset may pass unobserved. One must therefore always question the patient and eye witnesses closely on the mode of onset of 'generalized' seizures, and carry out an EEG examination, even when the diagnosis seems indisputable, for a large number of seizures apparently generalized from the start are found to be partial epilepsy secondarily generalized.

The evolution of partial discharges originating on the spot (primary discharges) depends upon the same factors of fatigue as in generalized discharges and perhaps also on the same phenomena of rhythmical inhibition. For this reason their EEG arrangement is usually the same as in generalized discharges. Rhythmic activity is first sustained in the same way at the initial frequency (indefatigability), then slowed progressively (growing fatigability), and finally interrupted by episodes of silence or slow waves which grow progressively longer (phase of exhaustion or inhibition), until at the end there is silence (phase of postictal extinction).

On the other hand, partial discharges remote from the epileptogenic lesion develop completely differently, in a way which defies all classification because of seizure variability. These discharges are characterized by slow sinusoidal or notched waves, or by polyphasic spikes with an initial positive phase, and they are notable for their long duration and their instability. At one moment a discharge may be rhythmical and of large amplitude and at the next it has lost these features. The discharge may be slowed or accelerated indifferently and sometimes even pass through two or three successive phases of speeding up and slowing down. Finally, there may or may not be postictal extinction, and in some cases the record becomes normal again immediately after the discharge has ended.

DISTINCTION BETWEEN TWO GREAT VARIETIES OF PARTIAL EPILEPSY WITH RESPECT TO CHARACTER OF THEIR

DISCHARGES. The various partial epilepsies have often been classified according to the structures in which the seizure develops, or at least in which it originates. Such a conception obviously presupposes that the discharge always originates in the same place, that it is always propagated along the same pathways and that it always provokes the same electroclinical signs. It also presupposes that the first symptom, the 'signal-symptom' or 'aura' is the same every time, points infallibly to the site of the lesion and guides the hand of the neurosurgeon.

Such rules, however, apply only to a small minority of the partial epilepsies, namely those provoked by a very limited irritative lesion whose discharge involves a closed neuronal system. In the majority of cases, however, these rules are only partially applicable, particularly when the epileptogenic lesion is extensive and when the discharge develops in complex neuronal systems where it is propagated irregularly and differently in various seizures and accordingly provokes complex and variable symptoms. In such cases, the 'signal-symptom' is clearly less valuable (54, 76, 79), for it may reveal a discharge propagated from a clinically silent structure and it may vary from one seizure to another according to the origin and propagation of the discharge.

Two varieties of partial epilepsy are distinguished in the Marseille school (59), according to propagation of the discharge to different anatomical systems.

a) In the first variety, the causal discharge originates in a structure essentially, if not exclusively, connected to one single other structure. Together they constitute a limited functional system, the two 'poles' (these two structures) being united by dense fibers. In this system, the discharge extends from one pole to the other but always stays limited within the system, for although other fibers unite each pole to other nervous formations, they are never grouped sufficiently densely to cause effective bombardment and to render these other formations epileptic. The most notable examples of these 'bipolar' systems in the brain are the corticothalamic sectors connecting the various specific areas of the cortex to the corresponding specific thalamic nuclei (54).

The EEG manifestations consist exclusively of discharges limited to the sector concerned and, in consequence, are recorded from a very localized region of the scalp. The interseizure discharges consist of sporadic spikes or spikes-and-waves which, in current EEG usage, reveal an 'epileptogenic focus'; the seizure discharges are spikes repeated rhythmically and slowing progressively, which constitute a 'partial seizure discharge expressed focally'.

It is evident that such a focus or discharge does not guarantee that the epileptogenic lesion is cortical, for it may just as well be at the subcortical pole of the system and nevertheless be expressed in the cerebral cortex. The clinical manifestations of the seizures depend upon the corticothalamic sector involved, appearing as clonic jerks when the sector of precentral cortex ⇌ ventrolateral nucleus is involved; dysesthesia for the sector of postcentral cortex ⇌ nucleus ventralis posterolateralis; visual phenomena for the striate region ⇌ lateral geniculate; and auditory phenomena for the superior temporal ⇌ medial geniculate.[13]

The discharges are not necessarily generalized throughout the whole of the corticothalamic sector. Some part only may be involved, for example, the Jacksonian twitching may affect only the face. Similarly, several adjacent sectors may be involved concomitantly or successively; for example, the Jacksonian jerking may accompany or be followed by dysesthesia in the corresponding part of the body.

b) In the second variety of partial epilepsy, the causal discharge originates in a nervous structure which is more or less diffusely connected with several other cerebral regions, constituting a multiple relay system. These systems are too numerous and at present too ill-defined to be described fully. In addition they are interconnected and a given cerebral structure may belong to several of them. We can however distinguish two great rhinencephalic systems: the hippocampus connected on the one hand to the limbic lobe and on the other hand to the hypothalamus and tegmentum; and the basal rhinencephalic formations (piriformoamygdaloid and olfactoseptal) connected on the one hand to the orbitoinsulotele-temporal cortex, and on the other to the epithalamus, hypothalamus and tegmentum mesencephali. There is also the most rostral part of the reticular formation of the brain stem which projects diffusely from the thalamus on to the whole of the cerebral cortex and which was previously discussed. This last system may be activated globally by way of the reticular afferents, as in generalized epilepsy, but it may often be brought into play in a fragmentary way in the partial epilepsies.[14]

The clinical manifestations are complex because they involve simultaneously or successively a large number of structures with different functions. Sensory, mental or motor symptoms may be associated or succeed each other and Gowers (92) has described cases in which a dozen visual, auditory, olfactory, illusional, hallucinatory and motor symptoms follow each other without interruption.

Vegetative and affective manifestations are particularly important since the discharges usually involve the rhinencephalon and diencephalon. These frequently include abnormal epigastric, abdominal and precordial sensations with reactional gestures: chewing, salivation, deglutition, and imperious needs to eat, urinate or defecate, as well as disorders of attention, anxiety, fear, anger, etc.

There usually is clouded consciousness and the appearance of more or less complex automatisms, since these discharges disturb the functioning of a large part of the brain and usually involve some of the diffuse cortical projection system which helps to regulate cerebral excitability and consciousness.

The electroencephalographic manifestations take the form of seizure discharges which may be classified as follows a) Localized discharges appearing as spike rhythms in the temporal region (with anterior temporal and middle temporal electrodes) or in the occipital region (with occipital, posterior temporal and posterior parietal electrodes), according to whether the discharge develops in the amygdalotemporal system or the pulvinaro-occipitoparietotemporal sector.

These localized seizure discharges are usually situated on the same side as the interseizure focus and its causal lesions, but fairly frequently they are situated on the opposite side (82). Such independent contralateral discharges may indicate a secondary vascular extension of the lesion to the other side (69) but may also indicate a functional 'unleashing' of these homologous contralateral structures which have acquired epileptogenic potentiality through being bombarded (78).

b) Diffuse discharges, constituted by a rhythm of waves gradually slowing or accelerating, more or less generalized over one or both hemispheres but often

---

[13] These seizures most commonly develop in the precentral cortex ⇌ n. ventrolateral nucleus sector, not because it more often contains the epileptogenic lesion but because it has the lowest convulsant threshold.

[14] These diffuse systems are often activated in the partial epilepsies through the rhinencephalic formations for two reasons: a) the latter, chiefly the hippocampus and amygdala, are frequently the seat of epileptogenic lesions (pararhinal sclerosis in the so-called 'temporal' epilepsies); and b) these rhinencephalic formations have the lowest convulsant threshold of all cerebral structures (see above).

redominant in the frontotemporal region. This occurs when the discharges develop in the diffuse thalamocortical system.

c) Complex discharges, in which localized and diffuse discharges are associated, either independently or concomitantly, and if the latter, either in or out of phase. This occurs when various cortical-subcortical systems are brought into play simultaneously or successively causing 'erratic' discharges.

d) Localized or generalized flattening of the basic rhythm occurs when the structure involved in the seizure is endowed with the property of desynchronizing the cortical electrical activity.

e) There may be no EEG manifestation of a seizure at all when the discharge involves subcortical structures with very poor cortical projection or when it is unable to cross the synapses leading to the cortex.

The interseizure discharges may be more or less diffuse for the same reason as the seizure discharges, but they are most often localized to the temporal region (and particularly the anterior temporal) or one or both hemispheres. This particular site is the most common, as Gibbs has well shown, because these interictal discharges usually originate in the diseased cerebral structures with the lowest convulsant threshold, that is to say, the tip of the temporal lobe and the basal rhinencephalic formations (piriform cortex, amygdala and hippocampus) which also project on to the teletemporal region (72, 121; and later authors).

Having described these two great varieties of partial epilepsy on the basis of pathological physiology, we shall further describe them in terms of anatomy, etiology, symptomatology and therapy.

a) The localized partial epilepsies not only show a local discharge but are usually caused by a localized superficial lesion, either atrophic or neoplastic. The causes are not numerous and include open head injuries with well-defined craniocerebral wounds, localized infections, chiefly periarterial or perivenous, local vascular accidents (malformations or thromboses) and small cortical or paracortical tumors. These lesions are discrete and, because they interfere with the normal functioning of only a small amount of cerebral parenchyma, the patient's mental make-up is usually normal between seizures, especially from the intellectual point of view. The lesion is usually cortical for the superficial pole of the corticothalamic sector is a much larger area and is more vulnerable than is its deep pole. Since the lesion involves the convexity of the cortex and spares the rhinencephalon and diencephalon, there is usually no disturbance of

character or behavior between seizures. On the other hand, interictal neurological symptoms are relatively frequent (mild hemiplegia, dysphasia or hemianopsia) for the lesion involves a corticothalamic sector with specific functions. Surgery may often be indicated when medical treatment fails in this type of partial epilepsy because of the precise and superficial localization of the lesion and because of its small size. The operation usually is easily performed and yields excellent results.

b) The diffuse partial epilepsies not only have a diffuse discharge but arise from diffuse sclerosis, predominating in the inferomedial aspect of the hemisphere, the 'pararhinal' region. The causes are numerous and varied but may be divided into three main groups, depending on the age at which the lesion is acquired: severe and prolonged compression of the head during delivery (156); cerebral edema in infancy or early childhood which accompanies various disorders clinically misnamed 'encephalitis', consisting of status epilepticus with coma and subsequent transient hemiplegia (57, 58); and closed head injuries in the adult (64). The principal pathogenic mechanisms in these three conditions are wedging of the hippocampal gyrus and the blood vessels supplying it into the tentorial incisure during compression of the brain at birth, or during intracranial hypertension secondary to cerebral edema in childhood, and injury of the orbitoinsulotemporal region by the sharp edge of the lesser wir.g of the sphenoid from the contrecoup accompanying closed head injuries. These two mechanisms are responsible for the two aspects of pararhinal sclerosis, incisural sclerosis (156), and vallecular (perifalciform) sclerosis (53, 57) which develops in relation to the tentorial incisure and around the vallecula sylvii in the region corresponding to the pararhinal region.

Because the lesions responsible for psychomotor epilepsy are so widespread and so severe and are located in the pararhinal region, these patients frequently show interseizure disturbances of intellect and particularly of character and of sexual, alimentary and social behavior (62).[15]

On the other hand, these diffuse and deep lesions do not involve the majority of the corticothalamic sectors and the important projection pathways which explains the fact that interseizure neurological mani-

[15] The basal part of the rhinencephalon acts as a controlling and regulating system of complex automatic activities, principally those adapted to the seeking of the opposite sex and to the pursuit, intake and ingestion of food (56). See the chapters in this work dealing with this region.

festations are rare. Finally, since the pararhinal region is so deeply situated, surgery is difficult and only exceptionally indicated, for it requires systematic anterior temporal lobectomy (Penfield) extended to the uncus, amygdala and hippocampus, or selective amygdalohippocampectomy (Niemeyer).

REFERENCES

1. ADRIAN, E. D. AND G. MORUZZI. *J. Physiol.* 95: 27, 1939.
2. ADRIAN, E. D. AND G. MORUZZI. *J. Physiol.* 97: 153, 1939.
3. AHLQUIST, R. P. *J. Am. Pharm. A.* 36: 414, 1947.
4. AJMONE-MARSAN, C. AND M. G. F. FUORTES. *Electroencephalog. & Clin. Neurophysiol.* 1: 283, 1949.
5. AJMONE-MARSAN, C. AND F. MAROSSERO. *Electroencephalog. & Clin. Neurophysiol.* 2: 133, 1950.
6. AJMONE-MARSAN, C. AND J. STOLL, JR. *A.M.A. Arch. Neurol. & Psychiat.* 66: 669, 1951.
7. ALAJOUANINE, T. AND H. GASTAUT. *Rev. neurol.* 93: 29, 1955.
8. AMANTEA, G. *Arch. ges. Physiol.* 188: 287, 1921.
9. AMANTEA, G. *Arch. sc. biol.* 12: 413, 1928.
10. ANDY, O. AND K. AKERT. *Electroencephalog. & Clin. Neurophysiol.* Suppl. 3: 48, 1953.
11. ANDY, O. AND K. AKERT. *J. Neuropath. & Exper. Neurol.* 14: 198, 1955.
12. ARDUINI, A. AND G. MORUZZI. *Electroencephalog. & Clin. Neurophysiol.* 5: 235, 1953.
13. ARELLANO, A., R. SCHWAB AND J. CASBY. *Electroencephalog. & Clin. Neurophysiol.* 2: 217, 1950.
14. ASUAD, J. *L'Épilepsie expérimentale. Contribution à l'étude de la Pathogénie des Convulsions.* Paris: Masson, 1940.
15. BAGLIONI, S. AND M. MAGNINI. *Arch. fisiol.* 6: 240, 1909.
16. BECHTEREW, W. *Neurol. Zentralbl.* 16: 199, 1897.
17. BICARD, N., Y. GASTAUT AND J. ROGER. *Epilepsia* 4: 73, 1955.
18. BINSWANGER, O. In *Nothnagel, Handbuch der Speciellen Pathologie und Therapie.* Vienna, 1913. [Cited by Muskens (149).]
19. BOUCHÉ, G. *Epilepsia* 5: 18, 1956.
20. BOUDOURESQUES, J. AND H. GASTAUT. *Rev. neurol.* 89: 155, 1953.
21. BREMER, F. *Proc. Soc. Exper. Biol. & Med.* 46: 627, 1941.
22. BREMER, F. AND V. BONNET. *J. physiol., Paris* 45: 53, 1953.
23. BUBNOFF, N. AND R. HEIDENHAIN. *Arch. ges. Physiol.* 26: 137, 1881–2.
24. BUSER, P. AND D. ALBE-FESSARD. *Compt. rend. Acad. Sc.* 236: 1197, 1953.
25. CADILHAC, J. Thesis. Montpellier, France: Université de Montpellier, 1955.
26. CHANG, H.-T. *J. Neurophysiol.* 16: 221, 1953.
27. CHAUCHARD, P., H. MAZOUE AND R. LECOQ. *Presse méd.* 16: 220, 1945.
28. CLEMENTI, A. *Arch. fisiol.* 27: 356, 1929.
29. CLEMENTI, A. *Arch. fishol.* 27: 388, 1929.
30. COHN, R. *A.M.A. Arch. Neurol. & Psychiat.* 71: 699, 1954.
31. CREUTZFELDT, O. *Schweiz. Arch. Neurol. u. Psychiat.* 77: 163, 1956.
32. CREUTZFELDT, O. D. AND R. W. MEYER-MICKELEIT. *Electroencephalog. & Clin. Neurophysiol.* Suppl. 3: 43, 1953.
33. CRITCHLEY, M. *Brain* 60: 13, 1937.
34. CURE, C. AND T. RASMUSSEN. *Electroencephalog. & Clin. Neurophysiol.* 2: 354, 1950.
35. DAVIES, P. W. AND A. REMOND. *A. Res. Nerv. & Ment. Dis., Proc.* 26: 205, 1946.
36. DAVIS, L. AND L. J. POLLOCK. *A.M.A. Arch. Neurol. & Psychiat.* 20: 759, 1928.
37. DE HASS, A. M. L., C. LOMBROSO AND J. K. MERLIS. *Electrocephalog. & Clin. Neurophysiol.* 5: 177, 1953.
38. DEMPSEY, E. W. AND R. S. MORISON. *Am. J. Physiol.* 135: 293, 1942.
39. DEMPSEY, E. W. AND R. S. MORISON. *Am. J. Physiol.* 135: 301, 1942.
40. DEMPSEY, E. W. AND R. S. MORISON. *Am. J. Physiol.* 138: 283, 1943.
41. DUSSER DE BARENNE, J. G., C. S. MARSHALL, W. S. McCULLOCH AND L. F. NIMS. *Am. J. Physiol.* 124: 651, 1938.
42. DUSSER DE BARENNE, J. G., W. S. McCULLOCH AND L. NIMS. *J. Cell. & Comp. Physiol.* 10: 277, 1937.
43. ERICKSON, T. C. *A.M.A. Arch. Neurol. & Psychiat.* 43: 429, 1940.
44. FEDEROV, L. N. *Ztschr. ges. exper. Med.* 72: 72, 1930.
45. FEDEROV, L. N. *Ztschr. ges. exper. Med.* 72: 82, 1930.
46. FEINDEL, W. AND P. GLOOR. *Electroencephalog. & Clin. Neurophysiol.* 6: 389, 1954.
47. FERRIER, D. *West Riding Lunatic Asylum Med. Rep.* 3: 30, 1873.
48. FESSARD, A. *Conférence à la Semaine Neurophysiologique de la Salpêtrière consacrée aux grands problèmes de l'Epilepsie.* Paris: Masson. In press.
49. FRANCK, F. AND A. PITRES. *Arch. physiol. norm. et pathol.* 2: 1, 1883.
50. FRENCH, J. D., B. E. GERNANDT AND R. B. LIVINGSTON. *A.M.A. Arch. Neurol. & Psychiat.* 75: 260, 1956.
51. FRITSCH, G. AND E. HITZIG. *Arch. Anat. Physiol. Wiss. Med.* 37: 300, 1870.
52. GASTAUT, H. *Electroencephalog. & Clin. Neurophysiol.* 2: 249, 1950.
53. GASTAUT, H. *Les Epilepsies.* Paris: Flammarion, 1950.
54. GASTAUT, H. *Encyclopédie Médico-Chirurgicale, Tome Neurologie,* Fascicule 17008. Paris: Encyclopédie Médico-Chirurgicale, 1951.
55. GASTAUT, H. *Riv. neurol.* 21: 1, 1951.
56. GASTAUT, H. *J. physiol., Paris* 45: 117, 1953.
57. GASTAUT, H. *The Epilepsies. Electro-clinical Correlations.* Springfield: Thomas, 1954.
58. GASTAUT, H. *Comptes rendus du Colloque de Marseille.* Bruxelles: Editions Acta Medica Belgica, 1955.
59. GASTAUT, H. *Encyclopédia Médico-Chirurgicale, Tome Neurologie,* Fascicule 37250. Paris: Encyclopédie Médico-Chirurgicale, 1955.
60. GASTAUT, H. In: *Les Grandes Activités du Lobe Occipital.* Paris: Masson, 1957.
61. GASTAUT, H., P. BENOIT, M. VIGOUROUX AND A. ROGER. *Electroencephalog. & Clin. Neurophysiol.* 6: 557: 1954.
62. GASTAUT, H. AND H. COLLOMB. *Ann. méd.-psychol.* 112: 657, 1954.
63. GASTAUT, H. AND M. FISCHER-WILLIAMS. *Lancet* 2: 1018, 1957.

64. GASTAUT, H. AND Y. GASTAUT. *Rev. oto-neuro-Ophtal.* 23: 257, 1951.

65. GASTAUT, H. AND J. HUNTER. *Electroencephalog. & Clin. Neurophysiol.* 2: 263, 1950.

66. GASTAUT, H. AND J. HUNTER. *J. physiol., Paris* 42: 592, 1950.

67. GASTAUT, H. AND H. LAMMERS. In: *Les Grandes Activités du Rhinencephale.* Paris: Masson. In press.

68. GASTAUT, H., R. NAQUET, M. BADIER AND A. ROGER. *J. physiol., Paris* 43: 737, 1951.

69. GASTAUT, H., R. NAQUET, E. BECK, J. CAVANAGH AND A. MEYER. In: *Comptes-Rendus du II Colloque Internationale sur l'Epilepsie Temporale.* Springfield: Thomas, In press.

70. GASTAUT, H., R. NAQUET AND M. FISCHER-WILLIAMS. *J. Nerv. & Ment. Dis.* 127: 21, 1958.

71. GASTAUT, H., R. NAQUET AND H. REGIS. *Comp. rend. Soc. de biol.* In press.

72. GASTAUT, H., R. NAQUET AND A. ROGER. *Rev. neurol.* 87: 224, 1952.

73. GASTAUT, H., R. NAQUET, R. VIGOUROUX, A. ROGER AND M. BADIER. *Rev. neurol.* 88: 310, 1953.

74. GASTAUT, H. AND E. PIROVANO. *Arch. psicol. neurol. e psichiat.* 10: 287, 1949.

75. GASTAUT, H., G. RICCI AND H. KUGLER. *Rev. neurol.* 89: 1, 1953.

76. GASTAUT, H., G. RICCI AND H. KUGLER. *Rev. neurol.* 89: 546, 1953.

77. GASTAUT, H. AND A. ROGER. *Rev. neurol.* 84: 94, 1951.

78. GASTAUT, H. AND A. ROGER. In: *Les Grandes Activités du Lobe Temporal.* Paris: Masson, 1955, p. 83.

79. GASTAUT, H. AND M. VIGOUROUX. *Rev. neurol.* In press.

80. GASTAUT, H., R. VIGOUROUX AND M. BADIER. *Rev. neurol.* 85: 505, 1951.

81. GASTAUT, H., R. VIGOUROUX, J. CORRIOL AND M. BADIER. *J. physiol., Paris* 43: 740, 1951.

82. GASTAUT, H., M. VIGOUROUX AND M. FISCHER-WILLIAMS. In: *Comptes-Rendus du II Colloque Internationale sur l'Epilepsie Temporale.* Springfield: Thomas. In press.

83. GASTAUT, H., VIGOUROUX AND R. NAQUET. *Rev. neurol.* 87: 607, 1952.

84. GASTAUT, H., R. VIGOUROUX AND R. NAQUET. *Electroencephalog. & Clin. Neurophysiol.* 5: 291, 1953.

85. GAUTHIER, C., M. PARMA AND A. ZANCHETTI *Electroencephalog. & Clin. Neurophysiol.* 8: 237, 1956.

86. GIBBS, F. A. AND E. L. GIBBS. *A.M.A. Arch. Neurol. & Psychiat* 35: 109, 1936.

87. GIBBS, F. A. AND E. L. GIBBS. *Atlas of Electroencephalography* (2nd ed.). Cambridge: Addison-Wesley Press, 1952.

88. GIBBS, F. A., E. L. GIBBS AND W. G. LENNOX. *Brain* 60: 377, 1937.

89. GLEY, P., M. LAPIPE, J. RONDEPIERRE, M. HORANDE AND T. TOUCHARD. *J. physiol. pathol. gen.* 38: 132, 1941.

90. GLOOR, P. *Electroencephalog. & Clin. Neurophysiol.* 7: 223, 1955.

91. GOODDY, W. *Brain* 79: 167, 1956.

92. GOWERS, W. R. *Epilepsy and other Chronic Convulsive Diseases; their Causes, Symptoms and Treatment.* London: Churchill, 1881.

93. GREEN, J. D. AND R. NAQUET. *IV Congrès International d'Electroencephalographie et Neurophysiologie.* Bruxelles: Editions Acta Medica Belgica, 1957, p. 225.

94. GREEN, J. D. AND I. SHIMAMOTO. *A.M.A. Arch. Neurol & Psychiat.* 70: 687, 1953.

95. GUTIERREZ-NORIEGA, C. *Rev. neuro-psiquiat.* 1: 85, 1938.

96. HALL, M. *Synposis of the Diastaltic Nervous System.* London: Mallett, 1850.

97. HAMOIR, J. L. AND J. TITECA. *Rev. neurol.* 80: 635, 1948.

98. HAYNE, R. A., L. BELINSON AND F. A. GIBBS. *Electroencephalog. & Clin. Neurophysiol.* 1: 437, 1949.

99. HOEFER, P. F. A. AND J. L. POOL. *A.M.A. Arch. Neurol. & Psychiat.* 50: 381, 1943.

100. HORSLEY, V. *Lancet* 2: 1211, 1886.

101. HUNTER, J. AND D. H. INGVAR. *Electroencephalog. & Clin. Neurophysiol.* 7: 39, 1955.

102. HUNTER, J. AND H. JASPER. *Electroencephalog. & Clin. Neurophysiol.* 1: 305, 1949.

103. INGVAR, D. H. *Acta physiol. scandinav.* 33: 137, 1955.

104. JACKSON, J. H. In: *Selected Writings,* edited by J. Taylor. London: Hodder and Stoughton, 1931.

105. JASPER, H. In: *Epilepsy and Cerebral Localization,* edited by W. Penfield and T. L. Erickson. Springfield: Thomas, 1941.

106. JASPER, H. *Electroencephalog & Clin. Neurophysiol.* 1: 405, 1949.

107. JASPER, H. AND C. AJMONE-MARSAN. *A. Res. Nerv. & Ment. Dis., Proc.* 30: 493, 1952.

108. JASPER, H., C. AJMONE-MARSAN AND J. STOLL. *A.M.A. Arch. Neurol. & Psychiat.* 67: 155, 1952.

109. JASPER, H. AND J. DROOGLEEVER-FORTUYN. *A. Res. Nerv. & Ment. Dis., Proc.* 26: 272, 1947.

110. JASPER, H. AND T. C. ERICKSON. *J. Neurophysiol.* 5: 333, 1941.

111. JASPER, H., R. NAQUET AND E. KING. *Electroencephalog. & Clin. Neurophysiol.* 7: 99, 1955.

112. JOHNSON, B. *J. Neurophysiol.* 18: 189, 1955.

113. JOHNSON, H. C., K. M. BROWNE, J. W. MARKHAM AND E. A. WALKER. *Proc. Soc. Exper. Biol. & Med.* 73: 97, 1950.

114. JOHNSON, H. C. AND A. E. WALKER. *Electroencephalog. & Clin. Neurophysiol.* 4: 131, 1952.

115. JOHNSON, H. C., A. E. WALKER, K. M. BROWNE AND J. J. W. MARKHAM. *A.M.A. Arch. Neurol. & Psychiat.* 67: 473, 1952.

116. JUNG, R. *Arch. Psychiat.* 183: 206, 1949.

117. JUNG, R. *Electroencephalog. & Clin. Neurophysiol.* Suppl. 4: 57, 1953.

118. JUNG, R. AND J. F. TONNIES. *Arch. Psychiat.* 185: 701, 1950.

119. KAADA, B. R. *Acta physiol. scandinav.* 24: Suppl. 83, 1951.

120. KAADA, B. R. *Nord. med.* 47: 845, 1952.

121. KAADA, B. R. *Ann. Rev. Physiol.* 15: 39, 1953.

122. KAADA, B. R., P. ANDERSEN AND J. JANSEN. *Neurology* 4: 48, 1954.

123. KARPLUS, I. P. *Wien. klin. Wchnschr.* 27: 645, 1914.

124. KING, E. *J. Pharmacol. & Exper. Therap.* 116: 404, 1956.

125. KIRIKAE, T., J. WADA, Y. NAOE AND O. FURUYA. *Folia Psychiat. Neurol. Japonica* 7: 181, 1953.

126. KLEITMAN, N. AND R. MAGNUS. *Arch. ges. Physiol.* 205: 148, 1924.

127. KOPELOFF, L. M., S. E. BARRERA AND N. KOPELOFF. *Am. J. Psychiat.* 98: 881, 1942.

128. KOPELOFF, L. M., J. G. CHUSID AND N. KOPELOFF. *Neurology* 4: 218, 1954.

129. KOPELOFF, L. M., J. G. CHUSID AND N. KOPELOFF. A.M.A. Arch. Neurol. & Psychiat. 74: 523, 1955.

130. LAVITRY, L. Thesis. Toulouse, France: Université de Toulouse, 1947.

131. LEWANDOWSKY, M. AND G. FISCHER. Die Funktion des Zentralen Nervensystems. Jena, 1907. [Cited by Marchand and Ajuriaguerra (134).]

132. MACLEAN, P. D. AND J. M. R. DELGADO. Electroencephalog. & Clin. Neurophysiol. 5: 91, 1953.

133. MAGOUN, H. W. AND R. RHINES. J. Neurophysiol. 9: 165, 1946.

134. MARCHAND, J. L. AND J. DE AJURIAGUERRA. Epilepsies. Paris: Desclée de Brouwer, 1948.

135. MARINESCO, G., O. SAGER AND A. KREINDLER. Rev. neurol. 1: 1329, 1932.

136. MARKHAM, J. W., J. M. BROWNE, H. C. JOHNSON AND A. E. WALKER. A. Res. Nerv. & Ment. Dis., Proc. 30: 282, 1952.

137. MAROSSERO, F. AND M. GARRONE. Electroencephalog. & Clin. Neurophysiol. 4: 230, 1952.

138. MCCULLOCH, W. S. Electroencephalog. & Clin. Neurophysiol. 1: 19, 1949.

139. MCCULLOCH, W. S. AND J. G. DUSSER DE BARENNE. Am. J. Physiol. 113: 97, 1935.

140. MCCULLOCH, W. S. AND H. W. GAROL. J. Neurophysiol. 4: 555, 1941.

141. METTLER, F. A. AND C. C. METTLER. J. Neurophysiol. 3: 527, 1940.

142. MORIN, F. AND J. D. GREEN. Anat. Rec. 115: 433, 1953.

143. MORISON, R. S. AND E. W. DEMPSEY. Am. J. Physiol. 135: 281, 1942.

144. MORUZZI, G. Arch. fisiol. 44: 109, 1945.

145. MORUZZI, G. L'Epilepsie Experimentale. Paris: Hermann, 1950.

146. MORUZZI, G. Electroencephalog. & Clin. Neurophysiol. Suppl. 4: 221, 1953.

147. MORUZZI, G. AND H. W. MAGOUN. Electroencephalog. & Clin. Neurophysiol. 1: 455, 1949.

148. MURPHY, J. P. AND E. GELLHORN. J. Neurophysiol. 8: 341, 1945.

149. MUSKENS, J. J. L'Epilepsie. Anvers: De Vos-Van Kleef, 1926.

150. NAQUET, R. Thesis. Marseille, France: Université d'Aix-Marseille, 1953.

151. NAUTA, W. J. H. AND D. G. WHITLOCK. In: Brain Mechanisms and Consciousness, edited by E. D. Adrian, F. Bremer and H. H. Jasper. Oxford: Blackwell, 1954.

152. NOELL, W. K. AND E. B. DOMBROWSKI. Cerebral Localisation and Classification of Convulsions Produced by Severe Oxygen Lack. Randolph Field, Texas: School of Aviation Medicine, 1947.

153. OLMSTED, J. M. D. AND H. D. LOGAN. Am. J. Physiol. 66: 437, 1923.

154. PAPEZ, J. W. A. Res. Nerv. & Ment. Dis. Proc., 21: 21, 1942.

155. PARMA, M. AND A. ZANCHETTI. Am. J. Physiol. 185: 614, 1956.

156. PENFIELD, W. A.M.A. Arch. Neurol. & Psychiat. 60: 107, 1948.

157. PIKE, F. H., C. A. ELSBERG, W. S. MCCULLOCH AND M. N. CHAPPELL. A. Res. Nerv. & Ment. Dis., Proc. 7: 203, 1931.

158. POGGIO, G., E. WALKER AND O. ANDY. A.M.A. Arch. Neurol. & Psychiat. 75: 350, 1956.

159. POLLOCK, L. J. AND L. DAVIS. A. Res. & Ment. Dis., Proc. 7: 158, 1931.

160. POPE, A., A. MORRIS, H. JASPER, K. ELIOT AND W. PENFIELD. A. Res. Nerv. & Ment. Dis., Proc. 26: 218, 1947.

161. PREVOST, J. L. Encéphale 2: 165, 1907.

162. PRUS, J. Wien. klin. Wchnschr. 11: 857, 1898.

163. RALSTON, B. AND C. AJMONE-MARSAN. Electoencephalog. & Clin. Neurophysiol. 8: 559, 1956.

164. RANSON, S. W., S. W. RANSON, JR. AND M. RANSON. A.M.A. Arch. Neurol. & Psychiat. 46: 230, 1941.

165. RANSON, S. W., S. W. RANSON, JR. AND M. RANSON. A.M.A. Arch. Neurol. & Psychiat. 46: 402, 1941.

166. RISER, M., J. GAYRAL AND J. PIGASSOU. Bull. Acad. Med. 129: 257, 1945.

167. ROGER, A. Thesis. Marseille, France: Université d'Aix-Marseille, 1954.

168. ROSENBLUETH, A. AND W. B. CANNON. Am. J. Physiol. 135: 690, 1941–1942.

169. RUF, H. Nervenarzt 22: 437, 1951.

170. RUSSEL, J. Cases of Suspended Cerebral Function Occurring among the Phenomena following Epileptic Fits. Medical Times and Gazette, 1882.

171. SAMAJA, N. Rev. méd. Suisse Rom. 34: 77; 173, 1904.

172. SCHLAG, J. D. A. Electroencephalog. & Clin. Neurophysiol. 8: 421, 1956.

173. SCHOEN, R. Arch. exper. Path. u. Pharmakol. 113: 257, 1926.

174. SCHROEDER VAN DER KOLK, J. L. K. On the Minute Structure and Function of the Spinal Cord and Medulla Oblongata and on the Proximate Cause and Rational Treatment of Epilepsy, translated by W. D. Moore. London: The New Sydenham Society, 1859.

175. SEGUNDO, J. P., R. NAQUET AND R. ARANA. A. M. A. Arch. Neurol. & Psychiat. 73: 515, 1955.

176. SHIMAMOTO, T. AND M. VERZEANO. J. Neurophysiol. 17: 278, 1954.

177. SHIMIZU, K., S. REFSUM AND F. GIBBS. Electroencephalog. & Clin. Neurophysiol. 4: 141, 1952.

178. SOREL, L. Arch. Belg. Med. Soc. Hyg. Med. du Trav. et Med. Leg. 13: 594, 1955.

179. SPERANSKI, A. D. A Basis for the Theory of Medicine. Moscow: INRA Cooperative Publishing Society, 1935.

180. SPIEGEL, E. A. Am. J. Psychiat. 87: 595, 1930–31.

181. SPIEGEL, E. A. AND T. FALKIEWICZ. Arb. Neurol. Inst. Wien 28: 67, 1925.

182. SPIEGEL, E. A., H. T. WYCIS AND V. REYES. Electroencephalog. & Clin. Neurophysiol. 3: 473, 1951.

183. STARZL, T. E. AND H. W. MAGOUN J. Neurophysiol. 14: 133, 1951.

184. STARZL, T. E., W. T. NIEMER, M. B. DELL AND P. R. FORGRAVE. J. Neuropath. & Exper. Neurol. 12: 262, 1953.

185. STEFENS, R. AND J. DROOGLEEVER-FORTUYN. Schweiz. Arch. Neurol. u. Psychiat. 72: 299, 1953.

186. STOLL, J., C. AJMONE-MARSAN AND H. JASPER. J. Neurophysiol. 14: 305, 1951.

187. TEMKIN, O. The Falling Sickness. A History of Epilepsy from the Greeks to the Beginnings of Modern Neurology. Baltimore: Johns Hopkins Press, 1945.

188. THOMAS, L. B., R. P. SCHMIDT AND A. A. WARD. Electroencephalog. & Clin. Neurophysiol. 7: 478, 1955.

189. TURTSCHANINOW, P. Arch. Exper. Path. u. Pharmakol. 34: 208, 1894.

190. VON BAUMGARTEN, R., A. MOLLICA AND G. MORUZZI. *Boll. Soc. ital. biol. sper.* 29: 1376, 1953.

191. VULPIAN, A. *Gaz. hebd. med. et chir.* 22: 202, 1885.

192. WALKER, A. E. AND H. C. JOHNSON. *A. Res. Nerv. & Ment. Dis., Proc.* 27: 460, 1948.

193. WALTER, W. G., V. J. WALTER, H. GASTAUT AND Y. GASTAUT. *Revue neurol.* 80: 613, 1948.

194. WARD, A. A. *J. Neurophysiol.* 10: 89, 1947.

195. WARD, A. A. AND M. D. WHEATLEY. *J. Neuropath. & Exper. Neurol.* 6: 292, 1947.

196. WHITLOCK, D. G., A. ARDUINI AND G. MORUZZI. *J. Neurophysiol.* 16: 414, 1953.

197. WILLIAMS, D. *Brain* 76: 50, 1953.

198. WORTIS, S. B. AND D. KLENKE. *Am. J. Psychiat.* 12: 1039, 1933.

199. ZANCHETTI, A. AND J. M. BROOKHART. *J. Neurophysiol.* 18: 288, 1955.

200. ZIEHEN, T. Dissertation. Berlin, Germany: University of Berlin, 1885.

201. ZIEHEN, T. *Arch. Psychiat.* 20: 584, 1889.

CHAPTER XV

Sensory mechanisms—introduction

LORD E. D. ADRIAN | *Trinity College, Cambridge, England*

THE ESSENTIAL ELEMENTS of the sense organs are the receptor cells which respond to physical and chemical disturbance and transmit information about it to the central nervous system. Naturally in these days they are fascinating material for the cell physiologist. The electron microscope gives him new data about their structure, and there are new biophysical and biochemical techniques for investigating their reactions. If all goes well, our understanding of the changes which take place in the receptors will soon have reached the molecular level.

The sense organs also provide ample material for the electrophysiologist who deals with them as constituent elements of the nervous system. The technique of recording nervous activity has reached great precision and the flow of information can be studied in the cell units and pathways of the central nervous system as well as in the peripheral nerves. In the animal kingdom there is still a vast range of receptor apparatus awaiting investigation and even in the vertebrate there is still a good deal of exploration to be done, particularly about the receptors which signal internal rather than external events.

Another line of research leads beyond the receptors and their afferent connections, for the physiology of the sense organs must include the study of their function as well as of the properties which make them react to the stimulus. Some of them, pain receptors for instance, may be no more than warning devices which signal whenever their environment sets them in action, but many are used actively to explore the environment and such use involves movement directed by the central nervous system. We look with our eyes, feel with our fingers and sniff to identify a smell. Activity directed by the central nervous system may also be needed to protect the sense organ when the stimulus is too strong. We may have to constrict our pupils and shade our eyes, or cover our ears or hold our breath. Since the receptors will give most information when the stimulus falls within a particular range of intensity, we have to study the different adjustments which keep it within that range.

The analysis of this kind of central control has been carried out most fully for the receptors which signal muscular contraction. The muscle spindle is a sense organ excellently adapted for investigations of this kind, for in it the signaling and adjusting mechanisms are coupled together in a single structure and its function is to guide the relatively simple operations involved in posture and limb movement. Recent information on the efferent innervation of the spindle has given us a much clearer picture in which it appears as an active participant in the feed-back mechanism which ensures smooth movement against a continuous postural background.

The action involved in adjusting the stimulus to the sense organ can vary greatly in scale and complexity, from a simple reflex contraction to an elaborate sequence of skilled movement, as when the microscopist places the slide in position, focuses first with the coarse adjustment and then with the fine and makes appropriate use of his ocular muscles, external or internal. In such operations the adjustment is carried out by muscles in the organ or elsewhere. But in addition we may have to consider a more direct central adjustment which does not operate through the muscular link but by efferent nerve fibers leading directly to the receptors or to some part of the pathway from them to the central nervous system. At present we know that there are efferent fibers to the retina and the olfactory bulb. There are indications of a control of this kind in the cochlea also and, although we do not know their function, we know that there are other nerve fibers which reach the peripheral receptors but are not directly connected with the receptor elements.

All the actions which focus the sense organs on the stimulus will evoke afferent signals of their own to be related to the signals from the organ itself. Thus the full report which comes to the central nervous system will be far more complex and informative than anything which could be furnished by any sense organ isolated from the body and controlled only by the electrophysiologist.

Our primary concern, to be sure, is with the receptors and their reaction to the stimulus. How and to what purpose their reaction can be influenced by the central nervous system opens up a different chapter more concerned with the central than the peripheral mechanism. But the receptors are there to decide the line of behavior which the organism should follow; they have to supply all the relevant information as to what is happening from moment to moment, and from this the central nervous system selects the items of particular importance. It is essential, therefore, to consider the sense organs not only as groups of receptors excited by particular physical or chemical events, but as organs capable of presenting a detailed report which will enable the event to be compared with others of the same class which have occurred before. The description must be as full as possible, yet it has all to be conveyed by trains of impulses in nerve fibers. Though we can record the impulses there are still a good many problems to be settled before we can reach a clear understanding of how the full description of the stimulus is handed on to the brain.

The eye, for instance, can inform us that there are patches of light on the retina of particular shape, intensity and color. We suppose that the shape is signaled by the distribution of the nerve fibers which convey the signals and the intensity by the number of impulses arriving at a particular region of the nervous system within a given time. Thomas Young suggested in 1807 that the color may be signaled by particular nervous elements sensitive to particular regions of the spectrum, but in spite of the many fresh data which recent work has given us, we have still to reach agreement as to the way in which the information of color is combined with that of intensity and area.

Again we are aware that the olfactory organ enables us to distinguish an immense variety of odors. We know that the temporal and spatial pattern of excitation in the organ may vary with the smell and

that some of the receptors vary considerably in their sensitivity to different kinds of odor. It seems probable that these different sources of information can be combined to give the full range of discrimination, but it is not yet clear how the combination is achieved.

The receptors in the skin and in the tissues beneath can give a great deal of information about the nature of the object in contact with it and active exploratory movements help us to judge shape, size, hardness, etc. But even a light contact on a passive surface will produce a discharge of impulses in a variety of afferent fibers of different diameter and rate of conduction coming from receptor organs of different structure. Zotterman's studies of the temperature receptors have shown that these at least form a group with a characteristic structure and behavior. With the receptors for touch, pressure and pain, however, we are still ignorant of the role of different types of axon and ending in producing sensation which can vary so much in quality and in the attention and action which it will arouse.

With all this to occupy us at the periphery we need not be in too great a hurry to follow the sensory discharge into the central nervous system where it will be far less easy to analyze. But there is one problem which deserves mention at the present time because we may be already on the way to its solution, or at all events to its investigation. It is the problem of access to the higher levels of the brain. The sense organs provide a running commentary on a great variety of environmental circumstances, but the organism has to select the particular reports which have an important bearing on its present and future behavior. The classical method of investigating the sense organs by comparing stimulus and sensation can throw no light on this selective treatment, for the subject has to fix all his attention on the one stimulus. He must look for a feeble illumination or a slight change of color or listen for a faint click or a just detectable change of pitch. When he lectures to a class, however, such stimuli may have no effect at all on his sensory experiences or on his course of action. Indeed this method of research, though it can tell us the effect of a particular sense organ on the attentive mind, cannot be expected to tell us how the other sense organs can be prevented from reaching it.

This problem of attention is not likely to be settled finally until we know far more about the processes involved in habit formation, in the factors which attach importance to particular stimuli and in those which balance conflicting claims from moment to moment. Clearly we attend to stimuli which are un-expected or are intense in themselves or likely to give rise to a chain of activity by reason of past association, but the afferent nervous discharges must be studied at all levels before we can say where and why some fail and some reach through to conscious-ness. Fortunately the investigation of the reticular formation has given a new impetus to the study of attention. With modern techniques the afferent signals can be traced in their passage through the intact brain and we can expect that soon there will be fresh data bearing on this penultimate problem of the sense organs. The ultimate problem of their effect on the mind is scarcely one for the physiologist to settle.

CHAPTER XVI

Nonphotic receptors in lower forms

HANSJOCHEM AUTRUM | *Department of Zoology, University of München, Germany*

CHAPTER CONTENTS

PROTOZOA: DIFFERENTIATION OF PROTOPLASMIC IRRITABILITY

PROTOZOA REACT TO STIMULI: heat, cold, chemical and mechanical irritation, gravity, and light influence their behavior. These stimuli therefore affect the protozoan cells. However, it is a significant morphological and physiological problem whether sensitivity to these stimuli is limited to certain parts of the protozoan cell, or whether the whole organism can be stimulated. Only if the former is true can we speak of receptors.

The body protoplasm and its surface is not much differentiated in the simpler protozoa, such as the amebae. There is therefore no reason to look for localized receptors. It appears, however, that the protoplasm of the ameba is not irritable under certain physiological conditions. The ameba does not react if a narrow light beam strikes the hyalin tip of the outer end of a pseudopodium (80, 82, 83). If the light beam strikes the endoplasm of a pseudopodium which is streaming toward the tip (and is in the sol state), the streaming of this pseudopodium is stopped and new pseudopodia are formed in other parts. If the light beam strikes the plasmasol some distance from the tip, streaming will be accelerated. Experiments with ciliates, such as *Paramecium*, also showed the susceptibility of the whole body to stimulation (61, 71, 72). Thus, separated pieces of cut *Paramecium* respond to chemical stimuli, e.g. by 0.5 to 1.0 per cent NaCl or 0.05 to 0.01 per cent H_2SO_4, and to temperature stimuli in the same way as do whole animals. There is also no difference between cut parts and whole animals in the response to gravity. This fact is of special interest since the sensitivity to gravity depends on the principle of the statocyst (68, 69): heavier substances included in the body exert a pressure on the underlying protoplasm.[1] However, there are no favored locations in the body of *Paramecium* sensitive to this pressure; it can be effective in every part and may produce orientation in relation to the gravitational field.

In contrast to *Paramecium*, only the anterior part of the ciliate *Spirostomum ambiguum* (which can grow to 4.5 mm in length) is sensitive to thermal and chemical stimuli according to the view of Alverdes (6) and Blättner (18). Excised posterior parts swim into dilute picric acid without reaction (18). However, very dilute picric acid attracts *Spirostomum* and is less toxic to it than to other ciliates such as *Paramecium* and *Stentor*. Therefore the findings of Blättner cannot be

---

[1] It is not known which inclusion bodies serve as statoliths causing excitation by the pressure they exert under normal conditions. Koehler assumes that all inclusion bodies may function as statoliths. They have to be only heavier than the cytoplasm (as for example the nucleus, the content of vacuoles and iron particles in experiments).

taken necessarily as proof that the posterior part of *Spirostomum* is not irritable to chemicals. This form responds to other chemical and mechanical stimuli in the anterior and posterior part.

A localized, receptorlike structure has so far been found in only a few flagellates. Many phytoflagellates (*Euglena* and others) possess an eyespot which contains the pigment astaxanthin (135). In *Euglena* there is a light sensitive plasma spot located in the concavity of this eyespot. The eyespot itself probably has a screening function to light (81, 84). There are other phytoflagellates (e.g. *Chlamydomonas*) which are sensitive to light throughout the body, even though they possess an eyespot, as shown by mutants without an eyespot (52). Therefore the question as to whether the eyespots are real receptors is still open.

The effector system of the protozoa is very complicated. It is certain that in no case do protozoan cells react according to the all-or-none principle. The degree of contraction of the pseudopodia of rhizopods depends on the intensity of stimulation; the stronger the stimulation the farther the contraction spreads along the excited pseudopodium; it will spread to other parts of the body if the stimulus is sufficiently strong (127). The contractile stalk of vorticellae can be completely or partially contracted depending on the intensity of the stimulation (29, 64). The rhythm of ciliary movements in some parts of the body of ciliates can be modified independently of the activity of the remaining cilia (65, 89).

COELENTERATES: CNIDOBLASTS AS INDEPENDENT EFFECTORS

The cnidoblasts are cells which are characteristic of the coelenterates (*Cnidaria*, polyps and medusae). The intracellular structures of the cnidoblasts are nematocysts which consist of a bubble-like capsule. The free pole is a long hollow thread which is introverted and coiled, as shown in figures 1 and 2. The opening of the capsule is usually covered by a cap. On discharge the cap bursts open and the thread is ejected by eversion. Different types of nematocysts are found in the same species. Furthermore, they are different in different species (56, 63, 118, 138).

So far as analysis with ordinary light microscopes is concerned, nematocysts are the most complicated structures formed by cells. Some cnidoblasts carry a fine spine or a cone of fused cilia on the free end, the cnidocil shown in figure 1; others lack this cnidocil. Cnidoblasts which are not yet differentiated (inter-

stitial cells) form new nematocysts during their whole life; the cnidoblasts migrate—sometimes in groups—into or between ectodermal cells and thus form batteries of nematocysts.

There exists a large number of morphologically different nematocysts (138), but only a few types have been analyzed physiologically. They show characteristic differences with respect to irritability and function.

1) The desmonemes (also called volvents) and stenoteles (also called penetrants) are used for catching food. They explode upon simultaneous stimulation by chemical and mechanical means (such as aquatic food organisms and meat); the cap bursts open and the thread is everted within 3 to 5 msec. The thread of the stenoteles, supported by spines at the base, penetrates the body of the food organism even through

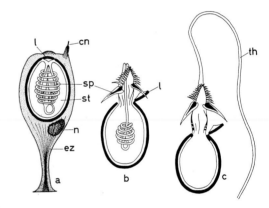

FIG. 1. Scheme of a stenotele nematocyst and its discharge. *a*, cnidoblast (ez) with nucleus (n), nematocyst (st), and cnidocil (cn); *b*, stenotele nematocyst during discharge; *c*, after discharge showing cap (l), spine (sp), and ejected thread (th). The cnidoblast is not drawn in *b* and *c*. Magnification, 555 ×. [From Kühn & Schulze (76).]

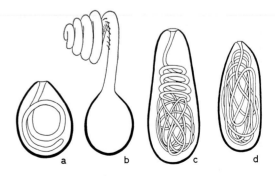

FIG. 2. Nematocysts of *Hydra* (cnidoblasts omitted). *a*, desmoneme prior to discharge; *b*, same after discharge; *c* and *d*, atrichous isorhizas. Magnification, 2200 ×. [From Kühn & Schulze (76).]

a well developed cuticle. The distal end of the thread of the stenoteles is open and by this means the poison stored in the capsule can be injected through the thread. The desmonemes on the other hand have a thread which is closed at its distal end and it winds only around the spines and other parts of the food organisms.

2) The atrichous isorhizas (also called small glutinants) serve *Hydra* by attaching the tentacles to the ground during the migration of the polyps.

3) Finally the holotrichous isorhizas are exclusively a defense mechanism. They explode only upon types of stimulation which cause no feeding reaction.

The discharge of the nematocysts occurs only upon direct stimulation; no nervous control exists. No nerve fibers can be found which lead to the cells containing nematocysts. With electrical stimulation only the nematocysts directly stimulated react (88, 90). Even repeated rhythmic stimulation by means of condensor discharges never causes a diffusion of excitation beyond the area directly stimulated. Thus the cnidoblasts contain irritable structures which act both as receptors and effectors and are independent of a nervous system.

Direct mechanical stimulation of the nematocysts on the tentacles of *Anemonia* or of the penetrants and volvents of *Hydra* does not normally lead to a discharge even though the cnidocils present are diverted (for example by epibiotic protozoa or artificially by chemically very clean, rounded glass needles). Neither is discharge obtained by chemical stimulation alone (such as extracts of meat or food organisms, proteins, amino acids or sugar). However the threshold for direct mechanical stimulation is considerably reduced by chemical stimuli produced by the food. The immediate releasing stimulus is therefore a mechanical one which however only becomes effective if the threshold is lowered in advance by certain substances present in the food.

The nature of these very specific chemical substances present in the food organisms is unknown. They are not proteins but they are firmly adsorbed on the proteins; they can, however, be extracted with ethanol or acetone (88).

The atrichous isorhizas serve to attach the tentacles to the ground during the migration of the polyps. They never respond to stimuli arising from food organisms. Chemical stimuli such as extracts of food organisms raise the threshold for this type of nematocysts. The duration of mechanical stimulation necessary to bring about discharge is greater for atrichous isorhizas than for stenoteles. Food inhibits chemically the discharge of the atrichous isorhizas (36).

In summary, it may be concluded that nematocysts respond to a mechanical stimulus. A simultaneous chemical stimulus, by raising or lowering the threshold, determines which kind of mechanical stimulus will explode the nematocysts. The change of the threshold insures that the reaction will be appropriate.

The cnidoblast is therefore a unique tissue element. As an independent effector it contains sensory, excitor and effector elements. The sensory element is in itself not simple and functions by means of two distinct sense organs, mechanical and chemical in nature. The cnidae may in fact be said to be double sense organs as well as effectors. There are no obvious analogies to this in the tissues of higher animals (88).

HIGHER INVERTEBRATES: EMERGENCE OF TRUE RECEPTORS

Anatomical Peculiarities

The receptor cells of the invertebrates are always primary sense cells; every sense cell has therefore a centripetal afferent nerve fiber. This is also the case in organs which in vertebrates have secondary receptor cells, for example the static and auditory organs.

In the simplest case, the sense cells are separate and are not yet united into an organ. Such scattered sense cells are found in all classes of invertebrates. They have the simplest shape in hydroid-polyps and actiniae; here they are located in the epithelium and have the shape of epithelial cells. They appear in the ectoderm as well as in the entoderm (fig. 3). They may be absent in the column ectoderm of the actinians, even if they are numerous in the ectoderm of the oral disc (88). Nevertheless, the column is sensitive to mechanical stimuli from the environment, although 4000 times less so than is the oral disc (91). Such single sense cells are found in the epithelium of lower and higher worms and molluscs, e.g. *Lumbricus* as shown in figure 4. The sense cells of the higher invertebrates are normally located subepithelially and send one peripheral fiber into the epithelium. These bipolar sensory neurons are illustrated in figure 5.

These single sense cells may have an auxiliary apparatus; for example, the hair-sensillae of the arthropods. These often, but not always, contain only one sense cell which sends a peripheral fiber into the interior of a hair which was formed by the cuticle (fig. 13).

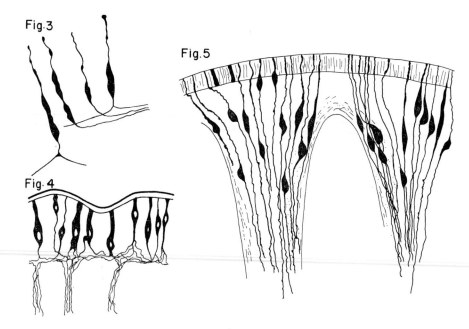

FIG. 3. Primary sense cells from the tentacles of the sea anemone *Cerianthus*. [From Hanström (50).]
FIG. 4. Primary sense cells from the epithelium of the earthworm *Lumbricus*. [From Hanström (50).]
FIG. 5. Bipolar sensory neurons from the skin of the slug *Arion ater*. [From Plate (92).]

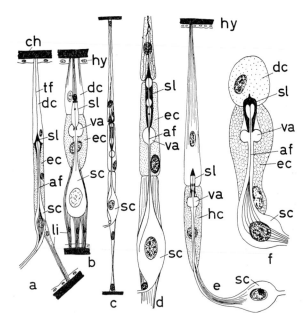

FIG. 6. Various types of scolopophorous sense cells (scolopidia) from the chordotonal organs of insects. *a* and *b*, amphinematic scolopidia; *c, d, e*, and *f*, mononematic scolopidia. *a*, simple chordotonal organ; *b*, scolopidium from the haltere of a muscid (fly); *c* and *d*, scolopidia from the tympanal organ of the cicada *Cicadetta coriaria*; *e*, scolopidium from the tympanal organ and *f*, from the subgenual organ of the grasshopper *Decticus*. af, axial fiber; ch, chitin cuticle; dc, cap cell; ec, enveloping cell; hy, hypodermis; li, ligament; sc, sense cell; sl, scolops (apical body of the sense cell); tf, terminal strand of the sense cell; and va, vacuole. [From Weber (137).]

Some single sense cells show a further anatomical differentiation. They have several short ramified fibers (dendrites) which lead to auxiliary cells. Examples of these are the stretch receptors at the joints in crustaceans (1, 5). As a rule, the stretch receptors send a fixed number of dendrites to a small bundle of muscle fibers (fig. 15).

The epithelial sense cells may be located in groups and thus form anything from primitive to highly specialized sense organs. If they are located in the epithelium, they may often carry fine hairs on their surface. Specific structures are often found in the sense cells; the most complicated of such intracellular structures are the apical bodies (scolopidia) in the chordotonal and tympanal organs (35) diagrammed in figure 6 and the rhabdomeres in the eyes of the insects (39, 47).

Some sense organs of invertebrates contain, side by side, sense cells which are morphologically differentiated in different degrees. An example is the sense cone on the last joint of the antennae of the Diplopoda; in this three different types of sense cells are located closely together (fig. 7).

The sense cells of an organ may be morphologically similar but differ in physiological respects; of three sense cells which are found in the chemosensory sensillae on the labellum of dipterans (flies), only two send peripheral fibers into the chemoreceptive part of the hair (fig. 11). These two cells react to are found in great numbers in all soft skinned invertebrates. Up to the present they have not been found in the turbellarians and echinoderms—probably for technical reasons. As a rule, these peripheral fibers form a plexus which can be located subepithelially in the connective tissue or subcuticularly above the epithelium. Such plexuses were first described in the classical works by Retzius (106) and von Apáthy (129). In arthropods such neurons with free terminals are limited to the soft skin of the joints and that between the segments (fig. 8). However, they are found also in the epithelium (hypodermis) of the mouth parts (fig. 9). The cells of these neurons are mostly located at some distance from the terminal ends of the dendrites. Sometimes, as in the above mentioned stretch receptors of the crustaceans, these dendrites are short.

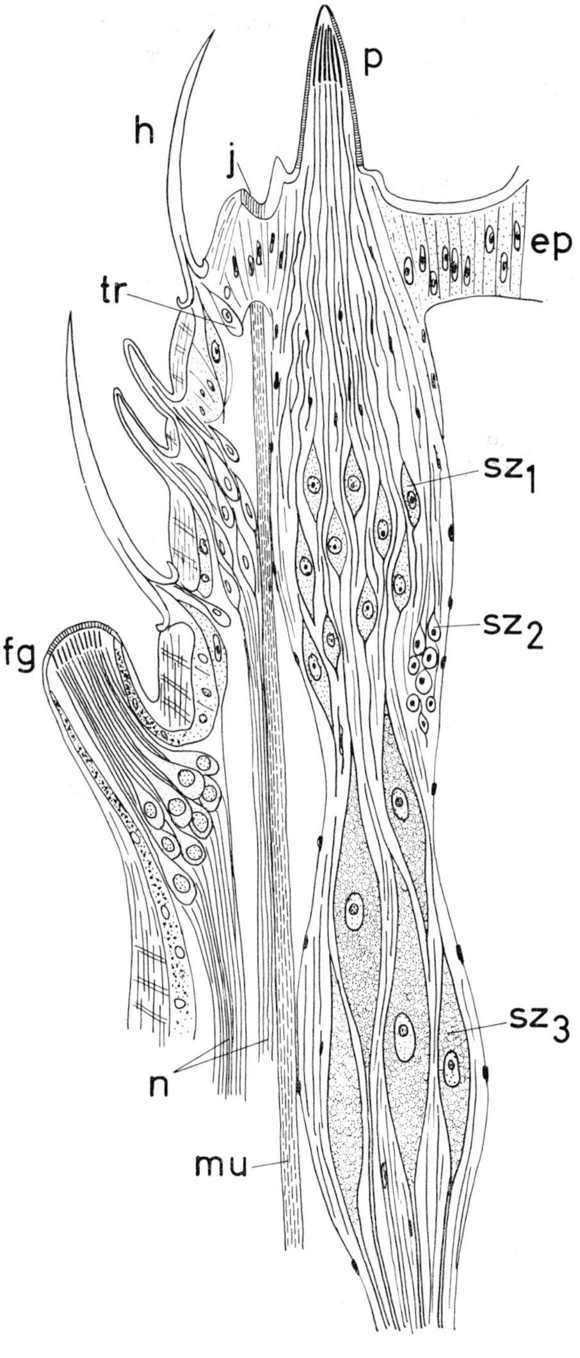

The simple type of receptors is common in invertebrates. On the other hand, some very complicated sense organs are found, for example the phonoreceptors and eyes of the insects, the eyes of the octopus, etc. Even in its highest form, however, the complexity never reaches that of the vertebrates.

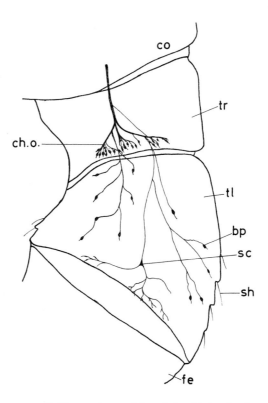

FIG. 7. Section of the last two segments of the antennae (7 and 8) of the diplopod *Polydesmus complanatus*. ep, epidermis; fg, finger-like organ (function unknown); h, sensory hair; j, skin joint; mu, muscle; n, nerve; p, peg-like sensilla; sc_1, sc_2, and sc_3, the three types of sense cells; tr, trichogen cell. [From Plate (92).]

different chemical substances; one neuron reacts only to sugar (with spikes of smaller voltage), the other one (with greater spikes) to salts, acids and alcohols (60).

Neurons with free nerve endings in the epithelium

FIG. 8. The trochanter joint of the third pair of extremities of an *Aeschna* larva. bp, bipolar sensory neuron; ch.o., chordotonal organ with bipolar sensory neurons; co, coxa; fe, femur; sc, sensory neuron with dendritic terminals at the joint; sh, sensory hairs; tl, trochantinus. [Redrawn after Zawarzin (144).]

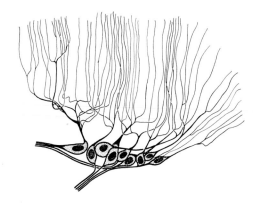

FIG. 9. Sensory neurons from the hypopharynx of the termite *Callotermes flavicollis*. The dendrites run between the cells of the hypodermis. [From Richard (107).]

The morphological differentiations in single organs are surprisingly versatile. [The special morphology and anatomy of the sense organs of the invertebrates may be found in the extensive monographs of Plate (92) and Hanström (50). They cannot be given here.] Physiological analysis has fallen far behind morphological description. The function of most structures and organs is not known and only in very few cases has been established by experimentation. The situation here is similar to that concerning the skin receptors of the vertebrates. The number of these is far larger than the number which has been analyzed or at present can be identified physiologically.

Comparison of the Senses of the Invertebrates with Those of Vertebrates

The functions of the receptors of the invertebrates are known in detail only in a few cases. There are, in addition to apparently very primitive organs, some which match or in some ways even surpass the effectiveness of those of the vertebrates. The absolute thresholds (from a physical point of view) are sufficiently well known only in a few instances to make possible comparison with the vertebrates. For the insects, accurate and comparable figures are available only for vibratory and auditory reception (10). The subgenual organs of the insects, shown in figure 16, which are most sensitive to vibration, e.g. in *Periplaneta* and *Tettigonia* (9), respond to amplitudes of vibration of the ground of 4×10^{-10} cm (with an optimal frequency of about 1400 cycles per sec.). The threshold for the perception of vibration in the human on the other hand is about 10^{-6} cm (67). The amplitude of movement of the membrane of the human tympanum at the threshold of hearing is of the same

order as the vibration threshold in the insects (143). The thresholds of the most sensitive sense organs of the invertebrates are as follows: the auditory receptors of the grasshopper, *Tettigonia*, 4×10^{-17} watt (11); the subgenualorgan of the cockroach, *Periplaneta*, 6×10^{-17} watt (11). For comparison, the auditory receptors of man require 8×10^{-18} to 4×10^{-17} watt (120). For the sense of smell one may also assume that the best threshold values of the insects match or surpass those of the vertebrates. The receptors of the invertebrates in some cases show potentialities which are not known in the vertebrates, such as perception of the direction of vibration of polarized light, sensitivity to ultraviolet and to the moisture content of the air (cf. p. 376) and perception of ultrasound.

The means by which comparable results are obtained are different in many cases. Vertebrates generally hear well in the range of 16 to 20,000 or 50,000 cycles per sec. Insects hear sound oscillations in the range to about 300 cycles per sec. by means of their hair sensillae (103, 104). The ears of the insects which are furnished with a membrane (tympanal organs) are actually too small to be stimulated by air vibration below a frequency of 1000 cycles per sec.; they are most sensitive in the ultrasonic range (beyond 10 to 20 kilocycles per sec.), according to Wever & Bray (139), Autrum (9) and Pumphrey (102). Tympanal organs cannot distinguish between pitches. However they are very sensitive to modulations of the amplitude of ultrasonic waves (53, 105) up to modulation frequencies of more than 300 per sec. (Autrum, H., unpublished observations); different frequencies of modulation can be distinguished. Amplitude modulation plays practically no part in the auditory reception of the vertebrates, but is however of decisive importance in the hearing and recognition of species-specific sounds of the insects with a tympanal organ.

Analogous differences of functional nature appear if the photoreception of the insects and vertebrates is compared (12, 14); the small spatial resolving power of the complex eye of the flying insects is compensated by a high temporal resolving power. The frequency of fusion of these eyes is as high as 250 to 300 flashes per sec.

Many proprioreceptors of the arthropods are basically different from the corresponding systems in vertebrates in both anatomical and physiological respects.

Reactions of Simple Receptors

The simple receptors of invertebrates serve as important models for the analysis of the function of single

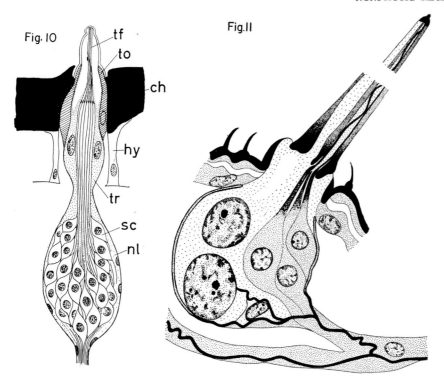

Fig. 10   tf
                          to
                          ch
                          hy
                          tr
                          sc
                          nl

Fig.11

FIG. 10. Sensilla basiconica from the antenna of a pupa of the wasp *Vespa vulgaris*. ch, chitin cuticle; hy, hypodermis; nl, neurilemma; sc, sense cells; tf, terminal strands; to, tormogen cell; tr, trichogen cell. [From Weber (137).]

FIG. 11. Diagram showing the histology of a labellar hair and associated cells in *Phormia*. The large trichogen and tormogen cells are at the left, and three neurons with silver stained processes at the right. The chemosensory area is confined to the silver-stained tip of the hair. The neuron in the middle of the group of three does not have any visible connection with the chemosensory area. [From Hodgson & Roeder (60).]

receptor cells. The lateral eyes of *Limulus* (51), the stretch receptor cells of crustaceans and the chemoreceptor sensillae of the flies are examples. It has been possible to analyze the functions of single receptor neurons in these simple organs.

Specific Types of Receptors

CHEMOCEPTORS. The chemoceptors of the invertebrates have been identified by physiological experiments in only a few cases: in Turbellaria, in which the auricular organs on the side of the head have been studied by Koehler (70) and by Müller (87); in *Limulus* by Waterman & Travis (136) and Barber (16); in crustacea by Hodgson (58); in insects by von Frisch (132), Wigglesworth (141), Frings & O'Neal (45), Frings & Frings (44), Hodgson (57), Grabowski & Dethier (48) and Hodgson & Roeder (60). [This field has been reviewed by Dethier (31), by Hodgson (58) and, particularly for molluscs, by Copland (28).] In

the turbellarians and molluscs these sense cells, which are located in the epithelium, carry fine hairs covered with mucus. Three types are found in the insects: sensillae placodeae, pore plates described by von Frisch (132); sensillae basiconicae, peg-like hair derivatives shown in figure 10; and sensillae trichodeae, hair sensillae drawn in figure 11. They are always supplied by more than one neuron. The covering cuticle is very thin (less than $1\ \mu$) and only partially sclerotized. The epicuticle has a low lipid content (108). The surface of the cuticle is always dry. These receptors are suited for quantitative experimental comparisons of different substances. [This topic has been reviewed by Dethier (31).] Therefore they are important for the general physiology of chemoreception.

In the vertebrates we distinguish between the sense of olfaction and the sense of gustation. An analogous distinction can be made in the insects but not in other groups. Hodgson (57) showed that the distinction between olfaction and gustation is unimportant at least on a cellular level, if it is based on the physical condition of the stimulus. A small group of morphologically identical receptors on the antennae and palpi of the beetle *Laccophilus* respond in the same way to chemical stimuli by substances whether they are dissolved in water or applied as gases.

Many authors assume that, besides the senses of olfaction and gustation, there is in insects a common chemical sense with separate receptors [cf. Dethier (30)]. The adequate stimuli for this common chemical sense are high concentrations of many substances which evoke defense reactions (e.g. ammonia, chlorine, essential oils).

There is no proof, and it is even improbable, that most animals can distinguish as many smells as can the human. Many, if not most, animals are probably specialized and able to respond only to one or a few smells in a very specific way. The females of *Bombyx mori* show no response in electrophysiological experiments to female sexual bait substances to which the males react with marked sensitivity. It may therefore be assumed that the receptors are highly specific with respect to this particular substance (113). On the other hand, the olfactory sense of the honey bee is strikingly similar to that of the human (131), even with respect to the ability to distinguish between stereoisomers (e.g. amyl acetate and methyl heptenone; *p*-cresol methylether and *m*-cresol methylether).

For the human sense of taste, four modalities are generally assumed: sweet, sour, salty and bitter. At present it is difficult to say whether the invertebrates have more or fewer of these modalities. The chemoceptors of *Limulus* are relatively insensitive to salty, sweet, sour and bitter solutions in electrophysiological experiments. However, they react violently to water extracts of marine clams (16). From about 30 substances which taste sweet to man, only a few are attractive for insects (for example saccharine is not effective). In this respect not only different insects, but also different organs of the same insect, react differently. Raffinose attracts almost all insects but not, however, the bees; the ant *Lasius niger* shows a positive reaction to sorbitol but the ant *Myrmica rubida* does not (130, 133). The water beetle *Hydrous* is able to distinguish between sugar, hydrochloric acid, sodium chloride and quinine in behavior experiments (17). Frings assumes that the distinction between the different modalities (salty, sour, sweet, bitter) generally is not dependent on the presence of different specific receptors for these substances in insects. Stimulation of the receptor cells with the lowest threshold is supposed to cause the sensation 'sweet' and the excitation of all receptors of one group

to cause the sensation 'sour'. The other modalities would be based on the evokation of receptor activity patterns which lie between these extremes.

Many terrestrial invertebrates respond to another modality, moisture; this topic has been reviewed by Dethier & Chadwick (33), by Roth & Willis (110) and by Dethier (30). The moisture receptors of the arthropods, as far as they can be identified, are indistinguishable from the other chemoceptors in morphological respects. According to experiments by Dethier (32) it is however very dubious whether clean water has a specific 'taste' for the contact receptors of the insects, since only two neurons are present in the hair sensillae of the fly *Phormia*. The hair can be adapted alternatively to water and to different concentrations of sugar; an alternative adaptation to sugar, sodium chloride or alcohol (which react upon the other neuron) is not possible. According to these findings there is only one receptor for sugar and water. A similar phenomenon was found in the vertebrates (145). It is not possible however to generalize and to apply these results to all hygroreceptors. It is quite possible that specific hygroreceptors exist, for instance in the human louse *Pediculus humanis corporis* (141).

The chemoceptors of insects are remarkably sensitive to temperature changes (43). The neuron which mediates sodium chloride detection in the fly *Phormia* reacts to a temperature increase of 0.1°C with a measurable increase of spike frequency according to Hodgson *et al.* (39).

Important progress has been made in recent years in the electrophysiological analysis of the chemoception of *Limulus* and insects (16, 19, 60, 112, 113, 122). Hodgson & Roeder (60) observed spikes of single neurons of chemical receptors in insects. Schneider (112, 113) found grouped spikes and slow potentials in the antennae of *Bombyx*.

The theories concerning the primary events in chemoceptor stimulation will not be discussed here but may be found in the relevant chapters of this work.

PROPRIOCEPTORS. Proprioceptors are defined by Lissmann (78) as sense organs capable of continuous registration of deformations (changes in length) and stresses (tensions and compressions) in the body. In the invertebrates they are known and have been experimentally tested only in the arthropods. The following types can be distinguished morphologically.

On the surface of the body are located: *a*) the peripheral endings of multipolar neurons without

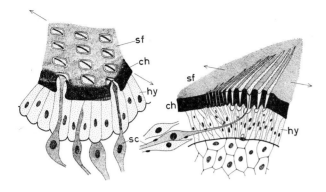

FIG. 12. Schematic drawings of the structure of an insect campaniform sensilla (left) and an arachnid lyriform organ, a slit sensilla (right). The arrows show the probable direction of the stimulus exciting the sensilla. These diagrams are based on drawings of the base plate sensilla on the haltere of *Calliphora* (Pflugstaedt, 1912) and of the lyriform organ on the patella of a spider. ch, chitin cuticle; hy, hypodermis; sc, sense cells; sf, surface (Vogel, 1923). [From Pringle (97).]

particular differentiation of the cuticle, the peripheral branches of which terminate between the cells of the hypodermis, e.g. in the skin over the joints in the appendages of *Limulus* (16, 98), or in the crustaceans (126); *b*) campaniform sense organs of the insects (fig. 12) and slit sense organs of the Arachnoideae (fig. 12) in which bipolar sense cells send their peripheral fibers to special differentiated structures of the cuticle at the membrane of the joints (66, 95, 97, 128); *c*) hair sensillae (sensillae trichodeae), which consist of single or larger groups of hairs, at the basis of which enter the peripheral ends of bipolar sense cells (fig. 13)—because of their location they are more or less affected by the relative positions of adjacent

segments of the appendages (95) or of the body, e.g. of the head according to Mittelstaedt (86), as shown in figure 14.

In the interior of the body are located: *a*) muscle receptors in insects, as shown by Finlayson & Lowenstein (40) and Slifer & Finlayson (121); *b*) organs suspended between two movable segments found in *Limulus* (16, 98) and Crustacea (especially the stretch receptor organs shown in fig. 15) (1, 2, 3, 4, 22, 23, 37, 38, 42, 74, 75, 140). To this latter group also belong with high probability many chordotonal organs which are found in the body of insects (fig. 18). This topic has been reviewed by Eggers (35) and by Snodgrass (123).

Proprioceptors in the wings of insects (124) and in the abdominal part of *Dytiscus* (62) have been found by physiological experiments; they are however not yet identified anatomically. In earthworms Gray *et al.* (49) found sensory discharges upon passive stretching and Prosser (100), during active movement.

The adequate stimulus for the multipolar sense cells on the skin of the joints of *Limulus*, for the campaniform organs of the insects and for the slit sense organ of the arachnoids is tension or compression of the cuticle covering the organ. The receptors in the muscles of the insects and the stretch receptors of *Limulus* and of the crustaceans respond to increase or decrease of the tension. All these organs are—with the exception of one of the two neurons in the stretch receptors of the crayfish—tonic receptors with slow and incomplete adaptation. The same holds true for the hair sensillae on the joints of the insects. Phasic receptors in close proximity to the tonic neurons are often found. They respond to an adequate stimulus

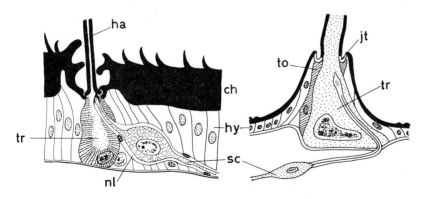

FIG. 13. Schematic diagrams of hair sensillae, that on the left from the cercus of the cricket *Liogryllus campestris* with an intraepithelial sense cell, and that on the right from the caterpillar *Pieris* with a subepidermal sense cell. ch, chitin cuticle; ha, chitinous hair; hy, hypodermis; nl, neurilemma; sc, sense cell; to, tormogen cell (secreting the chitinous joint membrane). [From Weber (137).]

FIG. 14. Diagram showing the method of excitation of the inner coxal hair plate by a fold of the intersegmental membrane of the second leg of the cockroach *Periplaneta*. cx, coxa; hp, hairplate; pl, pleuron. [From Pringle (95).]

with a short series of impulses and rapidly adapt; these are in *Limulus* the big cells located in the depth, and in arachnoids organs which are not exactly identified anatomically but are located close to the slit organs. The stretch receptors of some crustaceans are composed of two sense organs lying close to each other; one reacts tonically and the other one phasically. Each of these sense organs consists of a single neuron which is located on a bundle of muscle fibers

in *Homarus* and *Cambarus*. In other crabs, such as *Carcinus*, many cells are combined in this organ. Some of these cells react tonically, others phasically. The tonic neurons show a resting discharge. The maximum of this resting discharge of single neurons in *Limulus* is present either at maximal extension or at maximal flection of the joint. The minimum of the resting discharge of the whole organ corresponds therefore approximately to a mean position of the membrane of the joint.

The stretch receptor organs between the abdominal segments of certain crustaceans, including *Homarus* and *Astacus*, have been studied carefully. They are of interest also from the standpoint of general physiology since the activity of single sensory neurons could be analyzed in them. The organs consist of two fine bundles of muscles, RM_1 and RM_2; a sensory neuron, SN_1 and SN_2, is attached to each of these. This neuron sends many dendrites to the muscle fibers. An afferent axon is emitted from each neuron (fig. 15). The efferent innervation consists of: *a*) motor fibers, innervat-

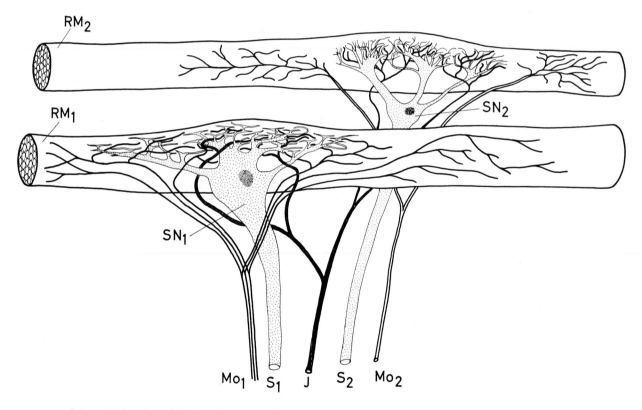

FIG. 15. Schematic drawing of the stretch receptors between the segments of the tail of the crab *Astacus fluviatilis*. RM_1, muscle bundle of the tonic receptors; RM_2, muscle bundle of the phasic receptors. SN_1 and SN_2, sensory neurons of the tonic and phasic receptors respectively; S_1 and S_2 their afferent axons; MO_1, three thin motor fibers of the tonic receptors; MO_2, thick motor nerve fiber of the phasic receptors; and I, an inhibitory axon. (By courtesy of D. Burkhardt.)

ing each bundle of muscles separately; *b*) a thick accessory fiber which is ramified into two branches in the vicinity of SN_2 (fig. 15), one branch innervating the area of the dendritic terminals of SN_2, the other branch innervating the dendritic terminals of SN_1; *c*) an additional thin accessory fiber innervating the terminals of SN_1 and SN_2 in *Homarus* (this is absent in *Astacus*); and *d*) a number of thinner fibers, the origin and terminals of which are not known exactly but mainly innervating RM_1.

The details may differ in the different species of the crustaceans and may be found in the discussions by Alexandrowicz (1, 2, 5) and Florey & Florey (42).

The adequate stimulus for these receptors is stretching of the muscle bundles. One of the two receptor cells of this organ (SN_2, the slow cell) has tonic qualities. The other one (SN_1, the fast cell) has phasic qualities. The same is valid for the corresponding muscle bundles on efferent stimulation, RM_1 yielding a fast twitch, RM_2, a slow response (74). The tonic receptor cell has a very low threshold to the adequate stimulus (stretch) and yields uninterrupted discharges with a low adaptation rate. The phasic cell has a high threshold and adapts very rapidly and completely. Excitation of the efferent nerve fibers leads to a contraction of the muscle bundles and in this way causes afferent responses of the sensory neurons (74, 140). The normal excitation originates in the dendrites. These become depolarized by stretch deformation producing a generator potential (37, 38). The generator potentials in the dendrites spread electrotonically and reduce the resting potential of the cell soma. Reduction of the resting potential (70 to 80 mv with relaxed receptor) by 8 to 12 mv in the slow cell and by 17 to 22 mv in the fast cell causes propagated impulses. The neuron therefore works according to the following scheme: stretch deformation of dendrite terminals→generator potential→electronic spread towards the cell soma (prepotential)→dendrite-soma impulse→axon impulse (37, 38).

Excitation of the inhibitory fiber (fig. 15) acts upon the generator mechanism in the dendrites and stops the discharge of the sensory neuron within a few milliseconds, even upon application of a strong stimulus (large stretch). This effect is caused by the following sequence of events. The impulses in the inhibitory fiber cause a postsynaptic effect in the dendrites of the sensory neuron. This drives the potential of the receptor cell towards an equilibrium level. The inhibitory effect can therefore be a postsynaptic depolarization or a hyperpolarization depending upon the existing state of the receptor cell. Through the stretch stimulus or its absence this may be pushed to either side of the equilibrium potential (37, 38).

The stretch receptors in the abdominal segments of the crayfish are physiologically similar to the muscle spindles of the vertebrates. Nevertheless all described proprioceptors are considerably different from the analogous organs of the vertebrates; they indicate not the functional condition of a single muscle, but of a whole body segment. These proprioceptors signalize the relative position of the parts of an appendage, e.g. the hair sensillae or the multipolar cells of *Limulus*, or they indicate the relative position of different segments of the body, e.g. the stretch receptors of the crayfish or the muscle receptors of insects. The campaniform and lyriform organs and the slit sense organs are located in such a way that they can register the forces which arise in the chitinous shell of the legs upon contact of the extremity with the ground. These organs therefore control the behavior and position of the animals (78, 93, 94, 95, 98).

Many of these organs are not designed to react to a single specific mode of stimuli. The proprioceptors of *Carcinus* respond both to the movement of the extremity and to vibration (22). The proprioceptors of *Dytiscus* (which are not localized anatomically) yield spikes during inspiration, expiration and to airborne sounds of about 100 cycles per sec. (62). The stretch receptors of *Cambarus* respond strongly to temperature changes with a frequency change of the discharges (41).

THERMORECEPTORS. Lower animals may lack temperature sensitivity completely. The sea anemone *Calliactis* is very sensitive to mechanical and chemical stimuli; however, a glass tube which touches the body wall can be heated so much that it causes burning of the ectoderm without producing any reaction (91). On the other hand most animals react to temperature. As a rule the parasites of warm blooded animals are especially sensitive, being attracted by warm objects. This has been shown for the leech and some insects, e.g. *Rhodnius* by Wigglesworth & Gillet (142) and *Cimex* by Sioli (119).

The temperature receptors of invertebrates have never been anatomically localized with precision. It is assumed to be highly probable that the pointed hairs on the antennae of insects are thermoreceptors. This is the case in at least some species, including *Rhodnius* (142) and *Pyrrhocoris* (46). At the base of these hair sensillae lie six sensory neurons.

The mechano- and chemoreceptors of the invertebrates very often respond to temperature by changes in the impulse frequencies in the afferent nerves (27, 41, 43, 59). The Q_{10} in the statocysts of the lobster is 4.5 for the nonadapting resting activity of the large spikes, according to Cohen *et al.* (27). This temperature sensitivity is therefore lower than that of the temperature receptors in the tongue of mammals, studied by Hensel & Zotterman (55), and of the ampullae of Lorenzi in rays, investigated by Hensel (54). On the other hand Bullock found marked mechanical irritability of the thermoreceptors on the head of the rattlesnake (21). The frequency of the afferent signals from many receptors of cold blooded animals depends not only on the adequate stimulus but also on the temperature. This temperature sensitivity of the sense organs of invertebrates raises a physiological problem which has hardly been investigated [cf. Bullock (20)].

A summary of the literature on the reactions of lower animals toward temperature is given by von Buddenbrock (130).

MECHANORECEPTORS: TACTILE SENSE. The receptors for this modality are well known only in a few cases. Sense cells of soft skinned invertebrates which are located in the epidermis and carry one or more long, hair-like spines are termed hypothetical tactile receptors. However, no full proof has been given in any case [cf. Müller (87)]. Passano & Pantin (91) adopt the view that a basal network of the sensory cells or the nerve net or the circular and parietal muscle sheets can be considered as receptors despite the fact that many primary sensory neurons occur in the ectoderm of the actinians. The tactile receptors of the insects are definitely known to involve long, movable hairs with joints in the chitinous skeleton at the base of which one or many peripheral fibers of bipolar sensory neurons end (fig. 13). They adapt rapidly if their resting position is changed. The adaptation is slow in certain spine-like hairs located on the legs of insects. The initial frequency of the impulses in the sensory axon depends on the velocity of displacement, according to Pumphrey (101). The transducer function of this sensory element was analyzed by Pringle & Wilson (99). They were able to show that the maximum of response (recorded by the frequency of impulses) precedes in phase the maximum tension of the stimulus upon application of harmonic, sinusoidally varying mechanical stimuli. This is a corollary of the adaptation shown by the sensory response to a transient stimulus.

MECHANORECEPTORS: VIBRATION SENSE. Specific, highly sensitive vibration receptors were found in the extremities of insects by Autrum (8, 11), by Autrum & Schneider (15) and by Schneider (115). These are groups of sensory cells which are spread in a sail-like fashion in the body fluid of the legs (fig. 16). They are furnished with peculiarly differentiated bodies, such as apical bodies, or scolopidia, as shown in fig. 6. Adequate stimuli are provided by vibrations of the ground. The subgenual organs respond preferentially to vibrations between 200 and 6000 cycles per sec., with maximum sensitivity between 1000 and 2000 cycles per sec. (fig. 17). The amplitude at threshold is about 4×10^{-10} cm at 1500 cycles per sec. for *Periplaneta*; consequently they are smaller than atomic dimensions.[2] The adequate physical stimulus is acceleration. These organs cannot distinguish between different frequencies. The high optimal frequency of the vibration receptors of many insects given in figure 17 can be understood if their small size is considered. Such high frequencies do not occur under natural conditions. It is therefore not necessary to distinguish the frequencies. Pulses and pulse-like vibrations of the ground are important for reactions of insects in the natural environment. These pulses possess high frequency components and during the initial tran-

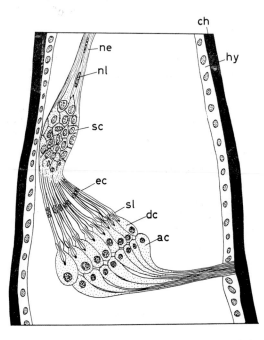

FIG. 16. Scheme of the subgenual organ in the leg of the ant *Formica*. ac, accessory cells; ch, chitin cuticle; dc, cap cells; ec, enveloping cell; hy, hypodermis; ne, nerve; nl, nucleus of a neurilemma cell; sc, sense cells. [From Weber (137).]

[2] The amplitudes of movement of the human tympanum are of the same order of magnitude at the threshold of hearing.

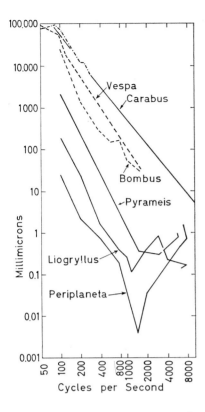

FIG. 17. Vibration thresholds at different frequencies for a few characteristic species of different sensitivity. [From Autrum & Schneider (15).]

sients stimulate the subgenual organs at their resonance frequency. The suddenness of the movement of the ground is therefore important for successful stimulation. This holds true also for the perception of vibrations in spiders, according to Liesenfeld (77); the vibratory stimuli which are emitted from the threads of the net require a sudden onset at full intensity, since spiders do not react to slowly increasing amplitudes. The type of the transients is the decisive stimulus. The same is true for the tympanal organ of the insects.

MECHANORECEPTORS: HEARING. Specific sense organs for which air sound waves are the adequate stimuli are known in arthropods. These are the hair sensillae, the antennae or the tympanal organs which contain a membrane, the tympanum.

The hair sensillae serve as receptors for air vibration of low frequency in spiders and many insects. The reactions of caterpillars (85), and the hairs on the anal cerci of the crickets and cockroaches, including *Periplaneta*, (104) have been carefully analyzed. The afferent nerve fibers of the hair sensillae respond to

low frequencies up to about 400 cycles per sec. in synchrony with the frequency of the stimulus and in some cases also at double the frequency. At higher frequencies, halving or quartering of the frequencies may appear.

The antennae of *Aedes aegypti* (109), *Anopheles* (125) and flies (24) carry many hairs which are not innervated. They are moved by air vibration and transfer this motion to the antennae and to the Johnston's sense organ. This is located between the second and third segment of the antennae and consists of many sense cells.

The adequate stimulus for the hair sensillae is the amplitude of displacement of the air particles not the sound pressure, according to Autrum (7, 10) and Pumphrey (102). They are thus displacement receptors.

The tympanal organs are sense organs with a tympanic membrane. Their primary neurons have scolopidia (cf. figs. 6 and 18). The structure of these organs has been reviewed by Eggers (35), and their physiology by Pumphrey (102), Autrum (8, 9, 13) and Schaller & Timm (111), as well as in the book edited by Busnel (25). The maximal sensitivity is in

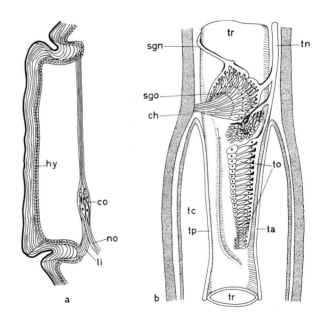

FIG. 18. *a*, chordotonal organ between abdominal segments of the larva of *Monohammus confusor* (after Hess). [From Weber (137).] *b*, auditory organ in the foreleg of the grasshopper *Decticus* (after Schwabe). ch, chitin cuticle; co, sense cells of chordotonal organ; hy, hypodermis; li, ligament; nv, nerve; sgn, nerve of subgenual organ; ta, anterior tympanum; tc, tympanic cavity; tp, posterior tympanum; tr, trachea. [From Autrum (10).]

the supersonic region, above 20,000 cycles per sec., as shown by Wever & Bray (139), Pumphrey (102), Autrum (8, 9, 10), and Schaller & Timm (111). The upper limit of hearing in some species is at 175 kilocycles per sec. Electrophysiological analysis has shown that the tympanal organs cannot distinguish the frequency of the sound. They consequently are not able to analyze sounds but react very sensitively to modulations of amplitude (53, 105). In the natural environment the stimulus is a sound of high frequency which is amplitude-modulated. Such a sound is important for their behavior. For example, the songs of crickets consist of sound with certain rhythms of modulation. The impulses in the tympanal nerve do not follow the frequency of the sound since these frequencies are too high but follow the modulation frequency to about 300 per sec., as shown in *Tettigonia* by Autrum (unpublished observations). The ultrasound therefore serves as a carrier frequency.

Acoustically these tympanal organs are displacement receptors as are the hair sensillae (8, 10, 102). The sensitivity of all acoustic displacement receptors depends on the direction from which the sound comes. The tympanal organs have for this reason, therefore, an 8-shaped polar diagram, which is important for the localization of the source of the sound (10, 13). In the same way sound reception by means of hairs is dependent on the direction (125).

STATOCYSTS. The statocyst of the invertebrates consists of a little ectodermal bag invaginated into the interior of the body. It is filled with fluid, has hairs in certain parts and contains one or more statoliths which are little stones or concretions of greater specific gravity than the fluid. According to the general scheme of function the statocysts are analogous to the otolith-containing organs of the vertebrates. Considerable differences are found in the anatomical details. Thus, the sensory neurons in the invertebrates are primary sense cells with an afferent axon and there are additionally nonliving cuticular hairs but no equivalent of the hair cells; in the vertebrates, by contrast, the hair cells are secondary sense cells and lack an axon.

The variety of the details is also very great in the invertebrates [cf. Hanström (50) and Plate (92)]. Statocysts are the first sense organs to appear in the phylogeny of the animal kingdom, being present in the coelenterates.

The adequate stimuli are gravity (static stimuli), acceleration (dynamic stimuli), or both. Compensatory reactions of the whole body, tonic reactions to certain muscles, or both, are directed from the stato-

cysts. The statoliths are important for static reactions (73).

The statocysts of crustaceans have been most carefully analyzed both by physiological behavior experiments by Schöne (117) and Dijkgraaf (34), and by electrophysiological studies by Cohen et al. (27) and Cohen (26). The adequate stimulus for the nerve ending is a bending of the cuticular hair, not pressure or pull of the statolith upon the hairs. Bending of the hairs medially causes a reflex rotational movement about the long axis in the same direction; bending towards the outside causes a rotation of the animal in the opposite direction. The sensory epithelium gives rise to a tonic impulse train which is independent of stimulation of the statolith. The stimulus bending the sense hairs produces either its own impulse or may modify the tonic impulses. Between the intensity of the stimulus (the bending) and the reaction (measured in the tonic reactions of the eye stalk) there exists a linear relationship. If the statoliths are removed on one side, the zero position will move to this side since the area of the statocyst which is adjacent to the sense hairs is inclined outward and therefore the statoliths in their normal position bend the hairs outward. Compensatory processes counteract these changes of the zero position. The position receptors are hook-shaped hairs in *Carcinus* and *Maja*, while the receptors for angular displacements are very thin thread-like hairs, 300 μ long (34). The statocysts of *Astacus* do not work antagonistically to each other, but in the same lateral position each produces the same tendency towards rotation. The impulses from both sides are simply added up in the central nervous system.

The results of Schöne (117) and Dijkgraaf (34) are in accordance with the electrophysiological findings of Cohen et al. (27) and Cohen (26) in that the statocysts react to rotatory acceleration around the axes [cf. Dijkgraaf (34)], to linear acceleration and to static position. A tonic discharge exists which remains even after removal of the statoliths. There exist rapidly adapting phasic elements and also tonic elements. The excitation of the latter depends upon the position and they adapt only slightly. Cohen found four types of afferent fibers, each reacting differently. The type I position receptor shows a nonadaptive impulse frequency which depends (within a certain angle to the normal position) upon the angle between the transverse axis and the normal position. The position receptor of type II may well be not a single receptor but may result from the coordination of several receptors. It *a)* maintains a characteristic nonadapting impulse frequency for each constant deviation from the horizontal axis and, in addition, *b)* yields adapting impulses during movements, which increase in frequency if the movement is carried out towards the position of the maximal static stimulation and decrease abruptly during movement away from this position. A third system of receptors responds to angular acceleration around every axis of the body. It shows a tonic discharge which is independent of the position when position is constant. This tonic discharge remains even after removal of the statolith. The response consists of a burst at the onset of rostrum-down, side-down, or contralateral horizontal rotation, followed by a depression at the termination of these movements. The opposite movements result in a reversed response sequence. The adaptation of the permanent discharge to the resting value is completed in less than 1 sec. This shows a striking similarity between the basic principles of the mode of function of the crustacean statocyst and the static apparatus of the verte-

brates studied by Lowenstein (79) and von Holst (134); in both cases the sine law is obeyed; the adequate stimulus is bending of the hairs; stimulus and reaction have a linear relationship; and the sensory epithelium emits a tonic impulse stream which is modified by the bending of the hairs. A loss of the tonic impulses on one side is compensated. This ability is important as the statocysts have to be supplied with statoliths from the outside after each molt, at least in some species. In this procedure it is not always possible to obtain statoliths of the same weight.

Orientation to gravity occurs in many cases without the help of statocysts, as is the case in insects according to Mittelstaedt (86), Pringle (96) and Schneider (114), but the eyes often play an important role in this adjustment (116).

Professor Autrum's chapter was translated from the German by Dr. and Mrs. Otto Scherbaum, Department of Zoology, University of California at Los Angeles.—Ed.

REFERENCES

1. ALEXANDROWICZ, J. S. *Quart. J. Microsc. Sc.* 92: 163, 1951.
2. ALEXANDROWICZ, J. S. *Quart. J. Microsc. Sc.* 93: 315, 1952.
3. ALEXANDROWICZ, J. S. *J. mar. biol. A. U. K.* 31: 277, 1952.
4. ALEXANDROWICZ, J. S. *Pubbl. staz. zool. Napoli* 25: 94, 1953.
5. ALEXANDROWICZ, J. S. *J. mar. biol. A. U. K.* 35: 129, 1956.
6. ALVERDES, F. *Neue Bahnen in der Lehre vom Verhalten der niederen Organismen.* Berlin: Springer, 1922.
7. AUTRUM, H. *Ztschr. vergleich. Physiol.* 23: 332, 1936.
8. AUTRUM, H. *Ztschr. vergleich. Physiol.* 28: 326, 1940.
9. AUTRUM, H. *Ztschr. vergleich. Physiol.* 28: 580, 1941.
10. AUTRUM, H. *Naturwissenschaften* 30: 69, 1942.
11. AUTRUM, H. *Biol. Zentralbl.* 63: 209, 1943.
12. AUTRUM, H. *Naturwissenschaften* 39: 290, 1952.
13. AUTRUM, H. *Ann. Inst. Nat. Rech. Agron. Ser. C. Ann. Epiphyt.* 6: 338, 1955.
14. AUTRUM, H. *Exper. Cell. Res.* In press.
15. AUTRUM, H. AND W. SCHNEIDER. *Ztschr. vergleich. Physiol.* 31: 77, 1948.
16. BARBER, S. *J. Exper. Zool.* 131: 51, 1956.
17. BAUER, L *Ztschr. vergleich. Physiol.* 26: 107, 1938.
18. BLÄTTNER, H. *Arch. Protistenk.* 53: 253, 1926.
19. BOISTEL, J. AND E. CORABOEUF. *Compt. rend. Soc. de biol.* 147: 1172, 1953.
20. BULLOCK, T. H. *Biol. Rev.* 30: 311, 1955.
21. BULLOCK, T. H. AND R. B. COWLES. *Science* 115: 541, 1952.
22. BURKE, W. *J. Exper. Biol.* 31: 127, 1954.
23. BURKHARDT, D. *Ergebn. Biol.* 20: 27, 1958.
24. BURKHARDT, D. AND G. SCHNEIDER, *Ztschr. Naturforsch.* 12b: 139, 1957.
25. BUSNEL, R. G. (editor). *Ann. Inst. Nat. Rech. Agron. Ser. C. Ann. Epiphyt.*, vol. 6, 1955.
26. COHEN, M. J. *J. Physiol.* 130: 9, 1955.
27. COHEN, M. J., Y. KATSUKI AND T. H. BULLOCK. *Experientia* 9: 434, 1953.
28. COPLAND, M. *J. Exper. Zool.* 25: 177, 1918.
29. DANISCH, F. *Ztschr. allg. Physiol.* 19: 133, 1921.
30. DETHIER, V. G. In: *Insect Physiology,* edited by K. D. Roeder. New York: Wiley, 1953, p. 544.
31. DETHIER, V. G. *Ann. New York Acad. Sc.* 58: 139, 1954.
32. DETHIER, V. G. *Quart. Rev. Biol.* 30: 348, 1955.
33. DETHIER, V. G. AND L. E. CHADWICK. *Physiol. Rev.* 28: 220, 1948.
34. DIJKGRAAF, S. *Experientia* 11: 407, 1955.
35. EGGERS, F. *Die stiftführenden Sinnesorgane.* Zool. Bausteine, Bd.2. Berlin: Borntraeger, 1928.
36. EWER, R. F. *Proc. Zool. Soc.* 117: 365, 1947.
37. EYZAGUIRRE, C. AND S. KUFFLER. *J. Gen. Physiol.* 39: 87, 1955.
38. EYZAGUIRRE, C. AND S. KUFFLER. *J. Gen. Physiol.* 39: 121, 1955.
39. FERNÁNDEZ-MORAN, H. *Nature, London* 177: 742, 1956.
40. FINLAYSON, L. H. AND O. LOWENSTEIN. *Nature, London* 176: 1031, 1955.
41. FLOREY, E. *Ztschr. Naturforsch.* 11b: 504, 1956.
42. FLOREY, E. AND E. FLOREY. *J. Gen. Physiol.* 39: 69, 1955.
43. FRINGS, H. AND B. L. COX. *Biol. Bull.* 107: 360, 1954.
44. FRINGS, H. AND M. FRINGS. *Am. Midland Natural.* 41: 602, 1949.
45. FRINGS, H. AND B. R. O'NEAL. *J. Exper. Zool.* 103: 61, 1946.
46. GERHARDT, H. *Zool. Jahrb., Abt. allg. Zool. Physiol.* 63: 558, 1953.
47. GOLDSMITH, T. H. AND D. E. PHILPOTT. *J. Biophys. & Biochem. Cytol.* 3: 429, 1957.
48. GRABOWSKI, C. T. AND V. G. DETHIER. *J. Morphol.* 94: 1, 1954.

49. GRAY, J., H. W. LISSMANN AND R. J. PUMPHREY. *J. Exper. Biol.* 15: 408, 1938.

50. HANSTRÖM, B. *Vergleichende Anatomie des Nervensystems der Wirbellosen Tiere.* Heidelberg: Springer, 1928.

51. HARTLINE, H. K., H. G. WAGNER AND E. F. MacNICHOL, JR. *Cold Spring Harbor Symp. Quant. Biol.* 17: 125, 1952.

52. HARTSHORNE, J. N. *New Phytologist* 52: 292, 1953.

53. HASKELL, P. T. *J. Exper. Biol.* 33: 756, 1956.

54. HENSEL, H. *Ztschr. vergleich. Physiol.* 37: 509, 1955.

55. HENSEL, H. AND Y. ZOTTERMAN. *Acta physiol. scandinav.* 23: 291, 1951.

56. HERTWIG, O. AND R. HERTWIG. *Jena. Ztschr. Naturw.* 13: 474, 1879.

57. HODGSON, E. S. *Biol. Bull.* 105: 115, 1953.

58. HODGSON, E. S. *Quart. Rev. Biol.* 30: 331, 1955.

59. HODGSON, E. S., J. Y. LETTVIN AND K. D. ROEDER. *Science* 122: 417, 1955.

60. HODGSON, E. S. AND K. D. ROEDER. *J. Cell & Comp. Physiol.* 48: 51, 1956.

61. HORTON, F. *J. Exper. Biol.* 12: 13, 1935.

62. HUGHES, G. M. *Nature, London* 170: 531, 1952.

63. HYMAN, L. H. *The Invertebrates. I. Protozoa through Ctenophora.* London: McGraw-Hill, 1940, p. 382.

64. JENNINGS, H. S. *Am. Natural.* 33: 373, 1899.

65. JENNINGS, H. S. *Behavior of Lower Organisms.* New York: Columbia Univ., 1906.

66. KASTON, B. J. *J. Morphol.* 58: 189, 1935.

67. KEIDEL, W.-D. *Vibrationsreception. Erlanger Forschungen Reihe B: Naturwissenschaften.* Erlangen: Universitätsbund e.V. 1956, p. 1.

68. KOEHLER, O. *Arch. Protistenk.* 45: 1, 1922.

69. KOEHLER, O. *Arch. Protistenk.* 70: 279, 1930.

70. KOEHLER, O. *Ztschr. vergleich. Physiol.* 16: 606, 1932.

71. KOEHLER, O. *Verhandl. deutsch. Zool. Gesellsch.* 36 (*Zool. Anz. Suppl. 7*): 74, 1934.

72. KOEHLER, O. *Verhandl. deutsch. Zool. Gesellsch.* 41: 132, 1939.

73. KREIDL, A. *Sitzber. Akad. Wiss. Wien, Math.-naturw. Kl.* 102: 149, 1893.

74. KUFFLER, S. W. *J. Neurophysiol.* 17: 558, 1954.

75. KUFFLER, S. W. AND C. EYZAGUIRRE. *J. Gen. Physiol.* 39: 155, 1955.

76. KÜHN, A. AND P. SCHULZE. In: Kükenthal *Leitfaden für das Zoologische Praktikum* (11th ed.), edited by E. Matthes. Stuttgart: Fischer, 1944.

77. LIESENFELD, F. J. *Ztschr. vergleich. Physiol.* 38: 563, 1956.

78. LISSMANN, H. W. *Symp. Soc. Exper. Biol.* 4: 34, 1950.

79. LOWENSTEIN, O. *Symp. Soc. Exper. Biol.* 4: 60, 1950.

80. MAST, S. O. *J. Exper. Zool.* 9: 265, 1910.

81. MAST, S. O. *J. Exper. Zool.* 22: 471, 1917.

82. MAST, S. O. *Biol. Bull.* 46: 55, 1924.

83. MAST, S. O. *Physiol. Zool.* 5: 1, 1932.

84. MAST, S. O. *Biol. Rev.* 13: 186, 1938.

85. MINNICH, D. E. *J. Exper. Zool.* 72: 439, 1936.

86. MITTELSTAEDT, H. *Ztschr. vergleich. Physiol.* 32: 422, 1950.

87. MÜLLER, H. G. *Ztschr. vergleich. Physiol.* 23: 253, 1936.

88. PANTIN, C. F. A. *J. Exper. Biol.* 19: 294, 1942.

89. PÁRDUCZ, B. *Acta microbiol. Acad. Sc. Hungaricae* 1: 175, 1954.

90. PARKER, G. H. AND M. A. VAN ALSTYNE. *J. Exper. Zool.* 63: 329, 1932.

91. PASSANO, L. M. AND C. F. A. PANTIN. *Proc. Roy. Soc., London, ser. B* 143: 226, 1955.

92. PLATE, L. *Die Sinnesorgane der Tiere. II. Allgemeine Zoologie und Abstammungslehre.* Jena: Fischer, 1924.

93. PRINGLE, J. W. S. *J. Exper. Biol.* 15: 101, 1938.

94. PRINGLE, J. W. S. *J. Exper. Biol.* 15: 114, 1938.

95. PRINGLE, J. W. S. *J. Exper. Biol.* 15: 467, 1938.

96. PRINGLE, J. W. S. *Phil. Trans.* 233: 347, 1948.

97. PRINGLE, J. W. S. *J. Exper. Biol.* 32: 270, 1955.

98. PRINGLE, J. W. S. *J. Exper. Biol.* 33: 658, 1956.

99. PRINGLE, J. W. S. AND V. J. WILSON. *J. Exper. Biol.* 29: 220, 1952.

100. PROSSER, C. L. *J. Exper. Biol.* 12: 95, 1935.

101. PUMPHREY, R. J. *J. Physiol.* 87: 6P, 1936.

102. PUMPHREY, R. J. *Biol. Rev.* 15: 107, 1940.

103. PUMPHREY, R. J. AND A. F. RAWDON-SMITH. *Nature, London* 137: 990, 1936.

104. PUMPHREY, R. J. AND A. F. RAWDON-SMITH. *Proc. Roy. Soc., London, ser. B* 121: 18, 1936.

105. PUMPHREY, R. J. AND A. F. RAWDON-SMITH. *Nature, London* 143: 806, 1939.

106. RETZIUS, G. *Biologische Untersuchungen* N. F. 4. Berlin: Friedländer, 1892, p. 1.

107. RICHARD, G. *Ann. Sc. Nat. Zool.* 13: 397, 1951.

108. RICHARDS, A. G. *Biol. Bull.* 103: 201, 1952.

109. ROTH, L. M. *Am. Midland Natural.* 40: 265, 1948.

110. ROTH, L. M. AND E. R. WILLIS. *J. Exper. Zool.* 116: 527, 1951.

111. SCHALLER, F. AND C. TIMM. *Ztschr. vergleich. Physiol.* 32: 468, 1950.

112. SCHNEIDER, D. *Ztschr. Naturforsch.* 11b: 121, 1956.

113. SCHNEIDER, D. *Ztschr. vergleich. Physiol.* 40: 8, 1957.

114. SCHNEIDER, G. *Ztschr. vergleich. Physiol.* 35: 416, 1953.

115. SCHNEIDER, W. *Ztschr. vergleich. Physiol.* 32: 287, 1950.

116. SCHÖNE, H. *Ztschr. vergleich. Physiol.* 33: 63, 1951.

117. SCHÖNE, H. *Ztschr. vergleich. Physiol.* 36: 241, 1954.

118. SCHULZE, P. *Arch. Zellforsch.* 16: 383, 1922.

119. SIOLI, H. *Zool. Jahrb., Abt. allg. Zool. Physiol.* 58: 284, 1937.

120. SIVIAN, L. J. AND S. D. WHITE. *J. Acoust. Soc. Am.* 4: 288, 1933.

121. SLIFER, E. H. AND L. H. FINLAYSON. *Quart. J. Microsc. Sc.* 97: 617, 1956.

122. SMYTH, T., JR. AND C. C. ROYS. *Biol. Bull.* 108: 66, 1955.

123. SNODGRASS, R. E. *Principles of Insect Morphology.* London: McGraw-Hill, 1935.

124. SOTOVALTA, O. *Ann. Entomol. Fenn.* 20: 148, 1954.

125. TISCHNER, H. *Acustica* 3: 336, 1953.

126. TONNER, F. *Zool. Jahrb., Abt. allg. Zool. Physiol.* 53: 101, 1933.

127. VERWORN, M. *Psychophysiologische Protistenstudien.* Jena: Fischer, 1889.

128. VOGEL, H. *Jena, Ztschr. Naturw.* 59: 171, 1923.

129. VON APÁTHY, S. *Mitt. zool. Stat. Neapel* 12: 495, 1897.

130. VON BUDDENBROCK, W. *Vergleichende Physiologie. I. Sinnesphysiologie.* Basel: Birkhäuser, 1952.

131. VON FRISCH, K. *Zool. Jahrb., Abt. allg. Zool. Physiol.* 37: 1, 1919.

132. VON FRISCH, K. *Zool. Jahrb., Abt. allg. Zool. Physiol.* 38: 449, 1921.

133. VON FRISCH, K. *Ztschr. vergleich. Physiol.* 21: 1, 1935.

134. VON HOLST, E. *Ztschr. vergleich. Physiol.* 32: 60, 1950.
135. WALD, G. *Harvey Lectures.* Ser. 41: 117, 1945–46.
136. WATERMAN, T. H. AND D. F. TRAVIS. *J. Cell & Comp. Physiol.* 41: 261, 1953.
137. WEBER, H. *Lehrbuch der Entomologie.* Jena: Fischer, 1933.
138. WEILL, R. *Trav. Stat. zool. Wimereux* 10 u. 11: 1, 1934.
139. WEVER, E. G. AND C. W. BRAY. *J. Cell. & Comp. Physiol.* 4: 79, 1933.
140. WIERSMA, C. A. G., E. FURSHPAN AND E. FLOREY. *J. Exper. Biol.* 30: 136, 1953.
141. WIGGLESWORTH, V. B. *Parasitology* 33: 67, 1941.
142. WIGGLESWORTH, V. B. AND J. D. GILLET. *J. Exper. Biol.* 11: 120, 1934.
143. WILSKA, A. *Skandinav. Arch. Physiol.* 72: 161, 1935.
144. ZAWARZIN, A. *Ztschr. wiss. zool.* 100: 272, 1912.
145. ZOTTERMAN, Y. *Acta physiol. scandinav.* 18: 181, 1949.

CHAPTER XVII

Touch and kinesthesis

JERZY E. ROSE
VERNON B. MOUNTCASTLE

Departments of Physiology and Psychiatry, Johns Hopkins University School of Medicine, Baltimore, Maryland

CHAPTER CONTENTS

INTRODUCTION

WE SHALL DEAL IN THIS CHAPTER with neural events which occur in the nervous system in response to mechanical stimulation of the skin and of some tissues beneath it. We shall focus our attention on those events which presumably provide the substrate for tactile and kinesthetic sensations.

In the past it was possible to study such sensations only by relating the introspective report of a human observer to the experimental manipulations at the periphery. In this way a large body of psychophysical data was gathered. The events which take place in the nervous system between the time an appropriate stimulus is applied to the receptive zone and the time sensation is reported were not accessible to systematic experimentation, and virtually all the knowledge about them was derived from clinical neurological and neurosurgical observations.

Even though an introspective report is still the only way by which sensations can be studied directly, a considerable body of electrophysiological data, relating the tactile and kinesthetic stimuli to the response in the central nervous system, has been collected in the past three decades. Perhaps because such data do not permit, at present, an interpretation of sensations in terms of neural events, their impact on theory has been quite modest. Even in recent accounts no need is felt to deal in any detail with the neural impulses farther centrally than the peripheral nerve. Since it is reasonable to believe that a detailed knowledge of central neural events is a prerequisite for any sound approach to the problem of sensations, we shall deal with the material pertaining to our subject in a somewhat unorthodox manner. Thus, we shall not review the formidable body of psychophysical data since such data are readily available in all texts of experimental psychology. Likewise, we shall deal with the morphology of the skin receptors only to the extent which is necessary for our purposes. We refer the interested reader to a recent review (268) which contains an extensive list of literature on this subject. On the other hand, we shall consider the electrophysiological data pertaining to the receptors and the peripheral afferent fibers and shall deal with the morphology and electrical activity of the central pathways and synaptic regions which appear relevant for tactile and kinesthetic sensations.

We propose to consider these sensations together since the available evidence indicates that the afferent impulses evoked by stimulation of skin and joints are handled in the central nervous system in a similar fashion and in the same synaptic regions. By kinesthetic sensations we understand the appreciation of movement and position of the joints. We shall use the term 'kinesthetic' which is current in the literature of experimental psychology instead of the term 'proprioceptive' which was introduced by Sherrington and which is almost universally used in physiological texts. For once it appears that a Sherringtonian concept tended to obscure rather than clarify the issues. It was already established by Goldscheider (99) that appreciation of movement of the limbs derives essentially from stimulation of the joints rather than muscles. In harmony with these findings there is, in our opinion, no evidence for and strong evidence against the notion that impulses provoked by stretch receptors in muscles provide information for perception of movement or position of the joints. Thus, it appears that classical proprioceptors may not contribute at all to the arousal of 'proprioceptive' sensations. Hence, the more neutral term of kinesthesis has been adopted.

Definitions

Since it is desirable to utilize electrophysiological data from animal experimentations in describing events leading to tactile and kinesthetic sensations, it is useful to consider such sensations in terms of the stimuli which provoke them and to assume that in mammals, other than man, comparable sensations arise when similar stimuli are applied. Three difficulties arise in this connection. First, the stimuli cannot usually be related to the receptors themselves, as would be desirable, but must be related to the tissues containing them; second, for the time being neural events cannot be related in any simple way to sensations; and third, not every activity in the central nervous system evoked by tactile and kinesthetic stimuli necessarily has a bearing on the arousal of sensations.

From the electrophysiological point of view then, one can speak in a strict sense only of the electrical signs of neural activity aroused by tactile or kinesthetic stimuli. We shall speak, however, specifically of tactile or kinesthetic activity if the stimuli evoke responses in the direct corticopetal pathways and appropriate synaptic regions since it seems fair to infer that at least this activity must be instrumental for the arousal of the appropriate sensations.

TACTILE STIMULI. We shall consider as tactile stimuli all those which cause displacement of hairs or deformation of skin without injury. Since most of the experimental data pertain to animals, it is usually not practical to distinguish between stimuli which cause sensations of touch from those of light pressure.

KINESTHETIC STIMULI. Stimuli pressing upon or displacing without injury the connective tissue underneath the skin, periosteum, bones, sheaths of tendons or muscle fascia, and capsules of the joints lead to sensations often referred to as deep sensibility. We shall be concerned in particular with those stimuli which cause displacement or compression of joint capsules and shall refer to them as kinesthetic. Under physiological conditions, of course, it is the contraction of the muscle which acts as a major kinesthetic stimulus. This fact, however, has no bearing on the assertion which is justified on page 410 that stretch receptors in the muscle itself play no direct role in the arousal of kinesthetic sensations.

Electrophysiological Methods for Study of Somatic Afferent Systems

When a light tactile stimulus is delivered to a small area on the body surface, it evokes a burst of impulses in afferent nerve fibers. This volley is relayed through afferent pathways and synaptic regions of the spinal cord, brain stem and thalamus, and invades the sensory areas of the cerebral cortex. An electrode placed at some point in the system samples the electrical signs of this evoked activity and provides a tool for study of its whereabouts and nature and of the patterning of the central reflection of the body form. The variables of the experiment are the form of stimulation used, the state of excitability of the neurons and the method of recording. Each deserves a comment.

METHODS OF STIMULATION. The somatic afferent system presents difficulties for experimental study for only exceptionally has it so far been possible to deliver quantitatively precise stimuli such as those available for activation of the auditory and visual systems. Various mechanical devices for quick displacement of hairs or skin or for rotation of joints are commonly used, but few of them provide a wide range of action. This had led many investigators to resort to electrical stimulation of nerve trunks to achieve an exact temporal positioning and pattern of the stimuli. It was often believed that a dependable correlation exists between certain groups of fibers, separable by stimulus strength, and certain modalities of sensations.

However, this correlation is far from exact, and it can hardly be doubted that the use of massive nerve volleys has led occasionally to conclusions of questionable physiological significance. The large electrical fields created around massive volleys traversing the central nervous system are likely also to lead to ephaptic excitation of neurons of perhaps completely unrelated function. Electrical stimuli delivered within or across the skin allow a topographical positioning of the stimulus, but since the volley evoked is a synchronous one it cannot, of course, be easily compared with that produced by a natural stimulus. A new advance in stimulation technique is badly needed.

EXCITABILITY STATES OF CENTRAL NEURONS. The remarkable safety factor of synaptic transmission at relays of at least some corticopetal tactile and kinesthetic pathways renders them in certain aspects relatively immune to the depressing effects of anesthetic agents. By contrast the activity evoked by tactile and kinesthetic stimuli in systems which do not conduct towards the cortex and therefore are not likely to contribute directly to conscious perception are extraordinarily susceptible to these depressing effects. This differential is of great advantage for it allows a detailed mapping of the place and patterns of the central projection of the sensory surface. However, the temporal capacity of the corticopetal systems for transmission as well as certain other functional characteristics are severely depressed by barbiturates.

The desire to retain a high level of excitability in an anesthetized animal has led many investigators to use chloralose as an anesthetic agent, frequently combined with a neuromuscular blocking drug. While connections revealed under these conditions undoubtedly exist, the abnormal excitability of the brain calls for particular caution in evaluating the findings obtained. Under these conditions the transmission capacity revealed is as seriously abnormal in one direction as it is in the other under deep barbiturate narcosis. Recently a combination of light barbiturate narcosis with neuromuscular blocking agents has allowed a somewhat closer approach to the normal state. An important advance has been made by Bremer (30, 31) by introducing the *encéphale isolé* preparation, although the high cervical transection makes such a preparation suitable for study of only certain sensory somatic problems. On the other hand, many investigators resort to the use of unanesthetized animals held motionless by neuromuscular blocking drugs. The latter method, apart from the hesitations one may have in using such preparations, hardly offers a solution of the problem for the neuromuscular blocking agents themselves have powerful effects upon central synaptic transmission. For this reason the method of recording from electrodes chronically implanted in the brain or upon its surface is now frequently employed. Recovery of the animals from the anesthetic allows the study of evoked electrical activity for periods of weeks or months under conditions closely approaching the normal. The developing technique of recording from single units by means of implanted microelectrodes promises to be fruitful.

METHODS OF RECORDING. An analysis of the electrical signs of neural activity evoked in the central nervous system by sensory stimuli is treated extensively in Chapters X and XII of this volume. Here we merely wish to point out that it is the initially positive slow wave which has proved of great value, particularly in the experiments designed to determine the locations of the responsive regions and the pattern of the sensory projection. The usefulness of this response is hardly minimized by the fact that its nature still remains obscure.

The method of single unit analysis introduced by Adrian precipitated a rapid advance in neurophysiology. So useful has it become that an appreciable share of present day research is based upon it. Both intra- and extracellular microelectrodes are commonly used. Successful application of the extracellular method requires that the unit observed be held under study for considerable periods of time in a relatively undamaged state. The method permits determination of response properties and topographic and modality attributes of a sample of cells at a given location which allows a reconstruction of the behavior of the population. A full reconstruction, however, would be possible only if the sample were sufficiently large and unbiased. This last requirement is probably not met, for it seems most likely that the smaller elements of the neural population are in fact rejected by the recording instruments presently available.

CURRENT THEORIES OF CUTANEOUS SENSATIONS

Classic Concept

According to the concepts developed by von Frey (244–247) pain, cold, warmth and touch represent the four basic modalities of cutaneous sensation and specific receptors can be assigned to each modality. The older anatomical and psychophysical findings were generally interpreted in the light of these notions and unqualified support of the orthodox view was given by the work of Woollard *et al.* (275), and earlier work by Weddell (264, 265) and Weddell & Harpman (266). The views of von Frey, however, did not remain altogether unchallenged and two formulations differing greatly from the classical concepts will be briefly considered.

Pattern Theory

Recently the Oxford group of workers (113, 154, 155, 220, 223, 267–269) seems to deny altogether the existence of modality specific receptors. The conclusion of the group is that different cutaneous sensations arise not as a result of selective activation of specific receptors but because different stimuli affect the same sets of fibers in a different manner. Thus, in the first order neurons different discharge patterns in the same fiber bundle, and not a selective activation of some fibers in the bundle, are thought to determine the different cutaneous sensations. The reasons for this deduction are that these workers were unable to relate specified endings to specific modalities in several skin areas (113, 155, 223) and that all modalities of sensations were obtained by stimulating the cornea (154) which is known to have free endings only. Moreover, histological evidence led them to believe that all endings in the skin are essentially alike since all arborize into fine, naked, axoplasmic filaments. They further conclude that a classification of encapsulated endings into various types is untenable since a large number of morphologically intermediate variants exists between the usually recognized types.

We believe that the Oxford workers did produce suggestive evidence that stimulation of free endings may cause sensations which can be classified in the broad spectrum of touch. Such findings however do not at all establish that specific endings do not exist, and the conclusions drawn from histological observations do not appear convincing. If a crisis exists in respect to evaluating the morphology of the endings, it is a crisis of abundance and not of scarcity. One hesitates to accept as a solution to the vexing problem of the morphology of the encapsulated endings a declaration that virtually all morphological differences between them are either insignificant or are due to artifacts of the technique.

In any case, a further elaboration of the idea of the discharge patterns led at least some workers of the Oxford group to opinions about touch which are closer to classical notions than one would expect.

Thus, Weddell *et al.* (267) conclude that the anatomical arrangement of the axoplasmic filaments of the encapsulated endings is such that one could expect them—in contrast to the free endings—to be highly sensitive to minimal deformations. A differential sensitivity to mechanical deformation, however, is all that could reasonably be required to declare such an ending as specific for touch or pressure. The difference, then, between the Oxford authors and the orthodox view in this instance reduces itself to the proposition that the Oxford workers presumably assume that discharge in some other fibers as well must necessarily occur before a touch sensation is recognized while we are inclined to think, with von Frey, that in principle such a sensation could arise if a single appropriate peripheral fiber were activated.

Concept of Head

An important difficulty in drawing conclusions from psychophysical experiments is the uncertainty about the classifying of some sensations which may still be called touch. This uncertainty is clearly at the root of the controversy as to whether or not stimulation of the free endings actually arouses tactile sensations. The interpretation of von Frey denies that this is the case and considers such sensations as akin to pain; the Oxford interpretation affirms the tactile quality of such sensations and denies the existence of specific receptors. Head and his collaborators (118) proposed that there are basically two different kinds of sensations subserved by a dual sensory mechanism at the periphery, the more generalized and, as they felt, more primitive or protopathic type and the more specific and advanced or epicritic system. The idea of the duality of cutaneous sensations was greatly elaborated by Head and this elaboration might have contributed to the present eclipse of his concepts. Although at first accepted by many, they were soon sharply criticized, and finally Walshe (262) in his review of the subject delivered a *coup de grâce* to these concepts by pointing out that the crucial introspective experimental observations of Head were not interpreted in the same way by any of the subsequent observers and that his theoretical elaboration was sometimes hazy and contradictory in details, often incompatible with the present knowledge and always speculative. However much one may disagree with some of Walshe's criticisms the fact remains that none of the experimental observations offered by Head in support of his ideas has been accepted by others. The conclusion that Head did not prove his point

is, however, irrelevant for an inquiry as to whether or not his central idea has merit. It is apparent that a protopathic system, if it exists, is likely to be represented anatomically by free endings. The question may then be asked whether stimulation of such endings results in sensations other than pain. There are some indications that this indeed may be the case. Evidence to this effect seems to be at present the chief support for the pattern theory of the Oxford workers, even though such findings could argue, in better harmony with other well established facts, for the existence of protopathic sensibility.

Another hint that a protopathic system may exist is offered by studies of action potentials in peripheral nerve. We shall discuss these in some detail later. Here it is sufficient to state that there is evidence that impulses evoked by tactile stimuli are conducted in both myelinated and unmyelinated fibers. Finally, the fact that activity aroused by tactile stimuli is conducted within the spinal cord in at least two independent ascending pathways could be utilized to argue that the idea of duality of the tactile system does not appear unreasonable.

It should be apparent from these remarks that it is not proposed at present to revive the concepts of epicritic and protopathic sensibility. We wish only to point out that an unqualified rejection of these concepts may be premature and that Head's ideas in some form may yet prove useful in the future.

SOME PROPERTIES OF PERIPHERAL SOMATIC AFFERENT SYSTEM

Receptors

It is convenient to consider the receptors both in this section and in the one which deals with the central events. In order to avoid repetition we shall consider here primarily those properties which have a bearing on their specificity.

SPECIFICITY OF RECEPTORS. Whatever opinions one may hold about the way tactile stimuli arouse sensations it is fundamental to recognize that there are some receptors which are specifically sensitive to such stimuli. Conclusive evidence in this respect is provided by studies of discharges, usually of single units, when mechanoreceptors are activated by natural stimuli. In many of these studies (4–6, 16–18, 29, 42, 68, 94, 124, 127, 161, 187) the existence of a specific receptor is inferred from the behavior of the neural discharge;

in some (12, 105–108), the receptors themselves were identified.

It was observed early and since confirmed by all workers in the field that the largest fibers in the cutaneous nerves are activated by certain types of tactile stimuli. It may be stressed immediately that the converse statement does not hold and that activity aroused by tactile stimuli is not limited to large fibers only. Since for technical reasons discharges occurring in large fibers are particularily convenient to study, the information given below regarding tactile receptors pertains to those which are connected to such fibers.

The specificity of tactile receptors manifests itself both in their exquisite sensitivity to mechanical stimuli and in their lack of sensitivity or high threshold for other than such stimuli. The threshold to mechanical stimuli is low, apparently commensurate with the capacity of the animal to recognize them, and the details of mechanical application of the stimulus are as a rule critical for evoking discharges. Direct measurements made on the mesenteric Pacinian corpuscles (105) indicate that the minimal movement of the stimulus probe necessary to excite the receptor is of the order of 0.5μ in 100 μsec.; the Pacinian corpuscle in the toe (107) showed a similar sensitivity. There are no figures available for any other ending. From qualitative observations, though, there is no reason to doubt that at least a number of them is equally sensitive.

The problem of sensitivity of mechanoreceptors to other than tactile stimuli has attracted but casual interest of most observers, chiefly because it is known that thermal and painful stimuli characteristically cause discharges in the smaller spectrum of fibers. Nevertheless, it was observed by Adrian & Umrath (5) that thermal stimuli did not excite the mechanoreceptors they studied, and Hogg (127) stated that thermal and chemical stimuli are less effective in the frog in activating large fibers than small ones and that the reverse is true for tactile stimuli. Hensel & Zotterman (124) recently presented interesting data on the response of some mechanoreceptors to cold. In the tongue of the cat they found mechanoreceptors not sensitive to strong thermal stimuli as well as thermoreceptors unresponsive to tactile excitation. In addition to these receptors they also found a group of fibers which responded both to pressure and to cooling. The response to cold differed in important aspects from the response of a typical thermoreceptor for the response occurred only to very low temperatures and rapid cooling (while thermoreceptors respond with a sensi-

tivity to about a tenth of a degree below 40°C) and it adapted to extinction within a few seconds (while a typical response to cooling persists for as long as the stimulus is applied). How to interpret such a response to cooling is an open question. It is conceivable that it represents a secondary effect due, for example, to a displacement of a mechanoreceptor through vasoconstriction, although this interpretation is considered as rather unlikely by the authors.

TYPES OF DISCHARGES. The mechanoreceptors in the skin can be divided into fast and slowly adapting types. Most receptors activated by displacement of hairs are fast adapting. Those responding to pressure adapt either fast or slowly. It is of interest that receptors activated by kinesthetic stimuli appear to have the same properties as the mechanoreceptors in the skin although the slowly adapting ones seem to predominate greatly in numbers (29, 225).

It is unfortunately not known how the morphological structure of the ending relates to the discharge pattern since, except for the Pacinian corpuscle, none of the other receptors has ever been studied in isolation. For that reason the significance of the capsule and of the accessory fibers is entirely obscure. Recently Boyd (28) and Skoglund (225) identified Ruffini's endings in the joint capsule as slowly adapting receptors and the modified Pacinian corpuscles as the fast adapting ones. These identifications, however, must be considered tentative since they are indirect. The Pacinian corpuscle, the best known receptor at present, is fast adapting (107). It is known for this receptor (106) that its adaptation to mechanical stimuli is a property of the receptor itself rather than of its fiber. Loewenstein (161), working on frog's skin, presented some data to suggest that a fast adapting receptor may be made to discharge for a long time if the tension in the receptor region is greatly increased, thus implying that whether an ending adapts quickly or slowly may be determined by the mechanical arrangement of the ending. If this be so, the degree of coiling of the terminals could be a determining factor in whether a receptor is fast or slowly adapting. The merit of this suggestion is at present difficult to evaluate.

RECEPTOR POTENTIAL. As already mentioned, the only receptor the functional properties of which have thus far been studied is the Pacinian corpuscle. It has been recently established by Alvarez-Buylla & de Arellano (12) that mechanical stimuli produce a local response which Gray & Sato (108) propose to call a receptor potential since this potential—in contrast to the local response of the nerve—is not affected by near absence of sodium. The receptor potential can summate and its amplitude depends on stimulus strength. It is set up in less than 0.2 msec. and is the earliest electrical event which is known to occur. While the mechanism of its generation is at the moment quite obscure, its occurrence provides a final indication—if such be needed—that the Pacinian corpuscle must be regarded as a full-fledged receptor. An electronmicroscopical description of its fairly complex structure has been given recently by Pease & Quilliam (195). The mechanism of excitation of Pacinian corpuscles is discussed by Gray in Chapter IV of this work.

Peripheral Cutaneous Nerve Fibers

IMPULSES IN PERIPHERAL NERVE FIBERS. Thus far we have discussed only to what extent discharges in single units reflect some properties of the receptors which initiate the impulses. We shall now turn to electrophysiological evidence derived from studies of cutaneous nerves. Since all experimental data are derived either from studies of single units or from studies of the electroneurogram, it will be useful to recall some properties of the peripheral fibers.

As is well known, a cutaneous nerve consists of fibers of different sizes. Fibers of different diameters do not, however, occur with equal frequency and the size-frequency distribution curve for any cutaneous nerve shows characteristically several peaks. It is customary to classify all fibers into A, B and C groups according to certain characteristics of their action potentials which are different for each of them. However, it is unnecessary to relate here these characteristics since in the cutaneous nerves only A and C fibers are known and the myelinated and unmyelinated fibers form the A and C groups, respectively.

It is known that the velocity of conduction in A fibers varies with their diameters. If an assumption is made that the amplitude of the action potential as recorded across the membrane is about the same for any A fiber but that the height of the externally recorded potential varies as the square of the diameter of the fiber, it is possible to estimate the size of the fiber from the externally recorded amplitude of the discharge in a single unit preparation. Making these assumptions for the entire nerve the shape of the compound action potential can be reconstructed with great accuracy if the fiber composition of the nerve is known. Conversely, it is justifiable to infer from the

different elevations of the electroneurogram the presence of fiber groups of specified diameters in a given nerve. Usually, Greek letters are used to denote the different elevations, each successive letter referring to a group of fibers of smaller diameter (fig. 1). Some confusion resulted occasionally in the past with the use of this notation, for different nerves do in fact differ in their fiber compositon and thus an elevation denoted by the same letter in different nerves may indicate at least somewhat different fiber groups. For the corresponding nerves in the same species the distribution of fibers is, according to Gasser (88), quite constant.

IMPULSES EVOKED IN FIBERS OF DIFFERENT SIZE BY TACTILE STIMULI. All workers agree that tactile stimuli activate the largest fibers in the cutaneous nerves and those who distinguish gentle contact (touch) from sustained displacement (pressure) invariably state that it is a gentle contact which activates the largest fibers. Maruhashi *et al.* (168) report that the diameters of the fibers activated by touch vary between 8 to 14 μ in the cat and 8 to 15 μ in the frog. They further found that movements of hairs activate fibers in the range of 6 to 12 μ, while diameters of fibers

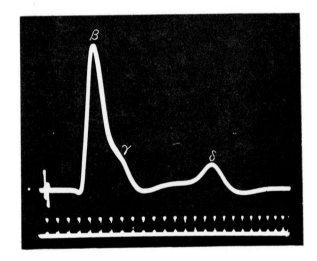

FIG. 1. Compound action potential of the saphenous nerve of the cat recorded at a distance of 54 mm from the locus of stimulation. Several elevations (denoted by Greek letters) are recorded because, in the nerve, fibers of different sizes are grouped around several peaks. Since the saphenous nerve lacks the largest afferents arising from the muscle stretch receptors no α elevation is indicated even though the sizes in the α and β groups overlap. The β and γ elevations as denoted here are sometimes referred to as α and β peaks. All elevations pertain to A fibers. The elevation due to C fibers is not shown. Time line: 5,000 cps.

excited by pressure are 3 to 5 μ in the cat and 4 to 5 μ in the frog. In addition, unmyelinated fibers of the C group were seen by them to be activated by mechanical stimuli both in the cat and frog.

The findings of the Japanese observers confirm the older observations of Zotterman (282) who, recording from strands of the saphenous nerve of the cat, noted that, apart from the usual discharges evoked by tactile stimuli in the large fibers, discharges were evoked in smaller fibers also by very light stroking of the skin. These potentials contribute to the delta elevation of the electroneurogram of the saphenous nerve and Zotterman judged the appropriate fibers to be in the range of 5 to 9 μ. He also noticed that with stroking of the skin the delta potentials are followed by a cascade of very small spikes which he felt must be conducted by the C group of fibers.

RELATION OF CUTANEOUS STIMULI TO ACTIVITY IN FIBERS OF DIFFERENT SIZE. Observations on single units indicate then that tactile stimuli can activate at least several groups of afferent fibers and, if the data of the Japanese workers are taken as a basis, the conclusion seems inescapable that no fiber whatever within either the A or C group can be eliminated by virtue of its size alone as potentially responding to tactile stimuli. Nevertheless, the data imply that a relation may exist between the size of a fiber and the exact quality of the mechanical stimulus which activates it. The conclusion that fibers of all sizes may be activated by mechanical stimuli must not imply that all fibers in the cutaneous nerve can be activated by them. If this were so, each fiber activated by other than mechanical stimuli would also be responsive to tactile stimulation. This is apparently not the case since at least some fibers which are selectively activated by thermal stimuli have been shown to exist (120–123, 281).

The problem of C fibers is of special interest. There is evidence available (22, 46, 149, 168, 282) that nociceptive stimuli can activate such fibers. From the experiments in which C fiber activity could be identified with certainty it has been inferred (46) that at least some thermal stimuli (warmth) can also cause C fiber activity. All workers who used single unit preparations and were concerned with this question (127, 168, 282) have concluded that not only nociceptive but cold, warmth and mechanical stimuli activate C fibers as well. It should be noted that with the single fiber technique it may not always be possible to decide that a C fiber and not a small A fiber has been activated. Nevertheless, the evidence suggests

indeed that C fibers can be activated by all modes of cutaneous stimulation.

In contrast to the findings about A fibers there is no conclusive evidence, either for or against, concerning selective sensitivity of single C fibers to various stimuli. It thus remains an open question to what extent the C fibers resemble the A system.

RELATION OF ELEVATIONS OF ELECTRONEUROGRAM TO MODALITIES OF SENSATION. The findings derived from observations of single units seem to agree with the studies which relate the different elevations of the compound action potential to the results of psychophysical and animal experiments in which the peripheral nerve is blocked by infiltration with local anesthetic, made ischemic or excited by electrical stimuli.

It has long been known for man that perineural injection of cocaine (or a similarly acting agent) blocks sensations in a preferential order in such a way that cold, warmth, pain and touch disappear in the order stated. There is some discrepancy among various observers whether it is cold or pain which disappears first, but there is an almost unanimous agreement that it is touch which disappears last. [For some discordant observations and a review of the literature see Sinclair & Hinshaw (221, 222).]

Since Gasser & Erlanger (89) demonstrated that cocainization blocks conduction in an orderly sequence, the smallest fibers being blocked first, it can be inferred that the largest fibers in the nerve are activated by tactile stimuli. This conclusion, of course, is but a confirmation of the firmly established findings discussed earlier. It should be stressed that cocaine block does not permit any conclusions as to whether smaller fibers which can be activated by touch exist, but it does imply that activity in a group of the largest fibers alone may be quite sufficient for the arousal of tactile sensations. Direct stimulation of an exposed nerve in man (119) leads to an identical conclusion since it is possible to excite only the largest fibers with an appropriate stimulus and since such stimuli lead only to an arousal of tactile sensations.

In contrast to a block produced by a local anesthetic, application of pressure over a limb of man leads to disappearance of sensations usually in the following order: touch, cold, warmth, pain. In experiments of Clark, Hughes and Gasser as reported by Gasser (87), compression of a limb of a cat led first to a conduction failure of the delta fibers and of the largest fibers in the nerve. The exact progress of the conduction failure was difficult to establish, but it was clear that the failure did not follow an orderly sequence according to fiber size. The important finding was that even after the entire spectrum of A fibers failed to conduct, the C elevation was only little impaired. It can thus be concluded that C fibers are more resistant to ischemia than is the A group and since manifestations of painful sensations are still evokable when only C fibers conduct, one can infer that painful stimuli must activate at least some C fibers. While this finding again agrees with what has been more recently shown by other methods, one can conclude in addition that activity in C fibers alone is apparently sufficient to arouse painful sensations. It could have been expected perhaps that some tactile sensations should be present as long as C fibers are conducting if it be true that mechanical stimuli excite such fibers. The negative findings may mean, of course, that there are no C fibers activated by touch. It may mean as well that activity in C fibers aroused by tactile stimuli under the experimental conditions tested are not interpreted as touch, or finally even that some perhaps obscure qualities of tactile sensations which actually were present were ignored by the experimenters and the experimental subjects alike.

SUMMARY. It appears that the available neurophysiological evidence in respect to the peripheral aspects of the tactile system does not support fully any of the current ideas regarding tactile sensations.

Despite the arguments advanced by the Oxford workers the evidence seems conclusive that there exist in fact specific tactile (as well as thermal) receptors. The evidence is also good that the fiber size may be indicative of connections with some specific receptors. Thus, the known thermoreceptors seem connected with small or medium sized fibers only, while the largest fibers in the cutaneous nerve are connected to mechanoreceptors. Bishop (21) points out further that the largest afferent fibers known in the peripheral nerves do not occur at all in the cutaneous branches, and it seems clear that these fibers are connected to the muscle stretch receptors. To this extent then von Frey's concepts appear valid. The fact that tactile stimuli can activate A fibers of different sizes may or may not be compatible with the classic ideas. What seems difficult to reconcile with von Frey's concepts is the suggestive evidence that C fibers (which presumably ramify in free endings only) are also activated by tactile stimuli. If this should be so a major question to be answered would be whether individual somatic C fibers are modality specific or whether an individual fiber is excited by tactile as well as by

thermal and nociceptive stimuli. If the latter should be the case, the classical concepts would clearly need a major revision obviously in the direction of the ideas expressed by Head.

CENTRAL TACTILE AND KINESTHETIC SYSTEMS

General Remarks

It is well known that the dorsal root fibers ramify upon entry into the central nervous system and, by means of their main branches and collaterals, establish synaptic contacts with several nuclear regions. It is convenient to divide into two classes those regions to which discharges aroused by tactile stimuli can be relayed. The first is formed by regions which are, or which can be reasonably assumed to be, instrumental for generation of tactile sensations. To the second class belong those regions which are either not at all sensory, as in the case of the anterior horn cells, or those which receive afferent information but for which there is no reason to believe that their function has an essential bearing upon tactile or kinesthetic experience. It is thus clear enough that the appearance of evoked neural activity in a given synaptic region following tactile stimulation may indeed mean that the region in question is relevant for tactile sensations. Such responses, however, may equally well merely indicate that some other activity, not necessarily even sensory in nature, is modulated by the activity of tactile receptors. Considerable confusion exists in the literature in respect to this problem, since many workers seem to believe that a response evoked anywhere in the central nervous system by tactile stimuli is *prima facie* evidence that the locus in question is linked somehow to tactile sensations. If one considers that most morphological groupings in the central nervous system establish synaptic contacts with more than one other morphological entity, the number of potentially activated synaptic regions may be expected to increase in geometrical progression with each synaptic relay. It is likely, therefore, that within a short time a signal in an afferent fiber could be relayed, at least in principle, to almost any grouping within the central nervous system.

Hence it is not unduly surprising if under certain experimental conditions a response to a tactile stimulus occurs in a region which anatomically appears to be an altogether unlikely locus. It is fortunate indeed for an analysis by electrophysiological methods that all potentialities for synaptic transfer are for a number of reasons actually not realized, and that tactile and kinesthetic stimuli activate usually only a limited number of synaptic regions, even though this number varies considerably under different experimental conditions.

In the sections which follow we shall concern ourselves almost exclusively with pathways and synaptic regions which are demonstrably significant for tactile and kinesthetic sensations. We shall not consider the problem of how stimulation of tactile and kinesthetic receptors may affect other activity in the central nervous system.

Classification of Central Tactile and Kinesthetic Systems

It is well known that tactile or kinesthetic discharges or both are conducted centripetally in the posterior columns of the spinal cord, in its anterolateral columns and in the trigeminal pathways. It also seems evident that such impulses can enter the central nervous system through the roots of the ninth and tenth cranial nerves, and there is good evidence (197) that some chorda tympani fibers may be activated by mechanoreceptors.

It is both convenient and almost certainly correct to consider together the systems arising in the posterior column nuclei and the one arising in the main sensory trigeminal nucleus. We shall refer to them as components of the medial lemniscal system. Likewise, we shall consider the spinothalamic system as consisting of two components. The first is the spinothalamic tract arising in the posterior horns of the spinal cord and the second is the spinothalamic tract arising in the spinal nucleus of the fifth nerve. We shall refer to the latter, following White & Sweet (273), as the bulbothalamic tract.

MEDIAL LEMNISCAL SYSTEM

Anatomical Definition

This system is the better known of the two, both anatomically and functionally. Anatomically we shall mention here only the centripetal terminations of the successive axons in the system. Some collateral connections relevant for our considerations will be discussed later. The spinal component of the system is formed by axons emanating from the cells of the spinal ganglia and ascending on the homolateral side of the cord in the posterior column and synapsing on cells in Goll and Burdach's nuclei; by axons originat-

ing from the cells of these nuclei, crossing (as far as is known, entirely) to the opposite side and ascending in the medial lemniscus to end upon the cells of the external component of the thalamic ventrobasal complex; and by axons originating in the cells of the latter element and projecting upon the postcentral cortex or its homologue.[1]

The trigeminal component of the lemniscal system arises in the main sensory nucleus of the fifth nerve. There is complete agreement among most observers that the main outflow of this nucleus consists of axons crossing to the opposite side. The pathway adjoins mediodorsally the medial lemniscus, forms an integral part of it and terminates in the arcuate component of the ventrobasal complex. The cells of the latter project, as do the cells of the external element, upon the postcentral cortex.

In addition to the crossed ventral pathways mentioned above, a dorsal pathway originating in the main sensory nucleus and reaching the thalamus via a tegmental route is frequently described. Considerable uncertainty prevails, however, about the origin of this tract, its components and its terminations in the thalamus. Wallenberg (261) described an uncrossed and a crossed component and believed that

---

[1] It is customary to consider n. ventralis posteromedialis and n. ventralis posterolateralis as the two tactile thalamic nuclei. We refer, however, to the principal tactile thalamic region as the ventrobasal complex and distinguish within this complex the arcuate or medial component, which receives the trigeminal projection, and the external or lateral component, which receives projections from the rest of the body (207). The reasons for this nomenclature are as follows. First, the two components of the ventrobasal complex are almost identical in their architecture and for that reason should not be divided into two separate nuclei. Actually in the rabbit such a separation is very difficult while in the cat and monkey it is best done on the basis of a dividing fibrous lamella. Second, most workers include into their n. ventralis posteromedialis a ventromedial element which is not activated by tactile stimuli and which displays structural characteristics of its own, which are different from those of the arcuate portion of the ventrobasal complex. Only Jimenez-Castellanos (136) and Jasper & Ajmone-Marsan (135) do not include this element in the n. ventralis posteromedialis. The latter workers, however, consider as a part of this nucleus a portion of the posterior thalamic group. Likewise, n. ventralis posterolateralis is with many workers not coextensive with the lateral component of the ventrobasal complex. Thus Olszewski (189), for example, distinguishes within his n. ventralis posterior lateralis an oral part which is not activated by tactile stimuli and a caudal part which corresponds probably exactly to the lateral component of the ventrobasal complex.

In respect to the sensory somatic cortical field we shall use interchangeably the following terms: first somatic field, postcentral cortex (areas 1 to 3 in primates), postcentral homologue and primary receiving area.

most but not all of the fibers of these tracts terminated before reaching the thalamus. Walker (254) confirmed in essence Wallenberg's observations and concluded that the uncrossed fibers predominate and that many terminate in the most medial portion of the arcuate nucleus. Other workers (40, 117, 191, 192) reported that the tract is uncrossed and that it terminates in the arcuate nucleus or in the centrum medianum, or in both. Recently Torvik (239) presented evidence on the basis of retrograde cell degeneration that the dorsomedial sector of the main sensory nucleus projects to the homolateral thalamus while the rest of this nucleus projects to the contralateral side, thus con-confirming some older observations (140) in this respect.

Since physiological evidence is conclusive that both the contralateral and ipsilateral face areas are represented in the arcuate sector of each ventrobasal complex, it is tempting to assume that the uncrossed tegmental trigeminal pathway exists and that it relays tactile and kinesthetic impulses from the homolateral face. Moreover, Hatschek's observation (117) that the uncrossed tract is particularly prominent in ungulates would fit with the findings of Woolsey & Fairman (277) that the ipsilateral cortical face areas are unusually large in the pig and sheep. However, there are also some reasons to doubt the correctness of this assumption. First, it is obvious from the controversy over whether this tract is both crossed and uncrossed, only uncrossed, or whether it exists at all (214), that different workers placed significantly different lesions in their animals and there is no convincing evidence that this tract necessarily arises in the main sensory nucleus. Second, it would be difficult to understand why homolateral tactile and kinesthetic impulses should utilize a tract which is quite different in its fiber composition from the ventral pathway and why the homolateral tract should lie so far apart from the contralateral one. Finally, the usual observation of recent workers that the tract ends in the most medial sector of the arcuate nucleus does not immediately establish that it relays tactile impulses, for in contrast to our own definition of the arcuate component most workers include in it not only the tactile thalamic trigeminal region but also a ventromedial element (differing considerably in structure from the arcuate nucleus) which in our opinion is not activated by tactile stimuli. It has been suggested (207) that this element may be connected with taste. It is of interest to point out that von Economo (243) suggested a long time ago that the

dorsal trigeminal tract is in fact concerned with gustatory impulses.

Physiological Properties

It has been known for a long time that destruction of the posterior columns in man leads to a loss of the capacity to appreciate the position and the movement of the limbs, and to an inability to recognize the vibrations of a tuning fork applied over the bone. The disturbances in tactile sensations were the subject of some dispute. It seems reasonable to believe, however, that there is a severe impairment in the appreciation of the spatial and temporal sequence of a series of stimuli. In addition, increases in threshold for tactile stimuli, a diminution in the number of 'sensory spots' and an impairment in proper localization of the stimulus is often described.

A general property of the lemniscal system is that the information concerning the form, nature, location and temporal sequences of the impinging stimuli is transmitted at each synaptic station with great security. From the point of view of its organization, the medial lemniscal system displays two striking features. The first of these is that the peripheral sensory sheet is projected centrally in a precise pattern, which is preserved to a considerable degree through the successive relays of the system, and is finally impressed upon the postcentral cortex. The second is that the system encompasses within a single topographical pattern several submodalities of the general sense of mechanoreception. We wish to discuss the system from these two viewpoints.

PROJECTION PATTERNS IN MEDIAL LEMNISCAL SYSTEM

Patterns in Dorsal Columns

The weight of the evidence indicates that the large majority of nerve fibers reaching the dorsal column nuclei by way of the dorsal columns are axons of first order neurons. It is not known that they are exclusively so, however, and it is possible that some unknown number arises from cells within the spinal cord, cells which are activated by dorsal root afferents and are therefore fibers of the second order. In the cat some 25 per cent of the dorsal root myelinated fibers which enter the dorsal columns at the segmental level are believed to reach the cells of the dorsal column nuclei directly (98).

Examination of Marchi degenerations in the dorsal

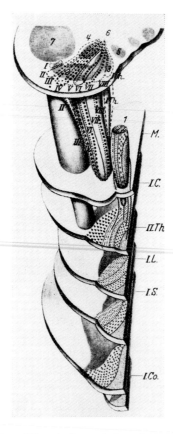

FIG. 2. Topical organization of fibers in the posterior column and in the posterior column nuclei. The upper two cross sections (M) refer to the medulla, the lower five to the coccygeal (I. Co.), sacral (I. S.), lumbar (I. L.), thoracic (II. Th.) and cervical (I. C.) levels of the spinal cord. The relative positions of fibers are indicated by dots for the coccygeal fibers and by crosses, dashes, dots and dashes and triangles for fibers of successively higher segments. 1: nucleus gracilis; 2 to 4: complex of nucleus cuneatus; 7: descending root of the fifth nerve. [From Glees *et al.* (97).]

columns following section of dorsal roots, or transection of the dorsal columns at various levels, indicates that the centrally projecting fibers are arranged in an orderly lamination (43, 65, 66, 70, 97, 258). Those from each successively higher segment are arranged in a series of successively more lateral laminae of fibers (fig. 2).

Patterns in Dorsal Column Nuclei

As figure 2 shows, this precise lamellar arrangement of the fibers of the dorsal columns is unchanged in the dorsal column nuclei. Fibers from the caudal segments terminate in the most medial portion of nucleus

gracilis, those from sacral, lumbar and at least the lower six thoracic roots terminate in successively more laterally placed dorsoventrally directed lamellae. Glees *et al.* (97) believe that all thoracic roots with the exception of the first terminate in this nucleus. Fibers from the upper thoracic and from the cervical roots terminate in nucleus cuneatus in a similar lamellar arrangement. Other fibers of the upper thoracic and of the cervical roots ascend in the dorsal columns and terminate in a topographically arranged pattern in the lateral cuneate nucleus, whose cells in turn project upon the cerebellar cortex.

The Marchi material suggests the existence of a considerable overlap between the terminals of neighboring fibers. However, it has been shown (97, 98) by using silver staining methods that intersegmental overlap is minimal, though intrasegmental overlap of the fields of termination occurs. This latter is accentuated by the numerous branching dendrites which reach into the synaptic fields of neighboring cells. The image of the body form thus composed by this projection is distorted to allow greater volume representation for those body parts which are heavily innervated by afferent fibers.

One looks to electrophysiological methods for finer details of the representation pattern. The lamination pattern in the dorsal columns has been confirmed (280). It appears, however, that only one study has been made of the projection pattern in the dorsal column nuclei, and that has been reported in only a short note. Using physiological stimuli Kuhn (145) has mapped the projection of the body surface upon the dorsal column nuclei. He found the ipsilateral body surface of the cat to be represented within the caudal portions of the dorsal column nuclei as an inverted figure of the animal, with the tail pointed dorsocaudally, extremities dorsally. No responses were recorded following stimulation of the contralateral side.

Unfortunately there are no experimental data to indicate the pattern of projection of the first order neurons of the trigeminal nerve upon the cells of the main sensory nucleus of the fifth. That a detailed and well differentiated pattern must exist therein is indicated by the pattern formed by the terminals of the second order elements within the thalamic relay nucleus (see fig. 3). This latter pattern contains also an ipsilateral projection of the peri- and intraoral structures which are partially superimposed upon the contralateral pattern of representation of the same

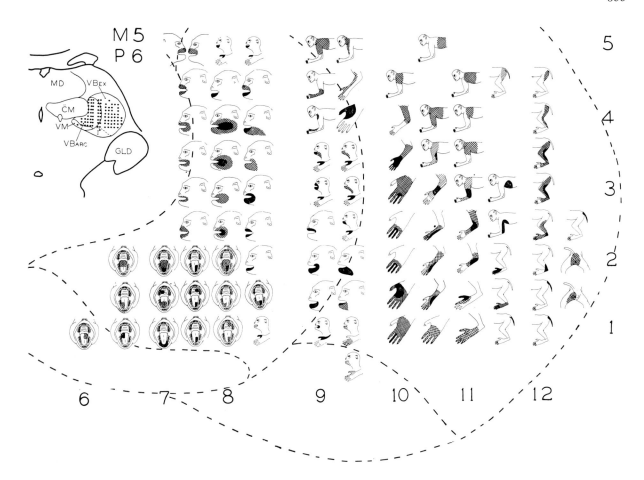

FIG. 3. Figurine map depicting the representation of the body surface in the ventrobasal thalamic complex of the monkey, *Macacus rhesus*, constructed from data obtained in an evoked potential experiment under deep barbiturate anesthesia. Inset drawing shows diagrammatically the thalamic structures in a Horsely-Clarke plane (frontal plane 6). Dots indicate points at which electrical activity was evoked by tactile stimulation of the body surface. For each dot in the inset an appropriately located figurine is shown. No responses were obtained elsewhere along the explored electrode tracks. Body areas, stimulation of which evoked large, smaller or small responses are shown in the figurines by solid black, cross-hatching or diagonal lines, respectively. The body is represented contralaterally except for the face and intraoral structures which are bilaterally represented. Numerals indicate the mediolateral and vertical Horsley-Clarke coordinates. *MD:* mediodorsal nucleus; *CM:* centrum medianum; *GLD:* dorsal lateral geniculate body; *VBarc:* arcuate component of the ventrobasal complex; *VBex:* external component of the ventrobasal complex; *VM:* ventromedial nucleus; *I:* the inferior portion of the ventral nuclear group. [From Mountcastle & Henneman (185).]

facial regions. Whether this projection depends upon ipsilateral axons from the main sensory nucleus traveling in the dorsal trigeminal tract is conjectural (see p. 398).

Patterns in Thalamic Relay Nucleus

DEFINITION OF THALAMIC RELAY NUCLEUS. Evidence from several experimental approaches indicates that

the ventrobasal complex, consisting of an external and an arcuate portion, is the thalamic relay for the medial lemniscal system. Tactile and kinesthetic activity is relayed through it to the first somatic area of the cortex. In carnivores and primates this region of the thalamus is distinguished from its neighbors in the ventral thalamic group by a special cytoarchitecture. It contains neurons which vary widely in size. These sizes are grouped around two means, though in the posterior third of the complex this difference is less obvious (50). It is the thalamic area as defined here which receives the terminals of axons of the ascending lemniscal system (40, 47, 48, 56, 67, 170, 200, 203, 242, 252, 260), and it is this thalamic complex alone which undergoes retrograde degeneration following lesions of the cortex confined to the postcentral homologue (49, 50, 143, 253). The method of local strychninization and observation of the induced behavioral changes yielded results in accord with these facts, though the method is too crude for any detailed analysis (59, 60). Finally, electrophysiological experiments are consistent with the notion that the principal area of the thalamus activated by tactile and kinesthetic stimulation of the body is coextensive with the ventrobasal complex (164, 182, 184, 185, 207). Two questions in this regard require further comment.

DIRECT SPINOCORTICAL AND BULBOCORTICAL PATHWAYS. It is an old suggestion that certain ascending sensory somatic fibers of spinal or dorsal column nuclei origin might reach the cerebral cortex directly without an intervening synaptic relay in the diencephalon. In 1890, Flechsig & Hösel (69) put forward this contention, having found some degenerations in the medial lemniscus of a patient who died following a lesion believed to be limited to the cerebral cortex. This idea was supported by Tschermak (240) but vigorously opposed by other workers who failed to confirm Flechsig & Hösel's observation and who concluded that the fibers of the medial lemniscus all terminate in the diencephalon. This latter view is widely supported by virtually all more extensive neuroanatomical studies and prevails even though some dissenting observations are occasionally described (186).

Recently Brodal & Walberg (35) and Brodal & Kaada (33) revived again the question of the existence of both the direct bulbocortical and the spinocortical tracts. The first is stated to arise from cells of the dorsal column nuclei and to project bilaterally upon the cerebral cortex by a pathway which joins the pyramidal tracts of either side. The second is believed to derive from neurons of the spinal cord and to ascend directly therefrom to the cortex in the pyramidal tracts. Both pathways are said to be activated by electrical stimulation of either cutaneous or muscle nerves. However, the anatomical evidence adduced by Brodal & Walberg does not appear to be sufficiently crucial to settle this old dispute, and the electrophysiological observations of Brodal & Kaada

need not imply the existence of such direct pathways according to the findings of Patton & Amassian (193) and of Landau (148).

IPSILATERAL PATHWAY FROM DORSAL COLUMN NUCLEI TO VENTROBASAL COMPLEX. It is clear from a large number of studies that, in so far as anatomical methods can determine, the entire upward outflow of the dorsal column nuclei ascends to the thalamus of the contralateral side and terminates largely within the ventrobasal thalamic complex. These observations accord well with the results of electrophysiological mapping experiments, which indicate that only the contralateral body surface is projected via the lemniscal system upon the ventrobasal complex, while the trigeminal component of this system does contain an ipsilateral component, partially overlaid with the contralateral one. This pattern of projection is further confirmed by our single unit observations in the thalamus (Mountcastle, V. B. & J. E. Rose, unpublished observations). Moreover, single unit studies of the postcentral homologue in cats and monkeys indicate that its cells are activated only by stimulation of the contralateral body surface, except for the trigeminal inflow (181; and Mountcastle, V. B. & T. P. S. Powell, manuscript in preparation). Many observers do not agree with these findings, however, and they report ipsilateral responses in the region of the thalamus, evoked by natural stimuli or by peripheral nerve, brachial plexus or dorsal column electrical stimulation (20, 51, 52, 90, 91, 116) although Berry et al. (20) found that direct electrical stimulation of one dorsal column evokes electrical activity only in the contralateral thalamus. The latter observation is of interest for it may provide a clue for the interpretation of the divergent findings. Evidence is accumulating (see p. 419) that in contrast to the medial lemniscal system the spinothalamic system does possess an ipsilateral component from the body surface, which may terminate partly or wholly in the segment of the posterior thalamic group which adjoins the ventrobasal complex posteriorly. It seems possible that the workers who obtained ipsilateral responses from stimulation of the body surface or nerves obtained them actually in the region which lies posteriorly to the ventrobasal complex. While this interpretation would harmonize the existing discordant findings, it would not immediately explain why ipsilateral stimuli fail to activate (at least under conditions of moderate anesthesia) the ventrobasal complex itself—as could be expected—unless one assumes that the functional significance of the ipsilateral inflow differs materially from that of the contralateral one.

PATTERNS IN TACTILE THALAMIC AREA. Detailed information regarding the pattern of projection of the lemniscal system upon its thalamic relay nucleus is provided by studies using the evoked potential technique. This method, as applied to study of the thalamus, involves passing a recording electrode down through the thalamus in successive rows of penetrations so placed as to explore the thalamic areas activated. At successive intervals during its downward passage the electrode is held stationary and the area of the body surface in which stimulation evokes electrical activity at a given point is determined. The figurine drawings which can be constructed from the data for each point are placed in proper relation to one another and to the thalamic nuclear outlines, as determined by study of the serial sections of the experimental brains (182, 184, 185, 207). The pattern of representation in the monkey is shown in figure 3.

Analysis of this figure reveals that the body surface of the monkey is represented as a distorted image of the animal. The face and head are represented within the arcuate portion of the ventrobasal complex, the body in its external element. The middorsal line of the body from nose to tail is represented across the top of the complex, the trunk and girdle regions, proximal and then distal parts of the extremities in successively more ventral positions. The only ipsilateral projection is that of the peri- and intraoral regions.

Perusal of such a figurine map makes it clear that a given small area of the body surface is not represented at a thalamic 'point' and only there. Stimulation of a small spot on the skin evokes intense activity at a limited thalamic locus and less intense activity over a considerable surround. It follows that a given thalamic locus can be activated to some degree from a considerable area of skin, which is smaller for some and larger for other parts of the topographical pattern. As the peripheral spot stimulated is shifted across the skin the peak activity shifts across the thalamic pattern, its submaximal and liminal fringes shifting with it. The problem is to understand the precision of spatial discrimination of which the organism is capable, which depends upon an anatomical substrate of 'point to area' and reciprocally, 'area to point' projection of the receptor sheet upon the central configurations. Some physiological mechanisms which appear of importance in this regard will be considered later.

When the representation pattern shown in cross-section in figure 3 is analyzed in three dimensions, it results that any given dermatomal (segmental) region of the body is represented in the ventrobasal complex in a narrow curving lamella of tissue, concave medially. Within such a narrow sheet the proximal skin areas of the dermatome are represented dorsally, the distal ventrally.

Extension of such studies to a series of mammals allows some estimate of the phyletic trends in thalamic tactile representation. The sequence of that representation is in principle the same in the rabbit, cat and monkey (fig. 4). The entire body surface is represented in each case, but striking differences in emphasis exist. In the rabbit, the bulk of the available tissue is given to the projection of head and face, while the cat possesses a balanced spinal and trigeminal projection. In the monkey the increased development of the hand and foot as tactile organs is indicated by an increased share of the pattern devoted to their representation.

This general pattern depicted by electrophysiological studies is a confirmation and extension of that

FIG. 4. Schematic outlines of body representation in the ventrobasal thalamic complex in rabbit, cat and monkey. The figures do not intend to depict with accuracy the actual relationships but aim to emphasize the dominance of the trigeminal representation in the rabbit, and the relative increase of the representation of the limbs in cat and monkey. The representation of the trunk and extremities is located quite anteriorly in the ventrobasal complex of the rabbit. In the cat and monkey this representation reaches progressively very much farther caudally.

demonstrated anatomically. The termination of gracilis neurons in the lateral and of those of the cuneate in the medial parts of the external component of the ventrobasal complex, and of the trigeminal tracts in its arcuate component, has been established by degeneration experiments (47, 67, 203, 253, 260). The same pattern is shown by the locations of retrograde degenerations produced by lesions of the face, arm or leg areas of the postcentral gyrus (49, 50, 143, 249, 253).

An important confirmation of the location of the somatic relay nucleus of the thalamus and the pattern in it has come from the study of patients in whom the ventral thalamic nuclei were stimulated by means of stereotactically placed electrodes in the course of thalamotomy for intractable pain (174, 175). Stimulation of the ventrobasal complex produced somatic sensations referred to bodily parts in topographic patterns similar to those in the monkey. The sensations produced by thalamic stimulation were referred only to the contralateral side of the body.

Patterns in Postcentral Homologue of Cerebral Cortex

Since sensory somatic cortical projection patterns are described by Terzuolo & Adey, Chapter XXXIII of this work, it may be read for a survey of this information and the description of relations between the sensory somatic fields and the motor areas.

Here we wish to stress a few generalizations important for our considerations. The first essential point which emerges from the extensive mapping studies made mainly by Woolsey and his collaborators is that the cortical pattern in every mammal studied is a representation of the body form itself, with distortions which are almost certainly due to differences in the peripheral innervation density. These in turn appear clearly related to the development of one or another part of the body of a given mammal as a tactile organ. Hence, the share of a body part in cortical representation apparently reflects the relative value of this part for tactile discriminatory acuity.

The second point to be made is that the thalamic pattern is projected *in toto* upon the cortical receiving area with only such further distortions as could be expected by the transfer of a three-dimensional pattern upon essentially a two-dimensional surface. While this statement is made on the basis of studies done only in rabbit, cat and monkey, there is no reason to doubt that it is true for other mammals as well. There appears to be no part of the thalamic relay

nucleus which is functionally independent of the cortex, a finding which is concordant with the observation that an adequate cortical removal results in virtually complete retrograde degeneration of the ventrobasal complex. There is, therefore, no reason to assume that this complex is a terminal station for any sensory somatic processes in any mammal, even though a contrary thought in this respect was frequently entertained in the past, and is implicit in the concept of 'thalamic sensations'. For any given mammal, the pattern of cortical representation is probably essentially similar not only to the respective representation in the ventrobasal complex but to that in the dorsal column nuclei as well. The available data in this regard are very limited. It is clear enough, however, that this holds true for the cat and the same can be deduced for the macaque. Moreover, the long, sentient and prehensile tail of the spider monkey *Ateles* is known to have a large representation in the dorsal column nuclei (43) and this rather unusual distortion of the pattern is fully reflected in the cortical representation (45). It appears then that all relay nuclei of the system participate fully in elaboration of the projectional pattern, as must be the case if the organization of this projection is correlated with the peripheral innervation density. While this conclusion appears to be almost self-evident, it may be useful to stress it since even modern neurological thinking is often unduly dominated by the concept of different functional levels. This tends to neglect the viewing of the synaptic regions of a system as integral parts of the whole, if such regions happen to lie at different topographical levels.

An important question as to the functional meaning of a morphological pattern is posed by the cytoarchitectonic differentiation of the postcentral homologue. While the number of fields distinguished here may vary according to different criteria of various workers, there is hardly any doubt that this region possesses a definite gradient of morphological change. In primates, areas 3, 1, and 2 are classically distinguished in an orocaudal sequence and all these fields together form the substrate for the representation pattern of the body as determined by the evoked potential technique. It is possible that differences in organization of thalamocortical projections underlie the cytoarchitectural differentiation of these fields. In this relation it was reported recently (50) that at least areas 3 and 2 differ substantially in this regard from each other. Area 3 has been shown to receive exclusive projections from the ventrobasal complex, while area 2 seems to receive only a collateral outflow from it. What this important finding may imply functionally is at present obscure.

MODALITY COMPONENTS OF MEDIAL LEMNISCAL SYSTEM

A second general property of the lemniscal system is that it handles, within a single topographical pattern, activity evoked by tactile as well as kinesthetic and other mechanical stimuli acting upon deep tissues. At each successive level of the system neurons subserving various forms of mechanoreception are intermingled in a common topographical pattern. Nevertheless, single unit studies indicate that the individual neurons at each level retain their modality specificity. This rather surprising observation requires an immediate comment. In work with an intact animal a given unit at a central station of the system can be driven by stimuli delivered to the skin or to the deep tissues. It is usually a simple matter to be certain which of the two contains the effective receptors, and this can be proved by direct surgical dissection of the peripheral tissues. Some difficulty does arise when the receptive fields lie in highly specialized regions at the apices of the limbs, such as the claws of the cat. Nevertheless, the lack of any evidence that stimuli to the skin and to the deep tissues can excite the same neuron is quite striking. Since all the findings are derived from anesthetized preparations it is conceivable, although we believe rather unlikely, that his apparent lack of any clear excitatory interaction

is induced by general anesthesia, however light. In any case, it is at present both convenient and necessary to consider separately the activity in the lemniscal system evoked by stimulation of the skin, touch-pressure, and that provoked by stimulation of periosteum, bones and joints, deep sensibility.

Touch-Pressure

ADAPTIVE PROPERTIES OF RECEPTORS AND OF CENTRAL NEURONS. It has been known for a long time (2, 3, 6) that the mechanoreceptors of the skin and the afferent fibers to which they are connected are not uniform in all their properties. One can classify these afferents according to the following criteria: the adequate stimulus required for each, the size and conduction velocity of the fibers concerned, the rate of adaptation to steady stimuli and the sizes of the peripheral receptive fields (168, 280, 282). When working with the intact anesthetized animal, however, it is useful to classify the cutaneous mechanoreceptors as (i) those which respond steadily to steady stimuli and (ii) those which adapt quickly to such stimuli (fig. 5). Neural elements at each of the central relay stations of the lemniscal system, which are driven by mechanical stimulation of the skin, fall readily into one or the other of these classes (2, 3, 6, 7, 181; Berman, A. L., unpublished observations, and Mountcastle, V. B. & J. E. Rose, unpublished observations). The type of adaptation of a given unit is, so far as has been observed, an unchanging functional property. In general, afferents related to hairs are quickly adapting, while

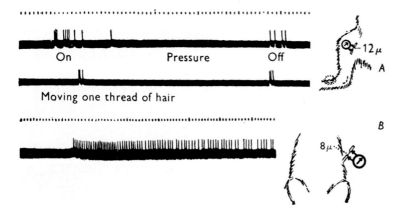

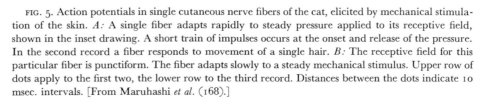

FIG. 5. Action potentials in single cutaneous nerve fibers of the cat, elicited by mechanical stimulation of the skin. *A:* A single fiber adapts rapidly to steady pressure applied to its receptive field, shown in the inset drawing. A short train of impulses occurs at the onset and release of the pressure. In the second record a fiber responds to movement of a single hair. *B:* The receptive field for this particular fiber is punctiform. The fiber adapts slowly to a steady mechanical stimulus. Upper row of dots apply to the first two, the lower row to the third record. Distances between the dots indicate 10 msec. intervals. [From Maruhashi *et al.* (168).]

slowly adapting 'skin pressure' units are driven by light mechanical stimulation of the skin surface. This correlation is probably not perfect, for some units excited by movement of specialized hairs have been observed which adapted slowly (68), and some rapidly adapting units have been noted whose peripheral receptive fields were located in hairless parts of the skin. Neurons responding steadily or with only an onset transient to mechanical stimulation of the skin have been observed at the level of the ventrobasal thalamic complex and in the postcentral homologue (181; and Mountcastle, V. B. & J. E. Rose, unpublished observations). Records of the action potentials of a postcentral cortical neuron responding steadily to a steady cutaneous stimulus are shown in figure 6. Results such as these indicate that neurons located at the various levels of the system reflect rather faithfully the discharge properties of either the peripheral receptors themselves or those of the first order neurons. At each level of the system the fast and slowly

adapting neurons are intermingled within a single topographical pattern.

PERIPHERAL RECEPTIVE FIELDS. Quantitative measurements of the cutaneous fields of distribution of single fibers have been very few. By recording unitary action potentials from fibers within the dorsal columns, Yamamoto et al. (280) found the peripheral fields to vary in size from a maximum of 2 to 3 cm² on the trunk, to a few square millimeters at the distal ends of the limbs. Working with single fibers in cutaneous nerves, Maruhashi et al. (168) have in general found similar results, though they emphasize that a) many large afferents may have truly 'spot-like' receptive fields, and b) that smaller (3 to 5 μ) slowly adapting afferents may have wide receptive fields in the range of 14 to 40 cm².

Only scattered data are available concerning the size of the fields which project upon neurons of the dorsal column nuclei and of the ventrobasal complex.

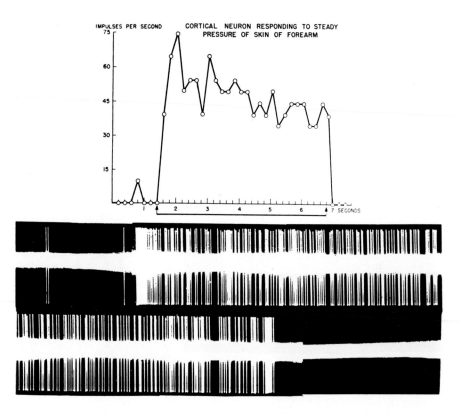

FIG. 6. Action potentials of a single cell in the postcentral gyrus of the monkey, *Macacus rhesus*. The neuron is driven by steady pressure applied to the cutaneous receptive field located on the volar surface of the contralateral forearm. Onset and release of pressure indicated by solid bar under the graph, which shows the number of impulses per second plotted at 200 msec. intervals. Experimental conditions described by Mountcastle et al. (183). [From Mountcastle, V. B. & T. P. S. Powell, manuscript in preparation.]

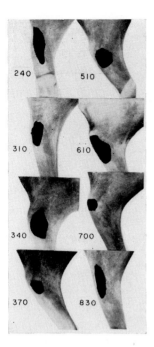

FIG. 7. Eight excitatory peripheral receptive skin fields of the cat's foreleg, stimulation of which activated eight single neurons in the contralateral postcentral cortex. The neurons in question were isolated at the levels indicated (in μ) below the cortical surface in the course of a single microelectrode penetration made perpendicularly to that surface. The fields are restricted in size and are almost identical in location. [Modified from Mountcastle (181).]

Some measurements, however, have been made of the fields which project upon neurons of the cerebral cortex (181). Several such fields are shown in figure 7, and the graph of figure 8 relates the sizes of the peripheral fields to their location upon the body surface.

PROJECTION OF PERIPHERAL RECEPTIVE FIELDS UPON CENTRAL NEURONS. Figure 9 indicates that not all parts of the peripheral receptive field of a thalamic neuron have an equal potency for excitation of that cell. The security of the relation varies from a maximum usually, though not always, near the center of the field to a minimum at its edge. The synaptic linkages converging upon the central neuron from afferent fibers innervating the edge of the field are apparently so few as to provoke only minimal activation of the cell, as measured by the early repetitive response (which will be defined below).

From data of this kind it is possible to reconstruct the pattern of events set in motion in the lemniscal system by a brief mechanical stimulus delivered to the skin. Before doing so it is convenient to describe the response properties of single neurons of the system.

Response Patterns of Neurons of Medial Lemniscal System

REPETITIVENESS OF RESPONSE TO SINGLE STIMULUS. All the evidence at hand from study of first order axons (168, 280) indicates that even very brief mechanical stimuli to hairs or skin surface elicit a short train of impulses in afferent nerve fibers (see fig. 5), even for quickly adapting elements. Such an afferent input elicits from the second (15), third (208) and fourth order neurons (183) short high frequency trains of discharges, a response pattern which is highly characteristic of the system (fig. 10). Amassian & DeVito (15) have shown that the early repetitive discharge in the cuneate nucleus occurs under different conditions of anesthesia, in the unanesthetized or decerebrate animal, and apart from variation of body temperature from 33 to 41 °C. It is important to emphasize that it occurs also when the afferent volley is made up of a single impulse in each synchronously active fiber. The repetitive discharge therefore is a general property of the postsynaptic cell at the first relay of the system, and indeed of those at each successive relay thereafter.

The repetitive response is not absolutely stable even in the deeply anesthetized animal. Here, when exactly the same peripheral stimulus activating a given neuron is repeated at slow intervals some variation in the number of impulses in the early repetitive response does indeed occur. In a population of such responses, many contain a characteristic number of impulses per response (the modal value) while some responses contain more and others fewer impulses (fig. 11). The shift in the modal value indicates sensitively the changing parameters of the stimulus, e.g. its intensity, frequency or position (see figs. 9, 10, 12 and 13).

RESPONSE OF SYSTEM TO SINGLE STIMULUS. Considering the variations in the response of a single neuron when the stimulus shifts across the receptive field it seems possible to reconstruct the events in a population of cells set in motion by a single stimulus, even though it has not yet been possible to record the activity of many single neurons simultaneously. A brief, strong peripheral stimulus sets up a burst of impulses in a number of afferent fibers. If the stimulus is brief enough only one impulse occurs in each fiber; if it is strong enough nearly all fibers are activated synchronously. The impulses are conducted into the cord and can be assumed to impinge upon a restricted

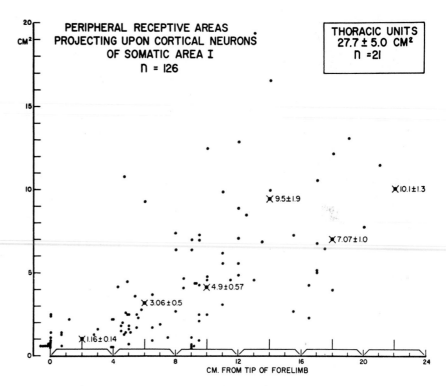

FIG. 8. Plot relating the size (in square centimeters) of excitatory cutaneous receptive fields for cortical neurons to the distances of the centers of those fields from the tip of the forelimb of the cat. Crossed dots locate means (and standard errors) for these fields when grouped into classes by 4 cm distances from limb tip. The receptive fields close to the tip of the limb are small in size and usually comparable in area. With the increased distance from the tip both the size of the fields and the variability between them increase greatly. [From Mountcastle (181).]

group of cells within the dorsal column nuclei. The cells in the center of the group will receive a maximum number of synaptic impingements and will discharge repetitive trains at high frequency, probably with shortest latency. Cells surrounding the center are presumably excited to discharge trains of fewer impulses at longer latency and at lower frequency, while cells at the edges of the discharge zone will discharge single impulses at even longer latencies. That a similar distribution of activity occurs among third order cells of the thalamic relay nucleus and among fourth order cells in the cortical receiving area can be deduced from single unit studies of those regions (13, 157–159, 183, 208).

RESPONSES TO TWO STIMULI AT DIFFERENT INTERVALS. Some information concerning the capacity of the somatic afferent system to relay activity has been obtained by measuring the ability of the system to respond to a second peripheral stimulus at various time intervals after the first. Marshall (166) and

Marshall *et al.* (167) have shown for the thalamic and cortical slow waves that the recovery time is greatly prolonged by anesthetic agents. Single unit studies have confirmed and extended these original observations (13, 183; and Mountcastle, V. B. & J. E. Rose, unpublished observations). The recovery time of single neurons in the unanesthetized animal is not yet known, though it probably is much briefer than the recovery time observed in an anesthetized animal. In the anesthetized animal, however, the anesthesia itself is not the only factor affecting the recovery time. At the same anesthetic level the unresponsive time of the system shortens as the strength of the initial stimulus decreases.

RESPONSES TO REPETITIVE STIMULI AT DIFFERENT FREQUENCIES. It is clear from study of individual neurons that the two-stimulus experiment does not at all specify the capacity of the system to respond when trains of stimuli are applied. Individual neurons at any level show one of two types of behavior. Figure 12

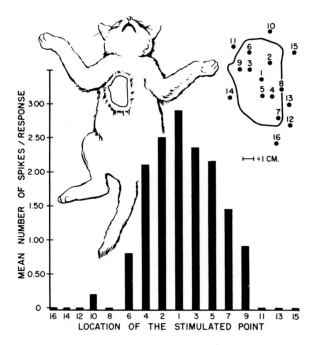

FIG. 9. Graph relating the average number of impulses discharged per response to the position of the stimulus at several points located in and around the receptive field. Inset drawing on the left indicates the location of the receptive field; inset drawing on right the positions of the stimulated points. Electrical stimulus of the same strength is delivered through a pair of needle electrodes thrust into the skin. The same unit located in the ventrobasal complex of the thalamus is responding throughout. Graph is based on 1208 responses. Cat under deep pentobarbital anesthesia. [From Mountcastle, V. B. & J. E. Rose, unpublished observations.]

illustrates the first type, shown here for a thalamic cell. Several characteristic phenomena for this type of response are as follows:

a) Equilibration. The neuron follows the stimulus rate beat-for-beat to a certain level, usually in the range of 30 to 70 per sec. When trains of stimuli at higher rates are delivered, the neuron continues to respond at about the same overall rate. There is no desynchronization, however, for each response occurs in a fixed and definite relation to a particular stimulus. The equilibration occurs because some stimuli randomly distributed throughout the train fail to evoke responses.

b) Early silent period. The records of figure 12 show that while the first stimulus elicits a response, the next few (i.e. numbers 2, 3, 4, 5, etc., in fig. 12) may be ineffectual. The succeeding stimuli, however, once again become effective. This early silent period is of about the same duration as the unresponsive time of

the system, as measured in the two stimulus experiment under the same experimental conditions. The important point is that the presentation of trains of stimuli 'recruits excitability' so that the system

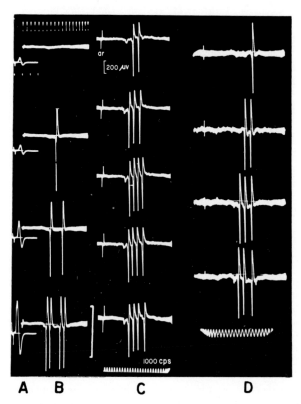

FIG. 10. Shifts in the number of impulses per response and changes in the latent periods with increased strength of the peripheral stimulus for three units located at successively higher synaptic regions of the medial lemniscal system of the cat. Stimulus strength increases in each column from above downward. Time lines for all columns, 1000 cycles per sec. *B:* Discharges of a single neuron of the cuneate nucleus evoked by stimulation of the ipsilateral radial cutaneous nerve. Note the shift in latencies and the increase in the number of spikes with increase in stimulus strength. The strength of the stimulus is indicated by the traces at the extreme left (*A*) which show increases in the size of the compound action potential in the radial nerve. [From Amassian & DeVito (15).] *C:* Increase in number of impulses of the early repetitive response of a single neuron of the ventrobasal thalamic complex evoked by increasingly stronger electrical stimuli (*ar*) delivered to the skin of the contralateral first digit of the forepaw. Traces show the modal number of the discharge train at each stimulus strength and a latency which is close to the mean latency at this strength. [From Rose & Mountcastle (208).] *D:* A similar series for a neuron located in the first somatic cortical field. Electrical stimulation of the skin of the contralateral foreleg. Each trace shows again the modal number for the discharge train at given strength of the stimulus and the latency, near to the mean latency at this strength. [From Mountcastle *et al.* (183).]

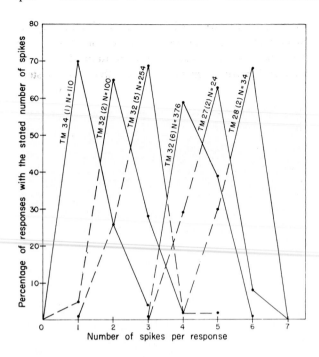

FIG. 11. Curves illustrating the distributions of response populations around their modal values for several neurons of the thalamic ventrobasal nuclear complex of the cat. Number of impulses per response to a brief peripheral stimulus graphed against the percentage of responses with the stated number of impulses. Although values on the abscissa are always integers, the points belonging to the same distribution are connected by lines to aid the eye. The number which follows the letters *TM* identifies the experiment, the number in parentheses identifies the neuron studied. *N* indicates the number of responses upon which each graph is based. Locus of peripheral stimulus constant for each unit. In each case the neuron is activated by electrical stimulation of the contralateral skin. Locus of stimulation: *TM* 34(1), second toe on hindfoot; *TM* 32(2), lower abdomen; *TM* 32(5), upper thigh; *TM* 32(6), ankle; *TM* 27(2), wrist; *TM* 28(2), wrist. Note that most responses in each series do not differ from the modal value by more than one impulse. [From Rose & Mountcastle (208).]

transmits at a higher frequency than that predicted by the recovery cycle studies.

c) Mode reduction. The records of figure 12 show finally that, when responding at higher frequencies, the cell discharges but a single impulse to each stimulus which is effective in contrast to the repetitive response to the first stimulus of the train. The repetitive response 'singles up' as a rule when the frequency of the stimuli increases beyond 10 to 15 per sec.

The equilibration type of response occurs in about 60 per cent of the neurons studied at thalamic and cortical levels. The remaining neurons display a different sort of behavior. While following the stimulus

rate up to values which differ greatly for different units, they respond to the presentation of still faster trains with but an initial response and are thereafter silent during the train, or discharge randomly at the spontaneous rate (see fig. 13). It is not clear at present whether the 'equilibration' and the 'cut-off' types of response can be obtained for the same unit by suitable manipulation of the stimulus. Most of the units observed which show the 'cut-off' response pattern follow only a low rate of stimulation. On the other hand, it seems to be true, at least occasionally, that a typical equilibration type of response becomes a cut-off type when the stimulus rate is made very high (200 to 300 per sec.).

AFFERENT INHIBITION. It has been shown recently (181, 198) that the afferent volleys evoked by peripheral stimuli while excitatory for some cells of the system will tend to inhibit others (fig. 14). All inhibitory phenomena are very sensitive to anesthetic agents and are probably at least partially abolished even under very light general anesthesia. Nevertheless, the inhibition of both the spontaneous and the evoked activity of central neurons has been observed for a considerable number of cells (198). The peripheral inhibitory receptive field for a given neuron (in the postcentral cortex) may surround or lie adjacent to its excitatory field. It is an interesting observation that a cell excited, for example by movement of a joint, may be inhibited by skin stimulation, although a purely excitatory intermodality interaction has not thus far been demonstrated for units driven from the skin and from deep receptors. In the cortex, pairs of cells which are in one case excited and in the other inhibited from the same receptive field have been observed at a single electrode position. They must therefore lie very close to one another. This suggests, of course, that afferent inhibition may play an important role in reducing the discharge zone of cells activated by a local peripheral stimulus. It need hardly be added that restricted, sharply focused discharge zones may be instrumental in recognizing a single localized peripheral event and in more complex discriminations as well.

SUMMARY. The single unit studies at several stations of the somatic afferent system have produced a considerable mass of data concerning the relation of a discharge of a single cell to the quantitative parameters of the peripheral stimuli. For a population of cells the data allow a reconstruction of the distribution of activity set up by a single brief peripheral stimulus occurring in that population. However, no informa-

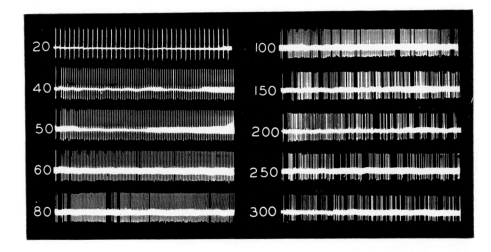

FIG. 12. Responses of a single neuron of ventrobasal thalamic nuclear complex of the cat to electrical stimulation of skin of the contralateral foreleg. The stimuli were delivered at different frequencies per second which are indicated by the numbers on the left. Note reduction of modal value and equilibration of response with increasing frequencies of stimulation, and the early silent period. Stimulus artefacts are not visible. [From Mountcastle, V. B. & J. E. Rose, unpublished observations.]

tion is yet available which permits a complete description of the sequential changes in neural events brought about by a natural stimulus in a completely unanesthetized animal. Underlying studies of this type is the assumption that perception of a local peripheral event depends in the first instance upon a local zone of cortical activity of abrupt onset, and that perception of more complex forms of stimuli (e.g. two-point discrimination, form and contour recognition, etc.) may depend upon the interaction of many such zones of activity. One of the problems in sensory physiology at the present time is to determine in some detail the patterns of cortical activity evoked by peripheral stimuli of some spatial and temporal complexity. It seems likely that single unit studies will advance the solution of this problem.

KINESTHESIS OR SENSE OF POSITION AND MOVEMENTS OF JOINTS

It is apparent that information concerning the orientation of the body in space and of the spatial relations between its parts depends upon afferent inputs from both somatic sensory and vestibular receptors as well as from the visual apparatus. The thesis is presented here that the somatic sensory component, which we shall refer to as kinesthesis or the sense of position and movement of the joints, depends

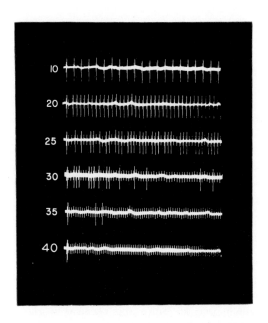

FIG. 13. Responses of a single neuron of the ventrobasal thalamic nuclear complex of the cat to electrical stimulation of the skin near the first digit of the contralateral forepaw, delivered at different frequencies. Note reduction of modal value as frequency increases from 10 to 20 or more per sec. At frequency of 40 per sec., or higher, the neuron responded to the first stimulus of a train and failed to respond thereafter: 'cut-off' characteristic. Small deflections are stimulus artefacts. [From Mountcastle, V. B. & J. E. Rose, unpublished observations.]

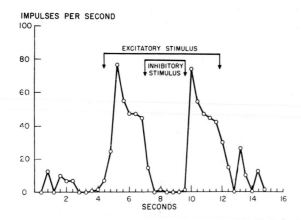

FIG. 14. Interacting effects of excitatory and inhibitory peripheral stimuli upon the discharge rate of a single neuron of area 1 of the postcentral gyrus of the monkey. Graph plots the average frequencies of discharge of the neuron in each successive 400 msec. period. Neuron excited by internal rotation of shoulder joint, indicated by upper bar, and inhibited by pressure upon skin of the palm, indicated by lower bar; both contralateral. Note that recovery from inhibition duplicates onset of excitation, with rapid onset transient and decline to a less rapid firing level. [From Mountcastle, V. B. & T. P. S. Powell, manuscript in preparation.]

upon the receptor organs associated with the joints. Activity set up in those receptors by the steady position or movement of the joints is relayed through the medial lemniscal system, in a topographical pattern at each precortical relay and in the somatic sensory cortex itself which is mutually interlocked with the pattern representing the cutaneous sensory sheet. Since this is contrary to the widely held belief that kinesthesis depends as well upon afferent input from muscle stretch receptors, the evidence for it will be presented in some detail.

Muscle Stretch Receptors and Kinesthesis

Evidence accumulates from recent research that the rate of discharge of the stretch receptors of muscle is not linearly or even constantly related to the length of the muscle per se. Since the classical work of Matthews (169) it has been known that the Golgi tendon organs discharge afferent impulses at a rate related to tension. The tension to which these receptors are subjected depends upon the length of the muscle, i.e. upon the joint angle, and upon the force exerted by the muscle against its load by its active contraction which in turn depends on the activity of the alpha motoneurons. It follows that the number of

active Golgi organs and their rates of discharge are not variables dependent solely upon the angle of the joint or joints across which the muscle works; these receptors cannot, therefore, inform reliably of joint position.

The spindle organ receptors of muscle are subject to even more complex influences. Matthews (169) had shown that these receptors are excited by stretch of the muscle but cease to discharge as the muscle is shortened by alpha motoneuron action. They may be completely silent when tension at the tendon is maximal. The work of Leksell (153) revealed, however, that the smaller efferent fibers of the ventral root, the gamma motoneurons, produce upon discharge an increase in spindle organ activity, even when the muscle shortens. These observations have been extended recently (102, 129–132, 144) and it is now well known that the gamma efferents condition afferent input from the spindles and thus play an important role in voluntary movement and reflex regulation. More recently Granit and his colleagues (62, 103, 104) have described the central nervous control of the gamma motoneurons and hence of spindle organ discharge, and Eldred & Hagbarth (63) their reflex regulation by cutaneous afferents. Further details of the function of the gamma efferent-spindle afferent loop are presented by Eldred in Chapter XLI of this work, and an excellent general review of the subject is provided in the monograph by Granit (101). The important point in the present consideration is that spindle activity may vary from zero to maximum independently of the length or tension of the muscle; these receptors, like the Golgi tendon organs, cannot signal muscle length or joint angle.

These facts alone are impressive for the argument that stretch receptors of muscle are not likely to inform of joint position. Complementary to them is the experimental observation of Lloyd & McIntyre (160) that the large stretch afferents from muscle do not project upwards in the dorsal columns but relay in the column of Clarke-Stilling into ascending systems terminating in the cerebellum. This observation has been confirmed and extended in an elegant series of studies (128, 150–152, 163) which showed that group I-a afferents from muscle spindle organs relay into the dorsal spinocerebellar tract. In addition, Oscarsson (190) has reported that group I-b fibers from tendon organs project upon the cells of origin of the ventral spinocerebellar tract. Complementary also are the negative observations that direct stretch of muscle produces no detectable response in the postcentral homologue of the cerebral cortex (182). Nor have single unit analysis studies revealed any cells at levels of thalamus or cortex which could be activated by stretch of muscle (181; Mountcastle, V. B. & T. P. S. Powell, manuscript in preparation; and Mountcastle, V. B. & J. E. Rose, unpublished observations).

Data obtained from experiments in which the system is activated by electrical stimulation of bared muscle nerves are somewhat discordant. Mountcastle *et al.* (182) reported that when the afferent volley was confined to group I afferent fibers (which innervate the annulospiral endings and the Golgi tendon organs), no responses were evoked in the postcentral homologue in anesthetized animals. Nor were such responses observed when the stimulus strength was increased to activate group II afferents (which innervate the flower spray stretch receptors). They did observe, again in anesthetized animals, that when group III fibers of the muscle nerves were activated cortical responses of long latency appeared. The peripheral endings of group III afferents are thought to be bare nerve terminals and there is no evidence that they are sensitive to mechanical changes in the muscle; it seems safe to assume that these endings are of no significance for position sense. Perhaps they, together with the C-fiber afferents, mediate the sensations of muscle fatigue and pain. These observations are in agreement with the observation that direct stretch of muscle evokes no detectable response in the cerebral cortex.

Some workers (84, 86, 171) find, on the other hand, that cortical responses do appear when the afferent volley is thought to contain the group II and possibly group I components. Perhaps these discordant results are due to the different muscle nerves used, for it is known that some fibers from joint receptors, periosteum and deep fascia, may travel in some muscle nerves and are of group II size (76, 225, 231–233). Whatever the final answer, it is clear that muscle stretch afferents are unlikely to play a role in position sense for they are under control of the gamma efferent loop and may discharge over their full frequency range at any muscle length.

Innervation of Joints

The tissues in and about the joints clearly receive a rich innervation; [the older literature on this matter has been reviewed by Skoglund (225)]. This innervation, the receptor organs in the ligaments and the joint capsules, and the functional properties of the receptors have been intensively studied in recent years. The articular innervation in a variety of animals and in man has been described by a number of workers (16, 18, 28, 29, 75–81, 215, 216, 225, 279). Afferent fibers from some joints have been shown to travel in both muscle and cutaneous nerves. The myelinated fibers vary in size between 2 and 16 μ and according to Gardner (76) the spectrum displays definite peaks between 2 to 5 and 7 to 10 μ, while Skoglund's measurements (225) suggest a unimodal distribution around a peak at about 3 to 6 μ. Articular nerves contain large numbers of unmyelinated fibers, some of sympathetic origin, while others are undoubtedly afferent dorsal root C fibers. It is clear then that articular nerves resemble in composition purely cutaneous ones.

Joint Receptors and Their Discharge Patterns

Some recent histological studies indicate three types of receptor organs in articular tissue (16, 18, 28, 76).

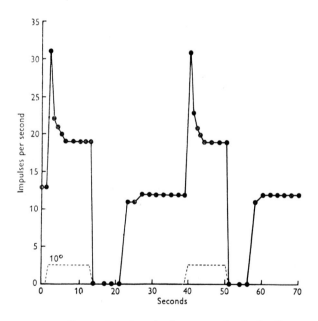

FIG. 15. Graph of the impulse frequency of a single afferent neuron innervating the capsule of the knee joint of the cat. Graph plots frequency of impulses against time as the joint is moved through 10 degrees of flexion and back again, as indicated by the dashed line. Note onset transient during movement, adaptation to a more or less steady frequency of discharge during steady joint displacement, rapid drop in frequency when joint moves away from excitatory position, postexcitatory silent period, recovery to 'resting' frequency of discharge, and almost exact repetition of the pattern of discharge when the movement is repeated. [From Boyd & Roberts (29).]

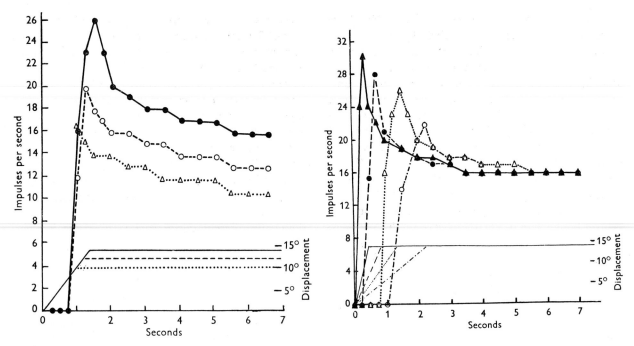

FIG. 16. *Left:* Graphs of the impulse frequency in a single afferent fiber innervating the capsule of the knee joint of the cat, showing frequency of discharge against time during flexion at a rate of 10 degrees per sec. carried through three different angles: open triangles, 10 degrees; open circles, 12 degrees; closed circles, 14 degrees. The upper curves show the frequencies of the impulses, the lower ones the angular displacements from a position of 132 degrees of extension, where this receptor did not discharge. Note that steady state frequency is higher for greater joint displacements. *Right:* Similar graphs for the same afferent neuron during movements of the joint between the same positions at four different rates: closed triangles, 35 degrees per sec.; closed circles, 17 degrees per sec.; open triangles, 10 degrees per sec.; open circles, 6 degrees per sec. The displacements are indicated by thin lines. Note that while onset transients differ, the steady impulse frequency in the final position is the same in each case. [From Boyd & Roberts (29).]

By far the most common are the 'spray-type' endings which resemble those described in the skin by Ruffini. They are located in the connective tissue capsule of the joints but not in its synovial lining membrane and are supplied by myelinated fibers ranging in diameter from 7 to 10 μ (225). They are well fitted by location and response properties to signal the steady position of the joint and the direction, rate and extent of joint movement (29, 225). They respond at low threshold with a rapid onset transient as the joint moves in a direction which causes their excitation (fig. 15). The rate of discharge during the movement is a function of its speed and extent (fig. 16); the steady state of discharge at a given excitatory displacement is independent of the rate at which the initial displacement occurred (fig. 17).

These slowly adapting receptors subserve angles of about 15 degrees. For any given joint different members of the population of receptors have their excitatory angles located at different positions along the

range of joint movement. Some have excitatory angles placed at one end of this range, responding at maximal rate at either full flexion, or full extension (figs. 17, 18). At least that is true for the knee joint of the cat which has been most intensively studied, but there is no reason to believe that qualitatively different conditions exist in other joints or other species, including man, for the articular innervation has been found to be remarkably uniform in all species studied.

A second slowly adapting receptor resembling in appearance the Golgi tendon organ has been found associated with the ligaments of the joints, and has been found to be innervated by fibers 7 to 10 μ in diameter. This type is much less numerous than the Ruffini type endings described above and possesses similar discharge properties (16, 225). Very rarely, first order afferents are observed which adapt very quickly to joint movement which excites them. Although some disagreement exists (76) they are thought to arise from modified Vater-Pacinian corpuscles

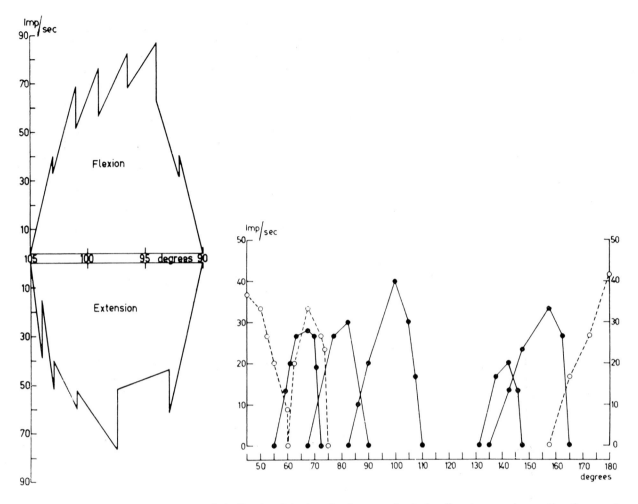

FIG. 17 *Left:* Graphs of the impulse frequency in single afferent neuron innervating the capsule of the knee joint of the cat, as the joint is moved in steps through the 'excitatory angle' for the receptor, in opposite directions. After each small step of the movement the frequency is allowed to reach an adapted rate. The two curves are almost mirror images. [From Skoglund (225).]

FIG. 18 *Right:* Graphs of impulse frequencies for eight single neurons innervating slowly adapting receptors in the capsule of the knee joint of the cat. The adapted impulse frequency is plotted against position of the joint in degrees. *Solid lines* show values for five units in one experiment; *dotted lines* show those for three units in another. The figure is not fully representative for the distribution of endings which are successively activated during full movement since in general endings which cause maximal adapted discharge rates are more numerous immediately before or at full flexion or full extension than in the intermediate positions of the joint. The sensitive ranges (15 to 30 degrees) are representative of the behavior of most endings. [From Skoglund (225).]

located in the pericapsular connective tissue (225). They are innervated by the largest afferents in the articular nerves.

Central Projection of Joint Afferents

The evidence that receptors in and about joints do indeed project into the lemniscal system was obtained by gross electrode recording of the electrical responses evoked in the ventrobasal thalamic complex and the somatic sensory cortex by mechanical stimulation of those tissues (182) and by electrical stimulation of articular nerves (83, 86). Such experiments indicate that the afferents from bones and joints form together with afferents from cutaneous receptors a common topographic pattern. Knowledge of this projection has been greatly extended by single unit studies. Some single elements in the ventral thalamic nucleus and in the postcentral homologue are activated by, and only by, movement of the joints (181; and Mountcastle, V. B. & J. E. Rose, unpublished observations). The great majority of these neurons respond not only to transient rotation of the joint to

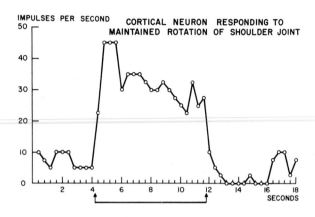

FIG. 19. Impulse frequency of a single neuron of area 1 of the postcentral gyrus of the macaque, plotted continuously as average frequency in each 400 msec. period. Neuron is a deep joint unit. At onset of rotation of the contralateral shoulder joint there is a rapid rise in discharge frequency which declines slightly to a more or less steady rate of discharge during steadily maintained joint rotation (period of stimulation indicated by black bar). Note rapid fall of frequency when joint is returned to its neutral position, and the postexcitatory period of low frequency discharge. [From Mountcastle, V. B. & T. P. S. Powell, manuscript in preparation.]

which they are related but continue to discharge impulses steadily when the joint is held within the excitatory angle, subserved by the unit (see figs. 19, 20). They adapt as a rule very slowly. The onset transient is a function of the degree and rate of joint movement; the subsequent steady state of activity is a function of joint angle only. In the cortex, as in the periphery, excitatory angles for different neurons related to a given joint are different, and some units of the group are active at any joint position. Phasic joint movements may recruit additional neurons, increase the discharge frequency in some neurons already active and decrease it in still others. From this description a generality is once again confirmed; the discharge patterns of central neurons of the lemniscal system are determined by those of the peripheral receptors to which they are linked.

It is an observation of interest that pairs of closely related cells in the cerebral cortex may be reciprocally related to a given joint. One of the pair is active and the other silent as the joint moves in one direction, and the reverse occurs when the movement alternates (181) (fig. 20). Whether the reciprocity is due to some central reciprocal inhibitory event or simply to alternate loading and unloading of appropriate groups of receptors on the two sides of the joint is unknown. In any case, it is likely that such a mutual interaction could serve to increase the discriminatory capacity in respect to the rate and extent of joint movement.

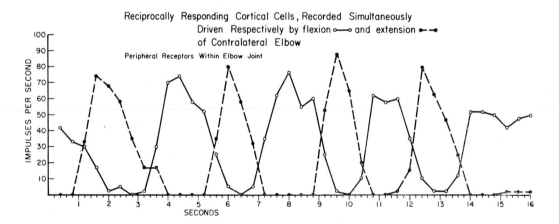

FIG. 20. Impulse frequency graphs of two neurons of postcentral homologue of the cerebral cortex of the cat. Discharges of the two units observed simultaneously at a single microelectrode position. Units responded reciprocally to alternating flexions and extensions of the contralateral elbow. Graphs plot continuously the average frequencies for each consecutive 400 msec. period. Impulse frequency reaches zero for each unit when the joint reaches the position maximally excitatory for the other unit. During fourteenth and fifteenth seconds the joint was held in steady extension, and the extension unit fires steadily, while the flexion unit is almost completely silent. [From Mountcastle (181).]

The thesis that the sense of position and movements of the joints is dependent upon joint receptors themselves fits well the clinical observations. However, we shall not discuss here the extensive clinical and psychophysical data available on this subject; we refer the interested reader to a series of articles by Goldscheider collected in a book (99). His careful work and his clear recognition of the joints as the source for kinesthetic sensations are unfortunately usually forgotten or disregarded in modern physiological texts perhaps because he was satisfied to treat these sensations within the concept of 'muscle sense' (*Muskelsinn*).

Projections of Deep Receptors Other Than in Joints

Studies of the modality properties of individual neurons of the lemniscal system at thalamic and cortical levels have shown a class of cells whose peripheral receptive fields lie in deep fascia (181; and Mountcastle, V. B. & J. E. Rose, unpublished observations). These fields are of similar shape and size as those for neurons driven from the skin (see fig. 7). The units are driven by very light mechanical stimuli to the fascia, and the threshold for activity is so low that even a very small displacement of the overlying skin may evoke their discharge. They may also be driven by pressure changes occurring in the deep fascial compartments when the enclosed muscles contract. It is reasonable to assume that this class of neurons functions in the overall sense of touch-pressure, for they respond to all but the very weakest of stimuli impinging upon the skin overlying their own fascial receptive fields.

Other neurons of this class are activated by direct pressure upon the periosteum. What role they may play in kinesthesis or some other aspect of deep sensibility is unknown.

FUNCTIONAL ORGANIZATION OF FIRST SOMATIC
CORTICAL FIELD

One of the central problems of neurophysiology at the present time is to understand the functional mechanisms of any given region of the cerebral cortex. Investigators proceed on the premise that if they can determine the patterns of neural activity entering a cortical region, the modifications of those patterns occurring across intracortical synaptic relays ('integrative action') and the spatial and temporal patterns of output from the region, they will then be able to reconstruct with some insight the way in which the particular cortical region operates. In the past few

years much effort has been expended to study the response properties of single cells in the first somatic field, the way these cells are activated from the thalamus, the relations of the unitary discharges to the evoked slow cortical wave on the surface of the cortex and in its depths and the relation of single cell discharges to the cortical EEG (13, 14, 157–159), matters recently reviewed by Albe-Fessard (7). Recently Mountcastle (181) has suggested on the basis of his studies that a vertical group of cells extending across all the cellular layers acts, as it were, as a functional cortical unit. Three observations are the reasons for this suggestion. *a*) The neurons of such a vertical group are all related to the same, or nearly the same, peripheral receptive field. This observation establishes also that the topographical pattern present on the surface of the cortex extends throughout its depth. *b*) The neurons of such a vertical group belong as a rule to the same modality group, i.e. they are activated by the same type of peripheral stimulus. This implies that a small group of thalamocortical fibers entering the cortex is activated by a single mode of peripheral stimulation and in turn activates a narrow vertical column of cortical cells. *c*) All cells of such a vertical column discharge on the average at more or less the same latency to a brief peripheral stimulus. The discharges are thus grouped within the time limits of a few milliseconds into an initial firing pattern. This observation is based, however, only upon the first response of cortical cells, the latency of which is known to be sensitive to various parameters of the peripheral stimulus.

The possibility that a vertical column of cells tends to behave as a functional unit appears acceptable anatomically both from the cytoarchitectural point of view and as regards the connections of such a vertical column as seen in the Golgi material (162). The subpial dicing experiments of several cortical fields (226, 227) could also be interpreted to imply that a complex cortical activity is still possible as long as the cortical organization in depth is preserved.

It is, of course, not implied by these observations that the cortex is organized into sets of isolated, vertically oriented tissue prisms. It appears, however, that at least for the incoming activity a columnar vertical organization is of special significance.

SPINOTHALAMIC SYSTEM

In comparison to our knowledge of the lemniscal system, that pertaining to the tactile activity of the spinothalamic system is quite inadequate since many basic questions concerning it are still not solved. As we define the system it consists of the spinothalamic tract arising in the posterior horns and of the bulbo-thalamic tract originating in the spinal nucleus of the fifth nerve.[2] The system is known to transmit impulses provoked by painful and thermal stimuli but there is adequate evidence as well that some tactile impulses are also relayed through it.

Location of Tactile Fibers in Spinothalamic System

It is customary to distinguish within the spinothalamic system of the spinal cord (though not in the bulbothalamic tract) a ventral and a lateral spinothalamic pathway. The first is assumed to conduct tactile impulses, the second is known to be important for arousal of painful and thermal sensations. The ventral spinothalamic tract is usually believed to lie in the medial aspect of the anterolateral column. Clinical experience in man indicates that some fibers in this column must be concerned with touch since tactile anesthesia results only if in addition to a destruction of a posterior column on one side a contra-lateral injury is present somewhere in the region of the anterolateral column. On the other hand, only partial impairment in tactile sensation occurs when either of these columns is selectively injured. In fact, it has been frequently believed in the past that a destruction of the anterolateral column alone does not lead to any deficits in tactile sensations. Foerster & Gagel (71), Foerster (70) and Kroll (141), however, using finer testing techniques were able to determine some such deficits after anterolateral cordotomies.

---

[2] Similar to the uncertainty which prevails in respect to the secondary trigeminal pathways arising in the main sensory nucleus of the fifth nerve (see p. 396), a considerable confusion and controversy exists in regard to the central course of the bulbothalamic tract. Wallenberg (259) who described this pathway maintained that it ascends in the dorsolateral portion of the reticular substance of the brain stem tegmentum. He believed that it terminates in the region of the centrum medianum and in the arcuate component of the ventrobasal complex. Bürgi's observations (36) imply that some of these fibers may end also in the n. lateralis posterior. Although Wallenberg's findings as to the course of this tract in the brain stem have been repeatedly confirmed (93, 241), many observers conclude that the bulbothalamic tract crosses to join the medial lemniscus and separates from it again at the level of the mid-brain to join the spinothalamic tract. We believe that Wallenberg's original description is likely to be correct and that contrary results are probably due to lesions involving the posterior column nuclei. For a contrary view and the review of the literature on this subject see Bürgi (36).

The deficits are generally described as an increase in threshold for tactile stimuli and a decrease in the number of 'sensory spots' without any readily detectable impairment in the capacity to localize the stimuli or to discriminate between them. These observations have been confirmed at all levels of the spinothalamic system by a number of subsequent workers who were interested in this problem (58, 109–111, 256, 270, 274). A striking aspect of tactile impairment is that tickle sensations disappear with some lesions of the anterolateral column and that with bilateral lesions severe disturbances of sensations in the sexual sphere are present.

Even though it is established that the spinothalamic system must relay some tactile impulses, any exact definition of the fibers concerned and therefore the very existence of a separate ventral spinothalamic tract as a tactile component of the spinothalamic system seems to be based mainly on suppositions. Foerster & Gagel (71) and Foerster (70) concluded that fibers concerned with temperature lie dorsally to the fibers concerned with pain in the lateral spinothalamic tract and they assigned on a hypothetical basis the anterior column to touch and pressure. Walker (255) modified this scheme and believed the fibers concerned with touch to lie in the most medial aspects of the anterolateral column and, although he emphasized the apparent overlap, he retained the basic sequence of separate fiber systems for temperature, pain and touch. Many recent observers stress the apparent or real overlap of fibers concerned with pain and temperature [for a review of the literature see White & Sweet (273)], but they are usually non-committal on the problem of touch. Apparently this is so because touch deficits resulting from anterior cordotomy, or tractotomies performed at the level of the medulla, pons or midbrain are of little or no clinical discomfort to the patients, because they are difficult to detect and evaluate without special tests, and because many observers were primarily interested in the problem of pain. In consequence, despite the very large number of operative procedures performed in man on the spinothalamic system there is still no conclusive evidence as to whether touch deficits, such as they are, result from injury of a separate sector of the spinothalamic tract or whether fibers concerned with touch are modality specific but are intermingled with other fibers of the system. Finally, it is possible that no modality specific tactile fibers exist within the system. The fact that after anterior cordotomies tickle sensations in the analgesic areas have been reported as always lost (70, 71), as almost always preserved (134) or only sometimes lost (273) could perhaps be interpreted to mean that at least some degree of separation exists between the fibers concerned with touch and those relevant for pain. This could be expected if the different observers differed in their routine sectioning of the anterolateral column in regard to the extent and the depth of the cut. However, more exact work is needed before one can conclude that the classical notions in respect to touch hold true for the spinothalamic system.

Origin of Spinothalamic System

The knowledge that large cutaneous fibers are activated by mechanoreceptors and that painful and thermal stimuli usually activate small fibers was obviously largely responsible for the deductions regarding the origin of the ventral spinothalamic tract. This tract is often conceived as originating solely from those posterior horn cells which themselves are assumed to be activated by the collaterals of the large myelinated fibers of the medial division of the posterior root. The lateral spinothalamic tract, on the other hand, is pictured as originating from cells which are discharged by the small fibers of the lateral division of this root. The evidence at hand is clearly discordant with such concepts since it is certain that tactile stimuli can activate A fibers of different sizes and since it is probable that even some C fibers can be so activated as well (see p. 394). It follows, therefore, that no cell in the posterior horn which emits an axon into the spinothalamic tract can be excluded at present as potentially responsive to tactile stimuli. The evidence secured with the retrograde degeneration method after cutting the anterolateral column (71, 146, 147, 178) implies that only the large apical, pericornual and basal cells of the posterior horn give rise to the spinothalamic tract. The findings of Kuru (147) suggest that the large cells just below the substantia gelatinosa give rise to the ventral spinothalamic tract and hence to the tactile component of the spinothalamic system if, indeed, it is true that the fibers carrying touch are running in a separate sector and if this sector lies ventromedially to the other fibers of the system. Curiously enough, no retrograde degenerations (after cutting of the anterolateral column) were observed in the substantia gelatinosa cells, which is one of the reasons for suggesting that these cells may actually represent a system intercalated between the axons of the posterior roots and the cells of origin of

the spinothalamic system (194). However, more evidence is needed to support this concept convincingly.

Termination of Spinothalamic System

Ever since the description of Edinger (61) there has been general agreement (44, 47, 53, 82, 96, 100, 180, 204, 263) that the spinothalamic tract is easily demonstrable in man and other primates. However, despite early descriptions of both the spinothalamic and the bulbothalamic components of this system in the rabbit (139, 259, 260) doubts have been frequently expressed as to whether the system actually reaches the thalamus in forms other than primates. The system is known to be composed mainly of small fibers (114) and it seems right to assume that only a fraction of them is actually traceable with the Marchi technique usually employed. It would appear that the poor myelination of the fibers accounts reasonably for the failure of some workers to trace the system to the thalamus although recently a claim has been made on the basis of studies employing silver technique (173) that, in comparison with the primates, actually fewer fibers of the system reach the thalamus in subprimate forms. In any case it seems clear that the spinothalamic system reaches the thalamus in all mammals studied and specifically so in the cat (95, 178) which is used so frequently in modern research. Although some fibers to the centrum medianum, to the parafascicular nucleus and to the intralaminar nuclei are often described, most workers are agreed that the system ends mainly in the ventrobasal complex of the thalamus. The spinal component is stated to end in the external element; the bulbothalamic component, in the arcuate element of this complex. As far as the tactile system is concerned, the classical concept assumes that the lemniscal and the spinothalamic systems converge upon the ventrobasal complex and that from here on corticopetal pathways are common to both.

It is possible that this concept may need a revision since it seems appropriate to suggest that besides the ventrobasal complex a region intercalated between this complex and the medial geniculate body may be a major terminal station for some spinothalamic fibers. The reasons for this suggestion are as follows.

Many observers in the past have been greatly disturbed by the scarcity of detectable terminations of the spinothalamic fibers in the ventrobasal complex. It is clear from descriptions by most of the writers cited that the spinothalamic tract can usually be followed with fair ease up to the region immediately medial to the medial geniculate body. It is the area between this region and the ventrobasal complex itself in which so many Marchi granules disappear with the result that the number of terminations in the ventrobasal complex is often only scanty. The point to be made is that this area, which is morphologically a part of the posterior nuclear thalamic group (209), is the critical region under consideration.

In the cat, this region will remain essentially preserved after an extensive ablation of the suprasylvian and lateral gyri and of the entire auditory region. It will degenerate completely if in addition to this massive removal the second somatic area is ablated as well. Nevertheless, the removal of the second somatic area alone will not cause any marked changes (209). It appears then that the axons of this thalamic region entertain connections (probably of collateral nature) with the second somatic area. This conclusion is harmonious with the findings of Knighton (138) who, attempting to determine the thalamic relay nucleus for the second somatic area, found that stimulation of the posterior segment of what he believed to be the n. ventralis posteromedialis activates the second somatic field. From his drawings one can be fairly confident that the actual locus of Knighton's critical area was that segment of the posterior nuclear group which is intercalated between the ventrobasal complex and the medial geniculate. A similar interpretation applies, in our opinion, to the findings of Stratford (235) who studied the corticothalamic projections of the second somatic area by means of the strychnine technique.

The evidence which suggests that the second somatic area may be activated by a thalamic grouping other than the classical tactile thalamic region agrees also with the findings of Woolsey & Wang (278) and Woolsey (personal communication) who determined that after ablation of the first somatic area in an acute or chronic experiment the responses in the second somatic area are not detectably affected.

It is tempting to assume that the second somatic area is activated solely by the spinothalamic system, an assumption which, if true, could shed new light on the function of this cortical region. This assumption, however, implies that a destruction of both anterolateral columns should eliminate potentials evoked by tactile stimuli in the second somatic cortex. While the evidence in this respect is scanty, the findings at hand imply that this is not the case.

Topical Organization of Spinothalamic System

We have already indicated that the available evidence is inconclusive for deciding whether tactile impulses are relayed within the spinothalamic system in a separate spectrum of fibers or whether they are transmitted partly or wholly by neurons which are also utilized by discharges provoked by painful or thermal stimuli. The existence of a specific tactile pathway is inferred primarily from the observations that thermal and painful sensations may be affected differentially by lesions of the spinal cord [for review of literature see White & Sweet (273)]. The observations that such dissociations are not easily produced even with shallow incisions into the spinothalamic tract and that they are altogether rare or nonexistent with extensive anterolateral cordotomies do not militate, we believe, against the concept of separate pain and temperature pathways as is occasionally argued.

Regardless of how the spinothalamic system may be organized in respect to different modalities of sensations, the evidence is conclusive that it is topically organized in respect to the body surface. Thus, the dermatomes are described as projecting in an orderly fashion upon the cells of substantia gelatinosa (237). It has been deduced early (196) and since amply confirmed by virtually all who perform anterolateral cordotomies that fibers concerned with the caudal portions of the body lie laterally to those related to more oral skin areas at any level of the spinal cord. The same basic sequence prevails in the medulla (57, 218, 219, 271), apparently in the pons, in the midbrain (257) and in respect to the terminations in the thalamus (44, 47, 263) although the details may vary somewhat at different levels.

Likewise, a topical organization of the trigeminal fibers is well established. The anatomical evidence indicates that the fibers of the mandibular, the maxillary and the ophthalmic divisions of the fifth nerve are arranged in a dorsoventral sequence in the spinal tract [for reviews of the literature see Aström (19) and Torvik (238)], and this sequence has been confirmed by electrophysiological studies as well (172). In man, the topical organization of this tract was inferred on the basis of clinical observations (234) and these deductions were proved substantially correct when pain-relieving operations were introduced. Although the opinions are not unanimous (64, 109, 111, 115, 133, 188, 202, 224), it is probable that in man, as in others mammals, there is also a topical organization of three trigeminal divisions in an orocaudal sequence. The fibers of the mandibular division do not reach as far caudally as do some fibers of the maxillary division nor these as far as do some fibers of the ophthalmic division. The clinical experience of some observers (32, 273) led them to believe that the spinal tract of the fifth nerve must be joined by some fibers relevant for pain and temperature sensations from the vagal, glossopharyngeal and intermedius nerves. While this inference needs further confirmation, it seems likely to be correct. The evidence in respect to the bulbothalamic tract is limited. Some data, however, clearly suggest that a topical organization of its fibers exists here as elsewhere in the spinothalamic system (55).

A statement that the spinothalamic system is topically organized, but that nevertheless considerable intermingling of fibers related to different segments of the skin takes place, seems a fair reflection of the opinions of the majority of neurosurgeons (272). This conclusion is based primarily on the common experience that shallow cuts into the spinothalamic tract tend to produce only transient analgesias of higher segmental levels of the body and that in order to secure lasting and complete effects a section as deep as practicable is usually necessary. If the fibers concerned with pain for all parts of the body were indeed known to lie quite superficially, such observations would constitute a proof for the existence of extensive overlap. In fact, however, the topographical position of such fibers is quite obscure. If they should lie deep, and if the transient symptomatology with shallow cuts results basically from contusion or compression and not transection of the relevant fibers, the actual overlap could be quite small. The important point is that the data in respect to the spinal trigeminal tract suggest that its topical organization is quite precise. If the clinical evidence regarding extensive overlap is not considered binding there is hardly any reason to suppose that the entire spinothalamic system is necessarily less precisely organized than is the system of the medial lemniscus.

Ipsilateral Pathways of Spinothalamic System

For many decades it has been a belief, and this view is still held frequently, that all the fibers of the spinothalamic tract originating in the cells of the posterior horn cross to the opposite side and ascend within the anterolateral column. With the introduction of cordotomy operations the view was advanced that in addition to a contralateral tract an ipsilateral component

of the spinothalamic system exists. Foerster & Gagel (71) and Foerster (70) advocated this view and gave several arguments for their belief. The most cogent were two observations: first, retrograde changes in some cells of the posterior horn occur on the side of the cord lesion (in addition to widespread changes on the contralateral side); and second, some deficits of tactile (and pain) sensations are demonstrable on the side of the operation.

Anatomically there are some reasons to believe that an uncrossed spinothalamic tract exists, for some cells of the posterior horn emitting axons into the anterolateral column of the same side have been described (27, 156, 201) and the occurrence of ipsilateral retrograde changes after appropriate cord lesions has been confirmed (147, 178). The observation that electrical stimulation of anterolateral column may evoke pain on the same side (236) and the rare occurrence of pain which is relieved by an ipsilateral cordotomy militate for the existence of the ipsilateral tract. Since the electrophysiological evidence in the cat and monkey is concordant with the findings in man it can be inferred that an ipsilateral as well as a contralateral spinothalamic tract presumably exists in all mammals.

SOME FURTHER OBSERVATIONS ON SOMATIC SENSORY SYSTEM

Relaying of Somatic Afferent Impulses

If the reasonable assumption is made that it is via the main sensory afferent pathways that electrical stimulation of the sensory nerve evokes early responses in the first and second somatic cortical fields it appears a simple matter to determine the location of the relevant paths in the cord or brain stem by appropriately placed lesions in these structures. However simple this method may be in principle it has proved itself quite difficult in practice for it yielded occasionally contradictory results in the hands of different workers and often inconsistent results in the hands of the same observers.

Thus, Bohm (25) and Bohm & Petersén (26) found in their experiments that selective sectioning of the posterior columns abolished responses in the somatic areas I and II (SI and SII). Bohm concluded rather boldly that the discharges in the anterolateral column are not relayed to the cortex. Gardner and his colleagues (83–86), on the other hand, who devoted much work to this problem, arrived at conclusions much more in accord with other data although some of their findings are puzzling. First of all, they established that the potentials evoked in the contralateral SI and SII (contralateral in respect to the stimulated nerve) can be relayed both through the ipsilateral dorsal column and through the contralateral anterolateral one. This is, of course, expected from the classical studies. However, such potentials seem to be relayed as well through the anterolateral column on the side of the stimulated nerve. While electrophysiological evidence concerning the existence of an ipsilateral pathway is, as already mentioned, quite in harmony with other data, the finding that the discharges in this tract can relay also to the contralateral cortex is anatomically not at all self-evident. Thus, despite some observations to the contrary it must be assumed that destruction of an anterolateral column causes only ipsilateral terminal degenerations in the thalamus. Likewise it is doubtful despite repeated affirmative reports that spinothalamic fibers actually cross partly within the posterior commissure. The latter doubt is reinforced by findings of Gardner & Morin (85) which imply that all crossings of sensory paths must take place below the midbrain. It appears then that, if the contralateral cortex is indeed activated via the anterolateral column of the same side as the stimulated nerve, the route by which this takes place is yet to be determined.

In preparations in which the anterolateral column of the same side was the only column available for conduction the contralateral cortical potentials were sometimes not evokable, and if evoked sometimes displayed longer latencies than in the intact animals (83). This suggests perhaps that other than the classical pathways might have been involved in the transmission of the discharges.

There is only fragmentary information available in regard to the ipsilateral responses in SII. It might be reasonable to expect that such responses are conducted through the ipsilateral spinothalamic pathway. However, out of three animals (83) in which this path was presumably cut the ipsilateral cortical responses disappeared in only one. Clearly, more data are needed before any conclusions can be drawn.

The question of the existence of an ipsilateral pathway from the nuclei of the posterior column to the ventrobasal complex aroused considerable interest. Several workers (26, 51, 116) using sectioning techniques concluded that such a pathway exists. However, in our opinion both the anatomical and the functional evidence (see p. 400) implies rather definitely that such conclusions must have been in error.

The problem of whether discharges evoked by stimulation of the afferent nerve may ascend within the spinal cord by other than the dorsal column or spinothalamic pathways has been considered repeatedly (41, 91, 176) and some evidence has been adduced that this may be the case. Morin (176) proposed that one such pathway runs in the dorsal part of the lateral column and that it synapses in the nucleus cervicalis lateralis. A crossing to the other side is believed to take place at the upper cervical levels. N. cervicalis lateralis, however, has been asserted (205, 206) to relay exclusively to the cerebellum, a finding strongly contested by Morin & Catalano (177).

In summary it appears that observations of evoked potentials after sectioning various fiber tracts have yielded thus far only limited data. The important finding is that impulses from both sides of the body are conducted in each anterolateral column. Some equivocal or contradictory results may be due in part to the difficulties in distinguishing in acute experiments the shock due to the acute lesion itself from the results of destruction of the relevant fibers. It is also possible that a massive electrical stimulation of the nerve might contribute to some confusing findings. Whatever the reasons may be for the difficulties encountered, much more systematic work is needed with this technique.

Centrifugal Pathways Impinging Upon Sensory Somatic Synaptic Regions

It is implicit in many present day concepts concerning the organization of the central nervous system that synaptic regions situated orally in a polysynaptic chain of an afferent system are capable of modulating the very inflow which arouses their activity. However well founded such ideas may be, no rigorous proof has thus far been offered for the existence of such circuits in the somatic sensory system, although recently suggestive evidence to this effect has been advanced. Thus, Brodal *et al.* (34) and Walberg (248) have described direct bilateral corticofugal connections to the sensory trigeminal elements and to the gracile and cuneate nuclei, arising not only from the sensorimotor area but from all major cortical regions as well. The former connections would clearly represent a 'feedback' system. It is certainly unexpected that virtually all cortical regions should affect the essential components of the projectional tactile system in a basically identical fashion. The lack of any somatotopical organization of the projection arising in the somatic fields is puzzling since all synaptic regions of the lemniscal system including the postcentral cortex are in fact organized topically quite precisely.

Electrophysiological evidence indicates that repetitive electrical stimulation of the sensorimotor cortex may depress the postsynaptic response which is evoked in the following regions: a) in the trigeminal nucleus by stimulation of the infraorbital nerves (125); b) in the posterior column nuclei by stimulation of the posterior columns (217); and (c) in the anterolateral column by stimulation of the contralateral dorsal roots (112). A destruction of the midbrain reticular formation (presumably the destruction of the midbrain tegmentum), on the other hand, was observed to enhance the postsynaptic response in the trigeminal nucleus when the infraorbital nerve was stimulated (126). In harmony with the latter observation King et al. (137) observed recently that responses recorded in the internal capsule to stimulation of the peripheral nerve displayed a reduced amplitude but also a decrease of the latent period when an EEG arousal was induced by repetitive electrical stimulation of the sciatic nerve, of the midbrain reticular formation or of the centrum medianum and n. centralis lateralis.

How to interpret these findings may be left an open question since, except for the work of King et al. (137), no quantitative data have been thus far offered to substantiate an effect which manifests itself by influencing the test response only quantitatively. It is, however, doubtful that the effects produced by stimulation of the sensorimotor area could have been mediated by the pathways proposed by the Norwegian workers since, if this were so, one could have expected indiscriminate effects from stimulation of any cortical region in either hemisphere, which apparently did not occur.

Activation of Brain Stem Reticular Formation by Sensory Somatic Discharges

In 1949, Moruzzi & Magoun (179) reported that electrical stimulation of the medial portions of the medulla, of the pontine and midbrain tegmentum, and of the dorsal hypothalamus and subthalamus produces generalized changes in the EEG which appear identical with those which result when the animal is aroused from sleep or alerted to attention. They suggested, therefore, that the central core of the brain stem represents an ascending activating system, the activity of the system being essential for wakefulness, the depression of this activity producing normal sleep or somnolence. A great deal of effort

has been expended in recent years, particularly by the research group of Magoun, by the group of Moruzzi in Italy and by Bremer and his colleagues, to substantiate this concept—which was suggested by the early work of Bremer (30, 31)—and to determine the functional organization of the reticular ascending system and the sources of its inflow.

Just to what extent and in which sense one can consider the reticular activating system as a functional unit (it is certainly not a unit morphologically) is at present still conjectural. Basic as this question may be for considerations of sensations in general, we shall not discuss it further since the present status of the problem is presented in detail in Chapter XLII of this work. However, we shall consider briefly the evidence regarding the activation of the brain stem by somatic sensory afferents since the available evidence suggests, we believe, a departure from conclusions usually reached on this subject.

Little is known about activation of brain-stem groupings by natural tactile stimuli. One may presume, however, that activity aroused by electrical stimulation of a nerve (it was usually the sciatic nerve which was stimulated) reflects, at least partially, activity aroused by tactile stimulation as well.

In a series of papers the California workers (72-74, 229, 230) concluded that, in addition to the medial lemniscal system, there exists in the brainstem a medially located, multisynaptic path, conducting centripetally, which is fed by collaterals arising from virtually the entire length of the medial lemniscus. They felt that this medial system must be composed of a multisynaptic chain of neurons since in comparison with the potentials in the lemniscal system those evoked in the reticular formation displayed much longer latencies and longer recovery time and were more sensitive to anesthetics. It is likely that the California workers understand by the medial lemniscal system, not only the system which we have defined under that term but also the spinothalamic tract. Nevertheless, all their data pertaining to the classical pathways seem to refer to the medial lemniscal system, as we understand it, and there is little doubt that collaterals of the classical medial lemniscal pathway are believed to activate the reticular ascending system.

While it is, of course, possible that the reticular potentials are indeed of medial lemniscal origin, it appears more likely that they are evoked, at least predominantly, through activation of the anterolateral columns in the spinal cord rather than of the medial lemniscus. There are several reasons for this belief. First of all there is little anatomical evidence that the fibers of the medial lemniscus emit any substantial number of collaterals. Ramón y Cajal (201) was emphatic in this respect and believed that only a few collaterals were given off to the region of the red nucleus and a somewhat larger number to the pretectal region. He seems to have been hesitant in respect to the medial lemniscal contribution to the mamillary peduncle. Other workers occasionally described some collaterals to other regions as well but there seems to be no convincing evidence that the medial lemniscus gives off any substantial number of collaterals below the midbrain. Matzke (170) recently stressed that the medial lemniscus does not decrease perceptibly in size from its origin to its termination.

The situation is different for the fibers arising in the posterior horns and ascending in the anterolateral column. We have considered thus far exclusively one component of the group, the spinothalamic tract, since it reaches farthest orally. However, it is well known that there are other fibers accompanying the spinothalamic tract which terminate below the thalamus and it is likely that at least some of them conduct impulses evoked by cutaneous stimuli. The fact that after anterolateral cordotomy only a small fraction of the degenerating fibers reach the thalamus led, as was discussed earlier, to doubts as to the existence of the spinothalamic tract in some mammals. It appears then that collaterals from the spinothalamic tract or other anterolateral column fibers terminating at lower levels could provide obvious pathways for relaying sensory-somatic activity to the brain-stem structures without any strain on the known anatomical facts concerning the medial lemniscus.

Second, it has been shown that the brainstem potentials evoked by stimulation of the sciatic nerve occur bilaterally (230). This observation is quite in harmony with the presumed existence of the ipsi- and contralateral tracts in the anterolateral columns. On the other hand, the occurrence of such ipsilateral potentials would be rather puzzling if they were mediated by the lemniscal system since, despite some protestations to the contrary, there is, we believe, no evidence for existence of an ipsilateral lemniscus arising in the posterior column nuclei.

Third, it has been shown that the potentials evoked in the ascending reticular system by stimulation of the sciatic nerve possess substantially longer latencies than do responses recorded at virtually any level of the lemniscal system (73). It is not at all clear why this should be so if a collateral inflow for the ascending activating system were indeed available almost at all levels from the medial lemniscus. If, on the other

hand, these potentials were evoked by mediation of predominantly small fibers of the anterolateral columns their long latencies could be readily understood even if the number of intercalated synaptic regions was quite small. That some potentials in the brain stem are, as could be expected, relayed through the anterolateral column has been shown recently by Collins & O'Leary (54). These workers studied a small region in the midbrain which was activated when smaller fibers (gamma and delta groups) of the radial or sciatic nerves were excited. They could show that the midbrain potentials survived (in contrast to the potential evoked in the ventrobasal complex) a destruction of the homolateral posterior column (homolateral to the stimulated nerve) but were abolished (again in contrast to the potentials evoked in the ventrobasal complex) when the contralateral anterolateral column was destroyed. It may be emphasized that the midbrain potentials displayed much longer latencies than did the potentials evoked in the medial lemniscal system, and in contrast to the latter were sensitive to anesthetic agents.

In summary, it appears that the sources of the sensory somatic inflow which activate the various brain stem structures are not yet established unequivocally. The evidence at hand seems to imply that the potentials recorded by the California workers in the reticular activating system relay mainly or solely through the anterolateral columns and the tracts arising from them rather than through the posterior column and the medial lemniscal system. However, these are indirect conclusions and it would be desirable to test them experimentally.

Cortical Fields Other Than the Primary Receiving Area Which Are Activated by Tactile Stimuli

We have thus far proceeded on the assumption that, among all the discharges in the central nervous system which are provoked by cutaneous and deep stimuli, only those which occur in the medial lemniscal or spinothalamic systems are relevant for the arousal of tactile and kinesthetic sensations. Clinical evidence suggests that this is likely to be so for all the synaptic regions below the cortical level. For the cortex itself the situation is less clear mainly because one is uncertain as to the extent of the cortical fields which are directly activated by the subcortical components of the classical systems. There is, of course, no doubt that the postcentral region in primates or its homologue in other mammals (which can be defined as the projection field of the ventrobasal complex of the thalamus) is the chief cortical representative of the medial lemniscal system. As such it must be in some way critically involved in the elaboration of tactile and kinesthetic sensations, and we have already considered some functional properties of this field. Nevertheless, there is evidence available that this region is not the exclusive recipient of all the discharges transmitted through the medial lemniscal and spinothalamic relays. While the evidence to this effect is fragmentary and much more work is needed to elucidate the details the general picture which emerges seems to be as follows. The postcentral family of fields (areas 1 to 3 of primates) appears to represent a focal region for tactile and kinesthetic activity. This activity is undoubtedly based primarily on the inflow from the ventrobasal complex. Surrounding this core region is a belt of cortical fields which receive, apart from any connections they may have with the postcentral region itself, some sensory somatic inflow directly from the thalamus. It is convenient to consider the evidence under several headings.

ANATOMICAL EVIDENCE. Most of the cells of the ventrobasal complex are definitely known to project exclusively upon the postcentral region, and it seems likely that all do so. Assuming this to be true, it follows that if impulses evoked by tactile stimuli are transmitted directly from the thalamus to some fields surrounding the postcentral region, they must be relayed through thalamic nuclei other than the ventrobasal complex. In fact evidence is available that a thalamic element intercalated between the ventrobasal complex and the medial geniculate body projects upon the second somatic field (see p. 418). It seems probable further that this element may be a terminal station for some spinothalamic fibers. Whether other thalamic elements of the ventral or posterior nuclear groups which partly surround the ventrobasal complex receive some medial lemniscal or spinothalamic fibers is not clear. It is tempting to speculate that for some this may be true since, if this were so, a number of electrophysiological observations would be readily understandable.

ELECTROPHYSIOLOGICAL EVIDENCE. It has been known since the early days of the evoked potential technique that the extent of the cortical areas activated by sensory somatic stimuli may vary with the anesthetic state. In deeply pentobarbitalized animals it is usually the classical first and second somatic fields which are activated by natural tactile stimuli. Under different anesthetic conditions, with no anesthesia at all, or when such drugs as chloralose are used, potentials

may appear in other regions as well, sometimes only when nerve volleys are used as stimuli (1, 8, 9, 14, 38, 39, 84, 92, 142, 165, 167, 276). [Other references are given by Buser (37).]

In the cat, which was most extensively studied, such additional regions in which potentials evoked by sensory somatic stimuli are likely to appear most consistently are the precentral homologue, the anterior portion of the lateral gyrus and the suprasylvian gyrus. It is known that a removal of the first somatic area (38, 278) does not abolish evoked potentials in the second somatic field. Recently it has been shown by Albe-Fessard & Rougeul (8) that responses in the lateral and the suprasylvian gyri are likewise not abolished by such a removal. Similar evidence has been offered (84, 142, 165) in respect to potentials evoked in the precentral region of the monkey by stimulation of the afferent nerves.

The fact that such potentials tend to appear under special conditions of stimulation or when the excitability of neurons is enhanced by drugs hardly diminishes the significance of the phenomenon if transcortical spread from the postcentral area can be excluded. Since this was done for several regions surrounding this area the conclusion seems warranted that, under certain conditions at least, some sensory somatic discharges may relay to other regions of the neocortex without mediation of the primary receiving field.

EXPERIMENTAL PSYCHOLOGICAL EVIDENCE. The electrophysiological evidence suggests then rather strongly that not only the postcentral region but also a belt of fields around it may be of significance for the capacity of the animal to appreciate and handle sensory somatic information. Nevertheless, it is reasonable to expect somatic area I to be the central region of the somesthetic system. The problem is to determine the exact role played by the different fields in the somesthetic capacity of the animal since it is obvious that these fields cannot by any means be functionally equivalent. Unfortunately only a small number of studies is available on the ability of an animal to perform somesthetic discrimination tasks after ablations of the postcentral field or other cortical regions. A systematic analysis has not proceeded very far perhaps because of the confusion which was created by the finding that simple somesthetic discriminations are still possible or can be relearned after removal of the first somatic field. The studies of Ruch & Fulton (210), who reviewed the older literature on the subject, although severely handicapped by lack of anatomical controls, were suggestive that this might be so in primates. Recent findings in rat (283, 285, 286), cat (284) and dog (10, 11) provide acceptable evidence for this statement. Ablations of somatic areas I and II together led to findings which may but need not be discordant. In the rat (283, 286) discrimination of roughness can apparently be relearned and form discrimination need not be lost after such ablations. Likewise form can be discriminated satisfactorily by the monkey with some retraining (143), even though a severe loss of tactile acuity is evident when placing reactions or grasp reflexes are tested. On the other hand, in the cat (284) and dog (11) a persistent inability of the animal to discriminate somesthetic stimuli has been reported after such combined removals. The findings in the cat can be dismissed since they are based on studies on one animal only. The findings of Allen on the dog require some comment. It appears from his description that the actual cortical removals exceeded considerably the anatomical limits of SI and SII. This might but probably does not account for Allen's divergent findings. What seems to be a more probable explanation of his results is that—in contrast to all other observers here considered who used a pair of discriminanda differing only in weight, roughness or form—Allen alone employed a differential conditioning technique to test the somesthetic defects of his animals. The response of the animal consisted of lifting his foreleg to a positive stimulus and not lifting it to a negative one. The positive and negative stimuli were respectively a light stroking of the back with the grain and against the grain or a light stroking with the grain once a second (positive) and three times a second (negative). The chief defect observed was the inability of the operated animals to withold the foreleg response when negative stimuli were applied. The response to positive stimuli was retained without impairment. In short, after the operations the animals tended to lift the leg to both the negative and positive stimuli and could not be retrained to make the differentiation. Since the task set by Allen for his animals was quite different and probably more subtle than those set by the other observers, the different results need not imply contradictory findings.

Even though older anatomical and physiological views have often held that the precentral and postcentral regions somehow form a functional unit of a higher order, it is only recently that the effects of postcentral and precentral ablation upon the somesthetic capacity of the monkey have been tested with modern techniques. As already mentioned, Kruger &

Porter (143) found no permanent deficits in somesthetic form discrimination after removal of the somatic areas I and II in their monkeys even though a severe tactile impairment of the limbs could be reasonably inferred to be present. Likewise, there was a perfect retention of the learned habit if the precentral gyrus alone was removed despite the severe motor deficits in the limbs. However, if both these regions were removed jointly on one side the two animals tested could not be trained to discriminate with the contralateral hand a three dimensional figure 'L' from its inversion. However, a visual discrimination task could be carried out utilizing that limb. Since this work reports permanent deficits, further studies along these lines are urgently needed. The reported lesions extended farther caudally than the anatomical limits of areas 1 to 3. It remains to be determined whether an inclusion of at least a part of the parietal region is necessary to produce permanent discrimination deficits.

The knowledge that some tactile responses from the ipsilateral side of the body reach the ipsilateral cortex (although we believe this is not true for the first somatic field) could suggest that learning of at least simple somesthetic discriminations takes place simultaneously in both hemispheres. Stamm & Sperry's (228) results are, therefore, somewhat surprising. In their cats the discrimination of form, softness and roughness performed with one paw had to be completely relearned only if the corpus callosum was sectioned. Clearly more data are needed to substantiate and further elucidate this problem.

The last set of available data we wish to consider pertains to findings after lesions of the parietal cortex. It was already suggested by the older work (211–213) that parietal lesions may produce some deficits in the capacity to discriminate somesthetic cues even though the animals could usually relearn the tasks. Such deficits after ablations of the parietal cortex which spared the postcentral region itself were definitely established by Blum (23), Blum et al. (24) and Pribram & Barry (199). Blum et al. (24) made the tentative suggestion that processes which determine the somesthetic discrimination capacity of the animal take place outside the postcentral region itself and specifically in the parietal region. The available findings hardly permit an evaluation of this suggestion. The data at hand are as yet too few in number, too limited in scope and not sufficiently systematic with respect to some cortical fields which are probably or possibly relevant. Some important observations, therefore, are subject to different interpretations. For example, the important finding of all workers that the removal of the postcentral region does not necessarily lead to any early or permanent deficits in somesthetic discriminations indicates strictly only that the postcentral region is not the sole cortical recipient and distributor of all the corticopetal tactile activity. This, of course, is also apparent from the electrophysiological considerations. Whether, however, such findings indicate in any way that the postcentral cortex is not relevant for processes determining the somesthetic discrimination capacity of the animal is another question. The anatomical and electrophysiological evidence leaves hardly any doubt that it must be relevant. The experimental psychophysical data are indicative that the postcentral region need not always be essential. It seems reasonable to consider the possibility that the answer may lie in the nature of the somesthetic task which the animal is trained to perform. If the somesthetic cues used in the experiments differed crudely from each other (and certainly most of them did so), it is possible that any somatic sensory inflow which reaches the cortex after removal of the postcentral region still contains enough information to enable the animal to perform the task. It seems probable that the unique role of the first somatic field will become apparent if the animal is asked to perform a task requiring the highly detailed and complex information which, as it appears, is available only to the primary receiving field. If this were so the postcentral cortex would be necessary for any tactile or kinesthetic discrimination task of sufficient complexity. Whether it alone is ever sufficient for learning of such a discrimination is yet to be determined. The chances are that the answer to this question will depend on what the animal is asked to do with the information it has available.

CONCLUDING REMARKS

It may be useful to discuss at the conclusion of this chapter experimental work which appears necessary for the clarification of some ideas regarding tactile and kinesthetic sensations.

In the section dealing with the neural events in the peripheral fibers it has been pointed out that a revival in some form of the basic concepts of Head may become advisable. What is well established is that specific tactile receptors exist; what can be deduced from some observations but what is by no means yet demonstrated is that generalized receptors, presumably responding to all modes of cutaneous stimulation, may exist as well. It seems futile to deny or ignore the convincing evidence regarding the specificity of some tactile receptors; it is probably too much to expect, on the other hand, that all experimental findings will yet become understandable within the framework of von Frey's concepts. It seems probable that the clouds over the classic concepts are real and that further work will establish the existence of generalized (in addition to the specific) receptors which will probably reopen the question of the existence of epicritic and protopathic sensibility.

Assuming that this development will take place the problem will be to determine to what extent the medial lemniscal and the spinothalamic systems are, respectively, activated by these two types of receptors. As far as the tactile activity is concerned there is hardly any doubt that specific receptors activate the medial lemniscal system. The available evidence indicates that this system could represent the tactile (and kinesthetic) epicritic system. The fundamental question as to whether this system can be activated as well by nociceptive and thermal stimuli must remain unanswered at the moment. In anesthetized animals only mechanical stimuli activate the medial lemniscal system. It is, however, not known whether this represents the true state of affairs or whether such findings are caused by anesthesia. The spinothalamic system could be the obvious representative of the protopathic system if the latter should exist. What little is known about its tactile activity is compatible with the idea that generalized receptors activate it. It is this system which—in sharp contrast to the medial lemniscal system—seems to distribute, together with other tracts arising in the posterior horns the sensory somatic activity throughout the brain stem. An extensive interlocking between the medial lemniscal and the spinothalamic systems occurs in two places. The first is the synaptic region of the posterior horns where the lemniscal activity plays upon the cells of origin of the spinothalamic system; the second is the ventrobasal complex of the thalamus where the spinothalamic activity in turn interacts with the medial lemniscal system. However, nothing at all is known as to the meaning of these interactions. From clinical studies it is clear that sensations of pain, temperature and tickle, and those accompanying sexual excitement depend upon the integrity of the spinothalamic system. Although this knowledge has been gained on large human material, very little is known for certain about the functional organization of the system, not even whether or not its fibers are modality specific. It is obvious that a number of basic problems of sensation could be profitably explored in man in connection with the frequently performed pain-relieving operations. Unfortunately such problems seem to be seldom of interest to clinical observers.

In regard to kinesthetic sensations considerable progress has been achieved in recent years. First of all, it is now apparent that the sense of position and of movements of the joints depends solely on the appropriate receptors in the joints themselves. There is no need to invoke a mysterious 'muscle' sense to explain kinesthetic sensations, and to do so runs contrary to all the known facts concerning the muscle stretch receptors.

A second point is that kinesthetic activity is relayed in the medial lemniscal system, as could have been expected from clinical experiences in man. Cells concerned with kinesthetic activity are intermingled at each synaptic level with the cells concerned with the activity evoked by tactile receptors, and the two groups are arranged in one common representation pattern. The individual cells retain, as far as is known, their modality specificity at least to the first stage of cortical activation.

A third fact of great interest is that receptors from bones, periosteum, deep fascia and sheaths of tendons activate the medial lemniscal system in exactly the same fashion as do the tactile skin and joint receptors. Whether kinesthetic and deep stimuli activate also the spinothalamic system is unknown.

At present the conclusion must be that touch, pressure, kinesthesis and deep sensibility are all very closely related. Yet this is not at all apparent from introspective observations, at least not for touch and kinesthesis. It seems likely that more will have to be known about cortical handling of the neural activity evoked by sensory stimuli before one can approach such problems on other than a purely speculative basis.

REFERENCES

1. ADEY, W. R., R. PORTER AND I. D. CARTER. *Brain* 77: 325, 1954.
2. ADRIAN, E. D. *J. Phsyiol.* 61: 49, 1926.
3. ADRIAN, E. D. *Proc. Roy. Soc., London. Ser. B* 109: 1, 1932.
4. ADRIAN, E. D., McK. CATTELL AND H. HOAGLAND. *J. Physiol.* 72: 377, 1931.
5. ADRIAN, E. D. AND K. UMRATH. *J. Physiol.* 68: 139, 1929.
6. ADRIAN, E. D. AND Y. ZOTTERMAN. *J. Physiol.* 61: 464, 1926.
7. ALBE-FESSARD, D. *J. physiol., Paris* 49: 522, 1957.
8. ALBE-FESSARD, D. AND A. ROUGEUL. *J. physiol., Paris* 47: 69, 1955.
9. ALBE-FESSARD, D. AND A. ROUGEUL. *J. physiol., Paris* 48: 370, 1956.
10. ALLEN, W. F. *Am. J. Physiol.* 147: 454, 1946.
11. ALLEN, W. F. *Am. J. Physiol.* 151: 325, 1947.
12. ALVAREZ-BUYLLA, R. AND R. DE ARELLANO. *Am. J. Physiol.* 172: 237, 1953.
13. AMASSIAN, V. E. *Electroencephalog. & Clin. Neurophysiol.* 5: 415, 1953.
14. AMASSIAN, V. E. *J. Neurophysiol.* 17: 39, 1954.
15. AMASSIAN, V. E. AND J. L. DEVITO. *Coll. Intern. centre nat. recherche Sci.* 67: 353, 1957.
16. ANDREW, B. L. *J. Physiol.* 123: 241, 1954.
17. ANDREW, B. L. *J. Physiol.* 126: 507, 1954.
18. ANDREW, B. L. AND E. DODT. *Acta physiol. scandinav.* 28: 287, 1953.
19. ÅSTRÖM, K. E. *Acta physiol. scandinav.* Suppl. 106, 29: 209, 1953.
20. BERRY, C. M., R. C. KARL AND J. C. HINSEY. *J. Neurophysiol.* 13: 149, 1950.
21. BISHOP, G. H. *Physiol. Rev.* 26: 77, 1946.
22. BISHOP, G. H. AND P. HEINBECKER. *Am. J. Physiol.* 114: 179, 1935.
23. BLUM, J. S. *Comp. Psychol. Monogr.* 20: 219, 1951.
24. BLUM, J. S., K. L. CHOW AND K. H. PRIBRAM. *J. Comp. Neurol.* 93: 53, 1950.
25. BOHM, E. *Acta physiol. scandinav.* Suppl. 106, 29: 106, 1953.
26. BOHM, E. AND I. PETERSÉN. *Acta physiol. scandinav.* Suppl. 106, 29: 138, 1953.
27. BOK, S. T. In: W. von Möllendorff, *Handbuch der mikroskopischen Anatomie des Menschen.* Berlin: Springer, 1928, vol. 4, p. 478.
28. BOYD, I. A. *J. Physiol.* 124: 476, 1954.
29. BOYD, I. A. AND T. D. M. ROBERTS. *J. Physiol.* 122: 38, 1953.
30. BREMER, F. *Compt. rend. Soc. de biol.* 118: 1235, 1935.
31. BREMER, F. *Compt. rend. Soc. de biol.* 118: 1241, 1935.
32. BRODAL, A. *Arch. Neurol. & Psychiat.* 57: 292, 1947.
33. BRODAL, A. AND B. R. KAADA. *J. Neurophysiol.* 16: 567, 1953.
34. BRODAL, A., T. SZABO AND A. TORVIK. *J. Comp. Neurol.* 106: 527, 1956.
35. BRODAL, A. AND F. WALBERG. *Arch. Neurol. & Psychiat.* 68: 755, 1952.
36. BÜRGI, S. *Arch. Psychiat.* 194: 67, 1955.
37. BUSER, P. *J. physiol., Paris* 49: 589, 1957.
38. BUSER, P. AND P. BORENSTEIN. *J. physiol., Paris* 48: 419, 1956.
39. BUSER, P. AND G. HEINZE. *J. physiol., Paris* 46: 284, 1954.
40. CARPENTER, M. B. *J. Anat.* 91: 82, 1957.
41. CATALANO, J. V. AND G. LAMARCHE. *Am. J. Physiol.* 189: 141, 1957.
42. CATTELL, McK. AND H. HOAGLAND. *J. Physiol.* 72: 392, 1931.
43. CHANG, H.-T. AND T. C. RUCH. *J. Anat.* 81: 140, 1947.
44. CHANG, H.-T. AND T. C. RUCH. *J. Anat.* 81: 150, 1947.
45. CHANG, H.-T., C. N. WOOLSEY, L. W. JARCHO AND E. HENNEMAN. *Fed. Proc.* 6: 89, 1947.
46. CLARK, D., J. HUGHES AND H. S. GASSER. *Am. J. Physiol.* 114: 69, 1935.

47. CLARK, W. E. LE GROS. *J. Anat.* 71: 7, 1936.

48. CLARK, W. E. LE GROS. *J. Ment. Sc.* 82: 99, 1936.

49. CLARK, W. E. LE GROS AND R. H. BOGGON. *Phil. Trans.* B224: 313, 1935.

50. CLARK, W. E. LE GROS AND T. P. S. POWELL. *Proc. Roy. Soc., London. ser. B* 141: 467, 1953.

51. COHEN, S. M. *J. Neurophysiol.* 18: 33, 1955.

52. COHEN, S. M. AND H. GRUNDFEST. *J. Neurophysiol.* 17: 193, 1954.

53. COLLIER, J. AND E. F. BUZZARD. *Brain* 26: 559, 1903.

54. COLLINS, W. F. AND J. L. O'LEARY. *Electroencephalog. & Clin. Neurophysiol.* 6: 619, 1954.

55. CRAWFORD, A. S. AND R. S. KNIGHTON. *J. Neurosurg.* 10: 113, 1953.

56. DÉJERINE, J. AND MME. J. DÉJERINE. *Compt. rend. Soc. de biol.* 2: 285, 1895.

57. D'ERRICO, A. *J. Neurosurg.* 7: 294, 1950.

58. DRAKE, C. G. AND K. G. MCKENZIE. *J. Neurosurg.* 10: 457, 1953.

59. DUSSER DE BARENNE, J. G. AND O. SAGER. *Zeitsch. ges. Neurol. Psychiat.* 133: 231, 1931.

60. DUSSER DE BARENNE, J. G. AND O. SAGER. *Arch. Neurol. & Psychiat.* 38: 913, 1937.

61. EDINGER, L. *Anat. Anz.* 4: 121, 1889.

62. ELDRED, E., R. GRANIT AND P. A. MERTON. *J. Physiol.* 122: 498, 1953.

63. ELDRED, E. AND K.-E. HAGBARTH. *J. Neurophysiol.* 17: 59, 1954.

64. FALCONER, M. A. *J. Neurol. Neurosurg. & Psychiat.* 12: 297, 1949.

65. FERRARO, A. AND S. E. BARRERA. *Arch. Neurol. & Psychiat.* 33: 262, 1934.

66. FERRARO, A., AND S. E. BARRERA. *J. Comp. Neurol.* 62: 507, 1935.

67. FERRARO, A. AND S. E. BARRERA. *J. Comp. Neurol.* 64: 313, 1936.

68. FITZGERALD, O. *J. Physiol.* 98: 163, 1940.

69. FLECHSIG, P. AND O. HÖSEL. *Neurol. Centralbl.* 9: 417, 1890.

70. FOERSTER, O. In: *Handbuch der Neurologie,* edited by O. Bumke and O. Foerster. Berlin: Springer, 1936, vol. 5, p. 1.

71. FOERSTER, O. AND O. GAGEL. *Zeitschr. ges. Neurol. Psychiat.* 138: 1, 1932.

72. FRENCH, J. D., F. K. VON AMERONGEN AND H. W. MAGOUN. *Arch. Neurol. & Psychiat.* 68: 577, 1952.

73. FRENCH, J. D., M. VERZEANO AND H. W. MAGOUN. *Arch. Neurol. & Psychiat.* 69: 505, 1953.

74. FRENCH, J. D., M. VERZEANO AND H. W. MAGOUN. *Arch. Neurol. & Psychiat.* 69: 519, 1953.

75. GARDNER, E. *Anat. Rec.* 83: 401, 1942.

76. GARDNER, E. *J. Comp. Neurol.* 80: 11, 1944.

77. GARDNER, E. *Am. J. Physiol.* 152: 436, 1948.

78. GARDNER, E. *Anat. Rec.* 101: 109, 1948.

79. GARDNER, E. *Anat. Rec.* 102: 1, 1948.

80. GARDNER, E. *Anat. Rec.* 102: 161, 1948.

81. GARDNER, E. *Anat. Rec.* 101: 353, 1948.

82. GARDNER, E. AND H. M. CUNEO. *Arch. Neurol. & Psychiat.* 53: 423, 1945.

83. GARDNER, E. AND B. HADDAD. *Am. J. Physiol.* 172: 475, 1953.

84. GARDNER, E. AND F. MORIN. *Am. J. Physiol.* 174: 149, 1953.

85. GARDNER, E. AND F. MORIN. *Am. J. Physiol.* 189: 152, 1957.

86. GARDNER, E. AND R. NOER. *Am. J. Physiol.* 168: 437, 1952.

87. GASSER, H. S. *A. Res. Nerv. & Ment. Dis., Proc.* 15: 35, 1934.

88. GASSER, H. S. *A. Res. Nerv. & Ment. Dis., Proc,* 23: 44, 1943.

89. GASSER, H. S. AND J. ERLANGER. *Am. J. Physiol.* 88: 581, 1929.

90. GAZE, R. M. AND G. GORDON. *Quart. J. Exper. Physiol.* 39: 279, 1954.

91. GAZE, R. M. AND G. GORDON. *Quart. J. Exper. Physiol.* 40: 187, 1955.

92. GERARD, R. W., W. H. MARSHALL AND L. J. SAUL. *Arch. Neurol. & Psychiat.* 36: 675, 1936.

93. GEREBTZOFF, M. A. *Cellule* 48: 91, 1939.

94. GERNANDT, B. AND Y. ZOTTERMAN. *Acta physiol. scandinav.* 12: 56, 1946.

95. GETZ, B. *Acta anat.* 16: 2 71, 1952.

96. GLEES, P. *Verhandl. Anat. Gesellsch.* April 1952, p. 48.

97. GLEES, P., R. B. LIVINGSTON AND J. SOLER. *Archiv Psychiat.* 187: 190, 1951.

98. GLEES, P. AND J. SOLER. *Ztschr. Zellforsch. u. mikroskop. Anat.* 36: 381, 1951.

99. GOLDSCHEIDER, A. *Physiologie des Muskelsinnes.* Leipzig: Barth, 1898.

100. GOLDSTEIN, K. *Neurol. centralbl.* 29: 898, 1910.

101. GRANIT, R. *Receptors and Sensory Perception.* New Haven Yale Univ. Press, 1955.

102. GRANIT, R. AND H. D. HENATSCH. *J. Neurophysiol.* 19: 356, 1956.

103. GRANIT, R., C. JOB AND B. R. KAADA. *Acta physiol. scandinav.* 27: 161, 1952.

104. GRANIT, R. AND B. R. KAADA. *Acta physiol. scandinav.* 27: 129, 1952.

105. GRAY, J. A. B. AND J. L. MALCOLM. *Proc. Roy. Soc., London. ser. B* 137: 96, 1950.

106. GRAY, J. A. B. AND P. B. C. MATTHEWS. *J. Physiol.* 114: 454, 1951.

107. GRAY, J. A. B. AND P. B. C. MATTHEWS. *J. Physiol.* 113: 475, 1951.

108. GRAY, J. A. B. AND M. SATO. *J. Physiol.* 122: 610, 1953.

109. GRANT, F. C., R. A. GROFF AND F. H. LEWY. *Arch. Neurol. & Psychiat.* 43: 498, 1940.

110. GRANT, F. C. AND L. M. WEINBERGER. *Arch. Surg.* 42: 681, 1941.

111. GUIDETTI, B. *J. Neurosurg.* 7: 499, 1950.

112. HAGBARTH, K.-E. AND D. I. B. KERR. *J. Neurophysiol.* 17: 295, 1954.

113. HAGEN, E., H. KNOCHE, D. C. SINCLAIR AND G. WEDDELL. *Proc. Roy. Soc., London. ser. B* 141: 279, 1953.

114. HÄGGQVIST, G. *Ztschr. mikroskop.-anat. Forsch.* 39: 1, 1936.

115. HAMBY, W. B., B. M. SHINNERS AND J. A. MARSH. *Arch. Surg.* 57: 171, 1948.

116. HARWOOD, T. H. AND R. H. CRESS. *J. Neurophysiol.* 17: 157, 1954.

117. HATSCHEK, R. *Arb. Inst. Anat. u. Physiol., Wien.* 9: 279, 1902.

118. HEAD, H. *Studies in Neurology.* London: Oxford, 1920.

119. HEINBECKER, P., G. H. BISHOP AND J. L. O'LEARY. *Arch. Neurol. & Psychiat.* 29: 771, 1933.

120. HENSEL, H., AND Y. ZOTTERMAN. *Acta physiol. scandinav.* 22: 96, 1951.

121. HENSEL, H., AND Y. ZOTTERMAN. *Acta physiol. scandinav.* 22: 106, 1951.
122. HENSEL, H., AND Y. ZOTTERMAN. *Acta physiol. scandinav.* 23: 291, 1951.
123. HENSEL, H., AND Y. ZOTTERMAN. *J. Neurophysiol.* 14: 377, 1951.
124. HENSEL, H. AND Y. ZOTTERMAN. *J. Physiol.* 115: 16, 1951.
125. HERNÁNDEZ-PEÓN, R. AND K.-E. HAGBARTH. *J. Neurophysiol.* 18: 44, 1955.
126. HERNÁNDEZ-PEÓN, R. AND H. SCHERRER. *Fed. Proc.* 14: 71, 1955.
127. HOGG, B. M. *J. Physiol.* 84: 250, 1935.
128. HOLMQVIST, B., A. LUNDBERG AND O. OSCARSSON. *Acta physiol. scandinav.* 38: 76, 1956.
129. HUNT, C. C. *J. Physiol.* 115: 456, 1951.
130. HUNT, C. C. *J. Gen. Physiol.* 38: 117, 1954.
131. HUNT, C. C. AND S. W. KUFFLER. *J. Physiol.* 113: 283, 1951.
132. HUNT, C. C. AND S. W. KUFFLER. *J. Physiol.* 113: 298, 1951.
133. HYNDMAN, O. R. *Arch. Surg.* 37: 74, 1938.
134. HYNDMAN, O. R. AND J. WOLKIN. *Arch. Neurol. & Psychiat.* 50: 129, 1943.
135. JASPER, H. H. AND C. AJMONE-MARSAN. *A Stereotaxic Atlas of the Diencephalon of the Cat.* Ottawa: Nat. Res. Council Canada, 1955.
136. JIMENEZ-CASTELLANOS, J. *J. Comp. Neurol.* 91: 307, 1949.
137. KING, E. E., R. NAQUET AND H. W. MAGOUN. *J. Pharmacol. & Exper. Therap.* 119: 48, 1957.
138. KNIGHTON, R. *J. Comp. Neurol.* 92: 183, 1950.
139. KOHNSTAMM, O. *Neurol. Centralbl.* 19: 242, 1900.
140. KOHNSTAMM, O. *J. Psychol. u. Neurol.* 17: 33, 1910.
141. KROLL, F. W. *Ztschr. ges. Neurol. Psychiat.* 128: 751, 1930.
142. KRUGER, L. *Am. J. Physiol.* 186: 475, 1956.
143. KRUGER, L. AND P. PORTER. *J. Comp. Neurol.* In press.
144. KUFFLER, S. W., C. C. HUNT AND J. P. QUILLIAM. *J. Neurophysiol.* 14: 29, 1951.
145. KUHN, R. A. *Tr. Am. Neurol. A.* 1949, p. 227.
146. KURU, M. *Gann* 32: 1, 1938.
147. KURU, M. *Sensory Paths in the Spinal Cord and Brain Stem of Man.* Tokyo and Osaka: Sôgensya, 1949.
148. LANDAU, W. M. *Science* 123: 895, 1956.
149. LANDAU, W. M. AND G. H. BISHOP. *Arch. Neurol. & Psychiat.* 69: 490, 1953.
150. LAPORTE, Y. AND A. LUNDBERG. *Acta physiol. scandinav.* 36: 204, 1956.
151. LAPORTE, Y., A. LUNDBERG AND O. OSCARSSON. *Acta physiol. scandinav.* 36: 175, 1956.
152. LAPORTE, Y., A. LUNDBERG AND O. OSCARSSON. *Acta physiol. scandinav.* 36: 188, 1956.
153. LEKSELL, L. *Acta physiol. scandinav.* Suppl. 31, 10: 1, 1945.
154. LELE, P. P. AND G. WEDDELL. *Brain* 79: 119, 1956.
155. LELE, P. P., G. WEDDELL AND C. M. WILLIAMS. *J. Physiol.* 126: 206, 1954.
156. LENHOSSÉK, M. *Der Feinere Bau des Nervensystems in Lichte Neuster Forschungen.* Berlin: Fischer, 1895.
157. LI, C.-L., C. CULLEN AND H. H. JASPER. *J. Neurophysiol.* 19: 111, 1956.
158. LI, C.-L, C. CULLEN AND H. H. JASPER. *J. Neurophysiol.* 19: 131, 1956.
159. LI, C.-L AND H. H. JASPER. *J. Physiol.* 121: 117, 1953.
160. LLOYD, D. P. C. AND A. K. MCINTYRE. *J. Neurophysiol.* 13: 39, 1950.
161. LOEWENSTEIN, W. R. *J. Physiol.* 133: 588, 1956.
162. LORENTE DE NÓ, R. In: *Physiology of the Nervous System,* edited by J. F. Fulton. New York: Oxford, 1949.
163. LUNDBERG, A. AND O. OSCARSSON. *Acta physiol. scandinav.* 38: 353, 1956.
164. MAGOUN, H. W. AND W. A. MCKINLEY. *Am. J. Physiol.* 137: 409, 1942.
165. MALIS, L. I., K. H. PRIBRAM AND L. KRUGER. *J. Neurophysiol.* 16: 161, 1953.
166. MARSHALL, W. H. *J. Neurophysiol.* 4: 25, 1941.
167. MARSHALL, W. H., C. N. WOOLSEY AND P. BARD. *J. Neurophysiol.* 4: 1, 1941.
168. MARUHASHI, J., K. MIZUGUCHI AND I. TASAKI. *J. Physiol.* 117: 129, 1952.
169. MATTHEWS, B. H. C. *J. Physiol.* 78: 1, 1933.
170. MATZKE, H. A. *J. Comp. Neurol.* 94: 439, 1951.
171. MCINTYRE, A. K. *Proc. Univ. Otago* 31: 5, 1953.
172. MCKINLEY, W. A. AND H. W. MAGOUN. *Am. J. Physiol.* 137: 217, 1942.
173. MEHLER, W. R. *Anat. Rec.* 127: 332, 1957.
174. MONNIER, M. *Acta neurochir.* Suppl. 3: 291, 1955.
175. MONNIER, M. *Rev. neurol.* 93: 267, 1956.
176. MORIN, F. *Am. J. Physiol.* 183: 245, 1955.
177. MORIN, F. AND J. V. CATALANO. *J. Comp. Neurol.* 103: 17, 1955.
178. MORIN, F., H. G. SCHWARTZ AND J. L. O'LEARY. *Acta psychiat. et neurol. scandinav.* 26: 371, 1951.
179. MORUZZI, G. AND H. W. MAGOUN. *Electroencephalog. & Clin. Neurophysiol.* 1: 455, 1949.
180. MOTT, F. W. *Brain* 18: 1, 1895.
181. MOUNTCASTLE, V. B. *J. Neurophysiol.* 20: 408, 1957.
182. MOUNTCASTLE, V. B., M. R. COVIAN AND C. R. HARRISON. *A. Res. Nerv. & Ment. Dis., Proc.* 30: 339, 1950.
183. MOUNTCASTLE, V. B., P. W. DAVIES AND A. L. BERMAN. *J. Neurophysiol.* 20: 374, 1957.
184. MOUNTCASTLE, V. B. AND E. HENNEMAN. *J. Neurophysiol.* 12: 85, 1949.
185. MOUNTCASTLE, V. B. AND E. HENNEMAN. *J. Comp. Neurol.* 97: 409, 1952.
186. NATHAN, P. W. AND M. C. SMITH. *J. Neurol. Neurosurg. & Psychiat.* 18: 181, 1955.
187. NESS, A. R. *J. Physiol.* 126: 475, 1954.
188. OLIVECRONA, H. *Arch. Neurol. & Psychiat.* 47: 544, 1942.
189. OLSZEWSKI, J. *The Thalamus of Macaca Mulatta.* New York: S. Karger, 1952.
190. OSCARSSON, O. *Acta physiol. scandinav.* 38: 144, 1956.
191. PAPEZ, J. W. *Anat. Rec.* 109: 405, 1951.
192. PAPEZ, J. W. AND W. RUNDLES. *J. Nerv. & Ment. Dis.* 85: 505, 1937.
193. PATTON, H. D. AND V. E. AMASSIAN. *Am. J. Physiol.* 183: 650, 1955.
194. PEARSON, A. A. *Arch. Neurol. & Psychiat.* 68: 515, 1952.
195. PEASE, D. C. AND T. A. QUILLIAM. *J. Biophys. & Biochem. Cytol.* 3: 331, 1957.
196. PETREN, K. *Arch. Psychiat.* 47: 495, 1910.
197. PFAFFMANN, C. *J. Cell. & Comp. Physiol.* 17: 243, 1941.
198. POWELL, T. P. S. AND V. B. MOUNTCASTLE. *Fed. Proc.* 17: 126, 1958.
199. PRIBRAM, H. B. AND J. BARRY. *J. Neurophysiol.* 19: 99, 1956.
200. PROBST, M. *Arch. Psychiat.* 33: 1, 1900.

201. RAMÓN Y CAJAL, S. *Histologie du Système Nerveux de l'Homme et des Vertébres.* Paris: Maloine, 1909.
202. RANEY, R., A. A. RANEY AND C. R. HUNTER. *Am. J. Surg.* 80: 11, 1950.
203. RANSON, S. W. AND W. R. INGRAM. *J. Comp. Neurol.* 56: 257, 1932.
204. RASMUSSEN, A. T. AND W. T. PEYTON. *Surgery* 10: 699, 1941.
205. REXED, B. AND A. BRODAL. *J. Neurophysiol.* 14: 399, 1951.
206. REXED, B. AND G. STRÖM. *Acta physiol. scandinav.* 25: 219, 1952.
207. ROSE, J. E. AND V. B. MOUNTCASTLE. *J. Comp. Neurol.* 97: 441, 1952.
208. ROSE, J. E. AND V. B. MOUNTCASTLE. *Bull. Johns Hopkins Hosp.* 94: 238, 1954.
209. ROSE, J. E. AND C. N. WOOLSEY. *Biological and Biochemical Bases of Behavior.* Madison: Univ. Wisconsin Press. In press.
210. RUCH, T. C. AND J. F. FULTON. *A. Res. Nerv. & Ment. Dis., Proc.* 15: 288, 1935.
211. RUCH, T. C., J. F. FULTON AND W. J. GERMAN. *Arch. Neurol. & Psychiat.* 39: 919, 1938.
212. RUCH, T. C., J. F. FULTON AND S. KASDON. *Am. J. Physiol.* 119: 394, 1937.
213. RUCH, T. C., S. KASDON AND J. F. FULTON. *Am. J. Physiol.* 129: 453, 1940.
214. RUSSELL, G. V. *J. Comp. Neurol.* 101: 237, 1954.
215. SAMUEL, E. P. *Anat. Rec.* 113: 53, 1952.
216. SASAOKA, S. *Jap. J. Med. Sc. I. Anat.* 7: 315, 1939.
217. SCHERRER, H. AND R. HERNÁNDEZ-PEÓN. *Fed. Proc.* 14: 132, 1955.
218. SCHWARTZ, H. G. AND J. L. O'LEARY. *Surgery* 9: 183, 1941.
219. SCHWARTZ, H. G. AND J. L. O'LEARY. *Arch. Neurol. & Psychiat.* 47: 293, 1942.
220. SINCLAIR, D. C. *Brain* 78: 584, 1955.
221. SINCLAIR, D. C. AND J. R. HINSHAW. *Brain* 73: 224, 1950.
222. SINCLAIR, D. C. AND J. R. HINSHAW. *Brain* 73: 480, 1950.
223. SINCLAIR, D. C., G. WEDDELL AND E. ZANDER. *J. Anat.* 86: 402, 1952.
224. SJÖQVIST, O. *Acta psychiat. et neurol.* Suppl. 17, 1938.
225. SKOGLUND, S. *Acta physiol. scandinav.* Suppl. 124, 36: 1, 1956.
226. SPERRY, R. W. *J. Neurophysiol.* 10: 275, 1947.
227. SPERRY, R. W., N. MINOR AND R. E. MYERS. *J. Comp. & Physiol. Psychol.* 48: 50, 1955.
228. STAMM, J. S. AND R. W. SPERRY. *J. Comp. & Physiol. Psychol.* 50: 138, 1957.
229. STARZL, T. E., C. W. TAYLOR AND H. W. MAGOUN. *J. Neurophysiol.* 14: 461, 1951.
230. STARZL, T. E., C. W. TAYLOR AND H. W. MAGOUN. *J. Neurophysiol.* 14: 479, 1951.
231. STILWELL, D. J., JR. *Anat. Rec.* 127: 635, 1957.
232. STILWELL, D. L., JR. *Am. J. Anat.* 100: 289, 1957.
233. STILWELL, D. L., JR. *Am. J. Anat.* 101: 59, 1957.
234. STOPFORD, J. S. B. *J. Anat.* 59: 120, 1925.
235. STRATFORD, J. *J. Comp. Neurol.* 100: 1, 1954.
236. SWEET, W. H.,, J. C. WHITE, B. SELVERSTONE AND R. NILGES. *Tr. Am. Neurol. A.* 1950, p. 165.
237. SZENTAGOTHAI, J. AND T. KISS. *Arch. Neurol. & Psychiat.* 62: 734, 1949.
238. TORVIK, A. *J. Comp. Neurol.* 106: 51, 1956.
239. TORVIK, A. *Am. J. Anat.* 100: 1, 1957.
240. TSCHERMAK, A. *Neurol. Centralbl.* 17: 159, 1898.
241. VAN GEHUCHTEN, A. *Névraxe* 3: 235, 1901.
242. VOGT, C. *J. Psychol. u. Neurol.* 12: 285, 1909.
243. VON ECONOMO, C. *Jahrb. Psychiat. u. Neurol.* 32: 107, 1911.
244. VON FREY, M. *Ber. sächs. Gesellsch. Wiss.* 46: 185, 1894.
245. VON FREY, M. *Ber. sächs. Gesellsch. Wiss.* 46: 283, 1894.
246. VON FREY, M. *Ber. sächs. Gesellsch. Wiss.* 47: 166, 1895.
247. VON FREY, M. *Abh. sächs. Gesellsch. Wiss.* 40: 175, 1896.
248. WALBERG, F. *Brain* 80: 273, 1957.
249. WALKER, A. E. *J. Comp. Neurol.* 60: 161, 1934.
250. WALKER, A. E. *J. Comp. Neurol.* 64: 1, 1936.
251. WALKER, A. E. *Koninkl. Nad. Akad. Wetenschap., Proc.* 40: 198, 1937.
252. WALKER, A. E. *Confinia Neurol.* 1: 99, 1938.
253. WALKER, A. E. *The Primate Thalamus.* Chicago: Univ. Chicago Press, 1938.
254. WALKER, A. E. *J. Comp. Neurol.* 71: 59, 1939.
255. WALKER, A. E. *Arch. Neurol. & Psychiat.* 43: 284, 1940.
256. WALKER, A. E. *Arch. Neurol. & Psychiat.* 48: 865, 1942.
257. WALKER, A. E. *Arch. Neurol. & Psychiat.* 48: 884, 1942.
258. WALKER, A. E. AND T. A. WEAVER, JR. *J. Comp. Neurol.* 76: 145, 1942.
259. WALLENBERG, A. *Anat. Anz.* 12: 95, 1896.
260. WALLENBERG, A. *Anat. Anz.* 18: 81, 1900.
261. WALLENBERG, A. *Anat. Anz.* 26: 145, 1905.
262. WALSHE, F. M. R. *Brain* 65: 48, 1942.
263. WEAVER, T. A., JR., AND A. E. WALKER. *Arch. Neurol. & Psychiat.* 46: 877, 1941.
264. WEDDELL, G. *J. Anat.* 75: 346, 1941.
265. WEDDELL, G. *J. Anat.* 75: 441, 1941.
266. WEDDELL, G. AND J. A. HARPMAN. *J. Neurol. & Psychiat.* 3: 319, 1940.
267. WEDDELL, G., W. PALLIE AND E. PALMER. *Quart. J. Microsc. Sc.* 95: 483, 1954.
268. WEDDELL, G., E. PALMER AND W. PALLIE. *Biol. Rev.* 30: 159, 1955.
269. WEDDELL, G., D. A. TAYLOR AND C. M. WILLIAMS. *J. Anat.* 89: 317, 1955.
270. WEINBERGER, L. M. AND F. C. GRANT. *Arch. Neurol. & Psychiat.* 48: 355, 1942.
271. WHITE, J. C. *Arch. Surg.* 43: 113, 1941.
272. WHITE, J. C., E. P. RICHARDSON, JR., AND W. H. SWEET. *Ann. Surg.* 144: 407, 1956.
273. WHITE, J. C. AND W. H. SWEET. *Pain. Its Mechanisms and Neurosurgical Control.* Springfield: Thomas, 1955.
274. WHITE, J. C., W. H. SWEET, R. HAWKINS AND R. G. NILGES. *Brain* 73: 346, 1950.
275. WOOLLARD, H. H., G. WEDDELL AND J. A. HARPMAN. *J. Anat.* 74: 413, 1940.
276. WOOLSEY, C. N., H.-T. CHANG AND P. BARD. *Fed. Proc.* 6: 230, 1947.
277. WOOLSEY, C. N. AND D. FAIRMAN. *Surgery* 19: 684, 1946.
278. WOOLSEY, C. N. AND G. H. WANG. *Fed. Proc.* 4: 79, 1945.
279. WRETE, M. *Acta Anat.* 7: 173, 1949.
280. YAMAMOTO, S., S. SUGIHARA, AND M. KURU. *Jap. J. Physiol.* 6: 68, 1956.
281. ZOTTERMAN, Y. *Skandinav. Arch. Physiol.* 75: 105, 1936.
282. ZOTTERMAN, Y. *J. Physiol.* 95: 1, 1939.
283. ZUBEK, J. P. *J. Comp. & Physiol. Psychol.* 44: 339, 1951.
284. ZUBEK, J. P. *J. Neurophysiol.* 15: 401, 1951.
285. ZUBEK, J. P. *Canad. J. Psychol.* 6: 183, 1952.
286. ZUBEK, J. P. *J. Comp. & Physiol. Psychol.* 45: 438, 1952.

CHAPTER XVIII

Thermal sensations

YNGVE ZOTTERMAN | *Department of Physiology, Veterinärhögskolan, Stockholm, Sweden*

CHAPTER CONTENTS

The different sensations of cold and warmth are produced by stimulation of separate specific nerve end-organs in the skin.
MAGNUS BLIX 1882 (9).

STRUCTURE OF RECEPTIVE FIELD

Topography of Thermal Senses: Cold and Warm Spots

SINCE THE DISCOVERY by Blix (9, 10) of cold and warm spots from which adequate or electrical stimuli elicited cold and warm sensations, respectively, numerous authors have described the distribution of cold and warm spots in the skin as well as in the mucous membranes of man. In general cold spots are far more numerous than warm spots, but the relation between the density of the two kinds of temperature sensitive spots varies a good deal in different areas. Hensel (45) in his review emphasizes the great errors inherent in finding these thermal spots by using punctiform stimuli such as Blix's cone affords. The highest density of thermosensitive spots is found in some areas of the face. Particularly sensitive to thermal stimulation are the eyelids and the lips. The forehead is very cold-sensitive but only moderately sensitive to warmth. The hairy parts of the head, the patellar region and the tongue are very slightly sensitive to warmth. The conjuctiva bulbi and the periphery of the cornea possess cold sensitivity but do not respond to warmth. Careful investigations on the distribution of temperature spots have been made for the whole body by Rein (72) and Goldscheider (32), for the genital organs by Hauer (39), Speiser (81) and Beetz (6), for the eye by Strughold & Karge (84) and Strughold & Porz (85), and for the mucous membranes of the mouth and the nose by Rein (72), Strughold (83), Schriever & Strughold (78) and Hirsch & Schriever (59). In these papers as well as in Goldscheider's review (32) topographical charts of temperature spots will be found. In table 1 the mean density of cold and warm spots is given for different areas of the body surface. The high temperature sensitivity of the tri-

TABLE 1 *Distribution of Warm and Cold Spots in Human Skin**

	Cold Spots†	Warm Spots‡
Forehead	5.5–8	
Nose	8–13	1
Lips	16–19	
Other parts of face	8.5–9	1.7
Chest	9–10.2	0.3
Abdomen	8–12.5	
Back	7.8	
Upper arm	5–6.5	
Forearm	6–7.5	0.3–0.4
Back of hand	7.4	0.5
Palm of hand	1–5	0.4
Finger dorsal	7–9	1.7
Finger volar	2–4	1.6
Thigh	4.5–5.2	0.4
Calf	4.3–5.7	
Back of foot	5.6	
Sole of foot	3.4	

* Number per cm².
† After Strughold & Porz (85).
‡ After Rein (72).

geminal area which in man is directly exposed to all weathers no doubt has special importance.

Concerning the thermal sensitivity of animals our knowledge is very scarce and scattered. Until recently cold-blooded animals were not believed to possess any specific thermoceptive organs. Sand (77) using electrophysiological methods discovered that the Lorenzinian ampullae of *Raja* reacted to cooling. The Lorenzinian ampullae of the elasmobranchs are situated laterally in the region of the head and consist of a group of small mucous cysts lying subcutaneously. They are supplied by afferent fibers from the facial nerve.

The facial pits of the pit viper (Crotalidae), which originally were believed to function as mechanoceptors specialized for the detection of air vibrations, were clearly shown by Noble & Schmidt (70) through behavioral experiments to detect the body temperature of the snakes' prey. They proved that snakes with the other principal sense organs of the head nonfunctional can still strike correctly at moving objects and can discriminate between warm and cold ones as long as the pits are uncovered. The organ consists of a small pit about 3 mm in diameter covered by a membrane 15 μ thick. This thin membrane is the innervated sensory surface. Leading off from microelectrodes, steel needles with tip diameter of about 3 to 7 μ inserted into the membrane, Bullock

& Cowles (12), Bullock & Diecke (13) and Bullock & Faulstick (14) proved that the afferent nerve endings serve as infrared receptors. They are, so far as we know at present, the most densely distributed warm receptors and the most effective organ for infrared detection within the animal kingdom. In mammals cold sensitivity seems to be located particularly on the bare parts of the nose and on the tip of the tongue. More details are not available as yet.

Depth of Thermal Nerve Endings

The fact that the reaction time for warmth is consistently longer than that for cold suggested that the warm receptors should be located deeper in the skin than the cold receptors (87, 91). This assumption had many proponents (1, 26, 27, 72). Bazett *et al.* (5) calculated the depth of the thermal receptors in the prepuce. The skin was stretched out into a flat sheet by means of small barbless fish-hooks. Sensitive spots belonging to one layer of skin could thus be stimulated from either side of the double fold. The rate of transmission of the temperature wave through the fold was determined by thermoelectrical recording; the value obtained of about 1 mm per sec. is in agreement with more recent measurements of Hensel & Zotterman (55). From this figure and the reaction time of the subject so stimulated it was possible to estimate the depth of the receptors.

The average depth of the warm receptors was thus found to be 0.3 mm. For the cold receptors the average depth was computed to somewhat less than 0.17 mm. The depths of the receptors for cold and warmth computed in this way were in good agreement with the average depth of the Krause and the Ruffini type of end organ respectively as determined histologically.

This and other previous methods based upon the subjective reaction time to thermal stimuli must be subject to rather large errors because a great number of uncontrollable reactions take place between the application of the stimulus and the conscious action of the subject, the time of which is many times longer than that of the actual peripheral events occurring in the thermal receptors themselves.

By using the method of recording the spike potentials in the specific cold fibers Hensel *et al.* (51) developed a method of physiological depth determination which eliminates the errors of the methods previously used. The method has been used for determining the depth of the cold receptors on the tip of the tongue of the cat and the dog but can of course in principle be applied even to human subjects.

The principle of the method consists of determining by means of small rectangular temperature steps the threshold temperature change, θ_s, for the cold receptors. A large well-defined cold pulse was applied then to the surface by means of a special thermode described in figure 14; then the lapse of time, t, from the beginning of the pulse until the appearance of the first cold fiber spike was measured. The time, t, is composed of the 'thermal latency,' t_θ, the time which the cold needs to penetrate into the receptor layer, and two constants: the nerve conduction time, t_n, of the cold fibers and the physiological latency, t_r, of the cold receptor. For the thermal latency, t_θ, from which the depth of the receptor can be calculated, we obtain

$$t_\theta = t - t_n - t_r.$$

When the thermal diffusion coefficient, a, of the living skin is known, it is possible to calculate to what depth the threshold temperature change, θ_s, has proceeded within the time, t_θ. This depth is the depth of the receptor. By means of a double beam cathode ray oscillograph for simultaneous recording of the electric response from the cold fibers and the temperature of the surface of the tongue, the beginning of the temperature course was easily determined with an accuracy of ± 0.002 sec.

Figure 1 shows a record of the discharge of cold spikes from a strand of the lingual nerve of the cat in response to a sudden cooling from 38 to 15°C and rewarming. Simultaneously the temperature of the silver bottom of a thermode on the tongue was recorded by the second beam. After an interval, $t = 0.023$ sec., from the beginning of the cooling, the first action potential from the cold fibers appeared. On rewarming, the last cold fiber spike disappeared after

an interval of 0.027 sec. from the beginning of the rewarming. The determinations of t were repeated several times for each preparation. As was shown by Zotterman (96) the shorter the interval, t, the larger the temperature steps. For the preparation of figure 1, for example, values of t between 0.015 sec. (for steps from 38 to 5°C) and 0.07 sec. (for steps from 38 to 34°C) were obtained. For the sum of the two constants t_n and t_r an interval of about 0.006 sec. was computed. The latency of the cold receptors, about 0.003 to 0.005 sec., is obtained by comparing the intervals, t, at large and small temperature steps. Using this value of t_r we obtained exactly the same depth at all temperature steps; at larger values of t_r the values of the depth were too small compared to the values computed when using medium or small temperature steps. From about 70 separate measurements on six cats the following values were obtained:

Relative threshold....	0.5	1	2
Average depth of receptors..	0.15 mm	0.18 mm	0.20 mm
Dispersion.....	±0.015 mm	±0.015 mm	±0.018 mm

The physiological depth determinations of the cold receptors are in good accordance with the histological observations made on serial slides from the same area of the cat tongue. The epithelium of the papillae has a height of 0.05 to 0.08 mm. The musculature of the tongue starts with a rather sharply defined border line at a depth of about 0.3 mm. Closely above the musculature of the tongue there is a well-developed net of blood vessels. Thus, according to these determinations, the cold receptors are situated subepithelially partly in the papillae and particularly at their base or just beneath them.

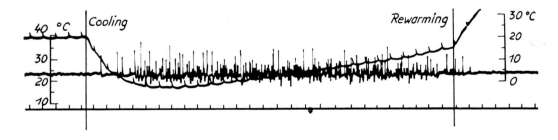

FIG. 1. Simultaneous records of cold potentials in a fine strand of cat lingual nerve and of temperature of silver bottom of thermode on tongue during sudden cooling from about 40° to 15°C and rewarming. *Left temperature scale* for cooling, *right scale* for rewarming. Time, 50 cps. [From Hensel et al. (51).]

Identification of Thermal Receptors

Since the recording of spike activity of single thermal nerve fibers by Zotterman and co-workers (22, 52, 96), there can be no doubt about the specificity of cold and warm nerve endings in the mammals as these thermal receptors discharging into functionally isolated nerve fibers responded to cooling and warming, respectively, but not to mechanical stimulation. The abundance of information about the function of the thermal receptors obtained in recent years from electrophysiological investigations has, however, not been followed by any corresponding widening of our knowledge of the morphological structure of the receptors. The old attempts to identify the receptors histologically by excision of human skin beneath the cold and warm spots, respectively, failed almost entirely [see von Skramlik (92)]. The statement in most textbooks that the Krause end bulbs are believed to be the receptor for cold and the Ruffini end organ that for warmth were based on histological studies by von Frey (91) and Strughold & Karbe (84) on sensory end organs within the cold sensitive periphery of the cornea. After mapping the cold spots on the conjunctiva bulbi, Strughold & Karbe dropped methylene blue into the eye and found a very good topographical correlation between the cold spots and the blue stained end bulbs observed in the corneal microscope. Similarly Bazett *et al.* (5) in their attempt to identify the end organs for temperature and touch in the prepuce injected methylene blue intra-arterially. They described seven different types of end organs, among which end bulbs of the Krause type were distributed in good agreement with the cold spots. Their average number was about 15 per cm² compared with 6 to 12 for the cold spots, but some of the end bulbs were so close together that their number obviously must exceed that found by mapping the cold spots. Further, there are reasons to believe that some nerve fibers branch and supply more than one end organ. Spots sensitive to warmth in the prepuce are few in number (one or rather less per cm²). The distribution of the Ruffini end organs agreed fairly well with that of the warm spots.

Whether the Krause end bulbs are the receptors for cold in other parts of the skin is still uncertain since conventional histological methods have failed to reveal any end bulbs of the Krause type in the skin underlying the cold spots. Recently Lele *et al.* (65) maintained that, in limited areas of the skin (as opposed to mucous membranes) in which encapsulated nerve endings are abundant (the palm of the hand, sole of the foot and parts of the dorsum of the digits), the diversity in size and configuration of their cellular and neural elements is such that any classification of encapsulated endings in the skin becomes purely arbitrary. On the other hand they draw attention to the fact that in both glabrous and hairy skin ensheathed nerve fibers arising from the cutaneous nerve plexus give rise at all levels in the skin (from the stratum granulosum of the epidermis to the junction of the dermis and the subcutaneous tissues) to a widespread series of fine naked axoplasmic filaments which interweave but do not fuse with one another. These unencapsulated nerve endings cannot be distinguished from one another on morphological grounds; they can be distinguished only by the fact that they are situated in a different stratum of the skin and thus lie among different tissue elements. Thus the morphologically nonspecific nerve endings found beneath the epithelium should be reduced in temperature and therefore be stimulated by cooling of the skin. The deeper endings situated close to the blood vessels are generally heated up by the blood so that a positive temperature gradient between the ending and the axons should be the usual mode of stimulation. According to Lele *et al.* the temperature modes are related not to the stimulation of morphologically specific endings, but to the manner in which nonspecific nerve endings of fibers in the skin are stimulated. These unencapsulated endings should thus, according to these authors, be looked upon "as universal receptors which give rise to bursts of action potentials, the pattern of which is related to the way in which the stimulus affects the skin." Consequently they also maintain that Johannes Müller's 'law of specific energies' and the thesis that there are specific nerve terminals which subserve specific sensory modalities is unsupported.

The absence of encapsulated nerve endings does, however, not exclude the possibility of functional specificity. The tongue of the frog does not contain any such endings although it contains afferent fibers responding specifically to touch, salt and water (98). In recent years it has often been suggested that the capsule of an end organ, for example in a Pacinian corpuscle, protects the nerve ending from being damaged when the organ is subjected to strong and lasting mechanical stimulation as in the beak of a wood pecker. The capsule should thus have nothing specifically to do with the energy transformation This would imply that the specific process of transformation should be inherent in the morphologically nonspecific naked nerve endings or in the structures where these are situated. The sensation experienced upon stimulation of the nerve ending may be more closely correlated with the most usual mode of stimulation—which, for the superficially situated 'cold' endings, is cooling of the skin. The discharges from these endings are then transmitted to specific cells of the cortex the activity of which will be labelled cold. So far it is easy to follow the idea of Lele *et al.* (65). But when these authors maintain that the thermal nerve endings respond even to mechanical and noxious stimuli they diverge from the experimental evidence, in that the activity of single temperature fibers of the cat and the dog cannot be influenced by mechanical stimulation of their receptive field at least within reasonable limits of stimulus strength. The nonspecific response of certain mechanoceptive fibers to cooling, as demonstrated by Hensel & Zotterman (53), requires a sudden temperature rise of more than 8°C. Since the cold fibers from the facial region of the cat which have been more closely studied (46) do not behave differently from those of the tongue, there can be hardly any doubt that these fibers possess endings which are specifically stimulated when the layer of the skin in which they are situated is cooled.

Afferent Nerve Paths

Judging from the relative spike height Zotterman (96) suggested that the cold fibers of the tongue of the cat were fairly thin myelinated fibers belonging to the δ-group of the class A fibers according to Gasser & Erlanger's nomenclature (fig. 10). Direct measurements of isolated single cold fibers from the saphenous nerve of the cat by Maruhashi *et al.* (68) gave diameters of 1.5 to 3 μ. These fibers showed a punctiform receptive field and were the smallest of the myelinated fibers. They were sensitive neither to light touch nor to pinprick. As the warm fibers give rise to spikes of somewhat higher amplitudes, they are considered to be of slightly greater diameters (54, 96).

The central course of the temperature fibers in man is only roughly known. After entering the spinal cord via the dorsal roots the thermal fibers form a lateral division which enters the dorsolateral fasciculus or the tract of Lissauer. The fibers ascend only one to three segments before terminating in the substantia gelatinosa Rolandi, a cell column capping the posterior horn with a seemingly uniform texture containing small cell bodies only and with no large myelinated fibers traversing it. The axons of its small cells cross the cord in the anterior gray commissure and ascend in the lateral spinothalamic tract (76). In syringomyelia the fibers crossing in the narrow space of the anterior gray commissure are often destroyed which leads to a well-known clinical syndrome characterized by loss of pain, warmth and cold on both sides of the body at the level of the segments involved while the sense of touch and pressure is preserved. In some patients there may be a dissociation between the degree of impairment of heat and cold sensation.

According to Häggqvist (36) as well as to Bailey & Glees (3) the majority of the fibers in the spinothalamic tract are 2 to 4 μ in diameter, 35 per cent are 4 to 6 μ and only a few fibers run up to 10 μ in diameter. Thus the dimensions of thermal and nociceptive peripheral fibers seem to be preserved in the second order of neurons. The spinothalamic tract is so organized that fibers ascending from the caudal region are pushed outwards by the accretion of crossing fibers at each successive segment (93). Fibers from the cervical part are thus situated most anterior and medially. This arrangement seems to maintain the topographical organization of the fibers into the cortical projection.

The small-sized temperature fibers of the trigeminal nerve follow the course of the pain fibers after entering the brain stem into the elongated spinal nucleus which extends through the medulla to meet the substantia gelatinosa Rolandi (28). Division of this tractus spinalis of the trigeminal nerve, the trigeminal tractotomy of Sjöqvist, in the medulla leads to an analgesia and also to a fairly complete thermal anesthesia in the opposite half of the face as well as to failure of tickling sensations (79, 97). The exact localization of the third thermoceptive neurons in the thalamus is not known. The spinothalamic tract fibers from different levels of the spinal cord terminate in the posteroventral nucleus of the thalamus but in doing so they interdigitate so much that the original peripheral topography of fibers mediating different modalities seems to be regained. In the ventral nuclei of the thalamus the finer topographical organization has been worked out by studying degeneration of the fibers in the medial lemniscus and the spinothalamic tract (13) but a still more detailed map was obtained by Mountcastle & Henneman (69) by studying the electric response appearing in the thalamus on stimulation of points on the body surface. The body surface is projected onto the thalamus, specifically onto the posteroventral nucleus which is the only part in which stimulation of the skin evoked any electric response, in such a way that the head is represented posteromedially, the tail anterolaterally, the back superiorly and the feet inferiorly. According to Ruch (76) this topography manifested in the thalamic terminations

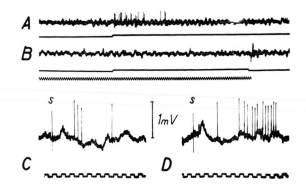

FIG. 2. Cortical cell responding specifically to cooling of the tongue (cat). *A*, water of 11°C and *B*, water of 37°C were applied to the tongue (signal on lower beam). Time, 50 cps. *C* and *D* show the same cell responding to electrical stimulation of the tip of the tongue. *S*, stimulus artifact. Note that the first spikes do not appear until the falling phase of the primary cortical response. Time, 5 msec. Negativity upwards in all records. [From Landgren, S., personal communication.]

of sensory systems is preserved in the thalamocortical projections. The medially situated arcuate nucleus receiving impulses from the face projects near the Sylvian fissure. The lateral part of the posterolateral nucleus, receiving impulses from the leg, projects near the mid-line. The projection from the arm is intermediate in both thalamus and cortex. As far as anatomical studies have revealed, the sensory body surface is projected upon the postcentral gyrus with spatial relations preserved but in an opposite direction compared with that in the thalamus. Lacking any direct evidence of the localization of the third thermal neuron in the thalamus we have to suppose that the original peripheral topographical organization of the thermal units is regained at this level.

Electrical stimulation of the somesthetic areas of the cortex made on conscious patients (16, 71) gives rise to localized sensations. The most usual responses are numbness, tingling and a feeling of movement and only more rarely warmth and cold are experienced. When recording from single cortical cells in the cat by means of fine microelectrodes, Cohen *et al.* (15) have found cells in the tongue sensory area which respond specifically to cooling of the tip of the tongue but not to mechanical or taste stimuli. Further investigations by Landgren (63) show that in response to cooling of the tongue cortical cold cells produce a discharge, the latency, frequency and duration of which is dependent upon the strength of the thermal stimulus. The shortest recorded latency of the specific

cortical cold cells to an electric shock to the tongue was 0.015 sec. compared to 0.005 sec. of a cortical touch cell within the same area. The shortest latency recorded to cooling of the tongue was about 0.02 sec. (fig. 2). The receptive fields of the specific cold cells were limited to the tip or the lateral edge of the tongue. Besides these specific cells other cells were found which responded to mechanical as well as to thermal stimuli, occasionally also to taste stimuli. These nonspecific cortical cells showed much longer latencies (0.08 to 0.30 sec.) which suggests that they cannot be primary. So far only one cortical cell responding specifically to warming the tongue was found. It thus looks as though the thermosensitive units are represented in the cortex topographically in much the same way as on the surface of the body. The fact that we have found in the somesthetic cortical areas cells which respond specifically to cold or to warmth does not exclude the possibility that there are peripheral afferent neurons which respond to thermal as well as to mechanical and noxious stimuli. Such neurons can, however, scarcely contribute to the specific thermal discrimination. For that purpose we have to reckon with the activity of specific peripheral neurons finally activating specific cortical neurons. All previous speculation of a possible frequency code is not only incompatible with Johannes Müller's law of specific sensory energies as currently conceived but also with recent electrophysiological investigations of the impulse traffic in sensory nerve fibers. Although many have looked for facts indicating some kind of frequency code there is to date very little evidence that frequency modulation in the sensory nerve can influence anything but the intensity of the cortical events underlying the sensation. This opinion will not be changed if nerve fibers are found with endings which are not strictly functionally specific. Some of the unmyelinated afferent cutaneous fibers are most probably activated by strong abnormal stimulation as well as by mechanical stimulation. The interference of these fibers with the activity of more strictly specific fibers may very well underlie such cutaneous sensations as hot and tickling which possess something more than one sensory quality. No nerve endings are absolutely specific as they are all excitable by electrical stimulation or by strong mechanical or chemical stimulation. Thus when we speak of specific nerve endings from a functional point of view, we refer only to such sensory end organs as are specific within reasonable limits.

CONDITIONS FOR THERMAL SENSATIONS

The variety of opinion concerning the conditions for thermal stimulation, which until lately has characterized the discussion of the temperature senses ever since Weber presented his famous theory in 1846, was to a great extent dependent upon imperfections in the physical methods used in studying the thermal movements in the skin as well as upon the use of subjective reports as an indicator of the stimulating effect. The main problems in the physiology of the thermal senses have been the question of whether temporal temperature changes or the absolute temperature levels were the adequate stimulus and the intimately connected question of the physical or physiological interpretation of adaptation.

Conduction of Heat in Skin

While the majority of writers have on the whole accepted Weber's opinion that the temporal differential quotient of the temperature change represents the adequate stimulus, there are others who like Hering (58) have given attention to the influence of the prevailing temperature in itself (37). Thunberg stated in 1905 in Nagel's *Handbuch* that this question cannot be settled until the physical constants of the external layers of the skin are so well known that the thermal exchange in the skin can be computed quantitatively. Following the work of Bazett *et al.* (5), Hensel (42, 43) succeeded in developing methods for the determination of intracutaneous temperature at exactly localized depths, a very fine thermocouple being introduced through a thin cannula or through an intracutaneous punctured channel.

Further, Hensel (43) constructed a precision-flow-calorimeter for measuring the steady heat flow given off from small skin areas. The Strömungskalorimeter—a flat cylindrical measuring chamber through which water of constant temperature flows with constant velocity—is placed on the skin above the two thermocouples which are situated at different depths. The amount of heat given off is then obtained from the flow velocity and temperature difference between inflowing and outflowing water. The mean error of the method is as low as about ±0.001 cal. per cm² per sec.

The thermal movement in nonstationary conditions depends not only upon the thermal conductivity of the tissue but also on its specific heat and density.

The determining constant, the thermal diffusion coefficient, a, is obtained by the following equation:

$$a = \frac{\lambda}{C\rho}$$

where λ (calories per cm per sec. per degree) represents the thermal conductivity, C (cal. per gm per degree) the specific heat, and ρ (gm per cm³) the density of the substance. As the determination of C and λ are problematic in the living skin, Hensel (44) elaborated a method for direct determination of the diffusivity, a. By means of the above described thermo-electrical methods the temperature movements were recorded at different depths of the skin when rectangular temperature pulses were applied to the surface by the application of metal bodies of constant temperature. From the curves obtained the diffusivity, a, could be determined in that the curves for various values of a were constructed and it was found at which value of a the computed curve best fitted the recorded curve. For human skin in depths up to 2 mm the values for a varied from 0.0004 to 0.0018

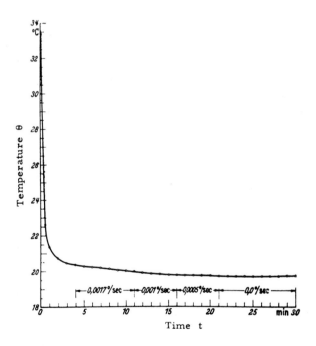

FIG. 3. Recorded intracutaneous temperature change at a depth of 0.6 mm on application of a thermode at 17°C on the skin at 33.5°C. A distinct cold sensation persisted throughout the whole experiment although the rate of change after 3 min. fell below the minimum value of 0.0025°C per sec. given by Gertz for the maintenance of a cold sensation. [From Hensel (42).]

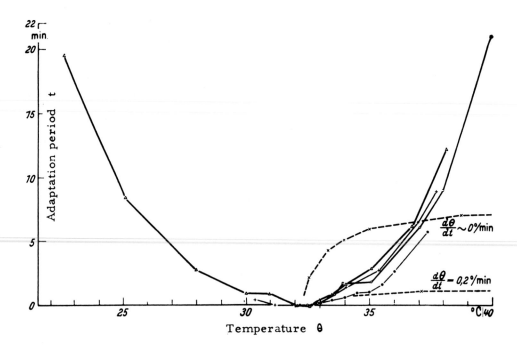

FIG. 4. 'Adaptation periods' (the time until the temperature sensation disappears) as a function of the stimulus temperature when using constant temperature for stimulation. The adaptation periods become longer as the stimulus temperature departs from the indifferent temperature (32.5 °C). *Broken lines* indicate periods as function of the stimulus temperature after which the intracutaneous temperature change at a depth of 1 mm has fallen below values of 0.2 °C per sec. and of 0.0 °C per sec. The adaptation periods do not at all coincide with the subsidence of the intracutaneous temperature change. [From Hensel (42).]

cm² per sec. according to depth of the layer and the cutaneous circulation.

By theoretical as well as by experimental investigation Hensel (44) showed that changes in the blood flow in the skin exerts much less influence upon the diffusivity (the thermometric conductivity) than it does upon the thermal conductivity.

Relation Between Temperature Change Recorded in Skin and Thermal Sensations

Using the methods described above Hensel (43, 44) made thorough investigations of the relation between the thermal sensations reported by the subject and the actual temperature movements in the skin when well defined thermal stimulation was applied to the skin.

In confirmation of earlier workers, Heilbrun (41) and Hensel (42) demonstrated that thermal sensations still persisted when the temperature of the skin had reached a constant level. With the above described method Hensel recorded the temperature movements at a depth of 0.6 mm when a rectangular

thermal step, t, was applied. As will be seen in figure 3, the rate of thermal change had gone down below the value of 0.0025° per sec. which Gertz (30) had found to be the minimum rate necessary to maintain a thermal sensation. After 20 min., when the temperature had been practically constant for some minutes, there was still reported a diminishing but quite distinct cold sensation.

In figure 4 the adaptation period (interval from the stimulus application until the disappearance of thermal sensation) and the interval until the temperature change stopped is plotted against the temperature applied to the skin. At temperatures below 20°C and above 40°C constant sensations appear. Hensel (42) found that the adaptation requires a longer time the more the temperature of the stimulus diverges from the temperature of the skin. But the cessation of the thermal sensation and the intracutaneous temperature changes do not coincide, as the sensation usually considerably outlasts the intracutaneous temperature movement. This is particularly the case at extreme temperatures.

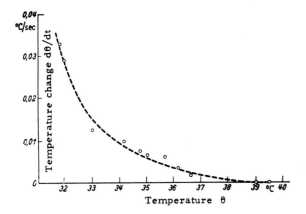

FIG. 5. Rate, $d\theta/dt$, of the intracutaneous temperature change at the subsidence of the warm sensation as a function of the prevalent temperature. (Forearm, skin temperature 31 °C, thermode area of 20 cm².) It will be seen that smaller values of $d\theta/dt$ are necessary for maintaining a warm sensation, the higher the prevailing temperature. [From Hensel (42).]

The rate $(d\theta/dt)$ of the intracutaneous temperature change at the moment of the subsidence of the warm sensation is shown in figure 5. Thus, the rate of temperature change believed necessary to maintain a sensation diminishes the more extreme the temperature until at certain threshold temperatures it attains the value of 0. Outside this threshold value a constant temperature acts as a stimulus eliciting a steady thermal sensation.

The experiments of Gertz (30) on the effect of approximately linear changes of temperature have been repeated using more accurate methods by Hensel (42). As will be seen from figure 6, the thermal sensations pass successively through all grades of sensation from cold to warmth, although the rate of change $(d\theta/dt)$ is kept constant. If at any stage of the procedure the temperature change is allowed to stop $(d\theta/dt = 0)$, the thermal sensation in question at once becomes definitely weaker.

With uniform rates of change of different slope the time factor (adaptation) will produce a shift of the threshold in such a way that the slower the rate of change the more will the sensory threshold be transferred to the extreme regions of temperature. A typical experiment is illustrated in figure 7 from which it must be concluded that in the determination of the thresholds for warmth and cold there must exist a mutual relationship between two factors: the prevalent temperature and the temporal slope $(d\theta/dt)$ of the intracutaneous temperature change.

Figure 8 gives a graphical description of the mutual relationship between the prevalent temperature and the temporal differential quotient, $d\theta/dt$, in relation to thermal sensations. The points of the curves represent average values from a great number of experiments. As will be seen, temperature changes of $+0.001°$ per sec. and $-0.001°$ per sec. are still effective at temperatures above 38° and below 25°. Out-

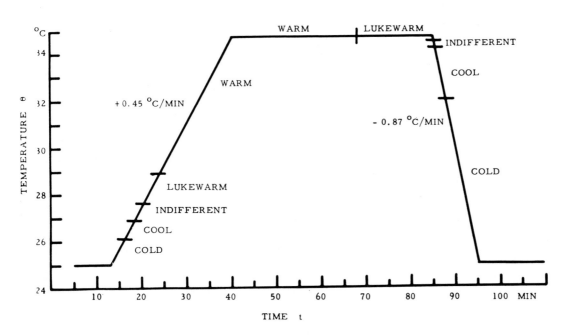

FIG. 6. Course of the temperature sensation at rectilinear warming and cooling of the foot in an ultrathermostate according to Höppler. [From Hensel (45).]

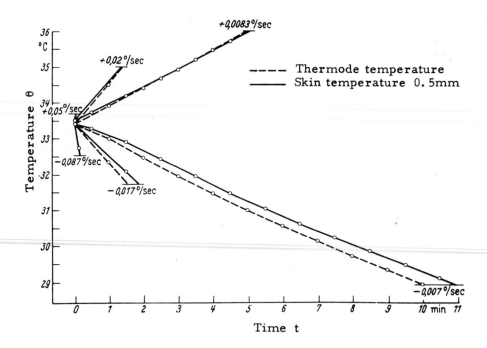

FIG. 7. Position of the warmth and cold thresholds on the forearm at rectilinear temperature changes of different directions and slopes (thermode area of 20 cm²). The slower the rate of change, the more distant from the indifferent temperature (33.4°C) the thresholds lie. [From Hensel (42).]

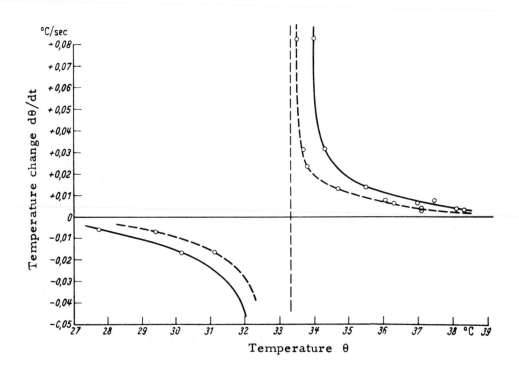

FIG. 8. Position of warm and cold thresholds in relation to the rate of temperature change, $d\theta/dt$, and the temperature θ of the skin. *Broken lines*, threshold sensation; *solid line*, distinct sensation. Initial temperature in all experiments, 33.3°C. [From Hensel (42).]

side this temperature region the required slope $d\theta/dt$ sinks further until it finally attains a zero value, i.e. where the temperature level itself is sufficient for elicitation of the sensation.

When the temperature change starts from different temperature levels (adaptation temperature), the thresholds for the warm sensation will reach different values (see fig. 9). With a constant rate of change of 0.0017° per sec. it is thus found that the threshold for warmth will depend upon the initial temperature to which the receptors have been adapted. The lower this initial temperature, the greater the heating has to be in order to elicit a sensation of warmth. For the cold sensation it is the other way when initial temperature is lowered. Here the cooling necessary becomes less and less intense until the temperature region is reached where a steady cold sensation ensues. For higher initial temperatures, the opposite holds. Here the cold receptors for equal cold steps become less sensitive the higher the initial temperature is taken (25, 37, 42).

It has long been recognized that the stimulated area and thus the number of stimulated thermal receptors must be of great importance in the production

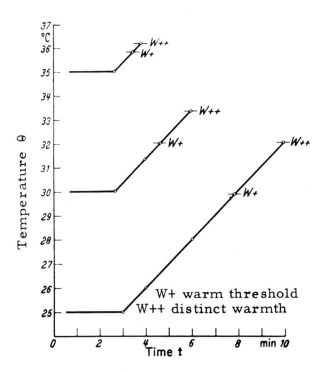

FIG. 9. Warm thresholds on forearm exposed to a rectilinear increase of temperature of 0.017 °C per sec. from initial temperatures of 25°, 30° and 35°. (Thermode area, 20 cm².) [From Hensel (45).]

of thermal sensations, although for long periods the use of more or less punctiform stimuli has been prevalent. The temperature sense in life situations is affected over much of the body surface as Hensel (45) emphasizes. This is *inter alia* seen from the fact that the cold and warm spots were not discovered until modern times (9), although they can be detected by the most simple devices.

Investigations on the temperature sensations when the whole body surface was exposed have been made by Maréchaux & Schäfer (67). In a climate chamber of the type used by Wetzler & Thauer the subjects were exposed to approximately linear increases of the temperature with a slope of 0.001 to 0.01 °C per sec. As the temperature of the chamber rose, the skin temperature of the different parts of the body rose relatively linearly. The average rate of the skin temperature rise during the most rapid rises amounted to 0.0015 to 0.003° per sec. and during the slowest rise to less than 0.001° per sec. Starting from a general coolish sensation the sensation of warmth appeared regularly in the following order: forehead-abdomen-hand-foot, in agreement with the investigations on more limited areas carried out by Gilsbach (31) and Hensel (42). The sensations produced appeared in this order: cold-indifferent-faintly warm-distinctly warm. Table 2 shows the warmth threshold temperature with slow rise of the chamber temperature. As will be seen it is not possible even with an extremely slow rate of temperature rise at less than 0.001° per sec. to avoid the production of a sensation of warmth when the temperature of the skin is above 35 °C. The region of thermal indifference when the whole body is concerned is thus limited to a small region between about 32 to 35 °C. Previous investigations of Rein & Strughold (73, 74), Stein & von Weizsäcker (82), Bohnenkamp & Pasquai (11), Hardy & Oppel (38) and Herget *et al.* (57) have all shown that there is a marked decline in the threshold when the number of stimulated sensory spots is increased.

Besides the temporal temperature gradient $(d\theta/dt)$ a spatial temperature gradient $(d\theta/dx)$ has been widely discussed. Ebbecke (26) observed that the release of blood flow into a previously clamped and cooled limb elicited an intense and unexpected sensation of cold. This led him to suggest that a cold sensation is produced by a temperature difference in the skin at the border line of the epidermis and the cutis, while a warmth sensation is produced by a temperature difference at the border line between the cutis and the subcutis, the direction of the temperature gradient being immaterial. This idea was confuted

TABLE 2. *Threshold Temperatures for Warmth During Heating of Body in Climate Chamber**

Rate of Increase degrees/sec.	Forehead °C	Abdomen °C	Hand °C	Foot °C	Integrated Skin Temp. °C
0.001	34.8±0.3	34.5±0.6	31.7±1.1	31.5±1.1	34.2±0.6
0.002–0.003	34.7±0.5	34.8±0.8	31.5±1.9	31.5±1.9	34.3±0.94

* Average values from 8 experiments [From Maréchaux & Schäfer (67).]

by Goldscheider & Hahn (33) who showed that subcutaneous injections of saline of 13°C elicited a distinct cold sensation while injections of 50°C saline elicited a sensation of warmth, whereas according to Ebbecke's view a sensation of warmth should have been produced in both cases.

From further experiments in which the temperature change and the change of the spatial gradient ran in opposite directions, Hensel (42) concluded that the intracutaneous temperature gradient or its temporal change cannot be the decisive condition for the production of a thermal sensation but the simple warming or cooling of the receptors, independent of the intracutaneous temperature gradient, is determinative. Bazett & McGlone (4) also observed that cooling from the lower surface of a double fold of the skin of the prepuce led to a sensation of cold in the upper surface. In their further investigations, carried out to test the validity of Ebbecke's spatial gradient hypothesis, they observed that sensations of intense warmth or heat were found to be induced on release of stasis in a limb maintained before, during and after stasis in a bath at the blood temperature level, so that on release no changes in temperature occurred and no thermal gradient was established. This warm sensation they attributed to a chemical stimulus derived from metabolic processes particularly in muscle tissue by means of a substance that varies in concentration both during asphyxia and as a result of temperature changes in a manner similar to that of acid.

According to Lewis *et al.* (66) and Zotterman (95) the sensation of tingling which occurs after the release of the blood flow to limbs in which the circulation has been arrested is attributable to an excitation of fibers in the nerve trunk in the area of compression. The sensation of tingling after release of the blood flow can be greatly enhanced by hyperventilation and its appearance can be entirely prevented by breathing 12 per cent carbon dioxide in oxygen (29). The sensation of warmth upon release has, however, a quite different time course from that of tingling which appears after a latency of 30 to 60 sec., and the sensa-

tion of warmth which is immediately experienced upon release is therefore most likely due to a stimulation of the receptors in the periphery, as Bazett & McGlone assumed. The only direct knowledge of the influence of ischemia on thermal receptors comes from Hensel (47) but is limited to the behavior of cold receptors. He noticed that ischemia abolished within a few minutes the steady discharge of the cold fibers. Upon release of the blood flow the discharge immediately reappeared reaching the initial frequency within 15 to 30 sec. In the same way as the steady discharge disappears during ischemia, the excitability of the receptor to cold increases is gradually paralyzed.

Although Lele *et al.* (65) repudiate "the spatial intracutaneous gradient theory which is based upon the assumed presence of specific encapsulated thermal receptors" on anatomical as well as on physiological grounds, they maintain that the thermal sensations reported in the presence of an absolutely constant surface skin temperature are due to a difference in temperature between different strata of the skin in which the terminals of the unencapsulated nerve endings and their nerve trunk lie. They suggest that the unencapsulated endings give rise to propagated disturbances when a difference of temperature exists between stem axons and terminals and that they are so arranged that the skin behaves as a thermopile type of 'bolometer' rather than as 'thermometer'. They believe that the anatomical arrangement of these unencapsulated nerve terminals in the skin is such that it is likely that different temporospatial patterns of action potentials will be evoked from the same area of skin when the temperature is raised or lowered. The patterns evoked will not be due to the fact that certain receptors have specific properties not possessed by others but due to the fact that numerous nonspecific receptors are disposed in different strata of the skin which are not at the same temperature. They further maintain that these endings, which subserve warm and cold sensibility can, if stimulated in the appropriate way, give rise to other sensations not associated with the thermal modality such as touch, prick, itch and sharp pain.

This opinion is quite incompatible with the electro-physiological findings of Zotterman (96), Hensel & Zotterman (52, 54) and Hensel (45, 46) that cold and warmth are subserved by specific peripheral neurons which are relatively inexcitable by mechanical stimuli. Hensel's thermoelectrical recordings show that a metal thermode through which water flows quickly dominates entirely the temperature conditions in the superior layers of the skin. The blood temperature has little or no effect. At a constant thermode temperature at 30°C or above, no appreciable temperature change was observed in the layer of the cold receptors in the tongue when the blood flow was arrested or released. The release of the blood flow to the tongue which previously had been ischemic for some minutes gave rise to an immediate return and enhancement of the steady discharge from the cold receptors previously paralyzed by the ischemia. The Ebbecke phenomenon can thus not be explained by thermal changes but by chemical changes induced by the ischemia. The effects of ischemia occur equally at all temperatures between 20 and 32°C and also when there is no thermal effect of the blood flow. They must all be due to oxygen lack (47).

Paradoxical Sensations

Strümpell (86) described patients with neurological diseases displaying specific anesthesia to cold and reported a very distinct heat sensation when the skin was touched by pieces of ice. The reverse was less often found, i.e. that heating the skin produced a sensation of cold. In 1895 von Frey (91) definitely established that the stimulation of single cold spots with heat above 45°C caused a sensation of cold which he named 'paradoxical cold sensation.' The existence of a paradoxical cold sensation has been generally accepted, while the corresponding paradoxical warm sensation still is under debate. Lehmann (64), Alrutz (1) and later Rein (72) failed to produce any paradoxical sensation of warmth. Thunberg (89) suggested in 1905 that this most likely is caused by the fact that the intensive cooling evokes a very intense cold sensation which masks the paradoxical sensation of warmth which in Strümpell's case of cold anesthesia was obtained unmasked. Recent electrophysiological studies (22) reveal that warm fibers actually respond to rapid cooling of 8 to 15°C but this has more the character of an off discharge of a phasic nature since it soon fades away. This behavior of the warm receptors or the peripheral parts of the warm fiber endings explains why this paradoxical

discharge of warmth is more difficult to detect (cf. page 448).

Thermal After-Sensations

Weber (94) had great difficulty in interpreting the phenomenon of the 'persisting cold sensation' experienced for instance when a cold metal object which has been pressed for about half a minute against the skin of the forehead is removed. In this famous experiment a cold sensation is thus experienced while the temperature of the receptor layer of the skin is gradually warming which according to Weber's theory should lead to a sensation of warmth. Weber himself suggested that this cold sensation was due to a further spread of the cooling to surrounding parts of the skin, a view which had been already rejected by Hering (58) because of the inadequate spread of the cooling compared to the marked rewarming of the cooled area. Alrutz (2) and Holm (60) suggested that the persisting cold sensation was due to paradoxical stimulation of the cold receptors by their sudden rewarming by the blood. The interpretation of Weber was again refuted by Holm (60) who anesthetized the cooled area of the skin leaving the surrounding area intact. In spite of normal thermal sensibility in the surrounding zone, no sensation of cold appeared. Further, Bazett & McGlone (4) recorded the skin temperature below the cooled area and proved that the cold after-sensation coincided with an actual rewarming of the skin although they believed as Weber that in their case the sensation could be attributed to a spread of the cooling to the surrounding skin.

More recently Hensel (42) has recorded the actual course of the intracutaneous temperature movement below as well as outside the thermode. He demonstrated that the spread of cooling to adjacent parts of the skin is very slight, the quantitative relation between the rewarming of the cooled area and the cooling of the surrounding being 18:1 at the time of the most intensive cold after-sensation.

Thus the cold after-sensation cannot be explained by a subsequent spread of cooling. At low skin temperatures a cold sensation can be present even when the temperature of the skin is gradually rising. This cold sensation is just a normal cold sensation due to the low temperature of the receptor layer of the skin. Electrophysiological studies of the activity of the cold fibers in the cat (cf. page 446) very substantially supports the view that the cold receptors at low temperatures are displaying a steady discharge which increases in frequency as the temperature slowly rises from 15 to 25°C.

Sensation of 'Hot'

Alrutz (2) suggested that the sensation of hot was a mixed sensation of warmth and 'paradoxical' cold although it is a subjectively simple sensation not divisible by introspective analysis and is qualitatively different from the sensations of cold and warmth. Thunberg (87), Kiesow (62) as well as Trotter & Davies (90) criticized this theory of Alrutz, maintaining that the paradoxical cold sensation can readily be apprehended and that the applied heat even stimulates other sensory fibers in the skin. Hacker (35) observed, however, in an experiment on himself in a traumatized region of the skin where no cold spots but numerous warm spots were found that no sensation of hotness was obtained but only of warmth. Goldscheider (32), however, rejected Alrutz' interpretation because the sensation of hot is felt most strongly in regions where the warmth sensibility is particularly good and not in regions where the cold sensibility is comparatively stronger than that of warmth.

Kaila (61) described an experiment on thermal receptors of the penis in man which greatly strengthens the original view of Alrutz (2). Usually the tip of the penis does not possess any sensibility of warmth while cold and pain is easily evoked. When the tip of the penis is dipped into water of 40°C, the subject experiences a rather unpleasant painful sensation; this temperature does not act on the cold receptors. If, however, the temperature is raised to 45°C, an intense sensation of cold is produced as this temperature stimulates the cold fibers. The sensation is, however, not really painful. When now a greater part of the penis is dipped into the water at 45°C, warm receptors are also stimulated and a specific sensation of pleasant heat appears.

This simple experiment is an example showing how simultaneous stimulation of different receptors can evoke the sensation of a specific quality in which it is not possible to recognize the elementary sensations which each of the specific receptors involved produce. Thus, when we speak of 'hot' as an elementary sensation, as Alrutz did, or as a 'fusion' the distinction is fictitious because the integration may be effected deeply below the 'threshold of consciousness.' Head (40) maintained that this occurred as early as the first synapse. For further analysis see page 452.

ELECTROPHYSIOLOGY OF THERMAL NERVE FIBERS

In recent years the function of the thermal receptors has been subjected to more objective investigation by the combination of effective methods for recording the temperature and the action potentials from the nerve fibers involved.

Specificity of Nerve Fibers in Mammals

The first recording of the specific electric response to thermal stimulation was made by this writer in 1936. He was generally able to see leading off from a fine branch of the lingual nerve a number of small action potentials with spike heights $\frac{1}{3}$ to $\frac{1}{10}$ of that of the largest spike potentials elicited by touching the tongue (fig. 10). When the tongue is washed with warm water these small spikes disappear to return shortly if the tongue is laid free in the air at room temperature. A faint draft over the tongue increases the number of impulses, and a sudden fine stream of air from a syringe on the receptive field elicits a dis-

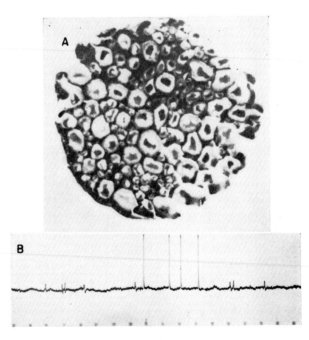

FIG. 10. A. Microphotograph of lingual nerve preparation. Magnification, 685. Largest fibers measure 10 μ in diameter. Alsheimer-Mann stain. B. Record from the same preparation showing the ratio between the spike heights of cold and touch impulses. The irregular discharge of the small cold spikes is due to the exposure of the tongue to air. The four large spikes were elicited by touching the tongue with a brush. [From Zotterman (96).]

tinct volley of small spikes. When the current of air is forceful enough to make a noticeable deformation on the tongue, larger spikes appear among an increased number of small ones (fig. 11 *B*). If the air in the syringe is successively warmed, a point is reached when the air stream does not elicit any small spikes, while the large ones still appear as soon as the pressure is raised sufficiently to occasion a noticeable deformation on the surface of the tongue.

When one drop of hot water (80°C) is applied to the tongue, two types of spikes may be observed besides the large spikes signalling the impact of the water drop (fig. 11*A*). A careful examination of the record reveals two types of spikes of which one derives from warm fibers and the other, a somewhat smaller and apparently more slowly conducted spike, derives from a pain fiber. In this way it was possible to show that cold and warmth as well as pain are mediated in specific nerve fibers (96).

Thermal Receptors in Cold-Blooded Animals

Electrophysiological investigations by Sand (77) on single fibers from the Lorenzinian ampullae of *Raja* showed that the receptors when kept at constant temperature were discharging continuously at a steady rate which varied with the prevailing temperature. Cooling caused an immediate increase in the frequency while warming led to the reverse effect.

Recent investigations by Hensel (49, 50) on *Scyllium* have confirmed Sand's original discovery in all details. At constant temperature the steady discharge in single fibers reaches a maximum of about 65 impulses per sec. at about 20°C. The temperature limits for steady discharge were 2 to 34°C. In this range of temperature, sudden cooling produces in single fibers a rapid increase in frequency up to 180 impulses per sec. followed by rapid adaptation to a low steady rate of discharge. The ampullae react definitely to a change in temperature of 0.05°C. Warming produces an immediate decrease or abolition of the discharge which then slowly attains a new steady value. The ampullae are not sensitive to mechanical stimulation and they thus behave qualitatively in every respect like the cold receptors of mammals. Quantitatively they appear to be even more sensitive.

The remarkable infrared receptors of the facial pits of the pit viper (Crotalidae) have been extensively studied recently by Bullock & Diecke (13). The nerve fibers from the facial pit usually show a continuous nonrhythmic discharge in the absence of environmental change. The adequate stimulus for increasing this activity is a relative increase in the influx or a decrease in the efflux of radiant energy in the middle and long infrared bands. Relative increases in efflux or decreases in influx reduce or inhibit the steady discharge. No response is obtained to sound vibration, a number of chemicals or heat-filtered light, but

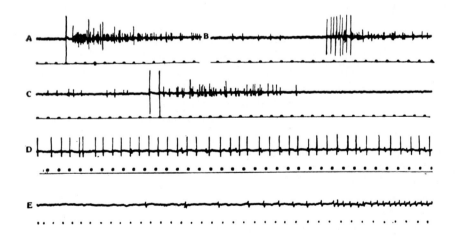

FIG. 11. Afferent spike potentials from different sensory fibers of a fine strand of the cat lingual nerve obtained by applying different stimuli to the tongue. *A.* The effect of a drop of water at 14°C falling on the tongue. *B.* First, the effect of a faint puff of air, which does not cause any visible deformation of the surface, followed by the effect of a stronger puff of air which makes a definite deformation. *C.* A drop at 80°C falling upon the tongue. *D.* The effect of pressing a pointed rod into the tongue. *E.* Squirting hot water (60°C) over the tongue. [From Zotterman (96).]

change in temperature by conduction from ambient media and mechanical deformation of the sensory membrane, do stimulate. It is concluded that these are minor or incidental in some fibers. Direct measurement of the change in temperature of water flowing over the membrane necessary to elicit a response gave values of 0.003 to 0.005°C.

Thus the nerves of the facial pit organs of rattlesnakes are composed of an essentially homogeneous population of warm fibers behaving principally as do mammalian warm fibers. But for the receptors of the pit organ the normal stimulus is chiefly radiant and not conducted heat, and several anatomical properties adapt it to a high sensitivity in terms of caloric flux.

Dodt (19) describes discharges from the glossopharyngeal nerve of the frog in response to temperature changes in the tongue of more than 3°C even in a temperature range below 15°C. This response appears only to warming, never to cooling. The response of these fibers to heating the tongue resembles in many ways that of mammalian warm fibers as well as that of the pit organ of the rattlesnake. Further experimental analysis is, however, necessary to decide whether this response to heating the tongue of the frog is due to the stimulation of nociceptive fibers or of more or less specific warm fibers.

Quantitative Relations Between Temperature Movements and Nerve Fiber Discharge

By use of well defined and thermoelectrically controlled thermal stimuli applied to the tongue of the cat, it has been possible to work out the fundamental relationships between the temperature and the activity of the thermal fibers. This work has principally been carried out in the writer's laboratory in a series of investigations by Hensel, Dodt and co-workers.

METHODS. For quantitative studies of cold receptors we have used fine strands of the cat's lingual nerve containing only one or a few cold fibers. Preparations containing single or a few warm fibers are best obtained from the chorda tympani of the cat. [For the operative technique see Zotterman (96), Hensel & Zotterman (53) and Dodt & Zotterman (22).] For thermal stimulation we used a metal thermode, open at the top, which had a free outflow on one side (fig. 12). The thermode had a gold-plated silver bottom of 20 x 30 mm and a thickness of 0.1 mm. From above, two constantly flowing jets of water at different temperatures were directed on to the bottom of the thermode in such a way that the jets could suddenly

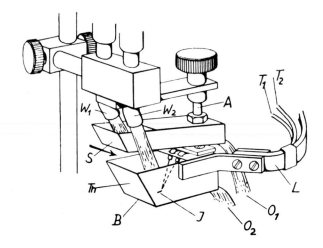

FIG. 12. Apparatus for applying rapid temperature changes to the surface of the tongue. *Th*, thermode; *B*, silver bottom; W_1 and W_2, water jets of different temperatures; O_1 and O_2, outflows; *S*, switch; *arrow*, movement of switch; *A*, axis of switch; T_1 and T_2, thermocouple wires; *J*, junction in bottom of thermode; *L*, lead strip. [From Hensel *et al.* (51).]

be interrupted. In this way it was possible to produce very rapid and exact temperature changes of the gold-plated silver foil. Soldered on the thermode bottom was a thermocouple with a diameter of 0.05 mm which enabled us to record the true temperature changes of the silver foil. Because of the rapid temperature change, which could exceed 300°C per sec., the temperature was recorded either by a microgalvanometer of Moll or by the second beam of the double beam cathode-ray oscillograph which was used for recording the action potentials. The thermode was adjusted on the tip of the tongue which rested on a cork plate. It can easily be shown both mathematically and experimentally that a constant temperature is reached in the receptor layer of the skin only negligibly later than at the surface of the tongue. In many experiments thermocouples were inserted to different depths into the tongue in order to record the temperature within the mucous membrane.

DISCHARGE AT CONSTANT TEMPERATURE. *Cold fibers.* When the thermode is adjusted at a constant temperature the frequency of the cold spikes attains a constant final value after a short interval. A record from a nerve preparation containing two cold fibers (one giving diphasic, the other monophasic spikes) will be seen in figure 13. The thermode was previously kept for a long time at a constant temperature of 34°C. Even at this temperature there was present a steady discharge of the monophasic fiber at a rate of 9 im-

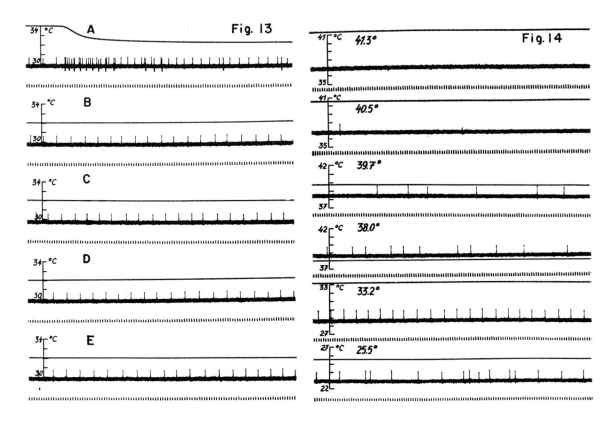

FIG. 13. Spike potentials from two cold fibers recorded on cooling the tongue of the cat from 34° to 32°C. *A*, the temperature drop; *B*, after 1 min.; *C*, after 2 min.; *D*, after 4 min.; *E*, after 15 min. [From Hensel & Zotterman (54).]

FIG. 14. Spikes recorded from a single cold fiber (cat) at different constant temperatures. Time marks, 50 cps. [From Hensel & Zotterman (54).]

pulses per sec. from which the three spikes can be seen before the cooling starts (fig. 13). The thermode was then quickly cooled down to 32°C. Immediately the frequency of the monophasic fiber rose to 35 impulses per sec. and simultaneously there was a discharge of the second diphasic fiber which, however, after a few seconds ceased again, while the discharge of the first fiber adjusted itself to a final constant frequency which after 1 min. attained a value of 9.3 impulses per sec. After that there is practically no more change. The cold receptor goes on discharging at a fairly regular rhythm for minutes or even hours with remarkable constancy if the temperature of the surface of the tongue is kept constant.

Figure 14 gives an example of the discharge of a single cold fiber after adjustment to a constant final value of frequency at different constant temperatures. At a temperature of 41.3°C there is no discharge in this fiber while already at a constant temperature of 40.5°C there is a low frequency of about 1 impulse

per sec. The upper limit at which a steady discharge of the cold fiber appears, called the steady threshold temperature for this particular cold fiber, lay between 41.3° and 40.5°C, i.e. above the ordinary blood temperature. At this temperature (38°C) the frequency of the steady discharge was 5 impulses per sec. and the maximum about 30°C. Below this temperature the steady discharge declines and at lower temperatures the discharge generally becomes irregular, occurring in beats of two or three impulses. Between 15° and 10°C the average discharge increases again (17) to disappear entirely between 12° and 10°C. No steady discharge of any cold fibers has been seen at a temperature below 8°C.

The diagram in figure 15 shows the steady discharge of a cold fiber as a function of the temperature. The experiment was conducted in such a way that the frequency was determined at definite temperature steps from warm to cold. After reaching the lowest temperature—in about 2 hr.—the impulse frequency

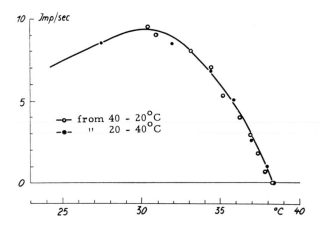

FIG. 15. Impulse frequency of the steady discharge of a single cold fiber as a function of the temperature of the tongue surface. The frequencies were first measured at temperature steps from 40° to 20°C and then again in reverse order. [From Hensel & Zotterman (54).]

was recorded once again when the temperature was raised in the same steps as before. It is seen that the points lie on the same curve. Even after hours of experiments exposing the receptors to widely differing temperatures, the steady discharge appears with the same frequency when the temperature of the tongue is restored to the initial value. The impulse frequency of the steady discharge of the cold receptors thus depends entirely on the temperature.

The steady discharge of cold fibers shows a maximum frequency of about 10 impulses per sec. The site of this maximum on the temperature scale varies in different fibers between 20° and 34°C, while the upper and lower temperature limits in extreme cases reach 10° and 41°C. The total frequency of cold impulses in the nerve, which is the sum of the discharges from the single cold fibers, reaches its maximum (fig. 16) at a temperature between 15 and 20°C (54).

Warm fibers. Judging from the relative spike height the fibers mediating warmth were conceived to be somewhat larger in diameter than the cold fibers (96). Preparations containing only warm fibers display a steady discharge to constant temperatures between 20° and 47°C. In single fiber preparations the frequency of this steady discharge varies in a consistent manner with the temperature, although the maximum discharge as well as the upper and lower temperature limits vary somewhat (fig. 17). The maximum usually was found between 37.5° and 40°C. At higher temperatures the steady discharge falls off

rather steeply. Above 47°C and below 20°C no steady discharge was noticed. The maximum frequency varied in single warm fiber units between 1.5 and 3.7 impulses per sec. (23). The discharge was never as regular as that of the cold fibers which may depend on the comparatively low frequency and also on the possibility that the warm fibers may divide peripherally to supply more than one end organ.

The low sensitivity of warm receptors to temperatures between 20° and 30°C also has an important bearing on the interpretation of Weber's phenomenon of persisting cold sensation (cf. page 443). When the cold object is removed from the skin there is a distinct pause in the cold sensation due to the postexcitatory depression of the cold receptors. When the cold sensation then slowly reappears, although the temperature of the skin is gradually rising, there will be very little interference from the scattered warm receptors. Thus the steady discharge of impulses from the cold receptors which display their maximum sensitivity in just this temperature range 25° to 30°C will stand out still more conspicuously.

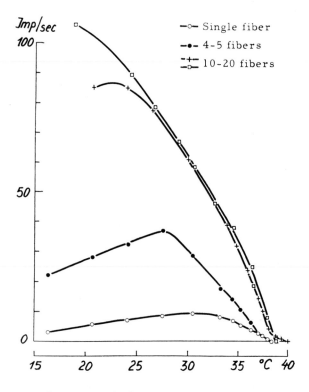

FIG. 16. Total impulse frequency of the steady discharge in different preparations of the cat lingual nerve as a function of the temperature of the tongue surface. [From Hensel & Zotterman (54).]

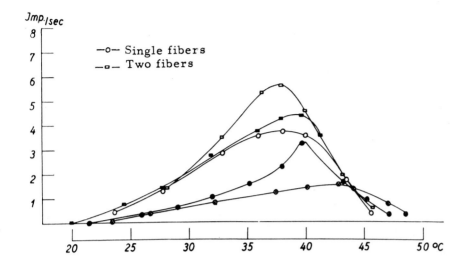

Fig. 17. Graph showing frequency of the steady discharge of different single and dual warm fiber preparations as a function of the temperature of the tongue surface. [From Dodt & Zotterman (23).]

RESPONSE OF THERMAL RECEPTORS TO TEMPERATURE CHANGES. For the investigation of the influence of temporal changes in temperature on the impulse frequency, rapid changes from one constant temperature level to another constant level were used. A purely rectangular shape of the temperature rise curve could not be obtained as the equalization of the receptor temperature takes a certain time, but a very rapid adjustment to a constant value was ensured.

Cold fibers. Sudden cooling of the tongue produces, as is seen in figure 18, a rapid discharge of the cold fibers which quickly declines to the final value of the steady discharge characteristic of the prevalent temperature. The maximum response of a single cold fiber seen when applying a very rapid cooling from 40° to 2°C was 140 impulses per sec. which is about 15 times as high as the maximum frequency recorded at a constant temperature.

In contrast to the steady discharge, the frequency of which is determined solely by the temperature, the maximum frequency at temperature changes is not so much dependent on the initial or final temperature as on the rate of the temperature change $(\mathrm{d}\theta/\mathrm{d}t)$. Rapid cooling can thus produce a discharge from cold receptors even in a rather warm temperature region above the upper temperature limit of the steady discharge as is shown in figure 18.

The maximum rate of discharge of the cold fibers in response to rapid cooling is, however, not exclusively determined by the rate of cooling $(\mathrm{d}\theta/\mathrm{d}t)$, as is evident from figure 19B. Applying equal temperature drops of 2°C at various initial temperatures, it was found that identical intracutaneous temperature changes elicited different grades of excitation in the cold receptors depending upon the range of temperature within which the change occurred.

Rapid warming of the cold receptors to a constant temperature leads to an immediate cessation of the steady discharge. If this temperature lies below the upper temperature limit of the steady discharge, the impulses reappear and adjust themselves at a frequency corresponding to the prevailing temperature (fig. 19). The length of this pause caused by warming the cold receptors depends upon the rate of warming and the range of temperature. Thus, while rapid cooling leads to an 'overshooting' excitation of the cold receptors, rapid warming of these receptors produces an 'overshooting' inhibition.

If the warming is small or follows at a relatively low rate, the cold impulses may not disappear at all but occur only at another frequency. Thus cold impulses were shown to appear even during warming of the cold receptors. This offers a ready explanation of Weber's 'persisting cold' sensation (cf. page 443) that below a certain temperature cold sensations may occur even when the temperature of the receptor layer of the skin is rising. The objection based on the spread of the cooling to surrounding parts of the skin was quite pointless in these experiments since, when thin nerve preparations are used, the receptive field

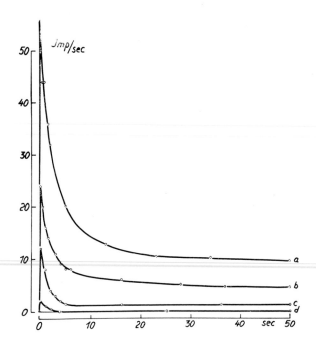

FIG. 18. Impulse frequency of a single cold fiber in the cat lingual nerve during induction of rapid temperature changes in the tongue. *A*, From 32° to 30°C; *B*, from 40° to 38°C; *C*, from 42° to 40°C; *D*, from 44° to 42°C. Cooling starts at time zero. [From Hensel & Zotterman (54).]

of the cold fibers is far smaller than the surface of the thermode in contact with the tongue. The cold receptors involved can thus be influenced only by the temperature changes below the thermode and not at all by any spread of cooling outside the thermode.

Warm fibers. The discharge of the warm fibers in response to thermal stimuli displays essentially the same characteristic features as does that of the cold fibers but in the reverse order. Thus rapid warming to a constant level produces an overshooting discharge after which the discharge adjusts itself fairly quickly into an irregular steady rhythm. The initial volley (fig. 20) appears after latencies varying from 0.15 to 0.55 sec. which was taken as indicating that the warm receptors were situated at varying depths in the tongue. Short latencies were observed particularly for temperature rises from 37° to 40°C, whereas latencies for corresponding rises in the range of 25° to 35°C were considerably longer. The discharge of a single warm receptor displays a much higher initial frequency compared with that of a cold receptor exposed to a corresponding drop in temperature, and the sequence of impulses thereafter is interrupted by sudden pauses in the discharge. The mean value of

the frequency falls, however, in an exponential way as does the discharge of the cold receptors.

Figure 21 shows simultaneous records from a strand of the chorda tympani (above) and from a strand of the lingual nerve (below). The former preparation contained warm fibers only while the lingual strand possessed cold fibers and one touch fiber. At a constant temperature of 23°C there is a steady discharge of cold fibers in the lingual preparation (below) while hardly any spikes are recorded from the chorda strand. When the temperature was raised to 38.5°C, a discharge of the warm fibers occurred while the steady discharge of the cold fibers disappeared. A quick return of the temperature to 23°C produced a small off-effect from the warm fibers at the same time as the cold fibers started their firing. When this procedure was repeated after 6 sec. (fig. 21), hardly any change in the response could be noticed. If however the temperature was raised to 44.8°C, a certain difference in the warm fiber response was noticed. First of all, the sudden rise elicits a much stronger initial frequency of warm impulses. Secondly, when the temperature dropped there appeared a

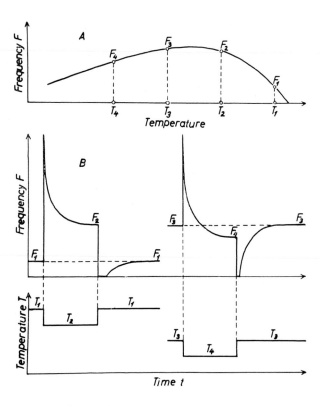

FIG. 19. Graphs showing *A*, impulse frequency of the steady discharge of a single cold fiber; *B*, frequency of a sudden temperature drop at different temperatures. [From Hensel (48).]

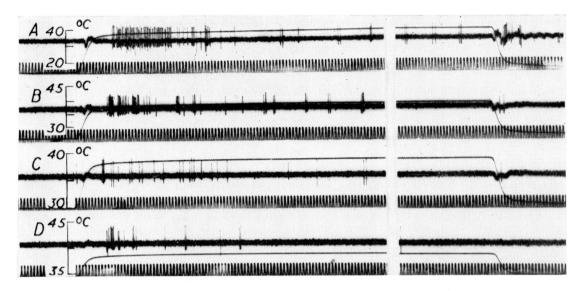

FIG. 20. Records showing the warm fiber response to sudden heating and cooling of the cat tongue at different levels. A, temperature rise, 14.2° to 38.6°C, latency 0.55 sec. B, 25.3° to 38.6°C, latency 0.46 sec. C. 50° to 38.6°C, latency 0.42 sec. D, 34.4° to 38.6°C, latency 0.47 sec. The latency of the off-effect, 'paradoxical warmth,' varied between 0.10 and 0.15 sec. [From Dodt & Zotterman (23).]

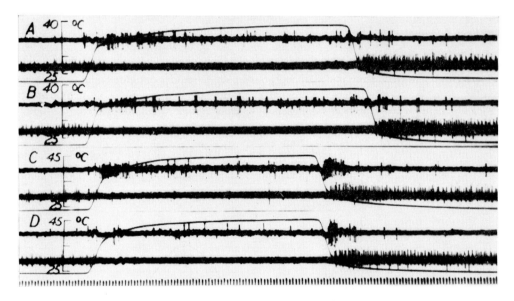

FIG. 21. Simultaneous recording from a warm fiber preparation of the chorda tympani and a cold fiber preparation of the lingual nerve. A and B, a rise from 23° to 38.5°C and back; C and D, from 23.8° to 44.8°C and back. B and D are recorded 6 sec. after the previous record. [From Dodt & Zotterman (23).]

strong off-discharge from the warm fibers. As can be seen in figure 21, this effect occurred after a very short latency, much shorter even than that of the cold fiber discharge. When the heating was repeated within 6 sec., the initial warm fiber response to heating to 44.8°C each time was very much reduced while the

off-effect from the warm fibers remained almost unchanged.

This off-effect of the warm fibers was observed whenever the temperature dropped about 8° to 15°C. It is more conspicuous the more rapid the change in temperature, but it appeared even at rather slow rates of temperature change. The response soon fades away when the temperature is kept below 20°C and is thus always of a phasic character in contrast to the steady paradoxical discharge of cold fibers when exposed to constant temperatures above 45°C. The fact that the latency of the warm fiber response to sudden cooling is only about a third of the shortest latency of its discharge to warming induced Dodt & Zotterman (23) to consider whether the former response of the warm fibers is due to an excitation of the warm receptor or to its nerve fiber. As was originally shown by Bernhard & Granit (7) rapid cooling of a nerve trunk excites class A fibers directly and such a rapid cooling also stimulates the endings of mechanoceptive fibers (53). This nerve fiber discharge in every respect is of the same character as the discharge of warm fibers to cooling. It has a relatively short latency, the length of which varies with the rate of cooling; the discharge is phasic, i.e. there is no steady discharge. When, however, the thermode was placed on the other side of the tongue where the more central part of the lingual nerve runs closely under the surface, no discharge of the warm fibers could be seen when this surface was suddenly cooled from 45° to 25°C.

An old question in the field of sensory physiology is whether sensation is in part due to direct stimulation of the sensory nerve fibers as well as of the receptors. In the function of thermoreception this question is, as we have seen, of particular importance. For that reason Dodt (18) made a thorough study of thermosensitivity of A fibers in the lingual nerve and compared the responses in specific cold, warm and mechanoceptive fibers upon thermal stimulation of the surface of tongue and of the lingual nerve, respectively. He found that all three types of afferent fibers were phasically excited by local cooling of the nerve trunk. In mechanoceptive fibers this occurred whenever the temperature drop was of a sufficient magnitude, regardless of the final value, the effect being optimally elicited when the nerve was at an initial temperature between 35° to 40°C. Cold fibers, however, were excited only when the nerve trunk was cooled to below a certain threshold value of about 20°C. Warm fibers were mixed in their reactions, some responding like mechanoceptive fibers, others having a distinct threshold. Warming of the nerve trunk never led to excitation of sensory A fibers.

The cold and the mechanoceptive fibers could be blocked by low and high temperatures, the cold fibers being blocked below 16° to 25°C and above 50° to 52°C, whereas the thresholds in mechanoceptors were in both types of block 5° to 8°C lower.

Cold fibers, excited by cooling the nerve to temperatures insufficient to cause blocking, show following the phasic excitation an impulse-free interval, the duration of which varies directly with the length of the excitatory burst and inversely with the background frequency of impulses coming from the receptor.

These findings suggest that under physiological conditions normal and paradoxical sensations of cold are due to the stimulation of the thermal receptors or the nerve fibers included in the end organ and never to a direct stimulation of their myelinated nerve fibers.

PARADOXICAL DISCHARGES. When the temperature of the tongue is raised above 45°C, a steady discharge of cold fibers is produced (24). This impulse activity increases slowly and attains a level corresponding to the prevailing temperature. This paradoxical discharge begins at 45°C and a maximum frequency of 7 to 7.5 impulses per sec. is attained at 50°C. The lower threshold temperature of this paradoxical discharge lies about 5°C above the upper limit of the usual range of temperature within which the cold receptors display a steady discharge (fig. 22). Paradoxical excitation of cold receptors at temperatures below 45°C does not occur. Thus the cold sensation which appears after a rise in the skin temperature from 20° to 35°C as described by Thunberg (88) is not due to any paradoxical excitation but to a reappearance of the usual steady discharge of cold fibers when the temperature approaches the final value of

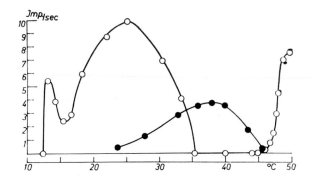

FIG. 22. Graphs showing impulse frequency of the steady discharge of a single cold fiber (*open circles*) and of a single warm fiber (*filled circles*) as a function of the temperature of the receptors within the range of 10 to 50°C. [From Zotterman (99).]

35°C. This phenomenon is only another example of 'persisting cold sensation' (cf. page 443). The low sensitivity of the warm receptors and the relatively high sensitivity of the cold receptors between 20° and 30°C has an important bearing on our interpretation of the Weber phenomenon of persisting cold sensation. When a cold object is removed from the skin, there is an obvious pause in the cold sensation due to the postexcitatory depression of the cold receptors. When the cold sensation then slowly reappears, although the temperature of the skin is gradually rising, there will be very little interference from the rather scattered warm receptors. Thus the steady discharge of impulses from the cold receptors which display their maximum sensitivity in just this temperature region, 25° to 30°C, will stand out still more conspicuously.

The question concerning the real existence of a paradoxical warmth sensation brought about by cooling has been the subject of much discussion (72). The reason for this is now quite obvious. We have to consider not only that cooling of the skin stimulates numerous cold receptors and that the ensuing cold sensation thus will mask the paradoxical warmth sensation but also the fact that the 'paradoxical' response of the warm fibers is of phasic character and soon fades away.

Thus we can conclude that the paradoxical sensation of cold experienced when the skin is heated to a temperature between 45° and 50°C has its physiological analogy in a steady discharge of specific cold fibers.

The paradoxical warmth sensation which generally is masked by an intense cold sensation has its counterpart in a phasic discharge of specific warm fibers to the cooling.

EFFECT OF TEMPERATURES ABOVE 47°C. The fact that the steady discharge of the warm receptors generally disappears at a temperature above 47°C must mean that above this temperature the quality of sensation which generally is described as hot has little to do with the feeling of warmth (cf. page 444). Alrutz' (2) suggestion that the sensation of heat was a mixed sensation of warmth and paradoxical cold must be revised to some degree. When the skin is suddenly heated from 35° to 50°C, there occurs first a sudden transient discharge of warm fibers accompanied by a paradoxical cold fiber discharge which continues as long as the temperature is kept at this level. To this paradoxical discharge of cold fibers a discharge of pain fibers is gradually added (96, 97). Skouby (80)

has recently found that the subjective pain threshold lies at temperatures of 47.1° to 48.5°C. Thus it can be concluded that, when temperatures of above 47°C are applied and after the temperature change in the skin has ceased, the sensation of heat then experienced is the resultant of a mixed inflow of paradoxical cold and pain impulses. This sensation is thus initiated only by warm and paradoxical cold impulses and to the persisting paradoxical cold discharge, pain impulses are gradually added as the temperature is kept at a constant value above 47°C. At still higher temperatures the heat will destroy the fibers. Heating the skin to more than 50°C very quickly not only inactivates the mechanoceptive fibers in the tongue (96) but also causes the steady paradoxical discharge of the cold fiber to disappear leaving the signalling duty entirely to pain fibers. This course of events was fully confirmed by recent experiments of Dodt (19).

INTRACUTANEOUS GRADIENT. In order to investigate the importance of the intracutaneous temperature gradient for the stimulation of the thermoceptors Hensel & Zotterman (55) recorded the action potentials from the cold fibers of the lingual nerve of the cat when cold stimuli were applied to the tongue so as to cause negative or positive intracutaneous temperature gradients (cf. page 446). The nerve preparations chosen were those containing cold fibers supplying only the upper surface of the tip of the tongue. In order to produce negative or positive temperature gradients, the tongue was cooled from either the upper or the lower surface, respectively, the temperature on both sides of the tongue being recorded thermoelectrically.

The cooling of the upper surface immediately gave rise to a strong discharge of cold spikes which instantly disappeared on rewarming (fig. 23). On cooling of the lower side no impulses appeared at first but within 1.5 to 3 sec., when the cold had penetrated the tongue and reached the upper surface, cold impulses appeared with increasing frequency. On rewarming of the lower surface the cold impulses persisted at first until the upper surface was also warmed again. In some experiments the cooling of the receptor layer was produced by injecting cold solutions into the lingual artery. This way of cooling produced the same cold receptor discharges as cooling the surface. The participation of deep thermoreceptors could be entirely excluded in these experiments, and the arrest of the blood flow in the tongue had no primary influence on these findings.

These experiments demonstrate that the stimulation

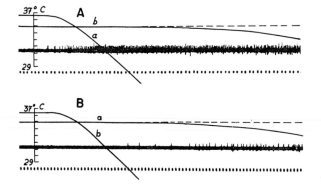

FIG. 23. Simultaneous records of cold impulses from receptor field on upper surface of cat tongue and of temperature of both surfaces. *A*, on cooling of the upper surface; *B*, on cooling of the lower surface; *a*, temperature of the upper surface; *b*, temperature of lower surface. Time marks, 15 cps. [From Hensel & Zotterman (55).]

of the cold receptors does not depend upon the direction or slope of intracutaneous temperature gradient. Thus temperature gradients between blood vessels and the receptors, which were suggested as the adequate stimulus, cannot be decisive since arrest of the circulation for a minute or so did not notably change the results obtained by the retrograde temperature gradient.

RESPONSE OF MECHANORECEPTORS TO THERMAL STIMULATION. When the tongue of the cat or dog is cooled, it is generally possible only to record small cold spikes in the lingual nerve, whereas the large touch and pressure spikes cannot be elicited by cooling. However, in a few cases cooling also sets up relatively large spikes in the lingual nerve. Hensel & Zotterman (53) investigated this phenomenon further and demonstrated that these larger spikes derived from mechanoceptive nerve fibers. These large spikes usually appear only with severe cooling and disappear within a few seconds at a constant low temperature, whereas small cold spikes appear with slight cooling and persist at constant temperatures for long periods (fig. 24). It was shown that this activity of mechanoceptive fibers could not be due to secondary mechanical stimulation of the pressure receptors by local vasoconstriction nor to stimulation of the nerve trunk by cooling. It is only medium-sized mechanoceptive fibers (8 to 10 μ) which were stimulated by cooling the surface; the larger pressure fibers (12 to 15 μ) were not excited.

These findings offer a ready explanation for the well-known phenomenon first described by Weber (94) that cold weights seem heavier than warm ones

('Weber's deception'). The pressure sensation caused by cooling the skin has been the subject of thorough examination by later workers. Kiesow (62) confirmed the existence of 'Weber's deception' and also succeeded in provoking sensations of pressure by application of ether and chloroform to the skin, and Goldscheider & Hahn (33), experimenting with various solutions and with cooled air, came to the conclusion that the mechanoreceptors could be stimulated by cooling.

Influence of Nonthermal Agencies

That menthol evokes cold sensations when applied on the tongue as well as on the skin is a well-known experience which has been exploited in manifold ways. It has likewise long been known that these cold sensations are not caused by physical cooling of the skin or the mucous membranes but by some chemical action directly on the cold receptors (32). Hensel & Zotterman (56) recorded the discharge of cold fibers after the application of menthol solutions upon the tongue using well defined thermal stimulation.

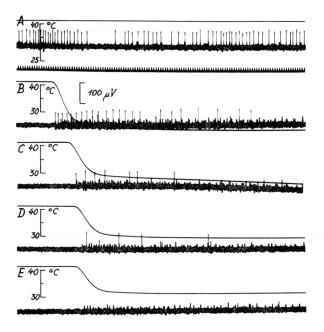

FIG. 24. Records from a thin strand of the cat lingual nerve obtained on applying mechanical and thermal stimuli to the tongue. The *thin line* shows the temperature of the surface of the tongue. *A*, pressure; *B*, cooling from 41° to 22°C; *C*, cooling from 41° to 26°C; *D*, cooling from 41° to 29°C; *E*, cooling from 41° to 32°C. Time marks, 50 cps. [From Hensel & Zottermar. (53).]

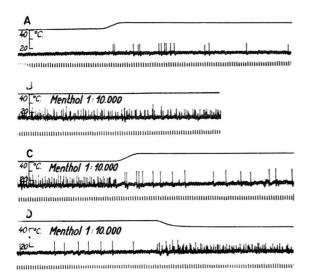

FIG. 25. Action potentials from cold and warm fibers in a thin strand of the cat lingual nerve after the application of menthol solution to the tongue. Under the action of menthol (1:10,000) there is at 40°C strong discharge of cold fibers which disappears on warming, to be followed by discharge from a warm fiber. [From Hensel & Zotterman (56).]

Aqueous menthol solutions of 1:10,000 lead to strong steady discharge of the tongue cold receptors at constant warm temperatures at which without menthol there is no discharge (fig. 25). At lower temperatures at which the cold receptors are steadily discharging without menthol, this substance produces a great increase of the steady cold impulse frequency. Further studies of Dodt et al. (21) of the effect of menthol on single fibers showed that menthol exerts an effect, not only on the cold fiber activity in the usual temperature range between about 10° and 38°C, but also on the paradoxical cold fiber discharge between 45° and 50°C. In agreement with Goldscheider these authors observed that menthol sensitizes the warm fibers also.

The effect of menthol on the cold and warm fibers can be completely compensated for by sudden heating and cooling, respectively, or by keeping the tongue at a constant higher and lower temperature, respectively. These measures can cause the cold and warm impulses provoked by menthol to disappear entirely. Thus it is not simply the question of a chemical 'inadequate' stimulation of the thermal receptors but of a sensitization of the thermal effect. The threshold of the menthol effect lies between the concentrations of 1:1,000,000 and 1:500,000.

Following the finding of Bing & Skouby (8) that the introduction of small amounts of cholinergic

substances into the skin produced an increased number of cold spots, Dodt et al. (21) investigated the effect on single thermal fibers. Minute amounts of acetylcholine shift the temperature range of the steady discharge of cold fibers towards the warm side and increase definitely the rate of the steady discharge of the receptors inside the normal range of temperature. Larger amounts produce a depression of the steady discharge and a narrowing of the temperature range recorded. Corresponding results were found with warm fiber preparations.

Dodt (20) has recently investigated the influence of carbon dioxide on the thermal receptors. An increase of the pCO_2 reduced the rate of the steady discharge of cold receptors, whereas it caused an increase of the steady discharge of warm receptors. The regulating structures will thus, under the action of carbon dioxide, receive a false picture of the actual thermal conditions in the periphery which will lead to a fall of the rectal temperature without any subjective discomfort.

THEORETICAL CONSIDERATIONS

Central Threshold

From the sensory physiological studies it appeared that three factors are governing the occurrence of a thermal sensation: a) the absolute intracutaneous temperature, θ, b) the rate of change of the intracutaneous temperature, $d\theta/dt$, and c) the area F, the extension of the stimulated field.

So far as the conditions for the occurrence of a thermal sensation can be expressed in physical-thermal terms, the excitation mechanism can be represented by a three-dimensional system of thermal-spatial-temporal factors which are mutually dependent on each other and to a great extent exchangeable. The threshold condition can thus be expressed as follows:

$$E \ni f(\theta, d\theta/dt, F)$$

where E is the abstraction class of the sensation, $\ni$ the implication sign of a probability implication (75). A sensation of cold, for example, would thus occur when a) θ is low, b) the rate of cooling, $d\theta/dt$, is sufficient, and c) the receptive field has a certain area (42).

The recordings of the action potential from peripheral cold fibers show that the total number, n, of impulses which in the time, t, arrive at the central organ also is a function of these three factors,

$$\frac{n}{t} \ni \phi(\theta, d\theta/dt, F)$$

i.e. the value of n/t becomes greater when a) the temperature is lower, b) the rate of cooling is greater and c) when the receptive field is enlarged—i.e. when the number of stimulated cold receptors is increased. The rate of n/t is nothing else but the central threshold which thus can be written,

$$E \ni \psi\left(\frac{n}{t}\right).$$

The results of the sensory-physiological studies are thus in very good accordance with those obtained from electrophysiological investigations on the specific thermal fibers.

The declining impulse frequency at constant temperature is the so-called 'physiological adaptation' of the thermal sense recorded objectively. As Hensel (42) concluded from his sensory-physiological studies, it should be more correct to avoid the use of the particular words, adaptation or change of excitability in order to express the temporal decrease of the excitation under a constant stimulus, as these expressions lead to a conception of a specific process separated from excitation. Adaptation is then assumed when a temporal change of the excitation occurs while the stimulus is kept constant. But this depends upon the definition of stimulation. When as in the thermal sense the temperature (θ) is the stimulus, adaptation appears at constant stimulation. If, however, the stimulus is the rate of temperature change, $d\theta/dt$, there will be no adaptation during constant stimulation. According to the usual definition, adaptation is therefore nothing else than an indirect description of the time factor of a sense organ based on its response to a specific mode of stimulation.

At constant temperature of the skin, the magnitude of n/t is dependent upon the temperature and the area of the skin. If the thermal receptors were evenly distributed, the thermosensible tonus would thus be a direct function of the integral skin temperature. This is, however, not the case as some parts, especially the trigeminal area, display a much greater density of thermal receptors and are thus likely to exert a more dominant influence upon the thermoregulation of the body. It is very likely that the central threshold of conscious cold sensations lies at a higher level than the threshold of the thermal receptor discharge (34, 54),

which implies that a certain part of the afferent thermoregulatory inflow occurs below the threshold of our consciousness.

Excitation Mechanism of Thermal Receptors

The fact that there is a distinct discharge of impulses from thermal receptors when there is a complete temperature equilibrium between the two sides of the receptor layer, i.e. when the spatial as well as the temporal temperature gradient is zero, shows that this activity does not depend upon any exchange of thermal energy. Thus there must occur in the receptors, processes—probably of a chemical nature—which are governed by temperature without any external exchange of energy in the skin.

For this reason it is not practicable to express the thresholds of the temperature sense—in analogy with the eye and the ear—in terms of a thermal energy.

The course of the receptor discharge at constant temperatures and particularly the effect of temperature changes suggests that we have to deal with at least two interacting processes, one exciting and one inhibiting. We can thus, according to Sand (77), assume that the frequency of the steady discharge of the cold receptor, n, is dependent upon the difference between two temperature dependent processes, E and I. The difference between these should give the impulse frequency, n (45, 54).

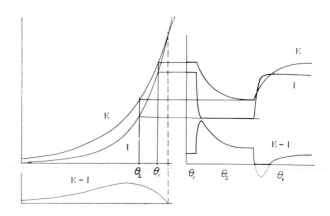

FIG. 26. Graphs illustrating discharging mechanism of a cold receptor. *Abscissae*, skin temperatures; *ordinates*, rates of impulse discharge. In the *lower left* is a plot of the steady discharge of a cold receptor assuming that the frequency of discharge (n) is a function of the difference between two temperature dependent processes E and I (*above*). On the right is illustrated the time course of the effect of sudden cooling from a temperature of θ_1 to one of θ_2 and back to θ_1. The intersection of the curves of E and I gives the upper threshold temperature θ_0 of the cold receptor. [From Zotterman (100).]

These functions E and I seem to resemble exponential functions with different constants as follows:

$$n = A[\underbrace{e^{\alpha(\theta-\theta_0)}}_{E} - \underbrace{e^{\beta(\theta-\theta_0)}}_{I}]$$

When the temperature $\theta = \theta_0$, $n = 0$. If $\alpha < \beta$, we obtain curves as shown in figure 26 where the difference curve, n, resembles the experimental curves of the steady discharge obtained from single cold fibers.

In the above equation only the temperature dependence has been considered. The time dependence can, however, be included in the equation in a manner which rather closely describes the 'adaptive' part of the response of thermal receptors, i.e. the response to sudden temperature changes. The equation can be written:

$$n = A[(a_1 - e^{-a_2 t})E - (b_1 - e^{-b_2 t})I].$$

The constants are dependent upon the previous excitatory level of the thermal receptor. Figure 26 shows how these functions can be used to predict the behavior of a cold receptor at a sudden drop in temperature from θ_1 to θ_2 and back again. For further details and the computation of the constants see Hensel (45).

REFERENCES

1. ALRUTZ, S. *Skandinav. Arch. Physiol.* 7: 321, 1897.
2. ALRUTZ, S. *Skandinav. Arch. Physiol.* 10: 340, 1900.
3. BAILEY, R. A. AND P. GLEES. *J. Physiol.* 113: 37P, 1951.
4. BAZETT, H. C. AND B. McGLONE. *A.M.A. Arch. Neurol.& Psychiat.* 27: 1031, 1932.
5. BAZETT, H. C., B. McGLONE, R. G. WILLIAMS AND H. M. LUFKIN. *A.M.A. Arch. Neurol. & Psychiat.* 27: 489, 1932.
6. BEETZ, F. *Arch. Gynäk.* 162: 106, 1936.
7. BERNHARD, C. G. AND R. GRANIT. *J. Gen. Physiol.* 29: 257, 1946.
8. BING, H. J. AND A. P. SKOUBY. *Acta physiol. scandinav.* 21: 286, 1950.
9. BLIX, M. *Uppsala läkaref. förh.* 18: 87, 1882.
10. BLIX, M. *Ztschr. Biol.* 20: 141, 1884.
11. BOHNENKAMP, H. AND W. PASQUAI. *Deutsche Ztschr. Nervenh.* 126: 138, 1932.
12. BULLOCK, T. H. AND R. B. COWLES. *Science* 115: 541, 1952.
13. BULLOCK, T. H. AND T. P. J. DIECKE. *J. Physiol.* 134: 47, 1956.
14. BULLOCK, T. H. AND D. A. FAULSTICK. *Fed. Proc.* 12: 22, 1953.
15. COHEN, M. J., S. LANDGREN, L. STRÖM AND Y. ZOTTERMAN. *Acta physiol. scandinav.* Suppl. 135, 1957.
16. CUSHING, H. *Brain* 32: 44, 1909.
17. DODT, E. *Acta physiol. scandinav.* 27: 295, 1952.
18. DODT, E. *Acta physiol. scandinav.* 29: 91, 1953.
19. DODT, E. *Acta physiol. scandinav.* 31: 89, 1954.
20. DODT, E. *Arch. ges. Physiol.* 263: 188, 1956.
21. DODT, E., A. P. SKOUBY AND Y. ZOTTERMAN. *Acta physiol. scandinav.* 28: 101, 1953.
22. DODT, E. AND Y. ZOTTERMAN. *Acta physiol. scandinav.* 26: 258, 1952.
23. DODT, E. AND Y. ZOTTERMAN. *Acta physiol. scandinav.* 26: 345, 1952.
24. DODT, E. AND Y. ZOTTERMAN. *Acta physiol. scandinav.* 26: 358, 1952.
25. EBAUGH, F. G., JR. AND R. THAUER. *J. Appl. Physiol.* 3: 173, 1950.
26. EBBECKE, U. *Arch. ges. Physiol.* 169: 395, 1917.
27. ENDRES, G. *Ztschr. Biol.* 89: 536, 1930.
28. GERARD, M. W. *A.M.A. Arch. Neurol. & Psychiat.* 9: 306, 1923.
29. GERNANDT, B. AND Y. ZOTTERMAN. *Acta. psychol. scandinav.* 11: 248, 1946.
30. GERTZ, E. *Ztschr. Sinnesphysiol.* 52: 1, 1921.
31. GILSBACH, C. *Die Wirkung grossflächiger Temperaturreize von verschiedener Steilheit* (Dissertation). Heidelberg, 1949.
32. GOLDSCHEIDER, A. In: *Handbuch der normalen und pathologischen Physiologie* XI: 131, 1926.
33. GOLDSCHEIDER, A. AND H. HAHN. *Arch. ges. Physiol.* 206: 337, 1924.
34. GRANT, R. T. *Ann. Rev. Physiol.* 13: 75, 1951.
35. HACKER, F. *Ztschr. Biol.* 61: 231, 1913.
36. HÄGGQVIST, G. *Ztschr. mikroskop.-anat. Forsch.* 39: 3, 1936.
37. HAHN, H. *Beiträge zur Reizphysiologie.* Heidelberg: Scherer, 1949.
38. HARDY, J. D. AND T. W. OPPEL. *J. Clin. Invest.* 17: 771, 1938.
39. HAUER, P. *Ztschr. Biol.* 85: 265, 1926.
40. HEAD, H. *Brain* 41: 57, 1918.
41. HEILBRUN, W. *Deutsche Ztschr. Nervenh.* 101: 290, 1928.
42. HENSEL, H. *Arch. ges. Physiol.* 252: 165, 1950.
43. HENSEL, H. *Ztschr. ges. exper. Med.* 117: 587, 1951.
44. HENSEL, H. *Ztschr. Kreislaufforsch.* 41: 251, 1952.
45. HENSEL, H. *Ergebn. Physiol.* 47: 165, 1952.
46. HENSEL, H. *Arch. ges. Physiol.* 256: 195, 1952.
47. HENSEL, H. *Arch. ges. Physiol.* 257: 371, 1953.
48. HENSEL, H. *Acta physiol. scandinav.* 29: 109, 1953.
49. HENSEL, H. *Ztschr. vergleich. Physiol.* 37: 509, 1955.
50. HENSEL, H. *Arch. ges. Physiol.* 263: 48, 1956.
51. HENSEL, H., L. STRÖM AND Y. ZOTTERMAN. *J. Neurophysiol.* 14: 423, 1951.
52. HENSEL, H. AND Y. ZOTTERMAN. *Acta physiol. scandinav.* 22: 96, 1951.
53. HENSEL, H. AND Y. ZOTTERMAN. *J. Physiol.* 115: 16, 1951.
54. HENSEL, H. AND Y. ZOTTERMAN. *Acta physiol. scandinav.* 23: 291, 1951.
55. HENSEL, H. AND Y. ZOTTERMAN. *J. Neurophysiol.* 14: 377, 1951.
56. HENSEL, H. AND Y. ZOTTERMAN. *Acta physiol. scandinav.* 24: 27, 1951.
57. HERGET, C. M., L. P. GRANATH AND J. D. HARDY. *Am. J. Physiol.* 135: 20, 1941.

58. HERING, E. In: Herrmanns *Handbuch der Physiologie*. III, Pt. 2: 415, 1880.

59. HIRSCH, L. AND H. SCHRIEVER. *Ztschr. Biol.* 89: 1, 1930.

60. HOLM, K. G. *Skandinav. Arch. Physiol.* 14: 249, 1903.

61. KAILA, E. *Handbuch der Psychologie*. Basel: Schwabe, 1951.

62. KIESOW, F. *Arch. Psychol.* 22: 50, 1911.

63. LANDGREN, S. *Acta physiol. scandinav.* 40: 202, 1957.

64. LEHMANN, A. *Die Hauptgesetze des Menschlichen Gefühlslebens*. Leipzig: Reisland, 1892.

65. LELE, P. P., G. WEDDELL AND C. M. WILLIAMS. *J. Physiol.* 126: 206, 1954.

66. LEWIS, TH., G. W. PICKERING AND P. ROTHSCHILD. *Heart* 16: 1, 1931.

67. MARÉCHAUX, E. W. AND K. E. SCHÄFER. *Arch. ges. Physiol.* 251: 765, 1949.

68. MARUHASHI, J., K. MIZUGUCHI AND I. TASAKI. *J. Physiol.* 117: 129, 1952.

69. MOUNTCASTLE, V. B. AND E. HENNEMAN. *J. Neurophysiol.* 12: 85, 1949.

70. NOBLE, G. K. AND A. SCHMIDT. *Proc. Am. Philos. Soc.* 77: 263, 1937.

71. PENFIELD, W. AND A. T. RASMUSSEN. *The Cerebral Cortex in Man: A Clinical Study of Localization of Function*. New York: Macmillan, 1950.

72. REIN, H. *Ztschr. Biol.* 82: 189, 1925.

73. REIN, H. AND H. STRUGHOLD. *Ztschr. Biol.* 82: 553, 1925.

74. REIN, H. AND H. STRUGHOLD. *Ztschr. Biol.* 87: 599, 1928.

75. RENQVIST-REENPÄÄ, Y. *Allgemeine Sinnesphysiologie*. Vienna: Springer, 1936.

76. RUCH, T. C. In: *A Textbook of Physiology* (17th ed.), edited by J. F. Fulton. Philadelphia: Saunders, 1955.

77. SAND, A. *Proc. Roy. Soc., London. ser. B* 125: 524, 1938.

78. SCHRIEVER, H. AND H. STRUGHOLD. *Ztschr. Biol.* 84: 193, 1926.

79. SJÖQVIST, O. *Acta psychiat. et neurol.* Suppl. 17, 1938.

80. SKOUBY, A. P. *Acta physiol. scandinav.* 24: 174, 1951.

81. SPEISER, M. *Arch. Gynäk.* 146: 137, 1931.

82. STEIN, J. AND V. v. WEIZSÄCKER. *Deutsche Ztschr. Nervenh.* 99: 1, 1927.

83. STRUGHOLD, H. *Verhandl. phys.-med. Gesellsch. Würzb.* 51: 31, 1926.

84. STRUGHOLD, H. AND M. KARBE. *Ztschr. Biol.* 83: 189, 1925.

85. STRUGHOLD, H. AND R. PORZ. *Ztschr. Biol.* 91: 563, 1931.

86. STRÜMPELL, A. *Deutsches Arch. klin. Med.* 28: 43, 1881.

87. THUNBERG, T. *Skandinav. Arch. Physiol.* 11: 382, 1901.

88. THUNBERG, T. *Skandinav. Arch. Physiol.* 12: 394, 1902.

89. THUNBERG, T. In: *Handbuch der Physiologie des Menschen*, edited by W. Nagel. III: 669, 1905.

90. TROTTER, W. AND H. M. DAVIES. *J. Physiol.* 38: 134, 1909.

91. VON FREY, M. *Ber. sächs. Gesellsch. Wiss.* 47: 166, 1895.

92. VON SKRAMLIK, E. *Arch. Psychol.* 4: 244, 1937.

93. WALKER, A. E. *A.M.A. Arch. Neurol. & Psychiat.* 43: 284, 1940.

94. WEBER, E. H. Wagner's *Handwörterbuch der Physiologie*. III, Pt. 2: 481, 1846.

95. ZOTTERMAN, Y. *Acta med. scandinav.* 80: 185, 1933.

96. ZOTTERMAN, Y. *Skandinav. Arch. Physiol.* 75: 106, 1936.

97. ZOTTERMAN, Y. *J. Physiol.* 95: 1, 1939.

98. ZOTTERMAN, Y. *Acta physiol. scandinav.* 18: 181, 1949.

99. ZOTTERMAN, Y. *Ann. Rev. Physiol.* 15: 357, 1953.

100. ZOTTERMAN, Y. In: *Fourth Conference on the Nerve Impulse*, edited by D. Nachmansohn. New York: Macy, 1954.

CHAPTER XIX

Pain

WILLIAM H. SWEET | *Department of Surgery, Harvard Medical School, Boston, Massachusetts*

CHAPTER CONTENTS

THE NATURE AND RANGE of the sensations covered by the word 'pain' elude precise definition. Aristotle (8) equated pain with unpleasantness whether arising from outside the body, within the body or within the 'soul' (as when one feels miserable). 'Pain or unpleasantness' stood for him as the opposite to 'pleasure' and he considered every action to be "accompanied by pleasure and pain." For Spinoza (65) pain was a focal form of sorrow which he called one of the three primary emotions. Pain, which he thought of as the emotion opposite to "pleasurable excitment," he "related to a man when one of his parts is affected more than the others; melancholy, on the other hand, when all parts are equally affected." As scientists now tend to use the word, 'pain' contains the Spinozistic implication that the unpleasant feeling is specifically referred to some place or places in the body. In any case it is this more localized kind of pain which is more amenable to physiologic study in contradistinction to diffuse states of unpleasantness.

But from the standpoint of the physician it is necessary to analyze and treat every type of disagreeable feeling of which people complain. It matters not whether the individual tags it by the label 'pain'. Thus in the area of the face which has undergone trigeminal denervation about 5 per cent of the patients have severe annoying sensations which they may call aches, but often they are at a loss for words to describe the peculiar sensation so extraordinary and unmatched by any of their previous experiences. Yet many so afflicted find the feelings sufficiently intolerable to seek major surgery for relief. Certainly such sensations are reasonably classified as an unusual form of pain, and the elucidation of the mechanism of severe unpleasantness referred to an anesthetic area in the presumed absence of an organic central lesion remains one of many challenges to the neurophysiologist.

Pain may be arbitrarily divided into two main elements, the initial sensation and the reaction to that sensation. As Beecher (15) has emphasized, the significance of the pain to the individual plays a major role in determining the extent of the second reactive component of the feeling. Thus he found that only 32 per cent of 150 war-injured men had pain severe enough to require a narcotic, whereas 83 per cent of 150 male civilians undergoing surgery involving much less trauma required narcotics. For the soldier the war wound marked the end of a gravely hazardous form of life, whereas no such compensation and, at worst, serious problems beset the operated civilian. Beecher interpreted the differing degree of complaint in these two settings as indicating "that the reaction or processing phase is very often of more importance in suffering than is the original sensation." Indeed the original sensation as well may appear as a symptom of protest, as from the person who develops a 'sick headache' at will; or the pain may come as a consequence of previous conditioning as in 'a painful memory.' Contrariwise, various cerebral deficiency states result in a reduced reaction to afferent impulses for pain which would normally evoke a lively response.

In this essay we shall devote most of the discussion to the sensation of pain as evoked by specific stimuli to sensory endings or pathways, recognizing, however, the vast importance of the psychological component of the response and the virtual impossibility of separating this from the primary awareness of pain.

PAIN AS A SENSATION WITH ITS OWN CENTRAL AND PERIPHERAL APPARATUS

The validity of searching for a special sensory mechanism concerned wholly or mainly with pain requires inquiry. The physiologist has not sought out specific nervous pathways subserving pleasure, the philosopher's antipode to pain; is it sensible to look for pain pathways? One can answer promptly that it is and has proved eminently fruitful to do so because

certain stimuli to certain areas almost invariably bring on pain in man, whereas the same constancy of relationship in no way applies to pleasure. One may venture to state that even the amorous male with the most Casanovian success has not developed a form and site of stimulus which constantly evokes pleasure in his partner, though in the absence of a critically reported series this can be no more than the author's disgruntled surmise.

Erasmus Darwin (53, pp. 121 and 125) thought pain to be the consequence of any excessive stimulation and a result of exaggeration of sensations of heat, touch, sight, taste or smell. This intensive theory of pain in one modification or another has found many supporters. And we can scarcely disagree with William James' (134) conclusion that it is certain that sensations of every order which in moderate degree are rather pleasant than otherwise become unpleasant when their intensity grows too strong. For example, in 1934 Nafe (198) drew attention to the fact that when smooth muscle was in spastic contraction at the extremes of heat and cold, 52°C and 3°C respectively, there was pain. At levels intermediate between these there was only a sense of warmth or coolness. As stimulation became more intense with a rise in temperature the quality of the sensation was altered from warmth, to heat, to pain; all mediated he thought by the same peripheral equipment and integrated at the thalamocortical level. More recently Gooddy (104) has argued that "any nervous pathways are potential pain pathways," i.e. that any pathway may provide "the impulse patterns that are associated with the perception of pain." In certain patients successive operations on peripheral nerves, posterior roots, spinal cord, thalamus and cerebral hemispheres may all fail to give permanent relief from pain. From such series of events, infrequent though they are, Gooddy reaches the extreme point of view that "unless the whole nervous system is destroyed, the abnormal patterns (evoking pain) gradually establish themselves anew."

The most clear-cut evidence to the contrary, that at least some pain is to be regarded as a particular form of sensation with its own pathways and not merely an intensification of other forms, is provided by patients with a lesion confined to the anterior quadrant of the spinal cord. This usually deprives them of the capacity to feel pain in response to a wide variety of noxa previously painful, yet proprioceptive and light touch sensibility are virtually unimpaired. This is the typical finding after the operation of anterolateral cordotomy. Although thermanesthesia is usually present along with analgesia, a rare patient after such a cordotomy may show only the former without the latter or vice versa, indicating that there are special pathways for pain and others for temperature sensation which are nearly, but not precisely, coextensive (296, p. 259). Schiff (238) one century ago made the fundamental observation that lesions of the spinal cord in rabbits, sparing only the posterior columns, resulted in animals which would make a number of responses to touch whereas they would ignore presumably painful deep stimuli. He recognized the similarity between this state and the clinical condition of analgesia without anesthesia to touch, described in man both by Beau and by Vieusseux [cited by Schiff (238), p. 253].

Such data, though, do not prove that impulses for pain and touch may not use the same fibers in peripheral nerves and there has been no histologic correlation between lesions of certain types of peripheral nerve fiber and a disassociated loss of touch or pain. Although such loss may occur in leprosy—the *Bacillus leprae* typically attacks only the peripheral and not the central nervous system—a focal degeneration of dorsal funiculi has also been seen in this disorder by Wilson (301, fig. 92, p. 753). Hence a purely peripheral lesion may not be taken for granted here as the explanation of a loss of pain without touch or the reverse. However, conduction by peripheral nerves can become impaired in such fashion that a differential loss of various forms of sensation occurs. Thus Herzen (127) was the first to note that pressure on a human peripheral nerve, the sciatic, caused initially loss of touch sensibility, shortly thereafter that of cold, much later that of warmth and finally of pain. Goldscheider (102) in the same year likewise observed a differential loss of sensory modalities, although in a different order, when a branch of a peripheral nerve was cocainized. He thought cold was blocked first, then, in sequence, warmth, pain and pressure. Modifications of the first method of compression or asphyxia of the nerve and of the second, pharmacologic block, have since been used extensively in a study of the specificity of nerve fibers for single modalities of sensation. Unequivocal proof that one peripheral fiber is devoted to but one type of sensory modality, pain, touch, cold or warmth has not been advanced as yet. The evidence bearing on this and on the question of special sensory end organs for pain will be presented later. Before studying the nervous system itself we may properly consider the tactics used in arousing its responses.

STIMULUS, SENSATION AND THEIR MEASUREMENT

Mechanical Stimuli

Quantitative assessment of pain involved, of course, measurement both of stimulus and sensation. In the earliest tactics one pricked the surface to be tested with needle points mounted either in fibers which bent at a calibrated force or on a calibrated spring—a method which remains the best for many clinical physiological studies.

Correlation with Tissue Damage

The adequate stimulus for pain, whether it is mechanical, thermal, electrical or chemical, is potentially or actually productive of tissue damage. Hence, the immediate zone of reception on which the stimulus is acting soon becomes modified in serial determinations at the same site. Thus Lewis (171, p. 106) pointed out that, if the skin of the front of the forearm is pricked with a needle just hard enough to cause pain, most of these pricks will subsequently show signs of tissue damage in the form of little circles of redness. Thermal radiation in order to evoke pain requires an energy (expressed in millicalories per second per square centimeter) which is 2000 times that of the threshold for warmth. In fact, Hardy *et al.* (118, pp. 23, 53), the workers responsible for these figures, state that the thermal radiation threshold for 'pricking pain' lies at a skin temperature of roughly 45°C, which is likewise the threshold temperature range for the production of skin damage, according to Moritz & Henriques (192). In agreement with this Benjamin (18) finds the threshold for the production of a cutaneous flare by heat is very close to the pain threshold.

Heat

Nevertheless thermal radiation which eliminates simultaneous contact and pressure sensations has formed the basis for much of the modern work on pain thresholds since the description by Hardy *et al.* (115) of their 'dolorimeter.' This apparatus permits control of the intensity and duration of applied heat and its measurement by a radiometer. With critical, careful use of this instrument so arranged as to provide a radiation time of 3 sec., it is their contention that the pain threshold is constant from person to person and in the same individual from time to time. The three investigators were the initial subjects and they studied themselves nearly every day for almost a year, directing the heat to an area of the forehead thoroughly blackened with India ink and obtaining values which all fell within ±12 per cent of the mean. They describe the subject's experience as follows: "The sensation is one of warmth, heat and burning which seems to 'swell' and then to 'draw together' into a prick at the end of the third second. Minimal after-sensations of heat and burning pain are common." This they call the pricking pain threshold. Bigelow *et al.* (26) also identified another threshold—that for 'burning pain.' This on the forehead is, they say, about 20 to 30 mcal. lower than the pricking pain threshold. When these workers extended their measurements to 150 individuals about the same mean intensity of stimulus, 0.21 gm cal. per sec. per cm², evoked 'pricking pain' with a maximal variation of ±15 per cent.

This uniformity is said to persist throughout a 24 hr. period of enforced wakefulness (241) in women before, during and after labor (135), and over much of the body surface (118). But Wolff & Goodell (304) also state that, if the subject is unable to concentrate on the testing procedure or "to maintain a detached, unprejudiced attitude" because of fatigue, lethargy, suggestibility or other reason, then the pain threshold varies greatly and is unpredictable.

A number of workers have been unable to confirm the described uniformity of pain threshold in these painfully collected data. Chapman & Jones (40) found the theshold of 200 normal subjects to vary much more widely—from −40 per cent to +50 per cent. Others who have reported inconstancy of thresholds by this technique include Clausen & King (44), Leduc & Slaughter (160), Schamp & Schamp (237) and Slaughter & Wright (252). Benjamin (20) agreed that the tactic of painting the skin with India ink resulted in absorption of nearly all (94 per cent) of the incident heat and its transmission into the skin by conduction, but found pain sensitivity in the palm less than in the forearm. Whyte (297) has advanced this cogent criticism: the validity of the method depends on the contention of Oppel & Hardy (203) that the rise in skin temperature produced by radiant heat is proportional to thermal intensity. If this were true, then at the increased radiant heat thresholds for morphine described by Wolff *et al.* (306) extrapolation of their curves would indicate that the skin temperatures would have reached about 54°C. The actual forehead temperatures of Whyte's subjects at the pricking pain threshold were about the same before and after morphine, ranging from 46.2 to 47.5°C. From this Whyte logically concludes that an increase in sweating or in blood flow to the skin may have occurred following the morphine rather than the presumed increase in nervous threshold. Beecher and associates have also been sharp critics of the contention that consistent thresholds are obtainable by the method. Denton & Beecher (63) found that an operator widely experienced in the radiant heat method, who was called in to correct their failure to get consistent data, was able to do so as long as he knew what drug had been administered; he failed when he did not know. They interpreted this to be a consequence of unconscious guidance by the operator of the subjective response he was seeking. Much space has been devoted to consideration of this single technique in order to point out the difficulties of precise measurement of a sensation as threatening to the individual as pain.

Electricity

Electrical stimulation has also been used to test cutaneous sensation. The threshold feeling, according to Bishop (27), varies depending upon the special sensitivity of the skin spot tested. Using a condenser discharge delivering a spark when the point of the stimulating needle was about 0.5 mm from the skin, he was able to stimulate without mechanical contact. With this device he found spots "mediating ordinary touch or light pressure" and others inducing the sensation of prick "which becomes pricking pain on a stronger stimulation." But he says that a "single stimulus applied to a single prick spot at the threshold is not painful but elicits a tactile experience usually accompanied by a faint aura of itch. This tactile sensation is not associated with a feeling of pressure. . . . On the other hand a single threshold stimulus applied to a touch ending is experienced as a slight tap." Distinctions between a tactile sensation with and one without pressure, and between a prick and pricking pain, certainly do not lend themselves to quantitative analysis. Mueller *et al.* (197), seeking to develop an electrical method for the testing of pain threshold, found the most clear-cut end point to be the sensation of prick but, in critical electrical measurements, they found the prick to occur during breakdown of skin impedance so that the electrical quantity was not purely an index of threshold pain but was dependent on the dielectric properties of the skin. Beecher (16) after a thorough review of the whole problem of the measurement of pain of both 'experimental' and 'pathological' types concludes that "no convincing demonstration has yet been given that the pain threshold is a constant from man to man or from one time to another in a given man." He attributes the variability to the 'psychic reaction component' rather than the 'original sensation.' Precise determinations of pain threshold find perhaps their greatest practical utility in the pharmacologic appraisal of analgesic agents—a subject beyond our scope. To me it appears that firmer conclusions are tenable when one works with stimuli in animals and man which, in normal man, consistently evoke unequivocal and unalloyed pain. The subsequent discussion will seek to emphasize such work.

Other methods for the study of pain either deliberately evoked or arising in pathological states will now be considered.

Distention of Viscera

Incision into and passing a needle through skeletal muscle are almost painless, and the abdominal viscera exposed under local anesthesia may be cut, torn or burned as long as the parietal peritoneum and roots of the mesentery are not stimulated (164). These viscera are capable of initiating impulses for pain upon the appropriate stimulus, however, and it was Lennander (165) who demonstrated that it was distension of the human kidney pelvis which was painful. Hurst (131) extended this principle, that distension is the pain-evoking stimulus for hollow viscera, to studies of the alimentary canal. Davis et al. (54, 56) have applied the same tactic to studies of the gall bladder. Rapid expansion of the capsule of solid organs like the liver and kidney also hurts.

Arterial Constriction with Ischemia and Arterial Dilatation

Both arterial constriction or occlusion to the point of ischemia and severe arterial dilatation at times associated with excessive pulsation in a part are productive of pain. Sutton & Lueth (257) thought that myocardial anoxia was the physiological stimulus for cardiac pain when they found that lightly anesthetized dogs gave responses suggestive of pain when a coronary artery was occluded by a ligature. Gorham (107) confirmed these results and added the observation that if three ligatures were placed in the wall of the coronary artery so that divergent traction on them would tend to distend the vessel, responses of 'pain' also occurred. The headache of migraine is one of the better studied examples of a pain probably brought on by arterial

dilation. Wolff, a prominent exponent of this view, summarized the evidence for it in 1948 (303, pp. 265 to 288). Histamine produces, among other effects, painful distension of arteries and presents a means of evoking headache experimentally, although this differs from that seen in migraine in at least eight respects according to Wolff (303, pp. 289 to 290). The reverse situation, ischemia as a cause of pain, is seen both in intermittent claudication affecting especially the lower limbs and in cardiac angina. Lewis, Pickering and Rothschild have developed a testing procedure (171, p. 97) involving voluntary manual gripping movements at the rate of 1 per sec. developing a tension of 20 to 28 lb. Such movements, normally painless for many minutes, soon cause pain if the circulation to the arm is stopped by inflation of a proximally placed cuff. Lewis (170) initiated and Kellgren (140) followed with another type of test, the injection of hypertonic saline into muscles, tendons, ligaments and joints to provide and permit the analysis of pain from these deeper structures.

Inflammation

Inflammation, arising from disease or produced experimentally, is apparently another process whereby previously painless stimuli appear to become painful; this is true for skin (172), for deeper somatic structures (150) and for the viscera (142). Thus the inflamed appendix hurts when pinched, but not the normal appendix.

Excellent summaries of various experimental methods appear in Hardy et al. (118, Chapter III) and in Beecher (16, Section V); Lewis (171, Chapter I) gives a useful catalogue of the effective stimuli for each of the pain-sensitive tissues of the body.

Quantitation of Severity of Pain

The purely subjective character of pain has given rise to great difficulty in efforts at quantitation, but Hardy et al. (118, p. 156) have thought that trained observers can distinguish as many as 21 different degrees of pain, from zero to maximum, arising from radiant heat. That is to say, there were 21 steps or 'just noticeable differences (jnd's)' as the amount of radiant heat was increased. They suggested a unit for pain sensation, a 'dol' equivalent to the sum of 2 jnd's; pain of ceiling intensity has a value of $10\frac{1}{2}$ 'dols.' Armstrong et al. (9) have found their trained group able to distinguish at least 8, possibly up to 16 units of pain intensity when a chemical excitant of pain is applied to the exposed base of a canthardin blister.

ANIMAL VERSUS HUMAN SUBJECTS IN PAIN STUDIES

Waterston (284) has pointed out that one's natural repugnance to investigating pain in man must be overcome because of "the value and importance . . . of the information which can be thus obtained and by this means only." The final and conclusive arbiter on all questions relating to any sensation must be man experiencing that sensation and able to describe it in words; this is particularly true of pain which by definition must have some degree of affective component of unpleasantness. I should agree without reservation with Hardy *et al.* (116, p. 2) that "the verbal report of the instructed subject is the most reliable evidence that the pain threshold has been reached." But it has seemed logical to many to assume that a maneuver which consistently evokes pain in man and provokes in him some form of motor response when pain is felt may be used in animals and the motor response of the creature taken as an end point indicative of pain. Unfortunately this conclusion is not without pitfalls. Such reasoning led Gerard (95, p. 335) to make a series of successively more rostral incisions into the spinal or descending trigeminal tract in cats, each incision about 1.5 mm rostral to the previous one.[1] She began at the midbulbar level at the obex and ascended until stimulation of the cornea no longer elicited the 'pain reflexes' of struggling, pupillary dilatation and rise of arterial pressure. Not until the cut reached the midpontine area did corneal stimulation fail to evoke such reflexes, so she naturally concluded that the pain fibers from the cornea terminate just below this point. But in man all such fibers terminate much lower, in fact all below the obex, because cutting of all of the descending trigeminal tract at this level produces enduring analgesia of the entire first division trigeminal sensory zone (75; 296, p. 457). It is possible that collaterals from corneal pain fibers may evoke reflexes without awareness of pain in both cat and man, and that these come off at more rostral levels than the obex; or it may be that the specific anatomy in cats differs from man. In either event lesions needed to stop 'pain reflexes' in the cat were

decidedly different from those required to stop pain in man.

Recently Goetzl *et al.* (100) found upon stimulation of the tooth pulp in unanesthetized cats and rabbits a rise in arterial pressure and a decrease in volume of the leg, spleen and kidney, whereas the reverse changes in arterial pressure and organ volume occurred when such stimuli were delivered to anesthetized animals. They concluded from these observations that the ability of the stimulus to produce a rise in arterial pressure depended upon actual perception of pain by the animal. Such a conclusion has dubious validity in view of Gerard's erroneous deductions from the rise of arterial pressure in her cats.

Animal experiments in the spinal cord have correlated even more miserably with work in man. Cadwalder & Sweet (37), after careful pre- and postoperative studies in dogs, found behavior after anterolateral cordotomy which they considered evidence of incomplete loss of cutaneous pain sensibility along with severe ataxia of the hind legs. Their post-mortem material demonstrated incisions of the type which produce total cutaneous analgesia and no ataxia in man. They quoted the work of six previous groups who obtained divergent results from similar animal work; three of the other groups had been unable to demonstrate any definite cutaneous sensory change in their animals after anterolateral cordotomy. Even in monkeys Mott (195) found no evidence of any loss of pain sensation after either unilateral or bilateral division of the anterior halves of the cord. In the cat Karplus & Kreidl (138) were unable to eliminate rostral response to painful stimuli applied to the hind legs even by complete hemisections, one on each side of the thoracic cord, five or more segments apart. Only when the incisions bisecting the cord were four segments apart or less did noxa to the legs fail to excite a response. From this they deduced that pain is transmitted by short chains of neurons crossing the cord from side to side. The conclusion from all these studies is that the bulk of somatic pain-conducting axons in many mammals including monkeys do not maintain a fixed position in the anterolateral columns of the cord. Happily from the standpoint of easy surgical relief of pain this position is usually the case in man. However, if one had only reflex behavior in man as a guide one might still be confused. Thus, when one of my patients, after cordotomy, stepped on an upturned nail, the analgesic leg briskly withdrew. Curious as to why the leg jumped, he discovered the heavy nail in the sole of his foot; he was consciously aware only of some local tingling.

---

[1] The trigeminal nerve enters the upper pons and one bundle of its fibers descends the length of the pons and medulla into the uppermost cervical segments, so the more rostral the incision the more toward the periphery the tract was being cut.

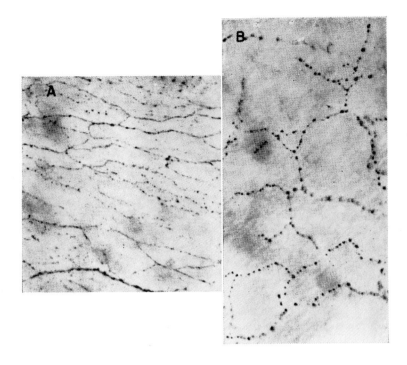

FIG. 1. Naked axons and terminals in the cornea of the monkey, stained with methylene blue. *A.* Beaded axons ramifying in the basal part of the epithelium ($\times$ 240). *B.* Epithelium only which has been stripped off substantia propria. Beaded nerve fibers are terminating extracellularly in end beads passing between cells in the middle third of the epithelium ($\times$ 400). [From Zander & Weddell (313).]

At a number of areas in the human body pain has been said to be the only sensation elicitable in the normal state. If this be true, it has seemed especially reasonable to excite such areas in animals and study the concomitant nervous behavior on the assumption that it may be correlated with pain perception. Appropriate stimulus of the most intensively studied such area, the cornea, has however been shown clearly to evoke other sensations than pain and will be discussed more fully. Even so, pain is the dominant and by far the most readily provoked sensation upon corneal stimulus in man and, in general, animal experiments in which the stimulus used would surely bring on pain in a normal man have been useful, especially in analysis of action potentials in nerves. Indeed Beecher (16) considers that a more dependable relationship has been established between the action of powerful narcotics and the 'experimental pain threshold' in animals than in man.

END ORGANS FOR PAIN

Normal Skin

The finding by Goldscheider (101) of points on the skin particularly sensitive to painful stimuli and of other spots which could be stuck painlessly with a fine needle has been followed by efforts to locate a

particular end organ, the nervous receptor for pain von Frey's (273, 274) exhaustive studies with calibrated hairs and thorns led him to insist on a distinction between the spots in which the sole threshold response to a point stimulus was a sense of pain and those in which it was a sense of pressure. Nerves end in the skin in a wide variety of complex patterns or specialized end organs (see other chapters for discussion), but the overwhelming majority of the fibers in the skin terminate both in epidermis and dermis without specialized groupings of cells about them, merely as fine naked freely ending axoplasmic filaments in an extracellular position. They interweave but do not fuse with one another (288). In the corneal epithelium such terminals are "disposed in depth throughout its whole extent," as well as "throughout the whole extent of the substantia propria." [See Zander & Weddell's (313) thorough original studies and analysis of the massive literature on the subject.] Figure 1 illustrates the appearances in two types of preparation. Weddell and others (personal communication) have also noted a gross variability from week to week in the number of clusters of corneal naked nerve endings simulating in appearance a Krause's end bulb, an observation which indicates that the normal nerve endings may be in a constantly changing dynamic state.

The multitudinous plexiform endings have been correlated with the multiplicity of 'pain points' found on examination with calibrated thorns. Strughold (256) found up to 200 per cm² and Woollard (307), testing sensation over a small area of his own thigh after removal of each of a succession of thin slices of skin, found pain to be the most superficial as well as the most extensive in depth of the modalities tested. In one region of his own epidermis which was especially sensitive to a needle tip he saw histologically a plexus of finely beaded nerve fibers. Woollard *et al.* (310) examined a biopsy of human skin taken just distal to an ulcer made 8 days earlier with solid carbon dioxide. Pain was the only sensation elicitable from the tissue and the subsequent microscopic examination revealed only fine naked nerve terminals. However, when Foerster & Boeke (cited in 77, p. 16) examined sections of skin in man following division of cutaneous nerves and beginning regeneration, they found in areas from which pain was the only type of sensation no free intraepithelial nerve endings. The positive findings of the previous authors are probably more significant. Despite the density of the pain points there are, however, spots analgesic to pain. Tindall & Kunkle (265) find that these are still demonstrable both during induced erythema (with lowered threshold) and during experimental ischemia (with raised threshold). They conclude that the analgesic spot represents a gap in the fiber network rather than a pain fiber with an unusually high threshold. The great ease with which pain is elicited from the cornea, the tympanic membrane and the dental pulp—all structures probably supplied only with delicate free filamentous nerve terminals and no specialized nerve endings—has convinced most workers that such endings can initiate nervous impulses giving rise to pain. [For the neurohistology of the tympanic membrane see Wilson (300).]

There has been less agreement as to whether or not other modalities of sensation might be evoked via these delicate nerve endings. Waterston (283) actually believed that the nerves of the normal epidermis mediate only touch, since he could slice this tissue painlessly from himself with a razor. In the skin shavings he saw nerve fibers ending in loops and fine arborescent figures. In Woollard's (307) detailed description of his similar studies he says that, when the first 5 x 22 mm slice of his skin was cut, he felt pain only at four previousy mapped 'pain spots'. But he must have felt touch during the rest of the slicing process and this is likely to have been mediated, at least in part, by the other fine nerve terminals in the epidermis. Personal repetition of studies with cali-

brated hairs and needle points along with a review of much of the voluminous literature on cutaneous sensation led us in 1955 (296, p. 10) to record agreement with Goldscheider's (101) original observation—that the threshold sensation to minimal stimulation with a minute pointed needle is one of touch at the great majority of all spots on the skin of the body. This I noted even in areas specifically recommended by von Frey (274) for eliciting pain in preference to touch, such as the skin over the eyelids, the biceps brachii and the clavicle. Consequently, the cutaneous sense of touch being even more widespread than that of pain, it seems likely that proper stimulus to many or even any of the most widespread endings, the fine unmyelinated type, elicits normally a sense of touch.

Cornea

Because the great majority of anatomists find only such fine endings in the cornea its sensation has been much tested. General teaching since von Frey (273) and in agreement with Lewis (171) has been that one may evoke only pain from the cornea. Since even a speck of grit on the normal eyeball is so intensely painful, repeated reports in the literature that a sense of touch may be elicited from the cornea found little general acceptance. However, many normal people do in fact describe only a sense of touch without pain or annoyance when a wisp of cotton rests on the cornea.

Lele & Weddell (163) have recently summarized 40 publications on corneal sensation and have carried out a series of critical experiments which may well become a classic of well-controlled study in the complicated field of sensation. In 25 of the 40 earlier publications the various authors record a feeling of touch upon corneal stimulation, and Lele & Weddell obtained this response invariably from each of 10 subjects when a fine nylon suture was brought into contact with the cornea. Reports of each subject never "included even a suggestion of pain". Contrariwise, a heavier nylon thread touching the cornea caused invariably a blink and a report of sharp pain. In their further studies a jet of air at warm, cold or neutral temperature, a warm or cool copper cylinder, or an infrared beam of radiation was applied to and restricted to the cornea. The stimulus excited an appropriate sensation of temperature in the overwhelming majority of instances.

From such findings it seems likely that the fine naked nerve endings in the surface layers of the body are capable of setting up impulses which will enable a man to distinguish not only a potentially noxious from a harmless stimulus—pain from touch—but warmth and cold as well.

Abnormal Skin

There are, however, areas of abnormally innervated skin in man from which only pain can be aroused. Weddell (285) studied biopsies of such skin from a patient with a lesion of the sciatic nerve and from a patient with a plastic tube pedicle of the abdominal wall. On histologic examination he saw in each specimen only fine nerve fibers giving rise to superficial nerve nets with beaded endings.

Special Cutaneous Sensory Endings

Discussion of the functions of the elaborate cutaneous sensory nerve endings of Meissner, Ruffini and Krause and of the deeper such endings, the Vater-Pacinian corpuscles and neurotendinous endings of Golgi is germane to our theme only to point out that many of them have a long slender 'accessory fiber' (Remak fiber or Timofevew fiber) with a fine unmyelinated naked nerve ending similar to those in the cornea. Assuming that the most elaborate forms of sensory nerve terminal subserve some specialized function such as touch, warmth or coolness, does excessive stimulation of such a receptor cause pain as well, and if so is that pain mediated via impulses in the accessory fiber? Woollard (308), in support of this hypothesis, has illustrated an 'accessory' fiber derived from what he calls the 'subepidermal pain plexus' terminating at a Krause's end bulb. Lavrenko (158) and Kolossov have shown that these accessory fibers are not connected with the sympathetic system; their specific association with pain remains at the moment a speculation. Trotter & Davies (270) regarded the sensation of 'hot' as a combination of warmth and pain, the sensation of 'cold' likewise would combine coolness and pain. With increasing thermal difference the sense of temperature disappears and pain alone is perceived. (See above for comments of Nafe on sensations arising from smooth muscle.) Elucidation of all the mechanisms of the combined forms of sensation is a task for the future; but one can say that the 'intensive' theory of pain is right to this extent, that sufficiently pronounced mechanical and thermal stimulation of fine unmyelinated nerve endings will cause pain.

Deeper Somatic and Visceral Receptors

Correlation of deeper somatic and visceral receptors with particular types of pain or other sensation is likewise in an elementary stage. Free unmyelinated nerve endings occur in serous membranes, the subserous coat of gut, intermuscular connective tissue, tendon surface and substance, deep fascia and periosteum—from all of which the suitable stimulus evokes pain. [For specific references see White & Sweet (296, p. 15).] The plexus of nerve fibers is much better developed in the adventitia and muscularis of arteries than of veins, according to Dogiel (66). This finding correlates well with the severe pain commonly felt on arterial puncture in man in contrast to the absence of or minor pain on venepuncture (283).

Terminating also in close relation to capillary walls are fine unmyelinated endings derived from sheathed stem fibers of dorsal root origin described by Weddell et al. (288). Their afferent function is further suggested by Landis' (151) observation in man that pain occurred when his micropipette penetrated these tiny channels.

TERMINAL SENSORY PLEXUSES

The nerve fibers ramifying in the subcutaneous tissue and skin are so interwoven as to give the impression of a continuous net or syncytium, but even in densely innervated areas such as the cornea Zander & Weddell (313) have never seen fusion between daughter axons originating from neighboring nerve fibers, although they have occasionally seen nets formed by fusion of daughter axons arising from the same parent fiber. Even though the stem nerve fiber from one dorsal root ganglion cell supplies a large area of skin, the capacity to perceive and localize pain correctly to a single spot is well known. It appears to be mediated by the multiple innervation of each 'spot' by branches from different stem fibers. Thereby a tiny area of skin gives rise to a pattern of excitation differing enough from its neighbor to permit localization and two-point discrimination. This disposition of stem nerve fibers was first seen by Bethe (23) at the sensory end organs of frog tongue. Boring's (30) penetrating analysis of sensation in his own forearm after deliberate division of a cutaneous nerve led him to the same concept. Weddell (285, 286) was the first to demonstrate histologically in human skin biopsies that a spot of skin especially sensitive to one modality of sensation was in fact supplied by two or more nerve fibers approaching from different directions. Moreover, in a patient with partial interruption of an ulnar nerve associated with impaired sensibility, a shaving of skin 3 cm² from the dorsum of the hand in the hypersensitive zone revealed in one area a single well-stained nerve fiber amid other unstained and presumably degenerated fibers. This fiber terminated in a net immediately beneath the epithelium, covering a roughly circular area of 0.75 cm in greatest diameter. This distance corresponded to the limen of two-point discrimination for pain in a similar normal area. The observation suggests that the appreciation of the dual nature of such stimulus requires the separation of the points by about the diameter of the terminal net of each fiber supplying the zone in question.

PERIPHERAL SENSORY NERVE FIBERS

Single Fiber Studies

Adrian (1, pp. 81–90) was the first to record electrical impulses from individual sensory nerve fibers in animals following a variety of peripheral stimuli. He and Zotterman promptly established that the spike potentials from a single axon are uniform in duration and amplitude, i.e. that the axon's impulse has an all-or-nothing character. Moreover they showed that no particular frequency of the discharge is characteristic for pain. Thus a needle prick evokes a discharge which varies between the usual limits for a number of types of stimuli of around 5 to 100 per sec. in each nerve fiber. Adrian pointed this out as evidence that pain is not the result of excessive stimulation of any type of receptor; if it were, one would expect a uniformly high rate of discharge. In confirmation of the conclusion that high frequency of discharge is not necessarily correlated with pain Adrian et al. (2) reported that puffs of air at high frequency directed to the skin of a frog would produce fiber discharges up to 300 per sec. Such stimuli did not seem to hurt unanesthetized frogs.

Echlin & Fessard (72) have also found in cats that they can drive receptors at frequencies over 400 per sec. so as to record synchronous afferent discharges from proximal points on nerves. The effective stimulus, a powerfully vibrating tuning fork placed against the skin over the bone of the tibia or ankle, would not cause pain in man—further evidence that high frequency of discharge in a sensory receptor or nerve need not give rise to pain in an afferent pathway not ordinarily concerned therewith.

Adrian however did note in animals that the dis-

charge following the painful stimulus of a heavy needle prick was prolonged up to 20 sec. The discharge after a light needle prick likely to evoke only a sense of touch in man lasted but 0.2 sec. or less (fig. 2). The initial frequency of the discharge was however the same with each type of stimulus. Although at the time of his writing the naked terminations of nerves were presumed to be exclusively receptors for pain, it would, as he said, "make for economy if one and the same nerve fiber could be used to signal nonpainful stimulation by a brief discharge and painful stimulation by a much longer one." He would account for the difference in sensation by a breakthrough of the long discharge into areas of the central nervous system inaccessible to its shorter counterpart. Such a mechanism would not preclude another apparatus for touch with particular receptors and fibers such as the nerve roots around hair follicles. In addition to prolonged discharge the pain receptors and fibers, as studied at the cornea for example, also show slow adaptation, i.e. they continue to transmit pain impulses as long as the noxious stimulus is present. Studies of single afferent fibers in the cat by Maruhashi et al. (185) are mentioned later.

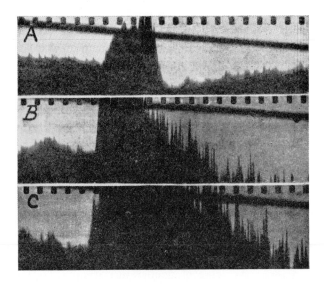

FIG. 2. Action potentials in cat's cutaneous nerve in response to touch and pain. Needle on weighed lever lowered on to the skin and allowed to rest there. A. Weight on needle 3 gm, very brief discharge. B. Weight on needle 43 gm, continued discharge. C. Weight on needle 99 gm, continued discharge. The 3 gm weight on needle used by Adrian for tracing A would, he says, be on human skin the stimulus for the sensation of contact. The discharge of impulses lasted about 0.2 sec. At weights above 20 gm a 'distinct prick' is felt on human skin. Discharges as in tracings B and C lasted as long as 20 sec. [From Adrian (1).]

Tower (267) has shown that stimuli to various portions of the field of ramification of the same fiber produce different responses in that one fiber; this introduces another variable in the data presented to the brain increasing the likelihood of precise spatial discrimination peripherally. She worked in the corneoconjunctival region of the cat using a preparation containing but one to three fibers. The stimuli with hairs, needles or glass rods were nearly all well above threshold and would presumably have caused pain at the human cornea. She made oscilloscopic recordings of the action potentials from the preparation, noting that one isolated nerve fiber yielding fairly large impulses fanned out over roughly one fourth of the cornea and some of the adjacent sclera. "Low threshold and slow adaptation characterized the central region of the terminal fields of individual fibers, and rapid adaptation more than high threshold, the peripheral parts." A strong stimulus near the center of the field of a fiber might push the frequency of the response nearly to the limit permitted by the refractory properties of the fiber, namely about 500 per sec. In general the frequency, duration and rate of adaptation of impulses within the field of one fiber were determined by site as well as by intensity of stimulus. When many fibers remained active, the normal situation of course, their fields overlapped in a fashion inextricable to the experimenter. But, presumably, the brain of the subject uses all this information, analyzing signals from fibers excited minimally which encircle fibers excited more vigorously to achieve better localization. The frequency of discharge in the most excited fiber would still reveal the intensity of the stimulus.

Fiber Diameters and Pain Conduction

Gasser (90) and his collaborators also have amassed evidence correlating physiological with anatomical properties of nerve fibers (see his Nobel Lecture, 1946). Their classification is based on the duration and form of the three components of the action potentials in the fibers—the initial negative spike, then the negative and finally the positive after-potentials. Their 'A' fibers embrace all of the medullated fibers in somatic nerves and some in the visceral nerves as well. The 'A' fibers are divisible into five subgroups designated in order of diminishing diameter by the letters alpha through epsilon. The velocity of conduction in these fibers varies directly with the diameter of the axon, ranging between 90 to 115 m per sec. for the largest fibers 16 to 20 μ in diameter

and around 10 m per sec. in the smallest myelinated fibers 2 to 4 μ in diameter (fig. 3). They have called the unmedullated fibers in sensory nerves 'C' fibers; these have a diameter of 2 μ or less and conduct at from 0.6 to 2 m per sec. Each component of a 'C' fiber's action potential lasts much longer than the corresponding part of the action potential of an 'A' fiber. The action potentials in most of the medullated fibers of visceral nerves differ so much from either of these that they have been placed in a separate category and called 'B' fibers. Usually a single elevation is present with no visible negative after potential. Gasser & Erlanger found no such fibers in the dorsal roots.

The more recently introduced designations of Lloyd (178) are also in current use. His Group I fibers from 20 to 12 μ are seen only in muscular branches of nerves; Group II fibers from 12 to 6 μ are seen infrequently in muscular branches but present a large peak in cutaneous nerves; Group III fibers mainly from 4 to 3 μ correspond to 'A' delta and occur in nerves to both muscle and skin; and Group IV are unmyelinated or C fibers.

Of the numerous efforts in animals to correlate pain with certain nerve fibers, the early experiment of Ranson & Billingsley (219) is still one of the more widely cited. As the posterior rootlets enter the spinal cord they divide into a lateral bundle of fine, mostly unmyelinated, fibers and a medial bundle of large fibers. These authors found that after section of the small (lateral) fibers stimulation of the remainder no longer evoked the 'pain reflexes' of struggling, altered breathing and arterial pressure, whereas after section of the large (medial) fibers these reflexes persisted. More specifically pain impulses have been associated both with the delta-epsilon 'A' fibers and with the 'C' fibers. The most direct evidence of association of pain with impulses in delta-epsilon fibers was obtained by Heinbecker et al. (125) from the cutaneous nerves of a man's leg which was later amputated. No sensation was evoked at operative exposure of the nerves until stimuli at a frequency of 12 per 5 sec. caused grimacing and a verbal report of unequivocal pain (as if he were being whipped). At the effective stimulus parameters there was a clear-cut delta elevation in the action potential from a companion nerve in the leg, but no 'C' fiber activity. The threshold for the 'C' fiber elevation in this nerve was five times as high. Earlier Bishop & Heinbecker (28) had established in animals that the thresholds of response to electrical stimulation of fibers in peripheral nerve trunks varied inversely with the fiber diameter. So in their study in

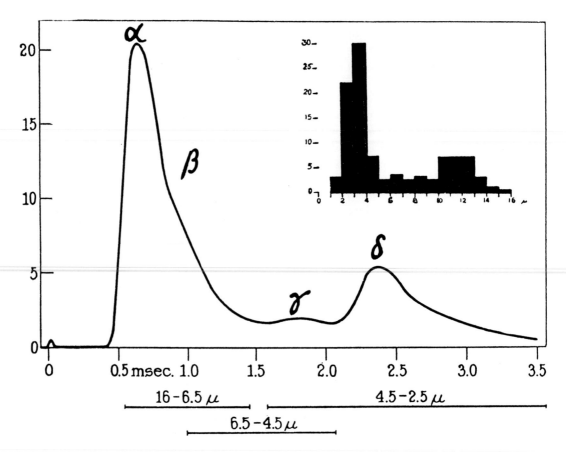

FIG. 3. Action potential form in a human sensory nerve. This curve was calculated from the fiber distributions. *Inset graph*, upper right, gives fiber distribution for the medial cutaneous nerve as fiber diameters. Beneath the curve is indicated the position of the axon potentials according to diameters of fibers, not axons. [From Gasser (89).]

man, since no pain had been caused by weaker stimuli activating fibers conducting more rapidly and at lower threshold than the delta-epsilon group, the authors thought these fibers were specific in their pain-producing power. Almost as direct evidence to nearly the same effect has been secured by Brookhart *et al.* (34) from the tooth pulp in cats and man, a structure chosen because of the assumption that pain is the only sensation experienced when it is stimulated. These workers saw in the cats the unmyelinated terminal arborizations join to form axons 1.5 to 6 μ in diameter with a median at 3 μ; the axons were nearly all invested with a myelin sheath, a fact already observed in human tooth pulp by Brashear (33). Brookhart *et al.* found that strength-duration curves of responses upon tooth pulp stimulation in both cat and man were similar to those obtained for 'A' gamma-delta fibers in the cat's saphenous nerve and markedly different from the 'A' alpha and 'C' fibers in the same

nerve. The index of excitation in the cat was the action potential recorded from the saphenous or trigeminal nerve and in man was the minimal sensation of pain. The conduction velocity of the responses in the cat's mandibular nerve ranged from 30 to 45 m per sec., putting them well into the 'A' gamma group. [The delta component conducts at 15 to 20 m per sec., according to Gasser (89).]

The strength of stimulus required to produce 'C' fiber activation *in vivo* has not been attained in critical human study, but Clark *et al.* (42) have shown that activity in these fibers also is correlated with nociceptive reflexes. Thus in deeply anesthetized animals a stimulus exciting 'C' plus 'A' fibers was followed by much larger reflexes than one exciting only 'A' fibers. Moreover the 'A' fiber conduction was not necessary for the production of reflexes which could still be evoked after block of all 'A' fibers by a pneumatic cuff surrounding the nerve. Zotterman (315) recorded only 'A' delta and 'C' fiber activity from the saphenous nerve of a cat when the corresponding skin was burned by a special stimulus applied without mechanical deformation of the surface. He obtained similar records upon etching the skin with acids. Maruhashi *et al.* (185) have recently studied preparations of single afferent fibers in the cat so that their conclusions as to fiber size are derived from direct measurement. They found one group of large and another of small 'nociceptive' fibers in the range 3 to 11 μ. Activity in such fibers was evoked by a pin prick or strong pull on a hair. The receptive field of a fiber in the toe pad was 2 x 2 to 3 x 3 mm; it was about 10 times larger in a hairy area. The extent of the field was clearly defined and within it the receptive spots were densely distributed. Following the stimuli used in these studies the impulse discharges were phasic and ended in about 0.2 sec.; but if a scalded area was stimulated mechanically a protracted after-discharge was present in both small myelinated and unmyelinated fibers.

Double Pain Responses or Second Pain

From the foregoing type of observation it has been concluded that pain is conducted in medullated 'A' fibers at 15 to 45 m per sec. and in unmyelinated 'C' fibers at less than 2 m per sec. The gap between the two groups of impulses is conceivably sufficient to permit a perceptible differentiation between the slow and the fast group and, indeed, long before the speeds of conduction in sensory nerves were known a double pain response to a single stimulus was described by many observers. Thus Rosenbach (225) in 1884 and Gad & Goldscheider in 1892 (86) thought the response to a pin was an immediate sensation of prick followed after an interval without sensation by a second prick. Thunberg (264) investigated what he considered to be two separate prick sensations with a great difference in reaction time between the two. Zotterman in 1933 (314) first associated the 'second' pain with 'C' fiber conduction. He confirmed the observation by Lewis *et al.* (173) that a compression cuff around the arm blocking the circulation causes early paralysis of the sense of touch, alters the pain sense, but does not cause analgesia even after arrest for 40 min. These two groups of workers fell in line with Gasser & Erlanger's (91) conclusion that arrest of the blood flow to the nerves causes a progressive loss of their function in accordance with the character of the fiber. The first fibers blocked are those in the 'A' delta elevation; with progression of asphyxia the larger medullated 'A' fibers are next affected; finally

after even the largest fibers are no longer conducting the 'C' fibers are blocked. Zotterman, using his compression cuff to switch off all the 'A' fibers, found that the pain which persists is felt only after a delay, and his measurement of the time of this delay agreed well with the reaction time for 'second' pain recorded by Thunberg. The conduction velocity in the sensory fibers (calculated from the reaction time) was not lower than 0.5 m per sec. which is only slightly below the conduction rate of the slowest 'C' fibers in mammalian nerves observed by Erlanger & Gasser. Upon checking the differences in time of appearance of the second pain in relation to the site stimulated, Lewis & Pochin (174) found the expected shorter time when thigh rather than toe was the area pricked. Thus calculated, the rate of conduction in the limb of the second response was again at the 'C' fiber speed of 0.5 to 1 m per sec. Confirmatory evidence of this concept has arisen from studies upon cocainization of nerve fibers. Gasser (89) found this drug blocked the 'C' fibers in his animals early, and then blocked the medullated 'A' fibers in the same way as asphyxia, i.e. beginning first with the smallest. He points out that "it is misleading to state that asphyxia blocks the large fibers first, while cocaine blocks the small fibers first." But cocaine does block the 'C' group before the 'A' group, and corresponding with this Lewis & Pochin (174) found that in man "cocaine reduces and ultimately abolishes the second pain response, before it similarly affects the first pain response." They are both agreed that there are great difficulties with any further attempt to correlate in a clear-cut way sensory function and fiber size, that the fibers belonging to different modalities must be widely distributed throughout the various fiber sizes and that there seems to be little possibility of associating any one sensation with an elevation in the electroneurogram. Sinclair & Hinshaw (248, 249), after an extensive study of compression and pressure block of peripheral nerves in man, subscribe wholeheartedly to the notion that such association is impossible. Even after a large number of experiments with procaine they found it impossible to generalize as to the order of loss of the various modalities of touch, pain, warmth and cold since by suitable adjustment of the experimental conditions "almost any desired order of sensory loss may be recorded."

Lewis (171) and Gasser (89) are agreed that both the fast and slow impulses evoke the same quality of sensation. Lewis adds that brief noxious stimulation produces the sensation of 'pricking' and that a prolonged noxious stimulation elicits a sense of 'burning.'

Hardy *et al.* (118, p. 133) on the other hand think there are two different qualities of pain independent of the duration of stimulation, that 'pricking' pain is predominantly 'fast' and primarily conveyed by myelinated fibers, whereas 'burning' pain is predominantly 'slow' and conveyed by unmyelinated fibers. Sinclair & Hinshaw (248, 249) had made a similar statement, but had added that "in the experience of pin prick, the factor which determines whether the subject reports a feeling of pain or not is probably not the initial prick conveyed by fast fibers, but what we may term 'unpleasantness' which arrives subsequently by the slower fibers." They also state that "after the slow unpleasantness is removed in pressure blocks there is a period when it is exceedingly difficult to determine whether a pin prick should be reported as 'sharp' or as 'sharp and painful'."

Landau & Bishop (150) have extended the analysis of pain sensation by the techniques of differential block by cuff pressure and procaine to subcutaneous tissue, periosteum, muscle and fascia. They elicited pain by both electrical stimulation and chemical inflammation. They concluded that the presumably 'C' fiber pain is "of slower onset, but of severer and more penetrating character and of longer after-effect." Periosteum, muscle and veins were found to be supplied by fibers of both types, whereas inflammatory pain from the subcutaneous injection of turpentine and from bee stings, as well as the pain following injection of 5 per cent sodium chloride solution, was assigned almost entirely to activity in 'C' fibers. Detailed consideration of their results reveals some inconsistencies, however; thus with procaine block to these deep endings which should block 'C' before delta fibers "only a partial loss of deep pain results before prick is blocked." The pricking pain should have been the last to go if the authors' hypothesis were to be fully confirmed.

Further evidence that two different qualities of pain may result from different types of responses of the same peripheral nerve was obtained by Pattle & Weddell (206) in an experiment which included direct exposure of one of Weddell's own digital nerves. The threshold sensation following single graded condenser shocks to the nerve was a "pain of unpleasant quality like a wasp sting." This response occurred at all strengths of shock from 0.1 to 6 μf capacity of condenser. But the discharge of a condenser of 7 μf capacity "produced a long-lasting, severe, aching pain, which was completely different in quality from the wasp sting reaction." The reaction time from stimulus to closure of an electrical contact by the sub-

ject was exactly 1.27 sec. for each type of pain, however. The study was carried out on a nerve in which only a few fibers appeared to be responding to stimuli following injection of the local anesthetic procaine which produced complete insensitivity of the whole distal phalanx of the finger. The two types of pain here are however manifestly different from the experiences recorded in experimental studies on double pain from the intact skin.

An astute maneuver to measure the conduction time for human pain sensation which eliminates the time from cerebrum to motor response has been described by Gordon & Whitteridge (106). The alpha rhythm of the human EEG can be disturbed by unexpected stimulus to the skin and in individuals in whom this response was clear-cut these workers found that the time between painful stimulus and alpha interruption averaged about 0.25 sec. at both normal fingers and toes. The delay was much greater when the base of finger or toe was compressed for an hour or more by a cuff occluding its blood supply. It averaged 1.04 sec. from the asphyxiated finger and 1.40 sec. from the asphyxiated toe. In the latter state they measured the fiber conduction time for the 'second' pain at about 1 m per sec.

Sinclair & Hinshaw (248, 250) and Sinclair (247) have put forward some sharp and cogent criticisms of much of this work on double pain and 'second' pain, pointing out that a delay between stimulus and perception of pain also occurs in procaine blocks, a situation in which the slowly conducting fibers are supposed to fail first. Critical scrutiny of the data obtained during the asphyxia caused by cuff compression also leads to doubts regarding the original interpretation.

Thus, Lewis & Pochin's (174) average figures in two subjects for appearance of second pain upon pin prick of a normal finger and toe and for appearance of delayed pain after a cuff block were about the same at 1.2 sec. But when each subject is considered separately, there is a statistically significant difference in both of them between the control and asphyxial readings. Moreover, Lewis & Pochin (174) found after cuff asphyxia that the latency of the pain response, the reaction time, rises abruptly from 0.3 sec. to be constant at 1.5 sec. Sinclair & Hinshaw (250) have recorded delays much in excess of this figure up to 5 sec.—longer than would be required for conduction from finger to brain of any normal 'C' fiber. Ashby (11) has likewise pointed out many recorded instances of much longer delays in tabes, and I have seen one such striking patient who showed a delay greater than 3 sec. upon stimulation of the forearm. If the delayed pain under abnormal conditions such as asphyxia is indeed pure 'C' fiber pain, then the abrupt rise in latency from 0.3 to 1.5 sec. described by Lewis & Pochin is consonant with the final failure of conduction in 'A' delta fibers. However, Wortis *et al.* (312) did not confirm this abrupt change; they found delays in the pain response at intervals during asphyxial compression studies in man to vary upon stimulus to the foot from 0.9 to 1.7 sec. Another major criticism rests upon the fact that reaction time to pain is influenced greatly by the intensity of the stimulus, there being a hyperbolic decrease in time with increasing intensity according to Piéron (212) and Eichler (73). In general the intensity of stimulus has not been maintained constant in the studies tending to identify delayed pain under abnormal conditions with second pain under normal conditions. Even the less complex sensation, touch, exhibits a reaction time which varies inversely with the intensity of the stimulus. It also varies with the cross sectional area of the stimulus and changes from day to day, from subject to subject and from testing site to testing site (162). Likewise thermal stimuli even when measured from the threshold intensity rather than from an absolute zero show the same type of variation as shown by Lele & Sinclair (161). Since the reaction time represents the sum total for initiation of conduction, for actual conduction over both afferent and efferent paths, for perception and judgement and for synaptic transmission, the assumption that changes in the reaction time are due to changes only in afferent conduction rate would seem unwarranted.

It will be noted that much of the work on second pain and double pain in nerve fibers has been carried out in abnormal situations of ischemia, pharmacologic insult or disease. Weddell *et al.* (289) have suggested that the delay in these abnormal conditions need not depend on the existence of two discrete groups of fibers conducting at different rates and that the delay could occur in the central rather than the peripheral nervous system as a consequence of simplification of the impulse pattern reaching the brain. Such an explanation fits more satisfactorily with the observation of gross variability in the delay and its occurrence with all maneuvers depressing conduction.

However, such an explanation does not account for the occurrence of second pain under normal conditions. I have never personally been able to convince myself that I could perceive two separate pains in response to a single noxious stimulus even after following Gasser's (89) prescription of flipping the back of my finger against a hot incandescent light bulb or metal hot water faucet. Weddell (personal communication) has had the same trouble. And it has been a mystery to us how Thunberg (264) and Lewis & Pochin (174) could measure such precise reaction times for a sensation we could not consistently discern.

It was with some relief that I read of Jones' (137) experiments. When she applied a rigidly mounted needle algesimeter calibrated in 0.25 gm steps to three different spots on the dorsal forearm of each of eight subjects, not one of them reported a double pain after any stimulus. (The point of the needle had been sharpened under a microscope to minimize the stimulation of pressure sensation.) The needles were not held by hand, as one infers was done by previous investigators, because the pain stimulus might vary. In another effort to elicit double pain she permitted the needle to remain at the site evoking a response. These 'adaptation trials' were carried out at the threshold for pain, 1 gm above threshold, and in four highly practiced subjects at 2 gm above threshold. The pain did not vary in a smooth way; instead "the course of adaptation showed fluctuations; in about one-fifth of the trials there were only two peaks which naive observers might possibly have interpreted as double pain." The four experienced subjects looked carefully for possible double pain, and with suprathreshold stimuli they reported it twice out of 20 trials; in two other trials there were other types of double sensation, one of cold and pain and another of pressure and pain. The possibility exists that a suprathreshold stimulus may excite two discrete receptors sequentially and Jones suggests this interpretation of the results. Woollard *et al.* (310) had already correlated 'first pain' with penetration of the needle point into the epidermis and 'second pain' with attainment by the point of dermal levels. This they did by measuring on the needle the depth at which each sensation was provoked and then correlating this with an actual histologic study of the skin in that area.

Thresholds to the pain upon electrical stimulus with a square-wave pulse from a Grass stimulator were also studied by Jones in 120 trials on each of the four experienced subjects. No double pain and no single delayed pains were felt. Jones regards this form of stimulus as well suited to analysis of the double pain hypothesis because if more than one receptor is stimulated they are all stimulated simultaneously. She points out that no experimenter has reported double pain with a single electric stimulus. Heat, on the contrary, one of the more effective stimuli in eliciting double pain, does continue to penetrate deeper into the tissues and to stimulate more remote receptors even after the stimulus is removed. Landau & Bishop (150) also found in eight normal, unprejudiced subjects "only three who could recognize a second pain response when the skin was tested with heat or brief mechanical stimuli." They ascribe the failure of brief stimuli to evoke delayed pain to a masking effect of the pricking pain. In any event it would seem to me that, since 'C' fiber activation in animals requires a much more powerful stimulus, Jones' studies at threshold levels and up to 4 gm above threshold may never have activated these fibers.

It would thus appear that the whole subject of pain conduction by nerve fibers of specific size is worthy of careful review. The technique of Dawson & Scott (58) of recording nerve action potentials through the intact skin in man may increase the feasibility of securing the crucial information. The method has already yielded valuable data on this score in the hands of Magladery et al. (183) who have found that the ischemia of cuff occlusion has a generalized depressant effect on the conduction in both afferent and efferent 'A' fibers in peripheral nerve trunks in man. They studied oscilloscopic records of the action potentials and correlated these with serial sensorimotor examinations as the cuff was inflated and deflated. Thus 17 min. after the onset of ischemia voluntary power was still relatively normal. But recognition "of all forms of sensory stimuli except those producing deep pain was diminished." With this one exception, no subject found one sensory modality impaired disproportionately to another. Figure 4 taken from their work shows the steady reduction in the potential from the rapidly conducting fibers as the ischemia continued. No 'C' fiber potentials appear in this record, obtained after a 'maximal single shock' to the ulnar nerve in the low forearm with recording over the ulnar nerve above the elbow.

In an important study in man by Collins, Randt & Nulsen (unpublished observations), the exposed sural nerve is being stimulated distally while action potentials are recorded oscilloscopically from a more proximal position. Such studies immediately precede and follow therapeutic incisions into the pain pathways of the spinal cord. Reporting on the five patients thus far studied, they say tentatively that the sensation corresponding to an 'A' gamma-delta elevation on the oscilloscope has been equivocal—

not clear-cut pain. But at the first intimation of 'C' fiber activation the patients have had severe pain; this has been the case also even if 'A' fiber conduction was profoundly depressed by local cooling of the nerve.

In relation to double pain an effort has been made to generalize even more widely regarding sense organs supplied by nerve fibers of significantly varying diameters by Katsuki et al. (139). They say that the thin fibers carry impulses from receptor elements of lower threshold to physiologic stimuli with a lower rate of adaptation, a lower maximal frequency of discharge and a greater tendency to continuous or spontaneous firing. Bullock (36) has drawn attention to the applicability of this principle to nine different sense organs, the thin fibers supplying the more sensitive and tonic, the thick fibers the more discriminating and phasic receptors. However his attempt to bring pain fibers into this concept stands up only in the roughest way under close scrutiny. He cites Maruhashi et al. in his support, but these workers actually describe distinct tonic or phasic behavior mainly in two groups of small myelinated nociceptive fibers in the toad all within

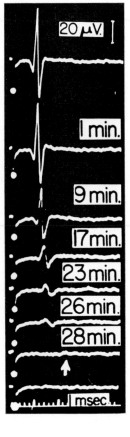

FIG. 4. Nerve action potentials in man following maximal single shocks to ulnar nerve in low forearm. Surface recording over ulnar nerve above elbow. Pressure cuff on upper forearm inflated to 200 mm Hg. *Top record*, before ischemia; *lower records*, the stated number of minutes after onset of ischemia. Time: 1 and 5 msec. [From Magladery et al. (183).]

the range of 3 to 5 μ in diameter Moreover the group responding tonically had a higher maximal frequency of discharge than that responding in phasic fashion. In line with Bullock's thought, however, was the finding in both these groups of lower maximal frequency than in the large myelinated nociceptive fibers 6 to 9 μ in diameter. These generally gave a phasic discharge to light pin prick, ending about 0.2 sec. after the onset of the stimulus. It is apparent that useful generalizations from the welter of facts before us regarding pain and impulses in nerve fibers are difficult.

PAIN IN ABNORMAL ANATOMICAL STATES AT PERIPHERY

Division of Cutaneous Nerves

Both the quality and the degree of pain sensibility become altered following injury to nervous pathways concerned with its conduction. The most painstaking and best controlled studies of the changes have been made by investigators who divided and then sutured the cut ends of one or more cutaneous nerves in themselves. They then followed the sensory status during the period of recovery. These workers included Rivers & Head (223), Trotter & Davies (270), Boring (30), Sharpey-Schafer (245) and Lanier *et al.* (157). All but the first group tended to agree with Trotter & Davies that "the changes consequent upon depriving a piece of skin of its nerve supply are distributed in a central area of absolute loss, surrounded by a zone of much less loss which is slight toward the periphery and deepens toward the center." They also observed that the "defect of sensibility to pain is precisely similar in character and distribution to the defects in sensibility to cold, to heat and to touch." In addition, Trotter & Davies found that there was an altered quality to many sensory stimuli on the tenth to twelfth postoperative day, lasting up to the sixth or eighth week. This developed in spotty, irregular fashion largely peripheral to the analgesic zone in the previously hypalgesic or so-called intermediate zone. Later a more extensive area of altered quality of sensation came on when regeneration began.

In the first 'hyperalgesic' stage they found that pain after pinprick has an abnormally unpleasant quality, radiates diffusely, tends to provoke a motor response, is poorly localized or may be a persistent severe burning which may reappear spontaneously afterwards. Two point discrimination is reduced in

the area and touch, although evoked only by stimuli normally above the threshold, may then have a painful quality. In the later stage of regeneration the same qualitative abnormalities can be elicited from the previously analgesic zone. These abnormal features may persist for many months and then gradually decline. In general these reports have been well confirmed but their significance remains widely debated and the mechanisms of production obscure. The names applied to the situation have been as varied as the hypotheses; 'hyperpathia', 'intensification', 'dyesthesia', 'over-reaction' and 'paradoxical pain' have been used. Hyperalgesia is probably the least appropriate term since it implies a lowered threshold to pain which is in fact usually not the case in this condition.

The development of the early phase of hyperpathia was correlated by Pollock (214) with the ingrowth of fibers from the adjoining peripheral nerves for two reasons: *a*) the early hyperpathia (and the other recovery of sensation) appears long before regenerating fibers could reach the skin; and *b*) such sensation is not lost if the regenerating nerve trunk is cut a second time. Weddell and associates (285) have in fact demonstrated unmyelinated fibers growing out from the intermediate into the originally anesthetic zone using methylene blue stain in man. More recently Weddell and associates (personal communication) have acquired evidence that a denervated sector of the cornea is reinnervated from three sources of nerve supply.

Head & Sherren (122) hypothecated that the normal sensations were mediated by 'epicritic' groups of nerves and that the abnormal qualities ensued only when 'protopathic' fibers were excited. Their complex formulation completely failed to fit the facts brought out by each of the succeeding workers who studied their own sensations before and after deliberate cutaneous nerve section. Cobb (46) in his work on patients with peripheral nerve injuries after World War I drew attention to the fact that Head's alleged areas of dissociation of sensibilities arose from comparing stimuli which were not quantitatively equivalent. He found, for example, that the areas of sensory loss were coextensive if one used a soft brush to test cutaneous touch and a needle point at 15 gm pressure for pain. Suffice it to say that despite the cogency of the criticisms of all of these workers it has required the devastating verbal scythe of Walshe (282), giving incisiveness to his keen critical powers, to sweep from the literature favorable reference to the 'protopathic' and 'epicritic' nervous systems of Head and associates. We are still left with the necessity of explaining the above abnormal features of the sensory response. Boring (30, p. 92) agrees with Head to this extent: the abnormal sensory intensity is achieved by the removal of an inhibition. More recently Landau & Bishop have identified the type of pain which they consider to be transmitted over normal 'C' fibers with the 'protopathic' forms of sensation of Head *et al.* (121) and conclude that block of delta-pain fiber responses releases "the perception of 'C' fiber pain in the otherwise normal subject."

An alternative explanation has been put forward by Weddell *et al.* (289) on the basis of their histologic studies of human skin at 39 sites from which the above abnormal qualities of pain were induced. Control studies were made at 20 other sites in cutaneous scars from which the pain did not have the abnormal unpleasant quality. In the former group the nerve nets and terminals were isolated from their neighbors instead of interweaving with them as occurs normally, and as was seen in those reinnervated scars which showed no abnormal quality in the senations aroused from them. Normally, as Boring (30, p. 95) first deduced, "single sensory spots are innervated by more than one nerve fiber and the multiple innervation is projected upon the central nervous system as multiple excitations." Weddell (285) demonstrated this, correlating neurophysiologic with clinical findings, and Weddell *et al.* (289) conclude that the complex pattern of impulses arising from such multiple innervation is essential to the normal quality of pain "of everyday experience," whereas if only a single pain fiber or terminal is excited then the pain is of characteristic unpleasant quality. This conclusion, that reduction in the density of innervation of an area will cause alteration in the quality of pain, has likewise been reached independently by Livingston (177). In a patient recovering from an injury to the median nerve at the wrist there was one area in which pain was of normal type until one of the main nerve trunks was blocked with procaine, whereupon pinprick became peculiarly unpleasant. This state was exacerbated when two of the three nerves were blocked simultaneously. Weddell *et al.* (289) have also studied the alterations in pain sensibility in themselves upon compression of the upper limb with a sphygmomanometer cuff. They found the first change to appear was a relatively abrupt alteration in the quality of the pain upon a needle prick; when fully developed at about the thirtieth minute of compression the prick caused a

"singularly unpleasant sensory experience," a slow swelling burning sting lasting for as long as 10 sec. and giving rise to a withdrawal reflex difficult to control. There was also an increasing interval between the application of the stimulus and its perception. They concluded that these typical features of 'unpleasant pain' were to be correlated with a gradual reduction in the number of fibers conducting impulses as the compression continued.

Isolation of the pain nets appeared to have no effect on the threshold of pain sensibility. In a number of biopsies these workers saw abnormal appearances of the nerve endings, ellipsoidal expansions which they called growth cones. The lowest thresholds to pain occurred in their patients in whom such growth cones lay just beneath the basal layer of epidermis. In such cases the mere passing of a camel's hair brush across the area was painful.

Foerster had earlier (77) suggested that the peculiar abnormalities of sensation (his hyperpathia) arose from the stimulation of an isolated 'pain point.' The similarity between this explanation and that of Weddell *et al.* is only superficial, however, because Foerster contended that as soon as other senory modalities such as touch and pressure were felt the hyperpathia began to recede, a viewpoint which is simply not substantiated by the observations of others. The sites at which pain has the abnormal quality are not directly correlated with anesthesia to touch. Figure 5 shows the results of an examination in which more spots hypersensitive to pinprick were in fact found outside of the anesthetic zone. Similarly Lanier *et al.* (157) in their study found an area in which, although touch sensibility was perfect, pain sensibility was diminished and unpleasant pain could be elicited from this region.

Figure 5 also illustrates another observation of Trotter & Davies (270, p. 170), namely that such patterns of 'hyperalgesia,' as they called it, were associated with veins. They say that often the skin over the vein itself was the most sensitive part of the patch. Although Cobb also thought that "these painful spots were usually along the course of a superficial vein," the explanation of this is unclear. Trotter & Davies originally regarded the hyperalgesia as a "secondary process due to the presence of some irritating substance produced as the result of the division and degeneration of the nerve."

But, in the light of another 17 years of rumination on the subject, Trotter (269) thought that the lack of complete insulation of regenerating nerve fibers would explain the raised threshold to stimuli and the

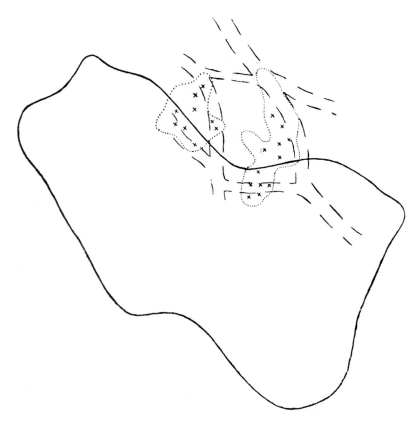

FIG. 5. Hyperpathia in relation to anesthesia following section of a cutaneous nerve. Examination 34 days after division of middle cutaneous nerve of thigh. *Within the continuous line:* anesthesia to camel's hair brush. *Within the dotted lines:* two areas abnormally sensitive to pin. *Broken lines* show course of superficial veins; *spots marked* X show maximal sensitivity to pin prick. [From Trotter & Davies (270).]

exaggerated explosive type of response upon effectual stimulation. Accompanying this concept was his notion that many types of fiber in their poorly insulated regenerating phase may conduct impulses giving rise to pain, since he presumed that pain was the only sensation evoked from the uninsulated, i.e. naked, unmyelinated end organs. He goes on to say, "With the advance of regeneration the fibers serving touch, heat and cold, become once more connected with end-organs, and then their insulation, by the junction of the neurilemma with the capsule of the end-organ, can be completed. The completely insulated fiber, having lost its temporary resemblance to the pain fiber, becomes once more sensitive to the finer stimuli and ceases to yield exaggerated responses." Later work already discussed which demonstrates the capacity of naked unmyelinated endings to transmit impulses concerned with touch cuts the ground from under the latter part of this reasoning, but the concept of lack of insulation has become more

appealing since the work of Granit *et al.* (109). These investigators showed that a generalized breakdown in 'insulation' occurs at the site of injury to the sciatic nerve in cats. This is so striking when the nerve is cut across that impulses set up in spinal ventral (motor) rootlets are transmitted to the sensory fibers at the cut and can be picked up via an oscilloscope from the dorsal (sensory) rootlets of the same segment. Such an 'artificial synapse' or 'fiber interaction' also develops at the crush of a knot tightened around a nerve and even appears from time to time after moderate pressures of 50 to 110 gm against a nerve insufficient to stop conduction beyond the point of compression. Granit *et al.* have assumed that pain fibers would be among the most easily excited by fiber interaction. These observations clearly present a mechanism whereby impulses traversing one fiber may abnormally pass to many at a site of injury, thereby permitting abnormal central excitation.

Hyperalgesic State After Trauma

We may now consider the special studies of Lewis (171) on the hyperalgesic state provoked in skin by controlled scratching, heat, freezing, ultraviolet light, or chemical or electrical irritation. These varied forms of trauma all produce a skin which is hyperalgesic in the strict sense of the word, i.e. a lighter needle prick will cause pain from it than from corresponding normal skin. In addition, an effective prick gives unusually intense, diffuse and long-lasting pain. Spontaneous pain is present which is worsened by relatively small amounts of warmth, more marked cooling or light contacts such as those from clothing. The zone of hyperalgesia gradually spreads after the injury—for example five minutes of faradization of the skin a little above the wrist provoked the above change over an area 18 cm long with a maximal width of 7 cm, an extent achieved within 11 min. (171, p. 69). The soreness in the area lasted several hours. Some days later repetition of the stimulation procedure led to nearly the same pattern of hyperalgesic zone. In general, such zones tend to correspond to the entire area of a cutaneous nerve, as shown by their agreement with the area of sensory elimination after anesthetic block of the nerve trunk. Moreover, direct stimulation of the cutaneous nerve trunk or any of its smaller branches will evoke the typical hyperalgesic pattern. Lewis advanced the view that a pain-producing substance developed at the site of injury which, by stimulus to local nerves, provoked the reaction over the whole arborization of a single cutaneous nerve. He also hypothecated that such reactions must be mediated by a new and distinct system of fibers which he called 'nocifensor' nerves. He was especially led to this conclusion by the fact that the pain terminals arising from a single nerve fiber have never been demonstrated histologically to cover so large an area as, e.g. 7 x 18 cm on the forearm. Maruhashi et al. (185) have come close to this electrophysiologically however. They found individual afferent fibers in the cat innervating oval areas ranging from 3 x 5 to 5 x 9 cm. Such fibers to which they give the special designation 'wide receptive fibers' were abundant in all skin nerves examined; they ranged from 2 to 5 μ in diameter. These fibers are probably not identifiable with the nocifensor system since afferent impulses can be evoked in them by 'extremely light touch' to the skin or to a hair in the fiber's large receptive field. Moreover such responses persist in areas 'deafferented' by excision of five lumbar root ganglia 3 to

4 wk. before the experiment. On the contrary the post-traumatic hyperalgesia of Lewis disappears from zones denervated by posterior rhizotomy. In the absence of any anatomical demonstration of an entirely different system of fibers specialized to mediate the hyperalgesic spread, this concept of nocifensor fibers has won little support. Walshe (282) and White & Sweet (296, p. 96) may be consulted for further arguments *pro* but mainly *con*.

CHEMICAL EXCITANTS OF PAIN

The concept that chemicals liberated at the site of injury provoke pain has been supported experimentally by Lewis (171, pp. 113 to 115). His extracts of freshly excised human skin caused pain when injected in tiny quantities intradermally. He thought the substance was not histamine since he found this to give itching rather than pain when it was pricked into the skin even in such high concentration as 1:30. Rosenthal (226), however, found that "as little as fifty-four molecules of histamine" injected intradermally will cause pain, and in a series of papers with several collaborators has presented evidence that histamine or a similar substance is the chemical mediator for cutaneous pain. Moreover Habgood's (113) analyses of the substance liberated upon antidromic stimulation of frog cutaneous nerve pointed toward histamine or an 'H-substance.' In addition he demonstrated that the chemical so produced could often evoke spontaneous discharge from an adjacent nerve twig (fig. 6). That a similar phenomenon may take place in man is intimated by Foerster's observations upon stimulation of distal ends of divided posterior roots at operation. This provoked burning pain in the skin which was eliminated by division of adjoining posterior roots. If then antidromically-induced liberation of a chemical which stimulates nerve endings will activate a separate but overlapping sensory unit, a wide area would be involved by a continuation of this process. The extent of the spread would tend to increase with the extent and severity of the original injury. And since Lewis had already obtained hyperalgesia by antidromic stimulation of cutaneous nerves in man, its explanation would not require either a separate system of nocifensor nerves or the wide receptive fibers of Maruhashi et al. (185).

The technique of applying fluids to the exposed base of a blister caused by cantharidin or heat, developed by Keele and his associates, has enabled

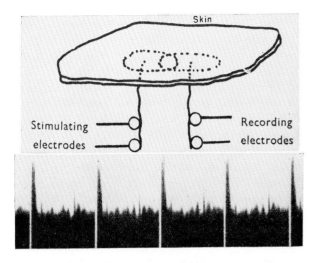

FIG. 6. Double nerve preparation from frog's skin showing chemical transmission of impulse from one nerve to the other. Antidromic stimulation of the peripheral end of one cutaneous nerve was often evoked by electrical stimulation of an adjoining cutaneous nerve with an overlapping field, the responses appearing either during or after the antidromic stimulation. The nature of the discharges is shown in the photograph of an action potential. *Vertical white lines* are synchronous with shock artefact and are 90 msec. apart; a succession of two fast spikes appears 3 to 4 msec. later; then one fast, four slow, one fast and two slow impulses regularly succeed in the recording electrodes following each stimulus to the other nerve. Direct conduction from one nerve trunk to the other and spread of current could be excluded. [From Habgood (113).]

them to study effectively the pain produced by chemicals. The method has given them more consistent results than intradermal injection or pricking of the skin through a drop of solution on it. They have demonstrated that tiny amounts of three identified substances found in tissues provoke pain when applied to the area exposed after removal of blistered skin. Both acetylcholine and histamine in concentrations of 10^{-5} gm per ml, and 5-hydroxytryptamine (serotonin) even in amounts as low as 10^{-8} gm per ml cause pain. The time of onset and duration of the pain are different and characteristic for each of the three. The two latter substances have already been associated with injured tissue, serotonin with platelet breakdown. Saline extracts of rat and human skin made by these workers were found to contain 5×10^{-6} gm per ml of histamine and to cause prolonged pain when applied to a blister base. Histamine alone in such concentration caused only itching.

The Keele group has found an additional pain-producing substance (PPS) in the blister fluid itself as well as in human plasma, serum and protein-rich inflammatory fluids obtained from pleural, peri-

toneal, joint or hydrocoele cavities (10). The PPS shows the peculiar behavior of appearing in these fluids only after they are 'activated' by contact with glass; but following activation the capacity to evoke pain declines rapidly to less than 10 percent of the peak within an hour at room temperature. The pain-producing activity of PPS correlates well with ability to cause contraction of the isolated rat uterus. By applications of this convenient method as well as by other tests they showed PPS to be different from serotonin and histamine and to resemble the polypeptide bradykinin more closely than any other substance yet tested. Bovine bradykinin produced pain in man indistinguishable from that of PPS in concentrations as low as 10^{-5} gm per ml. A continuation of this type of study may lead to knowledge of the actual substances which are stimulating pain endings *in vivo*. In general the minutiae of the mechanisms whereby stimuli are transduced into nervous impulses remain wide open for investigation.

POSTERIOR AND ANTERIOR ROOTS

The distribution of the nerve fibers transmitting pain via each posterior root has been largely worked out for the cutaneous supply. Various diagrams of these so-called dermatomes obtained by a number of methods have been collected by White & Sweet (296, pp. 26 to 30); such data are more fragmentary for the deeper structures (296, pp. 22 and 23). The possibility that afferent fibers may also enter the cord by way of the anterior roots has continued to be supported by bits of evidence over the past 75 years. White & Sweet (296, pp. 31 to 36) have collected and analyzed their own and others' data on this subject. Studies not mentioned in that account include those of Maruhashi *et al.* (185), who measured the size of small myelinated fibers they found associated with ganglion cells on the course of ventral roots in cats. These practically coincided with their afferent fibers "with wide receptive field" (discussed above), and they regard it as "certain that these fibers provide an exception to the Bell-Magendie law." However, these fibers were stimulated by touch rather than noxious maneuvers. We were unable to find *a*) record of any patient in whom anterior rhizotomy stopped pain unassociated with muscle spasm, *b*) report of altered response to objective sensory tests after anterior rhizotomy or *c*) written account of failure to stop pain by posterior rhizotomy followed by success after a later anterior rhizotomy. We are hence without positive evidence that pain impulses in clinically significant numbers transverse the anterior roots to enter the spinal cord in man.

PAIN AND AUTONOMIC NERVOUS SYSTEM

This system of nerves was defined by Langley (155) as efferent and distinguished from the somatic nervous system by a peripheral synapse. He was willing to regard as autonomic afferent fibers only "those which give rise to reflexes in autonomic tissues and which are incapable of directly giving rise to sensation." He considered all other afferent fibers somatic. We have since his time become progressively more aware that most of the nerves of gross anatomy named 'autonomic' contain pain fibers. This is true in virtually all of the sympathetic and pelvic parasympathetic nerves to the torso; the distribution of these insofar as they are known has been diagrammatized by White [see figs. 127, 130, 131, 133 and 134 in White & Sweet (296)]. Evidence for the presence of pain fibers in these nerves has been gleaned both upon stimulation and after denervation. These visceral pain fibers differ from autonomic efferents in their probable nonstop course through the paravertebral ganglia to enter the posterior roots of the spinal nerves.

Sympathetic Nerves

The concept that the efferent sympathetic pathways leave the cord only from the lowermost cervical to the upper lumbar segments and enter the sympathetic chain via the white rami communicantes is so well-established that it has led to ready acceptance of Langley's statements that the afferent fibers travelling with the sympathetic nerves also return impulses to the spinal cord only by way of these white rami. Thus in one study (156) leading toward this conclusion he deduced that sensory fibers of the cat's major accelerator nerve, the chief sympathetic nerve to the heart, entered the cord only by the top 5 white rami. He found in general that stimulation of the central ends of the gray rami produced "no observable physiological effect" in cats (155). Largely by histologic study of degenerating myelin after section of various nerves he concluded that the cell bodies of the afferent fibers travelling with the sympathetic nerves are only in the posterior root ganglia of the nerves with white rami. For example, upon section of the cervical sympathetic trunk below the superior cervical ganglion he found complete degeneration of the fibers rostral to the cut and extending up to the ganglion (153). This conclusion unfortunately rested on the misconception that there are no nonmedullated afferent fibers (154) which we now know to be wrong. His histologic studies would have failed to demonstrate degeneration in these. Ranson (218) reached the same conclusions, again relying heavily on microscopic studies of myelin degeneration. He said, "Histologically it is possible to trace sensory fibers through the sympathetic system because of their relatively large size." These statements were all made before the 'C' fiber days of Gasser and Erlanger, and the conclusions reached from them require modification not only because of that work but also because of later observations in man.

To begin with the neck, we point first to Leriche & Fontaine (168) who studied pain in 10 operations on nine patients by faradic stimulation to the superior cervical ganglion and to the rami communicantes of the second and third cervical nerves. The pain was referred mainly behind the ear and to all the teeth in the lower jaw. Stimulus to the trunk just below the ganglion caused pain of similar locus which was often very intense and might even last several days. Leriche (167) explained this on the basis of stimulation of vasomotor fibers in the area of pain rather than ascribing it to direct stimulation of afferent fibers in the sympathetic nerves. Foerster *et al.* (79, p. 147) likewise produced pain upon stimulation of the cervical sympathetic trunk at every operation thereon undertaken under local anesthesia. The pain was referred somewhere to the ipsilateral side of the neck or head. But they added the observation that stimulus to the caudal cut end of the cervical sympathetic trunk likewise caused pain of the same severity and distribution. From this they concluded that the stimulus was indeed to afferent fibers directly and that these were entering the spinal cord lower down. Frazier's (82) results on stimulation both to carotid vascular plexuses and superior cervical ganglia were less consistent, but in three of four patients upon stimulation at some point in the above zones pain was described in the ipsilateral head or neck. Peet (209) has also produced pain in the trigeminal zone "in a number of patients" upon electrical stimulation of the superior cervical ganglion.

To determine the mechanism of this pain Davis & Pollock (55) carried out a series of experiments in cats. They found no evidence of pain on stimulation of the intact cervical sympathetic trunk, and Langley

(152) and Cleveland (45) found none on stimulation of the caudal end of this trunk after it had been cut below the superior cervical ganglion. These represent another instance in which studies in man yield results relative to pain opposite to conclusions drawn from work in animals. However, the cats of Davis & Pollock behaved as though in pain upon stimulation of the superior cervical ganglion rather than of the trunk below it and they continued to do so after: *a)* all its branches were cut except those to the carotid plexus, *b)* the posterior roots of the upper 12 spinal nerves were cut and *c)* the trigeminal posterior root and the upper 11 spinal anterior roots were cut. Only when *b* was combined with trigeminal posterior rhizotomy were the pain responses stopped. Since Davis & Pollock accepted the evidence of Langley and Ranson that there are no afferent pathways in the cervical sympathetic trunk, they explained their findings on the basis that they were setting up efferent sympathetic impulses. These were presumed to produce a peripheral effect which in turn stimulated the ordinary accepted sensory pathways.

Helson (126) reported critical sensory measurements on patients of Frazier who had undergone trigeminal denervation of the second and third divisions. He found that such patients reacted violently if a hot cylinder was kept on the face more than a few seconds. But in three patients in whom thoracic sympathectomy had been added to the trigeminal rhizotomy he could sear the skin with a hot cylinder and evoke only a sense of pressure. Hence he agreed with Foerster *et al.* (79) that the cervical sympathetic nerves contain afferent fibers.

During our own stimulations of the sympathetic nerves in the neck, pain occurred in 9 of 10 individuals; but it was not elicited from all portions of the trunk or superior cervical ganglion when small bipolar electrodes with points less than 1 mm apart were used, whereas an effective stimulus (at similar voltage) applied to almost any point on a nerve of the cervical plexus caused pain. The details of the responses are summarized by White & Sweet (296, pp. 84 to 89); we concluded that there must be great variation in the distribution of pain fibers within the cervical sympathetics in man which would account for Frazier's vacillating opinion as to whether or not they were present at all (82). However the appearance of pain upon stimulus to central ends, either of cut peripheral sympathetic branches or of cut gray rami communicantes, made it clear that true afferent fibers do occur in them. Activation of efferent sympathetic fibers with subsequent conduction via cranial

sensory fibers in nervus trigeminus or intermedius could be excluded as the mechanism of pain in such instances and in another patient in whom the fifth, seventh and eighth cranial nerves had been divided.

That the sensory inflow back to the cord is not confined to the white rami communicantes was further shown in five other patients in our series in whom stimulus to each member of one or more pairs of rami elicited pain. In several of these each end of each cut ramus was stimulated; pain was elicited only from the end toward the spinal nerve. The pain came immediately upon stimulation, was obtained at about the same threshold and had the same reference as that from the intact ramus. One is unable to distinguish the white from the gray ramus in any given pair, but our results indicate that the pain afferents travelling with the sympathetic are not restricted to the portals of entrance to the central nervous system used by the efferent sympathetic fibers, i.e. the white rami from C8 to the upper lumbar area. Instead pain afferents may perhaps reach the spinal cord via any of the gray or white rami.

The presence of many pain fibers in the cardiac and splanchnic branches of the sympathetic trunk has been widely demonstrated by stimulation. Cannon (38) buried electrodes in contact with the vagus or splanchnic nerves in cats. After the wound was healed stimulation of the latter nerves made the animals restless and the presence of pain was inferred. Vagal stimulation caused only respiratory effects. White *et al.* (295) thought they relieved experimental cardiac pain in dogs by resection of the upper four thoracic ganglia and Davis *et al.* (54) concluded that the pain of their animals on distension of the gall bladder was stopped by splanchnicectomy. Balchum & Weaver (13) reached the same conclusion regarding the pain of gastric distension in the 158 dogs they studied. Leriche & Fontaine (168) provoked pain in the heart and precordial region by stimulation of the lower pole of the stellate ganglion in two patients. In a third patient who had never had angina pectoris, faradization of the stellate ganglion seemed to bring on an intense anginal attack. In at least three other individuals with clinical angina an attack has been elicited during dissection at the stellate ganglion [Jonnesco and Bouchard cited in (168); (167, pp. 375 to 376)]. The effectiveness of upper thoracic sympathectomy in eliminating afferent fibers for pain from the heart is attested by two large series of patients relieved thereby of severe angina pectoris, reported by Lindgren & Olivecrona (176), and by White & Bland (294).

Electrical stimulation of the central end of the cut great splanchnic nerves produced some of the more painful experiences seen in man by Foerster (77, p. 32). When the patient is under spinal anesthesia pain upon splanchnic stimulation is referred somewhere in the chest above the level of analgesia, according to Adson (3) and Leriche (166). On the other hand, in patients in whom we have stimulated the central stump of the greater and lesser splanchnic nerves under local anesthesia the pain has always been referred to the ipsilateral abdomen. Such pain appeared at the same low threshold without delay and was of about the same intensity as that evoked from the twelfth intercostal nerve several centimeters lateral to the rami communicantes (296, p. 83). Such pain also ensued upon stimulation of the twigs of origin of the greater and lesser splanchnic nerves from the sympathetic trunk and from their rostral cut ends. From all of these nerves no sensation occurred upon high voltage stimulation of their caudal cut ends.

Bilateral sympathectomy from the midthoracic through the third lumbar ganglia and including the splanchnic nerves from the T7 ramus to beyond the celiac ganglion (performed for hypertension) yielded a series of patients for study of abdominal visceral sensation by Ray & Neill (221). They found the pain sense absent in these patients in the stomach, intestine (except the rectum), extrahepatic biliary tract, pancreas, kidney and ureter. The stimuli for pain included distension by balloons of hollow viscera, and traction and faradic stimulation of all the structures mentioned. Studies after unilateral sympathectomy revealed a homolateral afferent supply for kidney, ureter, the two sides of the colon and possibly the gastric mesentery; the remaining organs had a bilateral supply. Bentley & Smithwick (22) had shown earlier that balloon distension of the duodenum and jejunum was no longer painful after thoracolumbar sympathectomy and splanchnicectomy. Bentley (21) stopped the pain evoked by transfixing an exposed duodenal ulcer with a needle when he procainized the splanchnic nerves. Numerous other animal and experimental studies confirm that the pain afferents from the abdominal viscera travel with the sympathetic nerves, and a substantial number of patients with pain arising in these viscera have been relieved by appropriate sympathectomy according to White & Sweet (296, pp. 652 to 676).

Gernandt & Zotterman (96) have made a con-tribution not readily feasible in man by recording oscilloscopically from the splanchnic nerve and from fine strands of mesenteric nerve in the cat. Slight pressure or touch to the small intestine gave no electrical impulses but pinching the gut or the mesentery produced delta fiber impulses conducted at up to 20 m per sec. and much slower impulses in 'C' fibers conducted at 0.5 to 2 m per sec. These authors concluded that intestinal sensibility is similar to that of skin deprived of its fast conducting afferents.

In the limbs the presence of afferent fibers in the sympathetic supply is less consistently demonstrable by stimulation in man, especially in the lower limb. However Leriche & Fontaine (168), Foerster et al. (79) and Harris (119) all record examples of pain referred to the upper limb upon stimulus to the inferior cervical or stellate ganglion. The author has seen one patient in whom electrodes applied to the first and second thoracic ganglia caused immediate pain in the entire ipsilateral arm and in whom this response recurred upon stimulation of the caudal end of the sympathetic trunk after section below the T2 ganglion—evidence that direct afferent fibers were stimulated. Similar evidence for the lower limb has been cited by Foerster et al. (79, p. 154) and by Echlin (71). White & Sweet have never succeeded in evoking pain in the leg by stimulation of the lumbar sympathetic trunk or rami. But the type of pain known as causalgia which may follow trauma to nerves especially in the limbs is consistently stopped by sympathectomy. This fact is extensively documented in table XIV of White & Sweet (296, p. 369). A possible explanation other than the elimination of direct afferent pathways in the sympathetics has been suggested by Doupe et al. (68), namely that at the site of injury artificial synapses appear permitting tonic efferent impulses in sympathetic nerves to excite somatic afferents for pain. If this is true the fiber interaction phenomenon of Granit et al. (109) has major clinical significance. Relevant also are experiments of Walker & Nulsen (280). They applied a chronic pull-out electrode to the sympathetic chain between the T2 and T3 ganglia and divided the trunk below this electrode in 12 patients. Only in the three who had causalgia did any pain appear in the arm and hand on stimulus postoperatively. In these three there was a consistent pattern in which the pain appeared only 4 to 20 sec. after the start of stimulus, usually a few seconds after piloerection over the whole upper limb. Maximal pain was not reached for 15 to 30 sec.; then, despite continuation of the stimulus, it slowly faded and disappeared 15 to 30 sec. after its peak. Although the sequence of events is too slow to suggest fiber interaction, efferent sympathetic discharges had apparently set up pain impulses at the periphery.

We are not aware that any observer has reported decreased appreciation of pinprick in man after sympathectomy, but van Harreveld & Smith (272) thought that extensive thoracicoabdominal sympathectomy produced additional loss of pain from the skin in seven of eight lower thoracic and upper lumbar segments studied in the cat. They isolated a dermatome by cutting three spinal nerves above and three below the one they left intact. The borders of this dermatome as determined by the motor response to pinching proved constant. After the sympathectomy there was then an added loss of sensitivity to pinching in a small often triangular zone at the cranioventral side of the dermatome. They suggested that these sympathetic afferents might go to the blood vessels of the skin.

Parasympathetic Nerves

Of the cranial autonomic nerves we shall mention only the vagus. That this carries afferent fibers from the trachea and bronchi is suggested by the finding of Morton *et al.* (193) who relieved the pain and cough of bronchogenic carcinoma by section of the homolateral vagus below its recurrent laryngeal branch. The presence of other afferent fibers perhaps from the thoracic esophagus is intimated by the observations of Grimson *et al.* (112). Their patients under spinal anesthesia experienced 'heartburn' and pain referred to the neck when the vagus was stimulated three inches above the diaphragm. Stimulation at or below the diaphragm caused no pain, so the vagi probably carry no such fibers from the abdominal viscera. This was also the conclusion of Cannon in his cats (38).

The problem of pain conduction by afferent sacral parasympathetic fibers is discussed by White & Sweet (296, pp. 671 to 674).

On balance it is our impression that afferent fibers for pain are to be found in so many of the autonomic nerves in man that no useful purpose is served by regarding these as comprising a purely efferent nervous system, the more so since a number of the considerations which led to the development of this concept by Gaskell & Langley have been shown to be invalid.

SPINAL CORD

Upon entry into the spinal cord the posterior root filaments divide into a lateral bundle of fine fibers and a medial bundle of large fibers. The small lateral fibers bifurcate at once into two short branches one of which passes rostrally, the other caudally, for a few segments in the dorsolateral fasciculus or zone of Lissauer (marginal zone of Waldeyer). Each branch gives off collaterals which pass into the posterior horn, according to Bok (29, p. 534). We have referred to the work of Ranson & Billingsley (219) in cats which places the pain fibers in the lateral bundle. Hyndman (132) has contended that incision into this zone in man produces an area of analgesia without complete loss of touch sensation. R. W. Rand, E. J. Penka and W. E. Stern, however, made in two patients a total of 15 electrolytic lesions in the zone of Lissauer and were unable to detect any sensory changes attributable thereto. They made an even more extensive series of rostrocaudal lesions in this zone in a monkey, 10 in number, 1 mm deep from the C6 through T1 cord segments. Examination post-mortem showed the lesions extending but little beyond the desired zone of destruction which had produced analgesia only of the ulnar aspect of the ipsilateral forearm and hypalgesia of the ulnar area of the hand. Because of the above-mentioned rostrocaudal fanning of the fibers, it is not surprising that an extended continuous lesion is required to produce any demonstrable sensory loss.

The posterior root fibers terminate around: *a*) the posteromarginal or pericornual cells which lie around the entire margin of the posterior horn, *b*) the more centrally placed cells of the nucleus proprius of the posterior horn and *c*) small cells lying within the substantia gelatinosa which caps the nucleus proprius, as shown in figure 7. Pearson (207) from studies of his Golgi preparations of spinal cords of human babies finds that these small cells in the substantia gelatinosa may intervene between some of the primary afferent terminals and the larger cells which lie in the nucleus proprius and in the pericornual regions. The latter two groups of cells give rise to the major crossed ascending afferent pathways in the cord. Pearson hypothecates that the primary afferent fibers which end directly in relation to these latter cells would be likely to give rise to 'fast pain,' whereas those cells containing a small intercalated neuron of the substantia gelatinosa might be those evoking 'slow pain.'

The pericornual cells are middle-sized ganglion

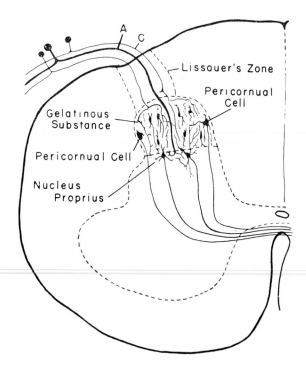

FIG. 7. Termination of pain fibers of the posterior root in human spinal cord. Large fiber *A* passes through the substantia gelatinosa to terminate near a cell of nucleus proprius. Small fiber *C* ends within substantia gelatinosa in relation to either: a pericornual cell, a cell of nucleus proprius, or a small cell within the substantia gelatinosa. Long axons crossing in the anterior commissure and ascending the cord arise from the nucleus proprius or pericornual group. [Modified from Pearson (207).]

cells lying in three main groups around the margin of the posterior horn, a special group at its dorsal tip, a reticular or lateral group adjoining the posterolateral column of white matter and an inner medial group adjoining the posterior white column. These extend the full length of the cord, and Kuru concludes that they give rise to the pain and temperature fibers (149, pp. 10 and 11). He has studied the retrograde cell degeneration in the posterior horns of patients who have had anterolateral cordotomy, with attention to those who have had incomplete analgesia and thermanesthesia below the expected level. He found a striking correlation between the segments of the cord showing chromatolysis of the pericornual cells and the dermal segments showing loss of pain and temperature sensation. The patients in whose pericornual cells below the level of operation he saw the greatest chromatolysis also had the greatest degeneration in the lateral spinothalamic tract. The larger cells occupying the more

centrally placed nucleus proprius of the posterior horn were not degenerated unless the anterior white columns were cut. They did show chromatolysis, however, in three patients whose incisions included the anterior white matter. In these three patients he traced degeneration in a distinct ventral spinothalamic tract, which he did not associate with loss of pain and temperature.

Anatomical details as to the number of segments required for crossover of the pain fibers through the anterior commissure, the likelihood of some fibers remaining uncrossed and the consistency with which fibers from a given area of the body occupy a particular portion of the opposite anterior quadrant of the cord are of great importance to the surgeon seeking to relieve pain but need not engross us here. White & Sweet (296, pp. 37 to 45) may be consulted for details.

Although the association of pain fibers with those for temperature in the anterior white quadrant is a close one there are a number of recorded results of dissociation of loss of pain from that of temperature. Analgesia to pinprick with little or no thermanesthesia was recorded following small, fractionally enlarged incisions for anterolateral cordotomy by Wilson & Fay (299) in one of two cases, by Stookey (255) in four cases, by Grant (110) in one case and by Foerster & Gagel (80) and Kuru (149) in 3 of 30 cases. The converse state of severe hypothermesthesia with preservation of normal pain sense has also been recorded by Frazier & Spiller (83) in a patient with a midcervical cord tumor. The paucity of such observations indicates that there usually are not two distinct bundles of fibers for pain and temperature, but the fact that such dissociation can occur suggests that individual fibers are concerned with impulses either for pain or for temperature. Such a thought is further intimated by the observation of Sweet (259) that bipolar electrical stimulation within the anterior half of the cord in man elicited responses purely of temperature (usually heat) in 46 per cent of the responses in which any subjective sensation occurred. The usual response was one of pain with or without a burning quality in 54 per cent of 200 stimulations.

A number of factors have conspired to make physiologic studies of pain in the central nervous system even more difficult than those of the peripheral somatic and autonomic systems. As mentioned earlier, pain pathways in the cords of animals appear to be more diffusely distributed and to ascend by multiple relays with crossing and recrossing of fibers. Furthermore, although the experience of pain is a more compelling usurper of conscious attention and tends to evoke more obvious motor activity than touch, pressure or the movement of a limb, these latter stimuli are accompanied by far more conspicuous signs of electrical activity appearing at a lower threshold. This is of course due to the fact that the latter modalities tend to traverse larger fibers and the recorded potential is in approximately linear relation to the diameter of the fiber, as shown by Gasser & Grundfest (92). Hence but few workers have carried their studies into the difficult realm of analysis of the smaller late potentials from noxious stimuli.

There are several facts which indicate that pain impulse conduction within the cord may involve unmyelinated as well as myelinated fibers. In the painstaking study of Häggqvist (114) 17,000 fibers in a single cross section of a young woman's cord at the T3 segment were measured. Samples were counted from each of the zones numbered in figure 8. Forty-two per cent of all the fibers in the whole cross section measured 2 μ or less in diameter, whereas in the anterolateral zones 6 and 7, the division of which would yield contralateral analgesia, 55 per cent and 61 per cent, respectively, of the fibers were of this small diameter.

Most of the histologic studies of fiber tracts including those for pain have relied on myelin or its degeneration products, but it would be a coincidence if the unmyelinated pain pathways were coextensive with pathways we can see in such stains as the Swank-Davenport (258) modification of the Marchi method. And indeed we shall see that in the brain

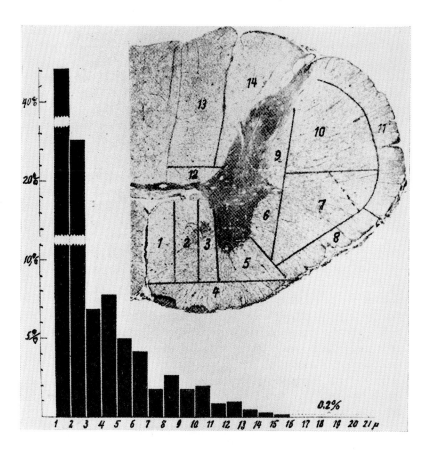

FIG. 8. Fiber sizes in the spinal cord. Cross section at T3 segment in which Häggqvist measured diameters of 17,000 fibers and subdivided the white matter into 14 zones on the basis of differing constellations of fiber sizes. The histogram below and to left indicates the percentage of fibers of each diameter in the entire hemisection. In the regions ventral and ventromedial to the anterior horn fibers less than 2 μ constitute 43 to 45 per cent of total. Since this is about the general average, these studies give no clue that the pain fibers lying here preponderate over tiny fibers with other functions. See text for different deductions with respect to zones 6 and 7. [From Häggqvist (114).]

stem the position of the pain pathways correlates poorly with the position of Marchi degeneration in spinotectal and spinothalamic fibers.

Impulses from somatic nerves were traced into the anterolateral column of the cat's spinal cord by Collins & Randt (49). They studied with 10 μ tip microelectrodes the responses evoked from stimulation of contralateral sciatic or superficial radial nerves, and compared these with the responses to be seen in the ipsilateral dorsal column. Velocities of impulses were compared for the two loci both in the peripheral nerve and in the cord. The responses in the anterolateral quadrant were related to the gamma component in the nerve. In the peripheral nerve they traveled at about 34 m per sec.; in the cord they averaged 24.9 m per sec. ranging from 19 to 33 m per sec. The dorsal column impulses while in the peripheral nerve traveled at about 85 m per sec. and slowed down to an average of 50.5 m per sec. in the cord. The typical anterolateral potential had slow rising and falling phases with superimposed spike activity which was maximal at the peak of the slower potential. The maximum voltages were from 50 to 75 μv, the total duration was 30 to 40 msec. The ratios of threshold potentials in the anterolateral column to the dorsal column were 2.6:1 for a 5 msec. shock, corresponding closely to the ratios of these potentials in peripheral nerve of 2.4:1. The anterolateral column potentials traverse this portion of the cord throughout its length as shown by their abolition in a cervical lead following thoracic anterolateral section (which leaves intact the cervical dorsal column potential).

Impulses from autonomic nerves were traced into the anterolateral column of the cord of rabbits, cats and dogs by Amassian (5). He recorded with microelectrodes the responses excited by stimulation of the splanchnic nerve. When this was increased to 15 v. with a 0.1 msec. shock a large fraction of 'A' gamma-delta fibers in the nerve was excited. A barrage of spikes could then be seen bilaterally in the anterolateral region of the cord close to the gray matter. Its long latency of 11 to 13 msec. and much greater duration of 25 msec. distinguished it from the posterior column wave. There is a striking similarity between these potentials and those recorded after stimulation of somatic nerves from almost the same spots in the cord, the splanchnic responses a bit medial to those from the somatic nerves. The high voltage required provoked reflex movements of the body wall, but such motor activity did not then set up the whole potential in the anterolateral column

because this was only partially reduced when the movements were stopped with d-tubocurarine. Amassian is appropriately cautious about correlating this pathway with that subserving visceral pain in man. Both clinical and experimentally induced pain in gastrointestinal and urinary viscera is usually stopped in patients by anterolateral cordotomy on the side opposite a laterally placed viscus. So the crossover of splanchnic pain fibers appears to be more complete in man than the fibers from which Amassian was recording. Visceral afferent pathways in the cat had already been shown to be incompletely crossed by Spiegel & Bernis (253) who found that stimulation of the central end of one splanchnic nerve caused 'pain responses' until both anterolateral columns were destroyed.

The following evidence indicates that impulses for pain may not ascend the cord exclusively via a single fiber running in the anterior or anterolateral white matter to reach the brain stem. a) Vigorous stimulation, as with bipolar electrodes at 100 or more v., consistently causes pain in an area apparently denervated by full anterior quadrant section as judged by analgesia to pinprick and to a variety of other forms of experimentally induced pain (296, p. 45). King's (141) careful measurements revealed that threshold voltage values for pricking pain on the analgesic side were only 40 to 50 per cent greater than on the normal side. That the pain impulses are not entering the cord at levels above the cordotomy incision, having moved rostrally along sympathetic pathways in the paravertebral trunks or along the aorta, is reasonably certain because the finding is the same following high cervical cordotomy. b) Direct bipolar electrical stimulation applied to the surface of the posterior and posterolateral columns of the cord in man causes severe tingling sensations like an electric shock. Foerster & Gagel (80) described such responses; we confirm that at low thresholds (of less than 0.01 v. in our hands) application of the electrodes to the fasciculus cuneatus causes reference to the ipsilateral leg or pelvis, and to the fasciculus gracilis causes reference to the ipsilateral arm. At higher thresholds one evokes similar responses contralaterally from the surface of the posterolateral column of white matter. That such pathways are rarely used in pain of clinical cause is clear from the high percentage of patients relieved of pain by anterior quadrant section. Possibly these observations have in fact no physiologic significance, and electrical stimulus to the exposed spinal cord may be a condition for which there is no physiopathologic counterpart. *c*) That the dorsal columns may, however, even if only rarely, carry impulses causing clinical pain seems a tenable hypothesis from the results of Browder & Gallagher (35). Their operative division of the dorsal column relieved, in three of four patients, pain referred to a phantom lower limb which seemed to be in a distorted posture. Moreover, tingling sensations perhaps like those evoked on posterior column stimulation may occur in the analgesic limb after cordotomy upon an unusually noxious event, such as running a nail into the foot.

MEDULLA OBLONGATA

The primary afferent neurons for pain and temperature arising from the face and head via trigeminal, nervus intermedius, glossopharyngeal and vagal routes collect in the descending or spinal trigeminal tract and terminate near cells in the lower part of the nucleus of that tract. The cells in this position extending from about the obex downward were called by Winkler the nucleus gelatinosus tractus spinalis (302, pp. 51 to 59) because they resemble those of the substantia gelatinosa Rolandi of the spinal cord. Olszewski's (202) more recent careful study of the nucleus in man and monkey is in general agreement. Section of the descending tract at about the level of the obex usually produces trigeminal analgesia as well as severe hypalgesia of the deeper areas of the face and head supplied by the afferent fibers in the seventh, ninth and tenth cranial nerves; so the correlation of the 'subnucleus gelatinosus' of Olszewski with pain and temperature function seems likely. Evidence on these points as well as on the finer details of topographic localization of the fibers from various portions of the head and face within the tract and their termination in the nucelus are summarized by White & Sweet (296, pp. 457 to 466).

The locus of spinothalamic fibers ascending from the secondary afferent neurons of the cord as determined by Marchi stain is illustrated in figure 9.

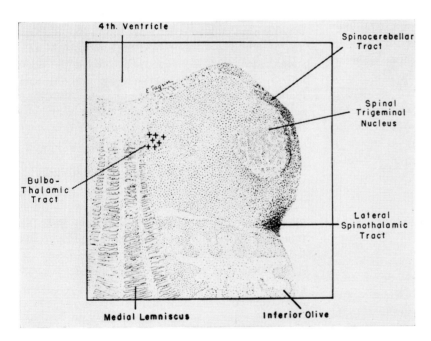

FIG. 9. Degeneration in the spinothalamic and bulbothalamic tracts at level of the inferior olive. The Marchi degeneration in the lateral spinothalamic tract (including spinotectal fibers) is that seen by Kuru in a patient all of whose pain fibers in the anterior half of the cord below C4 segment had degenerated. We show the locus of the bulbothalamic tract as that area of absence of Weigert-stained fibers described by Wallenberg in a patient who had post-mortem a softening in the ventral two-thirds of the descending trigeminal tract and its nucleus. The ictus had occurred 5 years earlier; the infarct it produced was of maximal size at the level of the obex, i.e. about the rostral end of the nucleus for pain fibers. We have referred to the secondary afferent pathway from this area as the bulbothalamic rather than trigeminothalamic tract since it probably includes the area of nervus intermedius, glossopharyngeus and vagus as well as trigeminus. [Modified from Kuru (149).]

The figures of other workers, such as Goldstein (103), Foerster & Gagel (80, p. 24), Walker (276), Rasmussen & Peyton (220), Gardner & Cuneo (87) and Poirier & Bertrand (213), are in general agreement. Although such degeneration has provided a subpial signpost to the localization of the pain fibers, it has failed utterly to intimate their full extent. This was first shown by clinical plus post-mortem studies of the lesions after thrombosis of vessels supplying the bulbar brain stem. These deductions were fully confirmed by the pioneering surgical work in man of Schwartz & O'Leary (242, 243), and of White (293) and by subsequent surgeons, Crawford (50) and D'Errico (64). Findings with respect to pain provoked by stimulation at operation were checked against depth of incision, postoperative analgesia and, at times, later post-mortem studies. These show that the pain fibers coming up from the cord occupy a much wider area just dorsal to the inferior olives extending 6 to 7 mm deep and continuing medially in the midst of the bulbar reticular formation nearly to the medial lemniscus. The quintothalamic or secondary afferent trigeminal fibers tend to lie in the more medial part of this area and to extend more dorsally as well (D'Errico). McKinley & Magoun (186) have shown from depth recording of action potentials in cats that there is indiscriminate mixing of the fibers from the three trigeminal divisions in this area, whereas the grouping of fibers related to trigeminal peripheral divisions is clearer in the descending trigeminal tract and nucleus, as shown by McKinley & Magoun (186) and Harrison & Corbin (120). Subsequent work in man has also shown that a discernible tendency to layering in the cord of the fibers from specific sections of the body becomes less consistent in the medulla.

More work is especially necessary on the course of pain fibers from face and head once they start up the brain stem. There is some evidence from Wallenberg (281) that these fibers separate into two deep bundles as they move rostrally. To the illustration from Kuru (fig. 9) has been added an indication of Wallenberg's notion of the location of these secondary fibers from the face at the mid-bulbar level.

Numerous fibers ascending from the cord move medially to terminate in the reticular formation of pons and medulla; their possible significance will be considered in the next section.

MESENCEPHALON

In the upper pons and midbrain pain fibers again become more superficial and hence more accessible to special analysis and surgical section in animals and man. Here their precise extent and location is less well-known than in the cord and medulla because of the smaller numbers of studies. In general, the fibers occupy a zone extending dorsally and medially for about 1 cm from the lateral mesencephalic sulcus. One example will suffice to indicate some of the unresolved discrepancies. Walker (278), the major pioneer in this field, following a trigeminal lesion in the monkey places the Marchi degeneration in the lower midbrain in a narrow zone 1 to 2 mm deep beginning right at the surface and extending dorsally a few millimeters from the lateral mesencephalic sulcus (fig. 10). Wallenberg (281) and van Gehuchten (271) working with the same method in rabbits found the degeneration exclusively in a much more medial position, and Wallenberg confirmed his impression in studies of degeneration in a patient (281). Moreover the spinothalamic tract demonstrable in Marchi stains at the level of the superior colliculus in man has dwindled to a tiny bundle. Having identified the bundle in Marchi stains, Glees & Bailey (99) then counted the fibers in this region in normal Weigert preparations; they found only about 1500 fibers. Of these two-thirds were 2 to 4 μ in diameter; most of the remainder measured about 4 to 6 μ; they were all in a small compact group only about 0.65 mm² in cross-section.

However, figure 10 also illustrates the area of surgical destruction in the largest lesion figured by Walker (278) which did not produce complete analgesia on the opposite face and lower limb (although it did on the torso and upper limb). Yet the lesion essentially blankets all of the variously described zones of myelin degeneration. It is again apparent that we need to know more about the unmyelinated fibers and perhaps about the role of relays of neurons in conduction of pain impulses.

The marked decrease in size at the upper midbrain of the Marchi-stained ascending afferent bundle following extensive cordotomy has long been shown to be due to departure from it of ventral spinocerebellar, spinoreticular and spinotectal fibers. The earlier descriptions, such as those of Foerster & Gagel (80), were confirmed by Morin et al. (190) who were the first to suggest that the spinoreticular

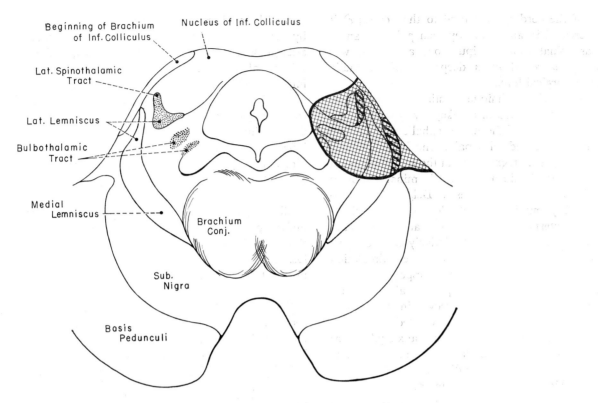

FIG. 10. Pain pathways in the mesencephalon. On the left side are shown: the lateral spinothalamic (including spinotectal) tracts as seen in Marchi degeneration after thoracic cordotomy in man by Rasmussen & Peyton (220), Gardner & Cuneo (87) and Glees (98); and the bulbothalamic tract as seen by absence of Weigert stained fibers seen following infarct by Wallenberg (281, legend to fig. 12). On the right side are shown, *diagonal hatching*, secondary afferent pathways in monkey as seen in Marchi degeneration: the upper medial area after mid-line myelotomy at L5 to 7; the lower lateral area after lesion in spinal trigeminal nucleus according to Walker (278). *Crosshatching:* Lesion in man which produced contralaterally a severe hypalgesia to pin prick on face, analgesia on upper limb and torso and hyperpathia on lower limb (277).

component might influence the perception of pain by effecting changes in cortical excitability via the reticular formation. Moruzzi & Magoun (194) had shortly before demonstrated the widespread cortical activation from electrical stimulation in the ventro-medial bulbar reticular formation. Now that stains for axonal degeneration are available Mehler *et al.* (188) have shown in monkeys, following antero-lateral cordotomy, that there is indeed "a massive fine-fibered, diffuse, medial spinoreticular system" passing to 11 of the nuclei in the pontobulbar reticular formation. They also saw in the midbrain fine spinotectal fibers passing to the lateral part of the central gray matter, the nucleus intercollicularis and deep strata of the superior colliculus. Bowsher (31) studied four patients following thoracic, cervical or bulbar division of pain pathways using the silver

stains for axonal degeneration either of Glees (97) or of Nauta & Gygax (199). His results show a striking similarity to those of the previous authors in monkeys.

Perhaps these spinotectal fibers, or bulbothalamic continuation paths from spinoreticular fibers, are responsible for a sharp spike potential found in the medial midbrain by Collins & O'Leary (48). When they stimulated the sciatic or superficial radial nerve in cats, they evoked the potential in a discrete region of the reticular substance dorsal to the rostral part of the red nucleus and lateral to the oculomotor nucleus. A relationship to pain was intimated by these facts: *a*) the potential was activated from peripheral axons of the gamma-delta group, the fastest of which were conducting at 45 m per sec.; *b*) its pathway was principally via the ventrolateral sector of the cord contralateral to the nerves; *c)* it was increased in amplitude by such painful maneuvers as spinal root manipulation; and *d)* it was promptly depressed by a deepening of anesthesia toward a surgical level.

By his special technique of stimulation Delgado (62) has also obtained in monkeys evidence that the inferomedial part of the mesencephalic central gray matter is concerned with pain. The lateral part of the mesencephalic tegmentum in the region occupied by the spinothalamic tract and trigeminal lemniscus has yielded similar responses. Delgado has implanted tiny multilead electrodes and then stimulated via external leads from these after the wound is closed and the animal is relatively free to move about. At the aforementioned points stimulation evokes the same sort of complex response that the normal monkey makes to a peripheral annoyance such as pinching his tail. Moreover in monkeys in which such responses had been elicited electrically the animal developed 'conditioned anxiety,' i.e. as soon as placed on the stimulation stage he screeched, bit and tried to escape. This did not happen in monkeys in which purely somatic motor or autonomic effects had been elicited. Hence Delgado assumed that the sensations evoked from the mesencephalic zones were painful and were remembered.

The possible significance of these pathways may be considered in relation to curious sensory changes which rarely appear following thoracic or cervical cordotomy, perhaps more often after bulbar spinothalamic tractotomy for pain and in many patients after mesencephalic tractotomy. Dogliotti (67), the first surgeon to divide pain pathways in the midbrain, reported that his three surviving patients had "diffused disagreeable sensations" in the half of the body contralateral to the incision. As described by Drake & McKenzie (69), in all six of their patients after the operation in the midbrain there was analgesia and thermanesthesia throughout the opposite side of the body and head for 3 to 15 days after operation. Then pinprick, deep pressure or thermal stimuli in all six patients and even light touch in one of them caused deep diffuse poorly-localized agonizing pain with strong withdrawal and grimacing. In three of the patients there was spontaneous burning pain in some part of the formerly analgesic area. Drake suggests that the impulses causing these pains traverse a secondary route via relay in the reticular formation which is not cut by the incision in the midbrain. Walker (279) had already noted "the diffuse, disagreeable sensation which may be elicited by cold, extreme heat or pinprick, especially by repeated stimulation" in some of his patients after mesencephalic tractotomy. He suggested that spinotectal tracts may be carrying such painful impulses to higher centers. Bowsher (31) also pointed out that bulbothalamic and tegmentothalamic tracts running in the reticular formation are separate from direct spinothalamic fibers between the level of the inferior olive and the thalamus. He suggests that the direct spinothalamic system transmits impulses for pain which is felt at once, is sharply localized and does not outlast the stimulus. He attributes to the medially placed spinoreticulothalamic system the diffuse poorly-localized pain with an appreciably slower conduction time which does outlast the stimulus. Since mesencephalic incisions in man have missed these fibers, this explanation would account for the type of persistent pain shown by such patients.

One further observation of Drake & McKenzie also fits in with this concept. One of their patients preoperatively had had severe pain in the face. Mesencephalic tractotomy replaced the original pain by a diffuse facial burning sensation. Division of all of the primary pain pathways from the face by bulbar trigeminal tractotomy then gave complete relief—perhaps because reticulothalamic pathways could no longer be activated.

THALAMUS

The fibers for touch and proprioception in the medial lemnisci mix with those for pain and temperature as they all terminate at the thalamic level. In man when vascular lesions destroy the nucleus ventralis posterolateralis severe sensory loss is found in the contralateral limbs and trunk; the facial fibers terminate in the nucleus ventralis posteromedialis (200, 229). These inferences from human material have been confirmed and extended by the more critical studies on Marchi material in lower primates carried out by Clark (43) and Walker (275, pp. 63 to 93). Moreover Walker's (275, p. 172) observations using the same technique have revealed that these same thalamic nuclei project in corresponding fashion to the postcentral gyrus of the same cerebral hemisphere. The nucleus ventralis posteromedialis sends fibers to the lowest or facial sector of the postcentral gyrus, and the most lateral parts of the nucleus ventralis posterior project to the superior part of the gyrus.

Foerster & Gagel (80), Rasmussen & Peyton

to or part of a focal seizure; *b*) as a more continuous pain; or *c*) as a dysesthesia appearing only when the surface of the body was stimulated. Michelsen (189) reviews earlier reports and adds five new cases of his own. Paroxysmal abdominal pain as a form of epilepsy has now been reported in several series of patients. O'Brien & Goldensohn (201) summarize the earlier work and add their own observations which indicate that in at least some of these patients organic cerebral lesions cause attacks of pain primarily referred to the abdomen, whereas in other patients the pain is secondary to abnormal gastrointestinal motility.

Lesions

Destruction of appropriate cortex and subcortical white matter may also cause hypalgesia, rarely analgesia. One of the early reports implicating the cerebral cortex with pain perception is Déjerine & Mouzon's (60) account in 1915 of a war casualty whose small cortical wound produced loss of pain sensibility in the contralateral arm. Kleist (143, pp. 426 to 428) collected 24 patients wounded in World War I in whom a localized parietal lesion brought about disturbances mainly in pain and thermal senses. In eight of these, hypalgesia was the only sensory loss. He noted analgesia changing during convalescence at times to an abnormally increased appreciation of stimuli, a hyperpathia. He ventured without confirmation post-mortem a precise placement of the cortical area for pain and temperature sensations in the posterior bank of the central fissure—in Brodmann's narrow fields 3a and 3b. Russell (233) after a study of men wounded in World War II reached essentially identical conclusions on all of the above scores. Davison & Schick (57) have also described two patients with hyperpathia combined with hypalgesia in whom autopsy revealed only cortical and subcortical lesions, completely sparing the thalamus.

Foerster (78, p. 146) pointed out that the subnormality in pain sensation after removal of the postcentral gyral representation for a limb soon returns virtually to normal; but subtle changes such as a reduction in the number of pain points or an increase in their threshold persisted for years in seven patients studied by Kroll (147). As early as 1909 Horsley (130) had noted that even after removal of the 'whole arm centre' in both precentral and postcentral gyri the pain sensation was 'notably diminished' though not abolished. Marshall (184) ably sum-

marizes the earlier work and adds studies on 12 more war-injured patients examined 5 to 34 years afterward. In some area contralateral to a shallow cerebral wound, all experienced slight or no pain when tested both with a heavy pin jab and by injection of 0.2 cc of 6 per cent sodium chloride into the muscles in an effort to provoke deep pain. He showed clearly the possibility of protracted focal severe disturbance of appreciation of pain from such lesions. Both he and Russell have commented on the anomalous situation that an extensive cortical injury may leave pain sensibility intact, whereas a small cortical wound in part of the same area in another patient may produce hypalgesia.

That a massive area of the cerebral cortex may in some way be associated with irritating sensation was shown by Dusser de Barenne and his collaborators (70) in experiments in lower primates. For example when they applied strychnine locally over a few square millimeters of the cortex anywhere over about the posterior half of the frontal lobe or the anterior three-quarters of the parietal lobe of the chimpanzee, they set up a diffuse irritation in face, arms or legs, depending on the area of cortex to which the drug was applied. The animal licked or scratched the skin of the zones concerned for about 30 min. more vigorously contralateral than ipsilateral to the side of the placement of the drug. The electrocorticogram showed 'strychnine spikes' within this extensive sensory region, according to Bailey *et al.* (12).

The ipsilateral cerebral representation of pain intimated by these studies is further suggested by these facts. Total hemispherectomy in man does not produce complete contralateral analgesia, but such a degree of cortical removal in the macaque and chimpanzee provokes almost complete degeneration in every thalamic nucleus except those in the medullary laminae which do not project to the cerebral cortex (279). This leaves the ipsilateral thalamus and cerebral cortex as the most likely sites mediating pain perception following hemispherectomy. Some individuals, e.g. Evans' patient reported by Walker (279), show but little disturbance of appreciation of pinprick anywhere except for some delay in response, whereas in two patients of Dandy (52) there was said to be loss of all contralateral cutaneous sensation below the face with a varying but lesser loss in the face. Gardner *et al.* (88) have recently given a resumé of the findings in their own and the earlier reported cases. They found a striking and constant retention of all modalities of sensation in the trigeminal area both in patients whose operation was for infantile hemiplegia and in those who had tumors. This extensive bilateral cortical representation for facial sensation including pain is consonant with the well-known similar motor representation. On the average the tumor patients showed the greater deficit, the lesion having been present a shorter time in a more adult brain. The contralateral parts showed an impairment of appreciation and localization of a sharp point, which increased progressively in the following sequence: face, trunk, thigh, upper arm, leg, forearm, foot and hand. A delay in the appreciation of all stimuli on the paralyzed side was short in the trigeminal area and longest in the distal parts of the limbs. Pain elicited from the abnormal side was more disagreeable than that from the normal side. Cold and hot stimuli were painful and could not be differentiated. When a pin was applied simultaneously to similar sites on the two sides, there was consistent extinction only below the elbow and knee on the paretic side.

Evoked Potentials

The somatic sensory areas I and II of the cerebral cortex of many mammals including monkeys have been outlined on the basis of cortical electrical potentials evoked by tactile stimuli to the body surface (311). There has been very little work to determine in animals the cerebral representation for painful stimuli; but in continuation of our assumption that 'A' gamma-delta impulses may be associated with pain, we shall summarize the work of Amassian (5, 6) on the cortical responses evoked from such fibers in the splanchnic nerves of carnivores. From tiny areas on the cortex at the junction of leg and arm representation in both sensory areas I and II in the dog and cat, he found brief initially surface-positive waves. These were obtained from both sensory areas contralaterally and from the ipsilateral area II in the cat when only splanchnic 'A' beta fibers were excited, as shown in figure 11. At much higher voltage, when 'A' gamma-delta activation was also visible in the record from the splanchnic nerve, a small deflection appeared on the returning limb of the primary response in area I as the only early cortical evidence of presumed activity of pain fibers. There was no change in the primary response from area II. Activation of the gamma-delta fibers also evoked a late secondary response generalized over the cortex. In the monkey, Ruch *et al.* (232) were able to find a splanchnic representation only in cortical area I.

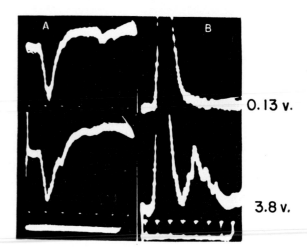

0.13 v.

3.8 v.

FIG. 11. Splanchnic A gamma-delta fibers and cerebral evoked potentials. Stimulating electrodes on splanchnic nerve distally. *Upper records* obtained with stimulus 0.13 v.; there is a maximal primary response from cortical area I (*upper left*) with no A gamma-delta discharge on the neurogram of the sympathetic trunk (*upper right*). *Lower records* obtained with stimulus 3.8 v. and pulse duration 1 msec., the A gamma-delta group is active (*second wave, lower right*), but the only cortical correlate therewith is a small deflection on the returning limb of the primary response (*lower left*). [From Amassian (5).]

A somewhat similar type of study has been carried out in the cat by Mountcastle *et al.* (196) working with nerves to muscle. They monitored oscilloscopically the ventral root instead of the stimulated exposed nerve and took as evidence of excitation of the Group III fibers, i.e. 'the delta pile,' the appearance of a late polysynaptic spinal cord reflex in the ventral roots. Only at stimuli sufficiently intense to excite these fibers did they evoke potentials in the contralateral cerebral cortex. Responses were seen in both somatic areas I and II; they were of higher amplitude in area II. Their latency at 18 to 19 msec. was about twice that of cortical potentials seen upon stimulation of adjacent cutaneous nerves. Because the small myelinated fibers in these muscle nerves are from 1 to 8 μ in diameter and conduct up to 40 m per sec., it was thought that their impulses might include some of nociceptive character.

Second Sensory Area in Man

Penfield & Rasmussen (211) have shown in man that sensation can be evoked from the secondary sensory area at the lowest part of the postcentral gyrus extending into the superior lip of the Sylvian fissure to include part of the parietal operculum.

Only a few of the reported sensations have been described as 'pricking.' However, Biemond (25) has described a remarkable case in which a complex of small confluent foci of softening was found in the cortex and white matter of the right parietal operculum (see fig. 12) and in the cortex of the insula. This lesion had been associated with severe hypalgesia over the entire left half of the body, as well as with a constant deep 'drilling' pain throughout this area worsened by any local stimulus. The senses of touch, proprioception, attitude, stereognosis, vibration, graphesthesia and discrimination were all intact! In figure 12 one sees also retrograde degeneration of a fiber bundle passing into the posteroventral nucleus of the thalamus where a marked cellular loss had occurred. This loss was worse in the caudal portion of the nucleus in which the spinothalamic fibers principally terminate. He also reports two other

less striking but similar patients in whom the findings in life and at autopsy also suggest that the second sensory area is related to the 'conscious pain sensation.'

A review of the earlier literature discloses that the lesion in Davison & Schick's (57) case 10 was largely in the second sensory area but with involvement also of the superior temporal and insular cortex. The sensory findings, similar regarding pain to those in Biemond's (25) case 1, included spontaneous and touch-evoked pains—although in this patient touch, vibration and stereognosis were impaired also. This case report, made before Adrian had described the second sensory area, may in retrospect be taken as confirmation of such an area in man and as adding evidence that it is especially concerned with the sense of pain.

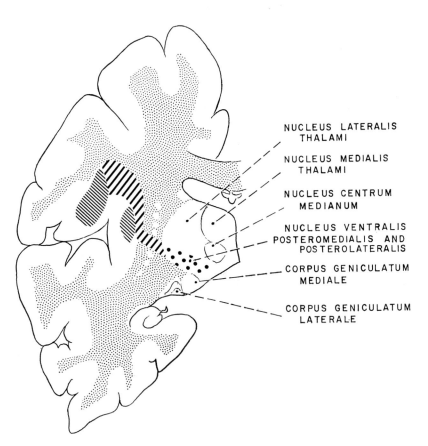

FIG. 12. Pain and the second sensory area in man. *Fine diagonal hatching:* areas of softening in the parietal operculum and cortex of insula; these extended in varying degree from the coronal plane of the anterior commissure in front to that of the lateral geniculate body behind. *Heavy diagonal hatching:* retrograde degeneration of fiber bundle as seen in Weigert-Pal stain for myelin, passing into posteroventral nucleus of thalamus via posterior part of internal capsule. *Heavy dots:* marked cellular loss in nucleus ventralis posteromedialis and posterolateralis, especially in caudal portion oi nucleus. [Based on data from Biemond (25).]

Reaction to Pain

The complexities of the cerebral mechanisms responsible finally for normal appreciation of and reaction to pain are at present largely beyond our knowledge.

Using the radiant heat method of Hardy *et al.* (115), Chapman (39) studied thresholds to 'pain perception,' i.e. the subjective end point signalled by the patient; and to 'pain reaction,' the first objective evidence of withdrawal, such as wincing, seen by the examiner. He found that a group of psychoneurotic patients, while presenting abnormal pain perception, showed an abnormally low threshold for pain reaction.

INDIFFERENCE TO PAIN. The contrary state, indifference to pain, has been seen temporarily in periods of severe emotional stress or in hypnosis, or over longer periods of time in hysteria, psychosis and postencephalitic states, and in mental defectives. In the latter two groups no effort has been made to correlate any particular lesions of the brain with this symptom. An extraordinary and rare phenomenon, described as 'a congenital insensitivity to pain' of many types, may occur in people otherwise apparently nearly normal. A detailed perusal of the case reports is required to appreciate the severity and variety of the injuries and noxious stimuli which such individuals have repeatedly sustained without pain (32, 51, 59, 81, 136, 148, 224, 236). Seven other case reports are cited by Madonick (182), although his own case, I think, belongs in the mental defective group mentioned above. A feature common to nearly all of these individuals has been their ability to distinguish with fair or great accuracy between the point and head of a pin or between slight differences of temperature. Yet they are indifferent to violent jabs and extremes of temperature and their utter lack of suffering is their striking characteristic. Boyd & Nie's (32) phrase "congenital universal indifference to pain" more clearly indicates the person's behavior and that the abnormality is central rather than peripheral. A number of them do experience discomfort upon cutaneous electrical stimulation at high levels, morbid distension of viscera, or other extreme noxa. The brain of no such person has yet been studied histologically, but the occurrence of various types of seizures or minor mental defect in several of them intimate that an organic lesion is present.

PAIN ASYMBOLIA. A state with slight similarity to the foregoing has been described by Schilder & Stengel (239) as 'pain asymbolia,' the situation in which there is "no analgesia in the common sense, but the psychic reaction to the sensation is absent." They (240) have observed this symptom in 10 patients with acquired organic cerebral disease and have implicated the anterior part of the lower part of the dominant parietal lobe. Autopsies on three of the patients showed various lesions of which they thought the common denominator was involvement of the supramarginal gyrus. However in these patients there was a concomitant sensory aphasia which made appraisal difficult, and at least in some of them there was a "dulling of the appreciation of pain" as well as an insufficient pain reaction. Moreover this dullness extended to a lack of concern over threatening gestures made toward the patient, intimating a general disturbance of the capacity to appreciate danger.

Rubins & Friedman (230) have contributed four more patients in whom this general clinical picture was present and in two of whom operative findings placed the lesion mainly in the dominant inferior parietal region. Although these patients recognized a pin as sharp, they did not withdraw from either painful stimuli or threatening gestures. But they also showed mild perceptive and more severe amnestic aphasia, right-left disorientation, inability to reproduce postural attitudes in space, Gerstmann's syndrome and idiokinetic apraxia. Hence, the 'asymbolia for pain' is by no means the isolated phenomenon seen in the syndrome of congenital indifference to pain. Hecaen & de Ajuriaguerra (123), adding a case report, note that in a number of other recorded patients as well as theirs the lesion extended into the posterior inferior part of the frontal lobe.

An even greater variety of locus of lesion was seen by Weinstein *et al.* (290) in 15 patients with pain asymbolia who did not have any aphasia. Such a group was selected for a special study of personality, and many of the patients had lesions in the nondominant hemisphere. Their heedlessness of noxious stimulation was often accompanied by inattention to disabled parts, by muteness, by hypokinesia or by depression. The authors considered all of these symptoms as to some extent an implicit denial of illness, perhaps related to actual verbal denial of illness or anosognosia. They considered such behavior related more to the personality background of the patient than to any specific lesion in the brain, and thought the premorbid personality of patients with 'pain asymbolia' was characterized by the habitual use of withdrawal and avoidance in stressful situations. It is apparent that the attribution of a depressed reaction to all noxa to a sharply focal cerebral lesion has dubious validity.

REACTIONS AFTER OPERATIONS ON FRONTAL LOBES. The modifications in the reaction of the individual to painful or distressing states provoked by removal of cortex or division of white fibers in the anterior two-thirds of the frontal lobe remain to be considered. Such lesions in an otherwise normal brain diminish the general reaction to constant pain of organic cause, such as advancing cancer, as well as the reaction to such psychological suffering as may be occasioned by the knowledge of impending death, an obsessive compulsive psychoneurosis or psychotic agitated depression. But the price paid for such relief includes inability to experience keen pleasure as well, i.e. there is a flattening of all affect and the development of a more or less apathetic state. In addition a wide variety of evidences of mental deficit may appear. The greater the area of frontal lobe removed or deprived of its normal connections by division of white matter, the greater the deficit. When most of the frontal white matter of a normally functioning human brain is transected bilaterally in the coronal plane just anterior to the lateral ventricles, there is often a serious disturbance of intellect and personality, as described by Rylander (234), Freeman & Watts (84, pp. 360 to 374), and Krayenbühl & Stoll (146). In an occasional patient these defects are mild enough to permit the individual to return to his work and retain for years a useful degree of pain relief (84, pp. 367 to 368; 205, pp. 452 to 453).

In an effort to secure a fruitful result with respect to pain but to preserve the personality, small lesions have been made. A total division of the white fibers on one side only, according to Koskoff et al. (145) and Scarff (235), produces a lesser deficit from which there is usually much recovery, unfortunately accompanied pari passu by return of pain. No significant difference in result re pain has been noted between division of fibers contralateral or ipsilateral to one-sided pain or between operations in the dominant or nondominant hemisphere. Bilateral inferior quadrant, bilateral medial or inferomedial lesions (111), removal of various small portions of the frontal lobes bilaterally, i.e. topectomy (216) or undercutting of various parts of the frontal cortex (244) have all been performed. Such patients have as yet been less thoroughly studied in relation to the correlation between locus of lesion and relief of pain, but the general pattern is similar in all. Contrary to the situation in

pain asymbolia, the lobotomized patient's reaction to individual noxious stimuli is, if anything, increased. He jumps at pinpricks and needle punctures and responds in the Hardy-Wolff-Goodell pain-threshold apparatus by wincing and pulling his hand away at a lesser stimulus after operation than before it, according to Chapman et al. (41). The general experience amply confirms Freeman & Watts' observations (84, pp. 371 and 372) that such events as rectal dilatation or childbirth are distressing to lobotomy patients. Moreover, following lobotomy when questioned about their preoperative pain they are likely to state that it is 'just as bad as ever' or 'terrible.' Yet they have few or no spontaneous complaints of pain, ask for little or no medication even if narcotic addiction appeared to be a problem before operation and are far less miserable even when mentation is almost normal. Patients with significant mental deficits may deny pain on direct questioning or even forget about the illness which is causing the pain. LeBeau (159, pp. 134 to 135 and pp. 226 to 290) and White & Sweet (296, pp. 287 to 333) summarize earlier reports and give accounts of their own experiences.

The behavior of the patients suggests that persistence either of noxious physical stimuli or disturbing thoughts sets off in the normal frontal lobes a potentiating mechanism which becomes a major factor in the total suffering of the person. That this mechanism may be to some extent specific to the frontal lobes is illustrated by the failure of bilateral anterior temporal lobectomy to modify the reactions to pain (296, p. 319).

That the mechanism may involve the diffuse thalamic projection system of Morison & Dempsey (191) is suggested by the following experiments. The thalamic nuclei of the macaque monkey giving rise to this projection system are the same ones which receive afferent impulses of somatic and visceral origin from the reticular activating system lying in the medial brain stem (85, 254). These impulses are distributed in certain thalamic association nuclei mainly to the frontal lobe anterior to areas 4 and 6. Magoun and associates have suggested that it is disturbance of the diffuse thalamic projection system which diminishes the affective component of sensory perception and deprives pain of its unpleasantness, the characteristic state following a frontal lobotomy, cortical undercutting or corticectomy. Since the dorsomedial nucleus of the thalamus is one of the main association nuclei for the diffuse thalamic projection system this explanation would also account for the similar condition following operative destruction of this nucleus. Thus Orchinik *et al.* (204), working with patients of Spiegel & Wycis in whom dorsomedial thalamotomy had been done, found reduced fearfulness of emotionally charged situations of many types. Yet there were "no changes in intellectual functioning, as measured by a standardized test."

Conclusion

Despite all of the foregoing data we are still unable to say what level of the brain must be attained or what constellation of nuclei and fibers must be active if pain is to be perceived. And not only do we not know the mechanisms involved in conversion of awareness of pain to the more grievous state of real suffering, we are uncertain as to the site and extent of lesion required to preclude the appearance of suffering.

ENDOCRINES AND PAIN

The recent introduction of total hypophysectomy in man as a palliative treatment for advanced cancer of the breast has provided an incidental and unexpectedly great reduction in or abolition of the pain in many of the patients so afflicted. Luft & Olivecrona (180) saw these favorable effects in 19 of 24 women in their series, and B. S. Ray has stated that his results are similar. The relief of pain occurs promptly after operation and is not due to cortisone since it continues when the drug is stopped. It has not been correlated with subsidence of tumor and has occurred both in patients who did and in others who did not give objective evidence of remission, as well as in patients who had either subtotal or complete hypophysectomy. These observations open for consideration the possibility that endocrine potentiation of nervous function is implicated in the full development of pain.

ITCHING AND TICKLING

In addition to the various sensations under the heading of pain discussed already there remain for consideration 'itch' and 'tickle.' Although the decisive feature of the stimulus which will lead it to provoke an itch is unclear, the nature of the sensation, i.e. the desire to scratch, is universally understood. An abundance of evidence now exists to indicate that itching is closely related to cutaneous pain. In a number of disorders involving a loss of pain with preservation of touch and proprioception, the capacity to itch in the analgesic zone was long ago shown to be lost (4, 266). This was fully confirmed in a recent study by Arieff *et al.* (7) both in patients with radicular and in those with cord lesions causing the dissociated decrease or loss in appreciation of a pinprick as painful. Itch disappears and reappears along with pain perception in the reversible states of asphyxial nerve block (174, 175) and of local anesthesia (227, 263). Rothman (227) has also noted that the converse is true, i.e. that sensitivity to pain and itching may be preserved in patients in whom there were zones of complete tactile anesthesia. He has also reported itching independent of the sense of temperature. Zotterman (315) interpreted some of his animal experimental results to indicate that peripheral afferent impulses mediating itching traverse C fibers, but the crucial proof was lacking, namely that the animal tended to scratch a zone from which C fiber potentials were arising.

As one moves into the central nervous system the correlation of itching with pain continues; it may be followed first with the central portion of the pain fibers of the primary afferent neuron. Thus operative division of the descending trigeminal tract in the medulla oblongata yielded complete trigeminal analgesia and thermanesthesia in a patient who had before operation such extreme itching that he scratched out all the hair in the left anterior quadrant of his scalp. Postoperatively the itching stopped and the hair grew back (296, pp. 459 and 512). Likewise division of pain fibers at the secondary afferent neuron by section of the anterior quadrant of the cord has stopped even itching of pathologically severe origin and intensity. This was first noted in Sicard & Robineau's patient (246) and in Banzet's (14) case 21, each with bilateral kraurosis vulvae. Further examples are mentioned by White & Sweet (296, p. 261). Bickford (24) produced itching by puncturing histamine solutions into the normal skin; a protracted itch followed the use of a 1:15 dilution. In five patients, including one with a cordotomy whose spinal lesion caused loss of pain to pin while touch was preserved, he could not evoke itching from the analgesic skin. Hyndman & Wolkin (133) were likewise unable to provoke itching by application of itch powder (from *Mucuna pruriens*) to the analgesic areas after cordotomy. Control areas of normal sensation did itch.

There is one discordant observation by Taylor (261). His patient with generalized bilateral itching continued to have this symptom in the analgesic zone following unilateral bulbar spinothalamic tractotomy.

But the itching postoperatively seemed 'deeper in' on the side which no longer felt a pin as sharp. No mention was made as to whether or not pain from deeper structures was stopped by this operation. There is also the possibility that the itching in this patient was of central origin since he felt it everywhere and had no primary skin disease. Intense itching appears to have been provoked by stimulus to the brain in cats upon intracisternal injections of morphine, physostigmine, pilocarpine or acetylcholine (144), and upon intraventricular injection of diisopropyl-fluorophosphate (DFP) or physostigmine (76). A centrally induced itch probably does not require intact spinothalamic pathways to achieve conscious recognition.

Investigations of the sense of tickle suffer from the difficulty one has in describing the sensation. For Pritchard (217) and Foerster (78) it is 'itching of the weakest intensity' and corresponding to this concept Rothman (228) describes the after-sensation following light strokes, firm strokes and burning stimuli on the skin as tickle, itch and burning pain, respectively—all mediated by 'C' fibers, he says. These speculations lack factual support. Foerster & Gagel (80) and Bickford (24), pursuing the subject into the spinal cord, found tickle sensation absent in the analgesic area after cordotomy; but patients of Peet (208), Hyndman & Wolkin (133) and White & Sweet (296, p. 261) said they could still be tickled in such areas. It scarcely seems worth fussing about.

PAIN AND INHIBITION

Head & Sherren (122) first described, and Foerster (77, p. 28) later confirmed, that division of a cutaneous sensory nerve lowers the threshold to pain in the underlying deep tissues, indicating that the superficial system exerts a moderating influence on the threshold and intensity of deep pain.

Zotterman (315) was one of the first to hypothecate a peripheral inhibiting mechanism on pain within a single nerve. He found only 'C' fiber discharge in the after-stimulation period when itching occurs. The relief of itching by rubbing suggested to him an inhibiting action of fast 'A' fibers on the slower 'C' fibers. Landau & Bishop (150) have extended this concept to account for at least some of the features of hyperpathia seen in lesions of peripheral nerves. They attribute the sensation upon pinprick after partial asphyxial compression of nerve to elimination of 'delta fiber pain.' The pricking pain then changes, is

more intense, more persistent and of a different and burning quality—the result they say of release of the central effect of 'C' fiber activation normally masked by activity of the delta fibers. We have already discussed objections to the concept that pricking and burning pain are mediated by delta and 'C' fibers, respectively. However in those explanations of hyperpathia following central lesions which attribute this state to isolated action of spinoreticulothalamic, spinotectal or other relay routes, there is also implicit the notion that the divided direct spinothalamic pathway normally activated by the same stimulus exerts an inhibiting action on the 'over-response.'

A number of observations point to an inhibiting interaction between rival stimuli resulting in decrease of pain. Thus Bender (17) found that causalgic pain following peripheral nerve injury was relieved by immersion of the opposite normal hand in water, and Graham et al. (108) abolished experimentally-induced itching on the skin of the back by pinprick in the same dermatome on the anterior chest. Hardy et al. (117) demonstrated another form of inhibition of one pain by another in the experimental situation of procaine block to a nerve trunk. Stimulation of the trunk proximal to this site then provokes a zone of hyperalgesia. Repeated pinpricks in this area, however, cause its borders to shrink; the investigators suggest that a central inhibition is occurring.

Further evidence for central inhibitory mechanisms for pain has been adduced by Foerster (77, pp. 77 and 78). In two patients with intramedullary cord lesions he made operative incisions into portions of the posterior columns; a severe cutaneous hyperpathia ensued limited to those areas corresponding to the incised pathways. He attributed this to removal of a mechanism inhibiting pain inherent in the normal pathways for touch and proprioception. In view of the extensive incisions into normal dorsal columns without such sequel reported by Browder & Gallagher (35), Pool (215) and White & Sweet (296, p. 407), Foerster's explanation of his results is no longer tenable. His surgery may have exacerbated effects of the original lesion in gray matter or nearby posterolateral white matter. Regarding the latter possibility, Foerster (77, pp. 79 and 80) has cited the evidence of Fabritius and Brown-Séquard that lesions in the deep posterolateral white matter provoke hyperpathia, i.e. that there is a corticofugal pain inhibiting pathway in this region.

An extraordinary patient has recently been well studied by Trent (268). Nearly four years after injury to the left temporoparietal cerebrum the man began to have pain in his right upper limb, maximal in thumb and axilla. This on examination proved to be accompanied by "hyperalgesia to pin prick, hyperesthesia to warm and cold" and intense pain from a vibrating tuning fork when applied over sharply defined areas of the limb and chest. Both the spontaneous pain, and the abnormal responses to pinprick, temperature and vibration were completely and immediately stopped by pressure on the anterior surfaces of the tips of the medial four right fingers; later, pressure only on the tips of fingers four and five sufficed to stop the pain. The inhibitory mechanism did not tend to fatigue and the patient could and did keep away the pain by keeping his fingers clenched to a fist. The purely clinical observations gave no clue to the mechanism of such inhibition.

The converse situation in which pain exerts an inhibitory effect on simultaneous perception of non-painful stimuli has been studied by Benjamin (19). He found that several forms of experimental pain all increased the thresholds of hearing over the total tonal range, flicker fusion, vibration at 60 cps and contact heat. The mean threshold raising effect was generally proportional to intensity of pain.

REFERRED PAIN

Under a variety of circumstances pain arising from impulses in one structure, usually deeply placed such as a viscus, is referred wholly or partly to some other area, usually superficial. The paucity of nerve endings in the deep tissues and the small volume of conscious sensation normally arising from these protected areas allow lesser opportunity for the cerebral cortex to build up a pattern of the internal image of the body as detailed as that of the surface. And indeed the cerebral mechanism for so doing is much smaller, as witness the tiny cerebral cortical area of splanchnic representation found by Amassian (5). If then noxious stimuli arising from deep structures converge upon the same neuron as such stimuli from the skin, the sensory centers may refer the origin of the stimulus to the far more frequent site of such origin—namely the skin.

That the peripheral neuron itself may be one of the sites of the convergence has been suggested by Sinclair et al. (251). The bifurcation of a single parent axon into two limbs, each passing into a different nerve trunk, has been demonstrated in fish by Wernøe (292), in amphibia by Adrian et al. (2) and probably in mammals by Lloyd (179), but not yet in man. However, the phenomena of summation, inhibition

and irradiation—all demonstrable in connection with referred pain—are more readily explicable on a central basis. Hence Weddell himself (287) is inclined to place the mechanism for referred pain mainly in the central nervous system.

Ruch (231) has drawn attention to one likely site of convergence of visceral and cutaneous afferents, namely the cells of the secondary afferent neuron in the posterior horn, because he finds many more 'pain fibers' in the posterior roots than axons in the spinothalamic tracts. If it is true that there are more primary than secondary afferent fibers potentially concerned with pain, then two of the former, one from a viscus, the other from skin, may well terminate in relation to a single dorsal horn cell. Excitation of the pool of such cells from a viscus may then result in erroneous reference to the skin.

Physiologic evidence for confluence of cutaneous and deep afferent pathways upon a single neuron has been acquired by demonstration of firing of the central neuron by either the cutaneous or the deep sensory nerve. Proof that it is indeed the same neuron responding is enhanced by the finding of 'occlusion,' i.e. that after excitation of the central neuron from one peripheral source there elapses an 'unresponsive period' during which it cannot be excited from the other peripheral source. Such convergence upon single neural units in the thalamic nucleus ventralis posterolateralis of the cat has been found by MacLeod (181) specifically related to delta afferent fibers in the splanchnic nerves and hence presumptively related to pain. In fact the majority of the cells responding to splanchnic delta afferents also responded to stimulation of the skin, usually that of the trunk but at times that of limbs or tail. Such thalamic cells were present both ipsilateral and contralateral to the splanchnic stimulus. The duration of the 'unresponsive period' of the pathway depended upon which peripheral field was stimulated first, and the response to stimulation of one of the fields was at times intermittent while that from the other field was consistent. Hence MacLeod, cited by Gordon (105), considered it unlikely that the confluence occurred peripherally in branches of the primary afferent neuron.

Widén (298) has also studied in similar fashion delta afferent fibers projecting to the anterior lobe of the cerebellum. This region was excited by stimulation of either a lower intercostal nerve or the splanchnic delta fibers and a high degree of occlusion between them was found. Although these studies are less clearly related to referred pain because of the lack of correlation between the cerebellum and conscious sensation, they provide another example of convergence of probable visceral pain and somatic afferent fibers upon a single central neuron.

Clinical observations have revealed that an added state, that of hyperalgesia or even tenderness upon pressure, may be seen in the area of skin to which pain is erroneously referred. Sinclair *et al.* (251) have explained this, in their peripheral theory, on the basis of antidromic impulses moving down the cutaneous branch of the parent axon (after stimulation of the visceral branch) to excite secondarily endings of other overlapping nerve fibers, perhaps via metabolites (171, p. 80). Wolff & Hardy (305) after studying referred pain and hyperalgesia in experiments on themselves favor the theory that an increasing central excitatory state presumably in the spinal cord is evoked by an increasing barrage of afferent stimuli. They noted, for example, that placement of the fourth finger in ice water caused pain which spread gradually from the immersed digit to those contiguous to it. They thought the referred pain did not develop quickly enough to be accounted for on the basis of branching primary afferent axons. Moreover procainization of the digital nerves in the painful finger out of the ice water did not stop the pain. It should have done so if antidromically conducted stimuli had produced an irritating metabolite or were otherwise secondarily activating adjoining nerves.

However, the spread of a central excitatory state would account for the varying findings following procainization of the cutaneous area of referred pain and hyperalgesia. Procaine injection may stop these manifestations (291), perhaps because it diminishes the excitatory state at central cells by virtue of stopping subthreshold impulses from the skin, but a variety of forms of experimental pain will break through and cause referred pain within or around the anesthetic zone of skin when the stimulus becomes more intense. These were the findings of Theobald (262) with respect to referred suprapubic pain caused by faradization of the uterus, and of Jones & Chapman, cited by White & Sweet (296, p. 74) relative to the cutaneous pain of experimental jejunal distention. In some studies procainization of the cutaneous area of reference did not stop the pain at all; this was the experience of Woollard *et al.* (309) whose direct stimulation of the phrenic nerve caused shoulder pain, and of McLellan & Goodell, cited by White & Sweet (296, p. 74) who distended ureters causing pain in loin and groin. These results can all be explained by assuming that the central excitatory state from such visceral stimulation was in itself adequate

to discharge the mechanism pertinent to cutaneous reference. Such increase in the central excitatory level may also arise from an increase in impulses from the cutaneous area. Thus Cohen (47) describes two patients with attacks of cardiac anginal pain never referred to the arm in question until in one instance the man fractured his elbow and in the other a blistered area developed after a vesicant plaster to the elbow region. Then both patients' anginal attacks included reference to the injured elbow.

Still another form of erroneous reference of pain may occur after injury to central pathways concerned therewith. Ray & Wolff (222) have studied four patients after anterolateral cordotomy in whom noxious stimuli of high intensity in the analgesic area induced pain of low intensity referred to the same or nearby segments on the opposite normally innervated side. The stimuli included squeezing of muscle, deep pressure against a diseased hip joint and application of heat at 80° to 90°C. The authors pointed out that some of the collaterals of entering primary afferent fibers proceed to synaptic relation in the posterior horns with internuncial neurons whose axons cross in the most dorsal part of the posterior commissure to terminate about cells in the posterior horns of the other side. The foregoing observations suggest that with sufficient background of facilitation and sufficient intensity of stimulation such indirect chains may transmit impulses which eventually excite the intact spinothalamic tract on the other side and are referred to the side opposite that stimulated. Inherent in this explanation is the assumption that with both spinothalamic pathways functioning before operation, there was some form of interference with the internuncial polysynaptic transmission. That such internuncial relays extend longitudinally in the cord as well is indicated by our observations (296, p. 257) and those of Holbrook & de Gutiérrez-Mahoney (128). We all found that some patients after cordotomy may refer pain to a much more rostral segment than that undergoing intense stimulation, still either in the analgesic area or above it; the pain experienced was much milder than that produced in normal circumstances by such stimuli. In both types of incorrect reference of the origin of impulses traversing less direct pathways, the patient interprets them as though they had travelled only the customary direct route.

We may well close this chapter with a quotation from Foerster & Gagel (80). "Pain has a vital significance; it is no wonder then that those physical processes associated with the psychic experience of pain have the broadest anatomical basis. The impulses leading to pain penetrate to and upwards within the central nervous system by a thousand devious routes. The wisdom of nature, which has placed pain as the guardian over life and health, has provided it with many paths and many back doors." Even the main avenues and mechanisms for pain are still poorly understood; the task of the neurophysiologist in this field lies largely before him.

REFERENCES

1. ADRIAN, E. D. *The Basis of Sensation*. London: Christophers, 1928.
2. ADRIAN, E. D., McK. CATTELL AND H. HOAGLAND, *J. Physiol.* 72: 377, 1931.
3. ADSON, A. W. *Proc. Staff Meet. Mayo Clin.* 10: 623, 1935.
4. ALRUTZ, S. *Skandinav. Arch. Physiol.* 17: 414, 1905.
5. AMASSIAN, V. E. *J. Neurophysiol.* 14: 445, 1951.
6. AMASSIAN, V. E. *A. Res. Nerv. & Ment. Dis., Proc.* 30: 371, 1952.
7. ARIEFF, A. J., S. W. PYZIK AND E. L. TIGAY. *A.M.A. Arch. Neurol. & Psychiat.* 77: 156, 1957.
8. ARISTOTLE. *Nicomachean Ethics*, translated by Sir David Ross. London: Oxford, 1954, Bk. II, 3.
9. ARMSTRONG, D., R. M. L. DRY, C. A. KEELE AND J. W. MARKHAM. *J. Physiol.* 120: 326, 1953.
10. ARMSTRONG, D., J. B. JEPSON, C. A. KEELE AND J. W. STEWART. *J. Physiol.* 135: 350, 1957.
11. ASHBY, M. *Brain* 72: 599, 1949.
12. BAILEY, P., J. G. DUSSER DE BARENNE, H. W. GAROL AND W. S. McCULLOCH. *J. Neurophysiol.* 3: 469, 1940.
13. BALCHUM, O. J. AND H. M. WEAVER. *A.M.A. Arch. Neurol. & Psychiat.* 49: 739, 1943.
14. BANZET, P. M. *La Cordotomie. Étude Anatomique, Technique, Clinique, et Physiologique.* Paris: Arnette, 1927.
15. BEECHER, H. K. *J.A.M.A.* 161: 1609, 1956.
16. BEECHER, H. K. *Pharmacol. Rev.* 9: 59, 1957.
17. BENDER, M. B. *A.M.A. Arch. Neurol. & Psychiat.* 54: 1, 1945.
18. BENJAMIN, F. B. *J. Appl. Physiol.* 5: 740, 1953.
19. BENJAMIN, F. B. *J. Appl. Physiol.* 8: 630, 1956.
20. BENJAMIN, F. B. *J. Invest. Dermat.* 26: 471, 1956.
21. BENTLEY, F. H. *Ann. Surg.* 128: 881, 1948.
22. BENTLEY, F. H. AND R. H. SMITHWICK. *Lancet* 239: 389, 1940.
23. BETHE, A. *Arch. mikroskop. Anat.* 44: 185, 1894.
24. BICKFORD, R. G. *Clin. Sc.* 3: 337, 1938.
25. BIEMOND, A. *A.M.A. Arch. Neurol. & Psychiat.* 75: 231, 1956.
26. BIGELOW, N., I. HARRISON, H. GOODELL AND H. G. WOLFF. *J. Clin. Invest.* 24: 503, 1945.
27. BISHOP, G. H. *J. Neurophysiol.* 6: 361, 1943.
28. BISHOP, G. H. AND P. HEINBECKER. *Proc. Soc. Exper. Biol. & Med.* 26: 241, 1928.
29. BOK, S. T. In: *Handbuch der Mikroskopischen Anatomie des Menschen*, edited by W. von Möllendorff. Berlin: Springer, 1929, vol. IV.
30. BORING, E. G. *Quart. J. Exper. Physiol.* 10: 1, 1916.
31. BOWSHER, D. *Brain* 80: 606, 1957.
32. BOYD, D. A., JR. AND L. W. NIE. *A.M.A. Arch. Neurol. & Psychiat.* 61: 402, 1949.
33. BRASHEAR, A. D. *J. Comp. Neurol.* 64: 169, 1936.
34. BROOKHART, J. M., W. K. LIVINGSTON AND F. P. HAUGEN. *J. Neurophysiol.* 16: 634, 1953.
35. BROWDER, E. J. AND J. P. GALLAGHER. *Ann. Surg.* 128: 456, 1948.
36. BULLOCK, T. H. *Fed. Proc.* 12: 666, 1953.
37. CADWALDER, W. B. AND J. E. SWEET. *J.A.M.A.* 58: 1490, 1912.
38. CANNON, B. *Am. J. Physiol.* 105: 366, 1933.
39. CHAPMAN, W. P. *Psychosom. Med.* 6: 252, 1944.
40. CHAPMAN, W. P. AND C. N. JONES. *J. Clin. Invest.* 23: 81, 1944.
41. CHAPMAN, W. P., A. S. ROSE AND H. C. SOLOMON. *A. Res. Nerv. & Ment. Dis., Proc.* 27: 754, 1948.
42. CLARK, D., J. HUGHES AND H. S. GASSER. *Am. J. Physiol.* 114: 69, 1935.
43. CLARK, W. E. *J. Anat.* 71: 7, 1936.
44. CLAUSEN, J. AND H. E. KING. *J. Phychol.* 30: 299, 1950.
45. CLEVELAND, D. A. *J. Comp. Neurol.* 54: 35, 1932.
46. COBB, S. *A.M.A. Arch. Neurol. & Psychiat.* 2: 505, 1919.
47. COHEN, H. *Tr. M. Soc. London* 64: 35, 1944.
48. COLLINS, W. F. AND J. L. O'LEARY. *Electroencephalog. & Clin. Neurophysiol.* 6: 619, 1954.
49. COLLINS, W. F. AND C. T. RANDT. *J. Neurophysiol.* 19: 438, 1956.
50. CRAWFORD, A. S. *A.M.A. Arch. Surg.* 55: 523, 1947.
51. CRITCHLEY, M. *Brit. M. J.* 2: 891, 1934.
52. DANDY, W. E. *Bull. Johns Hopkins Hosp.* 53: 31, 1933.
53. DARWIN, E. *Zoönomia, or The Laws of Organic Life*. London: J. Johnson, 1794, vol. I.
54. DAVIS, L., J. T. HART AND R. C. CRAIN. *Surg. Gynec. & Obst.* 48: 647, 1929.
55. DAVIS, L. AND L. J. POLLOCK. *A.M.A. Arch. Neurol. & Psychiat.* 27: 282, 1932.
56. DAVIS, L., L. J. POLLOCK AND T. T. STONE. *Surg. Gynec. & Obst.* 55: 418, 1932.
57. DAVISON, C. AND W. SCHICK. *A.M.A. Arch. Neurol. & Psychiat.* 34: 1204, 1935.
58. DAWSON, G. D. AND J. W. SCOTT. *J. Neurol. Neurosurg. & Psychiat.* 12: 259, 1949.
59. DEARBORN, G. VAN N. *J. Nerv. & Ment. Dis.* 75: 612, 1932.
60. DÉJERINE, J. AND J. MOUZON. *Rev. neurol.* 28: 1265, 1915.
61. DÉJERINE, J. AND G. ROUSSY. *Rev. neurol.* 14: 521, 1906.
62. DELGADO, J. M. R. *J. Neurophysiol.* 18: 261, 1955.
63. DENTON, J. E. AND H. K. BEECHER. *J.A.M.A.* 141: 1051, 1949.
64. D'ERRICO, A. *J. Neurosurg.* 7: 294, 1950.
65. DE SPINOZA, B. *The Philosophy of Spinoza*. New York: Carlton House, 1927, p. 217.
66. DOGIEL, A. S. *Arch. mikroskop. Anat.* 52: 44, 1898.
67. DOGLIOTTI, M. *Anesth. et analg.* 17: 143, 1938.
68. DOUPE, J., C. H. CULLEN AND G. Q. CHANCE. *J. Neurol. Neurosurg. & Psychiat.* 7: 33, 1944.

69. DRAKE, C. G. AND K. G. McKENZIE. *J. Neurosurg.* 10: 457, 1953.

70. DUSSER DE BARENNE, J. G. In: *Handbuch der Neurologie*, edited by Bumke and Foerster. Berlin: Springer, 1937, vol. 2, p. 268.

71. ECHLIN, F. *J. Neurosurg.* 6: 530, 1949.

72. ECHLIN, F. AND A. FESSARD. *J. Physiol.* 93: 312, 1938.

73. EICHLER, W. *Ztschr. Psychol. Physiol. Sinnesorg.* 60: 325, 1930.

74. ERICKSON, T. C., W. J. BLECKWENN AND C. N. WOOLSEY. *Tr. Am. Neurol. A.* 77: 57, 1952.

75. FALCONER, M. A. *J. Neurol. Neurosurg. & Psychiat.* 12: 297, 1949.

76. FELDBERG, W. AND S. L. SHERWOOD. *J. Physiol.* 125: 488, 1954.

77. FOERSTER, O. *Die Leitungsbahnen des Schmerzgefühls und die chirurgische Behandlung der Schmerzzustände.* Berlin: Urban, 1927.

78. FOERSTER, O. In: *Handbuch der Neurologie*, edited by Bumke and Foerster. Berlin: Springer, 1936, vol. 6, p. 358.

79. FOERSTER, O., H. ALTENBURGER AND F. W. KROLL. *Ztschr. ges. Neurol. Psychiat.* 121: 139, 1929.

80. FOERSTER, O. AND O. GAGEL. *Ztschr. ges. Neurol. Psychiat.* 138: 1, 1932.

81. FORD, F. R. AND L. WILKINS. *Bull. Johns Hopkins Hosp.* 62: 448, 1938.

82. FRAZIER, C. H. *A.M.A. Arch. Neurol. & Psychiat.* 19: 650, 1928.

83. FRAZIER, C. H. AND W. G. SPILLER. *A.M.A. Arch. Neurol. & Psychiat.* 9: 1, 1923.

84. FREEMAN, W. AND J. WATTS. *Psychosurgery in the Treatment of Mental Disorders & Intractable Pain* (2nd ed.). Springfield: Thomas, 1950.

85. FRENCH, J. D., E. K. VON AMERONGEN AND H. W. MAGOUN. *A.M.A. Arch. Neurol. & Psychiat.* 68: 577, 1952.

86. GAD, J. AND A. GOLDSCHEIDER. *Ztschr. klin. Med.* 20: 339, 1892.

87. GARDNER, E. AND H. M. CUNEO. *A.M.A. Arch. Neurol. & Psychiat.* 53: 423, 1945.

88. GARDNER, W. J., L. J. KARNOSCH, C. C. McCLURE, JR. AND ANN K. GARDNER. *Brain* 78: 487, 1955.

89. GASSER, H. S. *A. Res. Nerv. & Ment. Dis., Proc.* 23: 44, 1943.

90. GASSER, H. S. *Les Prix Nobel en 1940–1944.* Stockholm: Norstedt, 1946, p. 128.

91. GASSER, H. S. AND J. ERLANGER. *Am. J. Physiol.* 88: 581, 1929.

92. GASSER, H. S. AND H. GRUNDFEST. *Am. J. Physiol.* 127: 393, 1939.

93. GAZE, R. M. AND G. GORDON. *Quart. J. Exper. Physiol.* 39: 279, 1954.

94. GAZE, R. M. AND G. GORDON. *Quart. J. Exper. Physiol.* 40: 187, 1955.

95. GERARD, M. W. *A.M.A. Arch. Neurol. & Psychiat.* 9: 306, 1923.

96. GERNANDT, B. AND Y. ZOTTERMAN. *Acta. physiol. scandinav.* 12: 56, 1946.

97. GLEES, P. *J. Neuropath. & Exper. Neurol.* 5: 54, 1946.

98. GLEES, P. *Acta neuroveg.* 7: 160, 1953.

99. GLEES, P. AND R. A. BAILEY. *Monatsschr. Psychiat. u. Neurol.* 122: 129, 1951.

100. GOETZL, F. R., C. W. BIEN AND G. LU. *J. Appl. Physiol.* 4: 161, 1951.

101. GOLDSCHEIDER, A. *Arch. ges. Physiol.* Suppl. 1: 1, 1885.

102. GOLDSCHEIDER, A. *Arch. ges. Physiol.* 39: 96, 1886.

103. GOLDSTEIN, K. *Neurol. Zentralbl.* 29: 898, 1910.

104. GOODDY, W. *Brain* 80: 118, 1957.

105. GORDON, G. *Proc. Roy. Soc. Med.* 50: 586, 1957.

106. GORDON, G. AND D. WHITTERIDGE. *Lancet* 245: 700, 1943.

107. GORHAM, L. W. *A. Res. Nerv. & Ment. Dis., Proc.* 23: 337, 1942.

108. GRAHAM, D. T., H. GOODELL AND H. G. WOLFF. *J. Clin. Invest.* 30: 37, 1951.

109. GRANIT, R., L. LEKSELL AND C. R. SKOGLUND. *Brain* 67: 125, 1944.

110. GRANT, F. C. *Ann. Surg.* 92: 998, 1930.

111. GRANTHAM, E. G. *J. Neurosurg.* 8: 405, 1951.

112. GRIMSON, K. S., F. H. HESSER AND W. W. KITCHIN. *Surgery* 22: 230, 1947.

113. HAGBOOD, J. S. *J. Physiol.* 111: 195, 1950.

114. HÄGGQVIST, G. *Ztschr. mikroskop.-anat. Forsch.* 39: 1, 1936.

115. HARDY, J. D., H. G. WOLFF AND H. GOODELL. *J. Clin. Invest.* 19: 649, 1940.

116. HARDY, J. D., H. G. WOLFF AND H. GOODELL. *A. Res. Nerv. & Ment. Dis., Proc.* 23: 1, 1943.

117. HARDY, J. D., H. G. WOLFF AND H. GOODELL. *J. Clin. Invest.* 29: 115, 1950.

118. HARDY, J. D., H. G. WOLFF AND H. GOODELL. *Pain Sensations and Reactions.* Baltimore: Williams & Wilkins, 1952.

119. HARRIS, W. *Brit. M. J.* 2: 112, 1936.

120. HARRISON, F. AND K. B. CORBIN. *J. Neurophysiol.* 5: 465, 1942.

121. HEAD, H., W. H. R. RIVERS AND J. SHERREN. *Brain* 28: 99, 1905.

122. HEAD, H. AND J. SHERREN. *Brain* 28: 116, 1905.

123. HECAEN, H. AND J. DE AJURIAGUERRA. *Rev. neurol.* 83: 300, 1950.

124. HECAEN, H., J. TALAIRACH, M. DAVID AND M. B. DELL. *Rev. neurol.* 81: 917, 1949.

125. HEINBECKER, P., G. H. BISHOP AND J. O'LEARY. *A.M.A. Arch. Neurol. & Psychiat.* 29: 771, 1933.

126. HELSON, H. *Brain* 55: 114, 1932.

127. HERZEN, A. *Arch. ges. Physiol.* 38: 93, 1886.

128. HOLBROOK, T. J. AND C. G. DE GUTIERREZ-MAHONEY. *Fed. Proc.* 6: 131, 1947.

129. HORRAX, G. *Surgery* 20: 593, 1946.

130. HORSLEY, V. *Brit. M. J.* 2: 125, 1909.

131. HURST (formerly HERTZ), A. F. *Lancet* 89: 1051, 1119, 1187, 1911.

132. HYNDMAN, O. R. *J. Internat. Coll. Surgeons* 5: 394, 1942.

133. HYNDMAN, O. R. AND J. WOLKIN. *A.M.A. Arch. Neurol. & Psychiat.* 50: 129, 1943.

134. JAMES, W. *The Principles of Psychology.* New York: Holt, 1890.

135. JAVERT, C. T. AND J. D. HARDY. *Anesthesiology* 12: 189, 1951.

136. JEWESBURY, E. C. O. *Brain* 74: 336, 1951.

137. JONES, M. H. *Science* 124: 442, 1956.

138. KARPLUS, I. P. AND A. KREIDL. *Arch. ges. Physiol.* 207: 134, 1925.

139. KATSUKI, Y., S. YOSHINO AND J. CHEN. *Jap. J. Physiol.* 1: 179, 1951.

140. KELLGREN, J. H. *Clin. Sc.* 4: 35, 1939.

141. KING, R. B. *Neurology* 7: 610, 1957.

142. KINSELLA, V. J. *Brit. J. Surg.* 27: 449, 1940.

143. KLEIST, K. In: *Handbuch der Ärztlichen Erfahrungen im Weltkriege.* Leipzig: Barth, 1934, vol. 4, pt. 2, p. 1416.

144. KOENIGSTEIN, H. *A.M.A. Arch. Dermat. & Syph.* 57: 828, 1948.

145. KOSKOFF, Y. D., W. DENNIS, D. LAZOVIK AND E. T. WHEELER. *A. Res. Nerv. & Ment. Dis., Proc.* 27: 901, 1948.

146. KRAYENBÜHL, H. AND W. A. STOLL. *Acta neurochir.* 1: 1, 1950.

147. KROLL, F. W. *Ztschr. ges. Neurol. Psychiat.* 128: 751, 1930.

148. KUNKLE, E. C. AND W. P. CHAPMAN. *A. Res. Nerv. & Ment. Dis., Proc.* 23: 100, 1943.

149. KURU, M. *Sensory Paths in the Spinal Cord and Brain Stem of Man.* Tokyo: Sôgensya, 1949.

150. LANDAU, W. M. AND G. H. BISHOP. *A.M.A. Arch. Neurol. & Psychiat.* 69: 490, 1953.

151. LANDIS, E. M. *Heart* 15: 209, 1930.

152. LANGLEY, J. N. *Phil. Trans. Roy. Soc., London* 183: 114, 1892.

153. LANGLEY, J. N. *J. Physiol.* 20: 55, 1896.

154. LANGLEY, J. N. *J. Physiol.* 25: 468, 1900.

155. LANGLEY, J. N. *Brain* 26: 1, 1903.

156. LANGLEY, J. N. *Lancet* 207: 955, 1924.

157. LANIER, L. H., H. M. CARNEY AND W. D. WILSON. *A.M.A. Arch. Neurol. & Psychiat.* 34: 1, 1935.

158. LAVRENKO, V. V. *Bull. Exper. Biol. Med., U.S.S.R.* (in Russian). 5: 37, 1938.

159. LeBEAU, J. *Psycho-chirurgie et Fonctions Mentales.* Paris: Masson, 1954, p. 429.

160. LEDUC, E. H. AND D. SLAUGHTER. *Anesth. & Analg.* 24: 147, 1945.

161. LELE, P. P. AND D. C. SINCLAIR. *J. Neurol. Neurosurg. & Psychiat.* 18: 120, 1955.

162. LELE, P. P., D. C. SINCLAIR AND G. WEDDELL. *J. Physiol.* 123: 187, 1954.

163. LELE, P. P. AND G. WEDDELL. *Brain* 79: 119, 1956.

164. LENNANDER, K. G. *Zentralbl. Chir.* 28: 209, 1901.

165. LENNANDER, K. G. *Mitt. Grenzg. Med. Chir.* 15: 465, 1906.

166. LERICHE, R. *Presse méd.* 45: 971, 1937.

167. LERICHE, R. *La Chirurgie de la Douleur.* Paris: Masson 1949.

168. LERICHE, R. AND R. FONTAINE. *Rev. neurol.* 32: 483, 1925.

169. LEWIN, W. AND C. G. PHILLIPS. *J. Neurol. Neurosurg. & Psychiat.* 15: 143, 1952.

170. LEWIS, T. *Brit. M. J.* 1: 321, 1938.

171. LEWIS, T. *Pain.* New York: Macmillan, 1942, p. 187.

172. LEWIS, T. AND W. HESS. *Clin. Sc.* 1: 39, 1933.

173. LEWIS, T., G. W. PICKERING AND P. ROTHSCHILD. *Heart* 16: 1, 1931.

174. LEWIS, T. AND E. E. POCHIN. *Clin. Sc.* 3: 67, 1937.

175. LEWIS, T. AND E. E. POCHIN. *Clin. Sc.* 3: 141, 1938.

176. LINDGREN, I. AND H. OLIVECRONA. *J. Neurosurg.* 4: 19, 1947.

177. LIVINGSTON, W. K. *J. Neurosurg.* 4: 140, 1947.

178. LLOYD, D. P. C. *J. Neurophysiol.* 6: 293, 1943.

179. LLOYD, D. P. C. *Physiol. Rev.* 24: 1, 1944.

180. LUFT, R. AND H. OLIVECRONA. *Cancer* 8: 261, 1955.

181. MacLEOD, J. G. *J. Physiol.* 133: 16P, 1956.

182. MADONICK, M. J. *Neurology* 4: 554, 1954.

183. MAGLADERY J,. W., D. B. McDOUGAL, JR. AND J. STOLL. *Bull. Johns Hopkins Hosp.* 86: 291, 1950.

184. MARSHALL, J. *J. Neurol. Neurosurg. & Psychiat.* 14: 187, 1951.

185. MARUHASHI, J., K. MIZUGUCHI AND I. TASAKI. *J. Physiol.* 117: 129, 1952.

186. McKINLEY, W. A. AND H. W. MAGOUN. *Am. J. Physiol.* 137: 217, 1942.

187. MEHLER, W. R. *Anat. Rec.* 127: 332, 1957.

188. MEHLER, W. R., M. E. FEFERMAN AND W. J. H. NAUTA. *Anat. Rec.* 124: 332, 1956.

189. MICHELSEN, J. J. *A. Res. Nerv. & Ment. Dis., Proc.* 23: 86, 1943.

190. MORIN, F., H. G. SCHWARTZ AND J. L. O'LEARY. *Acta psychiat. et neurol. scandinav.* 26: 371, 1951.

191. MORISON, R. S. AND E. W. DEMPSEY. *Am. J. Physiol.* 135: 281, 1942.

192. MORITZ, A. R. AND F. C. HENRIQUES, JR. *Am. J. Path.* 23: 695, 1947.

193. MORTON, D. R., K. P. KLASSEN AND G. M. CURTIS. *Surgery* 30: 800, 1951.

194. MORUZZI, G. AND H. W. MAGOUN. *Electroencephalog. & Clin. Neurophysiol.* 1: 455, 1949.

195. MOTT, F. W. *Brain* 15: 215, 1892.

196. MOUNTCASTLE, V. B., M. R. COVIAN AND C. R. HARRISON. *A. Res. Nerv. & Ment. Dis., Proc.* 30: 339, 1952.

197. MUELLER, E. E., R. LOEFFEL AND S. MEAD. *J. Appl. Physiol.* 5: 746, 1953.

198. NAFE, J. P. In: *Handbook of General Experimental Psychology,* edited by C. A. Murchison. Worcester: Clark Univ. Press, 1934, chapt. 20.

199. NAUTA, W. J. H. AND P. A. GYGAX. *Stain Technol.* 29: 91, 1954.

200. NICOLESCO, J. *Compt. rend. Soc. de biol.* 115: 1556, 1934.

201. O'BRIEN, J. L. AND E. S. GOLDENSOHN. *Neurology* 7: 549, 1957.

202. OLSZEWSKI, J. *J. Comp. Neurol.* 92: 401, 1950.

203. OPPEL, T. W. AND J. D. HARDY. *J. Clin. Invest.* 16: 525, 1937.

204. ORCHINIK, C., R. KOCH, H. T. WYCIS, H. FREED AND E. S. SPEIGEL. *A. Res. Nerv. & Ment. Dis., Proc.* 29: 172, 1950.

205. PARTRIDGE, M. *Pre-Frontal Leucotomy.* Springfield: Thomas, 1950.

206. PATTLE, R. E. AND G. WEDDELL. *J. Neurophysiol.* 11: 93, 1948.

207. PEARSON, A. A. *A.M.A. Arch. Neurol. & Psychiat.* 68: 515, 1952.

208. PEET, M. M. *A.M.A. Arch. Surg.* 13: 153, 1926.

209. PEET, M. M. *A.M.A. Arch. Neurol. & Psychiat.* 22: 313, 1929.

210. PENFIELD, W. AND E. BOLDREY. *Brain* 60: 389, 1937.

211. PENFIELD, W. AND T. RASMUSSEN. *The Cerebral Cortex of Man.* New York: Macmillan, 1950, p. 44.

212. PIÉRON, H. *Compt. rend. Soc. de biol.* 103: 883, 1930.

213. POIRIER, L. J. AND C. BERTRAND. *J. Comp. Neurol.* 102: 745, 1955.

214. POLLOCK, L. J. *A.M.A. Arch. Neurol. & Psychiat.* 2: 667, 1919.

215. POOL, J. L. *Ann. Surg.* 124: 386, 1946.

216. POOL, J. L. *Tr. & Stud. Coll. Physicians Philadelphia* 19: 49, 1951.
217. PRITCHARD, E. A. B. *Proc. Roy. Soc. Med.* 26: 697, 1933.
218. RANSON, S. W. *J.A.M.A.* 86: 1887, 1926.
219. RANSON, S. W. AND P. R. BILLINGSLEY. *Am. J. Physiol.* 40: 571, 1916.
220. RASMUSSEN, A. T. AND W. T. PEYTON. *Surgery* 10: 699, 1941.
221. RAY, B. S. AND C. L. NEILL. *Ann. Surg.* 126: 709, 1947.
222. RAY, B. S. AND H. G. WOLFF. *A.M.A. Arch. Neurol. & Psychiat.* 53: 257, 1945.
223. RIVERS, W. H. R. AND H. HEAD. *Brain* 31: 323, 1908.
224. ROE, W. *Proc. Roy. Soc. Med.* 43: 250, 1950.
225. ROSENBACH, O. *Deutsche med. Wchnschr.* 10: 338, 1884.
226. ROSENTHAL, S. R. *Proc. Soc. Exper. Biol. & Med.* 74: 167, 1950.
227. ROTHMAN, S. *Arch. Dermat. u. Syph.* 139: 227, 1922.
228. ROTHMAN, S. *A. Res. Nerv. & Ment. Dis., Proc.* 23: 110, 1943.
229. ROUSSY, G. *Rev. neurol.* 17: 301, 1909.
230. RUBINS, J. L. AND E. D. FRIEDMAN. *A.M.A. Arch. Neurol. & Psychiat.* 60: 554, 1948.
231. RUCH, T. C. *A Textbook of Physiology* (16th ed.), edited by J. F. Fulton. Philadelphia: Saunders, 1949, p. 360.
232. RUCH, T. C., H. D. PATTON AND V. E. AMASSIAN. *A. Res. Nerv. & Ment. Dis., Proc.* 30: 403, 1952.
233. RUSSELL, W. R. *Brain* 68: 79, 1945.
234. RYLANDER, G. *A. Res. Nerv. & Ment. Dis., Proc.* 27: 691, 1948.
235. SCARFF, J. E. *J. Neurosurg.* 7: 330, 1950.
236. SCHACTER, M. *Praxis* 45: 681, 1956.
237. SCHAMP, J. R. AND H. M. SCHAMP. *J. Dent. Res.* 25: 101, 1946.
238. SCHIFF, J. M. In: *Lehrbuch der Physiologie des Menschen.* Lahr: Schauenburg, 1858, vol. 1.
239. SCHILDER, P. AND E. STENGEL. *Ztschr. ges. Neurol. Psychiat.* 113: 143, 1928.
240. SCHILDER, P. AND E. STENGEL. *A.M.A. Arch. Neurol. & Psychiat.* 25: 598, 1931.
241. SCHUMACHER, G. A., H. GOODELL, J. D. HARDY AND H. G. WOLFF. *Science* 92: 110, 1940.
242. SCHWARTZ, H. G. AND J. L. O'LEARY. *Surgery* 9: 183, 1941.
243. SCHWARTZ, H. G. AND J. L. O'LEARY. *A.M.A. Arch. Neurol. & Psychiat.* 47: 293, 1942.
244. SCOVILLE, W. B., E. K. WILK AND A. J. PEPE. *Am. J. Psychiat.* 107: 730, 1951.
245. SHARPEY-SCHAFER, E. *Quart. J. Exper. Physiol.* 19: 85, 1928.
246. SICARD, J. A. AND ROBINEAU. *Rev. neurol.* 1: 21, 1925.
247. SINCLAIR, D. C. *Brain* 78: 584, 1955.
248. SINCLAIR, D. C. AND J. R. HINSHAW. *Brain* 73: 224, 1950.
249. SINCLAIR, D. C. AND J. R. HINSHAW. *Brain* 73: 480, 1950.
250. SINCLAIR, D. C. AND J. R. HINSHAW. *Quart. J. Exper. Psychol.* 3: 49, 1951.
251. SINCLAIR, D. C., G. WEDDELL AND W. H. FEINDEL. *Brain* 71: 184, 1948.
252. SLAUGHTER, D. AND F. T. WRIGHT. *Anesth. & Analg.* 23: 115, 1944.
253. SPIEGEL, E. A. AND W. J. BERNIS. *Arch. ges. Physiol.* 210: 209, 1925.

254. STARZL, T. E. AND D. G. WHITLOCK. *J. Neurophysiol.* 15: 449, 1952.
255. STOOKEY, B. *J. Nerv. & Ment. Dis.* 69: 552, 1929.
256. STRUGHOLD, H. *Ztschr. Biol.* 80: 367, 1924.
257. SUTTON, D. C. AND H. C. LUETH. *A.M.A. Arch. Int. Med.* 45: 827, 1930.
258. SWANK, R. L. AND H. A. DAVENPORT. *Stain Technol.* 9: 129, 1934.
259. SWEET, W. H. *J.A.M.A.* 142: 392, 1950.
260. TALAIRACH, J., H. HECAEN, M. DAVID, M. MONNIER AND J. DE AJURIAGUERRA. *Rev. neurol.* 81: 4, 1949.
261. TAYLOR, C. W. *J. Neurosurg.* 11: 508, 1954.
262. THEOBALD, G. W. *Lancet* 257: 41, 1949.
263. THÖLE. *Neurol. Zentralbl.* 31: 610, 1912.
264. THUNBERG, T. *Skandinav. Arch. Physiol.* 12: 394, 1902.
265. TINDALL, G. T. AND E. C. KUNKLE. *A.M.A. Arch. Neurol. & Psychiat.* 77: 605, 1957.
266. TÖRÖK, L. *Ztschr. Psychol. Physiol. Sinnesorg. Abt. II* 46: 23, 1907.
267. TOWER, SARAH S. *A. Res. Nerv. & Ment. Dis., Proc.* 23: 16, 1943.
268. TRENT, S. E. *J. Nerv. & Ment. Dis.* 123: 356, 1956.
269. TROTTER, W. *Brit. M. J.* 2: 103, 1926.
270. TROTTER, W. AND H. M. DAVIES. *J. Physiol.* 38: 134, 1909.
271. VAN GEHUCHTEN, A. *Névraxe* 3: 237, 1901.
272. VAN HARREVELD, A. AND H. M. SMITH. *J. Neurophysiol.* 15: 313, 1952.
273. VON FREY, M. *Ber. sächs. Gesellsch. Wiss.* 46: 185, 1894.
274. VON FREY, M. *Ber. sächs. Gesellsch. Wiss.* 48: 175, 1896.
275. WALKER, A. E. *The Primate Thalamus.* Chicago: Univ. Chicago Press, 1938.
276. WALKER, A. E. *A.M.A. Arch. Neurol. & Psychiat.* 43: 284, 1940.
277. WALKER, A. E. *A.M.A. Arch. Surg.* 44: 953, 1942.
278. WALKER, A. E. *A.M.A. Arch. Neurol. & Psychiat.* 48: 884, 1942.
279. WALKER, A. E. *A. Res. Nerv. & Ment. Dis., Proc.* 23: 63, 1943.
280. WALKER, A. E. AND F. NULSEN. *A.M.A. Arch. Neurol. & Psychiat.* 59: 559, 1948.
281. WALLENBERG, A. *Arch. Psychiat.* 34: 923, 1901.
282. WALSHE, F. M. R. *Brain* 65: 48, 1942.
283. WATERSTON, D. *J. Physiol.* 77: 251, 1933.
284. WATERSTON, D. *Lancet* 224: 943, 1933.
285. WEDDELL, G. *J. Anat.* 75: 346, 1941.
286. WEDDELL, G. *J. Anat.* 75: 441, 1941.
287. WEDDELL, G. *Proc. Roy. Soc. Med.* 50: 581, 1957.
288. WEDDELL, G., W. PALLIE AND E. PALMER. *Quart. J. Microsc. Sc.* 95: 483, 1954.
289. WEDDELL, G., D. C. SINCLAIR AND W. H. FEINDEL. *J. Neurophysiol.* 11: 99, 1948.
290. WEINSTEIN, E. A., R. L. KAHN AND W. H. SLOTE. *A.M.A. Arch. Neurol. & Psychiat.* 74: 235, 1955.
291. WEISS, S. AND D. DAVIS. *Am. J. M. Sc.* 176: 517, 1928.
292. WERNØE, T. B. *Arch. ges. Physiol.* 210: 1, 1925.
293. WHITE, J. C. *A.M.A. Arch. Surg.* 43: 113, 1941.
294. WHITE, J. C. AND E. F. BLAND. *Medicine* 27: 1, 1948.
295. WHITE, J. C., W. E. GARREY AND J. A. ATKINS. *A.M.A. Arch. Surg.* 26: 765, 1933.
296. WHITE, J. C. AND W. H. SWEET. *Pain: Its Mechanisms and Neurosurgical Control.* Springfield: Thomas, 1955.
297. WHYTE, H. M. *Clin. Sc.* 10: 333, 1951.

298. WIDEN, L. *Acta physiol. scandinav.* 33: Suppl. 117, 1955.

299. WILSON, G. AND T. FAY. *A.M.A. Arch. Neurol. & Psychiat.* 22: 638, 1929.

300. WILSON, J. G. *Am. J. Anat.* 11: 101, 1911.

301. WILSON, S. A. K. *Neurology* (2nd ed.), edited by A. N. Bruce. London: Butterworth, 1955, vol. II, p. 703.

302. WINKLER, C. *Manuel de Neurologie.* Haarlem: Bohn, 1921, vol. 1, pt. 2, p. 51.

303. WOLFF, H. G. *Headache and Other Pain.* New York: Oxford, 1948.

304. WOLFF, H. G. AND H. GOODELL. *A. Res. Nerv. & Ment. Dis., Proc.* 23: 434, 1943.

305. WOLFF, H. G. AND J. D. HARDY. *Physiol. Rev.* 27: 167, 1947.

306. WOLFF, H. G., J. D. HARDY AND H. GOODELL. *J. Clin. Invest.* 19: 659, 1940.

307. WOOLLARD, H. H. *Brain* 58: 352, 1935.

308. WOOLLARD, H. H. *J. Anat.* 71: 480, 1937.

309. WOOLLARD, H. H., J. E. H. ROBERTS AND E. A. CARMICHAEL. *Lancet* 222: 337, 1932.

310. WOOLLARD, H. H., G. WEDDELL AND J. A. HARPMAN. *J. Anat.* 74: 413, 1940.

311. WOOLSEY, C. N. AND D. FAIRMAN. *Surgery* 19: 684, 1946.

312. WORTIS, H., M. H. STEIN AND N. JOLIFFE. *A.M.A. Arch. Int. Med.* 69: 222, 1942.

313. ZANDER, E. AND G. WEDDELL. *J. Anat.* 85: 68, 1951.

314. ZOTTERMAN, Y. *Acta med. scandinav.* 80: 185, 1933.

315. ZOTTERMAN, Y. *J. Physiol.* 95: 1, 1939.

CHAPTER XX

The sense of taste

CARL PFAFFMANN | *Psychology Department, Brown University, Providence, Rhode Island*

CHAPTER CONTENTS

THE SENSE OF TASTE, as distinct from the other chemoceptors, olfaction and the so-called common chemical sense, is associated with specialized receptor organs, the taste buds, which in land-inhabiting vertebrates are located in the mouth. In aquatic animals and insects chemoreceptors may be distributed over the body surface or on special appendages (68, 152, 197). In man taste stimulation is associated with the sensation qualities of salty, sour, bitter and sweet.

Of the three chemoceptors, common chemical sensitivity is the least differentiated and requires relatively high concentrations for stimulation. Indeed, the distinction between chemical sensitivity of the mucous membranes or moist skin surfaces and general pain sensitivity has been questioned (60, 112, 161). Some chemical irritants may be classed as lachrymatories or suffocants (144), depending upon their sites of action, but this may be a differentiation largely because of the surrounding structures. A familiar dissociation of taste and smell often occurs in the temporary anosmia during the common head cold. Under normal circumstances, exclusive stimulation of taste can be insured by placing dilute odorless solutions on regions of the tongue possessing taste buds. But many stimuli will activate all three senses with varying degrees of overlap.

The chemical senses are often classed among the lower senses (198) perhaps because of simplicity of morphology, relative paucity of information conveyed and relative unimportance in the sensory life of man. Indeed, the loss of taste is hardly as incapacitating as the loss of vision or hearing, at least to civilized man. At the same time, the chemical senses mediate such adaptive functions as food selection or the rejection of noxious stimuli, particularly in the case of lower organisms where dramatic examples may be cited (104, 177).

RECEPTOR ANATOMY

The taste buds in man and other mammals are located primarily on the edges and dorsum of the tongue, and adjacent surfaces of the upper margin of the gullet, epiglottis, soft palate and pharynx (124, 150, 198). On the tongue, taste buds lie in the upper surface of the mushroom-shaped fungiform papillae, in the grooves of the foliate papillae, which are a set of three to eight folds at the side of the tongue near the base and in the circular trench of the vallate papillae which form a chevron-like row of from 6 to 15 papillae on the dorsal surface of the base of the tongue (see fig. 1). The slender keratinized filiform papillae over most of the dorsum contain no taste receptors. In certain animals like the rodents, taste buds occur on the anterior hard palate, especially in and around the nasoincisor ducts (115).

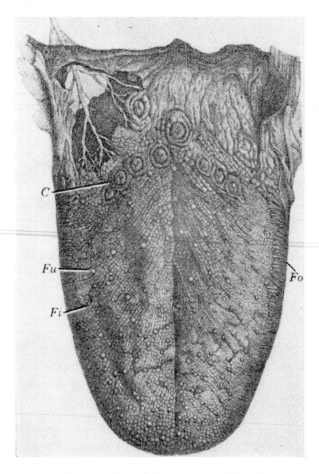

FIG. 1. Dorsal surface of the tongue partially dissected to show the nerves to the posterior part. The circumvallate (*C*), fungiform (*Fu*) and filiform (*Fi*) papillae are shown. The foliate papillae (*Fo*) are not clearly visible in this view since they are on the lateral surface of the tongue. Taste buds occur in *C*, *Fo* and not in *Fi*. [From Warren & Carmichael (199).]

in diameter at the thickest part. In a wide variety of species these values range from 27 to 115 μ for length and 14 to 70 μ for width. Two kinds of cells have been described, *a*) the thicker supporting cells and *b*) the more slender gustatory cells from which a fine terminal hair projects into the taste pore, but these may be different stages in the age or functional state of but a single type (124). During maturity a continuous process of atrophy and growth maintains the population of receptor cells at a relatively stable level.

In children, taste buds are more widely distributed over the hard palate, soft palate, pharyngeal walls and fungiform papillae of the middorsum of the tongue. In the adult, fungiform papillae are restricted to the sides and edges of the anterior tongue (198). Each fungiform papilla contains 3 to 4 taste buds. Taste buds of the circumvallate papillae show a marked atrophy in old age (11). The total number of taste buds in man is probably of the order of 10,000. It has been suggested that in humans the taste papillae reach full development at puberty and remain so until the age of 45 when regressive changes set in (4). In animals atrophic changes followed castration but could be reversed by hormone replacement therapy (5). Such atrophic changes, however, do not appear to diminish taste sensitivity in a preference test (184; Warren, R. P. & C. Pfaffman, unpublished observations). In man the decrease in number of taste buds with age is correlated with a decrease in sensitivity. Young adults recognized sugar solutions at a lower mean threshold, 0.41 per cent (0.012 M) compared to 1.23 per cent (.036 M) for elderly subjects (179).

The taste cell is a modified epithelial cell. The taste buds degenerate and disappear entirely after

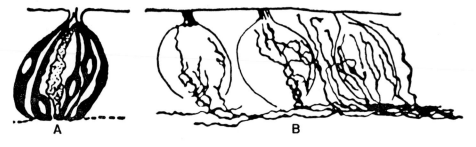

FIG. 2. Golgi preparations of taste buds and associated nerve endings. *A*. Taste cells and a 'sustentive' element. *B*. Nerve endings, sense cells not shown (after Retzius). [From Crozier (62).]

Taste buds are goblet-shaped clusters of cells oriented vertically in the epithelial layer with a small pore opening to the mucosal surface (fig. 2). Human taste buds measure from 60 to 80 μ in length and 40 μ

section of the taste afferent fibers. When nerve fibers regenerate to the periphery, taste buds also regenerate (149, 152).

Intrageminal nerve fibers arise from a subepithelial

network of fibers to enter the taste bud. Here they branch a number of times to entwine about and make contact with the surface of both the taste and supporting cells. Two to three nerve fibers may enter each bud and each fiber may connect with one or more sense cells. Extrageminal nerve fibers with fine terminations also arise from the same network of fibers to innervate the surrounding epithelium (124).

NEUROANATOMY

The lingual nerve to the anterior two thirds of the tongue subserves touch, temperature, pain and taste. The taste afferent fibers leave this nerve in a small strand, the chorda tympani nerve, which passes through the middle ear cavity close to the tympanum to enter the brain stem as part of the seventh cranial nerve. In some instances an alternative pathway via the greater superficial petrosal nerve seems indicated (63, 145, 188). The chorda tympani nerve also contains the efferent fibers for salivation, and temperature and tactile sensory fibers. The taste fibers are moderately small myelinated fibers less than 4 μ in diameter (70, 205). In the chorda tympani nerve of the cat, 18 per cent of the afferent fibers are unmyelinated (less than 1.5 μ) and the remaining are myelinated, ranging from 1.5 to 6.0 μ in diameter (77). Taste fibers from the posterior tongue travel in the glossopharyngeal and those from the larynx and pharynx in the vagus (see fig. 3).

The gustatory fibers of the seventh, ninth and tenth nerves run into the tractus solitarius together with its nucleus in the medulla. This tract extends from the posterior two thirds of the fourth ventricle caudally to the closed part of the medulla where it lies dorsal to the central canal, but the fibers of the seventh and ninth nerves terminate in the rostral portion of the nucleus (172). Insulated wire electrodes inserted into the medulla at this locus yield potentials when chemical stimuli are applied to the anterior tongue region (95). A response to the tactile stimulation occurs when the solution flow begins, but the response is brief compared with the continued discharge to taste solutions. Responses from the anterior tongue tactile stimulation and anterior tongue taste stimulation can be recorded from the same electrode loci using a 40 μ insulated wire electrode. Taste and the somatosensory pathways are closely related at this level.

Lesions in the anterior nucleus solitarius produce degeneration in fibers of the opposite ascending

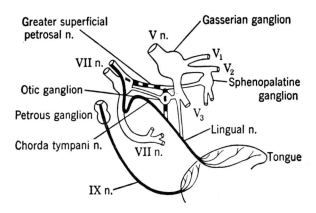

FIG. 3. The nerve supply to the tongue. The *solid lines* indicate the most common pathways for the taste impulses. The *broken line* indicates an alternative path from the chorda tympani believed to exist in a limited number of cases. [Modified from Cushing, 1903 and Schwartz & Weddell, 1938; from Pfaffmann (161).]

medial lemniscus close to the fibers of the ventral trigeminothalamic pathways (7, 81). Lesions in the region of the medial lemniscus produced by a stereotaxic instrument were associated with elevated thresholds in a two-bottle preference test with quinine solutions (155).

Patton & Ruch following Börnstein (30) have emphasized that the central pathways for taste are closely associated with the somatosensory systems for the face which at the level of the thalamus synapse medially in the arcuate nucleus (182). Degenerating fibers following lesions in the region of the nucleus solitarius were found in the arcuate nucleus (81), and retrograde degeneration was noted in the medial part after ablation of the cortical taste area (82). Destruction of a large portion of the arcuate nucleus in the monkey was followed by an elevation in the quinine preference threshold (157). Unilateral impairment of gustatory and cutaneous sensitivity has been reported following unilateral tumor of the medial part of the arcuate nucleus opposite to the sensory disturbance (3). The failure to find tactile representation in the ventromedial nucleus in spite of the fact that it adjoins the tactile representation of the inner mouth and tongue of the medial part of the ventrobasal complex led to the suggestion that taste as well as interoceptive fibers may terminate in the ventromedial complex (146, 182). Monkeys with ageusia resulting from cortical ablation showed lesions in the ventromedial complex (13). Taste-sparing cortical lesions of the inferior Rolandic cortex are associated with severe degeneration throughout the arcuate nucleus except for the dorsomedial tip (155).

The close association of taste pathways with the somatosensory and also motor mechanisms appears to hold true at the cortical level. Bremer (31) showed that ablation of the masticatory cortex in rabbits is associated with a taste deficit. Changes in the electrocorticogram from this same area were observed in unanesthetized rabbits when quinine solutions were placed on the tongue (72). A corresponding area on the orbital surfaces of the rat brain (25) was identified by the evoked potential method following electrical stimulation of the chorda tympani and glossopharyngeal nerves. This corresponds to the region from which masticatory movements could be elicited by electrical stimulation (130) and thus is a sensory motor area. Ablation of this area in the rat led to an elevation of the two-bottle preference thresholds for quinine solutions. No taste deficits were noted in two animals in which most of the neocortex except for the combined chorda tympani and ninth nerve receiving areas was removed. Further studies of the deficits produced by cortical ablation indicate that under certain high drive states no apparent taste deficit can be demonstrated. A thirsty normal animal and a thirsty animal with a cortical lesion will show the same aversion to quinine. Both have higher thresholds for quinine than the normal animal with water present ad libitum. Thus, the removal of the cortical taste area does not make the animal ageusic but instead renders the animal less discriminating in an ad libitum situation (23, 24).

The chorda tympani nerve area of the rat and cat lies in the face somatic area (156, 201). Much of the surface-positive cortical response to electrical stimulation of the chorda tympani is due to the tactile afferent fibers in that nerve. It has not been possible to record an evoked cortical potential with gross surface electrodes with adequate taste stimulation. However, ultramicroelectrode probings in the tactile tongue area of the cat did yield single units that responded to taste but not to touch or temperature. Other units in this area showed convergence of tactile, thermal and gustatory impulses (128). The taste units appeared to be less chemically specific than the single afferent fibers for they responded to almost all types of gustatory stimulation (50).

In monkeys and chimpanzees, lesions of the face motor and sensory areas along the free surface of the lower Rolandic cortex did not produce taste deficits in preference tests (155). Taste deficits occurred only when the lesions involved the buried opercular and parainsular cortex. Bagshaw & Pribram (13) have shown that the insular and anterior supratemporal as well as parainsular cortex all must be included to lead to an elevation of threshold. Some elevation of threshold followed ablation of the operculum plus insula, but not with restricted ablation of the insula or insula and anterior supratemporal plane.

In man, a series of patients with bullet wounds of the inferior postcentral region showed reduced gustatory and tactual sensibility of the tongue (30). Penfield & Boldrey (159) elicited gustatory sensations in conscious human patients by electrical stimulation of the lower end of the postcentral gyrus. Thus, the evidence implicates the region of the cortex of the operculum, insula and supratemporal plane of the temporal lobe.

Patton (155) notes that not only is there the close approximation of the taste to the somatosensory system but that taste localization fits into its orderly topographical arrangement. Taste does not have a special primary cortical receiving zone with exclusive gustatory functions.

RECEPTOR MECHANISMS

Functional Characteristics

No simple relation can be established between chemical stimuli and taste quality except perhaps in the case of acid. Equally sour concentrations of hydrochloric, sulfuric, nitric, phosphoric and acetic acids are said to be indistinguishable from each other when odor is excluded (56); but sucrose, dextrose and lactose do not have exactly the same taste (44); and stimuli that elicit the bitter taste can be discriminated from each other. The taste qualities of inorganic salts are complex and only sodium chloride has a pure saline taste, yet in threshold solutions this is variously reported as sweet or bitter (173, 181).

The tongue surface is not uniformly sensitive to punctate stimulation. The middorsum is insensitive to all tastes. Sweet sensitivity is greatest at the tip, sour at the sides, bitter at the back, while salt sensitivity is relatively homogeneous but greatest at the tip (96). Individual papillae have been found to react exclusively to salt, to sweet or to sour, or to come combination of two, three or four of the basic taste stimuli (120). Certain drugs have a differential effect on sensitivity. Gymnemic acid, an extract of the leaves of an Indian plant *Gymnema sylvestre*, reduces sensitivity for sweet and bitter but leaves salt and sour relatively uninfluenced (191). Such observations led to the view that taste consisted of four different modalities, salt, sour, bitter and sweet, each with its particular type of receptor even though no obvious histological differences distinguished taste buds from different regions of the tongue (147).

Electrophysiological studies show that the chorda tympani nerve discharge elicited by taste solutions on the tongue, varies with concentration above the threshold. In figure 4 the basic taste stimuli can be ranked in order of effectiveness: quinine, hydrochloric acid, sodium chloride, potassium chloride and

sucrose but the exact order or magnitude of response varies with species. In rodents (rat, guinea pig and hamster) sodium chloride is more effective than potassium chloride, whereas in carnivores (raccoon, cat and dog) the converse is true. There is very little response to sugar in the cat, somewhat more in the rat and still more in the hamster and guinea pig. The quinine response is better in the cat than in the rat or rabbit (21, 163).

A typical single fiber discharge from the rat chorda tympani is shown in figure 5 (164). The threshold varies from unit to unit so that as concentration increases there is an increase both in the number of units active and in the frequency of discharge. The fiber in figure 5 also responded to hydrochloric acid and potassium chloride. A wider sample of the 'spectrum' of sensibilities of different fibers in the rat chorda tympani is shown in figure 6. The pattern of sensitivity varies from fiber to fiber. Although some elements (A and B) are relatively specific, others (especially I) have a broader sensitivity. These different sensitivities cannot be readily grouped into the basic four types of classical theory. Studies (121) in which micropipettes have been inserted into the individual cells of the taste bud show the same kind of sensitivity pattern in the receptor cells themselves. This important observation disposes of the possibility that the overlapping sensitivities of single fibers of the chorda tympani result from the branching of fibers and termination upon more than one type of

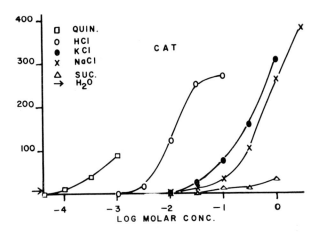

FIG. 4. Height of integrator deflections to stimuli of different concentrations in one cat preparation. *Ordinate* gives deflections in arbitrary units. [From Pfaffmann (164).]

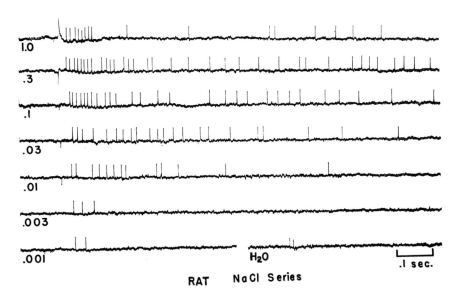

FIG. 5. Response of a single element from the rat sensitive to NaCl. This element also responds to HCl and KCl. Responses to quinine and sucrose were insignificant. [From Pfaffmann (164).]

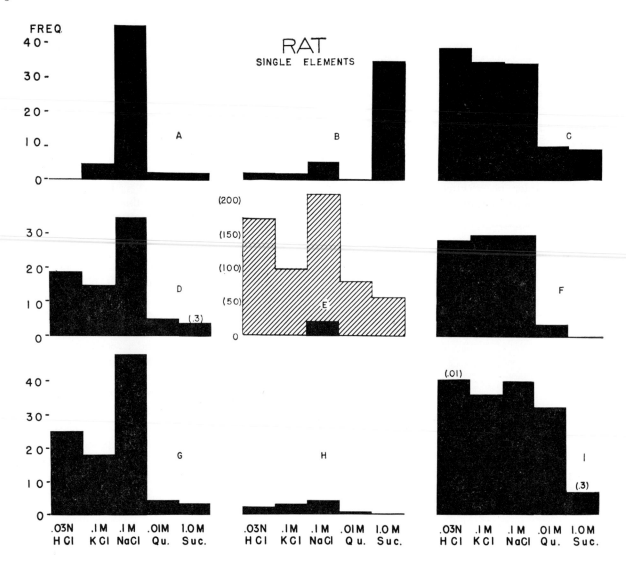

FIG. 6. Bar graphs summarizing frequency of response during the first second to five standard taste solutions in nine different single fiber preparations in the rat. Sucrose of 0.3 M was used as test solution in elements *D* and *I*, 0.01 M HCl in element *I*. In all other cases concentrations are as shown on *abscissa. Cross-hatched bar graph* superimposed on figure for element *E* shows relative magnitude of integrator response for test solutions. *Figures in parentheses* give magnitudes in arbitrary units. Note that only elements *D* and *G* resemble the response of the total nerve. [From Pfaffmann (164).]

receptor cell. The problem of chemical specificity is one of specificity within the individual cells, i.e. to different sites or loci on the cell membrane.

The specificity of the receptor unit cannot be adequately described by the response to only one concentration of a test stimulus. Figure 7 shows that fiber *B* (the same as fiber *B* in fig. 6) can be stimulated by sodium chloride at concentrations of 0.1 M and higher. This might be labelled as a salt-sugar unit. Since gymnemic acid applied to the tongue

leads to a clear-cut decrement in the response to sugar with no change for sodium chloride, it appears that only the sucrose sites on the cell is blocked, not the 'salt-sucrose' cell itself. The differential suppression of sugar sensitivity, often cited as evidence for separate modalities of taste, can be equally well encompassed by a theory of specific sites on the cell membrane.

The two fibers, *A* and *B* of figure 7, respond to both sodium chloride and sucrose, but *A* is more reactive to sodium chloride and *B* is more reactive to

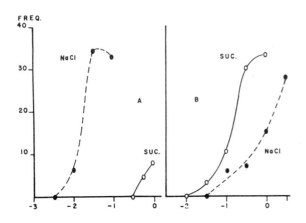

TABLE 1. *Fiber Type Response**

Stimulus	'Water' Fiber	'Salt' Fiber	'Acid' Fiber	'Qui-nine' Fiber	Sensation Evoked
H_2O (salt $<$0.03 M)	+	o	o	o	$\rightarrow$ water
NaCl (0.05 M)	o	+	o	o	$\rightarrow$ salt
HCl (pH 2.5)	+	+	+	o	$\rightarrow$ sour
Quinine	+	o	o	+	$\rightarrow$ bitter

* According to Cohen *et al.* (49).

FIG. 7. Graph comparing relative specificities of two different elements in rat. Each is sensitive to NaCl and sucrose (as well as other stimuli). Element *A* is relatively more sensitive to NaCl; *B* is relatively more sensitive to sucrose. *Ordinate* gives frequency in the first second of discharge. [From Pfaffmann (164).]

sucrose. At all concentrations of sodium chloride, the frequencies in *A* are higher than that in *B*; at all concentrations of sucrose, *B* is greater than *A*. Such a two-fiber system, therefore, signals sodium chloride when *A* is greater than *B* and sucrose when *B* is greater than *A*.

Thus different information may be conveyed by the same nerve fiber depending upon the activity in a second parallel afferent fiber. From figure 7 it can be seen that a discharge of 6 impulses in *B* with no activity of *A* is correlated with, that is, signals .05 M sucrose. A discharge of 6 impulses in *B* plus a discharge of 32 impulses in *A* is correlated with or signals 0.1 M sodium chloride. Intensity would be correlated with an increase in overall frequency of discharge.

Such a model may be expanded by adding more fibers to provide a greater variety of combinations of discharge pattern. If sensory quality depends upon such patterns, we might expect quality of sensation to change as the afferent population is reduced, for example when the stimulus concentration approaches threshold. Such changes in quality are well known (see table 3).

The further discovery that in certain species water alone leads to an increase in afferent activity (136, 164, 206) provides still another dimension by which discrimination can be mediated. Thus, a decrease in stimulus concentration will be associated with an increase in afferent activity. The base line or 'zero' taste, therefore, is not provided by pure water but

perhaps by the natural environment of saliva. Cohen *et al.* have elaborated the pattern concept with a schema (shown in table 1) incorporating the water receptor (49). This elaborates the earlier model described by Pfaffmann (160), but it is not clear that such 'typing' best describes the taste receptor spectrum (75). Increasing concentrations, for example, may bring in other stimuli so that a wider sampling of stimuli might change the 'types.'

It is clear from recent electrophysiological evidence that the taste receptors do not always fall into four basic receptor types corresponding to the basic taste qualities. The individual sensory cells are differentially sensitive to chemicals, probably because of differences at sites on the cell membrane. The chemical specificity of the taste cell can best be described as a cluster of sensitivities which varies among different receptor cells. Any one cell is reactive to a varying degree to a number of different chemical stimuli, many of which fall in two or more of the four classical basic taste categories.

Sensitivity and Mechanisms of Stimulation

SOUR. It has long been known that the sour taste is associated with the hydrogen ion and that, in a rough way, the degree of sourness is related to the degree of dissociation. Strong acids (fully dissociated) are more sour than equinormal solutions of a weak acid like acetic (114, 174). Neutralizing the acid eliminates the sour taste, but not all acids are sour. Amino acids are sweet and picric acid is intensely bitter.

Inspection of taste threshold data often reveals wide discrepancies from one investigator to another. Table 2 summarizes selected data on the acid lower thresholds. The range of variation among different references cited is shown, such variation being probably partly the result of valid individual differences among subjects and partly the result of differences in methods of determining thresholds. Threshold may be given as a sensitivity measure, i.e. the minimum con-

TABLE 2. *Acid Thresholds in Man (in Normal Concentrations)*

Substance	Formula	Mol. Wt.	Median	Range	n	Ref.*
Hydrochloric	HCl	36.5	.0009	.00005–.01	(10)	a, c, b, g
Nitric	HNO_3	63.1	.0011	.001–.0063	(4)	g
Sulfuric	H_2SO_4	98.1	.001	.00005–.002	(5)	a, c, g
Formic	HCOOH	46.0	.0018	.0007–.0035	(3)	f, g
Acetic	CH_3COOH	60.1	.0018	.0001–.0058	(9)	a, c, b, d, e, f, g
Butyric	$CH_3(CH_2)_2COOH$	88.1	.0020	.0005–.0035	(2)	f, g
Oxalic	$COOHCOOH \cdot 2H_2O$	126.1	.0026	.0020–.0032	(2)	f, g
Succinic	$COOH(CH_2)_2COOH$	118.1	.0032	.0016–.0094	(3)	f, g
Lactic	$CH_3CHOHCOOH$	90.1	.0016	.00052–.0028	(4)	b, f, g
Malic	$HOOCCH(OH)CH_2COOH$	134.1	.0016	.0013–.0023	(3)	b, g
Tartaric	$HOOC(CHOH)_2COOH \cdot H_2O$	168.1	.0012	.000025–.0072	(8)	a, b, d, e, f, g
Citric	$(COOH)CH_2C(OH)(COOH)CH_2COOH$	192.1	.0023	.0013–.0057	(4)	b, g

This table is based on values cited in von Skramlik (198) and certain more recent studies. Data from earlier literature in other compilations were not incorporated because of frequent errors of computation observed therein or uncertainties of method or technique of experimentation. Values shown are the median of several values, the number being shown in column n. The ranges of values are also reported. Hahn's (90) values of .003 N for all acids (except butyric and malic acids) were not included in this table.

* a, Cragg (59); b, Fabian & Blum (74); c, Gibson & Hartmann (83); d, Hopkins (110); e, Knowles *et al*. (123); f, Taylor (195); g, (Paul and Bohnen, Corin, Richards, Heymann, Richet, Renqvist) cited by von Skramlik (198).

centration at which a difference from water can be detected or as a recognition threshold, i.e. where the quality can be recognized. The former are usually lower.

Weak organic acids appear more sour than would be expected from their degree of dissociation. At threshold, the hydrogen ion concentration of acetic acid is less than that of hydrochloric acid. Liljestrand (135) found that the pH of weak organic acids at threshold ranged from 3.7 to 3.9, for strong mineral acids from 3.4 to 3.5. The findings of equal pH (approximately 4.4) for organic and inorganic acids (59) or equal normality of .003 N for all acids (89) are at variance with the more common result of different pH and different normalities at threshold (12, 26, 114, 158, 174, 195).

Cragg (58) noted that subjects with a more alkaline saliva required more concentrated hydrochloric acid solutions to match an acetic acid standard. The sour taste of buffers and of solutions of the monobasic salts of organic acids can be detected at pH values which are lower than those of inorganic acid solutions (12, 135, 158). Buffer solutions held in the mouth retain the sour taste longer than does plain acid. The pH of acetic acid changes less than the pH of hydrochloric acid after being held in the mouth.

The relative stimulating efficiency of suprathreshold concentrations studied by means of equal sourness matches between different acids and the standard, hydrochloric acid, is shown in figure 8. On the basis of hydrogen ion concentration, the organic acids

acetic, carbonic, tartaric, lactic and acetylactic acids were all more sour than hydrochloric acid (16, 103, 158).

These effects are not due solely to the buffering action of saliva. When acid solutions are applied by a flow system applicator so that the saliva is thoroughly rinsed off, equal afferent nerve discharge was not achieved with equal pH, equal normality or molarity (20). Figure 9 shows the magnitude of response in the chorda tympani discharge produced by different acids of the same pH.

Thus, some basic physiological mechanism complicates the relation between sourness and acidity. Richards (174) suggested that the hydrogen ions might react with some substance on the receptor surface so that, as these ions in a solution of the organic acid were taken up, further dissociation would replace them. Others (103) refer to the potential as well as actual hydrogen ion concentration as a determiner of sourness. Kenrick (116) and Beatty & Cragg (16) noted that the amount of phosphate buffer (pH 7) necessary to bring equisour concentrations of different acids to a pH 4.4 was proportional to the sourness defined by the normality of an equisour hydrochloric acid solution. Ostwald & Kuhn (151) noted a parallel between the sourness and the swelling of gelatin in different acids. Sourness has been attributed to the rate at which the acid penetrates the cell or intracellular spaces (61) or to adsorption on the cell surface (195).

Acid stimulation of the integument of lower organ-

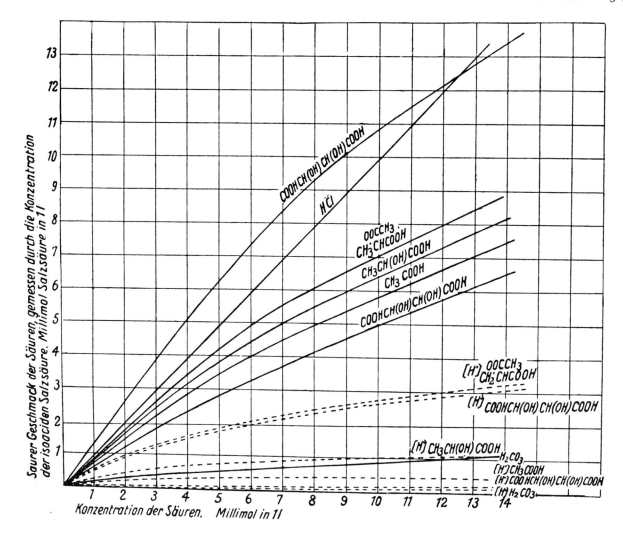

FIG. 8. Equal sourness matches. *Ordinates* give concentrations of HCl required to match the sourness of other acids at concentrations shown on the *abscissae*. *Broken lines* give hydrogen ion concentrations of weak acid and salts. [From Paul-München (158).]

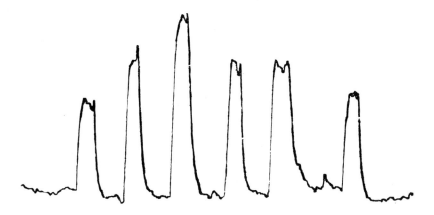

FIG. 9. Integrated response of the rat chorda tympani nerve to hydrochloric, citric, formic, oxalic, acetic and hydrochloric acids (*reading from left to right*) at pH 2.5. Duration of response, 10 to 20 sec. [From Beidler (20).]

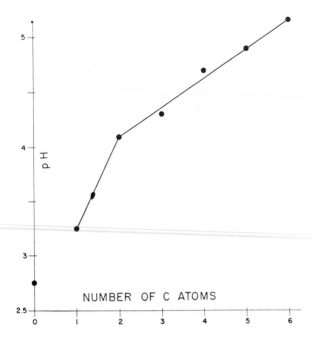

FIG. 10. pH required to elicit a constant reaction time in the sunfish, for hydrochloric acid and a series of normal aliphatic acids of increasing carbon chain length. [From Allison (8).]

TABLE 3. *The Taste of Salts at Different Concentrations**

M	NaCl	KCl
0.009	no taste	sweet
0.010	weak sweet	strong sweet
0.02	sweet	sweet, perhaps bitter
0.03	sweet	bitter
0.04	salt, slightly sweet	bitter
0.05	salty	bitter, salty
0.1	salty	bitter, salty
0.2	pure salty	salty, bitter, sour
1.0	pure salty	salty, bitter, sour

* From Rengvist (173).

isms (fish, frogs, barnacles, mollusks, worms) is probably due to the general sensitivity and thus simpler than in the case of taste. Stimulation by mineral acids in this case is determined by pH, but normal aliphatic acids stimulate at lower hydrogen ion concentrations, the efficacy increasing systematically with increasing chain length (8, 9, 54, 55) (see fig. 10). Similarly, the nonpolar parts of the molecule in a series of n aliphatic alcohols add to stimulating efficiency with increasing number of carbon atoms (53). The same holds for a series of alcohols and glycols for taste in man and in insect chemoception (66). In the insect studies a wider sampling of organic molecules was employed. Stimulation appeared to be associated with increasing lipoid solubility attendant upon increased chain length and the introduction of functional groups that reduced water solubility (65, 68, 69). The hydrogen ion is clearly an important determinant of the sourness of acids, but it alone does not determine stimulating efficiency.

SALTY. All substances with a salty taste are soluble salts composed of positive and negative ions in the solid (crystalline) state which dissolve in water to produce a solution of these ions. Sodium chloride is the only substance said to possess the 'pure salty taste' except that the threshold concentrations of this salt taste sweet (see table 3). Other salts display the same phenomenon but yield complex salty tastes at suprathreshold values.

Both the anion and cation contribute to the taste quality and to the stimulating efficiency (80). Thus, whereas .04 M sodium chloride is distinctly salty, sodium acetate of the same concentration has no salty taste. In a series of sodium salts, the quality of the taste elicited will vary with the anion. A similar effect can be noted in a chloride series with different cations. In a series of halides of the monovalent alkali metals (plus ammonium) the low molecular weight (below 110) salts are predominantly salty in taste, while the higher molecular weight (over 160) salts are bitter (122). Salts of heavy metals such as mercury have a metallic taste but some lead salts, especially lead acetate (sugar of lead), and beryllium salts are sweet.

The thresholds for different salts have been variously reported to be equimolar for the cation (92), for halogen salts (84), inversely related to the molecular weight (80), directly related to cation mobility (79). Table 4 shows the median values based on a sampling of a number of different threshold studies in man.

von Skramlik (198) attempted to specify objectively the complex taste of salts by means of the following taste equation: $N = xA + yB + zC + vD$ in which x, y, z, and v are molar concentration values and A stands for sodium chloride; B, quinine sulphate; C, fructose; and D, potassium tartrate; and N is the molar concentration of the salt being matched. Although individual differences among subjects are clearly apparent in the matches, certain trends or consistencies can be noted.

The degree of saltiness of a series of salts is given by the ratio of M NaCl/M 'salt' required to match the

TABLE 4. *Salt Thresholds in Man (in Molar Concentrations)*

Substance	Formula	Mol. Wt.	Median	Range	n	Ref.*
Lithium chloride	LiCl	42.4	.025	.009–.04	2	h
Ammonium chloride	NH$_4$Cl	53.5	.004[a]	.001–.009	3	c, h
Sodium chloride	NaCl	58.5	.01[b]	.001–.08	8	b, c, d, e, g[d]
			.03[c]	.003–.085	10	b, f, g, h
Potassium chloride	KCl	74.6	.017	.001–.07	6	c, h
Magnesium chloride	MgCl$_2$	95.23	.015[a]	.003–.04	3	h
Calcium chloride	CaCl$_2$	110.99	.01	.002–.03	6	b, c, h, i
Sodium fluoride	NaF	42.00	.005	.001–.04	1	a
Sodium bromide	NaBr	102.91	.024	.008–.04	2	h
Sodium iodide	NaI	149.92	.028	.004–.1	3	h

* a, Cox & Nathans (57); b, Fabian & Blum (74); c, Frings (79); d, Hopkins (110); e, Janowitz & Grossman (111); f, Knowles *et al.* (123); g, Richter & MacLean (181); h, von Skramlik (198); i, Höber & Kiesow (106).

[a] Mean value.   [b] Sensitivity threshold.   [c] Recognition threshold.

[d] Hahn (92) has reported one subject with a threshold for NaCl of less than 13×10^{-9}M. This is difficult to interpret for the value is far beyond the values commonly reported.

TABLE 5. *Mean Salt Quotient (M NaCl/M 'Salt') for Different Salts*

	Cl	I	Br	SO$_4$	NO$_3$	HCO$_3$
NH$_4$	2.83	2.44	1.83	1.26	1.03	
K	1.36	0.54	1.16	0.26	0.14	0.23
Ca	1.23					
Na	1.00	0.77	0.91	1.25	0.17	0.21
Li	0.44	0.57	0.79		0.23	
Mg	0.20			0.01		

Quotients show the molar concentration of NaCl required to match the saltiness of the comparison salt.

* From von Skramlik (198).

saltiness ignoring all other components. Table 5 showing the mean values for each of several series of salts gives the following cation series in the case of the chlorides: NH$_4$ > K > Ca > Na > Li > Mg. This closely resembles the series found (79) in a comparative study of rejection thresholds in animals and detection thresholds in man. Frings' (79) attempt to relate a single property, cation mobility, to the stimulating efficiency of electrolytes across all species is premature in view of the demonstrated species differences in sensitivity based on electrophysiological study (21, 163). The typical series for carnivores: NH$_4$ > Ca > Sr > K > Mg > Na > Li may be contrasted with that for the rat: Li > Na > NH$_4$ > Ca > K > Sr > Mg which is typical of the rodent class. The differences in the relation of sodium to potassium in the two orders is striking. Sodium is very effective in rodents but relatively ineffective in carnivores, whereas potassium is relatively ineffective in both. Beidler *et al.* (21) have pointed out that the sodium/potassium ratios in the red blood cells are

high (16.1) for carnivores and low (0.12) for rodents, perhaps indicative of a species difference in the physicochemical make up of the membranes of the receptors. The seriation NH$_3$ > K > Na > Li found in the withdrawal reaction of the frog and other lower aquatic forms when these solutions are applied to the integument is probably due to the less differentiated common chemical sensitivity (52, 109, 153).

The anion series based on table 5 for sodium salts is SO$_4$ > Cl > Br > I > HCO$_3$ > NO$_3$. Among invertebrates the following seriation has been described: I > Br > NO$_3$ > Cl. In the chorda tympani of the rat, the anion has a much smaller effect than the cation but the following series can be noted: Cl = Br > NO$_3$ > citrate > SO$_4$ > CO$_3$ (18).

Such ionic seriations (variously called Hofmeister series, lyotropic series, etc.) can be demonstrated in a number of other phenomena as the penetration into cells or adsorption on surfaces (105). Beidler (19) has recently developed a theory which provides some basis for choosing among these possibilities. His basic taste equation is:

$$\frac{C}{R} = \frac{C}{R_m} + \frac{1}{K R_m}$$

where C equals the concentration of the stimulus, R is the response magnitude of chorda tympani discharge, R_m is the maximal response magnitude and K is an equilibrium constant. A plot of C/R against C yields a straight line with a slope equal to $1/R_m$ and a y intercept equal to $1/KR_m$. The equation is similar to Langmuir's adsorption isotherm and to the

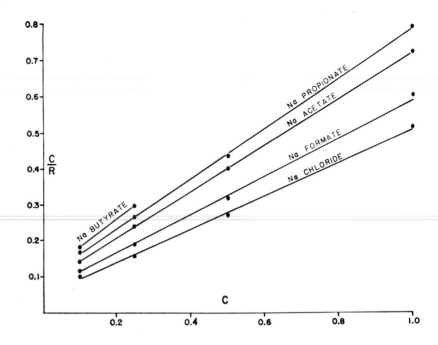

FIG. 11. Ratio of molar concentration and magnitude of integrated chorda tympani response plotted against molar concentration of stimulus. Explanation in text. [From Beidler (19).]

equation expressing the binding of ions by proteins. The equation describes the responses to different organic sodium salts (see fig. 11). From the low values of ΔF, the change in free energy, the relative independence of response magnitude of temperature or pH, the conclusion is drawn that the ions are loosely bound to the taste receptor surface by a nonenzymatic process much like that which occurs in the binding of ions by proteins or naturally occurring polyelectrolytes, such as nucleic acid or polysaccharides (19). Such binding may be the initial step in a series of reactions leading ultimately to stimulation of the receptor and depolarization of the associated afferent nerve fiber. Species differences are attributed to differences in the detailed configurations of the reacting molecular sites on the receptor surfaces.

SWEET. The sweet taste appears to be associated primarily with organic compounds, except for certain inorganic salts of lead and beryllium. The aliphatic hydroxy compounds which include alcohols, glycols, sugars and sugar derivatives constitute one of the better known classes. Other stimuli are aldehydes, ketones, amides, esters, amino acids, sulfonic acids, halogenated hydrocarbons, etc. A sampling of threshold values for the commoner sweet stimuli is given in table 6.

The complex relations between structure and the sweet taste cannot be adequately explained by any present systematization (51). Oertly & Myers (148) listed a number of sweet-producing molecular arrangements and postulated that, to be sweet, a substance must contain a 'glucophore' and an 'auxogluc.' Examples of their analysis are given in table 7. However, saccharin and dulcin are but two of the many exceptions.

In an homologous series, the taste of the members often changes from sweet to bitter with increase in molecular weight. In the higher members of an homologous series, it is said (144) that taste eventually disappears when the products become insoluble. On the other hand, as previously noted, an increase in molecular weight associated with increasing chain length in an homologous series is paralleled by a decrease in water solubility and an increase in taste stimulating efficiency. This was shown for alcohols and glycols at threshold (66). Some (62) have hypothesized that sweetening power is often associated with low water solubility, but numerous exceptions make this a difficult rule to maintain.

The importance of the spatial arrangement of the molecule is strikingly clear in the case of homologues in which small changes may produce striking dif-

TABLE 6. *Sweet Thresholds in Man (in Molar Concentrations)*

Substance	Formula	Mol. Wt.	Median	Range	n	Ref.*
Sucrose	$C_{12}H_{22}O_{11}$	342.2	.01 [†]	.005–.016	3	a, c, e
			.17 [‡]	.012–.037	7	a, b, d, e, f
Glucose	$C_6H_{12}O_6$	180.1	.08	.04–.09	3	a, b, f
Saccharin (sodium)	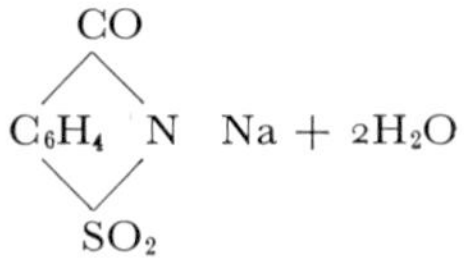 CO	241.1	.000023	.00002–.00004	3	f, g
	C_6H_4 N Na + $2H_2O$					
	SO_2					
Beryllium chloride	$BeCl_2$	80.0	.0003			a, f
Sodium hydroxide	NaOH	40.1	.008	.002–.012		b, f

* a, Fabian & Blum (74); b, Biester & Wood (27); c, Schutz & Pilgrim (186); d, Janowitz & Grossman; e, Richter & Campbell (179); f, von Skramlik (198); g, Warren, R. W. & C. Pfaffmann (unpublished observations).

[†] Detection threshold.

[‡] Recognition threshold.

TABLE 7. *Possible Structural Basis for Sweet Taste**

	Glucophore	Auxogluc
Glycol	CH_2OH—$CHOH$	H—
Glycerol	CH_2OH—$CHOH$	CH_2OH
Glucose	—CO—$CHOH$	CH_2OH
Glycine	$COOH \cdot CHNH_2$—	H—
Chloroform	—CCl_3	H—
Ethyl nitrate	—$CHONO_2$	CH_3

* According to Oertly & Myers (148).

ferences in taste. For example, of the homologues of *m*-nitroaniline, which is sweet, only 2-nitro-p-toluidine is sweet.

Sweet   Sweet   Tasteless

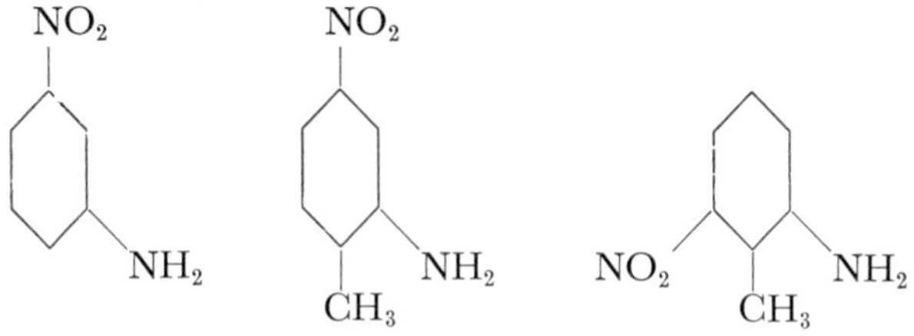

Very slightly bitter

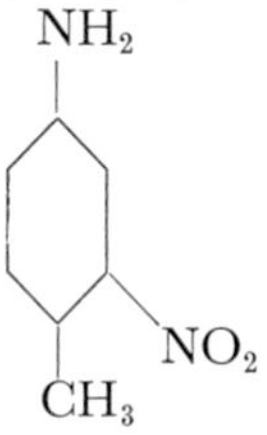

Saccharin is one of the better known physiologically inert synthetic sweetening agents. The salts of saccharin, especially the sodium salt crystallose, are sweet presumably due to the anion

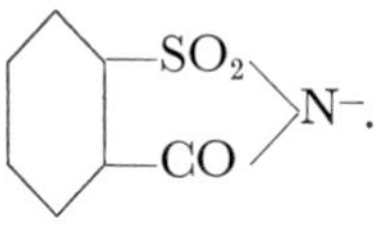

Where substitution of the hydrogen in the imide group occurs to form *N*-methyl saccharin, the compound is tasteless presumably because ionization cannot occur,

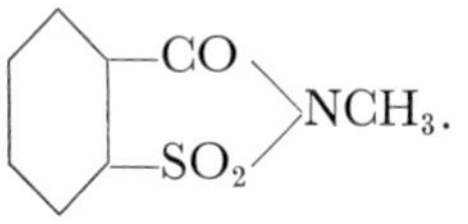

Several other intensely sweet substances are dulcin, cyclamate (Sucaryl) and the 4-alkoxy-3-amino-nitrobenzenes. The *n* propyl derivative of the latter class, called P-4000, is said to be the sweetest known compound but its use as a synthetic sweetening agent is limited by its toxicity (29, 131).

Stereoisomerism is of significance in taste as in other physiological systems. In fact, one of the earlier examples of the biological significance of optical activity was provided by asparagine of which the dextro form is sweet, the levo form tasteless. Freshly prepared solutions of alpha **D** glucose are sweeter than beta **D** glucose which predominates in solution after mutarotation has occurred (44).

Mention has already been made of the selective and reversible action of certain drugs like gymnemic acid which reduces sensitivity to sweet and bitter but leaves salt and sour unaffected (191). The effect may be demonstrated most simply after chewing a few of the dried leaves. A similar action is described for yerba santa, an extract of the leaves of *Eriodicyton californicum*. Topical application of weak concentrations of cocaine depress taste in the order, bitter > sweet > salt > sour. Stovaine in proper concentrations will eliminate sweet and bitter and reduce sensitivity to salt and acid followed by hypergeusia for salt. Cocaine ageusia may be followed by hypergeusia for sweet and bitter. The Sudanese plant *Bumelia dulcifica* is said to change sweet and bitter to sour.

The extract from the *Gymnema* leaves, after purification and recrystallization, yields a white powder with a melting point of 199°C and a molecular weight of 805. This appears to be a glycoside which yields glucose, arabinose and a small quantity of glucuronalactone upon hydrolysis. The hydrolysate has no effect on taste. Other substances in the crude extract do not influence the inhibitory action. Not only is the sweet taste of such diverse substances as sucrose and saccharin suppressed, both are equally reduced in sweetness, i.e. at suprathreshold levels equal sweetness matches remain unchanged (Warren, R. M. & C. Pfaffmann, unpublished observations).

The differential action of this drug is clearly shown in the electrical activity of the chorda tympani nerve (fig. 12), although the effect does not last as long as the perceptual effect in man. A similar reversible effect can be produced by the salts of heavy metals, silver and mercury, but not by arsenic, arsenous acids or potassium ferricyanide. This suggests competitive blocking of a mechanism which is nonenzymatic (88). These results are in striking agreement with those obtained in invertebrate contact chemoception (67, 68). The evidence from functional studies contraindicates an enzymatic process in stimulation gener-

ally in spite of the demonstration of enzymes in the neighborhood of taste cells (14).

Action potential studies have shown that an individual afferent receptor neural unit might respond not only to sugar but also to a salt like sodium chloride. Thus, specificity to a chemical agent must be specificity of sites within or on the individual sense cells. Presumably, different sites are specifically sensitive to sugar on the one hand and salt on the other (in addition to a wide variety of other substances). Gymnemic acid does not block the receptor cell as a whole but only the sucrose site.

Threshold and suprathreshold equal-sweetness comparison methods have been employed to study relative sweetness of different stimuli. Although the exact values may vary from experimenter to experimenter, the relative order of sweetness among the sugars, for example, is the same. In equimolar concentrations the order of sweetness is: sucrose > fructose > maltose > glucose > lactose (44). The relation between concentration and sweetness changes with concentration (see fig. 13). There are very wide differences in the stimulating efficiency of sweet stimuli. Close to threshold, saccharin is 500 to 700 times less concentrated than sucrose of equal sweetness. As yet there is no indication why some synthetic agents are so effective. In general, the available evidence suggests that the initial step in sweet stimulation may be a process like that already elaborated for salts. The response to sugar is resistant to enzyme poisons and pH change but not to surface active competitive inhibitors.

BITTER. Bitter, like sweet, is elicited by members of many chemical classes and is often found in association with sweet and other taste qualities. Increasing molecular weight of inorganic salts is associated with increasing bitterness (see p. 516). An increase in length of the carbon chain of the organic molecules may be associated with a change from sweet to bitter. Many sweet substances have a concomitant bitter taste or aftertaste (e.g. saccharin). This double or multiple taste quality is especially apparent as the stimulus moves from the front to the back of the tongue where bitter sensitivity is especially developed.

The best known class of bitter substances is the alkaloids which are complex nitrogenous compounds, often highly toxic, such as quinine, caffeine, strychnine and nicotine (144). Nitro compounds are often bitter (such as picric acid) especially if three or sometimes two nitro groups are present. The following groups are often associated with bitter taste: (NO_2) >

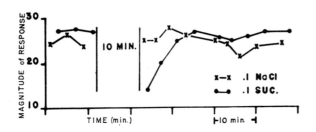

FIG. 12. Differential suppression of taste response to sucrose (*suc.*) and sodium chloride (chorda tympani discharge) by gymnemic acid after 10 min. application to surface of tongue. [From Hagstrom (88).]

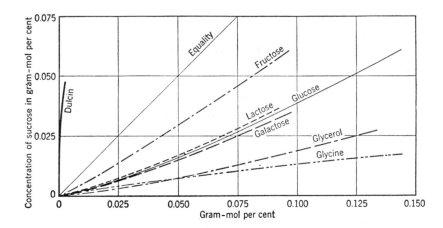

FIG. 13. Curves showing the concentrations at which different substances taste as sweet as various concentrations of sucrose. Gram-mol per cent is $\frac{1}{10}$ the value of the molar concentration. [From Cameron (44).]

TABLE 8. *Bitter Thresholds in Man (in Molar Concentrations)*

Substance	Formula	Mol. Wt.	Median	Range	n	Ref.*
Quinine sulphate	$(C_{20}H_{24}N_2O_2)_2H_2SO_4$	746.90	.000008	.0000004–.000011	3	b, f, k
Quinine hydrochloride	$C_{20}H_{24}N_2O_2HCl$	360.88	.00003	.000002–.0004	3	g, k
Strychine monohydrochloride	$C_{21}H_{22}N_2O_2HCl$	370.75	.0000016		1	k
Nicotine	$C_5H_4NC_4H_7NCH_3$	162.2	.000019		1	k
Caffeine	$C_8H_{10}N_4O_2$	194.1	.0007	.0003–.001	2	i, k
Phenyl thiourea (PTC)	$C_6H_5NHCSNH_2$	152.21				a, c, d, e, h, j
tasters			.00002† }	{ .0000002 to	6	
nontasters			.008† }	{ >.017		
Urea	$CO(NH_2)_2$	60.1	.12	.116–.13	2	c, k
Magnesium sulfate (Epsom salt)	$MgSO_4 \cdot 7H_2O$	246.49	.0046	.0042–.005	2	k

   * a, Blakeslee (28); b, Hanig (96); c, Harris (99); d, Hartmann (cf. 48); e, Harris & Kalmus (100); f, Kiesow (118); g, Parker & Stabler (154); h, Richter & Clisby (180); i, Schutz & Pilgrim (186); j, Setterfield, Schottl & Snyder (cf. 48); k, von Skramlik (198).
   † Modes.

2, $\equiv$N, $=$N$\equiv$, —SH, —S—, —S—S—, and —CS—. Some typical threshold values for the human are shown in table 8.

The importance of structure and specific chemical grouping is shown by the phenomenon of 'taste blindness,' a specific relative insensitivity to a number of

$$\overset{\displaystyle S}{\underset{\displaystyle \|}{}}$$

substances possessing the $>$NC— group. Phenylthiocarbamide (PTC) is widely used as a test for 'taste blindness.' The actual distribution of taste-blind individuals found depends upon the manner of administering the PTC, the percentages of 'nontasters' in Caucasians having been variously reported to be between 3 per cent and 40 per cent. A graded series

of solutions yields no sharp cutoff at one threshold concentration but rather a bimodal distribution.

This deficiency is inherited as a Mendelian recessive characteristic. Evidence for such taste defects were found in anthropoid apes (28, 48, 100). Rats, however, rejected PTC solutions with no evidence of the defect. PTC is intensely toxic to the rat when administered by stomach tube. This property was utilized in the preparation of a rat poison 'Antu' from a chemically related but tasteless compound (178, 180).

The inability to taste $\overset{\displaystyle S}{\underset{\displaystyle \|}{>}}$NC— may be overridden by other chemical groups as in thiourea, NH_2CSNH_2, which is sour to all persons. Many of the substances with which taste blindness may be demonstrated are antithyroid compounds (99). Taste blindness is not correlated with sensitivity for other bitter stimuli or the other taste qualities. This suggests a high degree of specificity for the particular chemical linkage together with some feature of the receptor mechanism. An attempt has been made to relate taste blindness to solubility of PTC in saliva (47). In view of the specificity of the linkage this does not seem to be a likely explanation.

The fact that sweet and bitter sensitivity are often associated in the case of certain stimuli and that both tend to be inactivated by the action of drugs or narcotic agents led one investigator to propose that both depend upon the action of a single receptor mechanism (194). Of all the taste mechanisms, that underlying bitter sensitivity is least well understood.

ELECTRIC TASTE. That electric currents can stimulate the sense of taste has been known almost since the discovery of electricity. Volta noted, for example, a sour taste when a circuit with two dissimilar metals made contact with the tongue. Such taste is elicited not only at the make and break of current but by the steady flow as contrasted with the more familiar stimulation of nervous tissue by short duration pulses. Anodal unipolar stimulation of the tongue with an indifferent electrode elsewhere on the body elicits a sour taste; cathodal stimulation yields a complex alkaline quality but, at cathodal break, sour is reported (198).

Early investigators often employed metallic polarizable electrodes. With an inert electrode like platinum, the following electrolytic change occurs when current flows through a weak salt solution. Electrons are introduced at the cathode toward which the positive hydrogen and sodium ions are attracted. A higher voltage is usually required to discharge the Na ion so that H ions are discharged and H_2 is liberated,

$$2e + 2H_2O \rightarrow 2OH^- + H_2$$

leaving Na^+ and OH^- ions. At the positive pole electrons come primarily from the OH^- ions which by their discharge leave an excess of H^+ ions.

$$4OH^- \rightarrow 2H_2O + O_2 + 2e$$

These together with the remaining Cl^- ions form a dilute solution of hydrochloric acid. These chemical effects would appear to account for the sour taste at the anode and alkaline taste at the cathode. In addition there is movement of cations toward the cathode and anions toward the anode with a resulting change in concentration in the vicinity of the electrodes.

With a nonpolarizable reversible electrode, electron transfer at the electrode is derived from the reaction $Ag \rightleftharpoons Ag^+ + e$. No discharge of OH^- or H^+ ions occurs. There is no electrolysis, but the subject still reports sour at the anode (40). Further work is desirable in view of one preliminary report that the anode produces a salty taste when a carefully constructed reversible electrode is utilized (71).

In general two hypotheses have been proposed to account for the electric taste. The first is the chemical theory in which it is believed that taste buds are stimulated by the concentration of ions resulting from electrolysis. Thus the sour of the platinum electrode is said to be due to the excess of hydrogen ions. The appearance of the same taste with a reversible electrode suggests the second view, namely that direct depolarization of the taste membrane occurs by virtue of the ionic transfer in the cell and across the cell membrane. In both cases, of course, the passage of current is an electrochemical reaction.

Direct stimulation of the nerve fibers so that the receptor organ itself is 'by-passed' can be ruled out, at least for direct current anodal currents. The taste threshold current is lower for the anode than the cathode, which is the reverse of the relation found for direct nerve stimulation. Furthermore the elevation of threshold after the topical applications of tetracaine was much greater for the anode than the cathode, suggesting that the anode stimulated the more superficial receptor but that the cathode stimulated the deeper nerve fibers. The strength duration curves of taste indicate a longer time constant for the anode than the cathode (38, 40).

Electrophysiological recordings of the single taste fibers show that anodal polarization of the tongue surface causes a discharge like that to chemical stimulation, except that the latency to the electrical stimulus is approximately 5 to 7 msec. whereas that to chemical stimulation is approximately 35 to 50 msec. (160). Thus the anodal electrical stimulus appears to act via the receptor cell but with a much shorter latency as though some initial step were by-passed.

The discharge to a steady anodal current continues, after an initial decrement, as long as the current flows. The same magnitude of cathodal current, however, causes an immediate inhibition of activity which lasts as long as the current flows. Upon break of the cathodal current, there follows a transient burst of activity. Other sense organs appear to show the same polarity relations, e.g. the tactile receptors of the frog skin and photo receptors of the *Limulus* eye, suggesting that these effects are not specific to taste (138, 139). These effects are just opposite to those seen in the axon where anodal block and cathodal excitation are found.

Studies of alternating current stimulation support the view that the receptor cell mediates the electric taste at low frequencies from 30 to 50 cps at which sour predominates. The low frequencies presumably can stimulate the receptor organs with their slower time constants. High frequencies around 1000 cps elicit a more complex bitter taste. The high frequencies may stimulate tissues with faster time constants, i.e. the nerve fibers themselves (41).

Intermittent square wave stimulation has been employed in studies of the so-called 'flicker fusion' of taste. The original studies (6) purporting to demonstrate gustatory flicker fusion at frequencies between 125 and 350 cps have not been confirmed (113, 170, 183), although it is true that something akin to fusion can be reported. The effect appears to be largely a tactual phenomenon which can be demonstrated in regions of the mouth and lips where no taste buds are found (170). Reports of true taste fusion (38) occur with extremely low frequencies in the range of from 0.5 to 10 cps.

Parameters of Stimulation

TEMPERATURE. The rate of most chemical reactions is increased by a rise in temperature. Early work showed that taste was optimal in a middle range variously reported between 10° and 20°C, 20° and 30°C and 30° and 40°C. At the extremes of 0° or 50°C the tongue is nearly insensitive especially after it has been immersed in solution (198). Komuro (125) studied intermediate values and reported a drop in threshold with temperature rise from 10° to 30°C, with some suggestion of an increase beyond 30°C for all stimuli. Chinaglia (46) found no change in threshold but did find a change in reaction time. The interpretation of reaction time data is somewhat equivocal because, in another study (143), no correlation was found between reaction time and threshold for sodium chloride over a wide temperature range.

Goudrian (86) showed that the apparent taste intensity of sugar solutions increased with increasing temperature between 10° and 40°C. Acid showed a

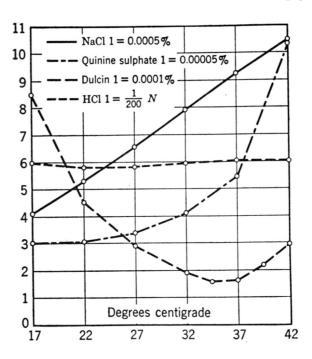

FIG. 14. The effect of temperature on taste thresholds for sodium chloride, quinine sulphate, dulcin and hydrochloric acid. The *ordinate* gives the thresholds in arbitrary units. The value of one unit on the ordinate differs for each of the four substances, as shown by the key in the figure. For example, one unit for NaCl equals 0.0005 per cent. [From Hahn (93).]

similar but not as regular or as striking a change. Salt and quinine fell in intensity with an optimum for salt at 10°C. The optimum for quinine was less consistent.

One of the better controlled studies is that of Hahn & Gunther (91) on absolute thresholds at different temperatures using the 'Geschmackslupe.' This device restricts the flow of solution to a specified region of the tongue so that a preadapting flow of water at the same temperature can be employed (see fig. 14). Sugar sensitivity increases, salt and quinine decrease and acid is unaffected by temperature rise. The greatest deviations occurred with different sweet stimuli. Glycol showed little change with temperature whereas beryllium salts and other sugars followed the sucrose curve. Certain acids showed slight upturn at either temperature extreme and different salts showed a flattening out or even a fall beyond 37°C. With different bitter stimuli there was only an increase in slope Hahn & Gunther's values do not include the extremes which cause insensitivity. If extended, their curves would probably have shown a rise in threshold at the low and high values.

One study among recent ones on the temperature effect using an electrophysiological method reported no change in response magnitude for sodium chloride at temperatures of 20°, 25° and 30°C (19). Another study with the larger temperature range found only a 10 per cent variation in magnitude response between 20° and 30°C, but larger effects outside these limits with sodium chloride (1). There was a sharp rise from 15° to an optimum of 22°C with a gradual fall from 22°C to 37°C and a greater drop at 45°C. Since a fall in neural response magnitude is equivalent to a rise in threshold, the electrophysiological results are in agreement with the human data showing that sodium chloride sensitivity falls off with temperature rise, particularly above 22°C.

In interpreting the temperature effects it should be remembered that biological systems have a normal functional range beyond which biological arrest usually occurs. With extreme cooling or excessive heating there may be irreversible changes (22). Thus biological systems with a mid-temperature region of optimal function, in general, yield U-shaped functions. It was the optimal range with which earlier workers were concerned. The more careful study of systematic changes within normal limits shows clearly that temperature increase does not increase all taste sensitivity. There is no simple temperature coefficient in the usual sense.

AREA AND DURATION. Stimulation of single papillae or of a limited area of the tongue by a single drop of solution usually results in higher thresholds or less intense suprathreshold tastes than does tasting by the whole mouth (44, 198). The expression $IS^x = K$ approximately describes the relation between threshold intensity, I, and surface area, S, with exponents of 0.73 for sodium chloride, 0.6 for citric acid, 0.93 for sucrose, and 1.42 for quinine hydrochloride. Threshold decreases with areas up to 60 to 90 mm². A similar relation also holds for the apparent intensity of suprathreshold solutions (43).

The relation between threshold and stimulus duration can be expressed as $t = C/i^n$ where t is duration, i is threshold and C is a constant. For sodium chloride and citric acid, n equals 1.5, for sucrose n equals 2.0. A similar relation with shorter durations holds for the electric taste (33). Similarly the apparent intensity of suprathreshold solutions depends upon duration. With long durations, the sensation of taste waxes slowly, reaching a maximum for quinine in 8 to 10 sec. and for salt in 4 to 5 sec. With electric taste the 'build-up' time is 1 to 1.5 sec. (42).

REACTION TIME. Most early workers report that bitter yields the longest, and salty the shortest times with sugar and acid intermediate (198). Because the stimulus intensity influences reaction time (169), it is necessary to specify this parameter. One recent study (32, 34) utilized a flow system in conjunction with an electrical measurement of the solution flow at the tongue surface or onset of current, in the case of the electric taste. Reaction times vary with different qualities and within the same quality. Reaction time is longest at threshold and shortest at the higher intensities, often by a factor of three or more. It seems reasonable, in view of the uneven distribution of sensitivity over the tongue surface, that reaction time for different stimulus classes would vary with the region stimulated. This parameter has not been investigated, however. An increase both in the area of stimulated surface or of hydrostatic pressure of the solution against the tongue surface decreases reaction time to some extent (108).

Adaptation

The continued flow of taste solution over the tongue leads to a diminution in subjective intensity and an elevation of the absolute threshold which is proportional to the intensity of the adapting stimulus (see fig. 15). The rate and form of the adaptation curve within the same quality may vary with different

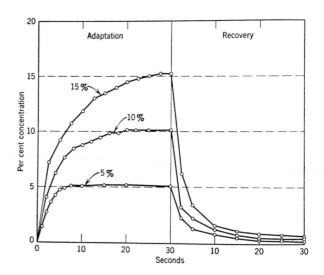

FIG. 15. Adaptation and recovery curves for NaCl. The *ordinate* indicates the threshold concentrations. The course of adaptation to three concentrations of NaCl, 5, 10 and 15 per cent, is shown for an adaptation period of 30 sec. and a recovery period of 30 sec. The unadapted threshold is 0.24 per cent. [From Hahn (92).]

stimuli, but the recovery curves tend to have the same shape (92). Subthreshold stimuli may elevate the threshold in a similar manner but to a lesser degree. Adaptation by acid adapts the sour taste for other acids, but in the case of bitter and sweet stimuli cross adaptation within these respective qualities may occur only between some but not all stimuli. More striking, however, is the case of salt where no cross adaptation was found among 24 inorganic salts studied (94).

It has commonly been assumed that sensory adaptation reflects the exhaustion of some receptive substance in the cell in a manner analogous to the bleaching of visual purple by light. The combination of the stimulus with such a receptive substance was assumed to be necessary for stimulation (129), and further that all stimuli eliciting the same quality would be mediated by the same receptor substance so that cross adaptation would result. Such a mechanism for the salts would require 24 different receptive substances in the taste cell. Hahn rejected this notion and hypothesized a specific inhibition of the cell receptor membrane (change in permeability) for the adapting stimulus only. The receptor cell itself was not rendered inexcitable (94). Analogous results were found in recent electrophysiological studies (20). No cross adaptation between calcium chloride and sodium chloride for example, was found, even though the single fiber analysis shows that calcium chloride and sodium chloride affected the same peripheral fiber and receptor cell (75).

Bujas has pointed out that the subjective intensity of taste does not always parallel the peripheral process. Maximal subjective intensity develops only after the stimulus has been acting for some seconds. During this 'buildup' period, however, the receptor sensitivity is falling as shown by the rise in threshold. Subjective intensity begins to fall off only later, showing that the magnitude of sensation is probably the result of a central and peripheral process working in opposition (37). Beidler has noted that the maintained steady discharge for sodium chloride in the electrophysiological record is at variance with the complete disappearance of salt sensation reported for all but the strongest concentrations in the human observer (2, 39, 127). This points to a process of central adaptation.

Adaptation to sucrose or sodium chloride enhances sensitivity to stimuli eliciting other qualities. Adaptation by quinine enhances sensitivity to sour and salt, but adaptation by hydrochloric acid does not affect the other qualities (64, 140). It is well known that distilled water appears sweet following a weak acid. The recent finding that water acts as a stimulus for certain taste endings and that the magnitude of such discharge can be modified by prior treatment with acids or other chemical stimuli suggests a peripheral locus for some of these effects (136, 164).

A positive after taste, i.e. persistence of the same taste quality after withdrawal of the stimulus, has been attributed usually to residual taste particles in the mouth or to slow desorption from the receptor surface.

Interaction when two disparate areas of the tongue are stimulated has been reported. Weak acid or sugar solutions were said to reduce the threshold for salt on the opposite side (119). An enhancement of salt sensitivity occurs with weak sugar solutions but inhibition or elevation of salt threshold occurs with stronger sugar concentrations. Such effects with stimulation of disparate sensory surfaces must have a central origin. Successive contrast effects of a similar nature also have been described (36, 198).

Unfortunately, there have been few systematic studies of masking and interactions with taste mixtures, except for efforts to duplicate complex tastes by mixing four components. One well-known interaction is the reduction of sourness by the addition of sugar or other sweetener. This has been studied by the electrophysiological method. The discharge of a nerve strand to a mixture of 10 per cent sucrose and an acid of pH 2.5 showed only an increase compared to the response to the sugar or acid individually (10). There was no peripheral inhibition. Such sour-sweet interaction, therefore, must have a central locus.

Intensive Relations

Differential sensitivity ($\Delta I/I$) as found by different investigators is summarized in table 9. Values from 1/10 (10 per cent) to 1/1 (100 per cent) with a modal value of 1/5 (20 per cent) have been reported depending upon the intensity level, amount of stimulus, criterion of judgment, etc., employed. Constancy of $\Delta I/I$ with intensity has been reported by some, whereas others reported a decrease in differential sensitivity at the high or low intensities, but the change in these latter instances was relatively small (approximately 10 times) compared with the 100 to 1000 times change found for vision and hearing. High differential sensitivity for one taste quality is not correlated with high sensitivity for others, and differences between subjects may be greater than the

TABLE 9. *Differential Thresholds ($\Delta I/I$) in Taste Modalities*

No. of Subjects	Sweet (Sucrose)	Salt (NaCl)	Bitter (Caffeine)	Sour (Citric Acid)	Ref.*
	$\frac{1}{9.1}$	$\frac{1}{6.6}$	$\frac{1}{4.7}$‡		e
2	$\frac{1}{3.1}$	$\frac{1}{3.8}$		$\frac{1}{5.2}$	b
1	$\frac{1}{5}$, $\left(\frac{1}{6.3}\right)$†				f
2		$\frac{1}{6.7}$			c
6–8		$\frac{1}{7.15}$			g
6	$\frac{1}{4.8}$, $\left(\frac{1}{3.7}\right)$†				§
2		$\frac{1}{3}$			d
1		$\frac{1}{4.5}$			a
10	$\frac{1}{5.8}$	$\frac{1}{6.7}$	$\frac{1}{3.3}$	$\frac{1}{4.5}$	h
Range in individual subjects	$\frac{1}{8} - \frac{1}{2}$	$\frac{1}{10} - \frac{1}{2.5}$	$\frac{1}{6.7} - \frac{1}{1.15}$	$\frac{1}{11} - \frac{1}{1.6}$	h
Median fraction	$\frac{1}{5}$	$\frac{1}{6.6}$	$\frac{1}{4}$	$\frac{1}{4.8}$	
Median ratio	20%	15%	25%	21%	

* a, Beidler (20); b, Bujas (35); c, Fodor & Happisch (76); d, Holway & Hurvich (107); e, Kopera (126); f, Lemberger (133); g, Sandullah (185); h, Schutz & Pilgrim (186).
† Saccharin.   ‡ Quinine.
§ Krogh & Jensen cited in (126). Values obtained by Keppler (117) were much lower than most values obtained by above authors and have been omitted from the table.

differences in the same subject for different intensities or qualities (186).

Attempts to measure or scale subjective taste intensity have employed different methods. One is the summation of just noticeable difference steps (JND's). In one study, successive JND steps were determined for two sweet substances, crystallose (sodium saccharin) and sucrose so that stimuli falling at equal JND steps above threshold could be specified (133). These concentrations, however, were not equally sweet when directly compared. At high concentrations, saccharin became relatively less sweet than sucrose of an equal JND scale value. As in the case of other modalities, the JND summation scale is not

a valid scale for subjective magnitude (193). This is also true when cross quality comparisons, e.g. saltiness versus sweetness, are carried out (35).

Another method, analogous to the equal loudness measurement in hearing, utilizes the direct match between one solution and an arbitrarily selected set of standards (44, 158). For sweetness, a series of sucrose solutions is often used; for sourness, hydrochloric acid, etc. This does not give taste intensity directly, only the relative taste effectiveness of different substances in eliciting equal taste intensities.

In recent years, a number of direct scaling methods have been developed, stemming from the work in audition. In one series of studies (17, 134) the fractionation method showed that subjective magnitude increased directly with the physical concentration, a special case of Stevens' general psychophysical law, $\Psi = s^n$, where Ψ is sensation, s is stimulus intensity, and n is an exponent, the exponent in this case being equal to one (193). Other studies using similar methods found that taste intensity increased as an exponential function of stimulus concentration, so that the exact relation between taste intensity and stimulus concentration is yet to be established (187).

Glucose is less sweet, molecule for molecule, than sucrose. Furthermore the ratios of concentrations for equal sweetness of the two sugars change with concentration. Sweetness does not increase equally with concentration for both (137). That this depends upon some basic receptor mechanism is suggested by the fact that the electrophysiological response in the chorda tympani nerve of at least one species, the rat, follows a rather different course for glucose than for sucrose as shown in figure 16 (89).

These relations also bear upon another effect, the so-called 'supplemental action' in mixtures of two or more sweetening agents. When glucose and sucrose solutions are mixed, for example, the sweetness of the mixture is greater than would be predicted by the simple addition of the equivalent sweetness values of each component stated in terms of the equisweet sucrose solution. When such mixtures are computed in terms of the equisweet glucose concentrations, however, the sweetness of the mixture is the sum of the components. There is simple additivity with no supplementary action (44). If it is assumed that the magnitude of nerve impulse discharge determines directly the magnitude of taste, i.e. sweetness, we note that the sensory effect for glucose is nearly linearly proportional to concentration, but for sucrose it is curvilinear, i.e. negatively accelerated. A graphical solution of the addition of 0.2 M glucose and 0.2

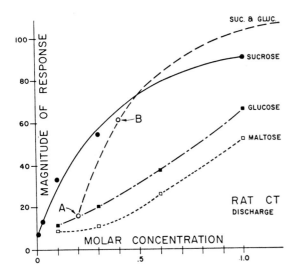

FIG. 16. Response of rat chorda tympani nerve to different concentrations of different sugars. The *dashed line SUC. & GLUC* is the summated response to be expected when sucrose solutions are added to 0.2 M glucose. See text for discussion. (From Hagstrom, E. C., unpublished observations.)

M sucrose solutions in a mixture can be made from figure 16 by adding the sucrose curve to the response of 0.2 M glucose at *A*, so obtaining the dotted line. The total sensory effect of the mixture should be the sum of the two functions at point *B*. *B* equals 62 units, a magnitude of nerve discharge that could be produced either by .34 sucrose or .94 glucose, individually. The empirical match to the original mixture can be stated as:

$$.2G + .2S = .34S \qquad (1)$$

In sucrose equisweet solutions where $.2G = .04S$, the equation (*1*) becomes

$$.04S + .2S = (\text{sucrose match}) \qquad (2).$$

But since the arithmetic sum of $.04S + .2S$ is .24 and not .34 (a difference of .10) there is supplemental action. That is, the empirical match shows a stronger sucrose concentration than could be predicted by the simple addition of equisweet sucrose solutions (i.e. the mixture is sweeter). Setting equation (*1*) in terms of glucose where $.2S = .74G$ we have:

$$.2G + .74G = .94G \ (\text{and} \ .94G = .34S).$$

The arithmetic sum of $.2G + .74G$ equals exactly .94G which is the same as the equivalent glucose value to match .34 sucrose. There is no supplemental action by this computation. The apparent supplemental action with one set of transformations but not the other is due to the attempt to add arithmetically one linear to one nonlinear function. This example, although derived theoretically from the electrophysiological response curves, can be matched almost exactly by empirical data from psychophysical experiments on man (44). Further study of taste mixtures by the electrophysiological method is desirable. The additive analysis presented in figure 16 is theoretical except that the response curves for the individual sugars are based upon experimental points.

BEHAVIORAL EFFECTS

Taste stimulation is most directly related to food taking and the rejection or avoidance of noxious stimulation. Hence, the manifold of four basic tastes of salt, sour, bitter and sweet can be reduced to two behavioral classes, acceptance or rejection. Certain substances are rejected in all concentrations; others may be accepted at low but rejected at high concentrations; still others may be accepted at all concentrations. Acceptance or rejection may also be influenced by postingestion effects, by the metabolic condition of the organism and by past conditioning or learning. Thus taste is only one of several determinants of appetitive behavior.

Richter (177) in his classical studies of self-selection demonstrated that the animal's behavior was a part of "the total adjustive mechanism working toward the constancy of the internal environment." The adrenalectomized rat will increase the intake of salt solution to such a degree that it not only survives but gains weight. It is significant that the albino rat under normal conditions, i.e. when not salt hungry or hormone deficient, displays a striking preference for sodium chloride and other sodium salts (15, 176, 203). This behavior is exaggerated after adrenalectomy as evidenced by a lowered preference threshold and greater intake of all salt solutions above threshold in preference to water. An excess of salt in the diet reduces the preference and may even wipe it out, leaving only an aversion over the entire stimulus range. Figure 17 summarizes these behavioral phenomena together with a plot of the magnitude of the afferent nerve discharge of the chorda tympani nerve in the rat. The solid line curves show the relative preference in per cent (cc salt/cc salt + cc H_2O) under four conditions: adrenalectomized, normal (*N*), with 5 per cent extra salt in diet and 10 per cent extra salt. The basic preference-aversion response (*N*) is shifted systematically by these changes in salt need. In the normal animal, the preference threshold lies above the concentration at which a discharge of nerve impulses can be detected. In the adrenalectomized rat the preference and electrophysiological thresholds are more nearly equal. The normal animal thus appears to taste the salt but does not ingest it. The adrenalectomized rat takes the salt solution when he can taste it (165).

The neural response curve of the receptor appears to be a stable property of the taste bud. The threshold, i.e. a minimum concentration necessary to elicit a discharge of the taste receptors, is essentially the same in normal and adrenalectomized rats (166). This has been confirmed in studies using the conditioned reflex method (45, 98). Thus the change in self-selection behavior cannot be explained by a peripheral change in sensitivity of the taste receptors. Of similar import is the finding of the constancy of the chorda tympani

response in insulin hypoglycemia (167). Insulin injection typically leads to a striking increase in the preference for sugar solutions in a free choice situation.

Richter has presented evidence that the compensatory increase in intake fails when the sensory nerves to the tongue are surgically removed (175). The attenuation in preference behavior in the normal animal after combined chorda tympani-ninth nerve deafferentation further supports the view that taste stimulation triggers the response to taste solutions (162). A rat with an esophageal fistula will show the salt preference even when the solution does not enter the stomach and cannot have a metabolic effect (192). At the same time the ingestion of water or salt solutions can be modified by stomach loading by intubation with sodium chloride solutions which 'by-passes' taste, but the effect is less than when the same amount of solution is taken by mouth so that the taste receptors are stimulated (132). Thus both taste and intragastric factors may influence drinking (204).

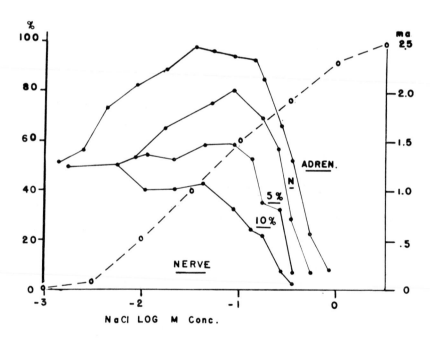

FIG. 17. A composite graph of the neural response (*broken line*) and the preference curves (*solid lines*) for different concentrations of NaCl. The neural response curve (*ordinate to the right*) shows the magnitude of the electrical activity in the chorda tympani nerve of a normal rat. Each *open circle* is a measure of the integrated electrical activity (in milliamperes, *ma.*) of the discharge at each concentration. The preference curves were obtained from four different groups of animals: adrenalectomized (*adren.*), normal (*N*), normal with 5 per cent additional salt in the diet (*5%*) and normal with 10 per cent additional salt in the diet (*10%*), respectively. Each point is the average preference (or aversion) indicated as a percentage (cc intake salt) ÷ (cc salt + cc H₂O) at each concentration. Each point is the average consumption for a 48-hr. period when both water and salt solution were continuously available. Salt solutions were presented in ascending order of concentration. [From Pfaffmann (165).]

The role of taste or other head receptor stimulation can be uncovered if the postingestion factors can be eliminated or minimized. In the brief exposure behavioral test which permits little ingestion, rats show a preference for the higher of two concentrations of sugar solution over a wide range of pairs. But such equally accepted solutions are not equally ingested in continuous drinking periods as brief as 20 min. in which the higher concentrations are usually consumed in lesser amounts (204). McCleary (142) has clearly demonstrated the role of intragastric osmotic pressure in this effect.

In another behavioral test, the Skinner box with sugar solutions as reinforcers, the rate of bar pressing on an aperiodic reinforcement schedule is faster, the higher the concentration of sugar (87). This schedule provides relatively little drinking per response and apparently minimizes postingestion factors. Furthermore, the concentrations of two different sugars, glucose and sucrose found to give equal rates of response, i.e. to have equal reinforcing value, correspond to the equally preferred concentrations in the short exposure test and to the equally sweet concentrations of these sugars for man. Thus, the direct sensory taste effect appears not only to instigate ingestion but to be capable of reinforcing the acquisition of other responses leading to ingestion. The usual measures of intake obscure the relation to sensory stimulation because of postingestion effects.

The nutritional consequences of sugar stimulation do not appear to be essential for such reinforcement. Nonnutritive saccharin solutions can also serve as reinforcers for the acquisition of a maze-running habit (189). The degree of reinforcement appears to be correlated with the amount of consummatory behavior elicited. Whether reinforcement power is determined by the magnitude of the afferent excitation per se or by the magnitude of the consummatory behavior elicited, is not yet clear.

The fact that certain taste stimuli control ingestion directly appears to be biologically determined, for nearly all organisms accept sugar solutions (78). Although there is evidence that direct injection of nutrient sugar into the blood stream may serve as a reinforcer of learning, there is no evidence that the 'sweet tooth' depends upon the concomitant nourishment. The drinking of nonnutritive saccharin solutions shows no sign of extinction which would be expected if the preference for saccharin were acquired by the association of the sweet taste with nourishment (189).

The aversion to certain stimuli like bitter appears to be relatively unmodifiable by experience. In one experiment, guinea pigs two days *post partum* were provided with a nontoxic but normally avoided solution as the only source of fluid until three weeks of age. This substance has an extremely bitter taste for man. Following this early exposure, preference tests showed that the avoided stimulus had been rendered somewhat more palatable, but in a retest three months later the effect had dissipated so that there was no difference between the control and experimental animals. The aversion had not been moderated by the early experience (168).

Thus the factors that control behavior in the taste preference and related situations are becoming clearer. Taste may trigger ingestion behavior but alone does not account for it. In many instances, feeding behavior is directed toward the physiological well-being of the organisms; but situations and habits may exist which are contrary to the physiological well-being. According to Young, "New habits tend to form in agreement with bodily needs, but established habits tend to persist as regulators of food selection even when the food selections are out of line with bodily needs." The limitations of self-selection are well documented (85, 101, 204).

Certain of these basic principles appear to be valid for man. Instances of enhanced salt craving reported by Richter included the case of a small boy who apparently compensated for adrenal insufficiency with an excessive intake of table salt (177). Patients in whom hypoglycemia had been produced for therapeutic reasons were reported to find strong sugar solutions more palatable than when blood sugar levels were normal (141). The bizarre taste cravings of pregnant women are well-known. The change is not one of taste sensitivity but one of changed likes and dislikes (97). The metabolic disequilibria of diabetic patients are often associated with strong cravings for sweet, although to satisfy this would run counter to the individual's well-being (177). Thus, although metabolic changes may be important factors in determining the hedonic value of a taste stimulus, such changes do not always automatically lead to self-corrective behavior.

The well-known fact that human subjects can taste certain substances when injected intravenously appears to support the view that taste sensitivity can be influenced by constituents in the blood stream (102). As already noted, neither the adrenalectomized nor hypoglycemic animal shows evidence of a change in taste sensitivity when studied electrophysiologically. In another study with this method, preliminary re-

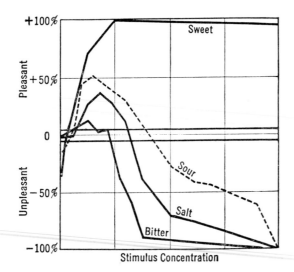

FIG. 18. Preponderance of 'pleasant' or 'unpleasant' judgments in relation to the concentration of taste solution. *Ordinate* gives per cent 'pleasant' minus per cent 'unpleasant.' The *abscissa* is proportional to the concentration, the full length of the base line standing for 40 per cent cane sugar, 1.12 per cent tartaric acid, 10 per cent NaCl and 0.004 per cent quinine sulphate (all by weight). [From Engel, as reproduced in Woodworth (200).]

sults showed no impulse discharge following intravenous injection of taste stimuli (Beidler, L. M., personal communication). Further electrophysiological studies of 'intravenous taste' are called for.

Sherrington (190) has noted that stimulation of the contact sense organs often initiates a chain of responses culminating in consummatory behavior. Taste along with tactile stimulation of the mouth leads directly to the retention, chewing and swallowing of food or its expulsion. Strong affective or hedonic tone appears to be a basic property of 'nonprojicient' receptor

stimulation as compared with the more neutral consequences of distance receptor stimulation.

Troland (196) divided receptor stimulation into classes of innate biological utility. These were nociception, associated with deleterious agents; beneception, with stimuli of biological utility; and neutroception, with stimuli of relatively neutral character. Different tastes might fall in either the beneceptor or nociceptor classes. These three classes correspond closely to the neutral, unpleasant or pleasant affective tone aroused by sensory stimulation (202).

Intensity as well as taste quality is a determiner of hedonic rating as shown in figure 18 (73). Quinine is mostly unpleasant and is increasingly so with increase in stimulus concentration. Sucrose is mostly pleasant but acid and salt are intermediate, showing a rise in pleasantness to a maximum and then a fall with increase in concentration. These hedonic curves appear to resemble the preference curves found in animal studies (see fig. 16), particularly for salt and quinine. Hedonic ratings of more complex tastes and flavors can be obtained with human subjects by means of rating scales, paired comparison judgments and other similar tests. These have had wide practical application in the food industry and the armed forces for assessing the palatability of food and rations. Such ratings can be reliable predictors of the actual acceptance in the field (171).

Acceptability of food by man, of course, is determined not alone by taste. Food habits, cultural conditioning, immediate social pressures or other complex psychological factors play a significant role in acceptability. Acceptability is not a property of food. The acceptance of food is a response of the organism, and taste as one component in flavor may play an important role in determining this response.

REFERENCES

1. ABBOTT, P. S. *The Effect of Temperature on Taste in the White Rat* (Thesis). Providence, R. I.: Brown University, 1953.
2. ABRAHAMS, H., D. KRAKAUER AND K. M. DALLENBACH. *Am. J. Psychol.* 49: 462, 1937.
3. ADLER, A. *Ztschr. ges. Neurol. Psychiat.* 149: 208, 1934.
4. ALLARA, E. *Arch. ital. anat. e embriol.* 42: 506, 1939.
5. ALLARA, E. *Riv. biol.* 44: 209, 1952.
6. ALLEN, F. AND M. WEINBERG. *Quart. J. Exper. Physiol.* 15: 385, 1925.
7. ALLEN, W. F. *J. Comp. Neurol.* 35: 275, 1923.
8. ALLISON, J. B. *J. Gen. Physiol.* 15: 621, 1932.
9. ALLISON, J. B. AND W. H. COLE. *J. Gen. Physiol.* 17: 803, 1934.
10. ANDERSSON, B., S. LANDGREN, L. OLSSON AND Y. ZOTTERMAN. *Acta physiol. scandinav.* 21: 105, 1950.

11. AREY, L. B., M. J. TREMAINE AND F. L. MONZINGO. *Anat. Rec.* 64: 9, 1935.
12. BACHARACH, E. *Ztschr. Biol.* 84: 335, 1926.
13. BAGSHAW, M. H. AND K. H. PRIBRAM. *J. Neurophysiol.* 16: 499, 1953.
14. BARADI, A. F. AND G. H. BOURNE. *Nature, London* 168: 977, 1951.
15. BARE, J. K. *J. Comp. & Physiol. Psychol.* 42: 242, 1949.
16. BEATTY, R. M. AND L. H. CRAGG. *J. Am. Chem. Soc.* 57: 2347, 1935.
17. BEEBE-CENTER, J. G. AND D. WADDELL. *J. Psychol.* 26: 517, 1948.
18. BEIDLER, L. M. *J. Neurophysiol.* 16: 595, 1953.
19. BEIDLER, L. M. *J. Gen. Physiol.* 38: 133, 1954.
20. BEIDLER, L. M. In: *Chemistry of Natural Food Flavors*, edited by J. H. Mitchell, Jr., N. J. Leinen, E. M. Mrak

and S. D. Bailey. Chicago, Ill.: Quartermaster Research and Engineering Command, 1957, p. 7.

21. BEIDLER, L. M., I. Y. FISHMAN AND C. W. HARDIMAN. *Am. J. Physiol.* 181: 235, 1955.

22. BĚLEHRÁDEK, J. *Biol. Rev.* 5: 30, 1930.

23. BENJAMIN, R. M. *J. Comp. & Physiol. Psychol.* 48: 119, 1955.

24. BENJAMIN, R. M. *J. Comp. & Physiol. Psychol.* 48: 502, 1955.

25. BENJAMIN, R. M. AND C. PFAFFMANN. *J. Neurophysiol.* 18: 56, 1955.

26. BERLATZKY, A. AND T. GUEVARA. *Compt. rend. Soc. de biol.* 98: 176, 1928.

27. BIESTER, A., M. W. WOOD AND C. S. WAHLIN. *Am. J. Physiol.* 73: 387, 1925.

28. BLAKESLEE, A. F. *Proc. Nat. Acad. Sc., Washington*, 18: 120, 1932.

29. BLANKSMA, J. J. *Rec. trav. chim.* 65: 203, 1946.

30. BÖRNSTEIN, W. S. *Yale J. Biol. & Med.* 13: 133, 1940.

31. BREMER, F. *Arch. internat. physiol.* 21: 308, 1923.

32. BUJAS, Z. *Compt. rend. Soc. de biol.* 119: 716, 1935.

33. BUJAS, Z. *Compt. rend. Soc. de biol.* 119: 835, 1935.

34. BUJAS, Z. *Compt. rend. Soc. de biol.* 119: 1360, 1935.

35. BUJAS, Z. *Acta Inst. Psychol., Univ. Zagreb* 2(1): 18, 1937.

36. BUJAS, Z. *Acta Inst. Psychol., Univ. Zagreb* 2(4): 12, 1937.

37. BUJAS, Z. *Acta Inst. Psychol., Univ. Zagreb* 3(3): 1, 1939.

38. BUJAS, Z. *Année Psychol.* 50: 159, 1949.

39. BUJAS, Z. *Acta Inst. Psychol., Univ. Zagreb* 17: 10, 1953.

40. BUJAS, Z. AND A. CHWEITZER. *Année Psychol.* 35: 147, 1934.

41. BUJAS, Z. AND A. CHWEITZER. *Compt. rend. Soc. de biol.* 126: 1106, 1937.

42. BUJAS, Z. AND A. OSTOJCIC. *Acta Inst. Psychol., Univ. Zagreb* 3: 1, 1939.

43. BUJAS, Z. AND A. OSTOJCIC. *Acta Inst. Psychol., Univ. Zagreb* 13: 1, 1941.

44. CAMERON, A. T. *Scientific Report Series No. 9.* New York: Sugar Research Foundation, 1947.

45. CARR, W. J. *J. Comp. & Physiol. Psychol.* 43: 377, 1950.

46. CHINAGLIA, L. *Riv. psicol.* 11: 196, 1916.

47. COHEN, J. AND D. P. OGDON. *Science* 110: 532, 1949.

48. COHEN, J. AND D. P. OGDON. *Psychol. Bull.* 46: 490, 1949.

49. COHEN, M. J., S. HAGIWARA AND Y. ZOTTERMAN. *Acta physiol. scandinav.* 33: 316, 1955.

50. COHEN, M. J., S. LANDGREN, L. STRÖM AND Y. ZOTTERMAN. *Acta physiol. scandinav.* 40: Suppl. 135, 1957.

51. COHN, G. *Die organischen Geschmacksstoffe.* Berlin: Siemenroth, 1914.

52. COLE, L. *J. Comp. Neurol.* 20: 602, 1910.

53. COLE, W. H. AND J. B. ALLISON. *J. Gen. Physiol.* 14: 71, 1930.

54. COLE, W. H. AND J. B. ALLISON. *J. Gen. Physiol.* 15: 119, 1931.

55. COLE, W. H. AND J. B. ALLISON. *J. Gen. Physiol.* 16: 895, 1933.

56. CORIN, J. *Arch. Biol. Paris* 8: 121, 1888.

57. COX, G. J. AND J. W. NATHANS. *J. Appl. Physiol.* 5: 395 1953.

58. CRAGG, L. H. *Tr. Roy. Soc. Canada* 31(3): 7, 1937.

59. CRAGG, L. H. *Tr. Roy. Soc. Canada* 31(3): 131, 1937.

60. CROZIER, W. J. *J. Comp. Neurol.* 26: 1, 1916.

61. CROZIER, W. J. *J. Comp. Neurol.* 26: 453, 1916.

62. CROZIER, W. J. In: *Handbook of General Experimental Psychology*, edited by C. Murchison. Worcester: Clark Univ. Press, 1934, p. 987.

63. CUSHING, H. C. *Bull. Johns Hopkins Hosp.* 14: 78, 1903.

64. DALLENBACH, J. W. AND K. M. DALLENBACH. *Am. J. Psychol.* 56: 21, 1943.

65. DETHIER, V. G. *J. Gen. Physiol.* 35: 55, 1951.

66. DETHIER, V. G. *Am. J. Physiol.* 165: 247, 1951.

67. DETHIER, V. G. *Quart. Rev. Biol.* 30: 348, 1955.

68. DETHIER, V. G. In: *Molecular Structure and Functional Activity in the Nerve Cell*, edited by R. G. Grenell and J. L. Mullins. Washington: American Institute of Biological Sciences, 1956.

69. DETHIER, V. G. AND L. E. CHADWICK. *J. Gen. Physiol.* 33: 589, 1950.

70. DODT, E. AND Y. ZOTTERMAN. *Acta physiol. scandinav.* 26: 346, 1952.

71. DZENDOLET, E. *Intensity-duration Relations for Taste using Electrical Stimulation* (Thesis). Providence, R. I.: Brown University, 1957.

72. ECTORS, L. *Arch. internat. physiol.* 43: 267, 1936.

73. ENGEL, R. *Arch. ges. Psychol.* 64: 1, 1928.

74. FABIAN, F. W. AND H. B. BLUM. *Food Res.* 8: 179, 1943.

75. FISHMAN, I. Y. *J. Cell. & Comp. Physiol.* 49: 319, 1957.

76. FODOR, K. AND L. HAPPISCH. *Arch. ges. Physiol.* 197: 337, 1922.

77. FOLEY, J. A. *Proc. Soc. Exper. Biol. & Med.* 60: 262, 1945.

78. FRINGS, H. *Turtox News* 24: No. 8, 1946.

79. FRINGS, H. *J. Comp. & Physiol. Psychol.* 41: 25, 1948.

80. GAYDA, T. *Arch. fisiol.* 10: 175, 1912.

81. GEREBTZOFF, M. A. *Cellule* 48: 91, 1939.

82. GEREBTZOFF, M. A. *Arch. internat. physiol.* 51: 199, 1939.

83. GIBSON, L. AND T. HARTMANN. *Am. J. Psychol.* 30: 311, 1919.

84. GLEY, E. AND C. RICHET. *Compt. rend. Soc. de biol.* 742: 1885.

85. GORDON, J. G. AND D. E. TRIBE. *Brit. J. Anim. Behav.* 2: 72, 1954.

86. GOUDRIAN, J. C. *Arch. neerl. physiol.* 15: 253, 1930.

87. GUTTMAN, N. *J. Comp. & Physiol. Psychol.* 47: 358, 1954.

88. HAGSTROM, E. C. Doctoral Thesis. Providence, R. I.: Brown University, 1957.

89. HAGSTROM, E. C. AND C. PFAFFMANN. *J. Comp. & Physiol. Phychol.* In press.

90. HAHN, H. *Klin. Wchnschr.* 11: 1504, 1932.

91. HAHN, H. AND GUNTHER, H. *Arch. ges. Physiol.* 231: 48, 1932.

92. HAHN, H. *Ztschr. Sinnesphysiol.* 65: 105, 1934.

93. HAHN, H. *Klin. Wchnschr.* 15: 933, 1936.

94. HAHN, H. *Beitrage zur Reizphysiologie.* Heidelberg: Scherer, 1949.

95. HALPERN, B. P. *Electrical Activity in the Medulla Oblongata following Chemical Stimulation of the Rat's Tongue* (Thesis). Providence, R. I.: Brown University, 1957.

96. HÄNIG, D. P. *Phil. Stud.* 17: 576, 1901.

97. HANSEN, R. AND W. LANGER. *Klin. Wchnschr.* 14: 1173, 1935.

98. HARRIMAN, A. E. AND R. B. MacLEOD. *Am. J. Psychol.* 66: 465, 1953.

99. HARRIS, H. *Nature, London* 163: 878, 1949.

100. HARRIS, H. AND H. KALMUS. *Ann. Eugenics* 15: 24 1949.

101. HARRIS, L. J., J. CLAY, F. J. HARGREAVES AND A. WARD. *Proc. Roy. Soc. London. ser. B* 113: 161, 1933.

102. HARTRIDGE, H. *J. Physiol.* 103: 34, 1945.

103. HARVEY, R. B. *J. Am. Chem. Soc.* 42: 712, 1920.

104. HASLER, A. D. AND J. A. LARSEN. *Scient. Am.* 193: 72, 1955.

105. HÖBER, R., D. I. HITCHCOCK, J. D. BATERMAN, D. R. GODDARD AND W. O. FENN. *Physical Chemistry of Cells and Tissues.* Philadelphia: Blakiston, 1945.

106. HÖBER, R. AND F. KIESOW. *Ztschr. physik. Chem.* 27: 601, 1898.

107. HOLWAY, A. H. AND L. M. HURVICH. *Am. J. Psychol.* 49: 37, 1937.

108. HOLWAY, A. H. AND L. M. HURVICH. *J. Exper. Psychol.* 23: 191, 1938.

109. HOPKINS, A. E. *J. Exper. Zool.* 61: 13, 1932.

110. HOPKINS, J. W. *Canad. J. Res.* 24F: 203, 1946.

111. JANOWITZ, H. D. AND M. I. GROSSMAN. *J. Appl. Physiol.* 2: 217, 1949.

112. JONES, M. H. *Am. J. Psychol.* 67: 696, 1954.

113. JONES, M. H. AND F. M. JONES. *Science* 115: 355, 1952.

114. KAHLENBERG, L. *J. Phys. Chem.* 4: 33, 1900.

115. KAPLICK, M. *Ztschr. Zellforsch. u. mikroskop. Anat.* 38: 571, 1953.

116. KENRICK, F. B. *Tr. Roy. Soc. Canada* 25: 227, 1931.

117. KEPPLER, F. *Arch. ges. Physiol.* 2: 449, 1869.

118. KIESOW, F. *Phil. Stud.* 10: 329, 1894.

119. KIESOW, F. *Phil. Stud.* 10: 523, 1894.

120. KIESOW, F. *Arch. ital. biol.* 30: 377, 1898.

121. KIMURA, D. AND L. M. BEIDLER. *Am. J. Physiol.* 187: 610, 1956.

122. KIONKA, H. AND F. STRÄTZ. *Arch. exper. Path. u. Pharmakol.* 95: 241, 1922.

123. KNOWLES, D. AND P. E. JOHNSON. *Food Res.* 6: 207, 1941.

124. KOLMER, W. In: *Handbuch der Mikroskopischen Anatomie des Menschen,* edited by W. Mollendorf. Berlin: Springer, 1927, p. 154.

125. KOMURO, K. *Arch. neerl. physiol.* 5: 572, 1921.

126. KOPERA, A. *Arch. ges. Psychol.* 82: 273, 1931.

127. KRAKAUER, D. AND D. M. DALLENBACH. *Am. J. Psychol.* 49: 469, 1937.

128. LANDGREN, S. *Acta physiol. scandinav.* 40: 210, 1957.

129. LASAREFF, P. *Arch. ges. Physiol.* 194: 293, 1922.

130. LASHLEY, K. S. *Brain Mechanisms and Intelligence.* Chicago: Univ. Chicago Press, 1929.

131. LEHMAN, A. J. *A. Food & Drug Officials U. S., Quart. Bull.* 14(3): 82, 1950.

132. LE MAGNEN, J. *J. Physiol. Paris,* 47: 405, 1955.

133. LEMBERGER, F. *Arch. ges. Physiol.* 123: 293, 1908.

134. LEWIS, D. R. *J. Psychol.* 26: 437, 1948.

135. LILJESTRAND, G. *Arch. neerl. physiol.* 7: 532, 1922.

136. LILJESTRAND, G. AND Y. ZOTTERMAN. *Acta physiol. scandinav.* 32: 291, 1954.

137. MACLEOD, S. *J. Exper. Psychol.* 44: 316, 1952.

138. MACNICHOL, E. F., JR., H. G. WAGNER AND H. K. HARTLINE. *XIX Internat. Physiol. Congr., Abstr. of Communic.:* 1953.

139. MARUHASHI, J., K. MIZUGUCHI AND I. TASAKI. *J. Physiol.* 117: 129, 1952.

140. MAYER, B. *Ztschr. Psychol. Physiol. Sinnesorg. Abt. II* 58: 133, 1927.

141. MAYER-GROSS, W. AND J. W. WALKER. *Brit. J. Exper. Path.* 27: 297, 1946.

142. McCLEARY, R. A. *J. Comp. & Physiol Psychol.* 46: 411, 1953.

143. McFADDEN, H. *J. Psychol.* 4: 349, 1937.

144. MONCRIEFF, R. W. *The Chemical Senses.* New York: Wiley, 1951.

145. MORUZI, A. AND LECHTINSKI. *Rev. neurol.* 70: 478, 1938.

146. MOUNTCASTLE, V. AND E. HENNEMAN. *J. Neurophysiol.* 12: 85, 1949.

147. OEHRWALL, H. *Skandinav. Arch. Physiol.* 11: 245, 1901.

148. OERTLY, E. AND R. G. MYERS. *J. Am. Chem. Soc.* 41: 855, 1919.

149. OLMSTED, J. M. D. *J. Comp. Neurol.* 31: 465, 1920.

150. OPPEL, A. In: *Lehrbuch der vergleichende mikroskopischen Anatomie der Wirbeltieren.* Jena: Fischer, 1900, vol. III.

151. OSTWALD, W. AND A. KUHN. *Kolloid-Ztschr.* 29: 266, 1921.

152. PARKER, G. H. *Smell, Taste and Allied Senses in the Vertebrates.* Philadelphia: Lippincott, 1922.

153. PARKER, G. H. AND C. B. METCALF. *Am. J. Physiol.* 17: 55, 1906-07.

154. PARKER, G. H. AND E. M. STABLER. *Am. J. Physiol.* 32: 230, 1913.

155. PATTON, H. D. In: *Textbook of Physiology* (17th ed.), edited by J. F. Fulton. Philadelphia: Saunders, 1955, p. 377.

156. PATTON, H. D. AND V. E. AMASSIAN. *J. Neurophysiol.* 15: 245, 1952.

157. PATTON, H. D., T. C. RUCH AND A. E. WALKER. *J. Neurophysiol.* 7: 171, 1944.

158. PAUL-MÜNCHEN, T. *Ztschr. Elektrochem.* 28: 435, 1922.

159. PENFIELD, W. AND E. BOLDREY. *Brain* 60: 389, 1937.

160. PFAFFMANN, C. *J. Cell. & Comp. Physiol.* 17: 243, 1941.

161. PFAFFMANN, C. In: *Handbook of Experimental Psychology,* edited by S. S. Stevens. New York: Wiley, 1951, p. 1143.

162. PFAFFMANN, C. *J. Comp. & Physiol. Psychol.* 45: 393, 1952.

163. PFAFFMANN, C. *Science* 117: 470, 1953.

164. PFAFFMANN, C. *J. Neurophysiol.* 18: 429, 1955.

165. PFAFFMANN, C. *Am. J. Clin. Nutrition* 5: 142, 1957.

166. PFAFFMANN, C. AND J. K. BARE. *J. Comp. & Physiol. Psychol.* 43: 320, 1950.

167. PFAFFMANN, C. AND E. C. HAGSTROM. *Am. J. Physiol.* 183: 651, 1955.

168. PFAFFMANN, C. AND R. P. WARREN. *J. Appl. Psychol.* In press.

169. PIERON, H. *Année Psychol.* 20: 42, 1914.

170. PIERREL, R. *J. Exper. Psychol.* 49: 374, 1955.

171. PILGRIM, F. J. *Am. J. Clin. Nutrition* 5: 171, 1957.

172. RANSON, S. W. AND S. L. CLARK. *The Anatomy of the Nervous System.* Philadelphia: Saunders, 1955, p. 232.

173. RENGVIST, Y. *Skandinav. Arch. Physiol.* 38: 97, 1919.

174. RICHARDS, T. W. *Am. Chem. J.* 20: 121, 1898.

175. RICHTER, C. P. *Tr. Am. Neurol. A.* 65: 49, 1939.

176. RICHTER, C. P. *Endocrinology* 24: 367, 1939.

177. RICHTER, C. P. *Harvey Lectures* 38: 63, 1942.

178. RICHTER, C. P. *Proc. Soc. Exper. Biol. & Med.* 63: 364, 1946.

179. RICHTER, C. P. AND K. H. CAMPBELL. *Am. J. Physiol.* 128: 291, 1940.

180. RICHTER, C. P. AND K. H. CLISBY. *Am. J. Physiol.* 134: 157, 1941.

181. RICHTER, C. P. AND A. MACLEAN. *Am. J. Physiol.* 126: 1, 1939.

182. ROSE, J. E. AND V. B. MOUNTCASTLE. *J. Comp. Neurol.* 97: 441, 1952.

183. ROSS, S. AND J. VERSACE. *Am. J. Psychol.* 66: 496, 1953.

184. ROWINSKI, DI, P. AND G. MANUNTA. *Arch. fisiol.* 53: 117, 1953.
185. SAIDULLAH, A. *Arch. ges. Physiol.* 60: 457, 1927.
186. SCHUTZ, H. G. AND F. J. PILGRIM. *J. Exper. Psychol.* 54: 41, 1957
187. SCHUTZ, H. G. AND F. J. PILGRIM. *Food Res.* 22: 206, 1957.
188. SCHWARTZ, H. G. AND G. WEDDELL. *Brain* 61: 99, 1938.
189. SHEFFIELD, F. D. AND T. B. ROBY. *J. Comp. & Physiol. Psychol.* 43: 471, 1950.
190. SHERRINGTON, C. *The Integrative Action of the Nervous System.* New Haven: Yale Univ. Press, 1948.
191. SHORE, L. E. *J. Physiol.* 13: 191, 1892.
192. STELLAR, E., R. HYMAN AND S. SAMET. *J. Comp. & Physiol. Psychol.* 47: 220, 1954.
193. STEVENS, S. S. *Psychol. Rev.* 64: 153, 1957.
194. TAYLOR, H. W. *Protoplasma* 4: 1, 1928.
195. TAYLOR, H. W. *J. Gen. Physiol.* 11: 207, 1928.
196. TROLAND, L. T. *The Fundamentals of Human Motivation.* New York: van Nostrand, 1928.
197. VON FRISCH, K. In: *Handbuch der Normalen und Pathologische Physiologie* 11: 203, 1926.
198. VON SKRAMLIK, E. In: *Handbuch der Physiologie der Niederen Sinne* 1: 7, 1926.
199. WARREN, H. C. AND L. CARMICHAEL. *Elements of Human Psychology.* Boston: Houghton Mifflin, 1930, p. 122.
200. WOODWORTH, R. S. (editor). *Experimental Psychology.* New York: Holt, 1938, p. 498.
201. WOOLSEY, C. H. AND D. H. LEMESSURIER. *Fed. Proc.* 7: 137, 1948.
202. YOUNG, P. T. *Motivation of Behavior.* New York: Wiley, 1936.
203. YOUNG, P. T. *Comp. Psychol. Monogr.* 19: No. 5, 1949.
204. YOUNG, P. T. *Am. J. Clin. Nutrition* 5: 154, 1957.
205. ZOTTERMAN, Y. *Skandinav. Arch. Physiologie* 72: 73, 1935.
206. ZOTTERMAN, Y. *Acta physiol. scandinav.* 37: 60, 1956.

CHAPTER XXI

The sense of smell

W. R. ADEY | *Department of Anatomy, University of Melbourne, Melbourne, Australia*

CHAPTER CONTENTS

At all stages of cortical elaboration an important function of the olfactory cortex, in addition to participation in its own specific way in cortical associations, is to serve as a non-specific activator for all cortical activities.

C. J. HERRICK, 1933

WHILE THE IMPORTANCE of the olfactory sense is greatly reduced in primates in comparison with other telereceptor mechanisms, such as sight and hearing, it can nevertheless provide significant information about events possibly remote in space and time. In-deed, olfaction may provide the only warning of serious environmental hazards, and in man it retains its importance in feeding and sexual functions. There remain many baffling aspects to even the most basic phenomena in the olfactory process, particularly in the mechanisms involved in excitation of the peripheral receptor and in the physiological patterning of activity through which fine differences in odors are presumably perceived.

OLFACTORY MUCOSA AND PERIPHERAL RECEPTOR

Arrangement of Olfactory Mucosa

The olfactory mucosa forms a restricted zone in man, lying in the dorsal and posterior part of the nasal cavity. To the naked eye it appears yellowish-brown in comparison with the rest of the mucosa, and it covers the upper parts of both the lateral wall of the nasal cavity and septum, extending over a total area of about 240 sq. mm (66). The olfactory mucosa is a pseudostratified columnar epithelium and, unlike the respiratory portion, has no distinct basement membrane or cilia. It lines the surface of nearly all the superior turbinate, a small part of the middle turbinate and the upper third of the nasal septum (fig. 1).

Inspired air traverses the inferior meatus and partially the middle meatus during normal breathing, and the olfactory area is thus above the main air current. Since a change in breathing, as in sniffing, causes adequate eddying of air into the upper olfactory area, it is apparent that aerodynamic factors may be intimately concerned in determining thresholds of excitability (56).

The olfactory receptors or hair cells are bipolar

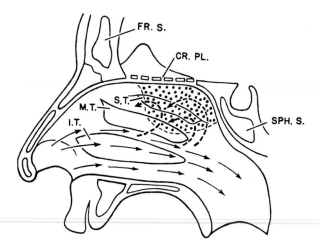

FIG. 1. Diagrammatic representation of the lateral wall of the nasal cavity, indicating the general extent of the olfactory epithelium (dotted). The main stream of inspired air passes below the olfactory region. Secondary eddying of air currents carries odors to the receptor region. Abbreviations: *CR.PL.*, cribriform plate, perforated by the olfactory nerves; *FR.S.*, frontal air sinus; *I.T.*, *M.T.*, *S.T.*, inferior, middle and superior turbinate bones projecting as ledges from the lateral wall of the nasal cavity; *SPH.S.*, sphenoidal air sinus.

and oval. When seen by light microscopy, they possess distally small terminal swellings from each of which five to six olfactory hairs commonly arise. In the rabbit, these cells are estimated to number 150,000 per sq. mm (35). Electronmicroscopy indicates that the hairs are considerably more numerous, with up to 1000 hairs per cell (23). Each hair is 1 to 2 μ long and 0.1 μ in diameter. In this way the surface area exposed by the receptor cell is greatly increased (fig. 2). Clark (32) points out, however, that near the periphery of the olfactory epithelium there is some intermingling of olfactory receptors and ciliated epithelial cells of the 'respiratory' region, and that this may lead to misinterpretations in electronmicroscopy of the olfactory hairs, which he considers to be coarser and to remain untapered at their free extremities.

Removal of the olfactory bulb in the rabbit produces a very striking degeneration in 48 hr., with almost complete removal of the debris of the mucosal receptors within three days (33). However, only about half the receptors degenerate after complete removal of the bulb, the remainder persisting unaltered up to six months after operation. The findings do not support the concepts that the axons of the residual elements may proceed to adjacent areas of the olfactory epithelium, rather than to the bulb, or

that they may give off collaterals sufficient to maintain the cells. The possibility is considered of a centrifugal system of fibers arising in the bulb and proceeding peripherally to the mucosa.

The secretions of the numerous serous and mucous glands in both the respiratory and olfactory regions of the nose bathe the entire cavity in a liquid sheath which is in a constant state of motion towards the nasopharynx. This sheath may be of basic importance in conveying odorous substances to the receptor cell, since varying degrees of water and fat solubility in the tissues of the mucosa may be related to the odorous properties of a particular substance (see below).

The electrical responses of the olfactory mucosa of the frog have been successfully recorded by Ottoson (76). Odorous air blown into the nasal cavity evokes a slow negative monophasic potential in the olfactory mucosa (fig. 3). The response is obtained only from the olfactory area of the mucosa and is not abolished by cocaine in concentrations sufficient to paralyze olfactory nerve fibers. It is abolished by small amounts of ether or chloroform vapor, and it is inferred that the response arises in the olfactory hairs. The amplitude of the response is, within certain limits, proportional to the logarithm of the stimulus intensity. Equal amounts of odorous material distributed in different volumes of air evoke responses of equal amplitudes. The shape and time course of the response is related to the strength of the stimulus. With an increase of odor intensity in the stimulating air,

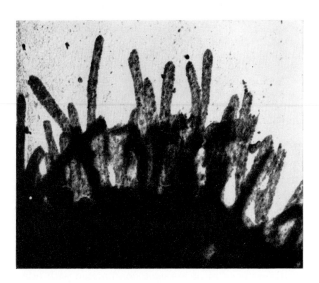

FIG. 2. Electronmicrograph of the surface of a human olfactory cell, showing a great number of thin finger-like processes 1.5 to 2.0 μ long. Magnification $\times$ 23,430. [From Bloom & Engstrom (23).]

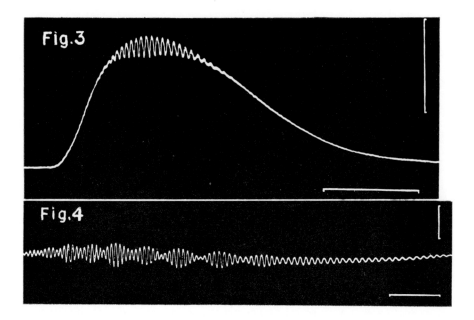

FIG. 3. Rhythmic waves superimposed upon the slow potential. Stimulus: amyl acetate. Volume of stimulating air, 0.25 cc. Vertical line 5.0 mv. Time bar, 1 sec. [From Ottoson (76).]

FIG. 4. Rhythmic waves evoked by continuous stimulation of the olfactory epithelium. Stimulus: 0.1 mole butanol. Velocity of stimulating air stream, 1.0 cc per sec. Vertical line 1.0 mv. Time bar 0.5 sec. [From Ottoson (76).]

the potential rises at a faster rate, the crest of the response broadens and the decay time lengthens. The 'wave form' of the stimulating air current is of great importance in determining the shape and time course of the response. The latency of the response to stimulation with butanol of different stimulus strengths varies from 0.2 to 0.4 sec.

Ottoson has found that during continuous stimulation the evoked response in the olfactory epithelium declines from the initial peak to a lower level which continues throughout stimulation (fig. 4). The amplitude of this residual response is lower at higher stimulus intensities. With repeated stimulation at short intervals, the first three or four responses are progressively diminished, with greater reductions at higher stimulus strengths. The sensitivity of the epithelium to different substances can be selectively reduced by repetitive stimulation, and rhythmic oscillations are often seen on the peak of the slow response evoked by strong stimuli.

Olfactory Bulb and Its Connections with Olfactory Mucosa

The olfactory nerve fibers arising from the hair cells penetrate the overlying cribriform plate of the ethmoid bone and enter the olfactory bulb. Electron-

microscopy of the olfactory nerves indicates a unique appearance, with large numbers of very small nerve fibers having a modal diameter of 0.2 μ. They number six million from one side of the nasal septum in the pig and are considerably more numerous from the turbinates (45). There appears to be a one-to-one relationship between receptor cells and axons. Their conduction velocity in the pike is 0.2 m per sec., thus resembling the last elevation in the C fiber action potential in the frog's sciatic nerve.

Within the outer layers of the bulb the fibers of the olfactory nerves enter into the formation of glomeruli (fig. 5). Each glomerulus is formed jointly by entering olfactory nerve fibers and also from the dendrites of more deeply situated mitral and tufted cells. These cells form the succeeding second order neurons on the olfactory pathway. The arrangement is an excellent one for spatial summation, since each glomerulus in the rabbit receives impulses from 26,000 receptors and passes this information through 24 mitral cells and 68 tufted cells (15, 16). The axons of the 60,000 mitral cells form the bulk of the lateral olfactory stria passing to higher olfactory centers.

Physiological and anatomical evidence confirms the existence of a regional projection pattern from the olfactory mucosa to the bulb. Impulses from the

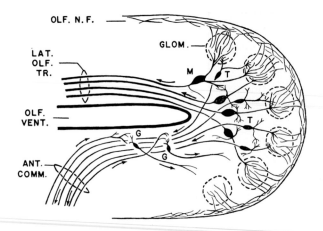

FIG. 5. General arrangement of the neural paths in the olfactory bulb. Fibers from the receptor cells are collected on the surface of the bulb (*OLF.N.F.*) and participate in the formation of more deeply situated glomeruli (*GLOM*) which also receive the dendritic processes of the mitral cells (*M*) and the tufted cells (*T*). Axons of mitral cells are mainly collected into the lateral olfactory tract (*LAT. OLF. TR.*) and run to the primary olfactory cortex. The finer axons of tufted cells pass into the anterior limb of the anterior commissure, reaching the opposite bulb where they synapse with deeply situated granule cells (*G*). Axons of granule cells are directed peripherally at least as far as the fields of the mitral and tufted cells. *OLF. VENT.* represents the olfactory ventricle present in lower mammals and continuous with the cerebral ventricular system.

anterior and dorsal parts of the olfactory mucosa reach the anterior parts of the bulb, whereas the ventral and posterior regions of the mucosa project to the posterior parts of the bulb (5). Although initial anatomical studies (35) did not support a topographic arrangement, more extensive investigations (31) have confirmed the general arrangement suggested by Adrian. The upper part of the olfactory epithelium projects mainly to the upper part of the bulb, and lower areas of epithelium to lower regions of the bulb; but anatomical evidence of an anteroposterior organization of the projections is less definite.

ESSENTIAL PROCESSES INVOLVED IN
OLFACTORY STIMULATION

Characters of Odorous Substances

No embracing picture can yet be advanced to categorize all odorous substances, since many are totally unrelated physically and chemically. Hill & Carothers (54) observed a relationship between the number of atoms in certain macrocyclic ring hydro-

carbon compounds and the nature of their odors. Thus compounds with 13 atoms possess a cedar-like odor, with 14, 15 or 16 atoms a musk-like odor, and with 17 or 18 atoms a civet-like odor. For example, pentadecanolide and decamethylene oxalate both have musky odors.

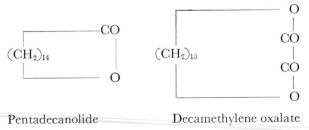

Pentadecanolide   Decamethylene oxalate

Hill & Carothers suggest that, within wide limits, the number of atoms in the ring, rather than the identity of the reactive groups, is the significant factor. However, many anomalies have limited attempts to extend this hypothesis. Moncrieff (68) has suggested that to be odorous a substance must be volatile and soluble in the tissues of the olfactory mucosa, the latter property involving varying degrees of water and fat solubility. The olfactory mucous membrane exhibits considerable powers of adsorbing odorous substances in the freshly isolated state, and this sorptive property may be intimately related to processes of excitation in olfactory receptors (69). Moncrieff further suggests that the disposition of an element in the electrochemical series may be correlated with odorous properties, since only seven elements are odorous (fluorine, chlorine, bromine, iodine, oxygen as ozone, phosphorus and arsenic), and six of these occupy the lowest places in the electrochemical series. The disposition of substitution groups in organic compounds is of great significance in determining both strength and quality of odors. Legge (64) has advanced the hypothesis that odorous substances may react with groups on the free surface of protein and lipoprotein films, leading to the rupture of a few bonds in incompletely spread proteins with a consequent enormous increase in their area. In view of the role played by —S—S— groups in the maintenance of protein structure, the rupture of bonds induced by odorous substances might explain the high dilutions at which mercaptans can be detected.

On the basis of records from the olfactory bulb, Adrian (10) has defined four groups of substances, and in each group has detected one substance capable of evoking a discharge limited to a single one of the units within the range of the electrodes. Acetone exhibits a high specificity in a group which includes amyl and ethyl acetate. Benzene behaves similarly in a group composed of aromatic hydrocarbons. Octane is similarly active in a group of paraffin hydrocarbons and heavy oils. Dipentane, cedarwood oil and eucalyptus oil (substances belonging to the terpenes and related compounds) likewise give single unit discharges.

The ability of various substances, including metal surfaces, to adsorb and retain foreign odors has been tested by Deininger & Sullivan (36). The great majority of metal surfaces not only pick up odors, but also modify and distort them, often so severely as to leave little suggestion as to the original contaminant. This perversion of the perceived odor is not related to the purity of the metal in the case of either copper or aluminum.

Enzyme Theories of Olfaction

Alexander (11) has suggested that odor-producing substances affect the catalyst balance of the olfactory cells. This theory has been elaborated by Kistiakowsky (60) in an hypothesis that substances having odor inhibit a reaction requiring a catalyst. These changes in the concentration of reaction products would cause excitation in specific receptor units. Sumner (81) has criticized this concept on the grounds that substances we smell, in the concentrations needed to smell them, would not be likely to have any effect on any known enzyme systems and would require an array of enzymes with new and unusual properties in the olfactory mucosa. Beidler (21) points out that some substances are effective olfactory stimuli in concentrations as low as 10^{-13} molar.

Even if an odorous substance should inactivate an enzyme, thus causing a change in concentration of certain substances, there is as yet no explanation as to how this change in concentration could stimulate olfactory nerves. Bourne (26) and El-Baradi & Bourne (38, 39) have detected significant amounts of alkaline phosphatase in the olfactory mucosa and in the taste buds of the tongue and have observed that vanillin inhibits this alkaline phosphatase. However, alkaline phosphatase is widely distributed throughout the body. Goldwasser, quoted by Sumner (81), suggests that the energy needed to stimulate olfactory receptors may come from Pauling's electrochemical energy source deriving from the modification of bonding angles within a molecule at the time that the molecule goes into solution.

Radiation Theories of Olfaction

Theories of electromagnetic radiation or molecular vibration in relation to olfaction have engaged many workers (20, 37, 74, 84, 90). However, there appears to be little or no experimental foundation for the concept that the essential properties of odor result from radiations inherent in molecular behavior (73). Indeed, a substance such as the deuteroxyl counterpart of n-butyl alcohol has exactly the same odor as the original n-butyl alcohol, although its infrared adsorption spectrum is different (89). On the other hand, certain d- and l-isomers differ in smell, although their infrared spectra are identical. No evoked electrical responses can be recorded from the olfactory mucosa if it is covered with a thin plastic membrane which transmits infrared radiation but impedes contact between the stimulating particles and the epithelium. There is no indication that olfactory receptors can be stimulated unless the odorous material is brought into contact with the epithelium (76).

Methods of Odor Measurement

SUBJECTIVE MEASUREMENT TECHNIQUES. Sources of error in the subjective assessment of odor quality and intensity have been discussed in a historical survey by Wenzel (87). It is obviously difficult to control such factors as the force of the observer's inhalation in methods involving the 'sniff' technique, nor does the administration of the odorous substance by a stream of air at constant pressure necessarily control mechanical factors involved in the eddying of air towards the olfactory receptors in the upper part of the nasal cavity.

Only a few of the many subjective methods will be discussed here, since all appear to involve significant possibilities of error in assessment of threshold, and there are conflicting opinions as to their relative merits. A number of early methods, typified by the olfactometer of Zwaardemaker (90), involved sniffing gradually increasing intensities of the odorous substance up to threshold concentration. In attempts to obviate subjective sniffing, both injection of a blast of air and a continuous stream of air have been tested by Elsberg & Levy (40). They defined the absolute olfactory threshold as the minimal blast of odorous air capable of producing a sensation of odor. Although the measurement so obtained is usually expressed in terms of volume, Jerome (55) has suggested that these threshold measurements are dependent on pressure of the air blast rather than on odor intensity. Jones (56) has also found that aerodynamic factors, especially pressure, determine the threshold in the blast injection technique and that the threshold so determined is not related to odor concentration.

Since neither subjective sniffing nor the substitution of an air blast for the observer's own sniff dispose of many of the difficulties in odor threshold measurement, Wenzel (88) has studied the reliability of threshold measurements during normal breathing with the subject's head placed in a camera inodorata. Here a plastic box encloses the subject's head, and the hair and face can be covered with plastic to eliminate their odors, leaving only the nostrils exposed. A continuous stream of pure air to which odors can be added is fed into the box. This method is claimed to give satisfactory results in threshold measurement without the need for prior training of the subject.

It has been claimed that subjects can match odors quantitatively by the use of a standard 'sniff' technique, using as test substances two aliphatic homologous series, comprised of the alcohols butanol (C_4) through duodecanol (C_{12}), and the acetate esters hexyl (C_6) through duodecyl (C_{12}), each prepared in serial dilutions (19). No attempt was made in these tests to instruct the subject in the technique of sniffing, reliance being placed on the subject's existing habits. Results were consistent in repeated trials, with odorosity decreasing as a function of molecular chain length, and also with dilution, for both alcohols and acetates.

Kuehner (61) has used an air-dilution method in determining olfactory thresholds and stresses the need to standardize the subject from day to day by exposing him to standard vapor concentrations. Extreme variations of sensitivity noted in individuals make it impossible to take odor measurements over extended periods without knowledge of the subject's sensitivity at the time of sampling. One breath of ammonia can reduce the sensitivity by 50 per cent for 24 hr. At the onset of a head cold, the sensitivity is sharply increased but later is depressed. A marked temporary reduction in sensitivity follows excessive drinking or smoking. Kuehner used air saturated with xylene vapor as a reference odor and in a prolonged series of experiments with two subjects exhibiting similar sensitivities found that its normal odor level was 380 times greater than threshold. Under the same conditions, nicotine saturated air to 3000 times the threshold intensity.

OBJECTIVE MEASUREMENT TECHNIQUES. Kuehner (61) claims that odorous substances are capable of react-

ing with oxidants and that the resulting deodorization is related to the amount of oxidant reduced. While efforts to find reproducible concentrations of individual odors in a complex, such as tobacco smoke, were unsuccessful, it was found that certain oxidants react with odor complexes in a reproducible manner, thus confirming the earlier observations of Lang *et al.* (62). Kuehner found a close uniformity in odor production by tobacco artificially burned in this system regardless of type, freshness and rate of combustion, and established that tobacco smoked by humans produced only 40 per cent of the odor level of that 'smoked' artificially, both in its reducing powers with oxidants and as determined subjectively under room conditions. This technique has been criticized by Turk (85) on the grounds that oxidant methods, which usually employ permanganates or ceric salts, may be inadequate because of a lack of relationship between quality or intensity of odorants and their reactivity toward a chemical oxidant. Such methods may indicate only the reducing or oxidizing qualities of the extraneous atmospheric gases and vapors.

Turk (85) has used infrared adsorption spectra of odorous substances as a means of qualitative analysis. Different functional groups, such as aldehyde, alcohol and ester linkages, show typical infrared adsorption frequencies. Thus the infrared spectrum of a mixture of compounds reveals information on the types of individual compounds therein, and by this means Turk has been able to detect vaporized mineral oil as a component of apple aroma in commercial apple storage rooms. It has already been mentioned that this method may not be free from error, since substances with similar odors may have different adsorption spectra and vice versa (87, 89).

ELECTRICAL PHENOMENA IN OLFACTORY BULB
ACCOMPANYING OLFACTORY STIMULATION

Patterns of Spontaneous and Induced Activity in Bulb and Effects of Anesthesia

The rhythmic waves that can be recorded from the surface of the bulb have been extensively investigated (4–10, 72, 86). Whereas Adrian's initial experiments suggested rhythmic discharges in the bulb synchronously with each breath, later experiments (5, 9) have shown that with filtered air no mechanical stimulation occurs. Both spontaneous waves and those which occur in response to strong olfactory stimuli have been recorded in the bulb.

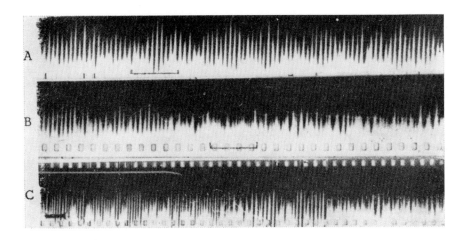

FIG. 6. 'Intrinsic waves' recorded in the olfactory bulb in light thiopental anesthesia. *A*: No olfactory stimulus. Frequency, 100/sec. *B*: Abolition of intrinsic rhythm by weak olfactory stimulation with amyl acetate. *C*: In another preparation, strong stimulation with amyl acetate abolishes the intrinsic rhythm with substitution of a slower induced rhythm. [From Adrian (5).]

SPONTANEOUS WAVES. These are usually smaller and less regular than waves evoked by olfactory stimulation and are associated with persistent activity in the cells of the bulb. They were described in the isolated olfactory bulb of the frog (47). Their frequencies are as high as 70 to 100 per sec (fig. 6). They are suppressed in the mammal by deep anesthesia and they accompany a persistent irregular discharge of axon spikes in the deeper layers. In medium anesthesia this discharge may be so large as to conceal any change induced by a weak olfactory stimulus. This continuous activity persists after complete destruction of the olfactory epithelium and after isolation of the bulb from the forebrain but ceases after interference with the blood supply of the bulb.

Adrian (5) regards this activity as largely spontaneous or intrinsic, expressing the continuous breakdown and repair of cells not stabilized by deep anesthesia. Although mitral cells certainly take part in this activity, there is some reason to suppose that it may originate in cells with short axons (granule cells) arranged in layers deep to the mitral cells. This is suggested by the fact that the intrinsic waves can exhibit considerably higher frequencies than the induced waves. If the induced waves indicate the maximum frequency of discharge of the direct olfactory pathway, a higher rhythm probably has a different origin.

In the phase of recovery from deep anesthesia, the bulb is quiescent unless stimulated, but a breath of odorous air will produce a few waves accompanied by scattered discharges in the mitral cells. With lightening anesthesia such a stimulus may start a longer train of waves of gradually decreasing frequency. Ultimately a stage is reached at which the bulb reacts with a train of waves which may continue indefinitely. This phenomenon has been named by Adrian the 'awakening reaction' of the bulb, and it is suggested that in medium or light anesthesia the granule cells have become capable of maintaining themselves in continued activity and that their activity leads to a continued discharge in the mitral cell axons.

WAVES AND UNIT ACTIVITY ACCOMPANYING OLFACTORY STIMULATION. In such animals as the cat and rabbit, strong olfactory stimuli elicit large sinusoidal oscillations in the bulb, usually at a fixed frequency and occurring only with each period of stimulation (fig. 7). These large regular waves are produced only by olfactory stimuli given at three or four times the threshold concentration, and may appear at frequencies of 50 to 60 per sec. against a silent background in moderately deep urethane anesthesia, and at 10 to 15 per sec. under allobarbital or pentobarbital. Their frequency does not bear any relationship to the quality or intensity of the stimulus.

In moderately deep allobarbital or pentobarbital anesthesia, with the bulb exhibiting regular intrinsic waves at a low frequency, an olfactory stimulus usually abolishes the waves at each inspiration. If the stimulus is strong the gap in intrinsic activity may be filled with induced waves. As anesthesia lightens, the rhythm becomes more firmly established and the

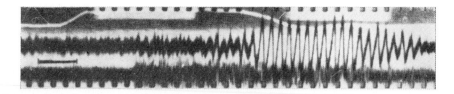

FIG. 7. Induced waves develop in the olfactory bulb after commencement of the olfactory discharge. Rabbit under deep urethane anesthesia breathing air containing amyl acetate. The upper oscillograph tracing shows the waves from the surface of the bulb; the lower shows the axon spikes from the white matter. Inspiration indicated by white line above. Time marker, 0.1 sec. [From Adrian (5).]

waves may be merely reduced or scarcely altered during stimulation. When the bulb is quiet in very deep anesthesia, a moderate olfactory stimulus sets up a mitral cell discharge with each inspiration, but no discharges are visible between inspirations. With lightening anesthesia, evoked discharges appear against a background of continuous irregular activity which ultimately becomes so prominent as to obscure entirely any change evoked by the stimulus. In very light anesthesia the olfactory stimuli regain some control over the mitral pathway, and both weak and strong stimuli evoke an obvious increase in discharge during each inspiration, with suppression of the mitral discharges in the periods between each inspiration.

The complete suppression of intrinsic activity in the bulb of the rabbit is seldom long maintained. The return of activity takes place more slowly when the smell is strong and the anesthesia light. Adrian (5) suggests that the phenomenon offers an explanation of olfactory adaptation as seen in man, although, as mentioned above, records from the mucosa during continuous stimulation indicate that at least some adaptation occurs at the receptor level (76).

Records from the olfactory bulb in man show a series of rhythmic waves at each inspiration while breathing tincture of valerian and benzene, whereas room air yields no response. No spontaneous waves of the type seen in the rabbit have been noted in man. Thiopental anesthesia abolishes all responses (80).

Unit activity recorded with microelectrodes in the olfactory bulb of a variety of animals favors the mitral cells as the site of origin of the axon spikes, with tufted cells and glomeruli possibly also contributing. Where it is possible to record both wave and spike components of the response, it is found that the fast spikes are evoked first, followed by the waves, with the spikes becoming synchronous with the waves as the wave response develops (5, 72).

Differential Excitation of Receptors

DIFFERENTIATION OF RESPONSE IN AREA. Substances soluble in water (e.g. amyl acetate, ethyl acetate, ether, acetone) have a lower threshold for spike discharges in the anterior part of the bulb, where mitral cells synapse with fibers from the anterior and dorsal parts of the mucosa (fig. 8). Conversely, substances soluble in lipoids (e.g. pentane, coal gas and benzene) have a lower threshold for spike discharges in the posterior part of the bulb which receives fibers from the posterior and ventral parts of the olfactory epithelium (9, 10). This difference does not necessarily imply a differential excitability of the receptors at the front and back of the organ and may well result from structural factors, difference in the velocity of the air current and in the composition of the surface film through which molecules of odorous substance pass to reach the receptor surface.

In records from the middle part of the bulb (9) there may be a single series of large spikes or a mixture of large and small spikes (fig. 9). The single series presumably represents a discharge from one cell, whereas small spikes come from neighboring units. Adrian found that at any one recording point one substance in low concentration would give a single series of large spikes. Each large spike thus appears to have a special relation to a particular stimulus. Units have been observed displaying this specific sensitivity to such diverse substances as trimethylamine, acetone, ethyl acetate, amyl acetate, pentane, octane, xylol, petrol, clove oil, oil of eucalyptus and thick machine oil. Despite the improbability of finding a few primary smells out of which all others can be compounded, Adrian (10) has defined four groups of substances with one substance in each group most frequently evoking a single unit discharge (see above). Strong concentrations of odorants will bring in other units, but critical regions will always exist where the concentration is only

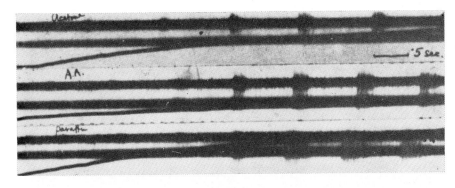

FIG. 8. Three records with double oscillograph system showing discharge from the oral and aboral regions of the rabbit's olfactory bulb. In each record the upper tracing is from the oral region and the lower from the aboral. The signal line shows increasing odor concentration. With acetone (top record) the discharge is confined to the oral region, with paraffin oil (bottom record) to the aboral and with amyl acetate (middle record) discharge occurs in both regions. [From Adrian (9).]

just great enough to excite and there the specific excitation will always show itself.

TEMPORAL DIFFERENTIATION OF RESPONSE. Adrian (10) suggests that at the beginning and end of each respiration the concentration of odorous substance is near threshold values. Physical and chemical properties of the substance will therefore determine the time course of the response. The integrated outline or envelope of the response as seen in oscillographic records will thus have a characteristic contour and a particular smell might be identified from this outline. Volatility and solubility in water both favor a rapid rise and decline of the discharge, with little persistence between one inspiration and the next. Thus the response to amyl acetate has a shorter latency and a more abrupt rise and fall than the longer latency responses to pentane. Increasing concentrations affect the areal differentiation but have no effect on the temporal pattern. Patterns of temporal integration have been recorded by the more elaborate techniques of Mozell & Pfaffmann (72) in determining the relative sensitivity of different parts of the mucosa and bulb to amyl acetate and heptane (fig. 10).

Mozell (71) has determined the neural response curve of the integrated spike discharge from four points on the olfactory bulb as a function of concentration of amyl acetate, heptane, ethyl ether and benzene. Discharge strength and duration increased approximately as a negatively accelerated function of concentration. The curves reached their asymptotes in about 1 to 1.5 log units of physical concentration. By contrast, the asymptote in other senses is not reached until the intensities have been increased several thousand times, or by 4 to 6 log units. It is

suggested that this may account for the relatively narrow range of subjective odor intensity discrimination. This study confirms the existence of a relatively gross anteroposterior spatial differentiation of responsive zones within the bulb for different substances.

Thus smells seem to be distinguished by a combination of detailed pattern and general region of excitation (10). Hainer et al. (52), in discussing an information theory of olfaction, also emphasize the importance of threshold phenomena in the conveyance of essential olfactory information.

CENTRAL CONNECTIONS OF OLFACTORY BULB

Olfactory functions were originally ascribed to many deep parts of the temporal lobe, including the hippocampal gyrus and hippocampal formation, and to certain regions of the frontal lobe, including the cingulate area. Much of the early work in this field can be seen in an English translation of certain works of Ramón y Cajal (78). Experimental determination of the sites of termination of the olfactory tract has indicated a much more restricted distribution of these fibers. Reviews by Brodal (27), Allison (15) and Pribram & Kruger (77) have discussed the morphological aspects of this problem.

Efferent Pathways From Olfactory Bulb

The majority of the axons of the mitral cells run caudally to be collected on the lateral and inferior aspects of the olfactory peduncle, forming the lateral olfactory tract or stria. In addition to the superficial pathways, there is a centrally placed group of delicate

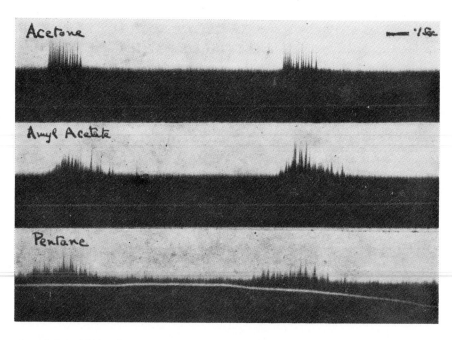

FIG. 9. Records from the middle region of the rabbit's olfactory bulb showing the differential sensitivity of neighboring mitral units. In this case, acetone gives only large spikes; amyl acetate gives large and small; and pentane gives only small spikes. [From Adrian (9).]

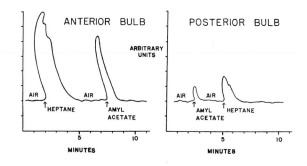

FIG. 10. Integrator records of the spike discharges from the anterior and posterior areas of the olfactory bulb following stimulation by heptane and amyl acetate. The responses indicate a differentiation in both space and time. [After Mozell & Pfaffmann (72).]

axons arising mainly from the tufted cells and traversing the anterior commissure to reach the opposite olfactory bulb. The existence of a medial olfactory stria conveying fibers from the bulb to the septal area appears unlikely (41). Although the tuberculoseptal tract is often stated to convey impulses from the olfactory tubercle to the septum, this tract arises largely in the nonolfactory part of the olfactory tubercle (15).

Extent of Primary Olfactory Cortex

NEUROANATOMICAL INVESTIGATIONS. Removal of the olfactory bulb in the rabbit (34) and monkey (67) is followed by degeneration of fibers running in the lateral olfactory tract to reach the olfactory tubercle, the frontal prepyriform cortex, the temporal prepyriform cortex, the cortical and medial amygdaloid nuclei and the bed nucleus of the stria terminalis. The general arrangement of these structures is shown in figure 11. An essentially similar distribution occurs in the marsupial phalanger (1). No degeneration has been seen in these studies in the hippocampal formation nor in the posterior pyriform cortex (entorhinal area), nor is there evidence of a medial olfactory tract establishing direct cingulate or septal connections.

Following inoculation of the olfactory mucosa of rhesus monkeys with poliomyelitis virus, Bodian (25) has found degeneration in the olfactory tubercle, the nucleus of the diagonal band, the prepyriform cortex and the periamygdaloid cortex. Some degeneration also occurs in the hypothalamus, the mid-line thalamic nuclei, the habenular nucleus and the globus pallidus. No degeneration was seen in the hippocampal formation or entorhinal area, nor in the lateral thalamus, putamen or caudate nucleus.

ELECTROPHYSIOLOGICAL INVESTIGATIONS. Responses can generally be recorded in animals exposed to olfactory stimuli from considerably wider areas than those which neuroanatomical studies have indicated as being directly connected with the olfactory bulb. Changes in electrical activity have been reported from the olfactory tubercle, the septal region, the prepyriform and periamygdaloid cortex and from the hippocampal formation (4, 14, 53, 65).

Direct electrical stimulation of the olfactory bulb has provided clearer information than the use of olfactory stimuli, since it allows some assessment of the temporal sequence of spread and may permit inferences to be drawn concerning the structures in monosynaptic connection with the olfactory bulb (22, 43, 58, 79).

In the cat under pentobarbital anesthesia, the bipolar record from the prepyriform cortex (with the lead electrode nearer the point of stimulation) shows an initial fast negative spike with a latency of 2.0 msec. and presumably resulting from conduction in the olfactory tract. This is succeeded by a biphasic response with an initial negativity peaking at 6 to 8 msec. In records from near the caudal border of the prepyriform cortex the diphasic response appears as a double negative wave. This second peak is eliminated by repetitive stimulation, possibly from synchronization of cortical activity, in such a way that the same elements which previously fired separately to produce two peaks discharge in unison to produce a single larger response (43). This is supported by anatomical studies in the primary olfactory cortex of the mouse (75) which have disclosed intracortical neuron chains possessing abundant and systematically distributed cells with short axis cylinders within these chains.

Similar records from the surface of the olfactory tubercle in the cat indicate two negative waves with latencies of 6.0 msec. and 11.0 msec. Records in depth show a single deflection peaking at 8.0 msec. Surface records from the pyriform lobe usually show two peaks, an initial diphasic wave with a latency of 8 to 10 msec., and a later deflection at 20 to 35 msec. Since this late response is not abolished by section of the lateral olfactory tract but only by complete transection of the prepyriform cortex, it is suggested that the late response in pyriform cortex depends on transcortical connexions between prepyriform and more caudally placed pyriform cortical areas (43).

Potentials similar to those in the cat are obtained in the monkey from stimulation of the olfactory

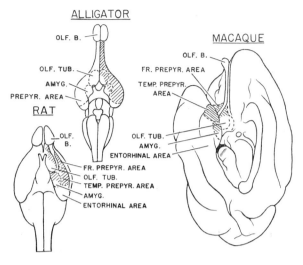

FIG. 11. The comparative extent of the primary olfactory cortex (*shaded area*) in alligator, rat and monkey, indicating the progressive reduction in the proportion of the cortical mantle receiving fibers directly from the olfactory bulb in higher vertebrates. Abbreviations: *AMYG.*, amygdala; *FR. PREPYR.AREA*, frontal prepyriform area; *OLF.B.*, olfactory bulb; *OLF.TUB.*, olfactory tubercle; *PREPYR.AREA*, prepyriform area; *TEMP.PREPYR.AREA*, temporal prepyriform area. [After Allison (15).]

bulb (58). A fast negative spike can be recorded in the olfactory tract, along the lateral and medial olfactory striae, from the rostrolateral portion of the olfactory tubercle and tip of the hippocampal gyrus. Second and third negative deflections appear after 7 to 11 msec. and 18 to 45 msec. in the olfactory tract, the cortex of the posterior orbital surface of the frontal lobe just external to the lateral olfactory stria, the rostrolateral posterior of the olfactory tubercle, the limen insulae and the anterior end of the hippocampal gyrus. In subjects under very light chloralose anesthesia, Kaada also noted responses in the posterior part of the hippocampal gyrus, the hippocampus and the septum lucidum.

Centrifugal influences may modify both the resting and induced electrical activity of the olfactory bulb (59). Stimulation of the prepyriform cortex, cortical amygdaloid nucleus and olfactory tubercle is followed by a depression of electrical activity in the bulb. Similar effects follow high frequency stimulation of the anterior commissure. These influences are thought to be mediated through the granule cells of the bulb and appear to exert tonic effects similar to those observed in the modulation of spinal afferent pathways (51).

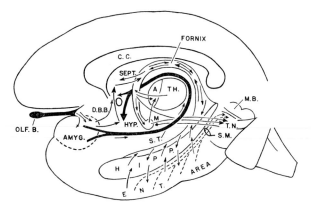

FIG. 12. Diagrammatic representation of intricate pathways through which the primary olfactory cortex may be brought into relation with certain 'rhinencephalic' structures and certain regions of the diencephalon and midbrain. The stria terminalis (*S.T.*) arises in the amygdala and terminates in part in the hypothalamus (*HYP.*). The amygdala probably also has more direct hypothalamic connections and is also connected with the septum (*SEPT.*) through the diagonal band of Broca (*D.B.B.*). The fornix bundles may convey activity in both directions between the hippocampus and the septum, the anterior thalamus (*A*) and hypothalamus, which terminates partly in the mammillary body (*M*). The mammillary body establishes anterior thalamic connections through the mammillothalamic tract. The hippocampus (*HIPP.*) is reciprocally connected with the entorhinal area (*ENT.AREA*). The tegmental nuclei (*T.N.*) and the periaqueductal grey matter of the midbrain (*M.B.*) may receive fibers from the entorhinal area through the stria medullaris (*S.M.*) and through the periventricular fiber systems. The tegmental nuclei may also be reciprocally connected with the mammillary body through the mammillotegmental tracts and the mammillary peduncle.

Higher Order Olfactory Connections

It is apparent from anatomical and physiological studies that the primary olfactory cortex is only indirectly connected with many of the cortical and subcortical regions included in classical accounts of the rhinencephalon. This is supported by the long latencies of responses recorded in the more remote regions. In the cat under pentobarbital anesthesia, whereas responses appear in the ventral part of the head of the caudate nucleus after 3.5 to 12.0 msec., and in the hippocampal gyrus, subiculum and anterior end of the hippocampus after 7.0 msec., slower responses are seen in the ventral parts of the hippocampus only after 10 to 33 msec., and in the caudal and dorsal regions of the hippocampus after 17 to 38 msec. Responses appear in the stria medullaris after 17 msec. and in the mammillothalamic tract after 25 to 34 msec. (22).

Certain studies have emphasized the possible role of such regions as the septum, the hippocampal formation and the adjoining pyriform cortex in mechanisms of alerting and emotional arousal. Although responses from olfactory stimulation can be recorded in these regions, they are also accessible to other sensory stimuli including those from tactile, visual and auditory modalities (46, 50, 57, 65). Maclean *et al.* (65) have recorded in the rabbit regular rhythmic discharges at 13 to 20 waves per sec. in the anterior pyriform cortex and in the hippocampal formation during respiration of smoke-filled air. Similar responses were evoked by gustatory and painful stimulation. They concluded that the hippocampus responds to olfactory stimuli in a less predictable manner and probably after a longer latency than the pyriform area. They did not seek responses in the posterior pyriform area (entorhinal area of the hippocampal gyrus).

Although a great body of evidence confirms the role of the anterior pyriform or prepyriform region as the major primary olfactory cortical area, pathways from it to adjoining rhinencephalic structures, such as the hippocampus, may well be circuitous (fig. 12). Thus neuroanatomical studies have indicated that the amygdaloid nuclei project largely via the stria terminalis bundles to the hypothalamus (3, 42, 44). The hypothalamus in turn establishes connections with midline and intralaminar thalamic nuclei (30, 70). Here further relays may pass via the fornix to the hippocampal formation (49, 50), and ultimately such activity may reach the midbrain tegmentum via the entorhinal area and the stria medullaris (2). Stimulation of the amygdala (48) has indicated widespread subcortical projections from both corticomedial nuclei (forming part of the primary olfactory cortex) and from basolateral nuclei. Short latency responses (presumably monosynaptic) appear in overlapping primary projection fields covering the basomedial part of the telencephalon and adjoining rostral pole of the diencephalon. From here responses pass by short multisynaptic relays through secondary projection fields which include a central core of grey matter stretching from the hypothalamus to the midbrain tegmentum. Short latency responses from the corticomedial group extend caudally into the hypothalamus further than those following basolateral stimulation, but no tegmental responses follow stimulation of the corticomedial nuclei. This study confirms the role of the stria terminalis as an important efferent pathway from the amygdala to the hypothalamus.

Behavior Studies of Olfactory Mechanisms

Excision of the olfactory bulb or damage to the anterior limb of the anterior commissure in the rat leads to a distinct impairment of olfactory discrimination. However, lesions involving the septum, the hippocampus, the fimbria, the fornix, the amygdala and the pyriform lobes are without effect on discrimination in tests involving the differentiation of wood shavings scented with oil of anise and creosote (82, 83). Brown & Ghiselli (28) also failed to find any impairment of olfactory discrimination after a variety of subcortical lesions. Experiments designed to test the role in olfaction of pathways through the anterior thalamic nuclei from the hypothalamus to the cingulate cortex have not disclosed impaired discrimination after total bilateral destruction of the anterior thalamic nuclei and their radiations, with additional involvement of the septum (63). In these experiments removal of the olfactory bulbs permanently abolished the discrimination between the odors of oil of wintergreen and of bread and milk, indicating that the reaction was based upon olfactory and not trigeminal stimulation. Cats are capable of finding food by olfactory cues after lesions destroying almost all the neocortex but leaving intact the anterior pyriform and periamygdaloid cortex (18).

Studies by Allen (12, 13) using conditioned responses have provided a more delicate measure of olfactory powers than simple discrimination tests. Using dogs, Allen subjected all animals to four tests which involved establishment of a conditioned foreleg response to clove vapor, ability to transfer this reflex to the opposite foreleg, ability to establish an absence of foreleg response to asafetida (negative conditioned reflex) and differentiation between two olfactory conditioned reflexes and, finally, ability to select by smell when blindfolded a paper package containing meat from three paper packets of like size and texture. Allen found that bilateral extirpation of the pyriform-amygdaloid areas abolished the negative conditioned reflex, the animals raising the foreleg to the odor of both cloves and asafetida after cortical resection. Additional ablation of the hippocampal formation was without effect on the olfactory performance, and in no case was the ability impaired in the blindfold test.

In view of the close subjective relationship between the senses of taste and smell, it might be expected that these senses would activate the same or adjacent cortical regions. Quantitative tests of the monkey's preference for water over a bitter quinine solution show, however, that the insularopercular cortex, rather than the amygdaloid complex and pyriform cortex, is primarily concerned in taste (17, 24). Human studies indicate that taste perception persists after complete destruction of the olfactory nerves (29).

REFERENCES

1. Adey, W. R. *Brain* 76: 311, 1953.
2. Adey, W. R., N. C. R. Merrillees and S. Sunderland. *Brain* 79: 414, 1956.
3. Adey, W. R. and M. Meyer. *Brain* 75: 358, 1952.
4. Adrian, E. D. *J. Physiol.* 100: 459, 1942.
5. Adrian, E. D. *Electroencephalog. & Clin. Neurophysiol.* 2: 377, 1950.
6. Adrian, E. D. *Année Psychol.* 50: 107, 1950.
7. Adrian, E. D. *Brit. M. Bull.* 6: 330, 1950.
8. Adrian, E. D. *19th Internat. Physiol. Congr., Proc.:* 151, 1953.
9. Adrian, E. D. *Acta physiol. scandinav.* 29: 5, 1953.
10. Adrian, E. D. *Brit. M. J.* 1: 287, 1954.
11. Alexander, J. *Colloid Chemistry* (4th ed.). New York: Van Nostrand, 1937.
12. Allen, W. F. *Am. J. Physiol.* 128: 754, 1940.
13. Allen, W. F. *Am. J. Physiol.* 132: 81, 1941.
14. Allen, W. F. *Am. J. Physiol.* 139: 553, 1943.
15. Allison, A. C. *Biol. Rev.* 28: 195, 1953.
16. Allison, A. C. and R. T. T. Warwick. *Brain* 72: 186, 1949.
17. Bagshaw, M. H. and K. H. Pribram. *J. Neurophysiol.* 16: 499, 1953.
18. Bard, P. and V. Mountcastle. *A. Res. Nerv. & Ment. Dis., Proc.* 27: 362, 1948.
19. Beck, L. H., L. Kruger and P. Calabresi. *Ann. New York Acad. Sc.* 58: 225, 1953.
20. Beck, L. H. and W. R. Miles. *Science* 106: 511, 1947.
21. Beidler, L. M. *Ann. New York Acad. Sc.* 58: 52, 1953.
22. Berry, C. M., W. D. Hagamen and J. Hinsey. *J. Neurophysiol.* 15: 139, 1952.
23. Bloom, G. and H. Engstrom. *Exper. Cell. Res.* 3: 699, 1952.
24. Blum, J. S., K. L. Chow and K. H. Pribram. *J. Comp. Neurol.* 93: 53, 1950.
25. Bodian, D. *Anat. Rec.* 106: 178, 1950.
26. Bourne, G. H. *Nature, London* 161: 445, 1948.
27. Brodal, A. *Brain* 70: 179, 1947.
28. Brown, C. W. and E. E. Ghiselli. *J. Comp. Psychol.* 26: 109, 1938.
29. Clark, E. C. and H. W. Dodge. *Neurology* 5: 671, 1955.
30. Clark, W. E. Le Gros. *The Hypothalamus.* Edinburgh: Oliver, 1938.
31. Clark, W. E. Le Gros. *Nature, London* 165: 452, 1950.
32. Clark, W. E. Le Gros. *Yale J. Biol. & Med.* 29: 83, 1956.
33. Clark, W. E. Le Gros. *Proc. Roy. Soc., London. ser. B* 146: 299, 1957.
34. Clark, W. E. Le Gros and M. Meyer. *Brain* 70: 304, 1947.

35. CLARK, W. E. LE GROS AND R. T. T. WARWICK. *J. Neurol. Neurosurg. & Psychiat.* 9: 101, 1946.
36. DEININGER, N. AND F. SULLIVAN. *Ann. New York Acad. Sc.* 58: 215, 1954.
37. DYSON, G. M. *Chem. & Indust.* 57: 647, 1938.
38. EL-BARADI, A. F. AND G. H. BOURNE. *Nature, London* 168: 977, 1951.
39. EL-BARADI, A. F. AND G. H. BOURNE. *Science* 113: 660, 1951.
40. ELSBERG, C. A. AND I. LEVY. *Bull. Neurol. Inst. New York.* 4: 5, 1935.
41. FOX, C. A. *J. Comp. Neurol.* 72: 1, 1940.
42. FOX, C. A. *Anat. Rec.* 103: 537, 1949.
43. FOX, C. A., W. A. McKINLEY AND H. W. MAGOUN. *J. Neurophysiol.* 7: 1, 1944.
44. FOX, C. A. AND J. T. SCHMITZ. *J. Comp. Neurol.* 79: 297, 1943.
45. GASSER, H. S. *J. Gen. Physiol.* 39: 473, 1956.
46. GERARD, R. W., W. H. MARSHALL AND L. J. SAUL. *Arch. Neurol. & Psychiat.* 36: 675, 1936.
47. GERARD, R. W. AND J. Z. YOUNG. *Proc. Roy. Soc., London.* ser. B. 122: 343, 1937.
48. GLOOR, P. *Electroencephalog. & Clin. Neurophysiol.* 7: 223, 1955.
49. GREEN, J. D. AND W. R. ADEY. *Electroencephalog. & Clin. Neurophysiol.* 8: 245, 1956.
50. GREEN, J. D. AND A. ARDUINI. *J. Neurophysiol.* 17: 533, 1954.
51. HAGBARTH, K-E. AND D.I.B. KERR. *J. Neurophysiol.* 17: 295, 1954.
52. HAINER, R. M., A. G. EMSLIE AND N. A. JACOBSON. *Ann. New York Acad. Sc.* 58: 158, 1953.
53. HASAMA, B. *Arch. ges. Physiol.* 234: 748, 1934.
54. HILL, J. W. AND W. H. CAROTHERS. *J. Am. Chem. Soc.* 55: 5039, 1933.
55. JEROME, E. A. *Arch. Psychol.* 274: 1, 1942.
56. JONES, F. N. *Am. J. Psychol.* 66: 81, 1953.
57. JUNG, R. AND A. E. KORNMÜLLER. *Arch. Psychiat.* 109: 1, 1939.
58. KAADA, B. R. *Acta physiol. scandinav.* Suppl. 83, 23: 1, 1951.
59. KERR, D. I. B. AND K-E. HAGBARTH. *J. Neurophysiol.* 18: 362, 1955.
60. KISTIAKOWSKY, G. B. *Science* 112: 154, 1950.
61. KUEHNER, R. L. *Ann. New York Acad. Sc.* 58: 175, 1953.
62. LANG, O. W., L. FARBER AND F. YERMAN. *Food Indust.* 17: 8, 1945.
63. LASHLEY, K. S. AND R. W. SPERRY. *Am. J. Physiol.* 139: 446, 1943.
64. LEGGE, J. W. *Australian J. Sc.* 15: 159, 1953.
65. MACLEAN, P. D., N. H. HORWITZ AND F. ROBINSON. *Yale J. Biol. & Med.* 25: 159, 1952.
66. MATESON, J. F. *Ann. New York Acad. Sc.* 58: 83, 1953.
67. MEYER, M. AND A. C. ALLISON. *J. Neurol. Neurosurg. & Psychiat.* 12: 274, 1949.
68. MONCRIEFF, R. W. *Ann. New York Acad. Sc.* 58: 73, 1953.
69. MONCRIEFF, R. W. *J. Physiol.* 130: 543, 1955.
70. MORIN, F. *J. Comp. Neurol.* 92: 193, 1950.
71. MOZELL, M. M. *J. Neurophysiol.* 21: 183, 1958.
72. MOZELL, M. M. AND C. PFAFFMAN. *Ann. New York Acad. Sc.* 58: 96, 1953.
73. NAVES, Y. R. *Perfumery Essent. Oil Rec.* 42: 147, 1951.
74. OGLE, W. *Med.-Chir. Tr.* 53: 263, 1870.
75. O'LEARY, J. L. *J. Comp. Neurol.* 67: 1, 1937.
76. OTTOSON, D. *Acta physiol. scandinav.* Suppl. 122, 35: 1, 1956.
77. PRIBRAM, K. H. AND L. KRUGER. *Ann. New York Acad. Sc.* 58: 109, 1953.
78. RAMÓN Y CAJAL, S. *Studies on the Cerebral Cortex,* translated by L. M. Kraft. London: Lloyd-Luke, 1956.
79. ROSE, J. E. AND C. N. WOOLSEY. *Fed. Proc.* 2: 42, 1943.
80. SEM-JACOBSEN, C. W., R. G. BICKFORD, H. J. DODGE AND C. PETERSON. *Proc. Staff Meet. Mayo Clin.* 28: 166, 1953.
81. SUMNER, J. B. *Ann. New York Acad. Sc.* 58: 68, 1953.
82. SWANN, H. G. *J. Comp. Neurol.* 59: 175, 1934.
83. SWANN, H. G. *Am. J. Physiol.* 111: 257, 1935.
84. TEUDT, H. *Prometheus* 30: 201, 1919.
85. TURK, A. *Ann. New York Acad. Sc.* 58: 193, 1953.
86. WALSH, R. R. *Fed. Proc.* 12: 150, 1953.
87. WENZEL, B. M. *Psychol. Bull.* 45: 231, 1948.
88. WENZEL, B. M. *Science* 121: 802, 1955.
89. YOUNG, C. W., D. E. PLETCHER AND N. WRIGHT. *Science* 108: 411, 1948.
90. ZWAARDEMAKER, H. *Arch. neerl. Physiol.* 6: 336, 1922.

CHAPTER XXII

Vestibular mechanisms

B. E. GERNANDT | *Department of Physiology, University of Gothenburg, Gothenburg, Sweden*

CHAPTER CONTENTS

THE INNER EAR contains an auditory portion, the cochlea, and a nonauditory portion for maintenance of equilibrium and orientation in three-dimensional space. The association of two apparently very different functions in a single organ may at first seem puzzling, but the explanation for this is found by studying the past history of the ear. In this chapter we are concerned only with the nonacoustic part which we shall refer to as the vestibular apparatus or the labyrinth. This lodges the three semicircular canals and two little membranous sacs, the utricle and the saccule. Their function is to respond to forces of acceleration, retardation and gravitation. In lower vertebrates, in fish and even in amphibians, the saccule seems to play an auditory receptor role in the absence of the cochlea. The labyrinthine function is phylogenetically older than that of hearing.

The labyrinth is by no means the only sensory organ concerned with the control of equilibrium. The ability of terrestrial man and his close relatives among the vertebrates to maintain equilibrium and orientation with respect to the environment also depends upon the stream of afferent impulses from other receptor systems. These are *a*) the eyes (perception of spatial relationships), *b*) the interoceptors of the muscles, tendons, joints and viscera and *c*) the exteroceptors of the skin (perception of position and movement of the body or changes in either function).

At the beginning of the nineteenth century Flourens (34) published the first exact observations on the function of the semicircular canals of pigeons and rabbits. He was able to induce forced movements of the head and body and involuntary rhythmical, conjugate deviations of the eyes following injury to the canals.

Since then an immense amount of research work has been carried out. The early part of this period was characterized by the struggle to separate the vestibular apparatus from partnership with the cochlea in the perception of sound and to attribute to it a function quite unrelated to that of hearing. In 1870, Goltz (46) was the first to arrive at the conclusion that the semicircular canals were sense organs concerned with maintaining equilibrium.

The use of classical histological methods and the observation of equilibrium disturbances resulting from operative interference with the internal ear (section or extirpation) have in the past been the two principal sources of knowledge concerning the structure and function of the labyrinth, but the answers given to various questions vary considerably in their value. From this it was realized that knowledge of behavior mechanisms in the normal subject was necessary in order to understand the nature and significance of defects associated with peripheral or central injuries. Recording of electrical activity from single fibers of the peripheral vestibular nerve or from nuclei within the central nervous system of different species has added much to our understanding of the function of the human labyrinth in spite of a number of difficulties posed by the anatomical differences from lower animals. Experiments on various members of the animal kingdom have shown that some of the responses will vary greatly from one species to another. However, the use of electrophysiological techniques for a more far-reaching study of the function, and the refinement in recent years of the ultrastructural analysis made possible by the electron microscope may allow more precise experimental studies of the correlation of function and structure. Some of our modern ideas about this correlation rest firmly on experimental facts; others, in the present incomplete state of knowledge, are mere speculations. The remaining ones range between these two extremes.

ANATOMY OF LABYRINTH

For understanding the function of the semicircular canals, the utricle and saccule, a clear concept of their anatomical position and their relationship to each other in space is paramount.

The bony labyrinth comprises a series of cavities tunneled in the compact petrous part of the temporal bone. The whole membranous labyrinth, consisting of a system of thin-walled sacs and ducts with a clear fluid, the endolymph, is enclosed within the osseous labyrinth, separated from its wall by the perilymph. In form it closely resembles the osseous labyrinth, except in its middle portion (fig. 1).

The membranous semicircular canals, three in number for each ear, are eccentrically suspended by fibrous strands in the osseous semicircular canals. They are smaller in diameter than the osseous canals and fill only about one fourth of the lumen. The canals are named according to their orientation in space, the horizontal (external, lateral), superior (frontal) vertical, and posterior (inferior) vertical, lying approximately at right angles to each other, one for each major plane of the body. Considering the two labyrinths together (right and left sides of the head), the two horizontal canals lie in the same bodily plane and form what may be termed a synergic pair. The synergic partner of the right superior vertical canal is the left posterior vertical canal. The left superior canal is parallel to the right posterior canal. The horizontal canal is slightly inclined downward and backward, so that it forms an angle of about 30° with the horizontal plane when the head is erect. The sagittal plane with the superior semicircu-

lar canal makes an angle of about 55°, open in front, and with the posterior canal, an angle of about 45°, open posteriorly (fig. 2).

The semicircular canals run from and open into the utricle by means of five apertures, one being common to the superior and posterior canals. At one end of each canal, near its junction with the utricle, is the swelling known as the ampulla. The horizontal and superior canals have the ampulla forward and the posterior canal has it backward.

The utricle is the larger of the two sac-like structures. It has an irregularly oblong shape, slightly compressed transversely. Its most caudal portion lies posteriorly, wherefrom it slopes anteriorly and upward (rostrally) at an angle of approximately 30°. The utricle communicates with the utriculosaccular duct and with the semicircular canals mentioned above.

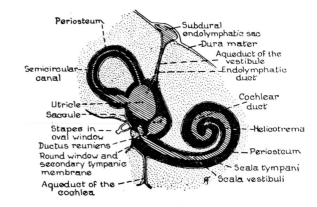

FIG. 1. Diagram of perilymphatic and endolymphatic spaces of the internal ear. [From Larsell (57).]

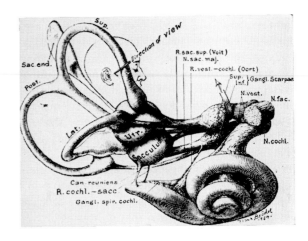

FIG. 2. The innervation and structural relations of human vestibular apparatus and cochlea. [From Hardy (52.)]

The saccule is a small, pear-shaped sac situated in the forepart of the vestibule. It lies below and medial to the utricle. The long axis of this sac is very nearly vertical; its dome-shaped portion is directed upward and its bluntly tapered portion downward and slightly posteriorly. From its posterior wall, a slender tube, the endolymphatic duct, arises to extend through the vestibular aqueduct into the cranial cavity; here it terminates outside the dura mater over the petrous portion of the temporal bone in a blind pouch, the endolymphatic sac. The endolymphatic duct and sac serve as a drainage mechanism for the endolymph. The ductus reuniens, finally, is a very slender duct which connects the saccule with the cochlear duct (scala media) near its basal end.

Crista

The sensory epithelium in the ampullae of the semicircular canals is collected into transverse crest-like elevations—the cristae ampullares—protruding toward the lumen and firmly attached to their bony foundations but free to swing at the other end. These are the receptor organs of the canals. The height of the crista corresponds to about one third the diameter of the ampulla. The epithelium is composed of two main types of cells, the hair (sensory) cells and the nonsensory supporting cells. Recent electronmicroscopic studies have revealed two types of hair cells that differ distinctly from each other both in structure and innervation (121). One type of cells is bottle-shaped, the other is more cylindrical (fig. 3). The former is mainly localized to the summit and the latter to the periphery of the cristae. The majority of them have a sterocilial structure, though one process from each cell has a kinocilium-like structure. The sensory hairs, or cilia, project into a gelatinous mass, the cupula, and there are found in a large number of canals (55, 56; fig. 4). The cupula may be regarded as a damped structure with a natural period, in the case of the pike of about 20 sec. (106), and acts as a spring-loaded over-critically damped torsion pendulum (50). Its chemical structure is not yet fully elucidated, but histochemical investigations conducted in recent years suggest that sulphomucopolysaccharides are important chemical constituents.

Macula

The receptor organs of the utricle and saccule are called maculae. The sensory epithelium exhibits again two kinds of cells, supporting and hair cells.

The macula is covered by a mucous or gelatinous substance which contains aragonite concretions (otoliths, otoconia) of calcium carbonate. The specific gravity of the otoliths, which ranges from 2.93 to 2.95, is thus greater than that of the surrounding endolymph. It has been shown that the otoliths of the utricular macula of mammals are of two, or perhaps three, distinct grades of fineness, each kind being situated in its own particular area of the receptor surface, which thus has a mosaic arrangement (61).

The macula of the utricle is situated on its anterior and medial walls, the two portions being joined at an angle of 140°. When the head is in the normal position, the macula of the utricle is in an approximately

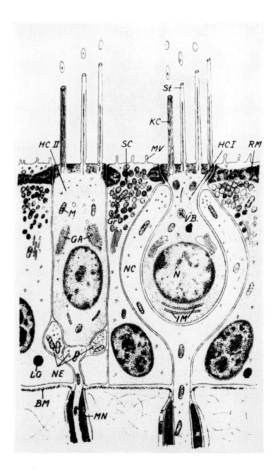

FIG. 3. The ultrastructural architecture of the cells and nerve endings of the crista ampullaris (guinea pig). *HC I*, bottle-shaped hair cell; *HC II*, cylindrical hair cell; *SC*, supporting cell; *St*, sterocilia; *KC*, kinocilia; *N*, nucleus; *GA*, Golgi apparatus; *IM*, intracellular membrane system; *VB*, vesicular body; *NC*, nerve calyx; *RM*, reticular membrane; *M*, mitochondrion; *NE*, nerve endings; *BM*, basement membrane; *MN*, myelinated nerve; *LG*, lipid granule; *MV*, microvilli. [From Wersäll (121).]

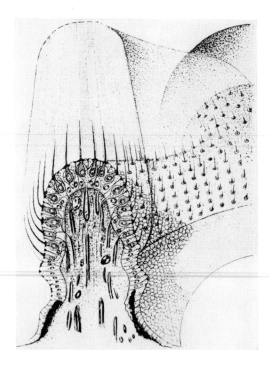

FIG. 4. Schematic three-dimensional diagram of one-half of an ampullar crista. [From Wersäll (121).]

horizontal position, with the otoliths lying on the hair cells. The saccular maculae are situated obliquely, forming an angle of about 30° with the vertical plane. Thus, when the head is in the erect position, the otoliths of the saccule are placed laterally on the hair cells, embedded in the substance that covers them.

INNERVATION OF SENSORY CELLS

Impulses from the peripheral receptors to the stations in the medulla are conducted by the vestibular branch of the eighth nerve. These fibers make up more than half of the nerve and number about 19,000. Most of them are large myelinated fibers (10 to 15 μ) but there are also medium and fine fibers (1 to 2 μ) (28, 59, 86, 90, 91). In addition, a large number of unmyelinated fibers with diameters between 0.3 and 1 μ have been described (121). Nerve fibers of varying diameter, as pointed out by Ramón y Cajal (90) and Lorente de Nó (59), have a characteristic distribution in each crista. Thus, the large fibers innervate the central region, those of medium size are distributed to the lateral regions, while the fine fibers go to the basal region.

Electronmicroscopic examination of the innervation of the sensory epithelium in the guinea pig by Wersäll (121) revealed two different types of nerve endings. The bottle-shaped hair cells have a nerve calyx enclosing the greater part of the cell, while the nerve branches form loops around the basal part of the cylindrical hair cells or terminate like bud-shaped nerve endings (fig. 3). Stimulation of the former type will give rise to impulses conducted mainly in one nerve ending, the nerve calyx, and only in one nerve fiber. The cylindrical hair cell, however, is usually innervated by branches from several different fibers; and several hair cells, often at relatively great distance from each other, are innervated by the same fiber. The difference, in principle, between the innervating characteristics of the two types of sensory cells may be of physiological importance but no investigations have, as yet, been able to reveal clearly the significance of the postulated different functions in the sensory epithelium of the cristae ampullares.

Recently Petroff (84) has published results of experiments with sectioning of the eighth nerve that might point to the existence of thin efferent fibers in the vestibular nerve. Such recurrent or feed-back connections of the auditory system have previously been described. Thus Rasmussen (92, 93) has found an efferent cochlear bundle that forms a plexus at the margin of the osseous spiral lamina around the afferent fibers. Galambos (35) was able to surpress the expected inflow of auditory nerve activity to normal acoustic stimuli by electrical stimulation of these efferent fibers. The function of the vestibular efferent fibers has not yet been studied.

The vestibular nerve has six main branches of origin: one each from the posterior, superior and lateral ampullae, and the utricle, and two from the saccule. Galambos & Davis (36) have found by histological methods that the auditory nerve in the interval from the internal meatus to the medulla contains nerve cell bodies which probably belong to the cochlear nucleus and are therefore second-order neurons in the auditory tract. There are reasons to believe that corresponding second-order neuron cell bodies can be found in the vestibular portion of the eighth nerve (38).

MODE OF ACTION OF VESTIBULAR APPARATUS

Though there must be an intimate coordination between activities of receptors situated in the ampullae of the semicircular canals and those in the vestibular sacs, the two sets of end organs are, as described, clearly different in detailed construction and they function in accordance with somewhat different principles. Interpretation of the particular functional role of the different sensory endings of the labyrinth has been exceedingly difficult because of the minuteness of the organ and the extreme inaccessibility of the structures. The recording of action potentials from the peripheral nerve or from the central nervous system in response to vestibular stimulation can, in many cases, serve as a revealing index of the validity of the older theories presented during the last century. In addition, this technique has been of considerable importance in furthering the study of the mode of action of the labyrinthine sensory endings (1, 6, 27, 38, 58, 68, 80, 94, 123).

Action of Semicircular Canals

The semicircular canals respond to any one of the following forms of adequate and inadequate stimulation: *a*) rotation (angular stimulation) of the head in a vertical, transverse or anteroposterior axis; *b*) artificial mechanical stimulation; *c*) caloric, irrigation of the ear with hot or cold water; and *d*) galvanic stimulation.

ADEQUATE STIMULATION. The anatomical fact that three semicircular canals are arranged in planes approximately at right angles to one another corresponds with the conclusion that their function is concerned with movements in the three dimensions. It is generally accepted that the cristae ampullares are receptors for the perception of rotatory movements.

The position of the cupulae is influenced by an increase or decrease of velocity of rotation, i.e. by positive or negative angular acceleration, but they are probably not influenced by linear acceleration (1, 53, 81, 88).

Several different theories have been presented during the last century to explain the physical changes in the canals resulting in stimulation of the receptor cells (the hydrostatic, hydrodynamic and pressure theories). Some are today only of historical interest. The literature for the first quarter of the twentieth century has been fully reviewed (13, 78, 85, 122) and, in addition, a number of reviews dealing with more recent studies have appeared (32, 104, 110, 119). According to the hydrodynamic theory of Mach, Breuer and Crum Brown, the only way in which the elastic cupular ridge may be swayed, one way or

another, is by the flow of endolymph. Any change in speed of rotation will cause a deflection of the cupula and the hairs of the sensory cells by a movement of the endolymph with a resulting differential push and pull upon the hairs. Owing to inertia, the endolymph of the involved pair of canals lags behind the progress of the wall of its containing tube and therefore executes a movement opposite to the direction of turning. The speed of endolymph movement in a semicircular canal during increased acceleration and the resulting deviation of the cupula have been calculated (95, 96, 106, 108, 109). Steinhausen (107, 108, 109) was able to demonstrate that the cupula, spreading to the sides and reaching to the roof of the ampulla, glides during its deflection in a swing-door fashion with a minimum of endolymph leakage. Some authors hesitate to accept the hydrodynamic theory because of the capillary nature of the canals and the viscosity of the endolymph (48, 73, 78). According to Maier & Lion (77), however, endolymphatic circulation is possible in the minute canals.

The hydrodynamic theory is strongly supported by experiments with direct observations on the exposed semicircular canals in fish. Through the injection of Chinese ink into the canals of the pike, which are relatively large and accessible, Steinhausen (107, 108, 109) was able to make visible the endolymphatic current with its corresponding deflection of the cupula. Dohlman (24) introduced a drop of oil into the canal and the fish (cod) was rotated while the behavior of the cupula was studied. As the rotation begins the endolymph in the canal moves, as shown by the shift in the position of the drop of oil, and the cupula becomes bent over in the direction of the endolymph movement (fig. 5). By using direct manometric measurement he found cupular movement from pressure changes equal to 0.05 ml of water (0.00004 gm).

The most effective stimulus to each ampulla is rotation of the head in the plane of its canal. But angular acceleration about any axis that lies obliquely to this plane may also tend to disturb the internal liquid (69, 111). A more or less combined stimulation of the ampullar cristae may be expected by movements of the head in any one of the intermediate planes. The utricle is shared by the three canals. Therefore, the question arises whether this does not cause an interference between the canals. Indeed, when the fluid in one canal is strongly affected by an acceleration, part of it may flow through into another canal. The other canals are, however, a shunt with a high resistance, so that the leakage is small (17, 20); and, for example, when angular stimulation produces

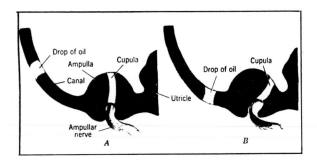

FIG. 5. The ampulla and semicircular canal in the living state before and during angular acceleration. The cupula, situated on the top of the crista, traverses the entire lumen of the ampulla. *A*, the cupula in its normal position; *B*, the cupula during angular acceleration. Note the shift of position of the oil droplet in the endolymph during acceleration. [From Dohlman (24).]

endolymph flow in the horizontal semicircular canals placed strictly in the horizontal plane, no flow is thought to occur in the vertical canals (30, 61).

Let us consider the case of rotation to the right after adjustment of the head so that the two horizontal semicircular canals, the synergic pair, are in the horizontal plane. During such a rotation the left ampulla is 'leading' its canal while the right ampulla is 'trailing' behind its canal. The endolymph, owing to the moment of inertia, will cause a deflection of the cupula of the right horizontal canal in the ampullopetal direction and an ampullofugal deviation of the cupula of the left horizontal semicircular canal. When the rotation is stopped, the two cupulae will be deflected in the opposite direction owing to a backflow of endolymph. Although movements of the endolymph stop in about 3 sec., the cupula seems to take about 25 to 30 sec. to return to its resting position. During this time, the subject will experience a sensation of rotation in the opposite direction. The stimulus to the cristae obviously arises from the swinging of the cupula set up by the endolymph. However, the cupula, being elastic, returns to its original position if the speed of angular stimulation becomes constant. Therefore, no response to movements of steady velocity occurs because the endolymph, subject to the frictional influence of its enclosing walls, takes up the motion of its canal and stimulation subsides.

The threshold for perception of angular acceleration has been studied by various methods (rotating chair, torsion swing, after-sensation time) and is now rather well-established. The torsion swing appears to be the most sensitive method for measuring this quantity (49). The minimum value for the perception of rotation varies with the indicator used and with the method of computation. Mach (72) and Dodge (22) found a threshold value of 2° per sec.² The product of the time and the acceleration required to reach the threshold of rotational sensation is constant. Thus, for reaching the threshold, the required acceleration is the greater, the shorter the time of its action. The lowest values reported for the human threshold are 0.2° per sec.² (113) and 0.5° per sec.² (5, 23, 49).

Some experimental results have led to the conclusion that the crista is a unidirectional receptor, capable of being stimulated only in one direction but irresponsive to deflection in the opposite direction (16, 70, 71, 78, 109, 123). Ewald (29) demonstrated that an ampullopetal cupular deviation in the horizontal semicircular canals evokes a stronger reaction than a corresponding ampullofugal deflection. In the vertical canals the effect of ampullofugal flow is more marked. There is no explanation for this functional difference, between the horizontal and vertical canals, a difference emphasized repeatedly by many authors.

More recent experiments, however, speak in favor of a bidirectional function of the semicircular canals (14, 61). The clearest evidence comes from experiments with electrical recording of the action potentials set up in the primary receptor fibers under conditions of natural stimulation (68, 69). By dividing the intracranial portions of the different nerve branches from the labyrinth into very slender filaments, it has been possible to obtain oscillographic records of the action potentials occurring in response to various kinds of stimuli, and under favorable conditions it is possible to continue the process of subdivision until only one or two sensory units are in functional connection with the recording device. Ashcroft & Hallpike (6) and Ross (94) made the first successful attempts to exploit this possibility, using frogs. Mowrer (80) recorded from the vestibular nerve of the common painted terrapin. Later Lowenstein & Sand (68, 69) made similar recording from the dogfish and ray and Ledoux (58) from the frog. They demonstrated a clear bidirectional response against a background of a resting discharge which is present even when the animal is in a state of absolute rest; their findings are in complete agreement with the assumption that the cristae are stimulated as a result of positive and negative angular acceleration. Increases or decreases in the resting discharge rate of the sensory cells in the crista are brought about by the deformation of their hair processes during deflections of the cupula. In the horizontal canals excitation occurs, and an increased impulse discharge can be recorded when the cupula is deflected in an ampullopetal direction, the stimulus being ampullopetal inertia movement of endolymph. With an increase of stimulus strength a clear recruitment of sensory units can be demonstrated. The maximum frequency is evidently related to the acceleration, but owing to the deceleration which follows it is impossible to say how rapidly the receptors would become adapted to the stimulus. For the study of adaptive behavior, a constant angular acceleration would have to be applied for a protracted period of time. Some results suggest that the receptors adapt slowly (1, 94) but Hallpike & Hood (51) and Lowenstein (64) came to the conclusion that the end organs show considerable adaptation under conditions of sustained cupular deflection.

An ampullofugal deviation of the cupula of the horizontal canal inhibits the spontaneous impulse activity. This demonstrates that a single receptor can signal rotation in either direction instead of one direction only. In the vertical canals the discharge of impulses is increased by angular displacements in which the ampulla is leading and an ampullofugal deviation of the cupula is elicited. An ampullopetal deviation will cause an inhibition. On cessation (or deceleration) of the angular stimulation, changes which are the reverse of the initial ones occur. If the speed of rotation is maintained at a constant level, the impulse frequency falls off until it has reached the spontaneous rate.

Adrian (1) was the first to use a higher mammal, the cat, for recording the discharge following varying stimulation of the labyrinth. The activity was recorded from the vestibular nuclei. Generally speaking, the results obtained have not shown any marked difference between the vestibular apparatus of the cat (1, 38) or rabbit (27) and that of the frog or the fish. There are gravity receptors to signal the posture and linear acceleration of the head, and rotation receptors to signal the turning movements (fig. 6). Some differences are found, however, but they are probably due to recording from second-order neurons (38). Units associated with the receptors of the horizontal semicircular canal showed an increase in impulse frequency in response to rotation toward the side of recording, while rotation in the opposite direction inhibited the activity. Sudden arrest of the rotatory movement resulted in a reduction in impulse discharge rate after ipsilateral and an increased discharge after contralateral acceleration. This type of response is interpretable on the basis of a mechanical tension-release theory for the hair cells, excitation being the result of stress, inhibition of release. In addition to this usual type of response, there were units which

showed an increased discharge in response to rotation in both directions (1, 27, 38). Both the ampullopetal and ampullofugal flow of endolymph had an excitatory effect. A mechanical tension-release theory would seem to be still more natural for these units than for units of the previous type (51). The hair cells may be assumed to be pulled upon by the movement of endolymph and cupula in both directions. This type of response appears in about 12 per cent of units. An inhibitory effect of rotation in both directions has been noted also during recording of the electrical activity from second-order neurons. This inhibition can hardly be regarded as due to a peripheral mechanism, a fact suggesting a difference in function between higher mammals and simpler organisms. An inhibition in both directions of rotation should, however, not provide greater difficulties to a tension-release theory than inhibition in one direction only. In both cases we have to account for the nature of the release by internal forces of tension for which so far there is no evidence. Once impelled, by the mechanical theory, to add unidirectional tensile forces inside the receptive organ to account for these findings, we might as well assume the existence of structures pulling upon the hair cells in such a well-balanced fashion that release follows when the cupula swings either way. Alternatively, the mechanical theory should be given up altogether in favor of the assumption that the impulses recorded are from cell bodies of second-order neurons, and that the pull on certain hair cells sets up inhibition at the first synapse, in the manner of the well-known retinal inhibition. This alternative seems to be the more probable. Another assumption is that these neurons may have

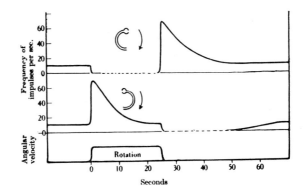

FIG. 6. Diagram to illustrate average time course of impulse discharge from a semicircular canal showing after-discharge and silent periods when acceleration and deceleration are separated by an interval of steady rotation. [From Adrian (1).]

been in synaptic connection with pathways derived from the opposite labyrinth (65).

INADEQUATE STIMULATION. The results obtained by using various forms of inadequate stimulation have supported the assumption that the flow of endolymph stimulates the cristae. Thus, the old experiment of Ewald with his 'pneumatic hammer' illustrates how the semicircular canals are stimulated. He was able to stimulate each canal separately in a pigeon by increasing or decreasing the pressure of the endolymph. Two small holes were made in an osseous semicircular canal near its smooth end. The hole farther from the ampulla was sealed with amalgam so as to block the membranous canal completely. The pneumatic hammer, a small metal cylinder with a moving piston, was cemented in the hole between the plug and ampulla. Compression or decompression of the endolymph caused an ampullopetal and ampullofugal endolymph flow, respectively. An increase in pressure in the horizontal canals caused the head and eyes to move toward the opposite side; decompression caused a weaker reaction in the reverse direction. Compression and decompression of the two vertical canals cause similar movements, but the effect of ampullofugal flow is more marked.

CALORIC STIMULATION. By this form of stimulation movements in the endolymph are produced (7). On irrigating the external auditory meatus with hot and cold water, labyrinthine reactions appear because convection currents are provoked in the endolymph of that semicircular canal which is placed in a vertical position and changes in the pressure on the ampulla result, causing the cupula to bend. The direction of the convection currents depends upon changes in the specific gravity of the endolymph resulting from heating or cooling. Thus irrigating the ear with cold water causes currents toward the ampulla of a vertical semicircular canal; on irrigation with warm water the endolymph rises. The effect of cold water is therefore the opposite of that of hot. The caloric test used in clinical otology and physiological experiments has the advantage over rotatory stimulation in that it permits the examination of one ear at a time. If the head is held in various positions, any one of the three semicircular canals can be stimulated; however, the posterior canal, lying deep in the bone, is influenced only slightly. Hot or cold water causes a greater change in the temperature of the endolymph in the part of the canal lying nearer to the external meatus than in the part more deeply situated. The temperature change first reaches the horizontal canal (23).

When the head is inclined 60° backward, the horizontal canals are brought into a vertical position. Irrigation of the left ear of a subject with warm water or the right ear with cold water produces involuntary, rhythmical conjugate deviations of the eyes (nystagmus) to the right and a tendency to fall to the same direction. The nystagmus appears after a short latency and lasts for a varying time according, *inter alia*, to the temperature employed and the duration of the irrigation.

A direct effect of thermal stimulation upon the peripheral nerve endings, in addition to the indirect effect based on movements of the endolymph, can not always be excluded (38). This is in accordance with the assumptions made by Bartels (8) and Breuer (11) that cold water may lead to a direct paralysis of the nerve endings and by Spiegel & Aronson (102) who found that the nystagmus due to continued caloric stimulation was independent of the position of the head.

GALVANIC STIMULATION. Another way to elicit reflexes from the labyrinth is by applying direct or alternating currents to the ear. Galvanic polarization produces impulse discharges similar to those occurring on natural rotatory stimulation (64). No movements of the cupula will occur during this form of stimulation (108). In the employment of this method of inadequate stimulation of the cristae or the peripheral nerve fibers themselves, an electrode is placed on one of the mastoids, another electrode on a distant part of the body (monaural stimulation) or on the other mastoid (binaural stimulation). In the latter case all six canals will be stimulated owing to the current spread. The galvanic stimulation will give rise to a mixture of horizontal and rotatory eye movements. When the cathode is on the right mastoid, the nystagmus is to the right and vice versa. A reflex movement of the head to the left will result if the cathode of the circuit is applied to the right mastoid.

Action of Otolith Organs

The anatomical, physiological and physical factors involved in the stimulation of the maculae are somewhat different to those influencing the semicircular canals. Breuer (12) realized that, although the endolymph is not in motion when the head is at rest, we nevertheless have a sense of position. He decided, therefore, that the otoliths within the utricle and saccule must be responsible for the static and positional sense. The mechanism of stimulation of the receptors has been controversial. According to the theory of Breuer, the gliding of the otoliths and bending of the hairs of the sensory cells caused by this gliding during changes of the position of the head is the stimulus. This theory has been rejected by later workers (7, 78). The effective stimulus is now thought to be the pull of gravity. The sensory cells will be differentially stimulated in different positions of the head since the otoliths will obey the law of gravity. When the stimulation of the utricular maculae on both sides is equalized, the sensation is that of normal position, with the vertex of the head up and its base down. Any disturbance of this equilibrium, as must take place in a changed position of the head, necessarily exerts a different pull of gravity upon the receptor structures. Experiments have demonstrated that the utricle is the source of responses to gravity, centrifugal force and linear acceleration (1, 63, 66, 67, 71, 94). By these various means of stimulation the otoliths are made to change their relative orientation with respect to the underlying macular surface. Electrical responses recorded from the frog by Ross (94) made it possible to distinguish between two types of gravity receptors. One type responds when the head is tilted out of the level position; the other type signals only the return of the previously tilted head to level. Cohen (15) describes four receptor types in the lobster. Adrian (1) recorded the potentials appearing in the vestibular nuclei of cats when the head is tilted. In a lateral tilt, with the recording side lowermost, the frequency of the discharge increased with increasing tilting (fig. 7). In no case was there an increase in frequency when the tilt was in the opposite sense, i.e. raising the side under examination and lowering the other. The frequency of the discharge declined very slowly as an expression of a slow adaptation of the receptors. It is interesting to note that the responses of different stimuli (tilting, rotation) were not found in the same parts of the vestibular nuclei. This may well indicate some sort of functional localization within the nuclei.

The utricle appears to be the organ of major importance in postural reflexes and in the differential distribution of muscular tone in the various labyrinthine reflexes.

The function of the saccule is more obscure and still imperfectly known. It can be destroyed on both

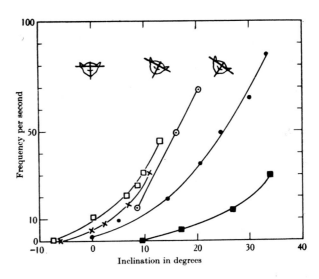

FIG. 7. Response of gravity receptors. Relation between tilt of the head and frequency of discharge in units from several animals. The degree of lateral tilt of the head is shown in the upper inset. The impulses were recorded from the right side while the head was being tilted to the right. [From Adrian (1).]

sides without disturbing labyrinthine reflexes, even in the rabbit, an animal in which these reflexes are highly developed. It has been considered that the saccule is not an essential part of the vestibular mechanism but rather an organ associated with the cochlea and designed for the perception of vibrational stimuli (6, 94, 123). Vibrations acting upon the mass of otoliths should thus transmit corresponding oscillations of pressure to the ciliate cells. More recent experiments by Lowenstein & Roberts (67) upon elasmobranchs have presented evidence that the fibers conducting impulses in response to vibrational stimuli are derived from the anterior two thirds of the saccular macula (and the papilla basilaris and macula neglecta). In higher vertebrates the saccule has probably lost its auditory function. It is unlikely that the sound vibrations transmitted from the oval window to the perilymph are further propagated in that part of the labyrinth represented by otolith organs and the three semicircular canals. The only exception may be the effect of very violent explosive sounds. The wave of pressure in the endolymph and perilymph set up by a sudden, very loud sound may be sufficient to stimulate the receptor cells of the semicircular canals, the utricle and the saccule. The subjective sensation is then one of vertigo, or of a sudden displacement in space. The reflex response to such stimulation is a sudden movement of the head, such as normally tends to compensate for an actual sudden change of position in space (112, 115). The direction and character of the movement depend upon which of the labyrinthine sense organs are most strongly stimulated. The semicircular canals can become sensitive to acoustic stimulation when they are artificially exposed to it, as, for instance, after a fenestration operation (12, 45, 112, 114). This does not mean, however, that sound perception is in the natural range of functions of the semicircular canals.

LABYRINTHINE PATHWAYS AND REFLEXES

The neural connections of the vestibular organ consist of numerous chains of neurons, reciprocally linked in many ways and having their synapses in various anatomical nuclei. All the chains work in intimate collaboration and the final pattern of reflex responses is attributable largely to the highly complex integrating activity of the center (62). The labyrinthine function is automatic, carried out in a reflex fashion, in other words, mostly below the level of consciousness. The brain centers through which the labyrinths elicit the various appropriate muscular reactions of the head, body, limbs and eyes—the righting, the postural and the ocular reflexes—represent an intricate mechanism. The nervous connections of the vestibular apparatus with the brain are, as yet, imperfectly known.

The impulses generated in response to stimulation of the peripheral receptors pass for the most part to Deiter's nucleus (the lateral vestibular nucleus), Schwalbe's nucleus (the medial nucleus), Bechterew's nucleus (the superior nucleus) and Roller's nucleus (the descending or spinal vestibular nucleus). In these nuclei originate, in turn, the ascending and descending tracts. For all practical purposes these four nuclei can be treated as a single functioning entity. Some axons pass directly to the cerebellum (2, 25).

The vestibular nuclei on each side of the medulla are connected with each other. This connection may be either direct (19, 31, 47, 90) or indirect by way of the reticular formation. Ramón y Cajal (90) describes a compact bundle of fibers within the vestibular nerve which passes directly from the vestibular (Scarpa's) ganglion across to the opposite side of the bulb without synaptic relay in the ipsilateral vestibular nuclei. Because these fibers spread out diffusely after crossing the mid-line, he was uncertain whether they terminate in the contralateral vestibular nuclei or within the contralateral bulbar reticular formation.

Ascending Fibers

Fibers arising from the medial and superior vestibular nuclei form the medial longitudinal fasciculus, the fibers of which end in the nuclei of the oculomotor nerves of the same and opposite sides. The tract is phylogenetically one of the every early ones to appear. It is present in cyclostomes and is known to be an important reflex pathway in fish. Its position and connections are very constant throughout the vertebral series.

NYSTAGMUS. The position of the eyes is very markedly influenced by stimulation set up in the labyrinth. This is of obvious importance since, as the body moves, compensation must be made by the eye muscles in order that the gaze may remain fixed on any object. In birds and reptiles most of the compensation is made by the neck muscles, and a head nystagmus appears during and after angular stimulation (12). As the body turns the eyes swing slowly in the opposite direction so as to maintain their fixation. Having turned as far as possible, they swing quickly back in the opposite direction to fix a new object which in turn they follow by a slow deviation. The slow movement in one direction is known as the slow component of the nystagmus, and the quick movement in the opposite direction is known as the quick component. The reflex latency of the slow component is 50 to 80 msec. (21). The magnitude of the quick and slow components is the same and by convention the direction of the nystagmus is designated as that of its quick component. Thus, when the quick component of a nystagmus is observed to be in the direction of the subject's right, it is called a nystagmus to the right. The movement of the eyes in nystagmus is in either the horizontal, frontal or sagittal plane. These different directions of the nystagmus can be easily demonstrated in man by rotating him with eyes closed in a revolving chair when different pairs of canals are brought into their maximal position (120). For example, to stimulate the horizontal canals maximally the head should be inclined forward about 30°. During rotation the quick component will be in the direction of rotation. When the rotation is stopped a postrotatory nystagmus will be observed; its quick component is in the direction opposite to that of the rotatory movement. This is due to the retardation of the endolymph which causes a deviation of the cupula, this time in the opposite direction. The post-rotatory nystagmus occurs, and lasts as long as the cupula needs to return to its starting position through its elastic recoil.

Thus we have seen that the impulses from the labyrinth are able to act on the different ocular muscles in an extremely precise manner. However, the details of the reflex arcs are as yet obscure. The slow phase of nystagmus is initiated from the labyrinth and has its center in the vestibular nuclei from which impulses are propagated, in part at least, through the medial longitudinal bundles to the eye muscles. The quick component is entirely central. Its neural mechanism must lie in the brain stem between and including the nuclei for the third nerves and the vestibular nuclei, for nystagmus occurs after transections of the brain above and below these levels (18, 60, 61). It is not abolished by ablation of the cerebellum. Lorente de Nó has located the center for the rapid phase in the reticular formation in the region of the abducens nucleus. It has also been found that nystagmus could still be produced after section of both medial longitudinal bundles (60, 61, 98). This finding is supported by experiments upon monkeys by Bender & Weinstein (9). There may be a double pathway from the vestibular nuclei to the nuclei of the ocular nerves—through the medial longitudinal bundle and through the reticular formation.

CORTICAL PROJECTION. It was previously implied that the vestibular apparatus had only subcortical projections. Recently, however, it has been well established by the work of a number of investigators using electrophysiological methods that the organ is represented by a projection area in the cerebral cortex of the cat, dog and monkey. Adequate stimulation (37, 39, 99, 101)—which is not easily graded or measured, nor brief enough for mapping out the exact boundary of the area—does not, in the light of more recent work, seem to be useful. The use of brief electrical stimulation of the vestibular nerve, in order to elicit a discrete evoked cortical response, has been of greater value (2, 54, 79, 117). The receiving area lies in the anterior ectosylvian gyrus and the posterior bank of the anterior suprasylvian gyrus. The projection is principally contralateral, but stimulation of the ipsilateral nerve activates a part of the same region. The response to electrical stimulation of the peripheral nerve occurs after a latency which suggests that the projection is direct from the thalamic relay nuclei (79).

The orderly features of the vestibular innervation and the projection of the vestibular fibers in the primary nuclei (1, 47, 103) have prompted the postulation that each vestibular receptor organ has its own exclusive representation on the cerebral cortex. Cortical responses to liminal electrical stimulation of three accessible vestibular branches can be recorded only from a more limited portion of the projection area as a whole (fig. 8). Stimulation of the nerve from the utricle of the cat evoked responses from the dorsal part of the area. Below and anterior to the latter focus, responses to stimulation of the nerve from the crista of the horizontal semicircular canal were recorded, and above it the cortical projection of the nerve from the superior crista was found (2) (fig. 9).

It has been demonstrated by neurotomy that the cortical response to stimulation of the vestibular apparatus requires neither an intact cerebellum nor an intact medial longitudinal fasciculus (4, 87). This proves that there are other ascending vestibular pathways conducting the impulses. According to Wallenberg (116) a vestibulocortical pathway appears to run parallel to the acoustic fibers (10). It should be noted that available results also suggest the existence of a corticovestibular connection, although it has been impossible to trace one (33, 100).

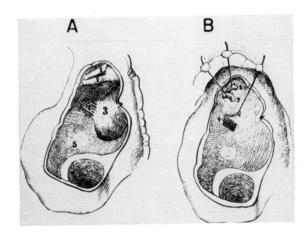

FIG. 8. Site of electrical stimulation of branches of the vestibular nerve. Ventrolateral view of the left vestibule, *A* before and *B* after removing the membranous labyrinth. Vestibular nerve branches from the ampulla of the superior canal, *1*; lateral canal, *2*; and utricle, *4*. The utricle is marked, *3*, and the saccule, *5*. In *B* three silver wires (*black lines*) are placed as stimulating electrodes and are held in place by dental cement attaching them to the cut edge of the bulla. [From Andersson & Gernandt (2).]

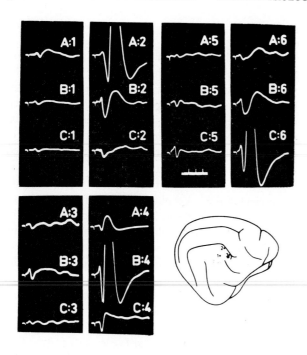

FIG. 9. Responses of various cortical areas to vestibular stimulation, recorded from points *1, 2* and *3* indicated on the drawing of the brain. *A:1, A:3* and *A:5* from the utricle; *B:1, B:3* and *B:5* from the superior ampulla; *C:1, C:3* and *C:5* from the lateral ampulla before local strychninization. *A:2, A:4* and *A:6* from the utricle; *B:2, B:4* and *B:6* from the superior ampulla; *C:2, C:4* and *C:6* from the lateral ampulla after strychninization. Time in 10 msec. intervals. [From Andersson & Gernandt (2).]

Descending Tracts

Through these connections vestibular impulses are conveyed to the primary motoneurons of the spinal cord. As far as origin and course are concerned the vestibulospinal tract seems to be the less complicated of the descending pathways. This tract, which originates, at least for the most part, from the large 'motor' type cells of the lateral vestibular nucleus, descends ventrally during its course in the medulla into the anterior funiculus of the same side of the cord. As stated, numerous anatomical connections exist between the vestibular nuclei and the reticular formation, and the fibers which constitute the reticulospinal tract have been traced from here into the lateral and ventral parts of the spinal cord (82, 83). Descending fibers forming the medial longitudinal fasciculus, being both homolateral and contralateral, are derived from the descending medial and lateral nuclei. Those fibers on the contralateral side all terminate in the cervical region, while those on the homolateral side may continue throughout the cord.

Vestibular and proprioceptive systems are both known to be active in posture and locomotion; streams of impulses arising from receptors in each of these systems must converge to influence the activity of the final common path. All reflexes which aim at preserving the normal posture of the body are collectively called 'postural reflexes' (26, 74, 75, 89); these are considered in Chapter XLI by Eldred in this work. The hyperextension of the extremities of a decerebrate animal can be modified by passively changing the position of the head. The compensatory movements of all four legs are elicited by the stimulation of the otolith organ and the proprioceptors of the neck muscles. These 'tonic labyrinthine' and 'tonic neck reflexes' operate in the same direction and consequently sum algebraically when both are elicited. The tonic labyrinthine reflexes can be studied separately after excluding the tonic neck reflexes by section of the upper cervical dorsal roots or by fixing the head so as to prevent any movements of it in relation to the body. It is then possible to move the animal about in different positions and thus ascertain the effects of the labyrinths upon the distribution of tone. For example, placing the animal on its back with the angle of the snout approximately 45° above the horizontal plane causes the extensor tone to become maximal; it is minimal when the animal is in the prone position with the angle of the mouth 45° below the horizontal axis. When the head is brought into other positions by rotation of the body around its transverse or longitudinal axis, intermediate degrees of rigidity between the two extremes result. These modifications in postural tone disappear if the labyrinths are destroyed. More precise experiments have made it clear that the reflexes are abolished by removing the otoliths from their maculae.

The ability to stay in an upright position is a universal property of man and higher animals. Five principal groups of reflexes of a somewhat similar type, responsible for the righting tendency, have been separated. Each one of these factors alone may bring a more or less normal upright position; but when they collaborate, greater precision and promptness in righting results. These responses can be studied in decorticate animals in which their reflex nature is quite apparent. One of them, which is dependent on the labyrinth, will be described briefly. In an animal blindfolded but with the labyrinths still intact the head tends to assume the natural horizontal position irrespective of the position in space of the remainder of the body. The reflexes causing righting of the head, initiated from the otolith organ, are called the 'labyrinthine righting reflexes'. The responding muscles are those of the neck. The tonic labyrinthine and righting reflexes are static ones and are not to be confused with the vestibular reflexes which are provoked by movements in space and initiated from the semicircular canals.

Since the classical investigations of Magnus and Sherrington upon the brain-stem influences on spinal motor activity were published, some more recent papers concerning the maintenance and control of static and phasic postural activites have appeared. Magoun and coworkers (76) have studied the role of the brain-stem reticular formation with respect to inhibition and facilitation of spinal motor activity. The importance of the vestibular nuclei as an excitatory mechanism for the cord has also, in the light of recent experiments, been reinvestigated (43, 44, 97, 105, 118).

It has been shown that the brain-stem reticular formation receives impulses relayed from somatic and auditory sensory structures. It is of interest from this point of view to be able to add the vestibular organ to the rest. By recording the impulse activity generated in response to adequate vestibular stimulation from isolated units in the reticular formation, it has been demonstrated that the formation is connected with both the homolateral and the contralateral vestibular nuclei (42). Thus the reticular formation forms an internuncial relay constituting a fundamental element of the reflex arc. The bilateral distribution of impulses from both labyrinths are changed in the relay into excitatory and inhibitory impulses which influence the motoneurons, i.e. the vestibular responses are organized for reciprocal action on flexors and extensors even when initiated from the reticular level (43).

Impulses conducted in the vestibulospinal tract will encounter fewer synapses on their way from periphery to periphery than those in the reticulospinal tract by way of the reticular formation. It is therefore possible to record a two-peak response to a single vestibular shock stimulus from a whole ventral root because the impulse volleys are transmitted along separate paths having different nuclear delays (40). The descending impulses occurring in response to vestibular stimulation will influence the activity of both alpha and gamma fibers. The small gamma efferents, however, are activated at a lower strength of stimulation than are the alpha fibers (3).

In studying the effect of the proprioceptive impulses upon the efferent discharge elicited by vestibular stimulation and recorded from a ventral root, it became obvious how strong and dominating this

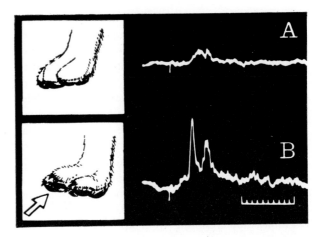

FIG. 10. Effect of foot joint stimulation on vestibular root response. In *A* is shown a control response recorded from ventral root L7. In *B* the response is augmented by manipulation of the tarsometatarsal joints of the ipsilateral hind foot. Time scale in msec. [From Gernandt *et al.* (40).]

proprioceptive control can be. The vestibular response, however strong it may be, will be inhibited by a muscular contraction (3). One kind of peripheral stimulation found to facilitate the vestibular response arises from manipulation of the joints of the foot ipsilateral to the recording site (fig. 10). Reinforcement of the vestibular response by afferent discharges arising from the foot joints will contribute to the increased stability and strength of the corresponding limb during standing, walking and jumping (40).

The effects of vestibular stimulation upon strychnine autorhythmic convulsive activity of the spinal cord has been studied in decerebrated cats. Inhibition of strychnine tetanus was obtained at all levels of the cord by tilting the head or the whole animal to the side, backward or forward. The inhibitory effect was characterized by a progressive decrease in frequency of the tetanic waves until a complete, but always reversible, inhibition occurred (41).

EFFECTS OF LABYRINTHECTOMY

As mentioned above, a distinction is made between two different functions of the vestibular apparatus. One is concerned with recording the position of the head in space, the other with reacting to any change in the rate of movements. The former function is mediated by the otolith organs, the latter by the ampullary cristae of the semicircular canals. The observation of equilibrium disturbances resulting from operative interference with the different parts of the labyrinth has been an important source of knowledge concerning the function of the two sets of end organs. It was Ewald who first drew attention to a tonic action of the labyrinth. The operation of double labyrinthectomy produces slackness of muscles in various parts of the body. This has been verified by McNally & Tait (70) who were able to show that denervation of the canals did not interfere with muscular tone, whereas denervation of the utricle did. The general effects of extirpation of the semicircular canals, so far as disturbances of equilibrium and occurrence of forced movements are concerned, resemble those resulting from operations upon the cerebellum.

If the organ on one side is destroyed, an abnormal asymmetrical posture of the head and trunk results from the unequal influence of the labyrinths on the tone of the neck muscles of the two sides. The result is a continuously acting righting reflex which causes the trunk to be curved and makes the animal tend to roll over and over. Cold blooded vertebrates are much disturbed by unilateral ablation of the labyrinths. Extirpation of the labyrinth in monkeys is followed by nystagmus with the quick component towards the normal side and rotation of head and neck to the same side. Rabbits, cats and dogs are rather less disturbed.

In man the effects are less enduring than in the monkey. A sudden ablation or a rapid destruction of one labyrinth causes a vertigo. Vestibular symptoms, such as nystagmus, past pointing, tendency to fall and vertigo, are frequently accompanied by symptoms pointing to an involvement of the autonomic system. Nausea and vomiting, lowering of arterial pressure, tachycardia and excessive perspiration may occur in the beginning. The intensity of the vertigo renders the sufferer unable to maintain erect posture. When examined in bed, the patient is poised in the least uncomfortable position and resists any head movement for fear that any alteration will increase the vertigo and bring on a spell of severe nausea and vomiting. The face is pallid and the skin is clammy. Diarrhea may alternate with the vomiting. The direction of the horizontal or rotatory nystagmus present is always to the healthy side. The vertigo likewise is to the healthy side. The distressing vestibular symptoms subside gradually and a complete recovery from the vestibular disability usually occurs at the end of one or two months.

A complete bilateral loss of vestibular function does not produce the vestibular syndrome that is found following an acute destruction of one labyrinth There is no nystagmus and no vertigo. A disturbance of equilibrium is always present and the patient, when deprived of the visual sense, is unable to maintain normal posture and locomotion. When submerged in water, he is disoriented and is as likely to swim downward as upward in attempting to reach the surface These symptoms are permanent, although partial compensation takes place.

REFERENCES

1. ADRIAN, E. D. *J. Physiol.* 101: 389, 1943.
2. ANDERSSON, S. AND B. E. GERNANDT. *Acta oto-laryng.* Suppl. 116: 10, 1954.
3. ANDERSSON, S. AND B. E. GERNANDT. *J. Neurophysiol.* 19: 524, 1956.
4. ARONSON, L. *J. Nerv. Ment. Dis.* 78: 250, 1933.
5. ARSLAN, K. *Rev. laryng.* 55: 79, 1934.
6. ASHCROFT, D. W. AND C. S. HALLPIKE. *J. Laryngol. & Otol.* 49: 450, 1934.
7. BÁRÁNY, R. *Physiologie und Pathologie des Bogengangapparates beim Menschen.* Vienna: Deuticke, 1907.
8. BARTELS, M. *von Graefes Arch. Ophth.* 76: 1, 1910.
9. BENDER, M. B. AND E. A. WEINSTEIN. *A. M. A. Arch. Neurol & Psychiat.* 52: 106, 1944.
10. BOHM, E. AND B. E. GERNANDT. *Acta physiol. scandinav.* 23: 320, 1951.
11. BREUER, J. *Arch. ges. Physiol.* 44: 135, 1889.
12. BREUER, J. *Arch. ges. Physiol.* 48: 195, 1891.
13. CAMIS, M. *The Physiology of the Vestibular Apparatus.* Oxford: Clarendon Press, 1930.
14. CAWTHORNE, F. E., G. FITZGERALD AND C. S. HALLPIKE. *Brain* 65: 138, 1942.
15. COHEN, M. J. *J. Physiol.* 130: 9, 1955.
16. CRUM BROWN, A. *J. Anat. Physiol.* 8: 327, 1875.
17. DE BURLET, H. M. AND C. VERSTEEGH. *Acta oto-rhino-laryng. belg.* Suppl. 13: 1, 1930.
18. DE KLEYN, A. AND V. SCHENK. *Acta oto-rhino-laryng. belg.* 15: 439, 1931.
19. DE VITO, R. V., A. BRUSA AND A. ARDUINI. *J. Neurophysiol.* 19: 241, 1956.
20. DE VRIES, H. *Progress in Biophysics and Biophysical Chemistry.* London: Pergamon Press, 1956, vol. 6.
21. DODGE, R. *J. Exper. Psychol.* 4: 247, 1921.
22. DODGE, R. *J. Exper. Psychol.* 6: 107, 1923.
23. DOHLMAN, G. *Acta oto-laryng.* Suppl. 5, 1925.
24. DOHLMAN, G. *Proc. Roy. Soc. Med.* 28: 1371, 1935.
25. DOW, R. S. *J. Neurophysiol.* 2: 543, 1939.
26. DUSSER DE BARENNE, J. G. *Handbook of General Experimental Psychology.* Worcester Clark Univ. Press, 1934.
27. ECKEL, W. *Arch. Ohren- Nasen- u. Kehlkopfh.* 164: 487 1954.
28. ENGSTRÖM, H. AND B. REXED. *Ztschr. mikroskop. anal Forsch.* 47: 448, 1940.

29. EWALD, J. R. *Physiologische Untersuchungen über das Endorgan des Nervus Octavus.* Wiesbaden: Bergmann, 1892.
30. FAVILL, J. *Arch. Neurol. & Psychiat.* 13: 479, 1925.
31. FERRARO, A., B. L. PACELLA AND S. E. BARRERA. *J. Comp. Neurol.* 73: 7, 1940.
32. FISCHER, J. J. *The Labyrinth.* London: Grune, 1956.
33. FITZGERALD, G. AND C. S. HALLPIKE. *Brain* 65: 115, 1942.
34. FLOURENS, P. *Recherches Expérimentales sur les Propriétés et les Fonctions du Système Nerveux dans les Animaux Vertébrés.* Paris: Crevot, 1824.
35. GALAMBOS, R. *J. Neurophysiol.* 19: 424, 1956.
36. GALAMBOS, R. AND H. DAVIS. *Science* 108: 513, 1948.
37. GEREBTZOFF, M. A. *Arch. internat. physiol.* 50: 59, 1940.
38. GERNANDT, B. E. *J. Neurophysiol.* 12: 173, 1949.
39. GERNANDT, B. E. *Acta physiol. scandinav.* 21: 73, 1950.
40. GERNANDT, B. E., Y. KATSUKI AND R. B. LIVINGSTON. *J. Neurophysiol.* 20: 453, 1957.
41. GERNANDT, B. E. AND C. A. TERZUOLO. *Am. J. Physiol.* 183: 1, 1955.
42. GERNANDT, B. E. AND C.-A. THULIN. *Am. J. Physiol.* 171: 121, 1952.
43. GERNANDT, B. E. AND C.-A. THULIN. *Am. J. Physiol.* 172: 653, 1953.
44. GERNANDT, B. E. AND C.-A. THULIN. *Acta physiol. scandinav.* 33: 120, 1955.
45. GERNANDT, B. E. AND M. VAN EYCK. *Arch. internat. physiol.* 61: 490, 1953.
46. GOLTZ, F. *Arch. ges. Physiol.* 3: 172, 1870.
47. GRAY, L. L. *J. Comp. Neurol.* 41: 319, 1926.
48. GREY, E. G. *Am. J. M. Sc.* 151: 693, 1916.
49. GROEN, J. J. AND L. B. W. JONGKEES. *J. Physiol.* 107: 1, 1948.
50. GROEN, J. J., O. LOWENSTEIN AND A. J. H. VENDRIK. *J. Physiol.* 117: 329, 1952.
51. HALLPIKE, C. S. AND J. D. HOOD. *Proc. Roy. Soc., London. ser. B* 141: 542, 1953.
52. HARDY, M. *Anat. Rec.* 59: 403, 1934.
53. JONGKEES, L. B. AND J. J. GROEN. *J. Laryng. & Otol.* 61: 529, 1946.
54. KEMPINSKY, W. H. *J. Neurophysiol.* 14: 203, 1951.
55. KOLMER, W. *Ergebn. Physiol.* 11: 372, 1911.
56. KOLMER, W. In: *Handbuch der Mikroskopischen Anatomie des Menschen (E, Gehörorgan).* Berlin: Springer, 1927, vol. 3, pt. 1, p. 250.
57. LARSELL, O. *Anatomy of the Nervous System* (2nd ed.). New York: Appleton, 1951.
58. LEDOUX, A. *Acta oto-rhino-laryng. belg.* 3: 335, 1949.
59. LORENTE DE NÓ, R. *Trab. Lab. Invest. Biol. Univ. Madrid* 24: 53, 1926.
60. LORENTE DE NÓ, R. *Labyrinthreflexe auf die Augenmuskeln.* Vienna: Urban, 1928.
61. LORENTE DE NÓ, R. *Ergebn. Physiol.* 32: 73, 1931.
62. LORENTE DE NÓ, R. *Arch. Neurol. & Psychiat.* 30: 245, 1933.
63. LOWENSTEIN, O. *Nature, London* 161: 652, 1948.
64. LOWENSTEIN, O. *J. Physiol.* 127: 104, 1955.
65. LOWENSTEIN, O. *Brit. M. Bull.* 12: 114, 1956.
66. LOWENSTEIN, O. AND T. D. M. ROBERTS *J. Physiol.* 110: 392, 1949.
67. LOWENSTEIN, O. AND T. D. M. ROBERTS. *J. Physiol.* 114: 471, 1951.
68. LOWENSTEIN, O. AND A. SAND. *J. Exper. Biol.* 13: 416, 1936.
69. LOWENSTEIN, O. AND A. SAND. *J. Physiol.* 99: 89, 1940.
70. McNALLY, W. J. AND J. TAIT. *Am. J. Physiol.* 75: 140, 1925.
71. McNALLY, W. J. AND J. TAIT. *Quart. J. Exper. Physiol* 23: 147, 1933.
72. MACH, E. *Grundlinien der Lehre von den Bewegungsempfindungen.* Leipzig: Engelman, 1875.
73. MACH, E. *Beitrage zur Analyse der Empfindungen.* Jena Fischer, 1886.
74. MAGNUS, R. *Körperstellung.* Berlin: Springer, 1924.
75. MAGNUS, R. AND A. DE KLEYN. *Arch. ges. Physiol.* 145: 455, 1912.
76. MAGOUN, H. W. *Physiol. Rev.* 30: 459, 1950.
77. MAIER, M. AND H. LION. *Arch. ges. Physiol.* 187: 47, 1921
78. MAXWELL, S. S. *Labyrinth and Equilibrium.* Philadelphia Lippincott, 1923.
79. MICKLE, W. A. AND H. W. ADES. *Am. J. Physiol.* 170: 682, 1952.
80. MOWRER, O. H. *Science* 81: 180, 1935.
81. MYGIND, S. H. *Acta oto-laryng.* Suppl. 70: 1, 1948.
82. NIEMER, W. T. AND H. W. MAGOUN. *J. Comp. Neurol.* 87: 367, 1947.
83. PAPEZ, J. W. *J. Comp. Neurol.* 41: 365, 1926.
84. PETROFF, A. *Anat. Rec.* 110: 505, 1955.
85. PIKE, F. H. *Physiol. Rev.* 3: 209, 1923.
36. POLYAK, S. *Ztschr. Anat.* 84: 704, 1927.
87. PRICE, J. B. AND E. A. SPIEGEL. *A. M. A. Arch. Otolaryng.* 26: 658, 1937.
88. QUIX, R. H. *J. Laryng. & Otol.* 40: 425, 1925.
89. RADEMAKER, G. G. J. *Das Stehen.* Berlin: Springer, 1931.
90. RAMÓN Y CAJAL, S. *Histologie du Système Nerveux de l'Homme et des Vertébrés.* Paris: Maloine, 1909.
91. RASMUSSEN, A. T. *Laryngoscope* 50: 67, 1940.
92. RASMUSSEN, G. L. *J. Comp. Neurol.* 99: 61, 1953.
93. RASMUSSEN, G. L. *Am. J. Physiol.* 183: 653, 1955.
94. ROSS, D. A. *J. Physiol.* 86: 117, 1936.
95. SCHMALTZ, G. *Arch. ges. Physiol.* 204: 708, 1924.
96. SCHMALTZ, G. *Arch. ges. Physiol.* 208: 424, 1925.
97. SCHREINER, L. H., D. B. LINDSLEY AND H. W. MAGOUN. *J. Neurophysiol.* 12: 207, 1949.
98. SPIEGEL, E. A. *Ztschr. Hals-Nasen-Ohrenh.* 25: 200, 1929.
99. SPIEGEL, E. A. *J. Nerv. & Ment. Dis.* 75: 504, 1932.
100. SPIEGEL, E. A. *A. M. A. Arch. Neurol. & Psychiat.* 29: 1084, 1933.
101. SPIEGEL, E. A. *A. M. A. Arch. Neurol. & Psychiat.* 31: 469, 1934.
102. SPIEGEL, E. A. AND L. ARONSON. *A. M. A. Arch. Otolaryng.* 17: 311, 1933.
103. SPIEGEL, E. A. AND I. SOMMER. *Neurology of the Eye, Ear, Nose, and Throat.* New York: Grune, 1944.
104. SPIEGEL, E. A. AND I. SOMMER. *Medical Physics.* Chicago: Yr. Bk. Pub., 1947, vol. I.
105. SPRAGUE, J. M., L. H. SCHREINER, D. B. LINDSLEY AND H. W. MAGOUN. *J. Neurophysiol.* 11: 501, 1948.
106. STEINHAUSEN, W. *Arch. ges. Physiol.* 228: 322, 1931.
107. STEINHAUSEN, W. *Ztschr. Hals-Nasen-Ohrenh.* 29: 211, 1931.
108. STEINHAUSEN, W. *Arch. ges. Physiol.* 232: 505, 1933.
109. STEINHAUSEN, W. *Ztschr. Hals-Nasen-Ohrenh.* 38: 19, 1935.
110. TAIT, J. *Medicine of the Ear.* Edinburgh: Nelson, 1948.

111. TAIT, J. AND W. J. McNALLY. *Phil. Trans. Roy. Soc. London* 224: 241, 1934.
112. TULLIO, P. *Das Ohr*. Berlin-Wien: Urban, 1929.
113. TUMARKIN, I. A. *Proc. Roy. Soc. Med.* 30: 599, 1937.
114. VAN EYCK, M. *Acta oto-rhino-laryng. belg.* 43: 303, 1953.
115. VON BEKESY, G. *Arch. ges. Physiol.* 236: 59, 1935.
116. WALLENBERG, A. *Deutsche Ztschr. Nervenh.* 117: 677, 1931.
117. WALZL, E. M. AND V. MOUNTCASTLE. *Am. J. Physiol.* 159: 595, 1949.
118. WARD, A. A., JR. *J. Neurophysiol.* 10: 89, 1947.
119. WENDT, G. R. *Handbook of Experimental Psychology*. New York: Wiley, 1951.
120. WENDT, G. R. AND R. DODGE. *J. Comp. Psychol.* 25: 9, 1938.
121. WERSÄLL, J. *Acta oto-laryng.* Suppl. 126: 1, 1956.
122. WILSON, J. G. *A. M. A. Arch. Otolaryng.* 1: 231, 1925.
123. ZOTTERMAN, Y. *J. Physiol.* 102: 313, 1943.

CHAPTER XXIII

Excitation of auditory receptors[1]

HALLOWELL DAVIS | *Central Institute for the Deaf, St. Louis, Missouri*

CHAPTER CONTENTS

INTRODUCTION

Auditory Information

THE EARS ARE SENSE ORGANS specialized for excitation by airborne vibratory energy. They belong in the general class of mechanoreceptors, together with the organs of touch, pressure, stretch and equilibrium. They are exteroceptors; the source of the acoustic energy is in general external to the body. They serve to transmit information concerning the character of the physical source as revealed by the rates of vibration, the intensity, the epoch and the overall temporal pattern of such vibrations. The ears also give information indirectly as to the direction from which the sound waves arrive.

Range and Differential Sensitivity[2]

The lower frequency limit of 'hearing' is usually set arbitrarily anywhere from 20 to 50 cps. Hearing merges gradually into sensations of touch, vibration, 'flutter', etc. The upper limit is about 20,000 cps in young ears but falls off with age. Differences in frequency of less than one per cent may be recognized. The dynamic range is very great, covering more than 12 logarithmic units (120 db) on the scale of acoustic energy (see fig. 6) from a lower limit close to the physical background noise of thermal energy (Brownian movement) up to limits set by acoustic injury to the sense organ. Differential sensitivity for intensity is in the order of magnitude of a tenth of a logarithmic unit, i.e. one db. Absolute differences in time of arrival of sound waves at the two ears as small as 10 msec., sensed in terms of the direction of the source, can be detected by practiced observers.

One physiological problem of hearing is to understand how the sense organ achieves such sensitivity, dynamic range and discrimination. Another is the means by which it encodes in nerve impulses the in-

[1] This work was supported by a contract between the Central Institute for the Deaf and the Office of Naval Research. Reproduction in whole or in part is permitted for any purpose of the United States Government.

[2] See especially the papers of Stevens & Davis (11) and of von Békésy & Rosenblith (22).

formation necessary for the central nervous system to achieve such discriminations. A third is the mechanism by which the mechanical forces of acoustic energy excite the nerve impulses in the sense organ.

Significance of Bitemporal Location of Ears

The location of the inner ears within the temporal bone of the skull gives them excellent mechanical protection. Certain details of anatomical architecture seem to give special acoustic isolation from the internal sounds of the body, including the sound of one's own voice (22). The location at the sides of the head provides an acoustic baffle between the two ears that insures the differences in intensity of sound waves and in times of arrival that are the basis of the sensing of direction of the incoming waves. The location in the head also allows the use of scanning movements of the whole head, which, in the human, replace the separate movements of large external ears. Acoustically, the human auricle is an organ of little significance.

GENERAL PLAN OF EAR

The external ear (fig. 1) includes the canal which extends diagonally inward about 27 mm (in man) to the tympanic membrane. This partition, however,

belongs to the middle ear or 'ear drum.' The middle ear is air-filled and is periodically ventilated for equalization of air pressure by opening of the auditory (Eustachian) tube. The latter connects with the nasopharynx. A chain of three small bones, the ossicles, in the middle ear form a system of mechanical levers that connect the outer tympanic membrane with a smaller inner opening, the oval window, into the inner ear. A second opening from middle to inner ear, the round window, is closed by the flexible round-window membrane. As we shall see, the chief acoustic function of the middle ear is to provide an impedance match between the air of the external ear canal and the fluid that fills the inner ear and thus to deliver acoustic energy efficiently to the inner ear where the sensory cells are located.

The auditory portion of the inner ear is a spirally coiled canal, called the cochlea because of its snail-like shape, within the temporal bone. It is fluid-filled and it is divided along nearly its entire length by a partition. This partition is actually a tube, the cochlear duct, which contains the sense organ proper, namely the organ of Corti, and its accessory structure, the tectorial membrane.

The coiled tube that contains the organ of Corti is roughly triangular in cross section (fig. 2). One side is formed by the fibrous, elastic basilar membrane, which extends from the inner bony core of the cochlea, the modiolus, to the spiral ligament which lines

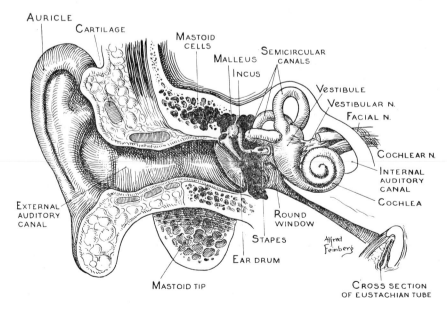

FIG. 1. In this semidiagrammatic drawing of the ear, the cochlea has been turned slightly from its normal orientation to show its coils more clearly. The opening for nerves through the bone to the brain cavity of the skull is quite diagrammatic. The muscles of the middle ear are omitted [From Davis (2).]

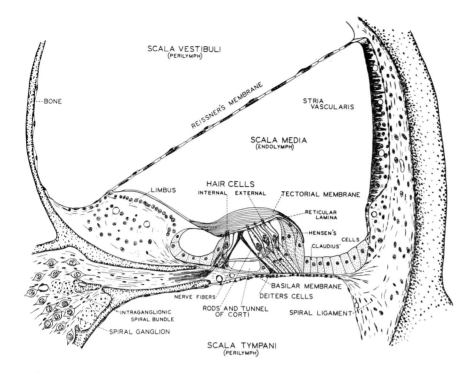

FIG. 2. Cross section of the cochlear partition of the guinea pig in the lower part of the second turn. [From Davis (5).]

the outer wall of the cochlear canal. The organ of Corti lies on the basilar membrane. The second, external, side of the triangle is largely covered by the stria vascularis, so called because it is richly provided with capillaries. This thick layer of specialized cells that face into the cochlear duct is thought to secrete the fluid, the endolymph, that fills the duct. The third side of the cochlear duct, Reissner's membrane, is thin but double-layered. It extends from the edge of the stria vascularis across to the modiolus and separates the space within the cochlear duct, the scala media, from the scala vestibuli. The basilar membrane separates the scala media from the scala tympani. The scala vestibuli and scala tympani are filled with perilymph, a fluid closely resembling cerebrospinal fluid.

The cochlear partition, including both the basilar membrane and Reissner's membrane, ends a little short of the apical end of the cochlear canal (fig. 3). Here the scala vestibuli and the scala tympani join through the helicotrema while the scala media ends blindly. At the other end of the scala tympani is the round window. The scala vestibuli opens into the central chamber of the labyrinth, the vestibule, close to the oval window. The length of the cochlear partition in man, from its origin between the oval and the round window to the helicotrema, is about 35 mm. The sensory surface of the cochlea is thus a long narrow ribbon, coiled in spiral form, mounted on an elastic membrane between two fluid-filled channels. This membrane is moved by the fluid which is driven acoustically at the oval window by the last of the ossicles, the stapes. The cochlear partition is the mechanical frequency analyzer of the ear.

FUNCTIONAL ANATOMY AND ACOUSTIC PROPERTIES OF EAR

Only those anatomical features of the ear will be described that are necessary for understanding how the ear acts as an acoustic impedance matching system, an acoustic frequency analyzer and a mechanical stimulator. Anatomy and physiological acoustics will be combined.

Middle Ear: Acoustic Impedance Matching[3]

The tympanic membrane is a light but fairly stiff cone with an apical angle in man of about 135° and

[3] See especially the papers of Stuhlman (13), von Békésy & Rosenblith (22) and Wever & Lawrence (24).

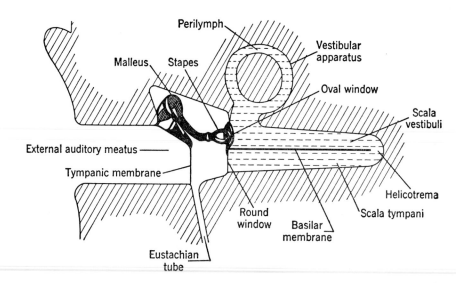

FIG. 3. Schematic drawing of the human ear. [From von Békésy & Rosenblith (22).]

with flexible edges. It closes the external canal diagonally. The long process of the first of the ossicles, the malleus, is attached radially to the inner surface of the tympanic membrane from the apex of the cone nearly to its upper edge (figs 4, 5). The similarity of the tympanic membrane to the paper cone of a loudspeaker or microphone is obvious and, like the cone of a microphone, it moves in and out as a whole when driven by sound waves—at least up to about 2000 cps. The malleus articulates with the second ossicle, the incus, but, except perhaps at very high intensities, the coupling between them is close and they move as one. The malleus and incus are suspended by ligaments in such a way that their only free movement is a rotation around an axis that is nearly tangent to the upper edge of the tympanic membrane. The membrane and the two ossicles turn on this axis as a unit. The rather large heads of malleus and incus serve as a counterweight for their long processes so that the center of gravity of the whole unit is very close to its center of rotation. The system is therefore not readily set in motion relative to the head when the head itself vibrates. This reduces the sensitivity of the ear to bone-conducted vibration.

The third ossicle, the stapes, nearly closes the oval window with its 'foot-plate,' but a flexible annular ligament allows it to swing like a door on an axis that is tangent to the oval window at its posterior end. The long process of the incus articulates with the head of the stapes and drives the latter in a bell-crank type of motion. When the foot-plate of the stapes moves, the fluid of the inner ear moves with it. Although the inner ear is a closed chamber, movement is possible because of the yielding of the elastic round window membrane (fig. 3). The latter thus moves in and out in approximately opposite phase to the foot-plate of the stapes.

The area of the human tympanic membrane is 50 to 90 mm². The area of the foot-plate is about 3.2 mm². The amplitude of movement of the center of each is about the same. In other words, there is very little mechanical advantage in the lever system in terms of amplitude of movement. The total force at the oval window is about the same as at the tympanic membrane, but it is concentrated in a smaller area; therefore, the pressure exerted on the fluid is greater. The overall system thereby matches the impedance of the air almost exactly to that of the inner ear. As a result, very little acoustic energy is reflected back from the tympanic membrane and nearly all is delivered to the inner ear.

Tympanic Reflex

Two small muscles, tensor tympani and stapedius, attach to the long process of the malleus and the neck of the stapes, respectively. Each tends to rock its ossicle into the cavity of the middle ear. The muscles are thus mechanically antagonistic but they act synergistically. They are fast striated muscles and probably not normally in tonic contraction. They do contract reflexly, with a latent period of about 10 msec., in response to fairly strong sounds. They also contract in

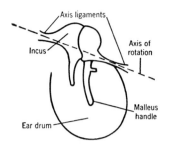

FIG. 4. Arrangement of incus and malleus showing how the mass is distributed around the axis of rotation. The maximum displacement of the drum occurs at its lower edge. [From von Békésy (18), after Bárány (1).]

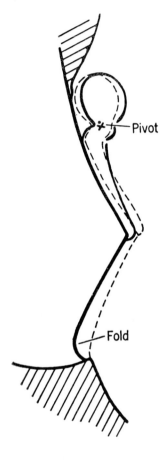

FIG. 5. The human tympanic membrane turns on an axis near its upper rim. A fold on the lower rim permits movement of the rigid eardrum cone. [From von Békésy (18).]

response to mechanical stimulation in the ear canal. The reflex contraction is not very well sustained. The contraction does not move the tympanic membrane significantly in man, but the increased stiffness (and perhaps damping also) of the ossicular chain reduces the transmission of low-frequency and of very-high-frequency sounds. The reflex seems to be primarily protective.

Frequency Characteristics of Ear

The middle ear has a resonant frequency of vibration of about 1700 cps but its movements are quite

heavily, although not critically, damped. The resonant frequency of the chain of ossicles is raised slightly when the tympanic muscles contract. The external ear canal has a resonant frequency at about 4000 cps, which gives an increase of sensitivity of about 10 db at this frequency. This resonance combines with that of the middle ear to give an overall acoustic frequency response of the ear that has a broad maximum from 800 to 6000 cps but which falls off rather rapidly above 6000 and, less rapidly, below 800 cps. The main features of the human threshold curve of acoustic sensitivity are apparently determined very largely by these acoustic properties (fig. 6).

Mechanical Properties of Inner Ear Structures[4]

In the inner ear the basilar membrane widens gradually from 0.04 mm at the stapes to 0.5 mm at the helicotrema. Certain other measurements, such as cross section of the cochlear canal and relative sizes of certain types of cell in the organ of Corti, are also graded from end to end; but the important variation that allows the cochlea to act as a mechanical acoustic analyzer is in the width of the basilar membrane. As a result of this variation the stiffness ('volume elasticity') of the cochlear partition varies by a factor of at least 100 from one end to the other.

The cochlear partition has significant stiffness and also mass. Contrary to earlier opinions it is not under tension. When cut the edges do not retract. The movements of the partition, like those of the middle ear, are quite heavily, but not critically, damped. Because of the gradation in stiffness and mass, different parts of the basilar membrane have different resonant frequencies, but the various parts cannot move as independent resonators. The basilar membrane and the organ of Corti on it are continuous structures. Their elements are coupled to one another elastically and also by friction. The endolymph and the perilymph provide some of the friction.

Traveling Wave Pattern of Cochlear Partition[5]

An increase in pressure on the footplate of the stapes caused by a sound wave sends a wave of acoustic pressure up the cochlea with a velocity that is determined by the laws of transmission of acoustic

[4] See especially the papers of von Békésy (20) and von Békésy & Rosenblith (22).
[5] See especially the papers of Tasaki *et al.* (17), von Békésy (20, 21) and von Békésy & Rosenblith (22).

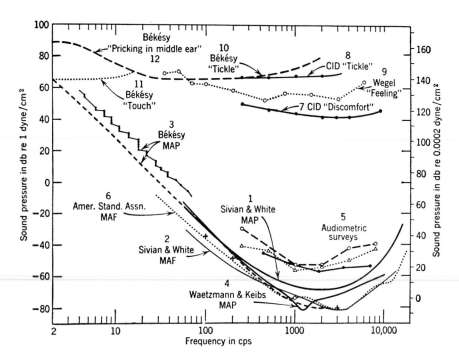

FIG. 6. The threshold of audibility and the threshold of feeling. *MAP*, minimum audible pressure at the eardrum. *MAF*, minimum audible pressure in a free sound field, measured at the place where the listener's head had been. [From Licklider (9).]

waves in a tube with a flexible wall. This velocity is less than the velocity of sound in water but it is so fast that the increase in pressure in scala vestibuli relative to scala tympani is virtually simultaneous throughout the length of the cochlea. The pressure wave travels much faster than the phase velocity of the traveling wave of mechanical movement that occurs in response to this difference in pressure between the two scalae. An over-all net movement of the cochlear partition towards scala tympani in response to this differential pressure occurs because the round window forms a flexible portion of the otherwise rigid walls of the bony labyrinth. The round window membrane bulges outward and thus allows inward movement of the stapes. Inside the cochlea, the cochlear partition bulges toward the round window.

When the movement is very slow, some fluid also flows through the helicotrema. But all parts of the cochlear partition do not move with equal promptness. The relatively stiff portion in the basal turn moves very nearly in phase with the driving force, but the more flexible apical portions, particularly those with a resonant frequency lower than the frequency of the acoustic wave that is driving the partition, tend to lag behind. As the acoustic wave reverses

its pressure, the portion that is 'tuned' to lower frequencies tends to overshoot and continues to lag behind the driving force exerted on it by the acoustic pressure in the fluid. Thus, because of the gradation of stiffness, a traveling wave of displacement appears on the cochlear partition (fig. 7). Furthermore, because of the continuity of the partition, the stiffer portion, moving almost as a unit, drives the more flexible portion.

The traveling wave increases in amplitude as it moves apically and reaches its maximum near the region where the resonant frequency of the basilar membrane corresponds to the frequency of the driving waves (fig. 8). The amplitude of movement falls off rather rapidly beyond this point; also the phase lag increases rapidly as the traveling wave moves on toward the apex. The velocity of travel therefore diminishes, and consequently the wavelength of the displacement pattern becomes shorter. A little distance beyond the position of maximum amplitude there is no significant movement at all. In the region of rapid diminution of amplitude the phase lag amounts to a full cycle or more.

If the driving frequency is increased, the position of maximum amplitude moves toward the oval window; if it is decreased, the maximum moves toward the

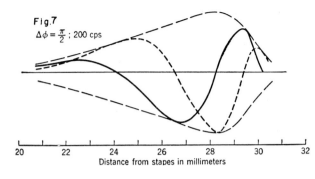

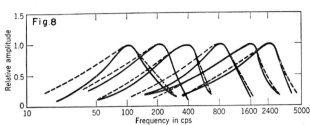

FIG. 7. A traveling wave on the cochlear partition for a 200 cps tone. The *solid line* shows the pattern at one instant, the *line with short dashes* a quarter of a period later. The envelope shows the maximal displacement at each point. [From von Békésy (19).]

FIG. 8. Resonance curves for six points on the basilar membrane. The *solid curves* represent measurements by von Békésy; the *dashed curves*, theoretical calculations by Zwislocki. [From von Békésy (22).]

apex (fig. 9). At about 100 cps in man, it is very close to the helicotrema. At 2000 cps there is very little movement beyond the mid-point of the cochlear partition. The extreme basal end of the partition, however, moves in response to all frequencies within the audible range.

The unsymmetrical traveling wave pattern of movement, with its rather flat maximum of amplitude and its abrupt apical reduction in activity, has been shown to be a necessary and predictable consequence of the principles of acoustic resonance in a system such as the cochlea with gradation of stiffness, mass, damping and coupling (21, 26). The traveling wave pattern has been reproduced in appropriate physical models and it has been observed directly in the cochlea under the microscope with stroboscopic illumination (20) and inferred from electrical recordings (17) (see fig. 15). It allows the cochlea to act as a mechanical frequency analyzer because the extent of activity and position of maxima vary as functions of frequency. It introduces additional features, such as asymmetry, progressive time and phase lag, and significant longitudinal as well as transverse bending of the cochlear partition, that contribute to the pattern of neural excitation that results from the movements of the partition.

Fine Structure of Organ of Corti[6]

The organ of Corti consists of sensory cells that are known as 'hair cells' because of their tufts of hair-like

[6] See especially the review by Davis (4).

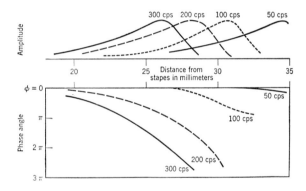

FIG. 9. Amplitude and phase angle of movements of the cochlear partition for four different frequencies as a function of distance from the stapes. At 50 cps the partition moves substantially in phase throughout. [From von Békésy (19).]

processes that extend into the scala media and supporting cells. The tectorial membrane, in which the outer ends of the hairs are imbedded, is an important accessory structure (fig. 2). It is obviously the analogue of the otolithic membrane of the utricle and of the cristae of the semicircular canals, sense organs that are sensitive to mechanical acceleration.

The ends of Deiters' cells that face the scala media form a stiff but openwork plate, the reticular lamina. The hair-bearing ends of the hair cells are firmly held in the openings of this lamina; their opposite ends, surrounded by the nerve endings of the auditory nerve, rest in cup-like supports that are also part of Deiters' cells. Between their upper and lower ends the external hair cells hang free in a fluid-filled space. The so-called 'rods of Corti' form, with the basilar membrane on which they rest, a stiff triangular supporting structure for the inner end of the reticular lamina. The outer edge of the lamina rests on a softer cushion of Hensen's cells. The outer portion of the basilar membrane, between Hensen's cells and the spiral ligament, carries the lower cuboidal cells of Claudius.

The flask-shaped hair cells forming a single row along the inner edge of the reticular lamina are known as internal or inner hair cells. There are about 3500 of them, each about 12 μ in diameter. The smaller (8 μ) cylindrical external hair cells are arranged in three or four rows external to the tunnel of Corti. There are about 20,000 of them in each ear.

Innervation of Hair Cells[7]

The afferent neurons of the auditory nerve are bipolar cells. The cell bodies, about 28,000 in each ear, are arranged in a long spiral ganglion parallel to the organ of Corti but within the bony modiolus. Their axons pass inward to the hollow core and thence, as the cochlear portion of the eighth cranial nerve, through the internal auditory meatus, to the cochlear nucleus of the medulla. The axon-like dendritic processes pass outward through the sieve-like bony and fibrous habenula perforata into the organ of Corti (fig. 2). They are myelinated up to the habenula perforata. Some of them, the internal radial fibers, pass directly to the internal cells and innervate one to three cells. Others cross the tunnel of Corti to the external hair cells. Some of these are radial fibers with a restricted area of distribution but most of them run apically or basally, or in both directions, for as much as several millimeters as the external spiral fibers. Each fiber innervates many external hair cells but not every cell along its course, and each cell typically receives more than one nerve fiber. The plan of innervation is illustrated in figure 10. The nerve endings around the lower ends of the hair cells appear under the electron-microscope as well-developed structures rich in mitochondria.

In addition to the afferent fibers, an efferent olivo-cochlear bundle from the contralateral olivary nucleus runs lengthwise of the organ of Corti as the intraganglionic bundle within the modiolus and just peripheral to the spiral ganglion (fig. 2). These efferent fibers distribute to the organ of Corti and apparently innervate the hair cells, particularly the inner hair cells.

[7] See especially the papers of Davis (4) and Wever (23).

Fine Movements of Organ of Corti

The fine movements of the organ of Corti and the tectorial membrane have been observed under the microscope by stroboscopic illumination and described in some detail by von Békésy (20). In any one segment the basilar membrane, organ of Corti, tectorial membrane, and usually Reissner's membrane also, move in phase with one another. The basilar membrane is fibrous and elastic, and basically it determines the traveling wave pattern of vibration described above. The cells of Hensen form a soft cushion supporting the stiffer plate of the reticular lamina. The tectorial membrane is hinged like the cover of a book along the edge of the limbus. It is composed of a system of diagonal fibers and also a jelly-like substance. It is a viscous elastic system that yields to slow movements but is quite resistant to quick movements. It returns rather slowly after being displaced.

Apparently, as the basilar membrane bulges 'upward' or 'downward' (fig. 11), the stiff reticular lamina tends to rock on the support of the rods of Corti around an axis at the attachment of the basilar membrane to the bony modiolus. The tectorial membrane swings on its attachment to the limbus. The result is a shearing action between the tectorial membrane and the reticular lamina (fig. 12). The 'hairs' arise from the cuticular plates of the hair cells which are set firmly in the reticular lamina, and their outer ends are firmly imbedded in the tectorial membrane. Therefore, as the basilar membrane bulges, the hairs are bent. The force of the movements of the cochlear partition is rather efficiently concentrated on this shearing action.

The movement described above is associated with an approximately radial displacement of Hensen's cells, as seen under the microscope, and a corresponding radial or slightly diagonal bending of the hairs. This movement is characteristic on the basal side of the position of maximal amplitude. On the apical side, however, due to the shorter wavelength of the traveling wave and sharper longitudinal bending of the basilar membrane, a longitudinal movement predominates and the hairs are presumably bent longitudinally instead of radially (fig. 13).

The exact significance of these different directions of movement in relation to the excitation of nerve impulses by the hair cells is still a matter of speculation, but the bending of the hairs is the final and

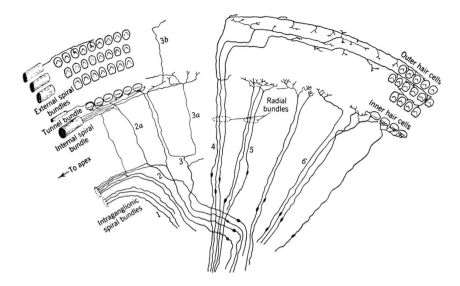

FIG. 10. Diagram of the innervation of the cochlea. The hair cells are indicated only in part. The principal types of fibers and the bundles that they form are: *1* and *2*, intraganglionic spiral fibers; *2a* and *3a*, internal spiral fibers; *4*, external spiral fibers; *5* and *6*, radial fibers. (Based on observations of Retzius, Solovcov and Lorente de Nó.) Not shown are the relatively scarce unbranched external radial fibers (Held). Type I is the continuation of the efferent olivocochlear bundle. [From Wever (23).]

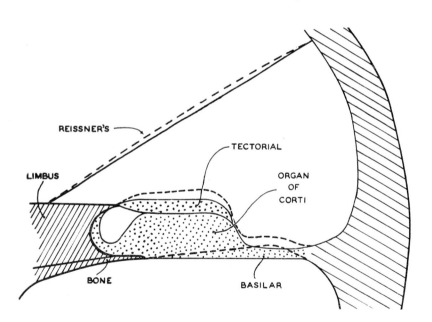

FIG. 11. Movement of the cochlear partition, based on descriptions by von Békésy. Explanation in text. [From Davis (3).]

critical mechanical event that has been recognized in the mechanism of stimulation. At this point the significant events apparently become electrical, for this bending of the hairs seems to release energy in the form of bioelectric potentials and these potentials are in all probability the important intermediate step in the mechanism of excitation of the auditory nerve fibers.

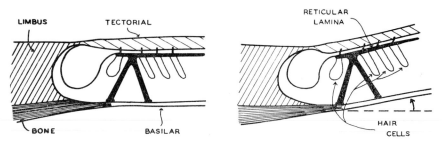

FIG. 12. Movement of the organ of Corti and the tectorial membrane, based on descriptions by von Békésy. The shearing action between two stiff structures, the tectorial membrane and the reticular lamina, bends the hairs of the hair cells. [From Davis (3).]

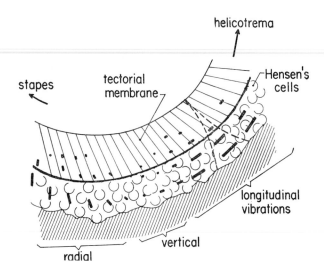

FIG. 13. The distribution of radial and longitudinal vibration along the organ of Corti for stimulation with a tone, seen through Reissner's membrane. [From von Békésy (20).]

FLUIDS AND BLOOD SUPPLY OF INNER EAR[8]

Blood Supply

The cochlea is supplied by the cochlear artery which enters the modiolus through the internal auditory meatus. The spiral ganglion is richly supplied with capillaries, and arterioles arch across the roof of the scala vestibuli to the spiral ligament. The stria vascularis, facing the scala media, is, as its name suggests, a veritable maze of small blood vessels with many anastomoses. The limbus is fairly well supplied with capillaries and a small arteriole often runs lengthwise on the tympanic surface of the basilar membrane.

[8] See especially the papers of Davis (4) and of Smith *et al.* (10).

The blood flow of the inner ear reflects, as would be expected, major alterations in systemic circulation, but it does not seem to be significantly affected by stimulation of the cervical sympathetic nerve.

Fluids

The perilymph, which fills the scala vestibuli and the scala tympani, is chemically almost identical with cerebrospinal fluid, and in fact the perilymphatic space is anatomically continuous with the subarachnoid space through the cochlear aqueduct. Essentially the same fluid also permeates the modiolus, the substance of the spiral ligament, and the tunnel of Corti and other spaces within the organ of Corti. The basilar membrane seems to be readily permeable to ions, and, in contrast to Reissner's membrane, offers little resistance to electrical current flow. The sensory cells are probably nourished from the scala tympani, not from the scala media.

The endolymph, which fills the scala media, differs sharply from perilymph in its ionic content. Unlike all other extracellular body fluids, it is high in potassium and low in sodium. It more nearly resembles intracellular fluid in this respect. Typical analyses of endolymph, perilymph and cerebrospinal fluid are given in table 1. The endolymph has sometimes been described as 'viscous,' but this is probably true only for certain fish and perhaps other lower forms.

The endolymph is probably secreted by the stria vascularis. Whether it is also reabsorbed wholly or only in part by the same structure is a matter of debate. The saccus endolymphaticus, an intradural extension of the endolymphatic system of the membranous labyrinth, may participate in secretion, in reabsorption or in both.

TABLE 1. *Composition of Spinal Fluid, Perilymph and Endolymph*

	Spinal fluid	Perilymph	Endolymph
Potassium (mEq/l.)........	4.2±0.5	4.8±0.4	144.4±4.0
Sodium (mEq/l.)...	152.0±1.8	150.3±2.1	15.8±1.6
Chloride (mEq/l.)..	122.4±1.0	121.5±1.2	107.1±1.4
Protein (mg %)....	21 ±2	50 ±5	15 ±2

Results (means and standard errors of means) of analyses of spinal fluid, perilymph and endolymph, made by Smith *et al.* (10). The endolymph was collected from the utricle, but cochlear endolymph gave similar although less reliable results.

ELECTRIC RESPONSES OF INNER EAR[9]

Action Potentials

The final output of the inner ear is nerve impulses in the auditory nerve. If these impulses are well enough synchronized into definite groups or volleys, as in responses to clicks or to successive sound waves of a low-frequency tone, the corresponding action potential waves can easily be recorded. They appear clearly when one electrode is on the round window and the other on the neck, but special placements are needed to record the action potentials without contamination by the other electric responses of the cochlea. With the usual electrode placements, the potentials are recorded as the impulses pass through the modiolus and just before they enter the internal auditory meatus.

The action potentials represent the familiar all-or-none 'spike' responses of nerve fibers. They show definite thresholds and are followed by refractory periods. One consequence of the refractory period is the phenomenon of 'masking.' The synchronized action potentials in response to a click or tone of moderate intensity are much reduced if a moderate random noise is presented at the same time. The noise stimulates the nerve fibers at random and the refractory periods prevent the usual synchronized responses of many fibers.

Other details of the nerve response in relation to parameters of the stimulus will be given below. The present point is that nerve action potentials are one of

[9] See especially the papers of Davis (3, 4) and of Tasaki *et al.* (15, 16, 17).

the electric responses of the ear and that they are in all ways similar to 'axon spikes' elsewhere.

Intracellular Potentials

Nearly all cells show a negative intracellular potential. Explorations of the cochlea and the auditory nerve with very fine microelectrodes reveal these intracellular potentials, ranging from −60 or even −80 mv relative to the potential of the perilymph in large cells such as Hensen's or Claudius' down to −20 or so in the cells of Reissner's membrane. The exact value seems to be a function of the amount of injury caused by the microelectrode, the greater the injury the lower the value. The hair cells, like the nerve fibers and supporting cells, are electrically negative internally.

Endocochlear Potential

The interior of the scala media, the endolymph, is electrically positive relative to the perilymph in the scala vestibuli and the scala tympani, and to the spiral ligament and extracochlear tissues in general. This potential is +80 mv (fig. 14). It is encountered abruptly at the point where the exploring electrode enters the endolymphatic space, although a relatively large (15 μ) electrode pushed through the stria vascularis usually reaches this potential level in a series of two or more steps. The change of potential in going from the interior of a hair cell through its cuticular layer into the scala media is from −70 to +80, or about 150 mv.

The endocochlear potential, formerly known as the endolymphatic potential, is so designated because it seems to be practically confined to the endolymphatic space of the cochlea. The corresponding potential within the utricle is not more than +5 mv. The endo-utricular potential is hardly more than the difference in potential found in the perilymph between the helicotrema and the basal end of the scala vestibuli or scala tympani. The latter potential gradient may well be due to unequal leakage through Reissner's membrane or other parts of the endolymphatic wall, but in any case it implies a considerable continuing current flow, dependent presumably on continuing metabolic activity.

The endocochlear potential is in fact closely dependent on an adequate oxygen supply. It falls, reversibly, to a very low level at the stage of asphyxia that is reached in extreme Cheyne-Stokes respiration

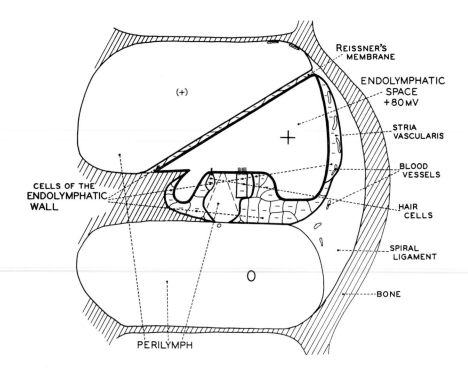

FIG. 14. Distribution of the positive 'endocochlear potential'. The 'endolymphatic space' of the scala media is shown in *heavy outline*. The negative intracellular potentials are also indicated. The tectorial membrane is omitted and only one external hair cell is shown. [From Tasaki (16).]

(in anesthetized, moribund guinea pigs). Full recovery requires only a few seconds after a large single gasping inspiration. It is also abolished rapidly by injection of cyanide or azide into the scala tympani or scala media. It is not immediately affected by injection of isotonic potassium chloride, choline chloride, or potassium glutamate into the scala tympani or scala vestibuli. It does fail, although less rapidly than with cyanide, following surgical injury to the scala media or the injection into the scala media of a solution that differs substantially in ionic content from the analytic figures for endolymph given in table 1.

The endocochlear potential is modified by displacement of structures within the cochlear partition. Displacement of the basilar membrane toward the scala tympani, as by injection of fluid into the scala media or an inward movement of the stapes, causes an increase in the positive potential by as much as 5 or 10 mv. Movement in the opposite direction, as by outward movement of the stapes, causes even greater reductions in the potential. Movements of Reissner's membrane alone are not effective, but movements of the tectorial membrane relative to the reticular lamina, when it is manipulated by a microneedle, produce just such changes in potential. The changes

are related to displacement, not to velocity, and are sustained as long as the displacement is maintained.

The source of the endocochlear potential has been identified positively. It is the stria vascularis (6). The changes in endocochlear potential described above are clearly associated with the organ of Corti, almost surely with the hair cells, but the resting positive endocochlear potential is not generated there. Perhaps a separate electric response to mechanical movement occurs in the hair cells and simply adds to the potential that is produced by the generator in the stria vascularis, or perhaps the potential of scala media is modified by a change of the electrical resistance to the continual leakage current that must flow from stria vascularis through the hair cells.

Cochlear Microphonic and Summating Potentials

The cochlear microphonic and two summating potentials (positive and negative) are all electric responses to acoustic stimulation. The cochlear microphonic is linearly proportional, up to a limit, to the displacement of the cochlear partition and thus, indirectly, to the instantaneous acoustic pressure. The microphonic thus reproduces the wave form of the acoustic stimulus (fig. 15). The summating potentials are proportional not to any instantaneous value of the acoustic signal but to a root-mean-square value, integrated over a very short time. Thus the summating potentials reproduce approximately the form of the envelope of the original acoustic signal. The positive and the negative summating potentials are opposite in sign. They can be separated by the greater vulnerability of the positive summating potential to oxygen lack and other injury and by the more apical site of generation of the negative response. The range of linear response of the summating potentials has not yet been determined.

The cochlear microphonic is generated at the cuticular surface of the hair cells. This is clearly proved by exploration with microelectrodes. The microphonic, and in all probability the summating potentials also, seem to reflect the bending of hairs in the appropriate direction. It is believed that, at intensities high enough to evoke the summating potentials, some kind of mechanical rectifying or detector action takes place in the inner ear to cause an asym-

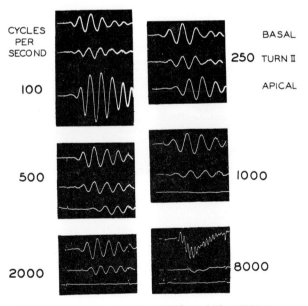

CYCLES PER SECOND

100

500

2000

250 BASAL
TURN II
APICAL

1000

8000

PAIRED ELECTRODES, SCALAE VESTIBULI AND TYMPANI, IN EACH TURN

FIG. 15. Cochlear microphonic responses to 'tone pips' of various frequencies recorded simultaneously from the basal, the second and the apical turn. The wave form of the acoustic signals is accurately reproduced. The time delay (phase difference) between the second and apical turns and the basal turn demonstrates the traveling wave pattern. The failure of 1000, 2000 and 8000 cps waves to reach the apical turn and of 8000 cps to reach the second turn demonstrates acoustical analysis. The displacements of the base line in the 8000 cps responses are summating potential. [From Tasaki (17).]

metrical, persistent one-way bend in the hairs of certain cells. In some cases the bending is probably across, in others lengthwise of, the organ of Corti. [A theory that includes this and several other aspects of the electrophysiology of the cochlea has recently been published elsewhere (4).]

Both the cochlear microphonic and the summating potentials are continuously graded responses, linearly related, up to a limit, to the intensity of the acoustic stimulus and with no true 'threshold' like that of all-or-none action potentials. No evidence of any all-or-none response in the sensory cells or of a refractory period has been found, even when the cochlear microphonic was recorded from an electrode inside a hair cell. Both the microphonic and the summating potentials show very little or no fatigue or adaptation.

The cochlear microphonic 'appears', in the sense that it reaches a root-mean-square value of a microvolt or thereabouts, at a much lower sound pressure level than the summating potential (except at the extreme high-frequency limit of response). The increase is linear with the sound pressure level up to about 90 db relative to 0.0002 microbar in the guinea pig but varies somewhat with frequency. The response then increases more slowly and usually goes through a maximum. At low frequencies harmonic distortion (peak limiting) occurs within the cochlea at even lower levels than in the middle ear. For high frequencies, however, the sinusoidal wave form of the microphonic is maintained even when the increase of amplitude with intensity has become nonlinear. This curious behavior is in sharp contrast to the peak limiting seen at low frequencies.

The summating potentials are not directly related to the nonlinearity of the mechanism of the cochlear microphonics although they may happen to first appear at sound pressure levels which lie near the beginning of nonlinearity. With increasing intensity the summating potentials do not reach a maximum but continue to increase up to limits that are set only by acoustic injury to the organ of Corti.

The cochlear microphonic, like the endocochlear potential, is closely dependent on an adequate oxygen supply. In anoxia both fall almost in parallel, and the minor differences are well explained by the changes in electrical resistance of Reissner's membrane, etc., which also occur in anoxia. This parallelism is a strong argument for a causal dependence of the microphonic on the endocochlear potential, but nevertheless the microphonic may also be abolished by certain injuries that leave the endocochlear potential unaffected. Two such injurious procedures are a) injection of a high-potassium solution like endolymph into the scala tympani (fig. 16), and *b*) poisoning with streptomycin just sufficient to cause degenerative changes in the hair cells.

Surgical injury or injections into the scala media of solutions of ionic makeup substantially different from endolymph causes a depression of the cochlear microphonic as well as the endocochlear potential, as in anoxia but more slowly. The parallelism between the endocochlear potential and cochlear microphonic here holds in general but is not exact.

In complete anoxia, and continuing for an hour or more post mortem, a small cochlear microphonic remains. This residue may depend, in part at least, on oxygen that diffuses to the basal turn through the round window, but perhaps it is generated in part by an anaerobic mechanism. This latter might be a transducer action like that of a condenser microphone. The primary aerobic cochlear microphonic, however, apparently represents an amplifier action in which energy from a pre-existing 'biological pool of energy,' such as is suggested by the endocochlear potential, is 'valved' or modulated by the mechanical bending of the hairs. In any case the sustained changes in the endocochlear potential noted above certainly represent a modulation of a biological source of energy and not simply a passive physical transducer mechanism.

The summating potential, as usually seen, is a displacement of the base line of the oscilloscopic record on which the cochlear microphonic is superimposed. It is a paradoxical fact that, with mild anoxia, abnormal ionic concentrations, etc., as the cochlear microphonic diminishes the negative summating potential increases (see fig. 16). The diphasic effect of anoxia, etc., is best explained by assuming *a*) that there is a positive as well as a negative summating potential, generated by a different set of sensory cells, and *b*) that the positive response is more sensitive to anoxia than the negative. The negative summating potential seems to be stronger, although higher in 'threshold' (of detection); only under more severe anoxia or ionic injury does it weaken and finally disappear. The positive summating potential is attributed to the inner hair cells which are known to be the more sensitive to anoxia.[10] With moderate stimuli in a fresh preparation the positive summating

---

[10] On the basis of more recent evidence (6), the negative summating potential is attributed to the internal hair cells and the cochlear microphonic and the positive summating potential are attributed to the external hair cells.

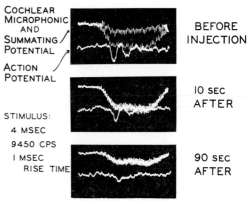

ENDO-TYRODE IN SCALA TYMPANI

COCHLEAR MICROPHONIC AND SUMMATING POTENTIAL

ACTION POTENTIAL

BEFORE INJECTION

10 SEC AFTER

90 SEC AFTER

STIMULUS:
4 MSEC
9450 CPS
I MSEC RISE TIME

DC REMAINED CONSTANT AT 75 MV

FIG. 16. A solution with high potassium and low sodium concentration like endolymph injected into the scala tympani depresses cochlear microphonic, summating potential and action potential before affecting the endocochlear potential in the scala media. Note the transient increase in summating potential at 10 sec. Downward deflections indicate the scala vestibuli to be more negative relative to the scala tympani (*top lines*) or the cochlea more negative relative to the neck (*lower lines*). [From H. Davis, unpublished observations.]

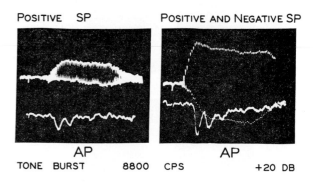

POSITIVE SP

POSITIVE AND NEGATIVE SP

AP

AP

TONE BURST   8800 CPS   +20 DB

FIG. 17. Action potentials, cochlear micophonics and summating potentials from the basal turn. An increase of 20 db in stimulus intensity causes the negative summating potential nearly to obscure the smaller positive response. Note N_1, N_2, and N_3 in the action potential response to the stronger tone burst. [From H. Davis, unpublished observations.]

potential may dominate (fig. 17). The reduction in positive summating potential causes the apparent increase in the opposing negative summating potential. The full sequence of changes may be even more complicated and depends in its details on the initial condition of the organ of Corti, the location of the recording electrodes and the frequency of the tone bursts used to elicit the responses.

AUDITORY NERVE IMPULSES[11]

Volleys and Latencies

The auditory nerve responds to a single click with a sharp, well-synchronized volley of action potentials, conventionally designated 'N₁'. If the click is of moderate strength, N_1 is usually followed about 1 msec. later by a smaller second wave, 'N_2'; and with still stronger clicks, a third still smaller wave, 'N_3', may be seen (fig. 17). N_2 and N_3 are due largely to repetitive firing in some but not all of the responding fibers, the interval corresponding to the refractory period of the nerve fibers.

The successive sound waves of a steady tone of frequency below 4000 cps give rise to similar, although smaller, volleys of action potentials. Between 4000 and 2000 cps the individual volleys are very small, but the frequency of the tone is nevertheless clearly reproduced in the action potential pattern, even though no one fiber responds to every sound wave. This pattern of occasional but synchronized response to a regular but intermittent stimulus such as sound waves is the basis of Wever's (23) 'volley principle' (fig. 18).

At very low frequencies in the guinea pig, both N_1 and N_2 may sometimes be seen in response to each sound wave, but both are rather dispersed in time. At 1000 cps and below, the sharp initial portion of N_1 is initiated in the lower turns of the cochlea in which the partition moves almost in phase as a unit. The sharp initial 'spike' is followed by a more diffuse 'tail' of impulses from the more apical regions.

Not only do different fibers have different latencies of response due to the travel time of the traveling waves but, as shown by studies of individual fibers, the latency of each varies from one response to the next. This variability leads to a less and less perfect synchronization of the impulses as the frequency is raised, and above 4000 cps no synchronization is visible on the oscilloscope or audible by ear. At the onset of a high-frequency tone burst, however, there is a very well synchronized N_1, N_2 and perhaps N_3 (figs. 16, 17). The latency of N_1, the sum of the whole group of fibers, is very stable in spite of the variability among individual fibers. The latency shortens from 2 msec. or more near threshold to about 1 msec. as intensity is increased. The shortest latency reported is 0.55 msec. The latency is a function of rise-time as

[11] See especially the papers of Davis (4) and of Tasaki (14, 15).

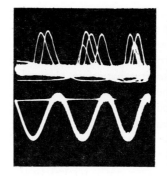

FIG. 18. Single-fiber spikes in two different fibers of the auditory nerve induced by 1000 cps pure tones about 55 db above human threshold. *Lower tracing* is sound stimulus recorded through a microphone. Exposure was about .015 sec. [From Tasaki (14).]

well as the intensity and perhaps also the frequency of the acoustic signal.

The latency of the action potentials is attributed chiefly to conduction time in the nonmedullated dendritic branches in the organ of Corti. It is measured from the beginning of the cochlear microphonic to the foot of the action potential spike, recorded as the volley passes through the modiolus. (No latency can be seen between mechanical displacement of the cochlear partition and the cochlear microphonic.)

The response to a brief high-frequency transient such as a click or the onset of a tone burst seems to be determined by the wave-group as a whole as if a rectifier-detector were operating in the ear. The summating potential is probably the electrical sign of just such a mechanical detector action.

At lower frequencies, below about 3000 cps, each sound wave acts more and more like an individual stimulus. Excitation apparently occurs during the 'falling phase' of the cochlear microphonic, i.e. while the scala media (and vestibuli) is becoming more negative relative to the scala tympani. This corresponds to the phase of outward movement of the stapes. The latency of responses to individual waves can be reckoned consistently and logically from the positive peak (in the scala media) of the cochlear microphonic; but latency measurements are complicated at low frequencies because of the progressive time delay of the traveling wave.

Single Fiber Activity

Many of the above statements concerning latency of response, all-or-none activity, etc., of auditory nerve impulses, derived originally from studies of the whole-nerve action potentials, have now been confirmed or extended by studies of single fiber activity.

The auditory axons are 2.5 to 4.0 μ in diameter. Tasaki succeeded in inserting hyperfine electrodes into individual axons in the modiolus near the internal auditory meatus while delivering brief tone bursts or steady tones to the guinea pig (fig. 18). The spike responses resembled those from myelinated fibers of similar size elsewhere. Injury discharge was sometimes seen and also responses clearly related to the auditory stimuli. The response to a brief burst or click was often repetitive as shown in figure 19, sometimes outlasting the stimulus by 20 to 30 msec. The minimum interval between impulses in such discharges was 1 msec. 'Spontaneous' impulses, i.e. not correlated with acoustic stimuli, were often seen in the same fibers that also gave clear responses to sounds. No inhibition of spontaneous impulses by acoustic stimuli was ever seen.

Some fibers regularly tended to give single, others repetitive responses. Some fibers had low thresholds, others high. Most fibers were partially selective with respect to frequency. Each showed a very sharp and very stable cut-off frequency above which it failed to respond even at high intensities of stimulation. At a frequency only slightly below the cut-off the fiber was most sensitive, but the rise in threshold with further reduction in frequency was very gradual (fig. 19). Nearly all fibers encountered had cut-offs above 1000

cps but in a few fibers a cut-off as low as 100 cps was found. The 'response areas' mapped out by Tasaki are much like those described earlier by Galambos and Davis for units now known to be second order (cochlear nucleus) neurons; but the high-frequency cut-off is rather sharper, the low-frequency decline is more gradual and inhibition of acoustic responses was never observed.

During continued tonal stimulation an apparently irregular discharge continued but at a gradually diminishing rate. This is the phenomenon of adaptation, for which there is also good psychoacoustic evidence. The continuing discharge was superficially irregular but actually, except for a few (presumably 'spontaneous') impulses, all the impulses from a given fiber fell in approximately the same phase relation to the tonal stimulus and the cochlear microphonic as explained above.

Concerning recovery from adaptation, fatigue, or both, the information from psychoacoustics has considerably outrun that from physiology. The recovery curve of N_1 of the composite nerve response is monotonic, unlike the recovery curve of psychoacoustic threshold. The partial depression of a second nerve response depends both on the intensity of the first click and on the duration of the interval following it, and it outlasts by 10 msec. the refractory period of the fibers.

The action potential threshold for clicks in guinea pig or cat may be within an order of magnitude of the human auditory threshold. With increasing power (in decibels), N_1 increases along a sigmoid curve, reaches a nearly flat plateau and then, with fairly strong stimuli, rises much more rapidly again. The tendency of single units to group into high-threshold and low-threshold classes may explain this nonlinear behavior of N_1 in the whole-nerve response. The maximum of response is uncertain, due to the onset of 'fatigue' or 'incipient acoustic trauma.'

Efferent Inhibitory Action[12]

Stimulation in the medulla of the olivocochlear tract of Rasmussen produces an inhibitory effect on the action potential response to clicks. N_1 is clearly reduced, but the cochlear microphonic is not affected. The effect is very specific with respect to the location of the stimulating electrodes, and the middle ear with its tympanic muscles is definitely not involved. The reduction appears some 20 to 30 msec. after stimula-

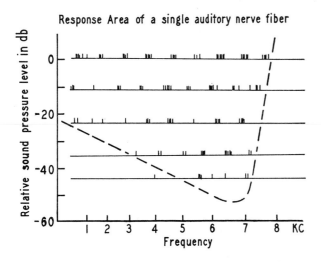

FIG. 19. Repetitive responses of a single auditory fiber to tone pips of different frequencies and intensities. *Dotted line* shows boundary of 'response area' of this fiber. [From Tasaki (14).]

[12] See especially the paper by Galambos (7).

tion has begun and increases up to about 250 msec. Rather rapid stimulation, 30 to 40 shocks per sec., is required. The optimal frequency is 100 cps. The long latency and the need for repetitive stimulation show quite clearly that this efferent inhibitory action is not related to the temporal priority of nearly simultaneous bilateral signals. It is apparently an expression of a rather general principle, namely central regulation of the sensitivity of sense organs. The functional relationships of this reduction in sensitivity are completely unknown.

THEORY OF AURAL ACTION[13]

This author has suggested elsewhere a series of possible mechanisms and interrelationships that, taken together, offer a presently tenable working hypothesis. This theory will be presented here in brief for its value in unifying many varied experimental observations, but the reader must recognize that several assumptions, interpretations and opinions, more or less plausible, are now added to the experimental facts.

Acoustic energy is delivered to the inner ear by the external and middle ears. The frequency characteristics of the external and middle ear determine to a large extent the shape of the curve of auditory sensitivity. The impedance match provided by the tympanic membrane and ossicles between air and intracochlear fluid is nearly perfect, except perhaps for frequencies below 500 cps, and contributes to the great absolute sensitivity of the ear. Other aspects of the middle ear structure and function are chiefly protective.

Acoustic pressure on the tympanic membrane causes movement of the foot-plate of the stapes and reciprocal movement of the round window membrane. The fluid movements between these two windows carry with them the elastic cochlear partition, but the pattern of movement of this partition, determined primarily by the graded stiffness of the basilar membrane, is complicated. The pattern is a sequence of traveling waves that move very rapidly at first, then more and more slowly, as they travel toward the apex. The amplitude increases gradually with travel to a rather flat maximum and then falls off quite sharply. The positions of this maximum and of the cut-off beyond it move toward the apex as the frequency is reduced and toward the base as the frequency is

raised. In this way the cochlea acts as a mechanical frequency analyzer and the 'place principle' is established as one element contributing to frequency discrimination.

The traveling wave pattern is an expression of phase differences in the movements of different segments of the cochlear partition. It is a necessary consequence of the graded stiffness of the cochlear partition, of the varying mass of fluid that moves with it and of the rather close coupling inherent in a continuous membrane such as the cochlear partition. The energy is transmitted in part through the fluid as an acoustic wave and in part along the membrane from segment to segment. The stiffer basal region, which for middle and low frequencies moves almost in phase, tends to drive the more flexible apical portion. The nearly-in-phase movements of the partition in the basal turn in response to low-frequency sounds cause nearly synchronous stimulation of impulses in many nerve fibers. Thus the frequency principle ('volley principle') contributes to the space-time pattern of nerve impulses in spite of the large phase differences that are associated with the fundamental traveling wave pattern.

The movements of the partition in the traveling wave pattern involve a bending of the basilar membrane in two dimensions, both across and lengthwise. The crosswise bending or bulging is sharpest at the position of maximal amplitude, but it is also significant for a considerable distance basally from the maximum. The longitudinal bending is sharpest in the 'cut-off' region on the apical side of the maximum and is probably negligible on the basal side.

As the basilar membrane, and the organ of Corti with it, bulge one way or the other, there is a shearing action between the stiff reticular lamina of the organ of Corti and the stiff and viscous tectorial membrane that lies in contact with it because the tectorial membrane pivots around a different axis, as illustrated in figure 12. The shearing action bends the hairs of the hair cells, which are attached both to the organ of Corti and to the tectorial membrane. This bending is the mechanical movement that is critical for stimulation. Protection against too great bending probably is provided by the attachment of tectorial membrane directly to the outer and inner borders of the organ of Corti.

The longitudinal bending causes longitudinal vibratory movements among the cells of the organ of Corti and presumably bends lengthwise the hairs of the cochlear partition. The external and internal hair cells are not equally sensitive to radial and longi-

[13] See especially the papers of Davis (3, 4).

tudinal bending of their hairs (19a). The differential stimulation of the two sets by the different directions of bending allows possibilities, through inhibitory neural interactions within the central nervous system, of sharpening the 'place' aspect of frequency discrimination.

The large traveling waves are known to produce eddies in the cochlear fluids on the apical side of the position of maximal amplitude. The forces that produce eddies we believe also tend to cause an unsymmetrical longitudinal shift or 'creep' of the tectorial membrane relative to the organ of Corti. Such a shift would cause a one-way longitudinal bending of the hairs. This is a mechanical rectifying action, and it allows the cochlea to 'detect' efficiently and respond with nerve impulses to high-frequency acoustic signals above 2000 per sec. Just as the cochlear microphonic is the electrical sign of a symmetrical vibratory bending of the hairs, we believe the negative summating potential is the electrical sign of an asymmetrical, rectified longitudinal shift. This shift is strongest on the apical side of the position of maximal excursion. The sustained bend of the hairs presumably acts as a steady stimulus to the hair cells that are affected, but compared to the alternating shearing movements revealed by the cochlear microphonic this mechanism is relatively insensitive. The rectifying action, as revealed by the negative summating potential, continues to increase, however, after the vibratory movements, and with them the cochlear microphonic, have reached their maximum. The rectifying action, no matter how it is produced, seems to be a mechanism that significantly extends the dynamic range of the ear.

The complete theory, as presented elsewhere, considers the mechanism of limitation of crosswise bending (and with it the cochlear microphonic) in more detail and it also includes a second rectifying action, associated with the crosswise bending, that depends on the viscous properties of the tectorial membrane. This second mechanical rectifying action and consequent one-way bias of the hairs is invoked as the basis of the positive summating potential, but this extension of the theory as well as a possible inhibitory action of the positive summating potential is admittedly more speculative than the postulate of the longitudinal 'shift' and its production of the negative summating potential.

The association of the cochlear microphonic with the bending of the hairs seems very well established. The mechanism that connects the two is completely obscure, however. A vague suggestion that the

mechanical distortion changes the electrical resistance of the upper ends of the hair cells has been offered but without supporting evidence (fig. 20). Whatever the mechanism, the bending of the hairs is supposed to account for not only the cochlear microphonic but also for both of the summating potentials. But these three electrical responses, it should be noted, are observed phenomena, not theories.

Consideration of the extreme sensitivity of the ear, and also the fact that the summating potential persists indefinitely if a static displacement of the tectorial membrane relative to the reticular lamina is maintained mechanically, leads to the conclusion that the energy of the electrical responses is derived from the metabolism of the tissues, not from the acoustic stimulus. The latter serves merely to 'valve' the flow of energy from the biological source. The result is an amplifier action in the sense organ prior to stimulation of the nerve fibers.

The endocochlear potential has been hailed as the obvious 'pool of biological energy' that is tapped by a valving action of the hair cells (3). Its mechanism is completely unknown but it seems to be a unique property of the cochlea. Its analogue in the utricle is not

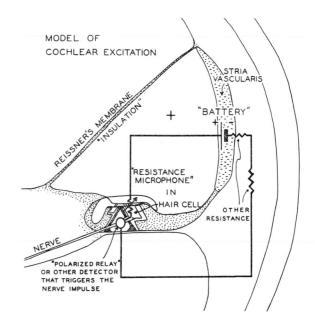

FIG. 20. An electrical model of excitation of nerve impulses in the cochlea. Additional 'batteries', not shown in the diagram, are located at the cell membranes of the hair cells and of the nerve endings. The return circuit from nerve endings to the stria vascularis is not restricted to the narrow anatomical path indicated in the diagram but is diffuse through all intervening tissues except the scala media. [From Davis (3)]

more than 5 mv at most. It is dangerous, therefore, to ascribe to the endocochlear potential anything more than an accessory function, namely to hyperpolarize the cuticular surfaces of the hair cells and thereby increase the sensitivity of the auditory detector. In the utricle the negative intracellular potential of the hair cells apparently must suffice as the 'pool of biological energy.'

The unique chemical composition of endolymph does not necessarily imply a high positive potential. The high potassium is present in the utricle; the potential is not. The two are probably unrelated. Perhaps the high potassium merely serves to maintain the proper colloidal state and consequent viscosity of the tectorial membrane!

The cochlear microphonic and the negative summating potential are believed to excite directly the nerve fibers in contact with the hair cells. Only a passive role as electrical conductors is ascribed to the nerve endings. There is no synapse-like delay in excitation. The phase relation of neural excitation to cochlear microphonic is correct for the electrical theory. The current flows from hair cell into nerve fiber and outward across the nerve membrane and thus can excite the nonmedullated dendritic terminals like one tremendous node of Ranvier or like nonmedullated fibers elsewhere. Spatial summation between the several hair cells attached to a given nerve fiber is clearly possible, as is also a facilitating action between summating potential and cochlear microphonic. A neurohumoral step between hair cell and nerve fiber is an acceptable addition to this simple electrical theory.

Transmission of Auditory Information[14]

We can now summarize the best present answers to the questions implied in the introduction concerning frequency and intensity discrimination and time differences.

Frequency (pitch) discrimination, the core of classical 'theories of hearing' (11, 23) is now considered to be a duplex function. We do not think of either a place principle (von Helmholtz) or a periodicity principle (Rutherford) but of a combined or duplex theory (Wever, Licklider).

The position of maximal stimulation, or more probably the cut-off boundary of strong stimulation, is certainly one part of the mechanism for identifica-

tion of frequency, particularly of high frequencies. The organ of Corti of the basal turn is essential for the hearing of high tones. Surgical injuries combined with behavioral tests in animals and disease in humans have established this fact firmly. Partial section of the auditory nerve may cause a complete high-tone hearing loss. Injuries to the apical end of the cochlea may cause a restricted low-frequency hearing loss but complete loss of sensitivity for the low frequencies does not occur. There is nevertheless a clear relation between frequency and position along the organ of Corti. Fine frequency discrimination is still a problem, however. The maxima of the 'resonance curves' of the cochlear partition (fig. 8) are much too flat, and the 'response areas' of individual nerve fibers (fig 19) are too asymmetrical to account for the known facts of frequency discrimination without some additional hypothesis. A model in which the skin of the forearm is exposed to traveling waves of tactile stimulation is surprisingly effective, however, in giving a sharp subjective location of the tactile sensation and in discriminating changes of frequency by changes in this location (21). The model reinforces the general opinion that a neural interaction, involving inhibition of the impulses from less strongly stimulated areas must be involved. Such inhibitory interaction at the level of the cochlear nucleus is already familiar.

Direct information as to the frequency of sounds below 4000 cps is also carried in the auditory nerve by the volley principle. This information is believed to contribute importantly to frequency discrimination and to the sense of pitch (8, 23). Opinions differ as to the upper frequency at which it ceases to be important and as to how the space and the 'periodicity' principles interact in the region of overlap. In any case the periodicity (volley) principle gains in importance and the place principle loses as the frequency is lowered.

Intensity discrimination and subjective loudness are usually attributed to the number of nerve impulses per second traversing the auditory nerve. Recruitment of additional fibers as intensity is increased is certainly one mechanism of increasing this number, and faster average rate of discharge per fiber is another. It is possible also that certain high-threshold fibers contribute more per fiber to loudness than do others, and it is by no means necessary to assume that loudness is a simple linear function of the total number of impulses per second.

Temporal information and also the binaural differences in time utilized in auditory localization are

---

[14] See especially the papers of Davis (4), Licklider (8), von Békésy (21) and Wever (23).

obviously transmitted in the form of time differences between volleys of impulses. In binaural localization the volleys in homologous nerve fibers are the important ones. The very small time differences that are known to suffice show that there is a statistical constancy in latencies, conduction times, etc., that is remarkable in view of the variability in the behavior of the individual unit. Here, as in fine discrimations in general, more time is required, often with repeated trials, for the best performance. The longer time allows for more complete averaging out of minor variabilities. This averaging out is primarily a function of the central nervous system rather than the sense organ. For frequency it allows very fine discrimination when ample time is allowed or, alternatively, good discrimination of time but with reduced discrimination for pitch when the duration of the stimulus is very short.

REFERENCES[15]

1. Bárány, E. *Acta oto-laryng.* Suppl. 26, 1938.
2. Davis, H. (editor). *Hearing and Deafness: A Guide for Laymen.* New York: Rinehart, 1947.
3. Davis, H. In: *Physiological Triggers and Discontinuous Rate Processes,* edited by T. H. Bullock. Washington: American Physiological Society, 1957.
4. Davis, H. *Physiol. Rev.* 37: 1, 1957.
5. Davis, H., R. W. Benson, W. P. Covell, C. Fernandez, R. Goldstein, Y. Katsuki, J.-P. Legouix, D. R. McAuliffe and I. Tasaki. *J. Acoust. Soc. Am.* 25: 1180, 1953.
6. Davis, H., B. H. Deatherage, B. Rosenblüt, C. Fernández, R. Kimura and C. A. Smith. *Laryngoscope.* 68: 596, 1958.
7. Galambos, R. *J. Neurophysiol.* 19: 424, 1956.
8. Licklider, J. C. R. *Experientia* 7: 128, 1951.
9. Licklider, J. C. R. In: *Handbook of Experimental Psychology,* edited by S. S. Stevens. New York: Wiley, 1951.
10. Smith, C. A., O. H. Lowry and M.-L. Wu. *Laryngoscope* 64: 141, 1954.
11. Stevens, S. S. and H. Davis. *Hearing, Its Psychology and Physiology.* New York: Wiley, 1938.
12. Stevens, S. S., J. G. C. Loring and D. Cohen (editors). *Bibliography on. Hearing.* Cambridge: Harvard, 1955.
13. Stuhlman, O In: *An Introduction to Biophysics.* New York: Wiley, 1943.
14. Tasaki, I. *J. Neurophysiol.* 17: 97, 1954.
15. Tasaki, I. *Ann. Rev. Physiol.* 19: 417, 1957.
16. Tasaki, I., H. Davis and D. H. Eldredge. *J. Acoust. Soc. Am.* 26: 765, 1954.
17. Tasaki, I., H. Davis and J.-P. Legouix. *J. Acoust. Soc. Am.* 24: 502, 1952.
18. von Békésy, G. *Akust. Ztschr.* 6: 1, 1941.
19. von Békésy, G. *J. Acoust. Soc. Am.* 19: 452, 1947.
19a. von Békésy, G. *J. Acoust. Soc. Am.* 25: 786, 1953.
20. von Békésy, G. *Ann. Otol. Rhin. & Laryng.* 63: 448, 1954.
21. von Békésy, G. *Science* 123: 779, 1956.
22. von Békésy, G. and W. A. Rosenblith. In: *Handbook o Experimental Psychology,* edited by S. S. Stevens. New York: Wiley, 1951.
23. Wever, E. G. *Theory of Hearing.* New York: Wiley, 1949.
24. Wever, E. G. and M. Lawrence. *Physiological Acoustics.* Princeton: Princeton Univ. Press, 1954.
25. Zwislocki, J. *Acta oto-laryng.* Suppl. 72: 1, 1948.
26. Zwislocki, J. *J. Acoust. Soc. Am.* 25: 743, 1953.

[15] Only general references, a few key papers, and the sources of the figures reproduced in this chapter are given. Fairly complete bibliographies will be found in references (4) and (12).

CHAPTER XXIV

Central auditory mechanisms

HARLOW W. ADES | *U. S. Naval School of Aviation Medicine, Pensacola, Florida*

CHAPTER CONTENTS

THE ASSIGNMENT IN THIS CHAPTER is to give an account of the cell and fiber groups of the brain which are more or less directly related to hearing. The coverage of this area is not necessarily uniform and probably expresses a certain degree of the author's bias, not only in choice of material but perhaps also in interpretation. The author, admitting to an unspecified degree of bias in both respects, finds it futile to offer apology but instead suggests to the reader the additional study of a recent review (32) and volume (109) to which text and bibliographic references will be found. The reference listing for this chapter is likewise not complete, especially in a historical sense, and the reader may remedy this deficiency by reference to the works just mentioned and also to the recent *Bibliography on Hearing* (98).

INTRODUCTION

The history of research on the central auditory pathway goes back only a few years into the last century, not even as far as the study of other sensory systems. The greater volume of significant work has been done in the last three decades only. This history can be divided into two phases which, while they began at different times, have been largely concurrent. The first necessarily concentrated on defining the neural structures which are primarily concerned with sound stimulation and those showing fiber connections, more or less direct, with the input from the cochlear nerve. The early functional studies suffered, as we now know, from the fact that the pathway of projection from ear to cerebral hemisphere is bilateral with only slight contralateral preference; consequently, clinical studies of one-sided damage to the brain produce only meager auditory deficits, and these can be demonstrated only by very sensitive tests. For this reason, study of central auditory mechanisms lagged behind studies on other sensory systems in which there is a great preponderance of contralateral projection. It is only with the advent of increasingly reliable physiological apparatus and the development of more sensitive behavioral testing in the past 25 to 30 years, that tracts, nuclei and cortical areas responsive to auditory stimulation have been reliably defined. This definition continues to be studied and revised, although attention to it has gradually given way to studies of the qualities of response rather than mere presence or absence of response.

The anatomical aspect of the first phase of central auditory study fared better than the functional and as well as that of other neural systems. The original work of Ramón y Cajal (75, 76), as far as the auditory pathway is concerned, has been amplified and embellished but remains basic. The cellular and fiber elements we traditionally consider as components of the central auditory system with few exceptions are the same as those which appear in Ramón y Cajal's diagrams.

The second phase of research on the central auditory pathway has concerned itself with the discovery of correlates between the characteristics of sound stimuli and the anatomicophysiologic mechanisms activated by them. From the beginning, two qualities of sound, frequency and intensity, have been the focal points of efforts to discover the neural correlates of hearing. There appear to be several interrelated reasons for this and for the consequent preoccupation with the pure tone stimulus in auditory research. Perhaps the most compelling force has been the influence of von Helmholtz who, soon after the middle of the nineteenth century, proposed the idea that the cochlea functions as a selectively resonant system in which tones of given frequency produce localized resonance of the basilar membrane. The implication of this is that the end organ functions as an analyzer of sound and delivers to the brain patterns of excitation which are already analyzed with respect to stimulus frequency. Besides the influence of von Helmholtz is that resulting from the relative ease with which pure tone stimuli can be controlled in terms of the standard parameters, frequency and intensity. As will be seen, the experimentalist's bemusement with pure tone has had both an advantageous and disadvantageous effect upon the course of central auditory research. However the relative good and bad may be evaluated, it is impossible to discuss central auditory function either historically or currently without giving a great deal of attention to pure tone studies.

There has been in recent years a growing trend away from pure tone studies of the central auditory system (at least in their simplest form). There are three reasons for this: *1*) 'Click' stimulation has been frequently used (where widespread rather than selective cochlear stimulation is desired) in order to avoid the experimental consequences of the frequency specificity which appears, at least to some degree, to be characteristic of the projection pathway. *2*) There is difficulty in studying the higher auditory centers by postablational hearing tests to separate the operated from the unoperated animals unless sound patterns more complex than pure tones or auditory functions requiring more than acuity and frequency discrimination are used. *3*) There is a feeling among some workers in audition that pure tone studies ignore

an essential temporal element in hearing which is introduced when clicks or other complex stimuli are used.

With this introduction, we can proceed to examine the available data relating more or less directly to the beginnings of neurological explanation of some of the simpler aspects of hearing as these are defined in psychophysical terms. As we do so, it will become apparent that few specific questions of this sort can be authoritatively answered at this time. It will be further apparent that, while considerable progress in thinking about central auditory problems has occurred in the last 25 years, few of even the earliest studies during this period are altogether obsolete, although interpretations and conclusions may be. Therefore, perhaps the best approach to the problem will be a semihistorical one in which we will attempt to develop, summarize and evaluate current trends of thinking.

CENTRAL AUDITORY PATHWAY

To define as central auditory mechanisms all neural elements which are activated by stimulation of the organ of Corti would impose an impossible task of description because sound stimulation may trigger neural activity of far-reaching systems eventuating finally in the activation of muscles. Consequently, arbitrary limits must be imposed on the description, if possible without causing a corresponding limitation on our thinking of the consequences of sound stimulation. One might choose, for example, to limit the definition of central auditory mechanisms to the classical pathway of Ramón y Cajal. This would include fibers and nuclei through which may be traced, anatomically, a clearly sequential series of connections from the ganglion of Corti to the cerebral cortex: cochlear nuclei, trapezoid body, superior olivary nucleus, lateral lemniscus and its nuclei, inferior colliculus, inferior quadrigeminal brachium, medial geniculate body and its fibers radiating to the cortical auditory projection area. However, strict adherence to the classical pathway would make it impossible to explain several phenomena observed in experiments on the response of medial geniculate body, cerebral cortex and cerebellum to sound stimulation. In the former case, for example, single neural elements of the medial geniculate body may be found with a latency of response far too long to be accounted for by impulses which are transmitted via the traditional pathway; hence, these impulses must be carried over a slower system, perhaps one not hitherto considered as auditory (36). A similar phenomenon has been demonstrated in the cerebral cortex (25). In the case of the cerebellum, the very fact that response to sound may be evoked requires some addition to the classical definition of central auditory mechanisms. Finally, while they have been mentioned from time to time for many years, fibers coursing within the classical pathway, but running perversely from rostral to caudal instead of ascending, have been until recently consistently ignored as functional units.

In considering the tracts and nuclei which we classify as 'central auditory mechanisms', we should keep in mind several functional requirements, some of which are specifically auditory but others are of more general neural significance, that is they are functional requirements of any neural system. Taking up the general requirements first, they have to do with two closely related characteristics of neural systems: *1)* the tendency for feed-back devices to occur, such as recurrent collaterals by which any neuron may by its own discharge feed back into itself, or similar mechanisms on a recurrent nucleus-to-nucleus basis, this sort of device apparently serving to amplify the effect of input into the system; and *2)* the apparent ability of the system, by its own activity, to modify, modulate or control that activity, a function which could be served by the same kind of recurrent feed-back circuits.

The more specifically auditory requirements have to do *1)* with the mechanisms by which sound is analyzed with respect to frequency and intensity, and the combinations and permutations of these, and the manner in which these are impressed upon the brain, and *2)* with the arrangements by which the activities of the auditory system impress themselves on integrative mechanisms of the brain and ultimately on motor systems through which responses to auditory stimulation may be mediated. It has been common to speak of this kind of function in terms of 'levels of integration', as though integration of auditory information could be classified as to its own complexity and to the complexity of response called for, and each category relegated to a particular rostrocaudal level. This concept may have a very general kind of validity, but it will become increasingly evident that its usefulness is questionable. It must be applied with great caution, and the delegation of degrees of perceptual judgment to one or another of the cell masses of the central auditory pathway represents a pattern of thinking which is more dangerous than helpful.

There appear to be significant differences between the pathway of projection from sensory end organ to cerebral cortex in the auditory system as compared with other afferent systems, for example the somatic sensory systems. The latter are characterized by a second-order link with a thalamic nucleus, whereas in the auditory the fibers reaching the thalamus are at least third order, and there are probably relatively few that are not of fourth, fifth or higher order. There is, in other words, in the auditory pathway a more complex and devious system of nuclear interruptions. One factor leading to this situation must have been that, since the cochlea and its central connections developed phylogenetically late as compared with other sensory systems, the ascending pathway had to be constituted from such scattered elements as were still open to modification in a neural matrix otherwise too fixed in pattern to permit of a new through pathway.

Figure 1 shows diagrammatically the main features of the known connections of the auditory pathway. Cerebellar connections are not shown. Connections with the reticular system are shown schematically. These are actually not known in anatomical detail, but some such connections must be present according to physiological evidence.

Cochlear Nuclei

The course and terminations of two types of dendritic processes of cells of the spiral ganglion of Corti have been studied and described by several authors (e.g. 28, 59, 75). Despite the rather elaborate differentiation thus revealed in the end organ of hearing, the course and terminations of the axons of the ganglion cells show no such corresponding differentiation; rather, the terminations display a pattern of organization of a different sort. For practical purposes then, our story of the central auditory pathway may begin with a group of fibers, showing little differentiation, entering the medulla at the inferior border of the pons as the cochlear portion of the eighth cranial nerve. Immediately the fibers begin to bifurcate and the resultant branches to pass to their terminations in dorsal and ventral cochlear nuclei (28, 75). Each fiber is said to terminate on 75 to 100 cells of the cochlear nuclei. This being true, it must also follow that each cell of the nucleus receives terminations from many incoming fibers because the total number of cochlear nucleus cells is only about 2.9 times the number of cells of the ganglion of Corti (22).

The cochlear nuclei are divisible each into several parts. The organizational pattern in the dorsal cochlear nucleus is laminar, that in the ventral is not but shows a similar degree of complexity and differenti-

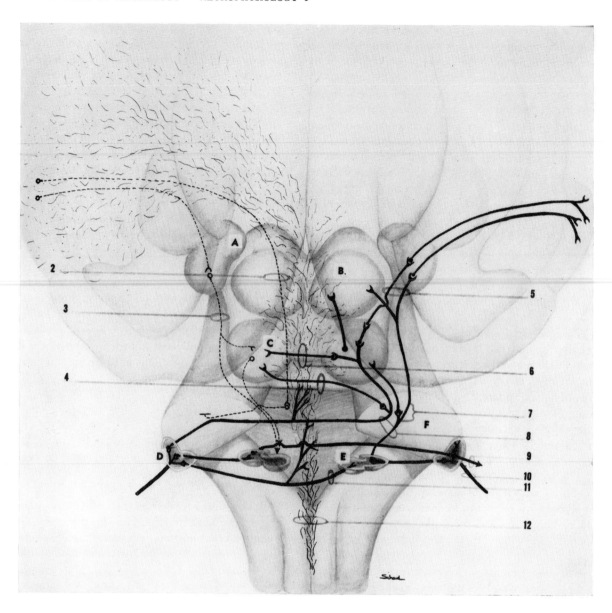

FIG. 1. Main features of the known connections of the auditory pathways in the cat. *A*, medial geniculate body; *B*, superior colliculus; *C*, inferior colliculus; *D*, cochlear nucleus; *E*, superior olive, *F*, cut section of brachium pontis; *2*, corticopontocerebellar pathway; *3*, recurrent fibers throughout the auditory projection pathway; *4*, commissure of Probst; *5*, brachium of inferior colliculus; *6*, commissure of inferior colliculus; *7*, nucleus lateral lemniscus; *8*, lateral lemniscus; *9*, olive cochlear bundle; *10*, cochlear nerve; *11*, trapezoid body; *12*, reticular system (diffuse projection to cerebral cortex).

ation. Both contain many cell types (28, 68) and several types of axon endings. Of the former, some are recognized as intranuclear short axon cells (28). In the light of present knowledge, there is little evidence to tell us what may be the functional significance of this complex organization or even its signifi-

cance in terms of distribution of efferent fibers from the cochlear nuclei. Rose *et al.* (84) have recently demonstrated a functional organization in terms of frequency but have not yet tied this firmly to the histological pattern. For the present, therefore, we have little choice but to ignore most of the organizational features of cochlear nuclei in describing the efferent fibers which leave them, particularly as the latter display a very great range of diameters (75).

Efferent Fibers from Cochlear Nuclei

Three principal groups of fibers emanate from the cochlear nuclei (13, 60). *1)* The dorsal (or superior) acoustic stria leave the dorsal nucleus to pass through the reticular formation under the medial longitudinal fasciculus, and, upon crossing the mid-line, pass ventrolaterally to the vicinity of the superior olivary nucleus. *2)* The intermediate stria arises from the dorsal part of the ventral cochlear nucleus, passes over the restiform body and crosses the reticular formation to the opposite side in an intermediate position. *3)* Fibers, which exceed in number the combined total of the other two striae, arise in the main body of the ventral cochlear nucleus, pass directly medially ventral to the restiform body, traverse the ventral part of the reticular formation and cross the mid-line as the trapezoid body (or ventral stria).

The three striae tend to draw together in the vicinity of the contralateral superior olivary nucleus where many of them terminate. In the course of their passage from origin to that point, there is a considerable diminution of fibers even before the mid-line is crossed due to termination of some fibers in the reticular formation and others in the ipsilateral superior olivary nucleus (13). The latter are of special interest insofar as they provide an essential part of an anatomical basis for ipsilateral rostral projection and possibly for reflex connections at the medullary level.

A few fibers emanating from the cochlear nuclei fail to be interrupted by synapses in either the ipsilateral or contralateral superior olivary nucleus (13) but turn rostrally and ascend through the pontine medulla in company with third order fibers which arise from the superior olivary nucleus, the combined elements being called the lateral lemniscus. Apparently all of the second order fibers which ascend in the contralateral lateral lemniscus terminate in either the nucleus of the lateral lemniscus or the inferior colliculus (13).

Lateral Lemniscus and its Nucleus

This tract ascends from the region of the superior olivary nucleus to the inferior colliculus and, in part, beyond, as the inferior quadrigeminal brachium, to the medial geniculate body in the thalamus. Between superior olive and inferior colliculus, the tract is com-posed of at least two, and probably more, different components, *1)* fibers having origin in the contralateral cochlear nuclei (13) and *2)* fibers taking origin from the ipsilateral superior olivary nuclei (13, 33, 69, 71, 75). It should be noted that since the superior olive receives second order fibers from both ipsi- and contralateral cochlear nuclei, the two components of the lateral lemniscus listed above can actually be subdivided into three with respect to cochlear origin of excitation carried by each: *1)* contralateral second order, *2)* contralateral third order and *3)* ipsilateral third order.

At this point it may be pointed out that our use of 'second order' and 'third order' is valid only if we assume a single synapse in each successive nucleus, for each chain of conduction as represented at one single point by a fiber of the lateral lemniscus. This assumption is neither necessary nor likely in view of the complexity of the nuclei so far encountered. It would seem more likely that a variable number of links in such chains of conduction might be introduced by the patterns of intranuclear conduction. Evidence on conduction time to the cochlear nucleus, trapezoid body and lateral lemniscus (5) indicates that there are at least some conduction chains in the system which are as direct as would be implied in speaking of second and third order fibers in the lemniscus; however, the protraction of the response to a very brief stimulus would also make one suspect the presence of chains with greater numbers of synapses.

The nucleus of the lateral lemniscus, unlike the other nuclei so far discussed, is neither compact nor does it show any recognizable organization. It consists of scattered groups of cells lying among the fibers of the tract. Some few of the tract fibers apparently terminate in synapse with these cells, and in turn they send their axons upward with the tract to terminations in the inferior colliculus, probably both ipsilateral and contralateral (by way of the commissure of Probst).

Some fibers of the lateral lemniscus, of third order or higher, pass lateral to the inferior colliculus and, becoming part of the inferior quadrigeminal brachium, continue with it to terminations in the medial geniculate body (3, 51, 75). The greater number of lemniscal fibers terminate in the inferior colliculus (13, 75).

Inferior Colliculus

The inferior colliculus (or posterior corpus quadrigeminum) receives a few fibers which project without interruption from the contralateral cochlear nuclei, many more from the ipsilateral superior olivary nucleus and a few (probably) from the nucleus of the lateral lemniscus, ipsi- and contralateral. The input to this nucleus, therefore, represents a degree of diversity and temporal dispersion still greater than that of the superior olive and cochlear nuclei. This is demonstrated by the relatively greater protraction of response to brief stimuli than is seen in the more caudally located stations of the pathway (5, 90).

The inferior colliculus is one of the most highly organized and largest nuclei of the brain stem. Indeed, its position, size, pattern of organization and multiplicity of afferent and efferent connections would make it seem more logical to consider it, together with the superior colliculus, suprasegmental rather than a brain-stem nucleus in the usual meaning. At any rate, the organization and fiber connections are such that, despite the fact that the inferior colliculus must function to some extent as a relay in the ascending auditory pathway, its significance can by no means be limited to its relay function. This will be discussed further in a different context in a later section of this chapter.

Inferior Quadrigeminal Brachium

The colliculus, in addition to efferent pathways to superior colliculus and pons (77), has, as its principal route of discharge, the brachium of the inferior colliculus (or inferior quadrigeminal brachium). This tract is composed predominantly of fibers arising in both ipsilateral and contralateral colliculi, those from the latter passing through the commissure of the inferior colliculus (111). In addition, there is present in the tract the group of lemniscal fibers, noted in the preceding section, that bypasses the colliculus. The entire brachium passes rostrally and somewhat laterally to terminate in the medial geniculate body.

Medial Geniculate Body

The medial geniculate body is the thalamic nucleus of the auditory pathway. It is described as having a pars principalis composed of small closely-packed cells arranged in a laterodorsally curving band, and a pars magnocellularis, lying medioventral to the pars principalis and composed of large cells (10, 23). There is some doubt that the magnocellular part should be considered a part of the true auditory thalamic relay, although the terminology which

makes it a part of the medial geniculate has been generally accepted for many years.

The pars principalis appears to be fairly homogeneous with respect to cell size and distribution, except for a slightly decreasing gradient of density from lateral to medial aspects (85). Thus, there is none of the conspicuous organizational complexity of the brain-stem acoustic nuclei. The principal input to the nucleus consists of the terminations of the inferior quadrigeminal brachium. Other than these, the only fibers reported as afferents to the nucleus are recurrent projections from the cortical projection area (62). Aside from a small number of fibers which are distributed rather diffusely to other parts of the thalamus (1) and a few which retrace the lower projection pathway (1), the main efferent outflow from the medial geniculate is the acoustic radiation. These fibers proceed by way of the posterior limb (sublenticular portion) of the internal capsule to part of the superior face of the superior temporal gyrus and adjacent insular and parietal opercular cortex in primates and the corresponding cortex in carnivors which lack a true temporal lobe. Discussion of the projection areas forms the subject matter of a later section of this chapter.

As noted above, the medial geniculate, pars principalis, shows little or no histologically demonstrable organization; however, there is other evidence indicating that there is, nevertheless, at least a spatial type of organization. This is inseparable from evidence of similar organization in other parts of the auditory system and a separate section will be devoted to spatial and tonotopic aspects of the projection pathway.

Auditory Connections with Cerebellum

Snider & Stowell (95) in 1944 reported the hitherto unknown fact that auditory stimuli (clicks) could regularly evoke responses from the cortex of the cerebellar vermis in cats. In subsequent experiments these findings were confirmed and the additional discovery made that stimulation by light flashes also elicits response in the same cerebellar area. The responses to auditory stimulation occur with latency so brief as to imply a fairly uncomplicated projection from the periphery. At the time of the original observations, no such cochleocerebellar path was known. Since then Niemer & Cheng (68) have deduced the existence of a pathway by which the ventral part of the dorsal cochlear nucleus sends fibers to terminations in the cerebellar vermis. Their evidence consists in the observation of retrograde chromatolysis in that nucleus as a consequence of destruction of the vermis. The tectopontile tract described by Rasmussen (77), which provides communication from the inferior colliculus to the pons, would also seem a possible avenue from auditory pathway to the cerebellum.

What may be the functional significance of such a system is a proper but as yet unanswered question. The further information that stimulation of the 'audiovisual' area of the cerebellum may evoke response in the cerebrocortical auditory area (94) and that stimulation of the latter elicits response from the former (42) may offer some help in answering the question. One suggestion, which has been made repeatedly by one of the more ardent advocates of a cerebellar contribution to audition, is that the cochleocerebellocerebral pathway provides an alternative pathway of auditory projection or integration (or both) to the cerebral cortex which may be implicated in the preservation of auditory function after interruption of the regular cortical projection pathway. This is neither a necessary nor a likely hypothesis. The fact that the cerebellum receives an auditory projection does not imply that it is implicated in the psychological phenomenon of audition *per se*.

The cerebral connections to the cerebellum are presumably those described by Mettler (62) as projecting from the cat's cerebral auditory area to the pons from which a pontocerebellar relay would be the expected pattern. A cerebellocerebral pathway from the cerebellar cortex to the cerebellar nuclei to the thalamus to the cortex would be a plausible or even probable explanation of the functional evidence that the auditory area of the cerebellum projects to that of the cerebral cortex. It is the more plausible when we recall the similar type of anteriorly directed projection of the brachium conjunctivum. The pattern of interprojection of cerebellar and cerebral areas is thus probably no different in relation to the auditory than to any of several other functional systems. The most likely explanation of cerebellar auditory (and visual) connections, therefore, would seem to be that these add the information of distance receptors to that of contact and proprioceptive receptors as these may modulate the cerebellar contribution to regulation of motor patterns.

Reticular Activating System

Like other sensory systems, the acoustic makes its contribution to the reticular activating system pre-

sumably at brain-stem levels. Certainly, it has been demonstrated that arousal can be induced by auditory stimuli in animals in which the standard acoustic projection pathway has been bilaterally interrupted (30, 57, 61, 96, 97). Thus, there is through the reticular system another route from brain-stem acoustic mechanisms to cerebral cortex, though this is of general rather than specifically auditory distribution. The ascending reticular system seems to be a diffuse and multisynaptic route, so the auditory and other specific modalities of input tend to be swallowed up in the more comprehensive functions of the ascending reticular system. It is impossible to say to what extent, if any, this system may serve a specific sensory function, though it would appear that this could not be extensive in the light of what we know about reticular function.

Descending Fibers in the Auditory Pathway

Fibers which proceed from rostral to caudal regions, that is from higher to lower stations in the auditory projection pathway, have been described at all levels from the cerebral cortex to the cochlea. In general these closely parallel the ascending system, although they may bypass nuclei with greater freedom. They are better known anatomically than physiologically with the possible exception of the olivocochlear tract which was described by Rasmussen (78–80). For a review of the available evidence and current studies of the descending auditory pathways, the reader is referred to Chapter XXXI by Livingston in this volume and to Galambos' recent review (32, p. 502). He indicates that, for the first time, a systematic anatomic study of these by adequate degeneration methods is under way. While the information is as yet meager, it is clear that a neural system which provides a possible mechanism by which the sensory system to which it belongs can achieve some degree of self-regulation may be of the utmost importance in providing explanation of complex functions, the means for which are not obviously available in the organization of the afferent pathway.

AUDITORY CORTEX

The development of knowledge of the cortical termination of the auditory projection system may be said to have begun with the observations of Ferrier (29) reported as part of a more general work in 1876.

Observations of the responses of cats to electrical stimulation of the brain, such as movements of the ears and turning of head and eyes, led Ferrier to identify as auditory in function the ectosylvian region. This area has remained the 'auditory area' ever since, although the exact limits of the cortex so designated have varied considerably with variations in method, investigator and, presumably, also with variation in the cat itself. For if there is one single incontrovertible fact which has emerged from a long series of investigations of this area, it is that a too faithful reliance on the correspondence between visible brain markings and functional significance in this or any other region in this or any other animal is a trap for the unwary.

Ferrier's observations apparently satisfied everyone for about 20 years because, for that period of time, no other work appeared, either to contradict or to modify Ferrier's conclusions. In 1899 Larionow (52) defined, also from experiments on cats, remarkably precise (though incorrect) boundaries of an S-shaped strip of cortex coursing along the gyral crest beginning at the middle ectosylvian gyrus, doubling back down the posterior ectosylvian gyrus and redoubling around the inferior end of the posterior suprasylvian sulcus for a short distance. Larionow was the first, though not the last, to see in his auditory strip a representation of an 'unfurled cochlea', an expression which has proved attractive to several workers through the years. Indeed, though Larionow unrolled his cochlea too far back, there is a note of prophecy and a modest degree of validity to the concept, as later events have shown.

A year prior to Larionow's report Vogt (104) had pointed out that the ectosylvian cortex of the carnivore is an area of early myelination. By the turn of the century, therefore, the feline auditory area had been located, though not precisely defined, by crude functional methods; the same area had been shown to have special histological characteristics and the idea of cochlear projection had been introduced. Thus, the ideas which were to guide the future study of the cortical auditory area were all present. The subsequent additions can be thought of as refinements and variants of method, the advent of good electrical recording methods during the 1930's constituting the only radical departure since. Even this has been used without much change in pattern of thinking until very recently.

There are several ways in which one might trace the development of knowledge of the auditory cortex. In order to show how we have arrived at our present knowledge and attitudes we will here adopt an approach which will be, in the main, sequential, but will deviate from strict chronology by first defining certain questions which were or might reasonably have been asked at the beginning and considering the successive steps which have been taken toward answering these. Thus, departures from strict chronology will be necessary when solutions to questions have been found not in what at the beginning might have been logical sequence. More often than not this has occurred when it was generally thought that, for example, question 1 had been answered and one might proceed to question 2, only to find in the course of investigation of question 2 that question 1 had not been answered as fully as it had seemed.

Given the general location of a functional cortical area, the next question is to determine the extent of the area. This question has been asked at least tacitly in nearly all investigations for over 50 years, even when the stated central question of a particular study was of a more esoteric nature. One reason which makes this determination an almost mandatory starting point for any study of the auditory cortex is that, because of individual variation, there are no configurative landmarks which can be relied on except in the most general way; therefore, if the experiment presupposes exact knowledge of extent of auditory projection, this must be determined for each animal as the starting point.

The animal most frequently used in experiments on the auditory area is the cat with the monkey (especially macaque) next most frequently; the dog has been used in only a few cases. Unless otherwise specified, the ensuing discussion may be assumed to refer to the cat as the experimental animal. Figure 2 shows the standard lateral view of the cat brain which will be used in subsequent figures in portraying the auditory area maps of several studies.

Vogt's myelination time studies represented the first application of a detailed morphological method of study to the auditory cortex. Campbell (21) in 1905 produced the first careful study of the region by the cytoarchitectonic method. Campbell's area is shown in figure 3. (In this figure, the total extent of the cortex considered to be auditory in function is shown in each case. Each portrays the original data as nearly as these could be projected from the original publication to the standard view of the cat brain used in all. Subdivisions are ignored for purposes of the immediate discussion but will be considered in the next section.) It is interesting to note that Campbell's auditory area is the most extensive of any but the latest published and is remarkably similar in some respects to the total composite area which would express the current area of substantial agreement of several authors.

In 1937, Kornmüller (50) published the first map of the cat's auditory cortex determined by recording electrical responses to acoustic stimulation. His map, seen in figure 3, includes an area confined to middle

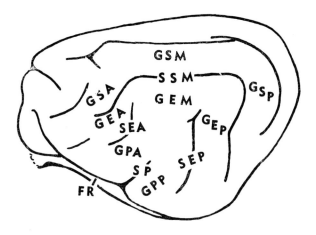

FIG. 2. Lateral view of brain of cat. *FR*, rhinal fissure; *GEA*, anterior ectosylvian gyrus; *GEM*, middle ectosylvian gyrus; *GEP*, posterior ectosylvian gyrus; *GPA*, anterior pseudosylvian gyrus; *GPP*, posterior pseudosylvian gyrus; *GSA*, anterior suprasylvian gyrus; *GSM*, middle suprasylvian gyrus; *GSP*, posterior suprasylvian gyrus; *SEA*, anterior ectosylvian sulcus; *SEP*, posterior ectosylvian sulcus; *SP*, pseudosylvian sulcus; and *SSM*, middle suprasylvian sulcus.

ectosylvian cortex. Between that time and 1941, two other such maps were published. Bremer & Dow (17) and Ades (1), using brief acoustic stimuli (clicks), defined the area responsive to such stimulation largely in the middle ectosylvian gyrus (fig. 4). The responsive area of Bremer & Dow extends to the pseudosylvian sulcus while that of Ades stops short of the sulcus. Bremer & Dow studied the cytoarchitectonic characteristics of the region also and found the somewhat smaller area shown in the same figure to satisfy the criteria of a sensory projection area. The study of Woollard & Harpman (110), in which they traced Marchi degeneration after electrolytic lesions in the medial geniculate body, defined the area shown in figure 4 as the projection area of that nucleus. It is interesting to note that the Woollard & Harpman map, based on anatomical findings, corresponds more closely with the Bremer & Dow electrical response map than the latter does with their own cytoarchitectonic map, which itself more nearly coincides with Ades' electrical response map.

The maps of the feline auditory cortex derived from the foregoing studies from 1933 to 1941 share the common feature of being considerably more restricted than the much earlier work of Campbell indicated. They were at the time regarded as being reasonably consistent with each other and probably substantially valid in defining the 'primary' auditory projection area, the only point of disagreement being the extent

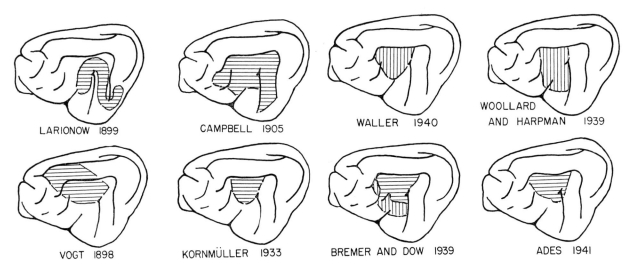

FIG. 3 (top). Auditory area of cat as described by individuals named, shown by *shaded areas.* All redrawn from originals on standard view.

FIG. 4 (bottom). Auditory area of cat as described by individuals named, shown by *shaded areas.* All redrawn from originals on standard view. In the map of Bremer & Dow, electrical responses to clicks could be obtained over both the *horizontally* and *vertically shaded* areas; cytoarchitectonically, the *vertically shaded area* satisfied the criteria for a sensory projection area.

of the lateral (ventral) margin of the area. The posterior ectosylvian cortex is the one part of the area that none of these studies implicated as auditory in function. This is a particularly curious circumstance in the light of evidence which began to accumulate rapidly the following year (1942) and which demonstrated that the posterior ectosylvian cortex is most definitely auditory.

Two virtually concurrent physiological studies extended the cortical sphere of auditory response to the posterior ectosylvian gyrus in 1942 and 1943. Both represented a departure from the preceding studies in that functional subdivision or organization rather than total extent of the auditory cortex became the principal theme although extension of the boundaries also came as a by-product. Both these studies and later ones which grew out of them demonstrated how much the factor of adequate instrumentation may influence validity of data. Ades (2) demonstrated what was then termed a 'secondary' auditory area (see fig. 5) occupying most of the posterior ectosylvian cortex. The experiments consisted in mapping the area responsive to clicks, then applying strychnine to the 'primary' area so defined and remapping the responsive area which now included the posterior ectosylvian. The latter area was originally termed 'secondary' because its response appeared to be dependent on and driven by that of the 'primary' middle ectosylvian cortex. This terminology was further motivated by a preoccupation, dating from Campbell's time, with the concept of primary sensory projection areas surrounded by or adjacent to sensory 'association' areas. Repetition of the same experiments with more nearly adequate instruments (14, 48, 49) has demonstrated that while the posterior ectosylvian, under the influence of strychnine, is driven by the middle ectosylvian, its response is not wholly dependent on transmission through the middle ectosylvian.

Woolsey & Walzl (113) published a report (actually a few months earlier than the one by Ades, though unknown to the latter until after his own report was in process of publication) which also extended the auditory area to the posterior ectosylvian cortex and also provided a basis for subdivision of the total responsive area but on a quite different basis than that suggested by the strychnine experiments. The experiments reported in this paper by Woolsey & Walzl are worthy of special note, as they represent a turning point in research on the auditory cortex which provides the basis for the modern view point. They employed a more adequate system of amplification and recording than had previously been used. This, together with stimulation of small groups of nerve fibers in the exposed osseous spiral lamina of the cochlea, afforded by far the most precise technique yet brought to bear on the problem. In addition, the results had great influence in dispelling the bemusement with the concept of primary and secondary areas, which, while it may still have some degree of validity, was in retrospect a concept which had done little to advance, and possibly something to retard, the development of understanding of cortical auditory function.

Woolsey & Walzl stimulated electrically small local groups of the exposed ends of cochlear nerve fibers in the osseous spiral lamina and recorded the cortical response. They were able to show that local stimulation of such small groups of fibers elicited a similarly localized response within the ectosylvian cortex. The pattern of projection was an orderly one such that in the more superiorly lying strip (fig. 5) stimulation at the base of the cochlea evoked response anteriorly while stimulation of the apex produced it posteriorly. In the more laterally lying strip, the pattern is reversed so that the base of the cochlea projects posteriorly and the apex anteriorly. These results were

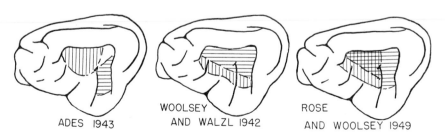

FIG. 5. Auditory area of cat as described by individuals named. All redrawn from originals on standard view. Ades: *Vertical shading*, 'primary area'; *horizontal*, 'secondary area.' Woolsey & Walzl: *Horizontal shading*, A I; *vertical*, A II. Rose & Woolsey: *Horizontal shading*, EP; *vertical*, A II; *cross-hatched*, A I.

confirmed by experiments reported by the same authors (108) in which the deficits in cortical response to click stimulation were noted after local lesions in the cochlea. These experiments then introduce in the auditory cortex an organization based on an internal integrity of the auditory projection pathway such that the anatomical pattern of the cochlea seems to be faithfully represented in the cortical receiving station. A fuller discussion of this 'point-to-point' feature of anatomical projection and its functional implications will be found in another section of this chapter.

Woolsey & Walzl introduced the terminology by which the two strips of auditory cortex noted in the foregoing paragraph were designated respectively 'A I' (the superior or dorsal strip) and 'A II' (the inferior or lateral strip). When this organization of the cortical auditory field was subjected to further study involving, in addition to electrophysiological methods, cytoarchitecture and retrograde degeneration in the medial geniculate body following selective extirpation of parts of the auditory cortex by Rose (83) and Rose & Woolsey (85), a further revision of the terminology became necessary. For, as their results showed, A I occupies a more limited area than originally designated by Woolsey & Walzl (fig. 5) and is the only part whose destruction leads to widespread degeneration in the pars principalis of the medial geniculate. Cytoarchitectonic study shows that A I and A II differ from each other and the anterior parts of both differ from the posterior. These findings lead to the map presented by Rose & Woolsey (fig. 5) in which the auditory area is now divided into A I, A II, and EP, the latter being compounded of the posterior parts of the original A I and A II. It will be noted that these areas now show varying degrees of correspondence to those of earlier studies. For example, A I now is closely similar to the more restricted electrically responsive area shown by Ades (1) and Kormüller (50) and to the cytoarchitectonic maps of Bremer & Dow (17) and Waller (106). It also corresponds to the posteroinferior portion of Vogt's (104) old map based on myelination time. A I plus A II now resembles the electrical map area of Bremer & Dow (17), the geniculocortical projection area of Woollard & Harpman (110), and corresponds with somewhat lesser fidelity to the anterior part of the Campbell (21) map. EP corresponds closely to the posterior ectosylvian 'secondary area' of Ades (2). It would appear that the restriction of responsive area shown in the earlier oscilloscopic studies may have been due to the relative weakness of responses in A II (except at its anterior end) and in EP which were

not detected by the comparatively poor instruments then available. The re-emergence of the EP area, as it is now commonly called, plus the reaffirmation by Kiang (49) that EP is to some extent functionally dominated by A I revives the question of the functional significance of such a cortical interrelationship.

At this point, while it has become apparent that the limits of the cortex which can be activated by acoustic stimulation may not have been completely and finally defined, it will be useful to depart briefly from the development of this essentially anatomical concept to consider some functional studies. These are of interest not only as they contribute to correlation of structure and function, but also as they reflect on the extent and internal organization of the auditory cortex.

The history of functional studies of the auditory cortex is, to a great extent, a history of increasing complexity of stimulus and experimental learning situations. It is also a study in progression of conceptualization of auditory function. It begins with the experimenter striving for valid criteria to show simply whether or not the experimental animal hears and continues at present as a search for ways in which auditory discriminative ability of animals can be accurately assessed.

Some of the earlier efforts to estimate the cortical contribution to hearing in animals took the form of hearing tests of greater or lesser refinement, following total or hemidecortication (12, 38). It was demonstrated that the decorticate dog can still acquire a crude conditioned response to sound although not nearly as readily as an intact animal. Although the animal could acquire the habit, his absolute intensity threshold was higher by 70 db (38). Other workers (12) were less impressed by the auditory deficit in decorticate cats. The decorticate animal, however, shows a general debility and inattentiveness which is more impressive than an auditory or any other specific sensory defect. This leads one to suspect that any test of hearing in such a preparation may be contaminated to a considerable degree by other deficits which have more to do with general integrative capacity than with hearing *per se*.

To avoid this difficulty, several workers resorted to extirpations of, as they thought, specifically auditory cortex. The theory was that if the cortical auditory projection area is removed, then the entire cerebral cortex is effectively eliminated from participation in any learning or conditioning process that involves stimulation by sound. If this were so, then any auditory function present before but absent after operation could be said to depend upon mediation through the auditory cortex. (Of course, as we now know, the geniculotemporal radiation is not quite the bottleneck it was then supposed. It is not the only avenue through which excitation aroused by sound may reach the cerebral cortex, and it may not be the only effective avenue by which such excitation can produce a specifically auditory cortical sign.) A series of studies in which various aspects of hearing were tested before and after auditory cortical extirpation were carried out beginning about 20 years ago. These yielded results which were surprising because of the difficulty encountered in seriously impairing auditory function. Several specific studies are considered in the following paragraph.

The earlier workers in this area were convinced that the intensity threshold of hearing for pure tones constituted the proper initial criterion of cortical auditory function. This led immediately to apparent discrepancies in results between different laboratories and even different individuals in the same laboratories (51, 58, 74) because, as ultimately became clear, the factor of recovery time between extirpation of the auditory cortex and retesting of thresholds is crucial. Those who were retested within a very short time showed varying degrees of threshold elevation, those who waited several days or weeks before being retested demonstrated little or no loss of acuity for pure tones. Finally Girden (37) demonstrated that in the dog, after incomplete lesions of the auditory cortex, initial losses in acuity gave way with continued testing and the thresholds returned nearly to preoperative levels. Even then, the blame for discrepant results tended to be fixed on differences in testing methods and on the degree of completeness of destruction of auditory cortex, the latter factor being complicated further by differences in understanding of extent of auditory cortex and by this kind of experiment itself being used as a criterion of determining that extent. Kryter & Ades (51) demonstrated that absolute intensity threshold to pure tones does not rise appreciably due to extirpation of auditory cortex in the cat, even when the cortical lesions in some instances extended considerably beyond the widest boundaries suggested for the area. By this time, workers were despairing of the intensity threshold to pure tone as a reliable indicator of cortical auditory function. It became apparent, in retrospect, that the confusion of previous studies had occurred, at least in part, because simple acuity as measured in this way is simply not dependent on cortical participation. It appeared logical then to seek some more complex manifestation of

auditory function which could be tested by a conditioning method and which might prove to be dependent on auditory cortex.

A series of studies directed toward that end began in 1946 with the report of Raab & Ades (74) indicating that, while of interest in other respects, the function of discrimination of differences in intensity of sound, measured in terms of difference limens, was not the cortex-bound function sought. This impression was confirmed by Rosenzweig (87). The next obvious point of attack was the ability of the animal to discriminate between small differences in frequency before and after extirpation of auditory areas. This kind of study has been done by Butler et al. (20), by Meyer & Woolsey (64) and by Allen (9). Before discussing these studies, it is necessary to digress briefly to note the addition of still another cortical area which shows signs of auditory function.

In 1945, Tunturi (103) described in the dog an area in which electrical response to auditory stimulation could be evoked. This area lies outside any of those previously described as auditory in the dog or as homologous areas in the cat. It lies in fact partly in the second somatic area (43). Also in 1945 Allen (9) using Tunturi's map found that, whereas ablation of the traditional auditory areas temporarily impaired but failed to destroy permanently the ability of dogs to discriminate widely different frequencies, this ability was permanently lost if the third auditory area of Tunturi were also destroyed. Later studies on the cat have confirmed the fact that auditory stimulation elicits response in the second somatic area (15, 16, 65, 70).

Meyer & Woolsey (64) trained cats to respond to change in frequency of a given tone at irregularly spaced intervals in a series of 2 sec. tones which were otherwise alike. Once the cats were trained, a rough difference limen for frequency was determined. They then extirpated, symmetrically, in varying combination the following cortical areas: A I, A II, EP, suprasylvian gyrus, temporal region (see fig. 6) and the cerebellar tuber vermis. Following operation, the animals were retrained and retested. It was found that if A I, A II, EP and S II (second somatic area) were completely destroyed on both sides, the animals could no longer achieve the frequency discrimination. No other combination of lesions had this effect and if remnants of A I and A II escaped damage, frequency discrimination was maintained. Butler et al. (20) used a basically similar plan but with what they felt was a more reliable and critical method of testing. In addition, they carefully analyzed the retrograde

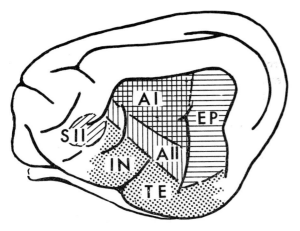

FIG. 6. Composite view of all areas of cat brain showing auditory function. A I, first auditory area; A II, second auditory area; EP, posterior ectosylvian area; S II, second somatic area; IN, insular region; TE, temporal area.

thalamic degeneration in their cats. The results in this series of experiments differ from those of Meyer & Woolsey in that ability to discriminate frequency was not permanently impaired even after complete lesions of A I, A II, EP and S II. Three significant points in explanation of the apparent discrepancy were offered by Butler *et al.* *1*) The testing methods, as have already been mentioned above were different. *2*) In the Meyer-Woolsey animals with loss of discrimination, the lesions, though listed as including A I, A II, EP and S II, actually extended ventrally nearly to the rhinal fissure (unlike those of Butler *et al.*). *3*) In the latter group, the posterior part of the medial geniculate, pars principalis, consistently escaped degeneration, although it was also noted that the nearer to the rhinal fissure the lesion approached, the farther posterior crept the degeneration in the medial geniculate. Thus, the tissue lying before and behind the pseudosylvian sulcus, hitherto largely immune to implication in the auditory cortical sphere, began to take on a most suspiciously acoustic flavor. That this trend is essentially correct has been demonstrated in recent experiments by Neff and his group and in the recent critical analysis by Rose & Woolsey (86) of thalamic degeneration resulting from lesions of the several subdivisions of auditory and apparently related cortex singly and in combinations.

Diamond & Neff (24) trained cats to respond to change in a simple tonal pattern. A three-tone sequence, for example, of low-high-low was presented repetitively for a variable number of times and then changed abruptly to high-low-high, at which point

the animal, in the course of training, learned to respond (by moving across the middle of a shuttle box) to avoid shock. Extirpation of A I failed to disturb the habit of discriminating the two patterns. With extensive damage to A II and EP in addition to A I, the habit was temporarily lost but could be re-established by further training. If the destruction of all three areas was complete, the tonal pattern discrimination could not be re-established even with a prolonged period of retraining. It is interesting to note that even small remnants of tissue which could be excited by sound, and which closely adjoined ablated areas, were sufficient to make possible retraining of the tonal pattern discrimination. In a second series of experiments, Goldberg *et al.* (39), having trained cats to both a simple frequency discrimination habit and to the tonal pattern discrimination, now extirpated bilaterally the region ventral to A II and EP (insular and temporal cortex shown in fig. 6), sparing A I, A II and EP as demonstrated by subsequent responsiveness to click stimulation and absence of severe degeneration in the medial geniculate. The results were quite surprising, both simple tone discrimination and tonal pattern discrimination being lost after operation. It proved possible to re-establish simple discrimination in about the same time as that required for original training. On the contrary, pattern discrimination could not be relearned even with prolonged retraining. The behavior of the animals in the test situation was not visibly different from preoperative behavior and, since the frequency discrimination habit was relearned, one cannot attribute the results to loss of learning capacity; rather the loss of pattern discrimination seems to be a specific auditory deficit.

Two salient features, then, emerge from the recent work of Neff and his group. *1*) The insular and temporal cortex of the cat are demonstrated to be of crucial importance to at least some aspects of auditory integrative function. *2*) Discrimination of tonal patterns (as distinguished from simple change in frequency) appears to be cortically bound.

One cannot help recalling (at least this author cannot) experiments in visual discrimination (4, 7) in which somewhat similar results were obtained after lesions of areas 18 and 19 and the temporal lobe in the monkey. It subsequently proved, however, that losses of discriminative ability in the monkey were less permanent if the monkey had been trained to learn quickly many different visually-guided discriminations rather than just one (81, 82). Although the evidence is insufficient, one cannot help but wonder if the insular and temporal cortex of the cat have a significance to the cat's auditory function similar to that of areas 18 and 19 and the temporal cortex to the monkey's visual function. Also, though prophecy is a questionable if not dangerous indulgence for ordinary people, one also wonders, given an animal whose sophistication is augmented by the learning of many rather than a single type of auditory discrimination, whether the particular habit (tonal pattern in this case) would remain as firmly corticalized.

Rose & Woolsey (85) introduce in their study an anatomical concept which goes a long way toward clearing up at least one aspect of the interrelationship between the subdivisions of the cat's auditory cortex and also toward providing anatomical support for the work of the Neff group. This is based on the shifting pattern of degeneration observed in the medial geniculate body as the cortical lesions are varied in pattern to include one or more of the subdivisions (fig. 6 indicates the areas and the terminology applied to them). It is considered that a cortical area receives an essential projection from a given thalamic nucleus if destruction of that area and only that area results in marked degeneration in the thalamic nucleus. If, however, two cortical areas are considered and if destruction of neither of these alone causes degeneration in a given thalamic nucleus, but simultaneous destruction of both does lead to severe degeneration in that nucleus, both cortical areas are said to receive sustaining projections from the nucleus. On this basis, Rose & Woolsey found that the only component of the cortical auditory complex which receives an essential projection from the medial geniculate (pars principalis) is A I. Since, however, simultaneous destruction of A I, A II, and EP result in much more profound medial geniculate degeneration than does A I alone, it is considered that both A II and EP receive sustaining projections from the geniculate pars principalis. Even the combination leaves the posterior third of the nucleus relatively unscathed. It is only when the cortical destruction is extended ventrally to include all of the cortex between A II and EP and the rhinal fissure (temporal and insular cortex as shown in fig. 6) that severe degeneration extends posteriorly to include the entire pars principalis. There is, therefore, projection from the posterior sector of the pars principalis to the temporal and insular cortex. That this is probably a sustaining projection is attested by the fact that the still limited evidence indicates insular and temporal lesions alone fail to produce severe posterior sector degeneration. Similarly, the pars magnocellularis degenerates markedly only when A I,

A II, EP, insular and temporal areas are all destroyed. Both posterior pars principalis and magnocellularis are largely preserved by the preservation of A I alone; consequently, it would appear that both emit rather widespread sustaining projections, but there is no evidence as yet of emission of essential projections. Finally, from the limited available evidence, the anterior part of the posterior nuclear group of the thalamus, in addition to the medial geniculate, must be suspected of having auditory connections. The critical evidence is lacking but this thalamic area, lying between auditory and tactile nuclei, probably sends a sustaining projection to S II, which itself has been shown to be excitable by auditory stimulation (15, 16, 19, 65, 70). Moreover, this auditory excitability, according to Rose & Woolsey (85), seems to be independent of medial geniculate-auditory cortex activity since it appears even when the medial geniculate body is profoundly degenerated. In contrast to this conclusion, Pribram et al. (73), noting an apparently similar system in the monkey, maintain that the responses in S II do drop out upon degeneration of the medial geniculate, and so come to the conclusion that the interconnection is by way of collaterals from the medial geniculate. Until this conflict is resolved, therefore, the question of the essential connection of this thalamic nucleus and cortical area with the cochlear projection pathway must be left open.

Returning briefly to efforts toward finding some auditory integrative function which is corticalized in the sense that the task cannot be accomplished without cortical participation, the work of Neff et al. (67) deserves special attention. They trained cats to make a response requiring localization of sound in space, correct performance being rewarded with food. Lesions were then made in A I in some cases and A I, A II and EP in others. Bilateral destruction even of A I, if complete, caused severe deterioration of performance in the test situation. That this behavioral deficit was specific to hearing was demonstrated by a normal capacity to learn a problem in the same situation if it were based on visual cues. As the authors point out, while the auditory cortex must play an important role in the function of localization of sound in space, it is less clear what the nature of this role may be. The evidence would allow several hypotheses but select none of them. The authors list the following. *1*) Intact auditory cortex is essential to learning the relationship between auditory signal and food reward. *2*) Intact auditory cortex is essential for maintaining attention to auditory signal, attention being defined as the ability of the animal to orient toward the signal and carry through its appropriately directed activity until the full response of opening a door and obtaining food is accomplished. *3*) Intact auditory cortex is necessary for accurate localization of sound in space. As indicated above, the data fail clearly to single out any of these. This, incidentally, is a common finding in behavioral experiments involving extirpation of brain tissue. It may be an inherent failing in all such experiments. However, this is of more concern from the standpoint of the neurology of learning than from that of specifically auditory integration.

We cannot leave the subject of definition of the auditory area without referring to the work of Lilly (55, 56) who has introduced a new method and a new dimension to this field of study. Using a square array of 25 electrodes covering an area of cortex of 1 cm², 25 amplifiers and glow tubes, each channel serving one electrode, and photographing at 128 frames per sec. the bank of glow tubes, Lilly has been able to demonstrate the patterns of spontanous electrical activity and those evoked by acoustic stimulation in the cat's auditory cortex. In this fashion, the simultaneous cortical surface activity can be recorded at 25 different zones and the changes at each noted in time sequence. Thus Lilly has demonstrated what he calls 'forms and figures' of cortical activity which combine the dimensions of time and space in a way not previously possible. The array was placed across the upper end of the posterior ectosylvian sulcus so that it covered part of the junctional area of A I and A II with EP. Lilly found that both spontaneous activity and the response to clicks followed a definite, repeatable pattern. Under deep anesthesia the response to clicks would appear first in one corner of the array, spread posteriorly to a boundary and there die out. Posterior to the boundary (i.e. in EP) spontaneous waves tended to originate and travel downwards along the posterior ectosylvian gyrus; however, under lighter anesthesia the response wave could trigger the 'spontaneous' EP waves, and at still lighter levels spontaneous waves were seen to originate in A I and travel across the border. In another series of experiments on unanesthetized monkeys, clicks set off waves of activity which were observed to travel systematically over the sensorimotor cortex. Thus, Lilly has at once made several interesting points, some of which are of specific interest in the development of knowledge of the cortical auditory equipment and others are of even greater significance to neurophysiological thinking in general. With respect to auditory function, he has shown that there

is a certain validity to the accepted subdivision of auditory cortex, albeit this may have been to some degree overplayed in the past because most previous workers (with one qualified exception in Bremer[1]) have used deeply anesthetized animals as the standard preparation. At the least, these studies present the interrelationship of auditory subdivisions from a new viewpoint. He has further demonstrated that the excitation of cerebral cortex which results from acoustic stimulation may be (or perhaps always is) considerably more widespread than is usually assumed, tacitly at least, in the plan of auditory experiments. This is somewhat disquieting from the standpoint of planning an experiment to demonstrate by electrophysiological method some facet of cortical auditory function; however, it is perhaps potentially comforting in even greater degree to those who work with behavioral methods and are constantly confronted with the necessity of explaining why an animal in which access to cortical integrative processes has presumably been denied to the acoustic system (by removal of receptive areas) can yet behave as though auditory stimulation still held meaning for him.

From a more general viewpoint, Lilly has neatly demonstrated the restrictive effect of anesthetization on cortical activity with respect to both time and space such that the functional separation of contiguous areas tends to be exaggerated. It should be an ample indication that while unguarded use of anesthesia in electrophysiological studies of the cortex may relieve some technical problems for the experimenter, it may simultaneously furnish the basis for an abundance of conceptual 'red herrings.' Lilly's work suggests further, however, that the enlightened, controlled use of anesthesia may be of most positive value in cortical studies by virtue of its capacity to separate functional areas whose boundaries tend to be inconspicuous in the waking animal.

The reader will note that, having begun with a hazy idea of the location and limits of the auditory cortex of the cat, these gradually became sharply defined through the years with improvement in instrumentation, method and thinking. At several points in this history, the matter seemed to have been settled. Each time this has occurred, someone

---

[1] Bremer's *encéphale isolé* preparation falls short of qualifying as equivalent to the intact preparation to the extent that it interrupts part of the reticular input; however, it is different from the deeply anesthetized animal to the extent that part of the reticular system is intact.

assuming this to be true and predicating a new study on this assumption has, by his findings, introduced some new confusion which has then required its own gradual resolution. We have now arrived at an interesting dilemma in which we recognize several types of auditory thalamocortical projection to a wide lateroventral extension of the auditory area as first defined and, in addition, projection from hitherto nonauditory thalamic nuclei to a cortical area originally considered to belong to the somesthetic system but now known to be excitable also by sound (and, indeed, by the nonacoustic labyrinth as well). Moreover, these latter-day auditory areas seem to play essential roles in the mediation of auditory-guided learned behavior. When we add to this the findings of Lilly which tend to blur functional if not anatomical boundaries, we begin to be less impressed than we once were with the possibility of singling out certain areas whose sole responsibility and exclusive prerogative lie in the realm of auditory integration. On the other hand, we must be equally careful to avoid the other horn of the dilemma by keeping in mind that, however dim the boundaries may become, the areas we call auditory do respond differently to sound than do other cortical areas and they do show differences among themselves.

Auditory Cortex in Primates

The foregoing section was based almost entirely on the brain of the cat. Comparable studies on the primate brain are far fewer in number and comparatively lacking in the area of behavioral studies. Otherwise, a history of developing knowledge of the primate cortical auditory areas would parallel that in the cat since neurophysiology traditionally uses the cat for pilot experiments which, after trial, modification and revision, can be applied to the monkey. The history of monkey experiments reflects the greater efficiency which is made mandatory by the expense of buying monkeys out of the characteristically meager operating budget for neurophysiological studies.

The early development of knowledge of the monkey auditory cortex is similar to that of the cat, often appearing in the same accounts, such as those of Ferrier, Munk and Campbell. It will suffice here to say that by the beginning of the twentieth century, inference, extrapolation and inspired guesswork, based on some knowledge of human and carnivore brains, had implanted firmly and widely

the belief that the primate auditory area is located somewhere in the superior temporal convolution. Fortunately in view of this, the facts, as they subsequently accumulated, support this belief.

Aside from the cytoarchitectural studies of the earlier neurologists, the modern investigation of the primate auditory area may be said to begin with the studies of Poliak in 1932 (72) based on Marchi studies of monkey brains after lesions in the medial geniculate body. He described the course and terminations of the auditory radiations, defining as the cortical projection area thus delineated the greater part of the superior surface of the superior temporal gyrus. The concentration of terminations was greater posteriorly than anteriorly, the focal zone coinciding with an elevation toward the posterior end of the concealed face of the gyrus which Poliak likened to Heschl's convolution in man. Poliak described a lesser concentration of fibers which reaches the lateral face of the superior temporal gyrus.

Walker (105) and Clark (23), both using the method of retrograde degeneration in the medial geniculate body following lesions in the superior temporal cortex, are in general agreement with Poliak on the location of the projection area of the medial geniculate; however, both outline a smaller area confined to the posterior part of the superior face of the gyrus. If the situation in the monkey is similar to that found in the cat by Rose & Woolsey (85), in which only A I of all the auditory region receives essential projection, it would be expected that only the corresponding area in the monkey would be revealed by the retrograde degeneration method. On the other hand, the Marchi method in conjunction with medial geniculate lesions should in addition demonstrate some of the fibers constituting sustaining projections to a wider area. No study of the primate auditory thalamocortical relationships comparable to the Rose and Woolsey study of the cat is available. There are, however, some hints derived from several other studies that similar principles may apply.

Electrophysiological efforts to map the primate auditory cortex, like the comparable studies of the cat, show the same sort of progression. They begin with a limited area and, with improvement of instruments and methodology, expand and become subdivided. There is, in the monkey, an additional handicap which limited the accuracy of the early studies. This arises from the fact the primate auditory area, unlike the feline, lies almost entirely in cortex concealed within the Sylvian sulcus, part of it, in fact, facing inward toward the insula. This makes necessary some special preparation in order to gain access for the exploring electrode. Earlier workers usually accomplished this by extensive removals of the overhanging frontal and parietal operculum, the latter of which, as later events have shown, actually contains some auditory responsive cortex. This was therefore missed until more recently Pribram and his coworkers (73) were able to expose the areas in question without major destruction of tissue.

The first electrophysiological demonstration of the simian auditory cortex, by Ades & Felder (6), used click stimulation and the usual exploration for cortical response. An area on the posterior part of the superior temporal plane was found to be responsive; this is shown in figure 7. This area is larger than those outlined by Clark and by Walker but confirms the general location. It is somewhat smaller than the area shown by Poliak (72) to receive geniculocortical fibers.

Licklider (53) and Licklider & Kryter (54), assuming the Ades-Felder definition of the auditory area to be correct, explored it while stimulating with short bursts of pure tone. They were able to demonstrate a degree of specificity of various parts of the area referable to frequency of stimulation. Bailey et al. (11) defined similar auditory areas from monkey and chimpanzee, in each case confined to the supra-

temporal plane, and confirmed the tonotopic distribution suggested by Licklider & Kryter. Walzl (107) and Woolsey (112), using different methods, also demonstrated a specificity of cochleocortical projection in the same area but found, in addition, a region of reversed order of projection on the upper (parietal) bank of the sylvian fissure, thus extending the boundaries of auditory cortex. The aspects of these and other studies which relate to topical projection, localized response to different stimulus frequencies or both will be considered in more detail in a section dealing specifically with that aspect of auditory projection.

The most extensive auditory area yet described for the monkey is that of Pribram et al. (73). They mapped the cortical areas from which electrical response could be evoked by clicks, exposing the depth of the Sylvian fissure and the insula by gently separating the lips of the fissure and wedging them apart in various ways. They do not relate in detail the means by which damage to the rich vascular tree of the middle cerebral artery was avoided; however, this surgical *tour de force* must have been accomplished because the effects of severe hemorrhage and ischemia in the region supplied by this vascular tree are not evident in the results. The cortex of the posterior supratemporal plane, superior temporal gyrus, insula and inferior parietal lobe all yielded responses to clicks (fig. 8). On the basis of latency of initial positive deflection and other criteria, the authors identify (by inference or direct statement) subdivisions of the total responsive area with those of the cat as follows: *1)* the posterior supratemporal plane with A I; *2)* the anterior margin of responsive area of supratemporal plane, posterior insula and posterior inferior parietal operculum with 'secondary' area of Ades & Bremer and, hence, EP of Rose & Woolsey; and *3)* the parietal operculum with S II. This analysis omits most of the responsive area of the posterior insula which corresponds roughly to the 'second' auditory area (or simian A II) of Walzl (107) and Woolsey (112). In this regard the data of Pribram et al. furnish no parallel to the Walzl & Woolsey data because the definition of A I and A II in the lexicon of the latter two authors hinges upon the presence in each of cochlear projections of mutually opposite orientation.

Pribram et al. include data on retrograde degeneration after lesions of the posterior supratemporal plane but not of any other part of their responsive area. So far as this goes, it confirms the impression

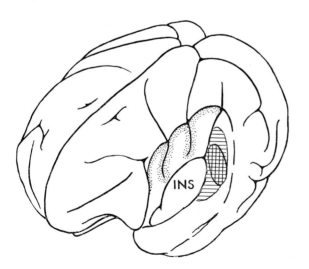

FIG. 7. View of monkey brain with operculum cut away to expose supratemporal plane. *Horizontal shaded area* shows 'click map' of Ades & Felder (6); *crosshatched area* within 'click map' shows area determined by Walker by retrograde degeneration to be medial geniculate projection area.

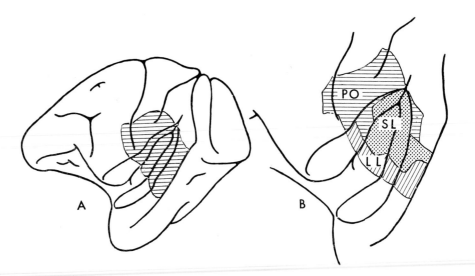

FIG. 8.   *A.* Lateral view of monkey brain, the sylvian fissure spread to show area responsive to clicks (*shaded*) according to Pribram *et al.* (73). *B.* Enlarged view of shaded part of *A*. *SL*, short latency area; *PO*, parietal operculum.

that the simian posterior supratemporal plane corresponds to the feline A I inasmuch as in each case destruction of the area leads to severe degeneration of all but the caudal portion of the principal part of the medial geniculate body. Pribram *et al.*, however, contrary to the findings of Rose & Woolsey, are quite positive in asserting that such a lesion and consequent thalamic degeneration effectively eliminates all conduction, not only to the simian counterpart of S II but also to the other normally responsive cortex of the ipsilateral hemisphere. From this they conclude that the pathway to S II follows collaterals from medial geniculate to some thalamic nucleus which projects to S II. This impression gains credibility from their observation that the negating effect of the lesion is not seen acutely (i.e. before consequent geniculate degeneration has taken place) but only some weeks later (i.e. after the effects have been felt in the medial geniculate). This conflict, except in the unlikely event it represents a species difference, can be resolved only by full analysis of the retrograde consequences of all combinations of suspected subareas in each species combined with electrophysiological delineation of responsive cortex in each instance after time lapse to allow degeneration and just before sacrifice. This is a large order, but it is both legitimate and feasible.

The reader will note that in the discussion of the primate auditory cortex, no functional counterparts of the feline insular and temporal regions have emerged. This probably represents merely a relative shortage of information on the monkey, a lack which may be filled in part by the additional information we hope will accrue from the arduous future study suggested in the last paragraph and in part from behavioral studies comparable to those in the cat. The behavioral studies on the monkey so far available are of little use inasmuch as they show no positive loss of auditory capacity and the lesions are incomplete (26, 27). At the least, in the outlook on the insular and temporal regions of the monkey, there is reason to hope because, if we accept the total area of Pribram *et al.*, a portion of the insula and all of the lateral surface of the posterior superior temporal gyrus are responsive to clicks but have not yet been claimed for any other anatomical, electrical or functional counterpart in the cat.

Finally, we may note that the definition of A II in the monkey rests in part on published data (107, 116) but in even larger part on logical though less well supported extension of that data. This is due, at least in part, to relative inaccessibility. In this connection, it may have been noted that of all the subdivisions in the cat's auditory cortex, A II seems to be the least firmly established. At no time since the initial definition of A II has it been as clearly valid an area as it was at that time. The experiments of Kiang (49), which explore the whole region in the cat by a combination of techniques, make the distinction between A I and A II more nebulous than it previously had seemed. It is possible this region may prove to be, as Kiang suggests, a transitional area or a fringe portion of A I.

TOPOLOGIC AND TONOTOPIC PROJECTION

An investigator entering upon the serious study of the neural aspects of audition 25 years ago inevitably found that the single most engrossing topic of study and speculation was that of the neurological basis of pitch perception. This was not at that time a new tendency, for von Helmholtz was in large part responsible for initiating it many years before by expressing the idea that the basilar membrane of the cochlea resonated in different, narrowly restricted regions to different frequencies of sound. It followed that if the cochlea is thus an analyzer of frequency, it must be reflected faithfully in the brain in order to make the results of its analytical efforts available to conscious processes. There was little opportunity to test this hypothesis rigorously until the advent, during the 1930's, of instruments which would reliably measure the neural results of stimulation by sounds. When this occurred, there was a rapid increment of interest in auditory neurophysiology and, in natural consequence, in study of the anatomy of the auditory pathway and of behavior as related to audition. It was quickly established that different parts of the cochlea do indeed respond differently to different stimulus frequencies, though not for the reasons nor in the manner which von Helmholtz thought, and this served to whet interest in the central reflection of the phenomenon.

Another factor in the rapid acceleration of interest in auditory neuroanatomy and neurophysiology was the then recent demonstration of a very precise point-to-point projection of the retina through the optic tract and lateral geniculate body to the occipital cortex. It was conceived that this sort of anatomical arrangement might be characteristic of sensory projection systems in general. Certainly a similar orderliness and topologic precision could be discerned in the somesthetic system, in which the functional counterpart of the visual field map was the body surface map. Why not a projection of the organ of Corti and a tonal map for the acoustic pathway?

The central auditory pathway, unfortunately for those theories, is more complex in its multinucleate interconnections than the visual or somesthetic pathways and it has not yielded easily to being fitted into the same general scheme. Nevertheless, the normal anatomy of the system is not without some indications of orderliness and a variety of experimental techniques has revealed even more. Likewise, on the functional side, no easy uncomplicated scheme of matching frequencies and fibers has presented itself. It has gradually become evident that this system is unique among sensory systems and presents problems peculiar to itself; however, it has also become more apparent that some relationship exists between anatomical location and location in the audible spectrum. Although it is somewhat awkward to do so, it will be best to consider structural and functional localization together, and the story will be more coherent if we largely ignore chronological sequence.

One of the more conspicuous features of the nerve supply of the organ of Corti and the termination of the cochlear nerve fibers in the cochlear nuclei is their orderly anatomical dispositions. At their entrance into the cochlear nuclei, the cochlear nerve fibers bifurcate along a curving line such that the linear relationship of their origins in the cochlea from apex to base is preserved (59, 75) with those from the apex bifurcating lateroventrally, those from the base, dorsomedially. The two branches of each fiber then pass respectively to dorsal and ventral cochlear nuclei and multiple terminations among the cells of these nuclei. Single unit responses in the dorsal cochlear nucleus to pure tone stimuli were shown by Galambos & Davis (34, 35) to respond selectively to tones of different frequency, each having its characteristic frequency. Very recently, Rose *et al.* (84), applying a similar microelectrode technique, explored the dorsal nucleus more systematically and demonstrated an orderly pattern of frequency response, the basic feature of which is that characteristic frequencies of the single units vary systematically from high at the medial (dorsal) edge to low at the lateral (ventral) edge. Less complete data indicate further that a similar arrangement is repeated in each of the two divisions of the ventral nucleus. If we accept for the moment that the base of the cochlea is concerned with high frequency reception and the apex with low (a concept which will need to be qualified presently), the frequency distribution in the cochlear nuclei corresponds to the pattern of nerve terminations. This study affords the first step toward an explanation of the as yet inexplicable meaning of the elaborate organization of the cochlear nuclei.

The story so far appears to be simple straightforward testimony in favor of the uncomplicated hypothesis that each narrow segment of the organ of

Corti responds to a correspondingly narrow frequency band and is connected by its own group of nerve fibers to an isolated part of the cochlear nuclei. True, upon arrival at the latter station, a rather disquieting multiplication of the end organ seems to take place such that the organ of Corti is projected not once but several times to the nuclei, this being accomplished by the systematic terminal branching of the cochlear axons. There are, however, aspects of this and related studies which are more fundamentally disturbing to the hypothesis in its simplest form. In both the microelectrode studies cited in the preceding paragraph, while the frequency response band of a given nuclear element was extremely narrow or punctate when the intensity of the stimulus was near threshold, as the intensity was increased the band became progressively wider, especially toward the low end of the scale. (There was little or no expansion of the response band to higher frequencies, even at very high intensity.)

When information on microelectrode studies of cochlear nerve fibers became available (99, 100, 101), one of the more striking features was the exaggeration of the principle just described for the second-order units in the cochlear nucleus. The individual units in the nerve also showed sharply restricted frequency specificity at threshold intensities but, upon increasing intensity, each fiber responded to a wider and wider range of lower frequencies but not to higher. Instead of responding each to its own frequency, therefore, it would be more correct to say that each fiber responds to all frequencies up to its high frequency limit and to none higher. This fits well with direct observation by von Békésy of cutoff points of vibration of the basilar membrane which vary with frequency of stimulus and involve all of the membrane up to the cutoff point (99, 100).

If the feature of auditory nerve function just described is true, then random partial lesions of the nerve should not, as was once supposed, result in hearing loss in the form of tonal islands but instead in losses at the highest frequencies with smaller lesions and a progressive high frequency loss as more and more fibers are involved. Relatively few fibers are stimulated by high tones, and so high frequencies are most vulnerable since in the spiral course of the nerve bundles also, it is inconceivable that any appreciable lesion could miss these. Hence, in lesions sparing only a few fibers, hearing should be preserved only for tones at the low end of the spectrum (since most or all fibers are sensitive to low frequencies, and the lower tones are therefore relatively invul-

nerable to any but complete section of the nerve). This is, in fact, the common finding in both animal and human studies of this kind (41, 66, 91, 92, 93).

Studies of localized frequency response of neural elements in stations lying between the cochlear nuclei and the auditory cortex are relatively few in number, although they are increasing currently. They rely mainly on the microelectrode techniques. Such studies have been made of the superior olivary nuclear complex (33, 99), the inferior colliculus (99, 102) and the medial geniculate body (31, 40). All of these share with each other and with the studies on cochlear nerve and nuclei the finding of elements which can be activated by tonal stimuli; of others, already discharging spontaneously, whose rate of (spike) discharge is increased by tonal stimuli; and of still others, already discharging, whose activity is inhibited by stimulation. An exception is seen in the work of Tasaki & Davis (100, 101) who found no fibers in the cochlear nerve whose activity was inhibited by stimulation.

The response band or area seems to undergo some change in shape at successively higher stations. In the nerve, it is characterized by a sharp high frequency cutoff and a long extension into lower frequency range. The cochlear nuclear elements show high frequency cutoff nearly as sharp as nerve elements but with a lesser expansion of the area into lower frequencies at higher intensities (31, 99, 101).

An abstract report of single unit recording from the several subdivisions of the superior olivary complex has just appeared (33), and a brief account of similar though less extensive experiments is included together with those on other nuclei (99). There is a greater variety of responsive units in these cell masses than in the cochlear nuclei, their relative numbers varying with location in the subdivisions and also with other factors. Some units (from the reports it is not clear what percentage) respond differentially to tonal stimuli. The response area of a given unit resembles closely those of cochlear nuclear units in that the high frequency cutoff is still sharp and the degree of extension into low frequency range about the same as for the nucleus. Sumi et al. (99) report that they found trapezoid elements responding to tones over 20 kc situated rostrally, those to tones below 300 cps caudally, and between these, 5000 and 3000 cps elements side by side. Thus there is indication of tonotopic localization of the projection thus far.

The inferior colliculus (99, 102) shows some differences and some similarities to the lower center with respect to single unit responses. The response areas are much narrower than in the more caudally situated nuclei. The threshold is just as sharp, but one is less impressed with the high frequency cutoff, there being some tendency for band width to widen toward the higher as well as the lower tones with increase in intensity, though the low tone bias is still prominent. The inferior colliculus has not been systematically explored, so we do not know to what relative degree each part of this complex organ may be populated with frequency-selective units. We can only be sure that such units can be found in considerable numbers.

The medial geniculate body responsive elements show, again, some similarities and some differences to the situation in the medullary nuclei. While there are many units which can be stimulated by pure tones, there are also many which cannot, though the latter group includes many units which do respond to clicks, noise or both. Of those responding to pure tones, it is noted the frequency bands to which they respond are broader at threshold than those of the other nuclei. Furthermore, the bands widen, with increasing intensity, almost equally toward higher and lower tones. The available data offer us little or nothing which would point to the existence of a nuclear plan or map of frequency-specific areas; however, this is really an open question which can be settled only by a more systematic survey of frequency-biased (if not specific) units throughout the nucleus.

A recent study of auditory cortical single unit response to pure tone (25) has demonstrated some units (few relative to brain-stem nuclei) which are responsive to tonal stimuli (as well as others responsive to other auditory stimuli). Tone-sensitive units are said to be usually maximally sensitive within a restricted frequency band, this band widening relatively little as intensity increases. In the terms we have been using, the response area follows the progressive tendency for narrowing of the band width overall while widening it somewhat at threshold. It should be emphasized that among the units sensitive to any kind of auditory stimulus, which altogether constitute less than 60 per cent of all units identified, those sensitive to pure tone represent only a small fraction. With respect to location of frequency-specific units, the findings indicate that those most sensitive to low frequencies predominate in the posterior A I field and high frequency units predominate in anterior A I, although in neither case

is the characteristic type the exclusive frequency sensitive type.

In review of the studies cited so far, it can be said that the sharply restricted frequency specificity of fibers for threshold intensity in the cochlear nerve persists in units of the medullary auditory nuclei but in the thalamus and cortex gives way to restricted though broader bands of threshold sensitivity. On the other hand, the very broad frequency response for tones below the high frequency cutoff, characteristic of the cochlear nerve fibers, diminishes steadily in width as we ascend the pathway and the sharp high frequency cutoff is lost. Thus, a given auditory nerve fiber may respond at threshold only to 2000 cps tone (for example) and, with increasing intensity may respond to all tones lower than 2000 cps, but will respond to no higher tones, no matter how intense; however, a cortical unit may respond at threshold to a restricted band centering at 2000 cps but respond at considerably higher intensity to a band not much wider. From the situation in the cochlear nerve where virtually all fibers are sensitive to tonal stimuli, we go to that in the cortex where only a fraction of the total elements are tone sensitive. Although we do not have very exact information on the percentage of tone-sensitive elements at all levels, the indications are that there is a proportional decrease, but no actual numerical decrease, and, more probably, some increase of elements whose prime preoccupation has to do with stimulus frequency.

Postponing for the moment any interpretation of the microelectrode studies, let us turn to other studies in which the basic questions have to do with overall specificity of projection rather than that of individual fibers or cells of the pathway. Both types of evidence will have to be incorporated into any effort at interpretation.

We have followed the upward progress of single tone-sensitive elements of the projection pathway and noted that through the several synapses and processing centers, a certain change in character of relative frequency sensitivity has occurred together with a dispersion of these elements among others which seem to have different concerns. It would now be well to examine the overall situation to determine if there is, indeed, any pattern of anatomical or physiological integration which can be discerned by correlation of elements or groups of elements at one end of the system with those of the other. Several relevant studies on cat, dog and monkey at once present themselves.

Let us consider first those primarily concerned with

anatomical integrity of projection. We have in the report of Woolsey & Walzl (113) a pure example of anatomical study of the neural projection of the cells of the spiral ganglion to the cortical projection area, by physiological means uncontaminated by the mechanical characteristics of the end organ. The only element of control lacking will be apparent as the experiment is briefly described. The procedure was: *1*) to expose the cochlear duct by removal of the external bony capsule, in the process of which the organ of Corti and basilar membrane were removed to expose the ends of the peripheral processes of the ganglion cell in the free border of the osseous spiral lamina; and *2*) to stimulate by brief electric shocks small groups of these fibers while exploring the suspected cortical areas for the responses and map these. The only methodological fault (which was unavoidable) is that, while the stimulus is electrically and geographically speaking quite localized, not all of the nerve fibers at any such local spot are. Some of them innervate only the inner hair cells immediately beyond the position of the stimulating electrode, but the rest innervate more widespread groups of outer hair cells, and the latter, to an unknown degree, may extend the cortical response area of a given point or perhaps blur its edges.

On the basis of these experiments, Woolsey & Walzl postulated a double cortical projection area (A I and A II as they have since come to be called and have been referred to in this chapter). Within A I, they found the basal end of the cochlea to project to the anterior part of A I and the apical to posterior A I, with intermediate cochlear stations projecting in orderly fashion between. A II showed a similar pattern except it was inverted, so that the basal cochlea is represented in posterior A II, the apical in anterior A II; however, it was less easy to trace the intermediate loci between these two focal regions. Part of this difficulty could be due to the fact the evidence is limited to the half of each cochlear spiral which can be surgically exposed, while the situation on the still inaccessible obverse turns must be logically inferred without demonstration.

We know from the foregoing that there is a direct relation of cochlear region to cortical area. Inferentially, we can postulate further from this work that high tones (basal cochlea) should excite anterior A I and posterior A II, while low tones should be represented in posterior A I and anterior A II. This has been experimentally tested by several investigators. The recent work of Erulkar *et al.* (25), using the microelectrode method, has already been mentioned.

With macroelectrode techniques, the cortical response to sustained pure tones (or noise for that matter) is less conspicuous than one might have thought, and it is difficult to evaluate reliably for purposes of mapping areas excitable by sound. This applies to the sound after it has been turned on during what Rosenblith calls a quasi-stationary state, the prefix, 'quasi', in this case representing the overwhelming burden of our ignorance of the continuously changing 'background' electrical activity, and the ways it may be influenced to change further by sound. The same handicap does not apply to the onset response to any kind of sound stimulus (onset can be seen as a high-voltage wave response, due presumably to arrival at cortex of a surge excitation), a fact which has been capitalized in the use of clicks, which are brief complex noises, and of tonal pips, which are brief pure tones in which the frequency characteristics are established and brought to threshold intensity within a very few cycles. Response to tonal pips has been used to map frequency-sensitive cortical areas and so has another method, the evoked strychnine spike technique. The latter depends upon the fact that a small part of the auditory cortical area can be sensitized with strychnine so that onset response of a tone to which the area is normally sensitive evokes a strychnine spike which, unlike the response of the untreated cortex, is so characteristic it cannot be lost in the background activity.

In earlier efforts at mapping the auditory cortex with respect to differential frequency sensitivity, both in cat and monkey, the tonal pip and tonal onset methods were used, recording from the untreated auditory cortex in anesthetized animals. In the cat (53), Licklider found that rough focal areas of maximal response to higher or lower frequencies could be found which are in general agreement with the more recent study of Hind (44). Licklider felt the situation could be better described in terms of gradients rather than restricted tonal foci because of the extensive overlapping.

Hind (44), using the evoked strychnine method, presented more extensive data and extended the frequency range studied. (It should be noted that the technique was originally worked out by Tunturi (103) and applied to study of the dog's auditory cortex. Tunturi's work will not be described here because, while in general agreement with others, the comparison of data on dog and cat is troublesome due to configural differences in the brain. We will, therefore, to conserve space and avoid confusion, confine the discussion to the cat studies which are more useful by virtue of wide comparability with others.) Hind found areas showing predilection for higher and lower frequencies. There is general agreement with Licklider's frequency map but, whereas the latter's highest tested frequency was 8 kc, Hind's study goes as high as 50 kc. Furthermore, Hind found two high frequency areas, namely anterior A I and posterior A II, and two low frequency areas, namely posterior A I and anterior A II. On both A I and A II, the area between high and low could be spoken of only as middle frequency range area, the data permitting no finer gradation. Hind's findings seem to agree with those of Woolsey & Walzl (113). Together, they indicate a broad correspondence between cochlea and cortical projection on the one hand and stimulus frequency and cortical frequency sensitivity on the other. Let us note that the data do not permit us to think here of a finely tuned system.

It is interesting to note that Hind was able, at each cortical point studied, by varying both frequency and intensity of stimulus, to outline areas of response which look very much like those of single units in the microelectrode studies. The focus of threshold frequency is not as sharp, and the response area widens rapidly both up and down the scale.

Similar studies to those in the cat are available for the monkey and the results, which will not be presented in detail, are similar. Woolsey (112) and Walzl (107) repeated on monkeys their earlier experiments on cats with similar results (cf. preceding section). Licklider & Kryter (54) described a pattern of frequency representation showing low frequencies toward the anterior part of the auditory area of the supratemporal plane (refer to fig. 8 for orientation) grading to high frequencies most posteriorly. This general arrangement was confirmed by Bailey et al. (11). Kennedy (47) explored the monkey's temporal region according to the same general plan as in Hind's study on the cat. She found no widespread response to tonal stimuli comparable to that responsive to clicks described by Pribram et al. (73), although she confirmed their findings with click stimulation. Kennedy did find the presumptive monkey A I area of the supratemporal plane responsive to tonal onset which, enhanced by strychnine, yielded frequency intensity thresholds for each point similar to those of Hind. Her composite map of frequency representation generally confirms but also extends (with respect to both area and frequency range) the study of Licklider & Kryter. It also considerably sharpens the picture for the monkey and shows the

pattern to conform to a plan of concentric octave bands, each oriented from medial to lateral. As in the cat, the overlapping of frequency range areas is at least as impressive as their separation, but the general trend is perhaps more clear-cut than in the cat; however, Kennedy shows no A II and this helps to to make the results look cleaner as compared to Hind's.

Summary and Discussion of Topologic and Tonotopic Projection

It can be taken as settled that a degree of frequency specificity is characteristic of some of the neurons of the central acoustic system. In numbers, these vary from a great many elements in the cochlear nerve, through progressively diminishing percentages of the total at intermediate recording stations, to an undetermined but certainly small proportion of elements in the auditory cortex. We must also reduce the term 'specificity' to its real proportions, a qualification which has often not been made in interpreting this kind of data. The term really applies well only if we are talking about threshold intensity and, even with this qualification, it applies best to the more caudally situated recording stations rather than to the thalamus or cortex. A second aspect of this specificity has to do with the manner and degree of expansion of the response area with increasing intensity. At the nerve, and to an only slightly lesser degree in the cochlear nuclei, the direction of the expansion is strictly toward the lower part of the scale and in degree is so wide as to make us think that some fibers are stimulated by high tones, many by intermediate tones and virtually all by low tones, given a stimulus of sufficient intensity. As we ascend this changes, so that among those cortical elements which are sensitive to tone each, though less sharply tuned at threshold, is comparatively greatly restricted in range of frequency sensitivity even at quite high intensity and expansion of response area is both up and down the scale. Thus, while 'attention' to the parameter of frequency is evident from cochlea to cortex, the original coding of this information, imposed by the mechanical characteristics of the cochlea, is changed, perhaps in the cochlear nuclei, perhaps aided by the superior olivary complex, perhaps even more gradually, so that in the more rostral parts of the pathway, tone-sensitive elements are in one way even more frequency-selective than those in the nerve.

We have spoken of progressive dispersion of tone-

sensitive elements in the upper reaches of the auditory pathway. This may be a misleading term. What
we really mean is that such elements become less and
less predominant from the standpoint of numbers,
or to state it another way, there is a progressively
increasing proportion of elements which have no
direct concern with the parameter of stimulus frequency. Many of these, however, do respond (as do
all the tone-sensitive units) to complex sounds (e.g.
clicks, noise) encompassing wide bands of the audible
spectrum. We do not know why this is true but, within
the bounds of known facts, it is not difficult to en-
vision a theoretical switching system by which tone
and noise sensitive and only noise-sensitive elements
would come to exist in parallel. We know that the
cochlear nuclei contain at least three projections or
replicas of the organ of Corti. According to the microelectrode evidence (84), these retain the original
coding of the cochlea; however, in the output of the
nuclear neurons, there is no inherent constraint to
preserve the original coding pattern. If, in the ensuing relays, we picture one group of cells each of which
receives approximately equal synaptic terminations
from all parts of one cochlear replica, it would presumably be responsive to summated volleys from a
sufficiently wide band of the replica, regardless of
position on the replica, and would therefore be responsive to stimuli of frequency bands of a given
minimal width, regardless of position on spectrum,
but not to narrow bands or pure tones. A second group
of cells, each receiving sufficiently concentrated synaptic terminations from a restricted part of the cochlear
replica, would respond to stimuli of frequency bands
of narrow proportions or even to pure tones. If in
succeeding relays the units of the second group began
to overlap each other somewhat, we would expect to
find the kind of changes which in fact have been found
in the response area of successively higher single
auditory units, namely some widening at threshold
but without a corresponding widening at higher intensity where small differences are insignificant.

That the units showing sensitivity to the various
segments of the audible spectrum retain, in the main,
their positions relative to each other in the ascent to
the cortex is evident, although there is also reason
to believe there is some degree of dispersion. This is
in accord with the observation, direct or incidental
by a variety of methods of many investigators on
several segments of the auditory pathway and on the
whole pathway from cochlea to cortex, that the arrangement of auditory elements, though often intricate with respect to nuclear organization, is always

orderly and maintains spatial relationships quite
faithfully. Macroelectrode studies of relative sensitivity of different regions of the auditory cortex confirm the impression that, relatively at least, tone-
sensitive elements of similar frequency range tend
roughly to group, though not to segregate themselves,
and maintain an orderly relationship to elements of
different frequency characteristics. These studies
also accord well with those which demonstrate projection of the cochlea to the cortex in a recognizable
pattern.

The less careful reader might, at this point, feel
we have established a good case for the primary relationship of frequency specificity and anatomical order
and for these conjointly as the prime organizational
feature of the auditory system. It must be re-empha-
sized that frequency tuning of auditory neural elements and of the overall grouping of these as measured by electrical response is relatively fine only at
threshold intensity and at higher intensity is an even
less convincing feature when compared to the precision of the psychophysical phenomenon of pitch
discrimination to which, presumably, we must relate
it. We can only suppose that the neurophysiological
facts so far known reveal to us only a part of the picture.

Efforts to translate the anatomicophysiological
phenomenon of tonotopic projection into terms of
hearing in animal experiments have been discourag-
ing but possibly needlessly so. There is good reason
to believe the meager success of such ventures is the
consequence of having asked the wrong questions,
these in turn growing out of unwarranted assumptions.
One double assumption of this sort is that pitch discrimination, of necessity, must depend upon intact
auditory cortical function because it is a 'complex'
auditory function. Neither part of this is necessarily
true. Compared to deficits of human auditory function resulting from temporal lobe lesions, pitch discrimination would be on the simple side. Deficits
in human subjects are not conspicuous unless they
involve actual auditory aphasia or unless the patient
is subjected to rigorous testing which goes far beyond
routine audiometry. It might also be pointed out
that it is impossible to prove the presence of a complex auditory deficit such as auditory aphasia unless
one can first establish that basic perception is essentially intact. The only auditory function which seems
to have been clearly tied to the cortex in animals,
namely discrimination between two three-tone patterns, would appear off hand to be of a very different
order of integrative complexity than aphasia. Sup-

posing, for argument, that pitch discrimination is a 'complex function', it still does not follow that the auditory cortex is the only or even the best neural matrix in which the discrimination may be made. If we consider the possibility that a kind of signal to noise ratio operates between frequency-sensitive and nonfrequency-sensitive elements, then the auditory cortex affords the poorest ratio of any part of the system. Finally, the animal behavioral experiments may be clouded to the extent that the learning and retention and conditioned response aspects of the method are neurologically inseparable from the purely auditory aspects.

OTHER ASPECTS OF CENTRAL AUDITORY FUNCTION

If it is apparent that the auditory system contains a tonotopic organizational pattern, it is equally apparent it is not filled by this pattern. Like many paths through a jungle, this tonotopic path through the auditory system has been found only because it was suspected and sought. It is also well to consider the jungle where other matters may be equally significant. By far the greater number of neural elements in the system cannot be demonstrated to have anything to do with this parameter (frequency) of the acoustic stimulus. Such has been the preoccupation with it, however, that any discussion of audition is inevitably dominated by it. Nevertheless, some investigative attention has, in fact, been otherwise directed and more should be. The remainder of the chapter will be devoted to several other aspects of central auditory function which have received some and require more attention.

Loudness

The neurophysiological correlates of loudness probably cannot be altogether divorced from those of pitch, although the subject was avoided almost entirely in the preceding section. The main reason for this was the desire to avoid confusion of issues in an area where much more is known of one side of the issue than of the other. A second, and hardly less compelling reason, however, is the status of our ideas about the neural mediation of loudness which is currently as or more confused than at any time in recent years.

Traditionally, loudness has been regarded, rather vaguely, as being expressed in terms of quantity of excitation. Whereas frequency was supposed to in-

volve the appropriate restricted group of fibers, loudness was supposed to be expressed in terms of a greater or lesser proportion of the total cross section of pathway excited. With the realization that, at least with respect to the cochlea, the total amount of end organ being stimulated and total number as well as site of origin of nerve fibers are involved in the analysis of frequency, it became apparent that the same device could not be used simultaneously for the factor of loudness, at least in a simple way. The possibility exists, however, that some interaction between inner and outer hair cells may lie at the bottom of the mechanical aspect of loudness. Whatever may be the cochlear, nerve and cochlear nuclear correlates of loudness, if the hypothesis proposed in the preceding discussion relative to a frequency recoding function of the nuclei is at all correct, the mediation of loudness might also take a different form in the ascending pathway.

It would probably be a mistake to suppose that loudness could be subserved by any of the possible upward projecting patterns without the addition of a factor of selective neural inhibition by recurrent elements. There is little evidence to call upon in this respect, and the possible significance of such elements will be discussed below in more general terms. For the moment, we can only exercise caution in theorizing about the mediation of loudness, bearing in mind that there is a large factor of relativity inherent in the concept and hoping that further investigation of the cochlear end organ will yield some suggestion as to direction.

Laterality of Projection

One of the more distinctive features of the central acoustic system, as contrasted to other sensory systems, is its tendency to bilateral reduplication and its bewildering array of commissural opportunities. It is obvious the system begins with two ears which are situated on opposite sides of the head, the openings of the external auditory meatuses 180° apart in terms of direction of orientation, plus or minus what few degrees of bias may theoretically be imposed by the presence of the pinna. This immediately suggests the possibility that source and direction of sound may be perceived in part as a consequence of the relative time of arrival or loudness or both of signal for the two ears. From psychophysical studies, it is clear that directionality is one of the properties of sound perception. It is not the function of this chapter to go extensively into the analysis of directionality as a function of binaural interaction; however, whatever may be the mechanism of such interaction, it is our concern to discuss whether, to what extent and by what means binaural interaction is reflected in the anatomicophysiologic organization of the central acoustic mechanisms. The evidence relevant to these questions is limited but does yield some useful information which we will examine presently.

A second question has to do with the extent to which each ear is bilaterally represented in the projection pathway. This question is probably not altogether separable from that of the central reflection of binaural interaction, although in certain contexts it may be. For this reason, discussion of the two questions will overlap, especially from the anatomical point of view.

The crucial anatomical problem in any theory of bilateral interaction must be the opportunity for side-to-side communication. There is no dearth of such opportunities in the auditory pathway. Crossing occurs at the trapezoid body, the earliest opportunity since this begins at the level of entrance of the cochlear nerves. The trapezoid crossing seems to provide not only the first but also the most essential crossing for maximum representation, both quantitative and qualitative, of the left ear in the contralateral hemisphere and vice versa (5). It is also at this level that the superior olivary complex, by virtue of its bilateral input from cochlear nuclei, provides many of the ascending fibers of the lateral lemniscus which represent either ear. Thus the basically bilateral projection of this system has its anatomical foundation almost at the level of entrance of the nerves.

Fibers of the lateral lemniscus cross at the somewhat diffuse commissure of Probst, just below the inferior colliculus. No functional significance of this commissure has been demonstrated (5).

A third opportunity for crossing of auditory nerve fibers occurs at the commissure of the inferior colliculus. The significance of this crossing appears to be largely local, carrying fibers from colliculus to opposite colliculus or, at most, to opposite medial geniculate (111). Its function with respect to the pathway as a whole, as measured by the influence of its presence or absence on cortical response to stimulation of the contralateral ear, seems to be negligible (5, 90).

The cortical auditory area, like other cortical areas, communicates by strong connections with its counterpart on the opposite hemisphere by way of the corpus callosum (62; also Ades, H. W., unpublished ob-

servations). The functional significance of this with special reference to audition is not clear.

A problem which particularly stimulated some of the early modern research in audition, and on which incidental observations have since been made, is that of the bilateral representation of each cochlea. This has been tested, more or less adequately, in various ways (5, 13, 18, 45, 46, 63, 88, 108, 113). Functionally, the results have generally indicated some difference but usually so small as to make it difficult to detect an effect on acuity of even the destruction of one ear. Most of the observations on cortical electrical response to contralateral versus ipsilateral and bilateral stimulation of the ears have revealed some small difference in representation. Similar results have been differently interpreted, apparently depending upon the point of view of the individual investigator more than on any other factor. One could sum up by saying the difference in representation of the two ears at one cerebral hemisphere is often statistically different but probably not practically different.

In a more ingenious way, however, Rosenzweig (89) has succeeded in demonstrating that, while quantitatively the difference in the effect of the two ears on the cortical area may appear nearly equal when one ear is stimulated at a time, there is nevertheless a more significant difference when the position of the stimulus is varied with respect to the two ears simultaneously stimulated. He found that when a sound is presented at one side, the cortical response is greater at the contralateral than the ipsilateral hemisphere—the farther to the side, the greater the difference. When the sound is in the median plane, the cortical activity is equal at the two hemispheres. Here we have, then, a clear correlation between auditory localization and differential response of right and left cortical auditory areas. We know, however, from the work of Neff et al. (67) that auditory localization is a function which is not abolished by destruction of the cortical areas. In a second group of experiments, Rosenzweig & Wyers (90) found some evidence for binaural interaction in the inferior colliculi, although not of the same kind as in the cortex.

Other than the studies cited briefly in the foregoing, the evidence on the bilaterality of auditory function is relatively scanty. The system has been more often than not treated without regard for, or with only incidental attention to, this structural and functional feature.

*Dispersion of Excitation, Recurrent
Pathways and Inhibition*

In this final section, the author would like to take up as a group certain considerations which have been touched upon in earlier sections of this chapter and by other authors. Presumably, these should ultimately apply to the elucidation of central auditory functions but are at present speculative and little supported by evidence. They must for the present be spoken of in general terms. The evidence which will be cited is more by way of justifying the speculation than of supporting a theory; indeed, we have no complete coherent theory to offer but only a number of facts, some connected, some possibly connected, and some suggestions of things which should be considered in future investigations.

One of the distinguishing features of the auditory system is the multiplication of elements at successively higher nuclear stations in the pathway (22). Coupled with this are the twin physiological phenomena of temporal dispersion of electrical response to brief (click) stimuli and amplification of response (5, 25, 32, 36). In this case, amplification takes the form of increased amplitude of response and temporal dispersion of extending the duration of response if, for example, we compare these factors from cochlear nuclei to medial geniculate body. The simplest way of accounting for these phenomena is by assuming the amplification to be the consequence of the larger number of units available to be fired in the larger, more rostral nucleus, and the temporal dispersion to be the consequence of the multisynaptic connections which result in a lateral lemniscus composed of several different orders of fibers. There are additional possibilities which might contribute to both phenomena. Each nucleus traversed contains within itself the neural matrix requisite (quantitatively speaking) to an internal temporal and spatial dispersion process in addition to that we are attributing to the pathway as a whole. The inferior colliculus constitutes, in one sense at least, a tract parallel to the lemniscal fibers which pass directly to the medial geniculate; lemniscal fibers diverge to the colliculus and fibers from it reconverge on the main path at the medial geniculate, providing a possible feed-back device which might augment the dispersion processes.

We also know, however, from many electrophysiological studies that amplification and temporal dispersion are only two of the things which may happen to a burst of activity in the auditory system aroused by so simple a stimulus as a click. The response may also be reduced in amplitude or obliterated by preceding or simultaneous auditory stimuli of the same or different type, depending upon where, when and how strong the two are relative to each other and upon where the recording is done. We may, at this point, recall the recurrent fibers mentioned in the early description of the pathway as still another feedback portion of a complex input to a given nucleus. When we recall that stimulation and inhibition are equally possible consequences of the firing of one neuron into another (depending on conditions at a given instant), we must realize the term 'feed back' as used here may be positive or negative with respect to the whole or a part of the pattern being processed in a given nucleus at a given time.

To make concrete the rapidly growing possibilities in the foregoing paragraphs, there is evidence, cited by Galambos (32) in a discussion of inhibition, that inhibition, intranuclear or that provided by recurrent fibers or both, may in the cochlear nuclei act to restrict the frequency range to which a given unit responds. He further indicates that other studies are in progress, both anatomical and physiological which we can hope will lead to an expansion of this factual nucleus.

We are not constrained to limit the possibilities of selective inhibition or other forms of modulation to the elements of the traditional projection pathway. It has already been pointed out in discussing the reticular formation that the auditory system feeds in some way into the brain-stem reticular system and thereby exerts its influence, in common with other sensory systems, upon the status of general cortical activity quite independently or indeed in the absence of an intact auditory projection pathway. Adey *et al.* (8) have recently demonstrated also that various cortical areas (including, as it happens, A I in the cat) fire freely back into the brain-stem ascending reticular system. There are many indirect suggestions in the literature which would lead one to believe that this system also may fire into the specific afferent pathways. This would provide a reciprocal arrangement at brain-stem levels which would permit interaction not only, in this case, between the auditory system and the cortex via the reticular system but also between the auditory and other sensory systems.

Any, all or none of the foregoing connections may exist and work in any, all or none of the ways suggested. But one thing is clear, namely that the central nuclei of the auditory system must operate on a plan which is far more complex than the simple projection pathway in terms of which we often speak. There is no reasonable doubt that each nucleus processes the information it receives from an input, complex both as to sources and patterns, in relation to events which have occurred or are occurring in centers above and below, auditory and nonauditory. It seems most unlikely that substantially further progress will be made toward explaining the facts of audition in neurophysiological terms without considering the intrinsic and extrinsic neural processes by which excitation aroused by sound is modulated in the central auditory system.

REFERENCES

1. ADES, H. W. *A. M. A. Arch. Neurol. & Psychiat.* 45: 138, 1941.
2. ADES, H. W. *J. Neurophysiol.* 6: 59, 1943.
3. ADES, H. W. *J. Neurophysiol.* 7: 415, 1944.
4. ADES, H. W. *J. Neuropath. & Exper. Neurol.* 5: 60, 1946.
5. ADES, H. W. AND J. M. BROOKHART. *J. Neurophysiol.* 13: 189, 1950.
6. ADES, H. W. AND R. E. FELDER. *J. Neurophysiol.* 5: 49, 1942.
7. ADES, H. W. AND D. H. RAAB. *J. Neurophysiol.* 12: 101, 1949.
8. ADEY, W. R., J. P. SEGUNDO AND R. B. LIVINGSTON. *J. Neurophysiol.* 20: 1, 1957.
9. ALLEN, W. F. *Am. J. Physiol.* 144: 415, 1945.
10. ARONSON, L. R. AND J. W. PAPEZ. *A. M. A. Arch. Neurol. & Psychiat.* 32: 27, 1934.
11. BAILEY, P., G. VON BONIN, H. W. GAROL AND W. S. MCCULLOCH. *J. Neurophysiol.* 6: 122, 1943.
12. BARD, P. AND D. MCK. RIOCH. *Bull. Johns Hopkins Hosp.* 60: 73, 1937.
13. BARNES, W. T., H. W. MAGOUN AND S. W. RANSON. *J. Comp. Neurol.* 79: 129, 1943.
14. BREMER, F. *Arch. internat. physiol.* 53: 53, 1943.
15. BREMER, F. *Rev. neurol.* 87: 65, 1952.
16. BREMER, F., V. BONNET AND C. TERZUOLO. *Arch. internat. physiol.* 62: 390, 1954.
17. BREMER, F. AND R. S. DOW. *J. Neurophysiol.* 2: 308, 1939.
18. BROGDEN, W. J., E. GIRDEN, F. A. METTLER AND E. A. CULLER. *Am. J. Physiol.* 116: 252, 1936.
19. BUSER, P. AND G. HEINZE. *J. physiol., Paris* 46: 284, 1954.
20. BUTLER, R. A., I. T. DIAMOND AND W. D. NEFF. *J. Neurophysiol.* 20: 108, 1957.
21. CAMPBELL, A. W. *Histological Studies on Localization of Cerebral Function.* Cambridge: Cambridge, 1905.
22. CHOW, K. L. *J. Comp. Neurol.* 95: 159, 1951.
23. CLARK, W. E. LeGROS. *J. Anat.* 70: 447, 1936.
24. DIAMOND, I. T. AND W. D. NEFF. In press.
25. ERULKAR, S. D., J. E. ROSE AND P. W. DAVIES. *Bull. Johns Hopkins Hosp.* 99: 55, 1956.
26. EVARTS, E. V. *J. Neurophysiol.* 15: 435, 1952.
27. EVARTS, E. V. *J. Neurophysiol.* 15: 443, 1952.
28. FERNANDEZ, O. *Laryngoscope* 61: 1152, 1951.
29. FERRIER, D. *The Functions of the Brain.* London: Smith-Elder, 1876.
30. FRENCH, J. D., M. VERZEANO AND H. W. MAGOUN. *A. M. A. Arch. Neurol. & Psychiat.* 69: 505, 1953.
31. GALAMBOS, R. *J. Neurophysiol.* 15: 381, 1952.
32. GALAMBOS, R. *Physiol. Rev.* 34: 497, 1954.
33. GALAMBOS, R. *Fed. Proc.* 16: 43, 1957.
34. GALAMBOS, R. AND H. DAVIS. *J. Neurophysiol.* 6: 39, 1943.
35. GALAMBOS, R. AND H. DAVIS. *Science* 108: 513, 1948.
36. GALAMBOS, R., J. E. ROSE, R. B. BROMILEY AND J. R. HUGHES. *J. Neurophysiol.* 15: 359, 1952.
37. GIRDEN, E. *Am. J. Psychol.* 55: 518, 1942.
38. GIRDEN, E., F. A. METTLER, G. FINCH AND E. A. CULLER. *J. Comp. Psychol.* 21: 367–385, 1936.
39. GOLDBERG, J. M., I. T. DIAMOND AND W. D. NEFF. *Fed. Proc.* 16: 47, 1957.
40. GROSS, N. B. AND W. R. THURLOW. *J. Neurophysiol.* 14: 409, 1951.
41. GUILD, S. R. *Acta oto-laryng.* 43: 199, 1953.
42. HAMPSON, J. L. *J. Neurophysiol.* 12: 37, 1949.
43. HAMUY, T. P., R. B. BROMILEY AND C. N. WOOLSEY. *J. Neurophysiol.* 19: 485, 1956.
44. HIND, J. E. *J. Neurophysiol.* 16: 475, 1953.
45. KEMP, E. H., G. E. COPPÉE AND E. H. ROBINSON. *Am. J. Physiol.* 120: 304, 1937.
46. KEMP, E. H. AND E. H. ROBINSON. *Am. J. Physiol.* 120: 316, 1937.
47. KENNEDY, T. Doctor's Thesis. Chicago: Univ. of Chicago, 1955.
48. KIANG, N. *Am. J. Physiol.* 183: 635, 1955.
49. KIANG, N. Doctor's Thesis. Chicago: Univ. of Chicago, 1955.
50. KORNMÜLLER, A. E. *Bioelektrische Erscheinungen der Hirnrindenfelder.* Leipzig: Thieme, 1937.
51. KRYTER, K. D. AND H. W. ADES. *Am. J. Psychol.* 56: 501, 1943.
52. LARIONOW, W. *Arch. ges. Physiol.* 76: 608, 1899.
53. LICKLIDER, J. C. R. Doctor's Thesis. Rochester, N. Y.: Univ. of Rochester, 1941.
54. LICKLIDER, J. C. R. AND K. D. KRYTER. *Fed. Proc.* 1: 51, 1942.
55. LILLY, J. C. *Am. J. Physiol.* 176: 493, 1954.
56. LILLY, J. C. AND R. B. CHERRY. *J. Neurophysiol.* 17: 521, 1954.
57. LINDSLEY, D. B., L. H. SCHREINER, W. B. KNOWLES AND H. W. MAGOUN. *Electroencephalog. & Clin. Neurophysiol.* 2: 483, 1950.
58. LIPMAN, E. A. *Am. J. Psychol.* 62: 215, 1949.
59. LORENTE DE NÓ, R. *Laryngoscope* 43: 1, 1933.
60. LORENTE DE NÓ, R. *Tr. Am. Otol. Soc.* 27: 86, 1937.
61. MAGOUN, H. W. *A. M. A. Arch. Neurol. & Psychiat.* 67: 145, 1952.
62. METTLER, F. A. *J. Comp. Neurol.* 55: 139, 1932.
63. METTLER, F. A., G. FINCH, E. GIRDEN AND E. A. CULLER. *Brain* 57: 475, 1934.

64. MEYER, D. R. AND C. N. WOOLSEY. *J. Neurophysiol.* 15: 149, 1952.

65. MICKLE, W. A. AND H. W. ADES. *Am. J. Physiol.* 170: 682, 1952.

66. NEFF, W. D. *J. Comp. & Physiol. Psychol.* 40: 203, 1947.

67. NEFF, W. D., J. F. FISHER, I. T. DIAMOND AND M. YELA. *J. Neurophysiol.* 19: 500, 1956.

68. NIEMER, W. T. AND S. K. CHENG. *Anat. Rec.* 103: 490, 1949.

69. PAPEZ, J. W. *A. M. A. Arch. Neurol. & Psychiat.* 24: 1, 1930.

70. PERL, E. R. AND J. U. CASBY. *J. Neurophysiol.* 17: 429, 1954.

71. POLIAK, S. *J. Anat.* 60: 465, 1926.

72. POLIAK, S. *The Main Afferent Fiber Systems of the Cerebral Cortex in Primates.* Berkeley: Univ. California Press, 1932.

73. PRIBRAM, K. H., B. S. ROSNER AND W. A. ROSENBLITH. *J. Neurophysiol.* 17: 336, 1954.

74. RAAB, D. H. AND H. W. ADES. *Am. J. Psychol.* 59: 59, 1946.

75. RAMÓN Y CAJAL, S. *Histologie due Système Nerveux de l'Homme et des Vertébrés.* Paris: Maloine, 1909, vol. I.

76. RAMÓN Y CAJAL, S. *Histologie du Système Nerveux de l'Homme et des Vertébrés.* Paris: Maloine, 1911, vol. II.

77. RASMUSSEN, A. T. *J. Comp. Neurol.* 63: 501, 1936.

78. RASMUSSEN, G. L. *J. Comp. Neurol.* 84: 141, 1946.

79. RASMUSSEN, G. L. *Anat. Rec.* 106: 69, 1953.

80. RASMUSSEN, G. L. *J. Comp. Neurol.* 99: 61, 1953.

81. RIOPELLE, A. J. AND H. W. ADES. *J. genet. Psychol.* 83: 63, 1953.

82. RIOPELLE, A. J., H. F. HARLOW, P. H. SETTLAGE AND H. W. ADES. *J. Comp. & Physiol. Psychol.* 44: 283, 1951.

83. ROSE, J. E. *J. Comp. Neurol.* 91: 409, 1949.

84. ROSE, J. E., R. GALAMBOS AND J. R. HUGHES. *Anat. Rec.* 127: 58, 1957.

85. ROSE, J. E. AND C. N. WOOLSEY. *J. Comp. Neurol.* 91: 441, 1949.

86. ROSE, J. E. AND C. N. WOOLSEY. *Cortical Connections and Functional Organization of the Thalamic Auditory System of the Cat.* Univ. of Wisconsin Symposium, Madison, Wisconsin, August, 1955. To be published.

87. ROSENZWEIG, M. *Am. J. Psychol.* 59: 127, 1946.

88. ROSENZWEIG, M. *Am. J. Physiol.* 167: 147, 1951.

89. ROSENZWEIG, M. *J. Comp. & Physiol. Psychol.* 47: 269, 1954.

90. ROSENZWEIG, M. R. AND E. J. WYERS. *J. Comp. & Physiol. Psychol.* 48: 426, 1955.

91. SCHUKNECHT, H. F. *Trans. Am. Acad. Ophth.* 57: 366, 1953.

92. SCHUKNECHT, H. F. AND W. D. NEFF. *Acta oto-laryng.* 42: 263, 1952.

93. SCHUKNECHT, H. F. AND S. SUTTON. *A. M. A. Arch. Oto-laryng.* 57: 129, 1953.

94. SNIDER, R. S. Office of Naval Research, Monthly Research Report, Aug. 1950, p. 15.

95. SNIDER, R. S. AND A. STOWELL. *J. Neurophysiol.* 7: 331, 1944.

96. STARZL, T. E., C. W. TAYLOR AND H. W. MAGOUN. *J. Neurophysiol.* 14: 461, 1951.

97. STARZL, T. E., C. W. TAYLOR AND H. W. MAGOUN. *J. Neurophysiol.* 14: 479, 1951.

98. STEVENS, S. S., J. G. C. LORING AND D. COHEN (editors). *Bibliography on Hearing.* Cambridge: Harvard, 1955.

99. SUMI, T., Y. KATSUKI AND H. UCHIYAMA. *Proc. Jap. Acad.* 32: 67, 1956.

100. TASAKI, I. *J. Neurophysiol.* 17: 97, 1954.

101. TASAKI, I. AND H. DAVIS. *J. Neurophysiol.* 18: 151, 1955.

102. THURLOW, W. R., N. B. GROSS, E. H. KEMP AND K. LOWY. *J. Neurophysiol.*, 14: 289, 1951.

103. TUNTURI, A. R. *Am. J. Physiol.* 144: 389, 1945.

104. VOGT, O. *Compt. rend. hebd. sean. et Mém. Soc. de biol.* 10: 54, 1898.

105. WALKER, A. E. *J. Anat.* 72: 319, 1937.

106. WALLER, E. H. *J. Anat.* 74: 528, 1939.

107. WALZL, E. M. *Laryngoscope* 57: 778, 1947.

108. WALZL, E. M. AND C. N. WOOLSEY. *Bull. Johns Hopkins Hosp.* 79: 309, 1946.

109. WEVER, E. G. *Theory of Hearing.* New York: Wiley, 1949.

110. WOOLLARD, H. H. AND J. A. HARPMAN. *J. Neurol. & Psychiat.* 2: 35, 1939.

111. WOOLLARD, H. H. AND J. A. HARPMAN. *J. Anat.* 74: 441, 1940.

112. WOOLSEY, C. N. *Fed. Proc.* 6: 437, 1947.

113. WOOLSEY, C. N. AND E. M. WALZL. *Bull. Johns Hopkins Hosp.* 71: 315, 1942.

CHAPTER XXV

Vision—introduction

H. K. HARTLINE | *Rockefeller Institute for Medical Research, New York City*

WE ARE INDEED 'CHILDREN OF THE SUN'. The ultimate dependence of living organisms on solar energy is probably one reason why animals came to evolve highly specialized sensory receptors for exploiting the sun's radiations. And since the green plants utilize wavelengths in that part of the solar spectrum reaching the earth's surface in greatest amount, it is not surprising that the receptors evolved by plant-eating animals and their predators also should operate in roughly the same range of wavelengths, which we in consequence call visible light.

Wavelengths of visible light are small compared with the size of the bodies of most animals and of many significant objects in their surroundings. Hence light reflected, scattered and absorbed in varying degrees by objects in an animal's environment makes an ideal physical agent for providing information about that environment. This possibility has been exploited by nearly all animal forms to a remarkable degree.

It is appropriate that a neurophysiologist taking up the study of vision should begin with a consideration of the extraordinary diversity in which eyes have evolved in 'lower' animal forms. An intimation of this diversity is given in the Milnes' chapter on invertebrate photoreceptors. Missing from this handbook is a comparable discussion of the eyes of the vertebrates, which, though of but a single type, nevertheless show a great variety of ingenious adaptations to meet special needs. Fortunately, this deficiency is easily remedied by reference to Walls' excellent and highly readable book, *The Vertebrate Eye* (17).

Of the great variety of visual organs that the animal kingdom has developed, many are no mean performers. Our own eyes, for all their defects, are excellent physical instruments, all the more remark-able for being constructed, by embryological magic, out of gristle and jelly. Yet man need not think he has the best of all possible eyes. He terms the short wavelengths 'ultraviolet', but they are visible to at least some insects. Polarized light elicits the entoptic phenomenon known as 'Haidinger's brushes', the orientation of which reveals the direction of the plane of the light's polarization. A few individuals are said to be able to perceive these brushes when viewing the blue sky with unaided vision. But as far as is known to the author, no race of men has utilized this as a sky compass, comparable to the use made by many of the arthropods of their ability to sense the plane of polarization of sky light. Man's eyes are remarkably sensitive; they can detect approximately 100 quanta, but many nocturnal vertebrates undoubtedly have a lower effective threshold. Our visual acuity is surpassed by that of some other animals, especially the acuity of birds of prey. Yet for all of this, man is at no very great disadvantage merely because the visual apparatus of other animals surpasses his own in some special directions. His visual equipment is not over-specialized, and it does many things very well.

Interest in light and vision dates back to antiquity. Nearly everyone has heard of the quaint idea of the Greeks, that light is an intangible ray-like emanation from the eye itself, exploring tactually the surroundings. (Indeed, if we were to assume that sensation could result only if such emanation were absorbed by what we term luminous objects, this idea would not be easy to disprove; in physics the optical principle of the reversibility of path is often invoked in theoretical discussions.) With a history of many interesting misconceptions, a sound understanding of the nature of light and the structure and function of the eye gradually emerged. By the time of Kepler many of the essentials of physiological optics were beginning to be clear. In the first few chapters of his book, *The Retina*, Polyak (11) summarized in scholarly and interesting style the early history of this subject, from the Greeks and Arabs through Medieval to Modern times.

As the science of optics developed, it took two paths. On the one hand, the physics of light emerged. Optics through most of its history depended ultimately on visual observations made by the human eye as the final detecting and measuring instrument. Only relatively recently have physicists been able to replace human vision to advantage by the photographic plate and by elaborate photoelectric detecting and recording devices. The laws of reflection and refraction were first derived by simple visual operations, conducted in a scientific manner. This history is discussed in some detail in a recent paper by Ratliff (13). Combined with the lens maker's art, the physics of lenses and mirrors developed into our present day geometrical optics. Physical optics is based on the observation of the maxima and minima detected by the eye in interference and diffraction patterns, and by brightness changes produced by polarization optics. Photometry was, and still is to some extent, dependent on the ability of a human observer acting as a null device to detect very small inequalities in brightness in an illuminated field. Even color vision, properly a subject belonging to physiology, has fascinated physicists from the time of Newton, when it formed the basis for the emerging science of spectroscopy. As these physical sciences developed, they in turn were applied to the eye itself, and physiological optics resulted.

Physiological optics had its great flowering in the last century, with the epochal work of von Helmholtz. In its essentials and in many of its details, the physics of the dioptric system of the human eye was put into satisfactory shape by Helmholtz, and is embodied as part of a broad study of visual physiology in his three monumental volumes *Handbuch der Physiologischen Optik* (16).

Physiological optics is by no means a finished subject, as shown plentifully in Fry's chapter. Even the physics of the eye, narrowly defined, invites creative effort today. In a broad sense, physiological optics is often taken to include most of visual physiology. Perhaps this is too broad a definition, but it is wise to avoid drawing arbitrary boundaries to this field.

Photosensitivity, that essential property that makes a visual organ possible, is conferred upon the specialized receptor cells of an eye by their possession of certain chemical substances that can absorb light (and therefore are pigments) and undergo photochemical change. This reaction must be such as to initiate a change of events in the irritable mechanism of the receptor, leading to the transmission of nervous influences along the optic pathway.

The visual pigment of the retinal rods of the vertebrate eye was discovered by Boll and carefully investigated by Kühne nearly a hundred years ago. The essential importance of 'visual purple' or 'rhodopsin' in vision was questioned for many years because of two misconceptions. First, it was argued that since no such pigment could be observed in the cones, none was there. True, the pigment of the cones is different from, though closely related to, that of the rods, and it is more difficult to detect; but modern methods are adequate for its detection in the cones and its extraction and study *in vitro*. The second, and less obviously fallacious argument was that the visual purple in a retina bleached on exposure to light, and yet photosensitivity remained. It was not realized that the restorative processes (already described by Kühne) would operate in light as well as darkness, and would lead to a 'stationary state' in which a small but significant amount of visual pigment would be present in the receptor for indefinitely long periods. Even in bright light, an active turnover of visual pigment, with photolysis and regeneration, takes place continually, and photosensitivity, while reduced, is still present. The clear, quantitative formulation of these ideas by Hecht in his classic studies of the photosensory mechanism of the clam, *Mya*, opened a new era of visual physiology. Before the advent of modern biochemistry, Hecht applied these ideas of photolysis, regeneration and the stationary state to basic visual phenomena such as light and dark adaptation, intensity discrimination and flicker. The experiments that he and his colleagues performed using animals and with human observers, and the theories they devised to explain their results, still play a fruitful role in the field of visual physiology (9). But by now it has become clear that Hecht's ideas, while basically sound, were oversimplified, and need to be reworked in the light of more recent biochemical developments.

At the present time, the significance of visual purple and the photosensitive substances related to it is firmly established. The biochemistry of these visual pigments is one of the most actively pursued and most exciting topics of receptor physiology, as amply demonstrated in Wald's chapter. The progress that has been made in the study of chemistry of the primary photosensitive substances of the rods and cones of the vertebrate retina, and the receptors of a few invertebrates, is indeed impressive.

It was a significant step when the visual pigments could be extracted from their loci in the outer limbs of the rods and cones, and bleached and resynthesized *in vitro*. Another important step has now been taken by Rushton and his colleagues (14), who have succeeded in measuring the bleaching and regeneration of visual pigments of both rods and cones in the living eye, as described in Wald's chapter. Operating on the principle of the ophthalmoscope, a sensitive photoelectric device is used to measure the light reflected back through the retina of a human subject. Rushton's studies are providing a link between the biochemical knowledge of the visual pigments, and the physiology of the living retinal receptors.

Biochemistry alone is not sufficient to solve the problem of the photoreceptor. In the living eye, visual pigments are part of highly organized cellular systems. New concepts of the fine structure of visual receptor cells are emerging from recent cytological investigations. In the developing vertebrate retina, the rods and cones originate as ciliated epithelial cells from the neural tube. [This subject has been reviewed by Detwiler (2) and by Walls (17).] The cilia become transformed (1) into the outer segments, which are long stacks of double-membrane disks (15). Remnants of the original ciliary structure remain visible to electron microscopy in the completely developed receptors (1, 12). In arthropods, the osmium-staining 'membranes' take the form of densely packed microvilli of the surfaces of the retinula cells, so that the rhabdom has a structure resembling a honey-comb (4, 10, 18). Rhodopsin is present only in the outer segments of the rods, and, as Wald points out in his chapter, constitutes a large fraction of their bulk. Presumably a similar arrangement of visual pigment holds for the cone outer segment and for the invertebrate rhabdomere as well. These cytological facts will have to be taken into consideration in any theory of the receptor mechanism.

A photoreceptor is a transducer of light energy into nervous action. The first step, the photochemical change in a specific visual pigment, is now quite familiar. The later steps, ultimately resulting in nervous excitation that is transmitted in the afferent nerve fibers, are almost completely unknown. Wald and Granit in their chapters have indicated some of the possibilities that are to be considered [see also (5) and (7)]. Presumably at least some of these processes in the photoreceptor are not basically different from those occurring in any other cell of the nervous system. Indeed, it would not be surprising if the entire photosensitive mechanism were the result of but a comparatively minor modification of a fundamental irritable structure of a cell. The photosensitivity of some ganglion cells, as discussed in the Milnes' chapter, and the fact that peripheral nerves can be photosensitized by dyes (3) makes this a not unreasonable expectation.

The final outcome of the excitatory processes initiated by light is the generation of trains of nerve impulses in the fibers of the optic pathway. Whether all photoreceptor cells themselves—the rods and cones in the vertebrate retina, the retinula cells in the arthropod compound eye, for example—actually generate trains of discrete impulses in their own fibers is not established; but some primary receptor cells do, and so do neurons closely associated with the receptors. Optic nerve fiber activity consists of the rhythmic succession of propagated 'all-or-none' disturbances typical of the activity of all neurons concerned with transmitting influences rapidly over large distances. Studies of the discharge of impulses in single optic nerve fibers have shown that many of the familiar phenomena of vision have their origin in properties of the receptors, or of the retinal neurons (6).

Intimately associated with the excitation of the visual mechanism are comparatively slow electrical changes measurable grossly as the retinal action potentials. These are discussed in Granit's chapter. As a result of studies employing microelectrodes that are small enough in some instances to penetrate single cells and record electrical activity from within them, the significance of various components of the retinal action potentials is gradually becoming clearer. It seems likely that an integral link in the excitatory process is a change in electrical polarization of cellular structures, brought about somehow by the photochemical system of the receptor. As in other parts of the nervous system, these electrical changes, because of the local current flow they engender, result in the initiation of relaxation oscillations in cellular membranes which, conducted, are the trains of nerve impulses that constitute the sensory message to the higher centers.

An eye is more than a simple mosaic of photoreceptor elements. The histological complexity of the vertebrate retina and of the compound eye of insects is ample evidence that, in the more highly developed eyes, sensory information from the transducer elements is acted upon almost immediately by highly organized ganglionic structures. The physiological studies that bear out this expectation are reviewed in Granit's chapter, where the conception of the retina as a nervous center is thoroughly developed. In the vertebrate retina, excitatory and inhibitory influences spread and converge, and interplay in a complex manner to generate patterns of optic nerve activity that are much more than mere copies of the patterns of light and shade on the receptor mosaic. Even in more primitive eyes, simple interactions of receptor units take place (8) that serve to accentuate certain significant features of the stimulus pattern, at the expense of exact fidelity of reproduction. Integrative nervous processes begin very early indeed in the visual pathway. More than this, Granit's chapter reveals that the visual receptor organ, like other sense organs, is under a certain amount of centrifugal control from the higher nervous centers. This new development in neurophysiology is already having far-reaching effects on our understanding of sensory physiology.

With the study of the physiology of the higher visual centers of the brain, taken up in Bartley's chapter, visual physiology merges with other branches of neurophysiology. In this area, contributions come from workers not primarily concerned with vision, for brain physiology involves the integration of all forms of neural activity that govern the organism's behavior. Quite properly, many references to the physiology of the visual centers will be found scattered in other chapters throughout this work.

In the analysis of central nervous system mechanisms, extensive use has been made of experimental animals in which parts of the brain have been ablated, fiber pathways interrupted or specific areas stimulated artificially. The resulting modifications of behavior then reveal important physiological rela-

tionships. Applied to the visual system, such studies require more than a casual familiarity with specific principles of retinal physiology and with overall visual performance. This is brought out in Bartley's chapter. Especially in the field of animal behavior it should be emphasized that great advances have been made recently by experimental psychologists. Animal behavior can now be controlled more effectively and studied with greater precision than was possible only a few years ago. The present day neurophysiologist must master these powerful new techniques or work in close collaboration with colleagues who have mastered them.

The aim of the studies that have been outlined above and taken up in detail in the chapters that follow is to understand vision. This broad aim can be expressed quite explicitly, so far as many of the behavioral manifestations of vision are concerned. The reactions of intact animals to stimulation by light and the reports of human observers in response to visual presentations have been studied by truly scientific methods for many years. Experimental psychology provides a vast amount of very detailed and very precise information about just how animals do react, what human subjects do report, in carefully controlled visual experiments. Students of visual phenomena have not neglected the analysis of their observations in attempts, often very successful, to provide an understanding of underlying mechanisms. Indeed, many such mechanisms are now being verified by direct neurophysiological experimentation. Psychological studies of vision are vitally important to the visual neurophysiologist, for it is this field of science that sets many of his ultimate problems. No matter how far we may progress in the analysis of the neurophysiological mechanisms of the visual pathway, our task of acquiring scientific understanding will not be complete without the complementary act of synthesizing our detailed knowledge into a coherent whole.

REFERENCES

1. DeRobertis, E. *J. Biophys. & Biochem. Cytol.* 2, Supplement: 209, 1956.
2. Detwiler, S. R. *Vertebrate Photoreceptors.* Experimental Biology Monographs. New York: MacMillan, 1943.
3. Fessard, A. *Recherches sur l'Activité Rythmique des Nerf Isolés.* Paris: Hermann, 1936, p. 130.
4. Goldsmith, T. H. and D. Philpott. *J. Biophys. & Biochem. Cytol.* 3: 429, 1957.
5. Granit, R. *Receptors and Sensory Perception.* New Haven: Yale Univ. Press, 1955.
6. Hartline, H. K. *Harvey Lectures* Ser. 37: 39, 1942.
7. Hartline, H. K., H. G. Wagner and E. F. MacNichol, Jr. *Cold Spring Harbor Symp. Quant. Biol.* 17: 125, 1952.
8. Hartline, H. K., H. G. Wagner and F. Ratliff. *J. Gen. Physiol.* 39: 651, 1956.
9. Hecht, S. *Physiol. Rev.* 17: 239, 1937.
10. Miller, W. H. *J. Biophys. & Biochem. Cytol.* 3: 421, 1957.
11. Polyak, S. L. *The Retina.* Chicago: Univ. Chicago Press, 1941.

12. PORTER, K. R. *Harvey Lectures* Ser. 51: 175, 1957.

13. RATLIFF, F. In: *Psychology: A Study of a Science* (vol. 4), edited by S. Koch. New York: McGraw Hill. In press.

14. RUSHTON, W. A. H. AND F. W. CAMPBELL. *Nature, London* 174: 1096, 1954.

15. SJÖSTRAND, F. S. *J. Cell. & Comp. Physiol.* 42: 15, 1953.

16. VON HELMHOLTZ, H. *Handbuch der Physiologischen Optik,* III Auflage. Hamburg and Leipzig: L. Voss, 1909. (English transation, J. P. C. Southall (editor). Menasha, Wisconsin: Banta, 1924–1925.)

17. WALLS, G. L. *The Vertebrate Eye and its Adaptive Radiation.* Bloomfield Hills, Michigan: Cranbrook Press, 1942.

18. WOLKEN, J. J., J. CAPENOS AND A. TURANO. *J. Biophys. & Biochem. Cytol.* 3: 441, 1957.

CHAPTER XXVI

Photosensitivity in invertebrates[1]

LORUS J. MILNE[2]
MARGERY MILNE[3] | *Durham, New Hampshire*

CHAPTER CONTENTS

EYE-MINDED MAN is prone to forget that the fundamental irritability of protoplasm includes a sensitivity to radiant energy in the spectral region he knows as light. An eye is a specialization with which a multi-cellular animal may gain additional information from a light stimulus. Usually it is a device allowing a central nervous system to be better informed about events in the surrounding environment. An eye implies a nervous mechanism of some kind, but the converse is not true.

In photosensitivity the initial event is absorption of photons—the quanta of radiant energy—by some substance which is altered by this addition. When compared to thermal reactions, most photochemical changes appear to be in a class by themselves characterized by temperature coefficients so small that they are described as 'temperature-independent.' Through the temperature range within which living things are active this is correct enough.

Since only the absorbed energy is effective in producing a photochemical change, every photosensitive mechanism must contain a chemical substance which can trap photons. When the concentration of such a substance is high enough so that a few per cent of incident photons are absorbed, we may detect the absorption as an opacity and recognize the absorbing substance as a pigment.

So far none of the pigments found to be responsible for photosensitivity in living systems are neutral in their absorption. They are not gray but colored because they absorb most at one wavelength and less at others. This feature determines the spectral sensitivity of the system.

For an animal to be informed continuously regarding the radiant energy reaching its surface, it must be able to produce continuously the pigment which is altered by the absorption of photons. In the dark this production would be expected to decrease in rate until the pigment reached a maximum concen-

[1] Contribution from the Scripps Institution of Oceanography, La Jolla, California, New Series No. 967. The information in this chapter has been assembled with the aid of research grants from the American Academy of Arts and Sciences, the American Philosophical Society, the Explorers Club and the Society of the Sigma Xi.
[2] Professor of Zoology, University of New Hampshire.
[3] Recently Visiting Professor of Biology, Northeastern University, Boston, Mass.

tration. Simultaneously the mechanism would attain its maximum sensitivity to light energy. In continuous illumination the system should reach an equilibrium such that the rate at which the pigment is altered by absorbed energy is equal to the rate at which the pigment is produced. The time required to reach maximum concentration in the dark has been found to be several times as great as that required to reach an equilibrium in continuous illumination. The former is a measure of dark adaptation and the latter of light adaptation.

Since radiant energy arrives a quantum at a time and, according to Einstein's law of photochemical equivalence, is absorbed only at the rate of one quantum per molecule affected, this initial step in photosensitivity has a statistical character. At low intensities of light, so few molecules may capture a photon in a given time that the organism ignores the scattered events. At a slightly higher intensity of stimulation, the frequency of capture would rise. If the lower limits for response to light are explored with a test flash of constant duration, some definite intensity level can be found at which a sensation of light is obtained 50 per cent of the time. At a slightly lower intensity, the response is obtained perhaps 30 per cent of the time. At a slightly higher intensity, perhaps 80 per cent of test flashes elicit a response. Both subjective and objective measurements of this kind show a range in 'frequency of seeing.' Some value, such as 50 per cent, can be defined as threshold.

Variation in response at threshold may be entirely attributable to variations in the quantum content of test flashes. Whether one molecule of pigment modified in a brief time (such as 0.1 sec.) is enough to trigger the entire photosensitive mechanism is still unsettled (10, 77, 97, 213). Different nervous systems may require several molecules of pigment to be altered almost simultaneously. In any case it is clear that photosensitivity has an efficiency approaching the theoretical limit of one quantum and one molecule.

Relatively few pigments are so unstable that a single photon can produce a chemical change. A photon simply lacks the amount of energy required to start most chemical reactions. From this it might be expected that photons with the largest content of energy would be most important in photosensitivity. In the wavelength band visible to the human eye, that giving the sensation of violet consists of photons with about double the energy of those in the red. Ultraviolet includes photons with an energy content double that of photons in the violet; but the seem-

ingly transparent media of terrestrial vertebrate eyes absorb the ultraviolet before it reaches the photosensitive retina. Aquatic organisms are shielded from ultraviolet by the water around them. Except under laboratory conditions, only the terrestrial arthropods (such as insects) appear to be stimulated visually by wavelengths shorter than 400 mμ.

The photosensitive pigments extracted from invertebrate and vertebrate eyes (152, 153, 276, 277) appear consistent in having their effective maximum of absorption between 400 and 700 mμ—well within the spectrum visible to man (fig. 1). Indirect evidence is available to indicate that the corresponding pigment or pigments in insects may be more affected by the ultraviolet components of sunshine than by energy absorbed at a secondary absorption maximum in the human range. Hence it is apparent that the chemical adaptations which permit photosensitivity in aquatic life and terrestrial vertebrates are related less to the energy content of the photons than to the wavelengths of radiant energy which penetrate most deeply into seas (480 mμ) and lakes (560 mμ). Sensitivity to ultraviolet seems to have come secondarily as a gain when some arthropods became both terrestrial and diurnal.

For extraction of photosensitive pigments in sufficient quantity for spectrophotometric analysis, considerable masses of photosensitive tissue are needed. So far this requirement has limited direct study to the large eyes of squids (20, 21, 65, 150, 229) and the stalked eyes of euphausiid crustaceans (143) which can be cut from hundreds of specimens taken with plankton nets. Most other invertebrates are either too small or too difficult to catch in adequate numbers for a biochemical approach. In consequence other avenues of investigation have been necessary for studying their photosensitivity.

The most valid approach is beset with technological difficulties. It consists of inserting microelectrodes into photosensitive cells and recording electrical events which follow stimulation of the cells by light. These changes in electrical potential clearly demonstrate the peripheral origin of nervous activity in visual systems (90) and suggest that depolarization of the photosensitive cell is responsible for initiating nerve impulses in its associated nerve fiber (177).

With some invertebrate eyes it is possible to study impulses in surviving nerve fibers emerging from photosensitive cells (88, 89, 281, 286). Far easier and more widely applicable is the less informative procedure of applying an electrode to the corneal surface of an intact eye and examining the gross potential

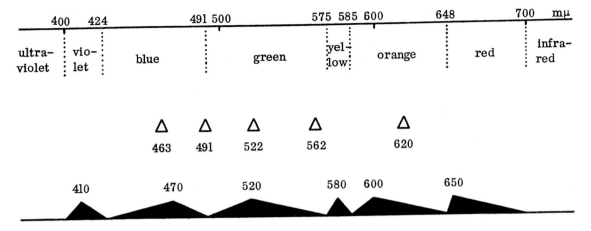

FIG. 1. The absorption maxima of extracted and synthesized photosensory pigments range across much of the spectral range visible to man. Commonly accepted boundaries (*top*) and representative centers (*bottom*) of appropriate wavelengths of light are shown for each hue sensation. Photosensory pigments include: *463*, euphausiopsin (Kampa, 1955); *491*, rhodopsin (Kühne, 1877) and cephalopsin (Bliss, 1948); *522*, porphyropsin (Wald, 1937); *562*, iodopsin (Wald, 1937); and *620*, cyanopsin (Wald, 1953).

changes which accompany illumination of the organ (6, 7, 87). Excised surviving eyes can be studied in the same way although without gaining from them any additional information (56, 211, 212).

Far more unknowns are encountered in trying to learn about an animal's photosensitivity from its behavior either under laboratory conditions or undisturbed in its natural habitat. Yet the vast bulk of physiological investigations on invertebrate vision employ methods of this type. In them one advantage can be seen: the reactions of the whole animal—even in an artificial environment—must be closer to its responses in normal life. By observing behavior, something more of the role of vision in ordinary situations can be gathered. Isolated measurements of electrical potentials are far more difficult to interpret on an ecological basis.

By far the most hazardous approach to photosensitivity in animals is also the commonest. It is deceptively easy to examine their photosensory structures anatomically and histologically and to infer how these structures may be used. Valuable evidence can certainly be obtained as to limitations imposed by structure; but without careful experimentation with living individuals, there is no way to be sure that the animal exploits its photosensory mechanism in its daily life.

In most groups of invertebrates the best that can be done in summarizing findings on photosensitivity is to relate the anatomical and behavior studies. This

is approached most simply on a structural basis or on a taxonomic framework (31, 77, 142, 193, 216, 269).

PHOTOSENSITIVITY IN UNICELLULAR ORGANISMS

Since both receptor and effector are component parts of the same cell in protozoans, photosensory specializations are more limited than among metazoans. Responses to light seem correspondingly restricted to movements of the whole cell or of its locomotory structures, such as flagella.

Cells Without Obvious Photoreceptors

There is no a priori reason to assume that the responses to light found in amebas need correspond to those in such flagellates as *Peranema*. In the former, an increase in intensity of illumination is usually followed by retraction of pseudopodia. The rate of locomotion of amebas appears to be affected significantly by the intensity of continued illumination. Initially the rate is modified by the state of dark adaptation of the cell (183). Hertel, who investigated the ultraviolet to 280 mμ as a stimulus (104), postulated that the radiations catalyzed the release of hydrogen peroxide within the cell and that these chemical changes accounted for behavior. Mast & Stahler (183) believed, instead, that the light produced a physical change in the elastic strength of the plasmagel, inhibiting the formation of pseudopodia.

In *Peranema* the whole cell, including its flagellum, appears to be sensitive to light (238, 239). A gradient can be detected from a minimum in the posterior end to a maximum in the flagellum. Even detached flagella will respond to increased illumination by bending, but no recovery seems possible. Hence both the receptor and effector substances must be widely distributed in the protoplasm, but the recovery phase depends upon transport of additional materials into the flagellum from the cell body where they are elaborated.

Cells With Obvious Photoreceptors

Definite organelles called stigmata are present in many flagellates and seem associated with a localized photosensitivity. Some stigmata are ball-like masses of opaque red or black pigment. This is the case in *Euglena* where the stigma is close to the double base of a single flagellum and must shade the flagellar bases from radiations reaching the cell from straight ahead. If it is assumed that shading allows the flagellar mechanisms to operate at full speed and illumination from the side inhibits the lashing movement, then the polarity of swimming movements with respect to a point source can be explained rather simply.

Cup-shaped and spoon-shaped stigmata are usual among colonial flagellates such as *Gonium* and *Volvox*. The concavity of the stigma is associated with the hypersensitive protoplasm and may be lined with a reflecting layer which serves as a concave mirror and concentrates the light at a focal point with the photosensitive region. Both *Gonium* and *Volvox* stigmata possess a lens as well. In *Volvox* the size of the stigmata decreases with distance of the cell from the anterior pole of the colony, and all stigmata are placed so as to face outward and slightly toward the anterior pole. The two flagella of each cell beat in different modes and at unlike rates according to the direction from which light reaches the stigma. Mast worked out the paths of the reflected and refracted rays (180, 182) but did not identify the functional connection between the photosensitive mass in the stigmatic area and the locomotor mechanism at the flagellar bases. It is clear, however, that when a *Volvox* colony is illuminated only from directly ahead on its axis of symmetry, every cell receiving radiations does so in ways which lead to symmetrical beating of the flagella. Under these circumstances the entire colony revolves on its axis and, unless the light intensity is excessive, approaches the source while so rotating. Unilateral illumination, by contrast, appears to modify flagellar movements on the illuminated side while vigorous beating on the shaded side gradually turns the colony until its axis is directed toward the source.

Mast (182) presented generalizations concerning the form and function of stigmata in unicellular and colonial flagellates, without mentioning the most remarkable of them all. In *Pouchetia* and related dinoflagellates, the lens associated with the stigma is enormous and spherical. The resemblance to a multicellular eye in these unicellular organisms is striking. No experimental work has been reported which might show the use to which *Pouchetia* puts this striking organelle.

PHOTOSENSITIVITY IN MULTICELLULAR ORGANISMS

With multicellularity a metazoan might be expected to show pronounced localization of photosensitivity into obvious eyes. Some metazoans manage quite well and respond to light without obvious specializations of this kind. Others, although equipped with eyes, seem to ignore visual cues for considerable parts of their life histories.

Photosensitivity Mediated Without Obvious Receptors

To this phenomenon the phrases 'dermoptic sense' and 'dermal photosensitivity' have often been applied (e.g. 133–135, 201). Table I indicates the taxonomic groups in which a generalized response of this kind has been demonstrated. Often a failure to recognize the presence of this photosensory system in animals with eyes has led to wrong conclusions concerning the effects of unilateral blinding.

Ganglionic Photosensitivity

In 1934, Welsh (290) and Prosser (218) discovered independently that the abdominal ganglia of the crayfish were photosensitive, permitting the animal to respond to light even after its eyes had been removed. Hess (113) found the same sensitivity in abdominal ganglia of the shrimp *Crangon* and the spiny lobster *Panulirus* but learned that photosensory cells were scattered along nerves in such remote parts of the body as the uropods. The role of ganglionic photosensitivity in controlling locomotor activity of the intact animal has received some consideration (232). Probably it is more important at the time of molt, before the new exoskeleton has de-

TABLE I. *Structural and Functional Aspects of Photoreceptors as Presently Known in the Various Taxonomic Groups of Invertebrates*

Representation

a = all
l = larval
m = most
s = some
v = noted

Group	Subgroup	Protoplasmic photosensitivity alone	Stigmata (intracellular organelles) also	General photosensitivity	Neuronal photoreceptors	Unicellular eyespots	Compound eyespots	Ocelli = simple eyes	Compound ocelli	Stemmata	Compound eyes (ommatidia)	Camera-style eyes	Retina direct	Retina inverted	Pigment-cell iris diaphragm	Muscular iris diaphragm	Tapetum	Migratory eye pigments	Muscular shift of lens	Hydraulic shift of retina	Muscular shift of retina	Muscular reshaping of lens	'Ladder retina'	Binocular field	Color vision
PROTISTA	Mastigophora		s																						
	Sarcodina	a																							
	Ciliata	a																							
COELENTERATA	Hydrozoa			v		s		s				m	s												
	Scyphozoa			v			m	s				a													
	Anthozoa			v																					
CTENOPHORA				v																					
PLATYHELMINTHES	Turbellaria			v		m		s					s	m										s	
	Trematoda			v		s																			
NEMERTINEA				v				s					s	m											
ASCHELMINTHES	Rotifera			v		m		s					a												
	Gastrotricha			v		m		s					a												
	Kinorhyncha			v		m																			
	Nematoda			v				s					a												
BRYOZOA				v																					
MOLLUSCA	Amphineura			v				m			s		a				s			s		s	s	s	
	Gastropoda			v				s			s	m	s			s			s		s	s	s		
	Pelecypoda			v	v	l	s	s			s	m	s			s					s		s		
	Cephalopoda			v							a	a			a				m				s		?
ANNELIDA	Archiannelida			v		m																			
	Polychaeta			v		s	s	s				s	m	s						s				s	
	Oligochaeta		v	v																					
	Hirudinea			v		m																			
CHAETOGNATHA				v					m				a												
TARDIGRADA				v		m																			
ONYCHOPHORA				v				a					a												
ARTHROPODA / Crustacea	Branchiopoda			v				m			m		a			m			s						s
	Ostracoda							m			m		a			m	s								
	Copepoda							m		s	m	s	a			m	s								
	Branchiura							m			m		a			m									
	Cirripedia							m			l		a		a										
	Malacostraca			v	v			s			m		a			a			s	s				s	s
	Trilobita							m			m		?			?									
	Xiphosura							a			a		a						s						
	Eurypterida							m			m		?			?									
ARTHROPODA / Arachnida	Scorpionida			v				m					a						s						
	Pseudoscorpionida			v				m					a						s						
	Phalangida			v				m							a				s						
	Acarida			v				s					a												
	Araneida			v				m				m	s				s			s				s	
	Solpugida							s					a												
	Pycnogonida							m						a											
ARTHROPODA	Chilopoda			v				m			s		m	s	s										
	Diplopoda			v				s	s			m	s												
ARTHROPODA / Insecta	Ametabola			v				s			m		a			s									
	Hemimetabola			v				s			m		a			m	s							s	
	Holometabola	l			l			s	s	s	m		a			m			s	s				s	s
ECHINODERMATA	Crinoidea			v																					
	Holothuroidea			v	v																				
	Asteroidea			v			s	s																	
	Echinoidea			v																					
	Ophiuroidea			v																					
HEMICHORDATA				v	v	l																			
CHORDATA	Urochordata			v	v			l							a										
	Cephalochordata			v		a																			

veloped its pigmentation and while light can penetrate more readily into the viscera.

Peripheral Photosensitivity

The degree to which light responses can be localized into effective behavior patterns without structural specialization of photoreceptors is certainly shown in the echinoid echinoderms. With the Mediterranean urchin *Centrostephanus*, von Üxküll found fairly rapid adjustments in orientation of the spines according to the direction from which the body was shadowed (275). A more detailed study of the Caribbean *Diadema* by Millott (188–191) confirmed von Üxküll's findings on behavior and established the fact that no special photoreceptor cells are present at the ends of the twigs from the radial nerves where these enter the dermis. Yet the entire body surface appears photosensitive, only the spines themselves lacking this type of irritability. The radial nerve must be intact for the responses to follow local stimulation. Even a kind of dark adaptation is present through concentration of pigment in dermal chromatophores, permitting more light to penetrate to the level in the skin at which the nerve twigs lie.

With another Caribbean urchin Millott was able to duplicate some of the spectacular findings of Dubois (59) on European *Strongylocentrotus*. Both echinoids have the habit of partially covering the aboral surface with debris picked up from the adjacent bottom. The Caribbean *Lytechinus* inhabits the coral reefs and boulder-strewn beaches to the limit of wave action at low tide and appears to use bits of coral as ballast in this buffeted zone; but if a narrow beam of light is directed on any portion of the aboral surface, the urchin transfers these opaque objects (or any bits of seaweed within reach of tube feet and pedicellariae) into the path of the beam, using them as a parasol. Urchins at greater depths, where the light is less intense, seem to carry debris only while sunlight is reaching them on the bottom (191).

Perhaps the best example of an extreme sensitivity to shadows was found by Millott with *Diadema*. When a single urchin was placed in a finger bowl of sea water under a checkerboard of electric lamps, it would rapidly point many spines in the direction of any single lamp in the pattern when this one was temporarily turned off. Identification of the direction in which so minor a change occurred must be mediated through an inherent polarity with maximum sensitivity to light reaching the body surface at right

angles, as well as through the general roundness such as Nagel postulated (201) (fig. 2 *right*).

A general photosensitivity with less striking responses has been demonstrated in other echinoderms: in the entire aboral surface of the sessile (and swimming) crinoid *Antedon* (163); over the whole body of the holothurians *Synaptula* (203) and *Holothuria* (41); over the aboral surface of asteroids from which the ocellate tips of the arms had been removed (258, 297); and in the ophiuroid *Ophiocoma* (37). Crozier found a difference (41) between the behavior of *Holothuria* and *Thyone* in that the latter holothurian moved away from a light source as an echinoid might—any angle of the body in advance. *Holothuria*, by contrast, showed a functional polarity, swinging around until the mouth was farthest from the stimulating light before moving off in this orientation.

Responses to light where no receptors seemed specialized toward sensitivity to radiations have been reported in blinded and intact members of many phyla: in the hydrozoan medusa *Gonionemus* (200); in luminescent ctenophores *Beroë* (122) and *Mnemiopsis* (197); in blind turbellarians (165); in blind rotifers (263, 264); in nematodes (104); in oligochaetes (110, 111, 114, 161) with identification of neuronal photoreceptors in which photosensitivity was localized; in the polychaete *Mercierella* (228); in the leech *Hirudo* (234); in bryozoans, both as larvae (*Pectinatella*) and adults (*Lophopus*), through kinetic responses of nega-

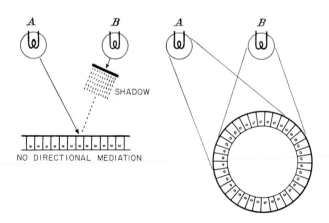

FIG. 2. Curvature of the body surface can provide an animal having general photosensitivity with a means for identifying the direction from which a light stimulus comes. Neither lamp *A* nor shadow *B* have a directional significance for a flat photosensitive tissue (*left*); but in a cylindrical or spherical organism (*right*) quite different cells are illuminated by the two sources, *A* and *B*. [After Nagel; from Milne & Milne (193).]

tive sign (179); in various pelecypods (201) but particularly *Mya* (94, 96, 148, 166); in the gastropod *Helix* on the basis of photosensitivity in spite of a gap found in the optic nerve from the tentacular eye (306); in the hemichordate *Dolichoglossus* (39, 111, 112); and in the adult urochordates *Ascidia* (93) and *Ciona* (96).

Photoreceptors in the skin of a soft-bodied animal, such as an oligochaete, vary greatly in degree of exposure depending on the extension and contraction of the superficial tissues in locomotion. In *Perichaeta*, Harper (85) found that a negative response might be shown to low-intensity illumination when the worm was tested while extended, yet the same test applied while the worm was contracted might lead to a positive response.

Quite a few eyeless invertebrates (particularly hydroid coelenterates and turbellarians) react positively to sunlight without giving proof that they are themselves photosensitive. These organisms harbor mutualistic algae (green 'zoochlorellae' or brownish green 'zooxanthellae') which carry on photosynthesis when illuminated. A response to chemical changes accompanying photosynthesis could account for the behavior of the animal partner in many instances. Even when the invertebrate possesses eyes as well as mutualistic algae, the role of vision in photic responses becomes suspect until proved definitely.

Translucent bodies which stud the exposable portion of the mantle in the giant clam *Tridacna* were described as eyes until Yonge (305) cleared up the misunderstanding. He found that these structures are, instead, an adaptation permitting daylight to reach deep levels of the mantle tissue where large numbers of mutualistic algae grow. *Tridacna* appears to depend for food primarily upon the success of the enclosed algae. It raises the plants in mantle greenhouses, and the supposed eyes are merely illuminators in the roof!

Photosensitivity Mediated Through Unicellular Eyespots

Addition of a cup of opaque pigment beside a photosensory cell seems but a small step in evolution but still a move toward development of an eye. This addition permits the receptor to be more definite as to the direction from which a stimulating light comes than when its own greater sensitivity to radiation passing along its axis is the sole means for differentiation. When photosensory mechanisms consist of a single receptor cell and an associated pigment mass, the term eyespot is useful—although earlier authors

have used the word far more loosely. Often a lens is associated with an eyespot, providing still more discriminatory possibilities and perhaps increasing the structure's sensitivity by gathering in more light.

Eyespots are present in such turbellarians as *Prorhynchus* (144) and in a number of parasitic trematodes, particularly at various larval stages of digenetic forms. Some trematode cercaria possess them; so does the miracidium of *Fasciola*. Instances of apparent degeneration have been identified (70), although no evidence has been given that would indicate a corresponding loss of sensitivity. In many nemertineans, one or more pairs of eyespots are present (123), but whether negative responses to radiation found in *Lineus* (194, 195) depend upon functional eyespots has not been proved. By ingenious experiments, Viaud has been able to distinguish between photosensitivity in rotifers mediated by their eyespots and those elicited on the basis of a general sensitivity (260–264). Eyespots are the only photoreceptors identified in archiannelids (125) and some polychaetes (117, 237). They are characteristically present in tardigrades (43) and larval hemichordates (243, 245). They are scattered along the nerve cord of cephalochordates (116, 141, 204), and appear to be the sole mechanism allowing response to radiations (204); possibly degenerate eyespots, devoid of pigment cups, were described by Joseph (141).

Photosensitivity Mediated Through Multicellular Eyes

COMPOUND EYESPOTS. Another small step toward effective vision consists of the grouping together of unicellular eyespots, forming them into an organized cluster with radially divergent axes. Structures of this kind—compound eyespots—have been reported in but three groups of organisms with no indication that they are part of an evolutionary sequence.

Both solitary and compound eyespots project from the mantle margin of pelecypods in the genera *Arca* (fig. 6) and *Pectunculus*. In *A. noae* a specimen 8.5 cm long had 235 of these sensory clusters. Neither Patten (206) nor Küpfer (159), however, indicated the degree to which the compound eyespots were used in a visual way.

The annelids *Potamilla* and *Branchiomma* (fig. 6) bear compound eyespots on the main stems of the cephalic branchiae (3, 27). Each sensory unit is isolated from its neighbors by pigment cells. Yet the known reactions of these polychaete worms seem no more complex than those of other genera in which the structure of photoreceptors is simpler (267).

The other group of invertebrates with compound eyespots conceals its photoreceptors so well that they were unknown before 1946. Most maggots (larval flies, insect order Diptera) give strong negative responses to any but very dim illumination, and many can orient themselves with remarkable accuracy. Yet it remained for Bolwig (22) to locate the photosensory structures using microdissection. He found a small group of rounded cells somewhat anterodorsal to the supraesophageal ganglion. In early first-instar larvae these cells are not fully developed; neither is photosensitivity. By the second instar, the cell group is well organized but not yet surrounded by opaque tissues; these larvae orient well, apparently by discriminating the faint shadow of their own translucent bodies. In the third instar, the growth of the pharyngeal skeleton provides an opaque cup around the compound eyespot without blocking the light from anterior directions; these larvae will follow the vectorial resultant path between two light sources. With later development, both overgrowth of the pharyngeal skeleton and increased opacity of the body reduce the accuracy of orientation and raise the threshold for response.

Eyes of types other than compound eyespots agree in having a layer of photosensory cells, i.e. a retina. It may line a pit (fig. 3, *left*) or lie below a lens (fig. 3, *right*). Where the retina consists of many cells so close to the dioptric elements that no clear image seems possible, the term ocellus (simple eye) may be applied. If a similar retina is remote enough from the dioptric system that a reasonable image is cast upon it, the phrase camera-style eye seems preferable; camera-style eyes usually have an accessory mechanism permitting accommodation. If the retina consists of only a ring of receptor cells, clustered around the proximal end of the dioptric system like sections of a citrus fruit, the structure is an ommatidium. Ordinarily ommatidia are grouped into a compound eye with the optic axes of the individual units diverging from one another on a quasiradial plan. Ocelli may also be grouped as compound ocelli, or 'aggregate eyes.' A puzzling intermediate between an ocellus and an ommatidium is found in the larvae of some holometabolous insects; for this structure the word stemma is useful.

OCELLI OR SIMPLE EYES. Ocelli with large lenses are located around the rim of many coelenterate medusae, but the degree to which their photosensitivity is used

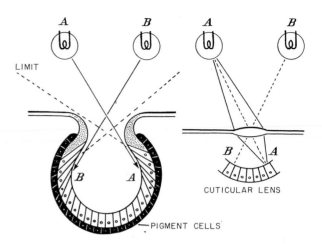

FIG. 3. A pigment-surrounded cup lined with photoreceptor cells (*left*), a cuticular lens above the retina (*right*), or a combination of the two, are characteristic of true eyes. A narrowing of the cup's aperture improves the ability of an eye to discriminate between events at *A* and *B* but reduces the amount of light admitted. A lens provides an aid to discrimination and also can collect more light, hence increasing the organ's sensitivity. [After Nagel; from Milne & Milne (193).]

to modify responses arising from a general responsiveness to light has never been established (e.g. 200). Nerve fibers from these eyes communicate with the diffuse nerve net and may be part of a much more direct sensory-motor mechanism than is found among animals with a highly developed nervous system.

Shallow and deep pigment cups without lenses are the characteristic ocelli in turbellarians. Their number ranges from one pair to many and their size from minute to relatively large. No phylogenetic pattern is discernible, and no correlation has been made with habits or habitat (133). Best known are the conspicuous ocelli of *Planaria* in which a pigment cup open laterally conceals the distal ends of the receptor cells (fig. 4). Hesse (115) related the visual field of each ocellus to the behavior of the intact flatworm. Taliaferro (249) found in addition that receptors in the posterior and ventral portions of each pigment cup are involved in responses wherein the animal turns toward the eye of that side, whereas stimulation of the remaining receptor cells is followed by a turn in the opposite direction.

Among nemertineans (123) and rotifers (263, 264) the presence of ocelli rather than eyespots has been noted in several genera. But no special significance has been sttributed to the more complex photosensory mechanism.

So wide a variation in ocellar structure is present

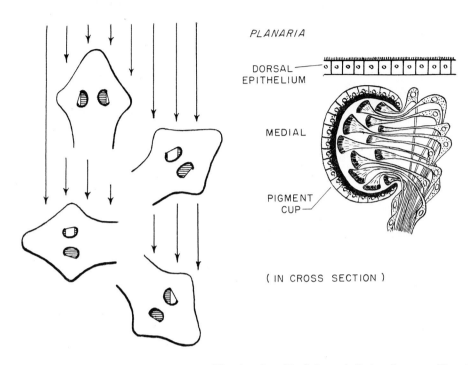

PLANARIA

DORSAL
EPITHELIUM

MEDIAL

PIGMENT
CUP

(IN CROSS SECTION)

FIG. 4. The dorsal ocelli of the turbellarian flatworm *Planaria* consist of opaque pigment cups open laterally, concealing the distal ends of photoreceptor cells. Shadowing of the photoreceptors by the pigment cups differs in horizontal illumination according to the orientation of the worm (*left*). Each receptor cell (*right*) is most sensitive to radiations passing through it parallel to the long axis of the portion within the pigment cup. [After Hesse; from Milne & Milne (193).]

among the many eye-bearing members of the phyla Annelida, Mollusca and Arthropoda that it is tempting to arrange them in parallel series (117, 193, 237). A phylogenetic basis for this series would be valuable (fig. 5), but no correlation has been found between form of ocelli and other structural features or with the normal habitats occupied. Hence it seems probable that the variation has no broader implications, and the parallels in embryonic development are fortuitous.

The several paired ocelli on the prostomium of the polychaete *Nereis* are of a single structural type with a cuticular lens over a cupped retina (162, 199). The most anterior pair may mediate negative responses to light and the others positive responses (105); an asymmetry of the retina in the anterior pair appears to adapt them to forward and lateral vision, whereas the other ocelli are directed more vertically upward (199). Brand (24) reported that the behavior characteristic of unilaterally blinded *Nereis* is shown even when any single ocellus is left intact on the operated side.

In the Atlantic palolo worm, the polychaete *Eunice*, each segment bears a single mid-ventral ocellus, but its function has not been found (111) since general

photosensitivity appears to account for responses observed.

The ocelli of leeches appear to be the chief specialized sensory organs and in the first five body segments occupy the positions corresponding to lateral-line organs in more posterior regions. Each ocellus is almost cylindrical with its longitudinal axis at right angles to the body surface; its nerve fibers connect on the medial surface. Whether they are phylogenetically related to tactile elements (293) or can legitimately be arranged in an evolutionary series (266) has not been proved. Their function may be related more to body pigment distribution (247) than to kinetic responses. As Parker pointed out (205), mere possession of photoreceptors does not imply that an animal can see.

The abundant small ocelli of amphineuran mollusks provide a comparable puzzle. An adult *Corephium* may have as many as 8500 of these structures, perhaps 3000 in the most anterior plate of the shell (198, 214, 215). Heath (92) traced their formation and concluded that they must be functional even in the adult. Crozier (40) could find only a general photosensitivity, however, in *Chiton*. It was most pronounced in the scaly girdle, where ocelli are lack-

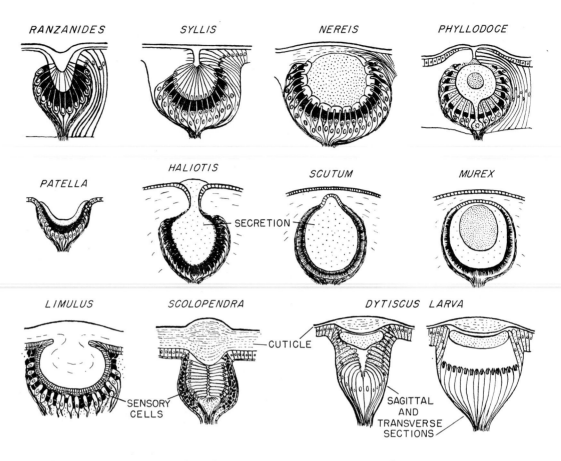

FIG. 5. A comparative series showing degrees of development in ocelli of polychaete annelids (*upper row*), gastropod mollusks (*center row*) and arthropods (*lower row*), the ocelli in longitudinal section in all instances. No phylogenetic interpretation seems indicated. [*Limulus* after Demoll, *Scolopendra* after Heymons, *Dytiscus* after Günther, others after Hesse; from Milne & Milne (193).]

ing, and extended over the soft ventral surface of the foot. Moreover, as the animal aged, its response to light changed from negative to positive.

Among the pelecypods, Nagel (201) distinguished a category of 'ikonoptic' organisms in which the structure of the ocelli seemed suitable for producing a poor image in the receptor cells. *Potamides* has a single layer in the retina, *Pecten* (fig. 7, *left*) a double layer; in both instances the ends of the receptor cells are turned away from the lens so that the retina is inverted (159, 209). Wenrich (291) investigated what he believed to be image-formation in *Pecten* in terms of the smallest white card intensely illuminated, movement of which would produce a shell-closing response in the scallop. A more probable explanation for his observed fact is that, at the light intensity used, the appearance or disappearance of the card in the visual field furnished the minimum effective change in brightness. Hartline (88) found by electrical means

that the distal (smaller) layer of retina mediates a strong off-response, whereas the proximal layer discharges nerve impulses whenever illuminated.

A remarkably gradual series can be arranged showing sectional views of gastropod eyes (fig. 5, *second line*), but the significance of the differences noted in terms of photic responses by the intact animal may be questioned (121, 216, 295). The sign of the response appears to be altered by many other factors, such as diet, wetness or dryness of the body surface (196), and whether the animal is inverted or upright (74). The role of general photosensitivity in these reactions has not been segregated from the supposed dependence upon vision through the ocelli.

On the basis of embryonic origins and neurologic connections, Hanström (82) classified ocelli in arthropods into three categories: *a*) the nauplian eyes of crustaceans, the ocelli of insects, the median eyes of trilobites, the ocelli of xiphosurans and the eyes of pycnogonids—all arising from a dorsal ectodermal mass in the embryo; *b*) the lateral ('secondary') ocelli of modern arachnoids and all eyes of diplopods and chilopods, arising through degeneration from the ommatidia of compound eyes produced by the lateral ectodermal mass of the embryo; and *c*) the ventral ocelli of trilobites and xiphosurans and the median ('primary') eyes of eurypterids and arachnids, arising from a ventral ectodermal mass in the embryo. No clear correlation can be noted between these categories and the detailed anatomical features of the ocelli in postembryonic life—features described and illustrated with great care by Grenacher (81).

In many planktonic crustaceans the median ocellus is the only eye present. Fundamentally it appears to be a double structure, but fusion may be remarkably complete. Many crustaceans which metamorphose lose their ocelli as they grow. An extreme example is found among barnacles (69): newly hatched nauplii have a bilobed median ocellus; a pair of compound eyes appears at the metanauplian stage, only to be extruded or to degenerate at metamorphosis; until this time the median ocellus remains unchanged, but then it separates into two, each half migrating into a lateral position and continuing as the sole photosensory specialization of the adult.

The ventral position of the median ocellus in *Branchipus*, *Artemia* and other branchiopods, many copepods, some trilobites and larval xiphosurans suggests that inverted swimming may be an ancestral habit. Inverted swimming is characteristic of *Limulus*, *Branchipus* and *Artemia*, and probably was also of trilobites. A median ocellus must be of help while dorsal compound eyes are directed toward the bottom rather than the sky. Persistent nauplian ocelli are known in some decapod malacostracans. In *Artemia* the ocelli can serve alone in mediating essentially all normal adult responses to light stimulation (171); exceptions, which depend upon function of the compound eyes, are the visual following of females by males and a convulsive reflex when a dark-adapted animal is suddenly illuminated.

Waterman (281) has provided a convenient table showing the groups of arthropods in which a median ocellus is known. At the same time he presented evidence from electrical recordings indicating that messages pass along the optic nerve fibers from *Limulus* ocelli comparable to those from the compound eyes. Their use by the animal's central nervous system remains a mystery.

Eight ocelli or less are characteristic of spiders (208); the arrangement and actual number varies from one genus to another. One pair, the 'primary eyes,' are simpler in having a direct retina and no tapetum, although the entire retina may be moved within the body through the contraction of paired muscles—perhaps in following the progress of prey or potential mate. The 'secondary eyes' usually have an inverted retina and often a tapetum; no movements of the retina are possible. Nervous connections to the two types of ocelli are consistent with this difference in structure and with Hanström's generalizations (82). The role of vision is difficult to demonstrate (128–130, 217, 294) in spiders, except in jumping spiders (127). These have been recommended as ideal laboratory material because they seem so unaware of confinement.

Among centipedes and millipedes which have ocelli, no responses to light have been described which could not be accounted for adequately on the basis of a general photosensitivity in the body surface.

Two, or at most three, ocelli are present in many insects (136, 137), but their role in normal living habits has been a puzzle (23, 52, 53, 108, 118, 126, 224). When only the ocelli are exposed, insects usually behave as though completely blinded. Some show responses which cannot be accounted for on the basis of general photosensitivity (25). Demoll & Scheuring (52) found considerable correspondence between the visual fields of the compound eyes and of the ocelli. This discovery, together with the observation that many insects with their ocelli covered respond more slowly to events in the visual field of their compound eyes, led to the notion that ocelli serve to measure general intensity of illumination and to control the level of tonic contraction in locomotor muscles.

Variation in proportion of parts and arrangement of retinal cells seems to have little effect in determining the role of insect ocelli (167–170, 303, 304). Some ocelli show a strong retinal astigmatism (fig. 5, *lower right*), those in some dragonflies (order Odonata) being particularly pronounced (252). In the orthopteran *Acridium* the ocelli are dimorphic in that those of the female alone show a double curvature on the proximal surface of the corneal lens—like a bifocal spectacle lens—producing two images at different distances (253). No explanation is available.

Ocelli in which the components of three-part lenses lie side by side, like the top of a clover-leaf roll, are found in the larvae of many urochordates. Mast (181) reported photosensory responses of this type of larva until the time of metamorphosis when the ocelli degenerate. Whether the remarkable lenses indicate fusion from an originally triplicate ocellar cluster is not clear from embryological studies (78). A comparable suggestion of multiple origin for the one to three ocelli in pelagic salps has received no support.

COMPOUND OCELLI OR AGGREGATE EYES. The grouping of separate ocelli, each with its own retina and pigment cup, into a pattern with roughly radial divergence of the optic axes seems to have arisen independently in many phyla through convergent evolution. In coelenterates a number of scyphozoans (cubomedusae) exhibit this arrangement (132). It is characteristic of chaetognaths in which three ocelli are clustered in each of two groups (120, 124). Among arthropods, compound ocelli resemble a compound eye in many millipedes and in males of the insect order Strepsiptera (227, 246). The millipede *Narceus* is hatched with only a single ocellus but adds others in a triangular area on each side of the head until a total of between 40 and 50 are present a few instars before sexual maturity (32).

Many starfish (asteroid echinoderms) bear a cluster of ocelli at the tip of their arms. Muscular movements of the arm tissues can alter somewhat the relative orientation of the separate ocelli (296), but the form of each photosensory unit appears fixed. A large central dioptric body must serve to concentrate radiations upon the receptor cells (242, 258), and photosensory functions seems indicated by the slow action potentials which develop upon illumination of the ocellar area (90). Some movements related to the direction of lateral illumination and of shadows have been described, but at least some of these may be due to a general photosensitivity in the dermis. The presence of carotenoid pigments in the compound ocellar tissues (192) could relate to a photosensitive substance. Alternatively these pigments may serve as filters which affect the spectral sensitivity of the organism.

STEMMATA. In the larvae of many members of the holometabolous insect orders, Neuroptera (*s. lat.*), Coleoptera, Lepidoptera, Trichoptera, Diptera and Hymenoptera, photosensory structures resembling isolated ommatidia are present. They disappear at metamorphosis and have no relationship to the compound eyes of the adult stage. Their distinctness from an ontogenetic standpoint led Landois (160) to consider them as an independent type of eye; he called them 'composite eyes,' but the term stemmata has been approved more widely.

Anatomical details have been described for those

of a larval water beetle *Acilius* (236), a lepidopteran caterpillar *Isia* (54, 55), a mosquito wriggler *Culex* (35) and several sawfly larvae (Hymenoptera) in a comparative study by Corneli (36). For the caterpillar, Dethier considered the diopteric system and found that a stemma with a one-part lens had an effective aperture between f/0.5 and f/1.0, whereas those with a three-part lens were slightly less spectacular collectors of light with effective apertures between 1.0 and 1.5. In all instances the caterpillar stemma had seven receptor cells arranged at two levels, a distal clump of three and a proximal group of four. No matter whether the corneal lens was simple or tripartite, only a single crystalline body was below it, close to the distal group of receptor cells. The stemmata were fixed in the firm head capsule at such angles to each other that their fields did not overlap. Dethier concluded that a coarse type of mosaic vision was possible.

Many caterpillars show clear responses to distant trees. Those of the nun moth *Lymantria* under experimental conditions will react to and approach pillars and vertical stripes of paint (131), whereas horizontal patterns seem to be ignored. Hundertmark, who explored this problem thoroughly, concluded that dark vertical patterns stimulated the larvae while their heads were being swung from side to side—a characteristic gesture of these caterpillars. Stimulation would then correspond to patterns crossing the visual field of stemma after stemma, and the astigmatism noted would have a basis in behavior rather than in structure.

COMPOUND EYES. True compound eyes are restricted to arthropods (fig. 6, *lower right*) and are represented among crustaceans, trilobites, xiphosurans, eurypterids, many fossil chilopods and diplopods, the centipede *Scutigera* and close allies, and most insects. Holometabolous insects possess them only as adults. In all situations they present a much more effective organization than compound eyespots or compound ocelli but show the same quasi-radial divergence of visual units.

According to Hanström (82), all true compound eyes arise from a lateral ectodermal mass in the embryo. In following these embryonic steps toward the final battery of ommatidia, Watasé (278) recognized no major variants in development. One rather fundamental difference has been overlooked in these and subsequent studies: in *Limulus* (and presumably all xiphosurans, perhaps eurypterids as well), the entire dioptric mechanism is molted. Other arthro-

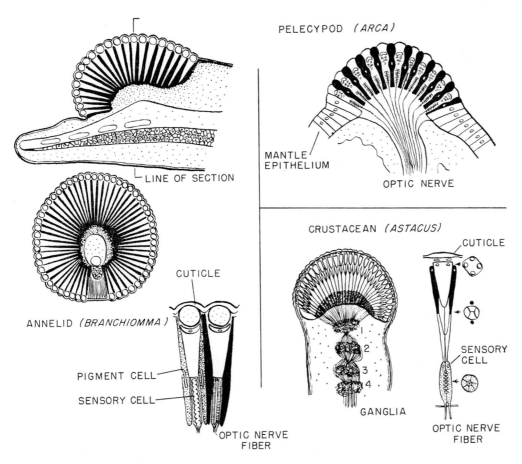

FIG. 6. Quasiradial divergence of photosensory units is characteristic of both compound eyespots and compound eyes. The former are exemplified by the pelecypod mollusk *Arca* (*upper right*) and the polychaete annelid *Branchiomma* (*left*), shown in lengthwise and transverse section and in detail. Each ommatidium of the compound eye (*lower right, detail*) consists of a cuticular lens, additional dioptric components on the ommatidial axis, a cluster of receptor cells whose nerve fibers penetrate the basal membrane and an investing sheath of pigment cells. At the *extreme right* are sections cut through such an ommatidium at levels as indicated. Commonly the optic nerve fibers pass to a series of ganglia close to the eye (*lower right*, longitudinal section of crustacean eye and stalk). [*Branchioma* after Hesse, *Arca* after Küpfer, *Astacus* after Giesbrecht; from Milne & Milne (193).]

pods which molt after acquiring compound eyes retain most of the dioptric mechanism, shedding only the corneal lens or a part of it.

There is reason to question that the conventional classification of arthropod ommatidia has a sound phylogenetic basis. The term 'exocone' is applied to those of crustaceans, trilobites, and beetles of the families Dermestidae, Elateridae and Lampyridae, in which the dioptric parts consist of a molted corneal lens and a nonmolted inward extension of corneal secretion. Elsewhere special cone cells ('Semper's cells') lie between the corneal lens and the receptor cells, and provide dioptric function. In 'acone' ommatidia the cone cells become transparent and refract

light; they occupy all of the space and are characteristic of the insect orders Dermaptera, Heteroptera, some Odonata, some Coleoptera and some nematocerous Diptera. In 'eucone' ommatidia the cone cells secrete a solid 'crystalline cone' within themselves, usually in such a way that the cone-cell nuclei remain distal to the cone; sometimes an anuclear portion of the cone cells lies proximal of the cone; this type is characteristic of the insect orders Thysanura, Collembola, Orthoptera, Homoptera, Neuroptera, Trichoptera, Lepidoptera, Hymenoptera, some members of Odonata, most of the Coleoptera and some nematocerous Diptera. The brachycerous Diptera are unique in having 'pseudocone' ommatidia in which the cone cells remain small and transparent but secrete distal to themselves a fluid or paste extending to the corneal lens and supposedly aiding in the refraction of light.

At the proximal end of the dioptric mechanism within the ommatidium is a ring of receptor cells, or two rings, one distal to the other. Two rings may be more primitive than one ring. In *Limulus* and some others, an eccentric receptor cell lies outside the ring but extends a terminal segment toward the dioptric system in a position central to the ring of other receptor cells. More commonly there is no eccentric cell, and the ring of receptors secretes a translucent rod in the core position as a rhabdom which conducts light energy along the optical axis to the more proximal parts of the receptor cells.

In rendering these dioptric structures visible in sections through a compound eye, it is customary to bleach the pigment from the cells which sheath each ommatidium. Exner (68) appears to have forgotten the existence of this pigment mantle while tracing the path of light rays. van der Horst (256) drew attention to the pronounced diaphragmatic effect of the mantle in many compound eyes, limiting the passage of light to so small an aperture that no image could be produced at the receptor level. Under these circumstances an individual ommatidium could do no better than serve as a photometer. Compound eyes which are used in daylight operate in this way, with each ommatidium isolated from its neighbors, and any picture of the outside world a synthesized one in the central nervous system, built on the mosaic of photometric information coming from the individual ommatidia.

Notthaft (202) took the extreme view that each ommatidium operated on an all-or-none principle. Either a target was included in its visual field enough to stimulate the receptor system, or not. Almost certainly this view is too severe. In *Limulus*, where the compound eye may be somewhat degenerate, the optic nerve fibers lack lateral connections and ganglion cells for a distance from the eye sufficient that electrodes can be applied and the response of individual ommatidia studied (75, 89, 90, 286). In juveniles, two or more nerve fibers per ommatidium may carry nerve impulses when the eye is illuminated, but in adults only one is conducting, seemingly the one arising from the eccentric cell. A wide range of sensitivity and of response is evident. But the function of the 9 to 19 other receptor cells in each ommatidium remains unknown. Both at threshold and under intense illumination, the ommatidium discharges impulses as a unit.

The directional sensitivity of single ommatidia in the compound eye of *Limulus* has been evaluated using the same electrical technique (282). Sensitivity is highest on the optic axis and falls off to a tenth or less for light sources 10 to 20 degrees on any side. The effective aperture of the ommatidium from a physiological point of view is thus to 40 degrees for high sensitivity and to 180 degrees for response to stimuli as much as four log units above threshold intensity. Yet the maximum angular separation of *Limulus* ommatidia is about 15 degrees, the minimum 4 to 5 degrees. Hence the overlap of visual fields of neighboring units must be extensive and the acuity which might be predicted (as Notthaft did) on the basis of number of ommatidia is probably not realized. Since the dioptric mechanism of the *Limulus* ommatidium is somewhat different from that of most other arthropods, however, these findings may not apply widely. Acuity may be far better elsewhere in the phylum.

The compound eye seems particularly efficient in detecting movements in its total visual field. This can be demonstrated under field conditions (34) or as a sensitivity to flickered light in the laboratory (298–301). When plotted on a probability grid, flicker-fusion curves are like visual-acuity curves in being essentially straight lines (298, 299). This may be due to a normal statistical distribution of sensitivities among the ommatidia; or it may arise through the recruitment of progressively more ommatidia in a convex eye as the intensity of stimulus rises. Crozier & Wolf (42) believed that the latter was the limiting factor in the crayfish *Cambarus*.

The intensity difference required for flicker detection by arthropods is greater than that for the human eye. At optimum intensity the honeybee requires one stimulus to be 25 per cent greater or less than the other (298, 299). For the fly *Drosophila* the difference must be of the order of 225 per cent (98, 99). For man 1.5 per cent is adequate in good illumination. Hence the visual field of the arthropod eye contains a gray scale with far fewer than the 500 steplike increments between black and white detectable by the human eye.

Evaluation of stimuli effective with a compound eye is more satisfactory if it can be made from electroretinograms rather than kinetic responses of the entire animal. Electrical records of this kind are possible either with a surviving eye (56) or an intact animal (87). Autrum & Stöcker (7) learned with this technique that insects show two very different ranges in flicker detection. The fly *Calliphora*, the wasp *Vespa* and the honeybee *Apis* responded to rates as high as

200 per sec., better than five times the performance of the human eye. In the cockroach *Periplaneta* and the grasshopper *Tachycines*, by contrast, any flickering rate higher than 5 or 10 per sec. was evidently fused and interpreted as a constant stimulus. The authors postulated that in the orthopterans an after-image was present, a phenomenon lacking in the dipterans and hymenopterans.

For the fly *Calliphora* the electroretinograms show that the effective angle of view of each ommatidium is about twice as great in the horizontal plane as in the vertical (6). Hence a target remains for a longer time within the visual field if it is moving horizontally; summation can permit its detection at a lower threshold than would be found in the same target moving vertically. The structural basis for astigmatism of this kind can be found in the dimensions and divergence of ommatidia. Ommatidia facing downward commonly are relatively shorter and have larger lenses than those facing upward; usually they diverge from one another more strongly. Autrum (6) generalized that in all insects which fly well the angle of view of each ommatidium in the horizontal direction is about twice that in the vertical.

In *Apis* the situation is somewhat more complex (11). The radius of curvature of the bee eye is smaller in the transverse plane than in the frontal, with a ratio near 2.5 to 1. The angle between ommatidia is regularly greater in the transverse than in the frontal plane, with a ratio of difference reaching about 2 to 1. In consequence maximum acuity lies in a plane inclined 65 degrees to the sagittal, and in this plane only in an arc from 47 degrees behind the anterior margin of the eye to 49 degrees ahead of the posterior margin.

The extremes of difference in dimensions and angular separation among ommatidia in a single compound eye are met in some deep-sea crustaceans and in insects belonging to the orders Homoptera (287), Ephemeroptera and Diptera (57, 58). In most of these the region with short ommatidia and large lenses is confined to one part of the eye, and the portion with long ommatidia, slight divergences and fine lenses forms a sort of 'turban' toward the top of the head. In many instances the owner of such a 'divided' eye is a predator. However, Rádl (221) concluded that it indicated a duality of embryonic origin and proposed a "duplicity theory.' Zavřel (308) extended this into a triplicity theory, but later workers have not supported either hypothesis.

de Serres (53) appears to have been the earliest to experiment with arthropod vision by painting over all or part of a compound eye with black varnish. He found many of the postural changes which became classic demonstrations of the 'muscle tonus' theory in rather recent texts of physiology. Light intensity, interpreted through the compound eyes, was believed to control the tonus of muscles involved in posture and locomotion. 'Circus' movements of unilaterally blinded arthropods were explained on this basis.

At the same time de Serres pointed out the 'false pupil' seen as a shifting dot or line in many living compound eyes. Ewing (66) described it more fully and concluded correctly that it represents ommatidial pigment visible in those few ommatidia facing an observer's eye. In cylindrical compound eyes, such as the stalked ones of the crab *Ocypoda*, it takes the form of a vertical line which follows the observer or camera lens through as much as a 360-degree field of view.

Dugès (60) noted that a false pupil can be seen simultaneously in the two compound eyes of many insects and suggested that they must have binocular vision. Demoll (47), working from sections of compound eyes, showed the extent of these binocular fields. It is easy to assume that binocular vision is important to predaceous arthropods and that they snatch for prey when the proper ommatidia in the two eyes are stimulated simultaneously by an object placed symmetrically in the binocular field. Distance estimation is evidently good in both naiad and adult stages of most members of the insect order Odonata (1, 8, 50), among the dipteran family Asilidae (185) and in tiger beetles.

The adaptability of the neural components in the eye-brain team appears to have been underestimated. In a matter of hours or days, the postural peculiarities and circus movements of unilaterally blinded arthropods often disappear entirely. Partially blinded odonatan naiads can adapt their behavior to approach prey monocularly, pivot and seize at the appropriate instant (1, 8). Whether marginal ommatidia can participate in this versatility has been questioned (9). It would be interesting to know whether variations in adaptability correspond to the zones found in the *Notonecta* eye (172), since in this heteropteran insect kinetic responses seem related to specific areas of the compound eye. Certainly ommatidia can serve in unusual reflexes (219, 220) but limitations may still be present.

Many, perhaps most, arthropod eyes show a sensitivity to the plane of polarization of light from the sky. Something of the kind has been suspected for many years to account for the homing ability of various hymenopteran insects. Wolsky (302) sought in vain to find an analyzer function in the corneal lenses of the coarse compound eyes of land isopod crustaceans. von Frisch credited the actual demonstration of polarization sensitivity to Autrum, although von Frisch's own reports (271, 272) antedate any of Autrum's published comments on the subject. von Frisch has found in the honeybee's 'sky compass' a basis for the ability of one bee to communicate to another by dancing within the dark hive the direction to a discovered supply of food (273).

Since von Frisch used an octagon of Polaroid film cut into symmetrically fitted equilateral triangles, it was natural that he should parallel this with the ring of receptor cells in each insect ommatidium. When the octagon was held toward the blue sky, some one diagonal was darkest, another lightest. The former corresponded to Polaroid triangles the axes of which were transverse to the plane of polarization in the sky area seen through the plastic. Possibly an image of comparable type was cast upon the ring of receptor cells and information of this kind interpreted by a single ommatidium.

In the dipteran *Volucella*, a ring of eight receptor cells and birefringence with extinction of one ray were reported (186), but the reality of the phenomenon described is open to question. Certainly each ommatidium may vary in its response to light as the plane of polarization of incident radiation is rotated around its optic axis, as may occur in *Limulus* (279, 280, 282, 283) or in *Drosophila* (244). But structural asymmetries of dioptric components in individual ommatidia and the obliquity with which many ommatidia in each eye meet the outer surface seem more responsible for the sensitivity found to the plane of polarization. The extent to which polarized light is available as a cue useful in arthropod navigation both in air and in water has been described by Waterman (280, 285). It has been shown experimentally (12) to be significant in the free behavior of fresh-water planktonic crustaceans.

In the earliest comprehensive account of the arthropod compound eye, Grenacher (81) recognized a difference in the distribution of pigment cells according to whether the organism was a day-active type or a crepuscular and night-active organism. In most of the latter, the pigment is not extended as a sheath isolating each ommatidium from the next but is clumped in such a way that light could pass obliquely from ommatidium to ommatidium. Exner (67, 68) traced the ray paths, and showed by diagrams how light entering many ommatidial lenses could be re-

fracted and fall on the receptors of a central visual unit. Grenacher's terms 'apposition' type for the eye with isolated ommatidia and 'superposition' type for the eyes used in dim illumination have been retained.

The same ommatidium may function alone by day and in concert by night through migratory movements of its pigment (145, 248). In crustaceans these changes in the eye are often matched by alterations in body color, the entire chromatophore system being under the control of hormones whose secretion is influenced by stimulation of the eyes by light (207). The literature on this subject has become extensive but most of it centers on hormonal aspects. In insects the corresponding shifts in ommatidial pigment may be independent of hormones (44, 49).

Normal structure of compound eyes has required extensive study because of the large number of variations within the wealth of genera in the phylum Arthropoda. Where possible, many writers on the subject have attempted to correlate form with function (30, 31, 48, 51, 61, 62, 119, 250, 268, 269). Numerous crustaceans bear their eyes on movable eyestalks and show compensatory movements of these when the animal or its visual field is rotated. Branchiopods show all gradations between a distinct pair of compound eyes and indistinguishable fusion into a single mass. The fused median compound eye of *Daphnia* consists of about 20 ommatidia and is somewhat unusual in that it can be rotated several degrees within the body through the action of a series of oculomotor muscles.

Ostracod compound eyes are commonly separate if a median ocellus is present but fused if the ocellus is lacking. Some lack compound eyes entirely. The luminescent *Cypridina*, however, has fully developed eyes.

Copepod compound eyes range from the median fused structure of *Cyclops* and *Calanus* through genera in which the two are completely separate. Branchiuran compound eyes must be regarded as degenerate. *Argulus* has four eye types present in each individual. Barnacles have compound eyes only during the metanauplian stage (69). Among chilopods only *Scutigera* and related genera possess compound eyes (84). Here each eye consists of not more than 200 ommatidia, each with two rings of receptor cells as in the thysanuran insect *Lepisma*.

Growth of compound eyes is inferred among trilobites because of the gradual increase in number of ommatidia found to accompany increase in body size within each species (226). In *Limulus* and other xiphosurans, both the number of ommatidia and the size of each increase at each molt (284), rapidly in early ages and more slowly later on. The same is true in crustaceans studied (14, 16, 149) and most insects (16, 173). The stick insect *Dixippus* is unusual in adding no new ommatidia, although the total increase in dimensions of each is 126 per cent and the eye area doubles from hatching to maturity.

Development of the compound eye appears to depend upon normality of the supraesophageal ganglion. Damage to this ganglion usually leads to failure of the eye to differentiate. In *Drosophila*, however, the various genetic mutants with degenerate eyes arise through factors acting on the eye itself and not indirectly through the nervous system (225). Degeneration of compound eyes in cavernicolous arthropods and deep-sea crustaceans is common and apparently follows a similar genetic course influencing the eye itself (83). Beddard (13) believed a relationship could be seen between depth and degree of degeneration of the compound eye, but so many instances of hypertrophy of these organs in deep-sea crustaceans have been described that the generalization is unsafe.

Regeneration following injury to the compound eyes seems possible in decapod crustaceans, although the regenerated part is not an eye but an antennalike organ. Trilobites alone are known to have regenerated ommatidia (138), this being recognized in terms of independence in the direction of the facet pattern in areas set off by scar tissue.

CAMERA-STYLE EYES IN MOLLUSKS. The remarkable convergence in anatomical organization between the large eyes of some cephalopod mollusks and those of vertebrate animals have led to frequent comment. Hensen (102) investigated the embryonic steps leading to the cephalopod types of eye. In all the organ arises as an invaginated vesicle. That of *Nautilus* is unique in proceeding no farther and hence remaining as a pinhole-camera eye (fig. 7, *right*).

In all other cephalopods the vesicle closes and sinks below the body surface. The double layer of tissue where the pinhole closed produces a pair of planoconvex lenses in contact with one another, as the sole structure focusing an image in these marine organisms. Distal to the lens an encircling ridge arises forming the muscular iris diaphragm (fig. 7, *center*). The whole eye sinks further below the surface at the bottom of a fresh invagination the rim of which closes over either partially or completely in forming a transparent cornea. A number of genera retain an open pore between the anterior chamber and the outside world, and sea water washes the front of the

lens. In some genera an additional encircling ridge forms around the eye, producing an approach to eyelids.

Deep-sea cephalopods often have eyes which are amazingly hypertrophied, sometimes supported on swiveling turrets (33). In these a binocular field seems probable, whereas in most surface and mid-water cephalopods the visual fields are completely separate. The apparent absence of blind cephalopods must be related to the number of kinds which bear luminescent organs in the depths.

Most cephalopods have a slit pupil which closes into a slightly hooked horizontal line. It is under direct control from the central nervous system and changes the degree of opening more in relation to emotional conditions than it does reflexly in relation to light intensity (259). Muscles provide for accommodation of the lens (151, 164) and demonstrate their action when the outer surface of the eye is stimulated electrically (2, 101). In *Octopus*, at least, the resting eye is myopic by 6 to 10 diopters, and accommodation is both positive for objects at close range and negative for distance (274).

Unlike the vertebrate eye, the cephalopod organ has a direct retina. Its optic nerve fibers may emerge from the eyeball as multiple bundles which fuse into a common optic nerve. Around them are the four oculomotor muscles which shift the eye in a wide range of movements, including rotational ones (121, 251).

Electroretinograms from cephalopod eyes (211, 212) have been as helpful as behavior in indicating the role of vision in these animals. In all cephalopods the nervous system is so highly organized, with visual cues related elaborately to tactile ones and perhaps taste as well, that simple responses are rarely elicited. Captive animals are seemingly affected strongly by their confinement, but will develop conditioned responses under skilful handling.

Camera-style eyes of quite different form are found in some other mollusks. a) In the sand-eating pulmonate gastropods *Onchidium*, *Oncis* and *Peronina*, the dorsal surface of the body bears short wartlike projections each with a single eye or with from two to seven of them in an irregular cluster. Each eye is about 0.2 mm in diameter and has a two-part refractive body between the rather flattened cornea and the inverted retina. The more distal refractive body alters in shape when a muscular collar surrounding it contracts. Presumably this is an accommodation mechanism. Natural history observations on a Bermudan *Onchidium* possessing eyes of this type suggest nothing

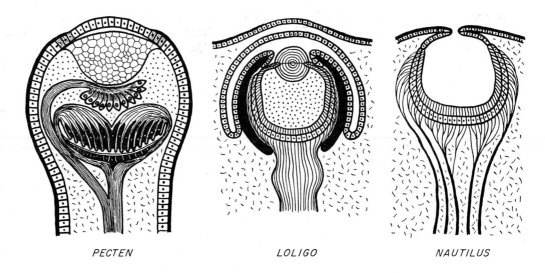

PECTEN   LOLIGO   NAUTILUS

FIG. 7. Mollusk eyes present a variety of optical systems. In the scallop *Pecten* (*left*), a cellular lens concentrates light on two levels of inverted retina. The distal layer mediates only the off-response leading to sudden closure of the shell valves. The proximal layer responds to steady illumination. A reflecting tapetum (shown as *opaque blocks* basal to the proximal retina) increases sensitivity and contrast discrimination at low intensities of light. In the cephalopod *Nautilus* (*right*), the eye becomes functional and matures as a pinhole-camera organ at an embryonic stage passed through in the development of all other cephalopod eyes. In the squid *Loligo* (*center*), extrinsic muscles orient the whole eye; intrinsic muscles provide both positive and negative accommodation and adjust the aperture of the slit pupil. [*Pecten* after Küpfer, *Loligo* and *Nautilus* after Hensen; from Milne & Milne (193).]

which might not be due to general photosensitivity (5).

b) Clams of the genus *Cardium* bear small eyes on short tentacles around the rim of the mantle. Each eye has a cellular lens mass in which the refractive index changes from distal to proximal and may provide an image on the rather coarse inverted retina. A cup-shaped extension of pigment cells surrounds the lens material and narrows to a distal pupil. The whole eye is invested in a muscular coat, the contraction of which alters the shape of the lens mass and may serve in accommodation. Nothing is known of the function of these eyes.

c) In the pelagic heteropods (gastropods) *Pterotrachea*, *Carinaria* and *Atalanta*, one small eye is borne projecting from the body contours on each side, like the port and starboard running lights on a ship. These highly modified eyes are directed forward and must have a binocular field in front of the animal, although no evidence has been presented to show that the animal makes use of them in sighting on objects of importance to it. Each eye has a large spherical lens at considerable distance from a 'ladder retina' with little ridges of receptor cells (fig. 8,

center) and a muscle whose contractions shift the lens (109), perhaps as a fine adjustment for focus.

CAMERA-STYLE EYES IN ANNELIDS. Fairly conventional camera-style eyes are found in the pelagic polychaetes *Alciopa* and *Eupolyodontes*. In the former (fig. 8, *left*) the two eyes at rest diverge widely, but contraction of three extrinsic muscles to each of them provides a basis for convergence, binocular vision and perhaps distance estimation (45). In *Eupolyodontes* the eyes face forward at rest (210). In all members of the family Alciopidae, the eye structure is comparable (79, 80). The large retina has direct receptors, a secreted mass of two consistencies separating the retina from the lens, an accommodation muscle (45), and a secretory cell (107) which responds well to electrical stimulation. Secretory action increases the volume of the distal mass behind the lens and pushes the lens forward, accommodating the eye for nearer vision. Muscular contraction should operate in the reverse sense. Unfortunately, no natural history details are available to indicate how and when these worms use their remarkable eyes.

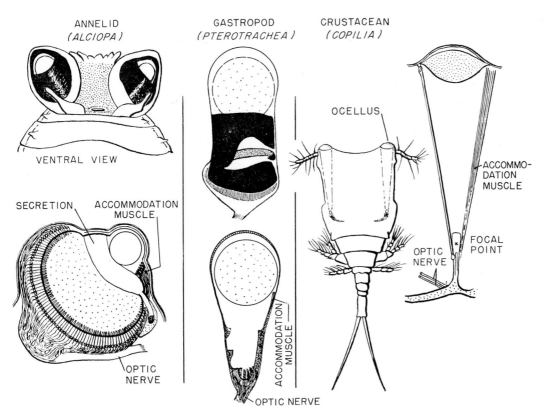

ANNELID
(ALCIOPA)

VENTRAL VIEW

SECRETION   ACCOMMODATION
MUSCLE

OPTIC
NERVE

GASTROPOD
(PTEROTRACHEA)

ACCOMMODATION
MUSCLE

OPTIC NERVE

CRUSTACEAN
(COPILIA)

OCELLUS

ACCOMMO-
DATION
MUSCLE

OPTIC
NERVE

FOCAL
POINT

FIG. 8. Camera-style eyes are found in several phyla of invertebrate animals, but the mechanism of accommodation varies considerably. In the polychaete annelid *Alciopa* it includes both a hydraulic system from a secretory gland, shifting the lens distally, and a muscle operating in the reverse direction (*left*). In the gastropod mollusk *Pterotrachea*, a muscle provides the basis for fine focusing on a series of receptor clusters known collectively as a 'ladder retina' (*center*). In the copepod crustacean *Copilia*, a small group of receptor cells at the focal point of the biconvex lens is shifted both toward the lens and swung laterally by muscular contraction. In both the mollusk and the crustacean the eyes apparently are useful only as sights but, like the annelid eyes with their extrinsic musculature, may have a binocular field in advance of the body. [*Alciopa* after Demoll; *Pterotrachea* after Hesse; *Copilia* dorsal view after Giesbrecht, detail after Grenacher; from Milne & Milne (193).]

CAMERA-STYLE EYES IN ARTHROPODS. Still less can be guessed as to the function of strangely simplified camera-style eyes in the planktonic copepod crustaceans known as corycaeids. *Copilia* carries two of them facing forward, widely separated in the body. *Sapphirina* has a pair close together. In *Corycaeus* their lenses are fused on the mid-line. Yet in all, the large lens in the body surface (fig. 8, *right*) appears to focus light on a little cluster of three or four receptor cells surrounded by a pigment sheath. A long slender muscle lengthwise at the side of the eye can shift the receptor cluster with reference to the lens in a way which may provide for both some accommodation and some sighting, perhaps in binocular vision. Nothing is known of the habits which would suggest a use for a visual mechanism of this kind.

PHENOMENA RELATED TO STIMULUS INTENSITY

Changes in the sensitivity and in the discriminatory capacity of multicellular eyes are often based in part upon other features in addition to photochemical changes and such obvious adjustments as those of iris diaphragms.

Pigment Migration within the Eye

A redistribution of pigment, either by active extension and contraction of pigment cells or by shifting of pigment granules within the protoplasm of stationary cells, follows changes in intensity of illumination on a variety of eyes: in the ocelli of the gastropod *Planorbis* (4, 241); in the stemmata of the lepidopteran caterpillar (235); in the ommatidia of crustaceans and insects (15, 46, 248, 254, 289, 309); and in the retina of cephalopod camera-style eyes (103, 106, 223). The redistribution serves to reduce the proportion of intense light reaching the receptor cells and to increase the proportion of dim light passing to retinal level.

In most insects that are active by day the pigment lies between the receptor cells when light intensity is high, and migrates below the basement membrane when the intensity is reduced. In mantid orthopterans and sphingid lepidopterans the mechanism is more like that in decapod crustaceans. During daylight the pigment is spread parallel to the crystalline cones and maintains isolation of one ommatidium from the next in typical apposition-eye organization; at night the pigment becomes concentrated distally, giving the eye a far darker appearance and permitting it to function on the superposition principle.

Either type of pigment movement may expose a reflecting layer in the eye. This may be either a 'basement tapetum' which serves to increase sensitivity and contrast at low light intensities by reflecting nonabsorbed incident light back through the receptor cells, or an 'iris tapetum' which reflects energy out of the eye again before it has reached the receptor-cell level. The latter is more developed among crustaceans (291), although found in some insects as well. If a basement tapetum is hidden by pigment movement at higher intensities of light, it is an 'occlusible tapetum' analogous to that found in some fish. No regularity is noticeable in either the chemical nature of the reflecting pigment or its systematic position. In *Limulus* the iris tapetum contains only guanine (146); the closely-related xiphosuran *Tachypleus* lacks a tapetum of any kind (284); the crayfish *Astacus* has an iris tapetum of uric acid (147); and the lobster *Homarus* one in which uric acid is supplemented by at least three additional substances, none of which is guanine (146).

So far, tapeta have been recognized either from eye histology or 'eyeshine' in only two phyla. Among mollusks it is present in the pelecypods *Pecten* (233) and *Cardium* (216). Among arthropods it is widespread in crustacean and insect ommatidia, in the ocelli of certain insects (216) and in the secondary ocelli of many spiders.

Spectral Sensitivity and Color Vision

Paralleling the spectral absorption characteristics of the photosensitive pigment in a receptor system is a spectral sensitivity shown through nerve impulses or responses in effector systems. With care an action spectrum can be plotted showing the energy required in a light stimulus at each wavelength in a series of tests to find the threshold of response. This graph is a spectral sensitivity curve; it regularly shows one or more maxima. The only exception reported, *Hydra*'s response to light (91), appears to be a uniform reaction at all wavelengths.

Even where two receptor systems are present in the same eye, there is no a priori reason to expect them to have different photosensitive pigments and hence a single action curve. In many vertebrate eyes the rod mechanism and the cone mechanism are known to have different spectral sensitivities, evident as a 'Purkinje shift' in the wavelength of maximum sensitivity and in the limits of the effective spectrum as the intensity is altered—reduced until the cones are inactive or raised until they dominate. A Purkinje shift has been detected in only one invertebrate so far (72), the fruit fly *Drosophila*.

A dual mechanism in the eye and a Purkinje shift does not indicate color vision; the dog has a Purkinje shift yet is color blind. Color vision depends upon differential mechanisms in the brain to which nerve impulses go separately from two or more unlike series of receptors active in the same intensity range. Color vision enables an organism to distinguish between radiant stimuli on the basis of inequalities of energy content at different wavelengths rather than upon intensity alone. A color-blind organism may distinguish between a series of grays but will confuse any color with some one shade of gray since only intensity discrimination is possible. The xiphosuran *Limulus* has been shown to have the peripheral basis for color vision (76) in that some ommatidia have greater sensitivity toward longer wavelengths, some toward shorter wavelengths; apparently this differential sensitivity at the ommatidial level is not used by the central nervous system since no discrimination between a spectral hue and a neutral source seems possible except on an intensity basis.

Scarcely any two individuals, let alone any two species, show the same range of spectral response. The human eye is regarded as sensitive to wavelengths from the extreme violet sensation at 400 mμ to the extreme red at 700 mμ. Many invertebrates are sensitive to wavelengths designated as ultraviolet (shorter than 400 mμ), even when these are not a normal part of their environment (as among aquatic organisms which are protected from radiation of this type by the spectral absorption characteristics of water). Many insects, which are active in sunlight containing ultraviolet, are more sensitive to this part of the solar spectrum than to the region visible to man (17, 18, 174, 175). In consequence it becomes important for man to learn more of what reflects ultraviolet, and hence may be visible to insects though not to him (26, 38, 175, 176).

Amebas travel as rapidly in the presence of radiations of long wavelengths (red) as in darkness but are increasingly sensitive as the wavelength of a stimulus is shortened (86). *Paramecium* tends to swim upwards in darkness, downward in light, and the direction is altered most effectively by shorter wavelengths (73).

The platyhelminth *Planaria* has been studied extensively in responses to spectral distribution in light stimuli. Erhardt (64) was able to account for earlier claims (19, 115) that *Planaria* had color vision upon intensity discrimination. Werner (292) concluded that much of the flatworm's response to ultraviolet arose through general photosensitivity and not the eyes; but Merker & Gilbert (187) found only non-directional kinetic responses when the eyes were removed, compared to a definite orientation with a single ocellus intact. They were able to plot the visual fields of *Planaria* toward ultraviolet and believed that responses were to the wavelengths used (366 to 313 mμ) rather than any secondary fluorescence.

Two separate receptor systems were described for the earthworm (255). One, mediating the shadow reaction, was most sensitive in the yellow portion of the spectrum and depended upon receptors distributed uniformly in the skin. The other, a more general photosensitivity related to rate of locomotion and the like, showed greatest sensitivity in the blue and was most developed toward the two ends of the body. In the leech *Piscicola*, pigment migration in surface chromatophores is an effector demonstration for which a spectral action curve can be drawn (140).

Using the threshold for retraction of the siphon as a kinetic cue to photosensitivity in the pelecypod *Mya*, Hecht (95) obtained a spectral action curve with limits somewhat short of those for the human eye. Its maximum fell at 500 mμ, suggesting that the neuronal photoreceptors in the mantle tissue of the clam have a photosensitive pigment similar to those extracted from organized eyes.

The fresh-water planktonic crustacean *Daphnia* appears to have at least three photosensory systems, one with greatest sensitivity in the ultraviolet (257), one in the yellow and the third in the blue. Only the latter two can have much importance under natural conditions (240). The response with maximum sensitivity to yellow is a positive horizontal swimming toward the radiant source. The response to blue is negative. Baylor and Smith at the University of Michigan have used the yellow and blue responses in an underwater trap which catches a wide variety of plankton organisms, crustaceans, acarid arachnids and insect larvae. Possibly photosensory mechanisms of this kind are involved in the vertical migrations made daily by many types of plankton, down during daylight, up at night.

Although the arthropod cuticle transmits freely a wide range of radiations from infrared to ultraviolet, only certain fireflies (nocturnal Coleoptera) have been found to respond to infrared stimuli (28). By painting the eyes of various butterflies with a clear red lacquer, Eltringham (63) was able to show that some kinds flew about naturally—able to see in red light—whereas others behaved as though blinded.

Sensitivity to ultraviolet is pronounced in most insects, and shown by many larvae as well (139, 184). Bertholf (17, 18) found a bimodal curve represented the spectral sensitivity of the honeybee. The peak in the ultraviolet was far higher than that in the spectrum visible to man and explained why these insects respond more to cues in ultraviolet components of sunlight than to reflectances visible to man. Lutz (174–176) examined the ultraviolet world of the insect and was able to produce conditioned responses in tropical hymenopterans (175) to patterns in white paints when one white reflected ultraviolet and another did not.

Conditioned responses in honeybees demonstrate that these insects do have color vision (270, 273). They can be trained to come for food to line spectra regardless of relative intensity (154–158). But a majority of insects, particularly the night-active ones, probably show no color vision, merely intensity discrimination based on a simple spectral-sensitivity curve (288). This may be modified from one genetic strain to another according to the eye pigments present and changes in the eye structure itself (71).

A neural basis for color vision has been described in insects (222, 230, 231); but whether even day-active species, operating in good light, make use of cues reaching them from differential mechanisms in the ommatidia is a point which must be established separately for each kind.

Form Perception and Pattern Recognition

If both the photosensory mechanism and the nervous system are sufficiently well organized and coordinated, the animal can give evidence of an awareness of surrounding events that is close to, if not identical with, consciousness. Identification marks and courtship gestures are significant in these terms. Insects which go habitually from one flower to another of the same kind demonstrate this type of discrimination; efficient pollination often depends upon it.

To be useful in form perception and pattern recognition, a photosensory mechanism must carry intensity discrimination the further step of detecting simultaneously in small areas of the visible field the differences in intensity which are significant. Several types of acuities are involved, all of them properly defined as the reciprocals of threshold intensities, whether linear, areal or angular. How large must a single object be to constitute an adequate stimulus? How far apart must two objects be for the gap between them to be visible? Can an object, such as a triangle, be significant in one orientation (say upright) but not another (say inverted)? Is alignment, or motion or distance significant to the organism as it views objects in the environment?

The camera-style eye and the compound eye appear most competent to interpret the world in terms of small differences in light intensity and to send messages to the central nervous system from which a picture of the environment can be assembled. Even for organisms with these eye types, pessimistic views have often been expressed. Frequently they represent inadequacy of experimental technique. "Absence of evidence is no evidence of absence." Thus Willem (295) concluded terrestrial mollusks could detect the presence of voluminous objects only when less than a centimeter distant, but von Buddenbrock (269) reported compensatory movements of the eyestalks to a rotating visual field much farther away. And various workers (100, 258) have had difficulty satisfying themselves that cephalopod mollusks respond to visual cues in the absence of simultaneous tactile and gustatory stimulation.

Plateau (217) obtained so few responses to the stimuli he gave to captive spiders that he concluded that they were essentially blind. Apparently some objects are recognized and others ignored, so that the acuities possible are not always demonstrated (208). No doubt Mallock (178) gave far too optimistic values of resolution in spider ocelli since he used the outmoded Rayleigh criterion in his calculations. Homann's estimates (127–129) correspond more closely with observed reactions.

Insect behavior seems to match reasonably well with predictions based on measurement of eyes and binocular fields (29, 47, 172, 173, 250, 307). Lack of accommodation—an ability claimed for ommatidia only once (265)—is of no significance in an apposition eye since no image is formed (256), or in a superposition eye since image resolution has been sacrificed for increased sensitivity. The mosaic style of vision tends to stress the importance of movement and find detail only at very close range.

REFERENCES

1. ABBOTT, C. E. *Turtox News* 27: 138, 1949.
2. ALEXANDROWICZ, J. S. *Arch. zool. exper. et gén.* 66: 71, 1927.
3. ANDREWS, E. A. *J. Morphol.* 5: 271, 1892.
4. AREY, L. B. *J. Comp. Neurol.* 26: 359, 1916.
5. AREY, L. B. AND W. J. CROZIER. *J. Exper. Zool.* 32: 443, 1921.
6. AUTRUM, H. *Experientia* 5: 271, 1949.
7. AUTRUM, H. AND N. STÖCKER. *Biol. Zentralbl.* 71: 129, 1952.
8. BALDUS, K. *Ztschr. vergleich. Physiol.* 3: 475, 1926.
9. BAUERS, C. *Ztschr. vergleich. Physiol.* 34: 589, 1953.
10. BAUMGARDT, E. L. M. *J. Gen. Physiol.* 31: 269, 1948.
11. BAUMGÄRTNER, H. *Ztschr. vergleich. Physiol.* 7: 56, 1928.
12. BAYLOR, E. R. AND F. E. SMITH. *Am. Natural.* 87: 97, 1953.
13. BEDDARD, F. E. *Voyage of H. M. S. Challenger, Zool.* 11(3, Part 33): 1, 1884.
14. BĚLEHRÁDEK, J. AND J. S. HUXLEY. *J. Exper. Biol.* 7: 37, 1930.
15. BENNITT, R. *J. Exper. Zool.* 40: 381, 1924.
16. BERNARD, F. *Bull. biol. France Belg.* Suppl. 23: 1, 1937.
17. BERTHOLF, L. M. *J. Econ. Entomol.* 20: 521, 1927.
18. BERTHOLF, L. M. *J. Agr. Res.* 43: 703, 1931.
19. BEUTHER, E. *Sitzber. Abhandl. naturforsch. Ges. Rostock* 1: 1, 1926.
20. BLISS, A. F. *J. Gen. Physiol.* 26: 361, 1943.
21. BLISS, A. F. *Biol. Bull.* 91: 220, 1946.
22. BOLWIG, N. *Vidensk. Meddelelser Dansk naturhist. Foren. Koebenhavn* 109: 80, 1946.
23. BOZLER, E. *Ztschr. vergleich. Physiol.* 3: 145, 1925.
24. BRAND, H. *Ztschr. wiss. Zool.* 144: 363, 1933.
25. BRECHER, G. *Ztschr. vergleich. Physiol.* 10: 497, 1929.
26. BRUES, C. T. *Proc. Am. Acad. Arts Sc.* 74: 281, 1941.
27. BRUNOTTE, C. *Compt. rend. Acad. Sc., Paris* 106: 301, 1888.
28. BUCK, J. B. *Physiol. Zoöl.* 10: 45, 1937.
29. BURT, E. T. AND W. T. CATTON. *Nature, London* 170: 285, 1952.
30. CARRIÈRE, J. *Quart. J. Microsc. Sc.* 24: 673, 1884.
31. CARRIÈRE, J. *Die Sehorgane der Thiere.* Munich: Oltenbourg, 1885.
32. CAUSEY, N. B. *Turtox News* 33: 200, 1955.
33. CHUN, C. *Verhandl. deutsch. zool. Gesellsch.* 13: 67, 1903.
34. COLLINS, D. L. AND W. MACHADO. *J. Econ. Entomol.* 28: 103, 1935.
35. CONSTANTINEANU, M. *J. Zool. Jahrb., Abt. Anat. Ontog. Tiere* 52: 253, 1930.
36. CORNELI, W. *Zool. Jahrb., Abt. Anat. Ontog. Tiere* 46: 573, 1924.
37. COWLES, R. P. *J. Exper. Zool.* 9: 387. 1910.

38. CRANE, J. *Zoologica* 39: 85, 1954.
39. CROZIER, W. J. *J. Exper. Zool.* 24: 211, 1917.
40. CROZIER, W. J. *J. Gen. Physiol.* 2: 627, 1920.
41. CROZIER, W. J. *J. Gen. Physiol.* 3: 57, 1920.
42. CROZIER, W. J. AND E. WOLF. *Biol. Bull.* 77: 126, 1939.
43. CUÉNOT, L. In: *Traité de Zoologie*, edited by P.-P. Grassé. Paris: Masson, 1949, vol. 6, p. 46.
44. DAY, M. F. *Biol. Bull.* 80: 275, 1941.
45. DEMOLL, R. *Zool. Jahrb., Abt. Anat. Ontog. Tiere* 27: 651, 1909.
46. DEMOLL, R. *Arch. ges. Physiol.* 129: 461, 1909.
47. DEMOLL, R. *Zool. Jahrb., Abt. Syst.* 28: 523, 1909.
48. DEMOLL, R. *Ergebn. Fortschr. Zool.* 2: 431, 1910.
49. DEMOLL, R. *Zool. Jahrb., Abt. allg. Zool. Physiol.* 30: 169, 1911.
50. DEMOLL, R. *Biol. Zentralbl.* 33: 727, 1913.
51. DEMOLL, R. *Die Sinnesorgane der Arthropoden, ihr Bau und ihre Funktion.* Brunswick, Germany: Vieweg, 1917.
52. DEMOLL, R. AND L. SCHEURING. *Zool. Jahrb., Abt. allg. Zool. Physiol.* 31: 519, 1912.
53. DE SERRES, M. *Phil. Mag.* 44: 107, 183, 274, 1814.
54. DETHIER, V. G. *J. Cell. & Comp. Physiol.* 19: 301, 1942.
55. DETHIER, V. G. *J. Cell. & Comp. Physiol.* 22: 115, 1943.
56. DEWAR, J. AND J. G. M'KENDRICK. *Proc. Roy. Soc. Edinburgh* 8: 179, 1873.
57. DIETRICH, W. *Zool. Anz.* 32: 470, 1907.
58. DIETRICH, W. *Ztschr. wiss. Zool.* 92: 465, 1909.
59. DUBOIS, R. *IX Internat. zool. Congres, Monaco* 1: 148, 1913.
60. DUGÈS, A. *Ann. Sc. Nat. Zool.* 21: 341, 1830.
61. EGGERT, B. *Zool. Anz.* 73: 33, 1927.
62. ELTRINGHAM, H. *Trans. Roy. Entomol. Soc. London*: 1, 1919.
63. ELTRINGHAM, H. *Butterfly Lore.* New York: Oxford, 1923, p. 117.
64. ERHARDT, A. *Biol. Zentralbl.* 52: 321, 1932.
65. ESCHER-DERIVIÈRES, J., E. LEDERER AND M.-L. VERRIER. *Compt. rend. Acad. sc. Paris* 207: 1447, 1938.
66. EWING, W. *Edinburgh J. Sc.* 5: 297, 1826.
67. EXNER, S. *Sitzber. Akad. Wiss. Wien (Abt. III)* 98: 13, 1889.
68. EXNER, S. *Die Physiologie der Facettirten Augen von Krebsen und Insecten.* Leipzig: Deuticke, 1891.
69. FALES, D. E. *Biol. Bull.* 54: 534, 1928.
70. FAUST, E. C. *Biol. Bull.* 35: 117, 1918.
71. FINGERMAN, M. *J. Exper. Zool.* 120: 131, 1952.
72. FINGERMAN, M. AND F. A. BROWN, JR. *Science* 116: 171, 1952.
73. FOX, H. M. *Biol. Rev.* 1: 219, 1925.
74. FRAENKEL, G. *Ztschr. vergleich. Physiol.* 6: 385, 1927.
75. GRAHAM, C. H. *J. Cell. & Comp. Physiol.* 2: 295, 1932.
76. GRAHAM, C. H. AND H. K. HARTLINE. *J. Gen. Physiol.* 18: 917, 1935.
77. GRANIT, R. *Receptors and Sensory Perception.* New Haven: Yale Univ. Press, 1955.
78. GRAVE, C. AND G. RILEY. *J. Morphol.* 57: 185, 1935.
79. GREEFF, R. *Sitzber. Gesellsch. Beförder. ges. Naturw. Marburg:* 115, 1875.
80. GREEFF, R. *Nova Acta Leopoldina* 39: 33, 1877.
81. GRENACHER, G. H. *Untersuchungen über das Sehorgan der Arthropoden, insbesondere der Spinnen, Insekten und Crustaceen.* Göttingen: Vanderhöck u. Ruprecht, 1879.
82. HANSTRÖM, B. *Kgl. Svenska Vetenskapsakad. Handl.* [3] 4: 1, 1926.
83. HANSTRÖM, B. *Arch. Entwicklungsmechn. Organ.* 115: 154, 1929.
84. HANSTRÖM, B. *Lunds Univ. Årsskr. N. F.* 30: 1, 1934.
85. HARPER, E. H. *Biol. Bull.* 10: 17, 1905.
86. HARRINGTON, N. R. AND E. LEAMING. *Am. J. Physiol.* 3: 9, 1899.
87. HARTLINE, H. K. *Am. J. Physiol.* 83: 466, 1928.
88. HARTLINE, H. K. *J. Cell. & Comp. Physiol.* 11: 465, 1938.
89. HARTLINE, H. K. *The Harvey Lectures* Ser. 37: 39, 1941.
90. HARTLINE, H. K., H. G. WAGNER AND E. F. MacNICHOL, JR. *Cold Spring Harbor Symp. Quant. Biol.* 17: 125, 1952.
91. HAUG, G. *Ztschr. vergleich. Physiol.* 19: 246, 1933.
92. HEATH, H. *Proc. Acad. Nat. Sc. Philadelphia* 56: 257, 1904.
93. HECHT, S. *J. Exper. Zool.* 25: 261, 1918.
94. HECHT, S. *J. Gen. Physiol.* 3: 367, 1921.
95. HECHT, S. *J. Gen. Physiol.* 3: 375, 1921.
96. HECHT, S. *Science* 53: 347, 1921.
97. HECHT, S. *Am. Scientist* 32: 159, 1944.
98. HECHT, S. AND G. WALD. *Proc. Nat. Acad. Sc., Washington* 19: 964, 1933.
99. HECHT, S. AND G. WALD. *J. Gen. Physiol.* 17: 517, 1934.
100. HEIDERMANNS, C. *Zool. Jahrb., Abt. allg. Zool. Physiol.* 45: 609, 1928.
101. HEINE, L. *Med. naturwiss. Arch.* 1: 322, 1907.
102. HENSEN, V. *Ztschr. wiss. Zool.* 15: 155, 1865.
103. HENSEN, V. *Zool. Anz.* 1: 30, 1878.
104. HERTEL, E. *Ztschr. allg. Physiol.* 4: 1, 1904.
105. HERTER, K. *Ztschr. vergleich. Physiol.* 4: 103, 1926.
106. HESS, C. *Zentralbl. Physiol.* 16: 91, 1902.
107. HESS, C. *Arch. ges. Physiol.* 172: 449, 1918.
108. HESS, C. *Arch. ges. Physiol.* 181: 1, 1920.
109. HESS, C. AND A. GERWERZHAGEN. *Arch. vergleich. Ophthalmol.* 4: 300, 1914.
110. HESS, W. N. *J. Morphol. Physiol.* 41: 63, 1925.
111. HESS, W. N. *Carnegie Inst. Washington Yr. Bk.* 30:382, 1931.
112. HESS, W. N. *J. Exper. Zool.* 79: 1, 1938.
113. HESS, W. N. *Carnegie Inst. Washington Publ.* 517: 153, 1940.
114. HESSE, R. *Ztschr. wiss. Zool.* 61: 693, 1896.
115. HESSE, R. *Ztschr. wiss. Zool.* 62: 527, 1897.
116. HESSE, R. *Ztschr. wiss. Zool.* 63: 456, 1898.
117. HESSE, R. *Ztschr. wiss. Zool.* 65: 446, 1899.
118. HESSE, R. *Zool. Anz.* 24: 30, 1901.
119. HESSE, R. *Ztschr. wiss. Zool.* 70: 347, 1901.
120. HESSE, R. *Ztschr. wiss. Zool.* 72: 565, 1902.
121. HESSE, R. *Das Sehen niederer Tiere.* Jena: Fischer, 1908.
122. HEYMAN, C. AND A. R. MOORE. *J. Gen. Physiol.* 7: 345, 1925.
123. HILTON, W. A. *J. Entomol. Zool.* 13(3): 49, 1921.
124. HILTON, W. A. *J. Entomol. Zool.* 13(4): 55, 1921.
125. HILTON, W. A. *J. Entomol. Zool.* 16(3): 89, 1924.
126. HOMANN, H. *Ztschr. vergleich. Physiol.* 1: 541, 1924.
127. HOMANN, H. *Ztschr. vergleich. Physiol.* 7: 201, 1928.
128. HOMANN, H. *Ztschr. vergleich. Physiol.* 14: 40, 1931.
129. HOMANN, H. *Ztschr. vergleich. Physiol.* 20: 420, 1934.
130. HOMANN, H. *Ztschr. Naturforsch.* b2: 161, 1947.
131. HUNDERTMARK, A. *Ztschr. Forst- u. Jagdwesen* 70: 225, 1938.
132. HYMAN, L. H. *The Invertebrates: Protozoa through Ctenophora.* New York: McGraw-Hill, 1940.
133. HYMAN, L. H. *The Invertebrates: II. Platyhelminthes and Rhynchocoela; the Acoelomate Bilateria.* New York: McGraw-Hill, 1951.
134. HYMAN, L. H. *The Invertebrates: III. Acanthocephala, Aschelminthes, and Entoprocta; the Pseudocoelomate Bilateria.* New York: McGraw-Hill, 1951.

135. HYMAN, L. H. *The Invertebrates: IV. Echinodermata; the Coelomate Bilateria.* New York: McGraw-Hill, 1955.
136. IMHOF, O. E. *Biol. Zentralbl.* 21: 189, 1901.
137. IMHOF, O. E. *Biol. Zentralbl.* 21: 459, 1901.
138. ISBERG, O. *Geol. Fören. i Stockholm Förh.* 39: 593, 1917.
139. JANDA, V. *Zool. Anz.* 96: 77, 1931.
140. JANZEN, R. *Ztschr. Morphol. Ökol. Tiere* 24: 327, 1932.
141. JOSEPH, H. *Biol. Generalis* 4: 237, 1928.
142. KAHMANN, H. *Tabul. biol. ('s-Grav.)* 22: 1, 1947.
143. KAMPA, E. M. *Nature, London* 175: 996, 1955.
144. KEPNER, W. A. AND A. M. FOSHEE. *J. Exper. Physiol.* 23: 519, 1917.
145. KIESEL, A. *Sitzber. Akad. Wiss. Wien (Abt. III)* 103: 97, 1894.
146. KLEINHOLZ, L. H. *Biol. Bull.* 109: 362, 1955.
147. KLEINHOLZ, L. H. AND W. HENWOOD. *Anat. Rec.* 117: 637, 1953.
148. KOLLER, G. AND G. VON STUDNITZ. *Ztschr. vergleich. Physiol.* 20: 388, 1934.
149. KOSSWIG, C. AND L. KOSSWIG. *Verhandl. deutsch. Zool. Gesellsch.* 38: 274, 1936.
150. KRAUSE, A. C. *Tabul. biol. ('s-Grav.)* 22: 200, 1951.
151. KROHN, A. *Nova Acta Leopoldina* 19: 41, 1842.
152. KRUGELIS-MACRAE, E. *Biol. Bull.* 110: 69, 1956.
153. KRUKENBERG, C. F. W. *Unters. physiol. Inst. Heidelb.* 2: 1, 1882.
154. KÜHN, A. *Nachr. Ges. Wiss. Göttingen. Jahresber. Geschäftsjahr. Math. physik. Kl.:* 66, 1923.
155. KÜHN, A. *Naturwissenschaften* 12: 116, 1924.
156. KÜHN, A. *Ztschr. vergleich. Physiol.* 5: 762, 1927.
157. KÜHN, A. AND G. FRAENKEL. *Nachr. Ges. Wiss. Göttingen. Jahresber. Geschäftsjahr. Math. physik. Kl.:* 330, 1927.
158. KÜHN, A. AND R. POHL. *Naturwissenschaften* 9: 738, 1921.
159. KÜPFER, M. *Vierteljahresschr. naturforsch. Ges. Zürich* 60: 568, 1915.
160. LANDOIS, H. *Ztschr. wiss. Zool.* 16: 27, 1866.
161. LANGDON, F. E. *J. Morphol.* 11: 193, 1895.
162. LANGDON, F. E. *J. Comp. Neurol.* 10: 1, 1900.
163. LANGELOH, H. P. *Zool. Jahrb., Abt. allg. Zool. Physiol.* 57: 235, 1937.
164. LANGER, C. *Sitzber. Akad. Wiss. Wien (Abt. I)* 5: 324, 1850.
165. LEMKE, G. *Ztschr. vergleich. Physiol.* 22: 298, 1935.
166. LIGHT, V. E. *J. Morphol. Physiol.* 49: 1, 1930.
167. LINK, E. *Verhandl. deutsch. zool. Gesellsch.* 18: 161, 1908.
168. LINK, E. *Zool. Anz.* 33: 445, 1908.
169. LINK, E. *Zool. Jahrb., Abt. Anat. Ontog. Tiere* 27: 213, 1909.
170. LINK, E. *Zool. Jahrb., Abt. Anat. Ontog. Tiere* 27: 281, 1909.
171. LOCHHEAD, J. H. *Anat. Rec.* 75, Suppl.: 64, 1939.
172. LUEDTKE, H. *Ztschr. vergleich. Physiol.* 26: 162, 1938.
173. LUEDTKE, H. *Ztschr. Morphol. Ökol. Tiere* 37: 1, 1940.
174. LUTZ, F. E. *Ann. New York Acad. Sc.* 29: 181, 1924.
175. LUTZ, F. E. *Am. Museum Novitates* 641: 1, 1933.
176. LUTZ, F. E. *Natural History* 33: 565, 1933.
177. MACNICHOL, E. F., H. H. WAGNER AND H. K. HARTLINE. *XIX Internal Physiol. Congr., Proc.:* 582, 1953.
178. MALLOCK, A. *Nature, London* 113: 45, 1924.
179. MARCUS, E. *Biol. tiere Deutsch.* 14: 1, 1925.
180. MAST, S. O. *J. Exper. Zool.* 20: 1, 1916.
181. MAST, S. O. *J. Exper. Zool.* 34: 149, 1921.
182. MAST, S. O. *Arch. Protistenk.* 60: 197, 1928.
183. MAST, S. O. AND N. STAHLER. *Biol. Bull.* 73: 126, 1937.
184. MAYER, A. G. AND C. G. SOULE. *J. Exper. Zool.* 3: 415, 1906.

185. MERLIN, D. *Zool. Bidrag Uppsala* 8: 1, 1923.
186. MENZER, G. AND K. STOCKHAMMER. *Naturwissenschaften* 38: 190, 1951.
187. MERKER, E. AND H. GILBERT. *Zool. Jahrb., Abt. allg. Zool. Physiol.* 50: 479, 1932.
188. MILLOTT, N. *Biol. Bull.* 99: 329, 1950.
189. MILLOTT, N. *Nature, London* 171: 973, 1953.
190. MILLOTT, N. *Tr. Royal Soc., London ser. B* 238: 187, 1954.
191. MILLOTT, N. *Endeavour* 16: 19, 1957.
192. MILLOTT, N. AND H. G. VEVERS. *J. marine Biol. A. U.K.* 34: 279, 1955.
193. MILNE, L. J. AND M. J. MILNE. In: *Radiation Biology,* edited by A. Hollaender. New York: McGraw-Hill, 1956, vol. 3, p. 621.
194. MINKIEWICZ, R. *Compt. rend. Acad. sc., Paris* 143: 785, 1906.
195. MINKIEWICZ, R. *Compt. rend. Acad. sc., Paris* 143: 934, 1906.
196. MITSUKURI, K. *Annot. Zool. Japon.* 4: 1, 1901.
197. MOORE, A. R. *Arch. sc. biol.* 8: 112, 1926.
198. MOSELEY, H. N. *Quart. J. Microsc. Sc.* 25: 37, 1885.
199. MOSELLA, R. G. *Boll. Ist. zool. Univ. Roma* 4: 166, 1927.
200. MURBACH, I. *Biol. Bull.* 14: 1, 1907.
201. NAGEL, W. A. *Der Lichtsinn Augenloser Tiere.* Jena: Fischer, 1896.
202. NOTTHAFT, J. *Abh. senckenberg. naturforsch. Gesellsch.* 12: 35, 1881.
203. OLMSTED, J. M. D. *J. Exper. Zool.* 24: 333, 1917.
204. PARKER, G. H. *Proc. Soc. Exper. Biol. & Med.* 3: 61, 1906.
205. PARKER, G. H. *Proc. Am. Philos. Soc.* 61: 107, 1922.
206. PATTEN, W. *Mitt. zool. Stat. Neapel* 6: 542, 1886.
207. PERKINS, E. B. *J. Exper. Zool.* 50: 71, 1928.
208. PETRUNKEVITCH, A. *J. Exper. Zool.* 5: 275, 1907.
209. PFLUGFELDER, O. *Zool. Anz.* 89: 276, 1930.
210. PFLUGFELDER, O. *Ztschr. wiss. Zool.* 142: 540, 1932.
211. PIPER, H. *Arch. Anat. Physiol., Physiol. Abt.:* 453, 1904.
212. PIPER, H. *Arch. Anat. Physiol., Physiol. Abt.:* 85, 1911.
213. PIRENNE, M. H. *Nature, London* 170: 824, 1952.
214. PLATE, L. H. *Zool. Jahrb.* 4, Suppl.: 1, 1897.
215. PLATE, L. H. *Zool. Jahrb.* 5: 15, 281, 1899.
216. PLATE, L. H. *Allgemeine Zoologie und Abstammungslehre. II. Die Sinnesorgane der Tiere.* Jena: Fischer, 1924.
217. PLATEAU, F. *Bull. acad. roy. Belg.* 14: 545, 1887.
218. PROSSER, C. L. *J. Cell. & Comp. Physiol.* 4: 363, 1934.
219. RABAUD, E. *Compt. rend. Acad. sc., Paris* 173: 606, 1921.
220. RABAUD, E. *Compt. rend. Soc. de biol.* 92: 603, 1925.
221. RÁDL, E. *Zool. Zentralbl.* 9: 82, 1902.
222. RAMÓN Y CAJAL, S. *Trab. Lab. Invest. Biol. Univ. Madrid* 7: 217, 1909.
223. RAWITZ, B. *Arch. Anat. Physiol., Physiol. Abt.:* 367, 1891.
224. REDIKORZEW, W. *Ztschr. wiss. Zool.* 68: 581, 1900.
225. RICHARDS, M. H. AND E. Y. FURROW. *Biol. Bull.* 48: 243, 1925.
226. RICHTER, R. *Zentralbl. Mineral. Geol.:* 344, 1922.
227. ROESCH, P. *Jena. Ztschr. Naturwiss.* 50 (N.F. 43): 97, 1913.
228. RULLIER, F. *Bull. lab. maritime Dinard* 30: 21, 1948.
229. ST. GEORGE, R. C. C. AND G. WALD. *Biol. Bull.* 97: 248, 1949.
230. SANCHÉZ, D. S. Y. *Arch. Neurobiol.* 3: 337, 1922.
231. SANCHÉZ, D. S. Y. *Trab. Lab. Invest. Biol. Univ. Madrid* 21: 143, 1923.
232. SCHALLEK, W. *J. Exper. Zool.* 91: 155, 1942.
233. SCHLICHER, J. *Verhandl. naturh. Ver. preuss. Rheinl. Westfal.* 82: 197, 1926.

234. SCHLÜTER, E. *Ztschr. wiss. Zool.* 143: 538, 1933.
235. SCHMITT-AURACHER, A. *Biol. Zentralbl.* 43: 225, 1923.
236. SCHÖNE, H. *Ztschr. vergleich. Physiol.* 33: 63, 1951.
237. SCHREINER, K. E. *Bergens Museums Årbok, Naturv.* 1897: 1, 1898.
238. SHETTLES, L. B. *J. Exper. Zool.* 77: 215, 1937.
239. SHORTESS, G. S. *Physiol. Zool.* 15: 184, 1942.
240. SMITH, F. E. AND E. R. BAYLOR. *Am. Natural.* 87: 49, 1953.
241. SMITH, G. *Bull. Museum Comp. Zoöl. Harvard* 48: 233, 1906.
242. SMITH, J. E. *Phil. Trans.* B227: 111, 1937.
243. SPENGEL, J. W. *Fauna e Flora Golf. Napoli* 18: 1, 1893.
244. STEPHENS, G. C., M. FINGERMAN AND F. A. BROWN, JR. *Ann. Entomol. Soc. Am.* 46: 75, 1953.
245. STIASNY, G. *Ztschr. wiss. Zool.* 110: 36, 1914.
246. STROHM, K. *Zool. Anz.* 36: 156, 1910.
247. STSCHEGOLEW, G. G. *Rev. zool. russe* 7: 149, 1927.
248. SZCZAWINSKA, W. *Arch. Biol. Paris* 10: 523, 1890.
249. TALIAFERRO, W. H. *J. Exper. Zool.* 31: 59, 1920.
250. TISCHLER, W. *Zool. Jahrb., Abt. allg. Zool. Physiol.* 57: 157, 1936.
251. TOMPSETT, D. H. *Liverpool Marine Biol. Comm. Mem.* 32: 1, 1939.
252. TÜMPEL, R. *Ztschr. wiss. Insektenbiol.* 8: 167, 218, 1912.
253. TÜMPEL, R. *Ztschr. wiss. Insektenbiol.* 10: 275, 1914.
254. UCHIDA, H. *J. Fac. Sc. Imp. Univ. Tokyo* Sect. IV, 3: 517, 1934.
255. UNTEUTSCH, W. *Zool. Jahrb., Abt. allg. Zool. Physiol.* 58: 69, 1937.
256. VAN DER HORST, C. J. *Acta Zool.* 14: 101, 1933.
257. VAN HERWERDEN, M. A. *Biol. Zentralbl.* 34: 213, 1914.
258. VAN WEEL, P. B. *Arch. neérl. Zool.* 1: 347, 1935.
259. VAN WEEL, P. B. AND S. THORE. *Ztschr. vergleich. Physiol.* 23: 26, 1936.
260. VIAUD, G. *Compt. rend. Soc. de biol.* 129: 1174, 1938.
261. VIAUD, G. *Compt. rend. Soc. de biol.* 129: 1177, 1938.
262. VIAUD, G. *Compt. rend. Soc. de biol.* 129: 1178, 1938.
263. VIAUD, G. *Bull. biol. France Belg.* 74: 249, 1940.
264. VIAUD, G. *Bull. biol. France Belg.* 77: 68, 1943.
265. VIGIER, P. *Compt. rend. Acad. sc., Paris* 138: 775, 1904.
266. VON APÁTHY, S. *Verhandl. intern. zool. Kongr. Berlin* 1901: 707, 1902.
267. VON BUDDENBROCK, W. *Der Biologe* 3: 231, 1934.
268. VON BUDDENBROCK, W. *Biol. Rev.* 10: 283, 1935.
269. VON BUDDENBROCK, W. *Vergleichende Physiologie. Band I: Sinnesphysiologie.* Basel: Birkhäuser, 1952.
270. VON FRISCH, K. *Zool. Jahrb., Abt. allg. Zool. Physiol.* 35: 1, 1914.
271. VON FRISCH, K. *Experientia* 5: 142, 1949.
272. VON FRISCH, K. *Experientia* 6: 210, 1950.
273. VON FRISCH, K. *Bees: their Vision, Chemical Senses, and Language.* Ithaca: Cornell Univ. Press, 1950.
274. VON PFLUGK. *Ber. ophthal. Gesellsch.* 36: 54, 1910.
275. VON ÜXKÜLL, J. *Ztschr. Biol.* 34: 319, 1897.
276. WALD, G. *Am. J. Physiol.* 133: 479, 1941.
277. WALD, G. *Am. Scientist* 42: 72, 1954.
278. WATASÉ, S. *Stud. Biol. Lab. Johns Hopkins Univ.* 4: 287, 1890.
279. WATERMAN, T. H. *Science* 111: 252, 1950.
280. WATERMAN, T. H. *Tr. New York Acad. Sc.* (2) 14: 11, 1951.
281. WATERMAN, T. H. *Proc. Nat. Acad. Sc., Washington* 39: 287, 1953.
282. WATERMAN, T. H. *Proc. Nat. Acad. Sc., Washington* 40: 252, 1954.
283. WATERMAN, T. H. *Proc. Nat. Acad. Sc., Washington* 40: 258, 1954.
284. WATERMAN, T. H. *J. Morphol.* 95: 125, 1954.
285. WATERMAN, T. H. *Science* 120: 927, 1954.
286. WATERMAN, T. H. AND C. A. G. WIERSMA. *J. Exper. Zool.* 126: 59, 1954.
287. WEBER, H. *Zool. Anz.* 108: 49, 1934.
288. WEISS, H. B. *J. Econ. Entomol.* 36: 1, 1943.
289. WELSH, J. H. *J. Exper. Zool.* 56: 459, 1930.
290. WELSH, J. H. *J. Cell. & Comp. Physiol.* 4: 379, 1934.
291. WENRICH, D. H. *Brit. J. Anim. Behav.* 6: 297, 1916.
292. WERNER, O. *Zool. Jahrb., Abt. allg. Zool. Physiol.* 43: 41, 1926.
293. WHITMAN, C. O. *Zool. Jahrb., Abt. Anat. Ontog. Tiere* 6: 616, 1893.
294. WIDMANN, E. *Ztschr. wiss. Zool.* 90: 258, 1908.
295. WILLEM, V. *Arch. Biol. Paris* 12: 57, 1892.
296. WILSON, N. *Tr. Linnean Soc. London* 23: 107, 1860.
297. WOLF, E. *Ztschr. vergleich. Physiol.* 3: 209, 1925.
298. WOLF, E. *J. Gen. Physiol.* 16: 407, 1933.
299. WOLF, E. *J. Gen. Physiol.* 16: 773, 1933.
300. WOLF, E. AND G. ZERRAHN-WOLF. *J. Gen. Physiol.* 18: 853, 1935.
301. WOLF, E. AND G. ZERRAHN-WOLF. *J. Gen. Physiol.* 20: 767, 1937.
302. WOLSKY, A. *Zool. Anz.* 80: 56, 1929.
303. WOLSKY, A. *Ztschr. vergleich. Physiol.* 12: 783, 1930.
304. WOLSKY, A. *Ztschr. vergleich. Physiol.* 14: 385, 1931.
305. YONGE, C. M. *Sc. Rep. Brit. Museum* 1: 283, 1936.
306. YUNG, E. *Arch. sc. phys. et nat.* 118: 77, 1913.
307. ZACHARIAS, O. *Monatschr. Mitt. Gesammtgeb. Naturwiss.* 7: 173, 1890.
308. ZAVŘEL, J. *Zool. Anz.* 31: 247, 1907.
309. ZIMMERMANN, K. *Zool. Jahrb., Abt. Anat. Ontog. Tiere* 37: 1, 1913.

CHAPTER XXVII

The image-forming mechanism of the eye

GLENN A. FRY | *School of Optometry, The Ohio State University, Columbus, Ohio*

CHAPTER CONTENTS

THE EYE PLAYS THE TRIPLE ROLE of gathering information, coding it and relaying it to the brain. In this chapter we are concerned only with the role which the eye plays as an optical device in gathering information.

In trying to explain this role I have started with a schematic eye which is free from some of the defects and complications of an actual eye. With this kind of an eye one can explain how an image is formed and what is meant by refracting power, refraction of the eye, size of the retinal image, etc.

The eye is not like a telescope which can be taken apart to find out how it works. Hence it is necessary to develop approaches which are not needed with an ordinary optical device. For example, the focal length of an eye cannot be measured directly and we have to substitute the concept of refraction to provide an index of an eye's performance as an optical instrument. An attempt will be made to explain how this and other measurements are made on a living eye. After explaining these basic concepts and methods of measurement, consideration will be given to the mechanism whereby the eye can change its focus.

The physiologist is by right more concerned with the response of the retina to light than the mechanics of applying light to the retina, but there are some special problems that arise in describing the stimulus applied to the retina to which attention must be given. In optics the word illuminance is used to describe the rate at which light is applied to the retina, but the physiologist wants to call this stimulus intensity. This is confusing because in optics the term intensity is reserved to designate the candlepower of a point source.

Furthermore, blur produces a pattern of illuminance on the retina which is quite different from the distribution of luminance in the visual field, and in most cases it is the blur inherent in the image-forming mechanism and not the structure of the retina which limits the ability of the eye to resolve fine detail.

Stray light in the eye also presents a problem. Although the stray light is feeble in comparison with the focused light which is applied to a small spot on the retina, it still has to be reckoned with in relating the light response of the pupil and the potential of the electroretinogram to the pattern of stimulation applied to the retina. We are dealing not only with the small number of photoreceptors responding to focused light but also with the millions of photoreceptors responding to stray light.

This chapter also includes a section on entoptic phenomena because they are used in various indirect ways to help us understand how the eye gathers information.

The study of the image-forming mechanism of the eyes has a long history because as soon as man began to think about himself as something separate from the external world, he assumed the reality of the external world and began to wonder how he could see external objects. At first he supposed that images were given off by objects and transmitted into the eye. He reasoned that these images must be reduced in size in order to get through the pupil. The discovery of the small images reflected by the cornea led to the belief that these images are responsible for vision, and the lens and not the retina was assumed to be the structure assigned to relay the images to the brain. This view lasted for centuries. About the beginning of the seventeenth century, Kepler (79, p. 116) discovered and described how an image is formed by a refracting surface. He then applied his concepts to the eye to show how the refracting mechanism of the eye must form an upside-down picture on the retina. The pinhole camera which was invented about the same time helped to demonstrate how an upside-down image could be formed, and finally Scheiner (79, p. 116) demonstrated the upside-down image on the back of an excised eye.

About this time attention was turned away from the nature of the image on the retina to the mechanism of accommodation by which the eye can change its focus. From the time of Kepler to that of Young (79, p. 158) various mechanisms were proposed including change in length of the eye, change in the curvature of the cornea, change in the position and shape of the lens and change in the size of the pupil. Young (86, p. 201; 79, p. 158) with a series of brilliant experiments at the beginning of the nineteenth century showed that the lens provides the basis for accommodation. Since then steady progress has been made in understanding the various aspects of image formation by the eye.

Helmholtz (79) has presented at the end of each of his chapters an historical summary and a bibliography which is useful to those interested in the early history of the subject. There are other general references that pertain to the early history (74, 77, 78).

IMAGE FORMATION

Gullstrand's Schematic Eye and Its Refracting Mechanism

In demonstrating the principles of image formation by the eye, it is customary to substitute for an

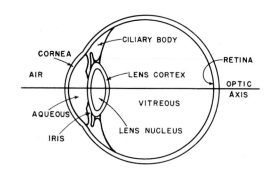

FIG. 1. Gullstrand's schematic eye, in which the dimensions and indices are as follows:

	mm
Thickness of cornea	0.5
Displacement of front surface of lens behind front surface of cornea	3.6
Displacement of nucleus from front surface of lens	0.546
Thickness of nucleus	2.419
Thickness of lens	3.6
Index of refraction of cornea	1.376
Index of aqueous and vitreous	1.336
Index of lens cortex	1.386
Index of lens nucleus	1.406
Radius of front surface of cornea	7.7
Radius of back surface of cornea	6.8
Radius of front surface of lens	10.0
Radius of front surface of nucleus	7.911
Radius of back surface of nucleus	−5.76
Radius of back surface of lens	−6.0

actual eye a schematic eye such as Gullstrand's (79, p. 392) which is illustrated in figure 1.

The front and back surfaces of the cornea, the front and back surfaces of the lens and the front and back surfaces of the nucleus of the lens are the refracting surfaces and constitute the refracting mechanism. The spaces bounded by these surfaces are assumed to be filled with homogeneous transparent media, but differ from each other in having different indices of refraction. The six refracting surfaces of Gullstrand's schematic eye are assumed to be spherical and centered on a common optic axis.

Formation of Image by Refracting Mechanism

The refracting mechanism forms images of objects placed in front of the eye. The simplest kind of object that can be so placed is a monochromatic point source of light as shown in figure 2. The point source Q gives off rays which are incident at the cornea. Because these rays diverge from the point Q this point represents the focus of the incident rays. These rays are said to exist in object space and the point Q is called an object point.

The pupil admits into the eye a certain number of the rays diverging fron the point Q, and after these rays emerge into the vitreous they are said to exist in image space. They converge at the point Q' which represents the image point which is conjugate to Q.

One can locate the image point corresponding to a given object point by tracing two or more rays through the refracting surfaces. Each ray entering the eye is refracted or bent at each surface in accordance with Snell's law of refraction, illustrated in figure 3. The ray in the first medium which is incident to the refracting surface makes an angle α with the normal to the refracting surface at the point of incidence. After it emerges into the second medium as the refracted ray, it makes an angle α' with the normal. Snell's law states that

$$n \sin \alpha = n' \sin \alpha'$$

where n represents the index of refraction of the first medium and n' the index of the second medium.

This method of locating an image point which involves tracing rays from surface to surface is tedious, and it is much simpler to locate first the so-called cardinal points and planes and then use these to locate the image point. For Gullstrand's schematic eye one may compute for any given wavelength a pair of nodal points N and N', a pair of principal points H and H' and planes, and a pair of focal points F and F' and planes (see fig. 4). The significance of these points and planes will become obvious as the discussion proceeds.

A ray incident to the front surface of the eye which is directed through the first nodal point emerges into the vitreous directed through the second nodal point and parallel to the incident path of the ray, as shown in figure 5. A second incident ray which passes through the primary focal point F emerges into the vitreous parallel to the optic axis. The emerging ray is also directed through the points V and V'. This is true because an incident ray which is directed through the point V in the primary principal plane must emerge into the vitreous directed through the point V' in the second principal plane which lies on a line through V parallel to the optic axis. This is a consequence of the fact that the principal planes are the conjugate planes of unit magnification. A third incident ray parallel to the optic axis emerges into the vitreous directed through the secondary focal point F'. All three of these rays which emerge into the vitreous converge at the image point Q'. It is obvious that once the cardinal points and planes are located we can predict the location of the image of any object point.

The cardinal points bear fixed relations to each other so that once the principal points and one of the focal points are given, the locations of the other points can be immediately determined by means of

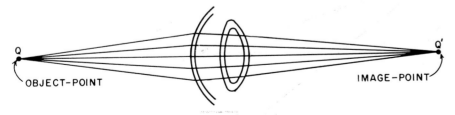

FIG. 2. Conjugate foci in object and image space.

the equation

$$H'F' = \frac{n'}{n}(FH) = FN = \frac{n'}{n}(N'F')$$

where n' is the index of the vitreous and n the index of air.

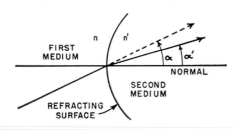

FIG. 3. Snell's law of refraction.

Refracting Power of the Eye

Since the locations of principal points and the ratio n'/n are relatively fixed from eye to eye and remain relatively unchanged as a given eye accommodates, the specification of the distance $H'F'$ tells us practically all we need to know about the refracting mechanism of an eye. Instead of specifying this distance, which is known as the secondary focal length, it is more usual to specify the refracting power F, but

$$F = n'/H'F'$$

The refracting power is expressed in diopters.

The refracting power of an eye is dependent upon the curvature of the refracting surfaces and the indices of the media. In all cases except for the back surface

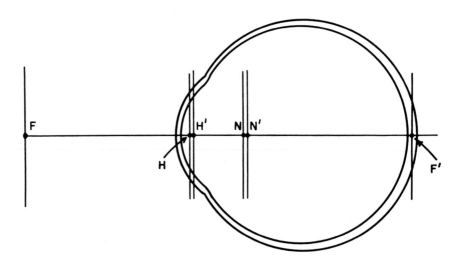

FIG. 4. Cardinal points of the Gullstrand schematic eye. In this eye the secondary focus F' falls 0.387 mm behind the retina, i.e. the layer of photosensitive elements that respond to light. The principal points H and H' are located 1.348 mm and 1.602 mm from the front surface of the cornea, respectively. $FH = N'F' = 17.055$ mm and $H'F' = FN = 22.785$ mm. The ratio $H'F'/FH$ is equal to the index of the vitreous.

FIG. 5. Ray tracing.

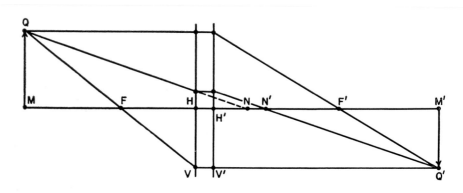

of the cornea, an increase in curvature increases the refracting power of the eye.

When we want to know how a change in index affects the refracting power of the eye, we have to approach the matter from a different direction. If we introduce a thin layer of air between the adjoining media, this will create two surfaces for each surface except the first, and each medium will be bounded on both sides by air. Introducing such layers of air would not affect the direction of the refracted rays. Figure 6 represents an exploded diagram showing each medium bounded on both sides by air. These elements form plus and minus lenses except in the case of the lens nucleus where a biconvex lens is formed, and in the case of the vitreous where we must deal with a single refracting surface. This analysis of the optical system makes it easy to visualize what happens when the index of a given medium changes. An increase in index will increase or decrease the total power of the eye depending upon whether the refracting effect of the particular element is plus or minus.

Helmholtz Schematic Eye

Helmholtz (79, p. 152) made use of a somewhat more simplified schematic eye than that employed by Gullstrand. In the Helmholtz schematic eye the cornea represents a single refracting surface at which the aqueous adjoins the air. Furthermore the lens is treated as having a uniform index throughout (see fig. 7).

The value which Helmholtz selected for the radius of the front surface of the eye approximates the average front surface of the cornea in the adult human eye. The displacement of the lens from the front surface of the eye also approximates the distance from the front surface of the cornea to the front surface of the lens as measured experimentally. The thickness of the lens and the radii of curvature also approximate the actual values. The value of 1.338 given to the

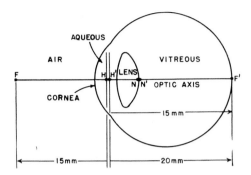

FIG. 7. The Helmholtz schematic eye

index of the aqueous and vitreous for sodium light (589 mμ) approximates the true value. A value of 1.455 has been selected for the lens because, if the lens substance is assumed to have a uniform index throughout, it gives the lens approximately the same refracting power as an actual lens immersed in vitreous. The indices selected by Helmholtz have been adjusted by Laurance (54) from 1.338 to 1.333 (or 4/3) and from 1.455 to 1.45 in order to give the eye primary and secondary focal lengths of −15 and 20 mm, respectively, which are round numbers.

The radii of curvature of the refracting surfaces, their locations and the indices of the media constitute the optical constants of the eye and are summarized for the Helmholtz schematic eye in table 1. All of these values refer to sodium light (589 mμ).

Reduced Eye

Helmholtz's schematic eye can be simplified still further, as has been done by Laurance (54), by using a single refracting surface as shown in figure 8. The interior of this eye is filled with a medium which has the same index throughout and is equivalent to that of the vitreous of the Helmholtz schematic eye, namely 1.333. The surface at which this medium makes contact with the air in front of the eye is the only refracting surface. The curvature of this surface has been arbitrarily increased to compensate for the absence of the lens so that the eye has the same refracting power as the Helmholtz schematic eye.

In the reduced eye the two principal planes coincide and are tangent to the front surface of the eye. The two nodal points coincide at the center of curvature of the front surface. The focal lengths are the same as in the Helmholtz schematic eye, and for most purposes the reduced eye is equivalent to the Helmholtz eye. It is very useful for visualizing certain

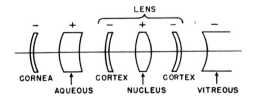

FIG. 6. Exploded diagram of the Gullstrand schematic eye showing the various elements with air spaces between them.

TABLE 1. *Optical Constants of the Helmholtz Schematic Eye*

Distance from cornea to front of lens...........	3.6 mm
Thickness of lens...........................	3.6 mm
Radii of curvature:	
Cornea................................	8 mm
Front surface of lens	10 mm
Back surface of lens........................	6 mm
Indices of refraction (sodium light)	
Aqueous...............................	1.333
Lens..................................	1.45
Vitreous...............................	1.333

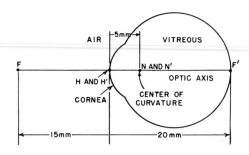

FIG. 8. The reduced eye devised by Laurance.

aspects of image formation as will become obvious later.

Role of Pupil in Image Formation

The pupil is an aperture in the iris which lies in contact with the front surface of the lens. The pupil varies in size because the muscles in the iris can make it either contract or dilate. The pupil is important in the formation of an image on the retina because by changing its size it can affect the illuminance and the blur of the image. It does this by limiting the size of the ray bundle which enters the eye from each object point. In terms of geometrical optics this means that it serves as the aperture stop of the system.

In order to understand the role of the pupil in image formation, it simplifies matters to make use of the imaginary entrance- and exit-pupils of the eye. The entrance-pupil is conjugate to the real pupil with respect to refraction at the cornea, and the exit-pupil is conjugate to the entrance-pupil with respect to the complete refracting mechanism of the eye. The entrance-pupil is larger than the real pupil and lies slightly in front of it. The exit-pupil lies behind the real pupil and is not quite as large as the entrance-

pupil. The entrance-pupil is the pupil which we see when we look at another person's eye. This is the pupil on which direct measurements can be made in visual experiments. Its position and diameter can be directly determined. The positions and sizes of the real and of the exit-pupil have to be calculated.

Chief Rays

Another concept which is needed in explaining the role of the pupil is that of a chief ray. The chief ray oi a bundle of rays entering the pupil of the eye from a given object point is the one which is directed through the center (O) of the entrance-pupil and which, after refraction at the cornea, passes through the center of the real pupil. After emerging into the vitreous, it is directed through the center (O′) of the exit-pupil, as shown in figure 9.

Blur Circles in Eye Free from Astigmatism

The major role of the pupil is to limit the size of the blur circles and ellipses formed on the retina when an eye is out of focus. The schematic and reduced eyes referred to above are all free from astigmatism for object points close to the optic axis because the refracting surfaces are assumed to be spherical and also centered on the optic axis. In this eye free from astigmatism, the bundle of rays from a given object point emerges into the vitreous as a cone or pencil of rays with the exit pupil forming the base and with the rays coming to a focus at the apex as shown in figure 10. This point is called the optical image and may lie on, in front of, or behind the retina. If the retina intercepts the bundle at the optical image so that the optical image falls on the retina, the retinal image in terms of geometrical theory is a point image; but if the optical image Q' falls in front of or behind the retina, the retinal image at Q'' is an out-of-focus blur circle. As is obvious from figure 10, the size of the blur circle is determined by the size of the exit-pupil.

Astigmatism

The bundle of rays from a point source does not always come to a focus at a point. The most common deviation from this ideal is called astigmatism. Figure 11 illustrates an astigmatic bundle of rays emerging from the exit-pupil. The planes which intersect at the chief ray constitute the meridians of the bundle. The vertical and horizontal meridians are the principal meridians because the rays come to a focus in these

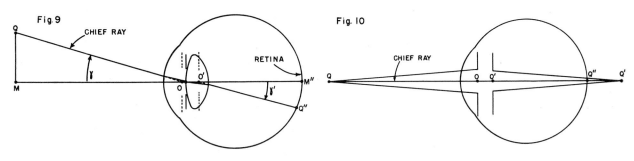

FIG. 9. Chief ray.   FIG. 10. Out-of-focus blur circle.

meridians. The rays in the vertical meridian focus at Q' and the rays in the horizontal meridian at Q''. Cross sections of the bundle at various distances from the exit-pupil are also shown in the figure. The cross section is in general elliptical but at Q' it becomes a horizontal line and at Q'' a vertical line. At one point in between it becomes a circle; and when this part of the bundle is intercepted by the retina, the effect is the same as throwing out of focus an eye which is free from astigmatism.

There are two principal causes of astigmatism. On the one hand the chief ray of the bundle may be oblique to one or more of the refracting surfaces. On the other hand one or more of the surfaces may be toroidal, i.e. a given surface may be shaped like the side of a barrel which is more curved in the direction around the barrel than up and down. It is obvious that in a multisurface system like the eye, there may be many combinations of toroidal and tilted surfaces and it becomes impractical to try to analyze all these various combinations.

In practice the resultant astigmatism is measured and treated without analyzing the contributions made by the separate surfaces. However, the toroidicity of the cornea may be independently measured and gross observations may be made of the tilt of the refracting surfaces.

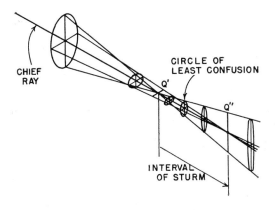

FIG. 11. Astigmatic blur ellipses.

Lines of Sight

Object points which lie on the incident path of a chief ray produce concentric blur circles or ellipses on the retina, and because of this the incident path of a chief ray is also called a line of sight.

Primary Line of Sight and Foveal Chief Ray

Of all of the lines of sight (or chief rays) which converge at the center of the entrance-pupil, there is

one which is all-important in the use of the eyes. When a person is told to fixate a given point with one of his eyes while the other is covered, he points that eye at the object. The pointing is not steady because the eye is subject to a fine tremor and also weaves back and forth and makes occasional jerks away from the object, but we can nevertheless think of the average fixating position of the normal eye as one in which the retinal image is centered on a given part of the retina which falls somewhere near the center of the fovea. The chief ray which penetrates this point is the foveal chief ray and the incident path of this ray is the primary line of sight.

Pupillary Axis and Angle λ

It is customary to specify the location of the foveal line of sight in terms of its relation to the pupillary axis which can be easily located by objective methods. The pupillary axis is a line normal to the front surface of the cornea and directed through the center of the entrance-pupil. It forms an angle λ with the primary line of sight which also passes through the center of

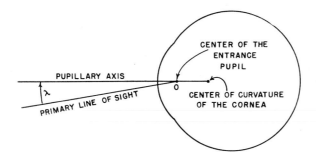

FIG. 12. The angle λ.

the entrance-pupil. The pupillary axis is usually about 5 degrees temporalward from the primary line of sight, as appears in figure 12.

Size of Retinal Image

The chief ray concept is also useful in dealing with the size of the retinal image of an external object. The angle γ subtended by two object points at the center of the entrance-pupil O is called the visual angle; it is the angle between the two lines of sight (see fig. 9).

The term 'size of the retinal image' refers to the linear distance between the retinal images M'' and Q'' of the two object points M and Q. When the eye is out of focus, the retinal images are blur circles and the size $M''Q''$ represents the distance between the centers of the two blur circles formed on the retina. If the angle γ' subtended by the centers of the two blur circles at the center of the exit-pupil is expressed in radians,

$$\gamma' = \frac{\text{linear separation of the centers of two blur circles}}{\text{distance from the exit pupil to the retina}}.$$

The ratio of γ' to γ is one of the more important constants of the eye. In the case of the Helmholtz schematic eye

$$\gamma'/\gamma = 0.81.$$

With this ratio and the distance from the exit-pupil to the retina specified, one can compute the linear separation of two blur circles on the retina for a given value of γ.

The expression 'size of the retinal image' is often misinterpreted to mean the size of the blur circle formed by a single object point, but this is something which is quite different from the linear separation between the centers of two blur circles.

REFRACTION AND ACCOMMODATION OF THE EYE

The eye has an adjustable focusing mechanism. The first section of this chapter has explained how the eye forms an image of an object when the focusing mechanism is fixed. This section describes how the changes in focus may be described and specified.

Refraction of the Eye

If a given point on the primary line of sight produces a bundle of rays which comes to a point focus on the retina, the eye is said to be focused for this point. Another way of stating this is to say that the object point producing the bundle is conjugate to the retina.

The spectacle point S (14 mm in front of the cornea) is used as the reference point for specifying the location of the point R which is conjugate to the retina, as represented in figure 13A. Stating the distance from R to S adequately describes the refractive state of the eye, but it is customary to use the reciprocal of this distance and call it the refraction of the eye. It is measured in diopters when the distance $\overline{RS}$ is given in meters.

When the eye is astigmatic, it is necessary to specify separately the refraction in the two principal meridians. To visualize this problem it is better to start with a point on the retina penetrated by the foveal chief ray and trace a bundle of rays back out of the eye through the entrance-pupil. The line of sight represents the chief ray of this bundle, and the principal meridians are the planes which intersect at right angles at the line of sight.

The 0 to 180 degree meridian which is the reference meridian for the location of the principal meridians lies in the plane of regard which is defined by the centers of the two entrance-pupils and the point of convergence of the two primary lines of sight. In figure 13B the line of sight is perpendicular to the paper and penetrates the front of the eye at A. The angles ϕ_1 and

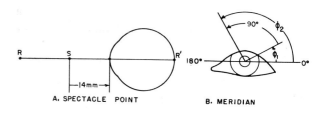

FIG. 13. Reference points and planes for specifying the refraction of an eye.

ϕ_2 represent the counterclockwise angular displacement of the principal meridians from the 0 to 180 degree meridian.

Accommodation

The refracting mechanism of the eye possesses the ability of accommodating itself for different distances; that is to say, the eye can focus on one object at a given moment and on an object at a different distance a moment later. This represents a change in the refractive state of the eye which is brought about by a change in form of the lens and a slight movement forward. The major part of this effect is mediated by the change in curvature of the front surface of the lens, and it greatly simplifies our concept of how the eye works if we assume that this is the only variable. If as in the schematic eye the pupil is centered upon the optical axis of the lens, chief rays through the center of the pupil cross the axis at the front surface of the lens and the refraction of such rays is not affected by a change in curvature. There is therefore no change in the ratio of γ' to γ.

Static Refraction of the Eye

When accommodation is relaxed, the point $\bar{R}$ for which the eye is accommodated in a given meridian is known as the far point (*punctum remotum*) for that meridian. The reciprocal ($1/\bar{R}S$) of the distance from the far point ($\bar{R}$) to the spectacle point (S) is defined as the static refraction of the eye and is measured in diopters. The spectacle point corresponds to the back surface of a spectacle lens and lies 14 mm in front of the cornea. For all practical purposes it coincides with the primary focal point.

Emmetropia is the condition in which the far point lies at infinity and in which the static refraction equals zero. Ametropia is the condition in which the far point does not lie at infinity but at some finite distance either in front of or behind the spectacle point. Myopia is the positive type of ametropia in which the far point lies at some finite distance in front of the spectacle point. Hyperopia is the negative type of ametropia in which the far point lies behind the spectacle point.

When an eye is equally ametropic in all meridians, it is said to have a spherical error of refraction which may be either hyperopic or myopic. When the static refraction differs in the various meridians, the eye is said to have an astigmatic error of refraction.

Correction for Ametropia

That lens which will permit an ametrope to see lines clearly in all meridians at 6 m with relaxed accommodation is called the distance correction. The myope needs a minus lens and the hyperope a plus lens, as shown in figure 14. In each case the refracting power of the lens is the same in all meridians and is equal numerically to the static refraction but opposite in sign. Myopia for example is a positive ametropia which is neutralized with a minus lens.

A person with astigmatism requires a lens which varies in power from meridian to meridian. Such a lens has a toric or cylindrical surface on one side and a plane or spherical surface on the other and is equivalent to a combination of a spherical lens with a cylindrical lens. The cylindrical lens compensates the astigmatic component of the refractive error, and the spherical lens compensates the residual spherical component.

In designing a lens for a given person many combinations of surfaces may be used on the two sides to provide the correction for the ametropia, and other factors have to be considered in selecting the particular curves to be used. The thickness and index can also be varied although the glass normally used has an index of 1.523 for sodium light. The lens may be designed to compensate for its own aberrations, to provide a specified amount of angular magnification in addition to refracting power and to minimize reflections, and some consideration is always given to breakage and weight on the face. Plastic lenses are sometimes used instead of glass lenses.

The ordinary ophthalmic lens is mounted with its back surface at or near the spectacle point 14 mm from the cornea and with its optic axis passing through the center of rotation of the eye.

A corneal contact lens is worn in contact with the cornea, while the scleral type contact lens contacts

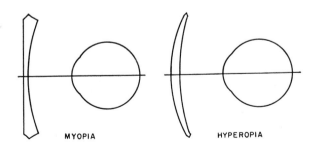

FIG. 14. Spectacle lenses for the correction of spherical ametropia.

the sclera around the cornea with a thin fluid layer between the contact lens and the cornea.

Specification of Amount of Accommodation in Play

Accommodation is measured in diopters and represents the reciprocal of the distance from the conjugate focus of the retina to the spectacle point when the distance correction is worn. Thus when the distance correction is worn the accommodation must be reduced to its zero level in order to see a distant object clearly.

The maximal amount of accommodation that can be elicited is called the amplitude of accommodation. The nearest point for which the eye can accommodate is called the near point of accommodation (*punctum proximum*). This varies with age as shown in figure 15. At the age of about 40, the near point recedes rapidly beyond the ordinary working distance of 33 to 40 cm. Various sets of data relating amplitude to age have been analyzed by Marg *et al.* (63). It is necessary to compensate for this loss of accommodation with a plus lens added to the distance correction. The added plus lens power at the near point is usually provided in the form of a bifocal which has enough plus lens power added in the segment to permit the eye to see clearly at a given working distance with one half of the accommodation held in reserve.

Aphakia

When the crystalline lens is missing, the eye is said to be aphakic. The lens may be surgically removed, it may be congenitally absent, or it may be dislocated so that it fails to cover the pupillary aperture. Clear vision can still be obtained by means of a lens mounted in front of it, but the eye no longer has any power of accommodation. The range of clear vision through any given lens is strictly a function of the depth of the focus of the eye.

In the first section of this chapter reference was made to the indices of the media and the curvature of the refracting surfaces and their distances in front of the retina. In the second section, reference was made to the distance from the conjugate focus of the retina to the spectacle point and its use in specifying refraction and accommodation. This section explains how such quantities are actually measured.

Indices of Media

Each medium of the eye has been assumed to be uniform in the schematic eye; but the cornea and the lens have a definite microstructure and can be treated as made up of layers of different indices.

The cornea has five different layers, the epithelium, Bowman's membrane, the stroma, Descemet's membrane and the endothelium. The index for the epithelium has been found to be 1.416 and that for the rest of the cornea, 1.372 (22, p. 728).

The index of the lens substance varies from 1.387 at the cortex to 1.406 at the center (22, p. 736). The variation in index of the lens from the center to the cortex affects its performance as an image-forming device. The problem can be formulated by visualizing a series of isoindical surfaces from the cortex to the center. In a meridian section these surfaces probably correspond to the course of the fibers as they arch around the nucleus from the axis back to the axis (79, p. 339).

The index of the aqueous is 1.336 and that of the vitreous is the same (22, p. 734).

The index measurements reported above have all been made with an Abbé refractometer which makes use of the principle of total reflection.

Purkinje Images

The Purkinje images are important because they provide us with many objective methods of studying the configuration, tilt and location of the refracting surfaces. The refracting surfaces of the eye can form images both by reflection and refraction. Images involving single reflection at the front and back surfaces of the cornea and at the front and back surfaces of the lens are known as the first, second, third and fourth Purkinje images (86, p. 48). These images may be seen by an observer located in front of the eye.

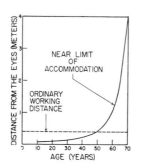

FIG. 15. Regression of the near point of accommodation with age. Based on Donder's data (20). It is assumed that the distance correction is worn.

Optic Axis of the Eye

It has been assumed in connection with the schematic eye that the refracting surfaces are centered on a common axis, but the extent to which this is true in the case of an actual eye can be tested by observing the Purkinje images of a point of light held close to the observer's eye. The subject is then made to follow a fixation target which is moved about until the Purkinje images line up or at least until the third and fourth ones line up. This puts the observer's eye on the path of a ray of light which passes through the lens normal to both surfaces, and the extent to which the center of the pupil and the center of curvature of the front surface of the cornea are displaced from the optic axis of the lens can then be directly observed.

In general the optic axis (in so far a such an axis exists) coincides with the pupillary axis, so that the optic axis deviates temporalward from the primary line of sight about 5 degrees and also about 2 degrees downward (86, p. 77). For the purpose of specifying this angle, it may be assumed that the two lines intersect at the center of the entrance-pupil.

The optic axis does not necessarily coincide with the anatomical axis of the eye which may be defined as the line connecting the geometrical center of the cornea (front pole) with the geometrical center of the sclera (back pole). However, the optic axis and the anatomical axis do approximately coincide in the average eye. Theoretically the anatomical axis of the eye should coincide with the line normal to the cornea at its geometrical center This is called the geometrical axis of the cornea.

Configuration of Front Surface of Cornea

The central portion of the cornea is usually spherical or toroidal. With a keratometer one can determine whether the cornea is spherical or toroidal and, if it is toroidal, the principal meridians can also be determined. Furthermore, one can measure the radius of curvature in each of the principal meridians of a toroidal cornea and in any meridian of a spherical cornea.

The central portion of the typical cornea which may be regarded as spherical or toroidal covers a region about 4 mm in diameter and outside of this area the curvature gradually decreases as the limbus is approached. The center of the optical portion does not necessarily fall at the center of the cornea (79, p. 311; 86, p. 68).

The exact form of the peripheral portion of the cornea can be investigated in a number of ways. One can view the profile of the cornea with a microscope or photograph the profile. One can examine it point by point with an ordinary keratometer by using a variable point of fixation. It can also be viewed with a keratoscope or photographed with a photokeratoscope. In this technique a reflected image of a series of concentric circles is used. In one of the later models (50) the concentric rings are arranged on a spherical surface concentric with the eye so that the reflected images cover the entire cornea. Another method is that of sprinkling powder on the cornea and then taking a stereophotograph which can later be analyzed like an aerial map. One can also take a mold of the cornea as in fitting contact lenses and then study the configuration of the mold.

Measurement of Internal Refracting Surfaces

One can measure the position of the margin of the iris with respect to the cornea and assume that this lies in contact with the front surface of the lens (79, p. 19, 334). The ophthalmophakometer (86, p. 80) and the Blix ophthalmometer (79, p. 326) make use of specular reflections at the surfaces to locate the positions of the vertices and centers of curvature of the surfaces. It is also possible to photograph the Purkinje images (1, 2, 6, 45, 49, 94) and to calculate the radii of curvature of the reflecting surfaces from this kind of data.

Fincham (26, p. 38) used diffusely reflected light to produce an optical section of the refracting surfaces, and by viewing with a microscope having a calibrated fore and aft movement he was able to measure directly the apparent separations of the surfaces. A similar arrangement can be used with a camera replacing the microscope (26, p. 44). A projective transformation of the photographic image gives a cross section of the eye. This method has the advantage of showing not only the configurations of the surfaces but also gives the internal structure of the lens.

The measurements made on an internal surface apply to the apparent surface viewed through the refracting surfaces lying in front of the surface in question. The concept of a thick mirror is helpful in this connection. The center of curvature of the apparent surface is the image of the actual center of curvature formed by the refracting surfaces lying in front, and the vertex of the apparent surface is also the image of the vertex of the actual surface.

X-ray Measurement of Axial Length of the Eye

A sheet of X-rays is produced by passing X-rays through two parallel slits, and the eye is held so that this sheet of rays traverses the eye perpendicular to the direction of regard, as shown in figure 16. Its intersection with the retina is a circle and, since X-rays so applied stimulate the retina, the subject sees a circle of light. The size of the circle can be made smaller and smaller by moving the sheet of rays toward the back of the eye, keeping it always perpendicular to the direction of regard. It reduces to a point as it becomes tangent to the retina. The distance of the cornea from this plane can then be measured by sighting on the profile of the cornea (23). (Care must be taken to keep the X-rays from passing through the crystalline lens.)

X-ray Determination of Location of Second Nodal Point

Two sheets of X-rays are produced by passing X-rays from a source through one slit and these then are passed again through two slits which are parallel to the first slit as shown in figure 17. These two sheets of rays are allowed to traverse the back of the eye which is pointed with its optic axis in a direction parallel to the slits. Two distant object points are adjusted so that their images fall on the two lines on the retina stimulated by the X-rays. Knowing the linear separation of the two X-ray images and knowing the angular separation of the two optical images at the second nodal point, one can compute the distance from the second nodal point to the retina.

Locating Conjugate Focus of Retina

It is assumed in this section that the astigmatism of the eye, if any be present, has been corrected and that the experimenter is interested only in locating the conjugate focus of the retina for the purpose of determining the refractive state of the eye or the amount of accommodation in play. In order to simplify our problem let us consider absolute presbyopia in which the eye has a fixed focus. The same thing occurs in an aphakic eye or in an eye which has been temporarily paralyzed with a drug. In this case a target is needed to control fixation and then some subjective or objective means must be provided for locating the conjugate focus of the retina.

Let us consider the subjective methods first. A target consisting of a point, a line or a row of small letters can be used for controlling fixation and locating the conjugate focus of the retina. The distance can be varied or lenses may be placed in front of the eyes. The natural pupil may be used or, if this has been dilated, a diaphragm with a pupil of normal size can be placed before the eye. The target must be fine enough so that the subject can tell when the focus is sharpest.

The Scheiner principle substitutes for the natural pupil two small holes or two parallel slits. If a single target is used the retinal image doubles when it is out of focus (fig. 18). The doubling is easier to detect when monochromatic light is used than when white light is used; still better the two beams can be transmitted through filters of different color. If the upper and lower halves of a vertical slit are seen through different parts of the pupil displaced laterally from

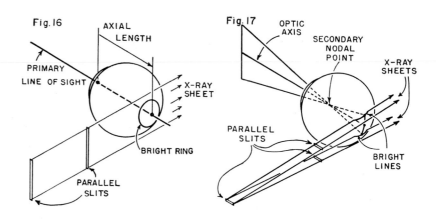

FIG. 16. X-ray measurement of the axial length of the eye.   FIG. 17. X-ray method of locating the second nodal point.

each other, the two halves of the slit are seen out of vertical alignment when the eye is out of focus (fig. 19). Monochromatic light is used in this case. Since the Scheiner technique makes use of only two small parts of the pupil, it may yield a different measure of accommodation than a measurement based upon the full pupil. This is a function of the spherical aberration of the eye. Consequently the Scheiner principle is primarily useful in measuring changes in accommodation.

The threshold principle involves having the target (usually a line) disappear when it goes out of focus. This test has the advantage that it can be used with a normal pupil.

The retinoscope (skiascope) is an objective device for determining the refraction of the eye. A small mirror throws a beam of light on the eye from a small source. The examiner looks through a small hole in the mirror and observes the light reflected from the retina back out of the eye. This makes the pupil appear bright, and moving the mirror modifies the distribution of the light in the pupil so that the examiner can tell when the eye is out of focus for the hole in the mirror. When the eye has a fixed focus, the subject can control his fixation by fixating the mirror image of the light source.

The coincidence optometer is another objective device which is a very valuable means for the objective determination of the refractive state. In this device an image is formed on the pigment epithelium in contact with the retina, and the light diffusely reflected from this surface forms an image in the plane conjugate to the retina. This image is viewed through an eye piece. The target and the focal plane of the eye piece are kept at the same distance from the subject's eye, but this distance can be varied to locate the conjugate focus of the retina. The operator may use blur as a criterion for the proper setting, or as in Fincham's instrument (24, 27) a modification of Scheiner's principle may be used. Fincham (unpublished observations) has also made use of a photoelectric cell with a feed-back which automatically focuses the instrument.

Campbell (15) has designed an optometer based on the use of a photocell and Scheiner's principle which automatically records changes in accommodation.

The indirect ophthalmoscope may be used like a coincidence optometer except that the blood vessels and demarcations on the retina are used instead of an image of an external target focused on the retina. In this way only the focus of the emerging beam is involved in the measurement.

With the direct ophthalmoscope the refracting mechanism of the subject's eye is used as a magnifier, the focal length of which can be varied with the auxiliary lenses mounted in the instrument.

The aberrations of the eye and the differences in criteria as to what constitutes a focus create a problem in trying to correlate the results obtained with subjective and objective methods.

A technique known as the fogging method has been developed for measuring the 'zero level' of accommodation by manipulating the stimulus pattern

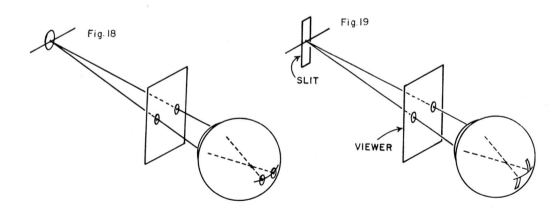

FIG. 18. Scheiner principle with doubling as the criterion of the retinal image being out of focus.

FIG. 19. Scheiner principle with vernier displacement as the criterion. Assume that the upper and lower halves of the slit are covered with polaroid with the axes at right angles, and that the two holes in the viewer are also covered with polaroid with the axes crossed at right angles.

to force accommodation to this level. A chart of small letters is used to control fixation and to stimulate relaxation of accommodation. Plus lenses are placed in front of the eye to relax accommodation and then additional plus lenses are used to get below the level to which accommodation can be relaxed. This 'fogs' the eye. Once the eye is 'fogged' the plus power is reduced to locate the level at which the 'fog' ends. This represents the 'zero level' of accommodation. The measurement can be carried out on the two eyes at the same time if they have previously been corrected for astigmatism and anisometropia. The target is placed at a distance of about 6 m to create an awareness of distance and also to relax convergence if the test is binocular.

In many experiments it is necessary to stimulate accommodation to various degrees. For most purposes it suffices to use a single target with fine detail to control fixation and accommodation. If the fine detail is clearly visible, it is assumed that the eye is in focus for the target. On the other hand it is often desirable to find out whether the amount of accommodation in play is leading or lagging behind the stimulus. One target is used for stimulating fixation and accommodation and, if both eyes are used, it also serves as a convergence stimulus. An independent target must be used to measure the amount of accommodation in play. This target is usually presented to one eye and a beam splitter is used to superimpose an image of the measuring target upon the stimulus target. The image of the measuring target must be adjustable so that it can be made to fall in front of or behind the stimulus target. A single bright point source is a good measuring target because it cannot compete with the more complex stimulus target in controlling accommodation. This is the principle underlying the stigmatoscope.

The threshold principle (56; 57, p. 485; 73) may be employed to avoid stimulating accommodation. As long as the target is invisible, it cannot stimulate accommodation and hence it is moved from the out-of-focus position to the just-visible point. This is done from both directions to determine the limits of the visible range. The mid-point is assumed to be the point of best focus.

It is of interest to know what happens to accommodation when the stimulus to accommodation is fixed and the stimulus to convergence is varied. The Scheiner principle can be used to good advantage in this kind of experiment because the changes in accommodation can be continuously tracked by having the subject adjust the target as the stimulus

to convergence is slowly decreased or increased (31). The Scheiner target avoids stimulating accommodation because the two beams entering the pupil are narrow.

The skiascope (32) or the coincidence optometer (30) may also be used in this kind of experiment to measure the amount of accommodation in play. However, the objective methods not only present criteria problems (34), but also the additional stimuli applied to the retina may affect the amount of accommodation. This, of course, is avoided in the case of the infrared skiascope (16, 49).

At low levels of illumination and in the presence of an optically empty field of high luminance, accommodation fluctuates. Westheimer (91) has been successful in measuring these fluctuations using intermittent exposure of a Scheiner target. The subject reports at each exposure. This target not only measures accommodation but also controls fixation. Chin & Horn (16) observed these fluctuations with an infrared skiascope.

An optically empty field at high luminance is provided by Knoll's 'blob' (47) which is a luminous patch with diffuse edges upon which the subject cannot focus. It is small enough, however, so that fixation can be controlled by looking at the center of the 'blob.'

Another problem is that of controlling convergence without stimulating accommodation and at the same time measuring the amount of accommodation in play. The 'blob' described above or a blurred line (58) can serve as a stimulus to convergence and the threshold, momentary exposure or infrared principle can be used in measuring the accommodation.

Tracking rapid changes in accommodation presents a special problem. Changes in the ciliary muscle potential (76) can be used as an index of changes in accommodation. Photographic records of the changes in size of the third Purkinje image have also been employed (1, 6, 45). Campbell's automatic recording optometer (15) should be useful for this purpose.

The amount of accommodation in play at a given moment following a stimulus to a change in accommodation can be measured by presenting a momentary exposure of a measuring stimulus at the selected time (3, 4, 7).

MECHANISM OF ACCOMMODATION

Intraocular Mechanism of Accommodation

Of all the structures which might be manipulated to focus the eye, the lens alone fulfills this role. Young

(79, p. 158; 86, p. 201) proved that the length of the eye does not change with accommodation by placing the front and back of one of his eyes between the jaws of a clamp and noting that there was no change in the pressure phosphene at the back of the eye as the eye changed accommodation. The X-ray method of measuring the length of the eye described above is now available for demonstrating this fact. Young also showed that the cornea does not change its curvature during accommodation by noting the reflections from the front surface. He also immersed his eye in water which has about the same index as the aqueous and showed that the power of accommodation was not impaired. The final proof offered by Young that the lens alone provides the mechanism of accommodation is the fact that the eye assumes a fixed focus when the lens is absent.

By measuring the curvature of the front and back surface of the lens and the distances of the two surfaces from the cornea, Helmholtz (79, p. 143) showed that the lens increases in thickness and moves forward slightly, that the curvature of the back surface also increases slightly but that the most important change is in the curvature of the front surface of the lens.

Helmholtz believed these changes to be brought about by a decrease in tension of the zonule which attaches the lens to the ciliary body surrounding the lens. The lens was regarded as a pliable body enclosed in an elastic capsule. Such a body tends to assume an ellipsoidal form when a centripetal tension is applied all along its equator but tends to assume a more spherical form when released from this tension.

Helmholtz believed that the release in tension on the zonule required for accommodation is brought about by a contraction of the ciliary muscle which acts partly as a sphincter in reducing the diameter of the ciliary margin and partly as a system of radial fibers pulling forward the choroid to which it is attached. This increases the pressure of the vitreous on the back side of the lens and neutralizes the tendency of the lens to bulge on its back side. The mechanical pressure of the iris on the peripheral part of the front surface of the lens would help to increase the curvature of the front surface.

Fincham (26, p. 42) has demonstrated in a patient with aniridia that the mechanical pressure of the iris is not an essential part of the mechanism of accommodation. In this case he could observe the decrease in diameter of the lens and of the margin of the ciliary body during accommodation. Fincham (26, p. 50) has described a person with an eye in which the lens substance had been dissolved out of the capsule and showed that when the other eye accommodated the

tension on the capsule decreased and left it free to dangle. Hensen & Voelkers (86, p. 199) demonstrated the forward movement of the choroid during accommodation by inserting a needle through the sclera and choroid near the ora serrata and then making the ciliary muscle contract. The protruding part of the needle moved backward as the choroid moved forward.

Young (86, p. 208) demonstrated that the spherical aberration of the eye becomes partially corrected when the eye accommodates and Tscherning (86, p. 211) used the specular reflections from the front surface of the lens to demonstrate that this was due to a flattening of the peripheral part of the front surface of the lens. The Helmholtz theory had not taken this fact into account.

It remained for Fincham (26, p. 59) to demonstrate that this is due to a variation in the thickness of the capsule. The details of the theory of how an elastic ellipsoidal membrane having zones of varying thickness from the pole to the equator affects the form of the lens as a result of a change in tension of the zonule have not yet been worked out.

Fincham (26, p. 17) demonstrated the elastic force of the capsule by puncturing the lens and noting that the lens substance protruded through the capsule. Also by direct experiment Fincham (26, p. 24) demonstrated that the zonule behaves like an elastic membrane. Furthermore, when the capsule of the lens is removed, the lens assumes a form of its own in which the decapsulated lens is more spherical (26, p. 65).

Hess (26, p. 52; 79, p. 398) observed that when a maximal effort of accommodation is made, tension on the zonule is relaxed so that the position of the lens in the eye is affected by gravity. This can be demonstrated by showing that the amplitude of accommodation is greater when the head points downward than when it points upward. The lateral displacement of the lens when the head is laid on one side or the other can be demonstrated entoptically when there exists a small opacity near the front or back pole of the lens. Hess concluded from this finding that it may not be necessary for the eye to make a maximal contraction of the ciliary muscle in order to relax the lens completely from the tension of the zonule.

Lancaster & Williams (53) have shown that when a maximal state of accommodation is maintained over a period of time, the lens develops a set so that it cannot immediately relax to the zero level of accommodation. It takes several minutes to overcome this set. Lancaster & Williams regarded this as evidence that the lens is completely released from the tension of the zonule at the maximum level of accommodation.

However, in some subjects the same type of effect occurs in lesser degree with submaximal amounts of accommodation.

Duane (21) showed that in a young man it takes the same time for homatropine to begin to take effect as in an older man and argued from this that the older man has the same excess of ciliary capacity above the capacity of the lens to respond as the young man.

It is necessary to look in some other direction to ascertain what fraction of the total ciliary contraction available is required to produce a diopter of accommodation at different ages. The answer is to be found in the study of the relation of accommodation to convergence as described in the next section.

It remains to be determined whether the lens layers become nonpliable one by one from the center out with the cortical layers remaining relatively unaffected or whether all layers get progressively less pliable with age but with the hardening process more developed at the center than at the cortex. The role played by the tensile strength of the individual fibers must also be considered.

The slit lamp technique of observing or photographing the internal structure of the lens, if systematically used at different age levels, might throw some light on this problem. It would also be important to study at different ages the time characteristics of the response of the lens to changes in tension of the zonule (7).

Ciliary Muscle Potential

Schubert (76) has recently developed a method for detecting and recording a potential which appears to be generated by contraction of the ciliary muscle. One electrode is applied to the sclera over the ciliary body and the other to some indifferent part of the body. Alpern (unpublished observations) has described the relation of size of this potential to the amount of accommodation in play. This new technique provides us with an opportunity to study the lag of the response of the lens behind the changes in the ciliary muscle.

Innervation Controlling Accommodation

Although the ciliary muscle is classified histologically as a smooth muscle and the branch of the third nerve supplying it is identified as a part of the parasympathetic system, the ciliary muscle behaves in many ways like a skeletal muscle. Marg *et al.* (64) have demonstrated that in the cat the amount of accom-

modation elicited in response to a square wave galvanic current applied to the ciliary ganglion is a function both of the strength of the current and the frequency of the stimuli. A submaximal response of any degree may be elicited.

Allen (2) has developed a method which can be used in the cat or dog for comparing the lag of the lens and the lag of the muscle. A faradic stimulus is applied to the region of the ciliary muscle. A needle pushed through the sclera into the choroid gives a record of the muscle response, and motion picture photography is used to measure the change in size of the third Purkinje image.

When the eyes accommodate, they also converge and the pupils constrict. This is known as the triad response. The convergence part of the triad response is called accommodative convergence because it is associated with accommodation. It has to be differentiated from fusional convergence which is a different kind of response.

Allen (1) devised an arrangement for suddenly switching from a stimulus at one distance to a stimulus at a different distance. The stimuli were presented to one eye only and the ensuing accommodative and convergence responses were tracked with recording devices. The accommodative response lags a little behind the convergence response (see fig. 20) and this may be due to the lag of the lens behind the response of the ciliary muscle. The results confirm the notion that the two types of responses are initiated through a common center.

The triad response is probably always brought into play by voluntary effort and it behaves like a postural adjustment of the arm which may be raised to a given level and held in that posture while the subject pays primary attention to some other aspect of his behavior. Under normal conditions of use of the eyes, the only

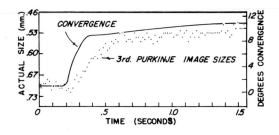

FIG. 20. Accommodative and accommodative convergence responses to a change in the stimulus to accommodation. The points represent sizes of the third Purkinje image measured in successive frames of a motion picture record occurring at a rate of 64 per sec. [From Allen (1).]

awareness of voluntary effort to readjust the triad mechanism is an awareness of switching attention from an object perceived to be located at one distance to an object perceived to be located at another distance (60). As a matter of fact a readjustment of the triad mechanism can be evoked when the subject is in total darkness by having him switch his attention from an imaginary far point to an imaginary near point (47). The problem of focusing the eye, however, is not quite this simple. If the subject starts by paying attention to a given object, then covers one eye and places a minus or plus lens in front of the other to throw the image out of focus, and then concentrates on the object or attempts to clear up the blur, the object eventually comes into focus without the subject perceiving any change in distance. We have yet to learn whether this response is a result of the voluntary effort to clear up the blur or a reflex response to the blur which is akin to the reaction of an automatic focusing device. Regardless of whether this accommodative response to blur is voluntary or reflex, it appears to involve the same tie-up with convergence and pupillary constriction as the accommodative response to a change in the distance of attention. Considerable attention is being devoted today to the problem of whether the eye can detect ahead of time from some aspect of a blurred image whether to increase or decrease accommodation to clear up the blur. Fincham (28, 29) has investigated the response to blur and has found evidence that the colored fringes on the target resulting from chromatic aberration determine the direction of the response. Allen (6) has also investigated what determines the direction of the response when the subject is confronted with a blurred stimulus with all cues of distance eliminated. In 19 of the 20 trials in which the response was recorded, the subject's first response was in the right direction and in only one trial did he make an initial response in the wrong direction which had to be corrected by a second adjustment. Astigmatism as well as chromatic aberration could provide the subject with a cue as to the right direction.

It is possible that the cortical center which controls the triad response transmits impulses simultaneously to the centers in the midbrain controlling convergence, accommodation and pupil constriction. On the other hand it is entirely possible that the triad innervation from the cortex is first transmitted to the center controlling accommodation and relayed from there to the centers controlling convergence and pupil constriction. This is possible because the brain-stem center controlling accommodation never responds without the simultaneous occurrence of a convergence and a pupillary response. However, the accommodative response could not be mediated either through the brain-stem center controlling convergence or through the center controlling pupillary constriction because these same centers mediate other types of pupillary and convergence responses which are not associated with accommodation.

The same center in the midbrain which mediates the pupillary part of the triad response also mediates the pupillary response to light. It is assumed to be located in the Edinger-Westphal nucleus.

Furthermore the brain-stem center which mediates the convergence part of the triad response also mediates fusional convergence. Both types of convergence induce an excycloductive movement of the two eyes, i.e. the two eyes rotate around their lines of sight with the tops of the eyes turning outward. This indicates that both types of convergence are mediated by the same mechanism in the brain stem. There is no cyclorotational movement associated with simple conjugate movements of the eye to the right or left (5).

On the other hand there is ample evidence that the brain-stem mechanism for accommodative and fusional convergence receives innervation from two different cortical centers in mediating these two types of responses. Fusional convergence is a reflex response to stimulation of disparate points of the two retinas. This is probably a feed-back type of response in which the eyes constantly tend to drift to the phoria position, i.e. that which they would assume if one eye were placed under a cover, but are brought back to the fusion position by the retinal disparity resulting from the drift.

Knoll (46) and Marg & Morgan (61, 62) have demonstrated that a marked pupil constriction is associated with a change in accommodation and accommodative convergence, but the pupil response associated with fusional convergence is almost negligible. The very fact that fusional convergence can be manipulated without affecting accommodative convergence is in itself evidence that it involves a separate cortical mechanism.

Reese & Hofstetter (73) have reported a case in which accommodation and accommodative convergence were absent, but positive fusional convergence was still operative. An ordinary concomitant squinter may have a normal amount of accommodative convergence but a total absence of fusional convergence.

The relationship of accommodative and fusional convergence (8, 31, 33) at various levels of accommo-

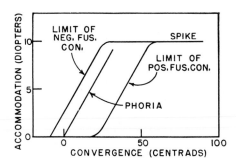

FIG. 21. Relation between accommodation, accommodative convergence and positive and negative fusional convergence in a normal 20-year-old subject.

dation is shown in figure 21. At each level of accommodation the phoria position of the two eyes represents the position of rest that the eyes assume when one of them is covered. At the same level of accommodation the two eyes can be made to converge toward or diverge away from this position of rest in response to stimuli upon which the two eyes can fuse, and the extent to which this can be done without changing accommodation gives us the limits of fusional convergence. The phoria line shows the relation between accommodation and accommodative convergence when the eyes are freed from fusion stimuli. The reciprocal of the slope of this line is called the ACA ratio. The 'spike' at the maximum level of accommodation which indicates that an increased amount of convergence can develop at that level was regarded by van der Hoeve & Flieringa (87) as evidence that the ciliary muscle can keep on responding after the lens reaches its limit to respond. van Hoven (unpublished observations) has shown in six subjects that this is not the case. He paralyzed one eye with homatropine and when the eye partially recovered, he measured the phoria at various levels of accommodation for each of the two eyes and he also measured the amplitude of accommodation of each eye by measuring the accommodative response at the maximum level of convergence. He showed that the amplitude is strictly proportional to the ACA ratio. This means that the lens is responding to changes in contraction of the ciliary muscle at the maximum level of accommodation. Hence it is the muscle and not the lens which determines the maximum level of accommodation. Fincham (30) independently performed the same kind of experiment except that he has also used physostigmine. This gives a hypermaximal spike which proves that the limit lies with the muscle or its innervation but not with the lens.

One can explain the 'spike' by assuming that the ciliary muscle reaches the limit of its capacity to contract before the cortical center controlling the triad responses reaches the limit of its capacity to initiate impulses.

The effect of age upon the ACA ratio is important (8, 18, 30, 40). If the ACA were proportional to the amplitude it ought to change as the amplitude changes with age. The studies made so far have not confirmed this relation. This raises the question whether the connection between accommodation and convergence is a matter of habit instead of dependence on some fixed anatomical arrangement.

Morgan & Olmsted (67) have shown that stimulation of the sympathetic supply to the eye produces a relaxation of accommodation to the extent of about 0.75 D below what is commonly regarded to be the zero level. Morgan (66) believed this effect to be mediated by a change in blood volume of the ciliary body, but Melton *et al.* (65) have demonstrated in a bloodless eye that the effect is still obtained. The mechanism involved has yet to be identified.

Night and Sky Myopia

In total darkness and in the absence of a stimulus to accommodation the refractive state of the eye comes to rest at a higher level than occurs when the eyes are looking at a test chart at 20 ft. (47; 48; 56; 57, p. 485; 71; 72; 84). The effect of low levels of illumination can partly be explained (84, 89) by the aberrations of the eye, but these explanations do not apply in sky myopia (92). In sky myopia as well as in night myopia an increase in accommodation of about 1 D above its zero level is found to exist. Moreover, Westheimer (91) has shown that under these conditions the accommodation is not fixed but exhibits slow oscillations up to a diopter in amplitude. These fluctuations have also been reported by Campbell (14) and by Chin & Horn (16).

VISUAL FIELD

The visual field of a given eye is a conical space with its apex at the center of the entrance-pupil which contains the chief rays for all parts of the retina that respond to light. In the ordinary use of the eyes a part of the field of view is cut off by the nose, eyebrow and cheek.

The direction of a point in the field of view may be specified in terms of its radial direction and eccentricity from the primary line of sight. Objects in the zero radial direction lie in the plane of regard to the left of the line of sight. Other radial directions are displaced clockwise around the line of sight and specified in degrees from 0 to 360. This is the same kind of notation as that used for cylinder axes mounted in front of the eyes. Eccentricity represents degrees between the primary and secondary lines of sight.

The limits of the visual fields for the right and the left eye are shown in figure 22. The combination of the two monocular fields with their centers coinciding represents the binocular visual field.

RETINAL ILLUMINANCE

In order for a person to see, it is necessary for the photoreceptors to react to the light falling on them by generating impulses which can be transmitted to the brain. The response of the photoreceptor is dependent not only on the amount of light directed toward it from the exit-pupil but also upon its structure and orientation with respect to the exit-pupil. The amount of light falling upon a given photoreceptor is dependent upon the amount of light admitted into the eye from the corresponding part of the field of view and upon the transmittance of the eye. We have in the eye not only the light which is focused by the image-forming mechanism at or near the retina but also a certain amount of stray light. These problems can all be treated in a quantitative way, although it is necessary to introduce a few photometric concepts and units. The units which have been used belong to the meter-kilogram-second system.

Light and Illuminance

Light is luminous energy, and a unit of this energy is called a talbot. Illuminance is a term which is used to describe the rate at which light is falling on a surface from all directions. The statement that one lux of illuminance is falling on a surface indicates that a total of one talbot of light is falling each second from all directions on a square meter of the surface.

Solid Angle

The simplest way to visualize a solid angle is to consider a certain area on the surface of a sphere. This area is said to subtend a certain amount of solid

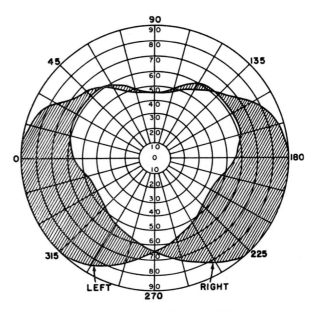

FIG. 22. Monocular and binocular visual fields.

angle at the center of the sphere. It is measured in steradians and is equal to the area of the surface divided by the square of the radius.

Luminance

Luminance is a term which may be used to describe the rate at which light is falling on the eye from a given direction. Consider any line of sight. The luminance in this direction as measured at the center of the entrance-pupil represents the illuminance per unit solid angle falling on a surface perpendicular to the line of sight at the center of the entrance-pupil. One unit of luminance is equal to one lux of illuminance per steradian of solid angle.

Retinal Illuminance

The illuminance E (luxes) at a given point on the retina corresponding to a given direction in the field of view is given by the following equation,

$$E = BtA \cos \theta / k$$

where

B = luminance in the given direction (nits),
t = transmittance of the eye,
A = area of the pupil (m^2),
θ = angle of incidence of the chief ray at the plane of the pupil, and

k = a constant which represents the ratio of a given area (m^2) of the retinal image to the corresponding solid angle (steradians) in the visual field.

Since t and k are constants and since cos θ in the usual case may be assumed to be equal to unity, Troland (85) proposed a unit of retinal illuminance which he called the photon (now known as the troland). The number of trolands at a given point on the retina is equal to the number of nits multiplied by the area of the pupil in square millimeters.

This unit is useful in an experiment in which an artificial pupil is used, but should not be used when pupils of different sizes are used unless the proper allowance is made for the Stiles-Crawford effect.

Transmittance of the Eye

The spectral transmittance of the eye from the cornea to the retina as measured by Ludvigh & McCarthy (59) is shown by the dots in figure 23. This includes consideration of the losses by reflection and scatter at the surfaces as well as the losses by absorption and scatter in the media. In considering foveal vision it is necessary to pay attention to the brown or yellowish spot of macular pigment covering the central 14-degree region of the retina which is called the macula lutea. The transmittance of the macular pigment in this region according to Wald (88) is given by the circles in figure 23 and the curve represents the product of the two transmittances

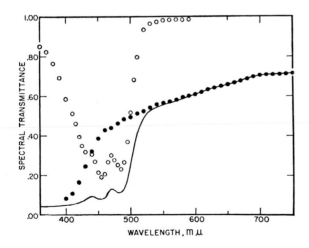

FIG. 23. Spectral transmittance of the ocular media. The *circles* represent the transmittance of the macular pigment, and the *dots* the transmittance of the media from the cornea to the retina. The *curve* represents total transmittance. [From Judd (44).]

giving the total transmittance of the ocular media. The absorption in the ultraviolet region depends largely upon the lens. In an aphakic eye enough ultraviolet reaches the retina so that objects invisible to the normal eye with ultraviolet illumination are easily seen by the aphakic eye.

Maxwell's spot, which can be seen when the eye alternates fixation from a gray surface to a purple surface of the same brightness, is probably dependent upon the macular pigment. Walls & Mathews (90) believe it to be a function of the distribution of different kinds of photoreceptors.

Polarization affects the amount of light reaching the retina as shown by Haidinger's brushes which are visible in looking at the blue sky through a polaroid filter. This polarization effect is attributed to Henle's fibers (22, p. 806) which radiate from the center of the fovea and connect the cones at the center of the fovea with bipolar cells which are displaced toward the edge of the fovea.

Stiles-Crawford Effect

Stiles & Crawford (83) have investigated the relative luminous efficiency of rays entering different parts of the pupil. The results in the horizontal meridian in a typical case are given in figure 24. Losses from reflection and scattering at the refracting surfaces and losses from absorption and scattering by the media may contribute to this effect but the most important factor is the angle of incidence at the photoreceptors. It is an effect which involves cones but not rods (82) which are normally oriented. It is not affected by polarization of the light (70). Phase differences in two beams entering different parts of the pupil (25) do not affect the efficiency of the beams when they are combined again at the retina, and hence the effect can be treated as if it were produced by a gradient filter covering the pupil which has a high transmittance at the center which tapers off at the edge.

Stray Light in the Eye

There are several sources of stray light in the eye (10, 35, 36, 55, 81): *a*) diffusion through the sclera and iris (10, 75); *b*) flare in the optical system (55), including the light reflected from the iris to the cornea and thence through the pupil to the retina, and also part of the light diffusely reflected by the retina which may be reflected back toward the retina by one

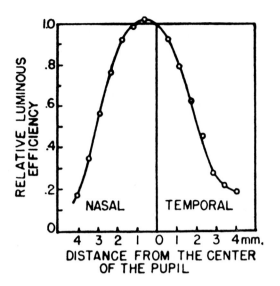

FIG. 24. The Stiles-Crawford effect. Data for the horizontal meridian of the right eye of B.H.C. (81). [From Fry (37).]

of the refracting surfaces; *c*) scatter by the media (12, 35, 36, 41, 55, 81) including the halos (22, p. 801) produced by diffraction associated with the microstructure of the lens and cornea; *d*) diffuse reflection from the pigment epithelium, choroid and sclera (19, 34), this light stimulating the photoreceptors in passing back through the retina (halation), and then passing through the vitreous to the other parts of the retina (after reaching some other part of the retina a part of the light may be further reflected); *e*) fluorescence of the lens (22, p. 820) and the retina (22, p. 821) when exposed to ultraviolet light; and *f*) bioluminescence in the photoreceptors which Judd (44, 69) has proposed may cause one of the images in the sequence following a flash of light. [The 'blue arcs' associated with the passage of impulses along ganglion cell axons across the retina are explained by some writers as a form of electroluminescence, but the evidence favors the direct electrical excitation of the underlying elements (68).]

In the actual use of the eyes a person is most likely to run into the problem of stray light in connection with the impairing effect of a peripheral glare source on foveal vision. The effect of the glare source on a given test object can be compared with the effect of a patch of veiling luminance superimposed on the test object (41, 42, 80). It is satisfactory to assume that this effect is mediated by stray light (12, 35, 36, 81) and hence the luminance of the veiling patch may be used as a measure of the stray light. In figure 25 the ratio of the veiling luminance B_v (nits) to the illumi-

nance E (luxes) in the plane of the pupil produced by a glare source is plotted as a function of the angle θ of the glare source from the primary line of sight.

Stray light is especially important in interpreting the results of electroretinography (11, 13, 38, 93) and pupillography (39). If the eye is exposed to a small bright stimulus, the electrical potentials or the pupillary response produced by the millions of elements feebly stimulated by stray light may completely mask the response of the few elements stimulated by focused light.

BLUR OF RETINAL IMAGE

The retinal image can be treated either as a geometrical or as a physical image. In treating the image of a monochromatic point source as a geometrical image, one assumes that the rays from the point source which pass through the pupil are uniformly distributed across the pupil. These rays can be traced to the retina and the illuminance at any part of the image is proportional to the concentration of rays at that point.

In treating the retinal image as a physical image, it is assumed that the light entering the eye is propagated in the form of waves and diffraction is taken into consideration.

The concept of a blur circle produced by throwing the eye out of focus and of a blur ellipse produced by astigmatism is based upon geometrical imagery. The

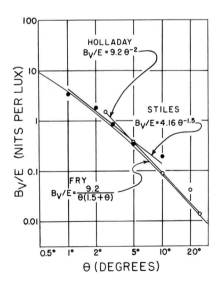

FIG. 25. The equivalent veiling brightness (B_v) of a glare source at various glare angles (θ). [From Fry (36).]

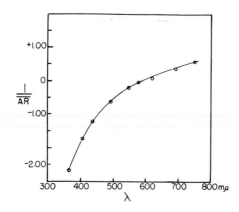

FIG. 26. Chromatic aberration data of Wald & Griffen (89), cited by Fry (37). $\overline{AR}$ is the distance from the cornea to the conjugate focus of the retina. λ represents wave length. [From Fry (37).]

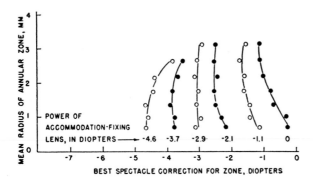

FIG. 27. Spherical aberration of an eye with various amounts of accommodation in play. [From Koomen *et al.* (52).]

light is assumed to be uniformly distributed over the blur circle or blur ellipse. This approach to the problem of throwing the eye out of focus is usually quite adequate.

Geometrical ray tracing is also adequate for describing and defining aberrations, but in order to evaluate the effect of aberrations upon the distribution of illuminance in the retinal image it is necessary to deal with the physical image.

The axial chromatic aberration of the eye can be measured by locating the conjugate focus of the retina for different wavelengths of light. Figure 26 gives the average data for the seven subjects of Wald & Griffin (89) expressed in terms of an eye focused on a yellow (589 mμ) point at infinity.

The spherical aberration of the eye can be expressed in terms of the conjugate foci of the retina for different zones of the pupil. Figure 27 shows the data of

Koomen *et al.* (52) for a typical eye for several different amounts of accommodation. Many arrangements (9, 34, 43, 51, 52) have been used for measuring the spherical aberration of the eye.

Chromatic dispersion (37, p. 89) of the eye is dependent upon the axial chromatic aberration of the eye and the lateral displacement of the pupil from the incident ray directed through the primary nodal point of the eye (see fig. 28). Blur produced by chromatic dispersion is akin to astigmatism in being radially asymmetrical. Other aberrations in the human eye, such as coma and radial and irregular astigmatism, have not been extensively studied.

Figure 29 shows the effect of diffraction (37, p. 57) upon the image of a monochromatic point source in an eye free from aberrations and astigmatism and in perfect focus. The geometrical image would be a point. Reducing the size of the pupil increases the blur due to diffraction and minimizes the effect of being out of focus and the effects of chromatic and spherical aberration. A pupil size of about 4 mm yields maximum sharpness of vision in an eye which is well-focused (17).

Once the distribution of illuminance for a single point is known, the distribution of illuminance on the

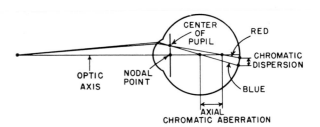

FIG. 28. Dependence of chromatic dispersion on axial chromatic aberration and lateral displacement of the pupil.

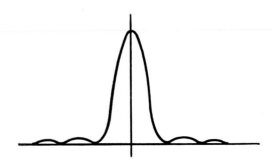

FIG. 29. Distribution of illuminance across the center of the physical image of a monochromatic point source in an eye free from spherical aberration and astigmatism and focused for the sharpest possible image.

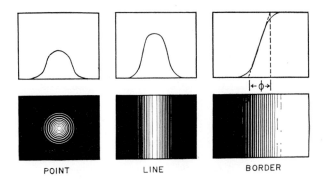

| POINT | LINE | BORDER |

FIG. 30. Distributions of illuminance in the images of a point, a line and a border, representing the same degree of blur.

nonuniformities in the illumination of the retina produced by nonuniformities of index and surface curvature.

A white surface viewed through a pinhole held near the primary focal point produces a shadow of the iris on the retina. The irregularities in the margin are clearly visible and changes in the size of the pupil can be observed directly. The Broca pupillometer (57, p. 237) is based on this method of viewing the pupil. This method of viewing also makes visible spots and folds in the cornea, star figures and incipient cataracts in the lens, and opacities in the vitreous body which give rise to the muscae volitantes. One can also see images of the blood corpuscles in the retinal capillaries as white spots. If the pinhole is oscillated back and forth, one can observe shadows of the large and also the minute blood vessels. The larger vessels form a branched tree known as the Purkinje figure.

This Purkinje figure formed by the blood vessels can also be viewed by illuminating a spot on the sclera or by forming a small bright image on the peripheral retina. By using two point sources, two shadows can be produced whose angular separation at the second nodal point can be measured. From this one can determine the distance of the vessel in front of the photosensitive elements.

Since the vessels move with the photosensitive elements, their shadows are not affected by the micronystagmoid movements of the eye; this provides a means of studying adaptation without involving micronystagmoid movements.

retina may be calculated for any pattern. The index of blur ϕ proposed by Fry & Cobb (37, p. 33) provides a method of specifying the amount of blur regardless of how it is caused. Figure 30 illustrates the distribution of retinal luminance across the images of a point, a line and a border. Although ϕ may be defined in terms of any one of these images, its meaning is best comprehended in the case of a line. It represents the ratio of the area under the curve to the height of the central ordinate. ϕ has the advantage that for any condition of observation it can be measured experimentally without analyzing the factors that contribute to it.

ENTOPTIC PHENOMENA

Entoptic phenomena include the shadows on the retina of opaque structures inside the eye and the

REFERENCES

1. ALLEN, M. J. Am. J. Optom. 26: 279, 1949.
2. ALLEN, M. J. Am. J. Optom. 27: 287, 1950.
3. ALLEN, M. J. Am. J. Optom. 30: 78, 1953.
4. ALLEN, M. J. Am. J. Optom. 30: 393, 1953.
5. ALLEN, M. J. Am. J. Optom. 31: 297, 1954.
6. ALLEN, M. J. Am. J. Optom. 32: 422, 1955.
7. ALLEN, M. J. Am. J. Optom. 33: 201, 1956.
8. ALPERN, M. Am. J. Optom. 27: 491, 1950.
9. AMES, A. JR. AND C. A. PROCTOR. J. Opt. Soc. Am. 5: 22, 1921.
10. BARTLEY, S. H. Vision, A Study of Its Basis. New York: Van Nostrand, 1941, p. 57.
11. BOYNTON, R. M. J. Opt. Soc. Am. 43: 442, 1953.
12. BOYNTON, R. M., J. M. ENOCH AND W. R. BUSH. J. Opt. Soc. Am. 44: 879, 1954.
13. BOYNTON, R. M. AND L. A. RIGGS. J. Exper. Psychol. 42: 217, 1951.
14. CAMPBELL, F. W. Brit. orthopt. J. 11: 13, 1954.
15. CAMPBELL, F. W. J. Physiol. 133: 31, 1956.

16. CHIN, N. B. AND R. E. HORN. J. Opt. Soc. Am. 46: 60, 1956.
17. COBB, P. W. Am. J. Physiol. 36: 335, 1915.
18. DAVIS, G. J. AND F. W. JOBE. Am. J. Optom. 34: 16, 1957.
19. DI FRANCIA, G. T. AND L. RONCHI. J. Opt. Soc. Am. 42: 782, 1952.
20. DONDERS, F. C. Accommodation and Refraction of the Eye, translated by W. D. Moore. London: New Sydenham Society, 1864, p. 204.
21. DUANE, A. Am. J. Ophth. 8: 196, 1925.
22. DUKE-ELDER, W. S. Text-book of Ophthalmology. St. Louis: Mosby, 1934, vol. I.
23. DUKE-ELDER, W. S. Text-book of Ophthalmology. St. Louis: Mosby, 1949, vol. IV.
24. EMSLEY, H. H. Visual Optics (5th ed.). London: Hatton, 1952, vol. I, p. 257.
25. ENOCH, J. M. J. Opt. Soc. Am. 48: 392, 1958.
26. FINCHAM, E. F. The Mechanism of Accommodation. London: Pullman, 1937.

27. FINCHAM, E. F. *Proc. Phys. Soc. London* 49: 456, 1937.
28. FINCHAM, E. F. *Brit. J. Ophth.* 35: 381, 1951.
29. FINCHAM, E. F. *Transactions of the International Optical Congress.* London: Brit. Opt. A., 1951, p. 105.
30. FINCHAM, E. F. *J. Physiol.* 128: 91, 1955.
31. FRY, G. A. *Am. J. Optom.* 16: 325, 1939.
32. FRY, G. A. *Am. J. Optom.* 18: 306, 1941.
33. FRY, G. A. *Optometric Weekly* 34: 153, 1943.
34. FRY, G. A. *The O-Eye-O* 15 (Autumn): 8, 1949.
35. FRY, G. A. *Illum. Eng.* 49: 98, 1954.
36. FRY, G. A. *Physiological Bases of Disability Glare.* Compte Rendu, Commission Internationale de l'Eclairage, Zurich, 1955, 1.4.2, U-F.
37. FRY, G. A. *Blur of the Retinal Image.* Columbus: Ohio State Univ. Press, 1955.
38. FRY, G. A. AND S. H. BARTLEY. *Am. J. Physiol.* 111: 335, 1935.
39. FUGATE, J. M. *J. Opt. Soc. Am.* 44: 771, 1954.
40. HIRSCH, M. J., M. ALPERN AND H. I. SHULTZ. *Am. J. Optom.* 25: 535, 1948.
41. HOLLADAY, L. L. *J. Opt. Soc. Am.* 12: 271, 1926.
42. HOLLADAY, L. L. *J. Opt. Soc. Am.* 14: 1, 1927.
43. IVANOFF, I. *J. Opt. Soc. Am.* 46: 901, 1956.
44. JUDD, D. B. *Colorimetry* (National Bureau of Standards Circular 478). Washington: U. S. Government Printing Office, 1950, p. 2.
45. KIRCHHOF, H. *Am. J. Optom.* 27: 163, 1950.
46. KNOLL, H. *Am. J. Optom.* 26: 346, 1949.
47. KNOLL, H. A. *The Effect of Low Levels of Luminance and Freedom from Optical Stimulation of Accommodation upon the Refractive State of the Eyes* (Dissertation). Columbus: Ohio State University, 1950.
48. KNOLL, H. A. *Am. J. Optom.* 29: 69, 1952.
49. KNOLL, H. A. *Am. J. Optom.* 30: 346, 1953.
50. KNOLL, H. A., R. STIMSON AND C. L. WEEKS. *J. Opt. Soc. Am.* 47: 221, 1957.
51. KOOMEN, M. J., R. SCOLNICK AND R. TOUSEY. *J. Opt. Soc. Am.* 46: 903, 1956.
52. KOOMEN, M., R. TOUSEY AND R. SCOLNICK. *J. Opt. Soc. Am.* 39: 370, 1949.
53. LANCASTER, W. B. AND E. R. WILLIAMS. *Tr. Am. Acad. Ophth.*: 170, 1914.
54. LAURANCE, L. *Visual Optics and Sight Testing.* London: School of Optics, 1926, p. 452.
55. LE GRAND, Y. *Rev. Opt.* 16: 201, 241, 1937.
56. LUCKIESH, M. AND F. K. MOSS. *Am. J. Ophth.* 20: 469, 1937.
57. LUCKIESH, M. AND F. K. MOSS. *The Science of Seeing.* New York: Van Nostrand, 1937.
58. LUCKIESH, M. AND F. K. MOSS. *A.M.A. Arch. Ophth.* 23: 941, 1940.
59. LUDVIGH, E. AND E. F. McCARTHY. *A.M.A. Arch. Ophth.* 20: 37, 1938.
60. MARG, E. *Am. J. Optom.* 28: 347, 1951.
61. MARG, E. AND M. W. MORGAN, JR. *Am. J. Optom.* 26: 183, 1949.
62. MARG, E. AND M. W. MORGAN, JR. *Am. J. Optom.* **27**: 217: 1950.
63. MARG, E., J. ONG AND D. HAMASAKI. *Am. J. Optom.* 33: 3, 1956.
64. MARG, E., J. L. REEVES AND W. E. WENDT. *Am. J. Optom.* 31: 127, 1954.
65. MELTON, C. E., E. W. PURNELL AND G. A. BRECHER. *Am. J. Ophth.* 40 (Pt. II): 155, 1955.
66. MORGAN, M. W., JR. *Am. J. Optom.* 23: 99, 1946.
67. MORGAN, M. W., JR. AND J. M. D. OLMSTED. *Proc. Soc. Exper. Biol. & Med.* 42: 612, 1939.
68. NEWHALL, S. M. *J. Opt. Soc. Am.* 27: 165, 1937.
69. NEWHALL, S. M. *J. Opt. Soc. Am.* 28: 177, 1938.
70. O'BRIEN, B. *J. Opt. Soc. Am.* 36: 506, 1946.
71. OTERO, J. M. *J. Opt. Soc. Am.* 41: 942, 1951.
72. REESE, E. E. AND G. A. FRY. *Am. J. Optom.* 18: 9, 1941.
73. REESE, E. E. AND H. W. HOFSTETTER. *Am. J. Optom.* 24: 123, 1947.
74. RONCHI, V. *Optics, the Science of Vision,* translated by E. Rosen. New York: New York Univ. Press, 1957, p. 24.
75. SCHOUTEN, J. F. *Koninkl. Ned. Akad. Wetenschap., Proc.* 37: 516, 1934.
76. SCHUBERT, G. *von Graefes Arch. Ophth.* 157: 116, 1955.
77. SHASTID, T. H. *Am. Encyclopedia Ophth.* 11: 8524, 1917.
78. SORSBY, A. *A Short History of Ophthalmology.* London: Bale, 1933.
79. SOUTHALL, J. P. C. (editor). *Helmholtz's Treatise on Physiological Optics* (translated from 3rd German ed.). Rochester: Opt. Soc. Am., 1924, vol. 1.
80. STILES, W. S. *Proc. Roy. Soc., London, ser. B.* 104: 322, 1929.
81. STILES, W. S. *Proc. Roy. Soc., London. ser. B.* 105: 131, 1929.
82. STILES, W. S. *Proc. Roy. Soc., London. ser. B.* 127: 64, 1939.
83. STILES, W. S. AND B. H. CRAWFORD. *Proc. Roy. Soc., London. ser. B.* 112: 428, 1933.
84. TOUSEY, R., M. KOOMEN AND R. SCOLNICK. *J. Opt. Soc. Am.* 43: 926, 1953.
85. TROLAND, L. T. *Principles of Psychophysiology.* New York: Van Nostrand, 1930, vol. II, p. 62.
86. TSCHERNING, M. *Physiological Optics,* translated by C. Weiland. Philadelphia: Keystone, 1924.
87. VAN DER HOEVE, J. AND H. J. FLIERINGA. *Brit. J. Ophth.* 8: 97, 1924.
88. WALD, G. *Science* 101: 653, 1945.
89. WALD, G. AND D. R. GRIFFIN. *J. Opt. Soc. Am.* 37: 321, 1947.
90. WALLS, G. L. AND R. W. MATHEWS. *New Means of Studying Color Blindness and Normal Foveal Color Vision.* Berkeley and Los Angeles: Univ. California Press, 1952.
91. WESTHEIMER, G. *J. Opt. Soc. Am.* 47: 714, 1957.
92. WHITESIDE, T. C. D. AND F. W. CAMPBELL. Flying Personnel Research Committee, Report 821, March, 1953.
93. WIRTH, A. AND B. ZETTERSTROM. *Brit. J. Ophth.* 38: 257, 1954.
94. WULFEK, J. W. *J. Opt. Soc. Am.* 45: 928, 1955.

CHAPTER XXVIII

The photoreceptor process in vision[1]

GEORGE WALD | *Biological Laboratories, Harvard University, Cambridge, Massachusetts*

CHAPTER CONTENTS

CHEMISTRY OF VISUAL EXCITATION

LIGHT INITIATES a nervous excitation in the outer segments of the rods and cones which, transmitted from one neuron to another to centers in the brain, ends in exciting visual sensations. To achieve this result probably the whole apparatus must be thrown into activity; yet all of it waits upon and, to a degree, retains the impress of the primary processes of excitation in the receptor cells.

The general arrangement of these processes is clear from first principles. Light to have any effect, chemical or physical, must be absorbed. The rods and cones must therefore contain substances which absorb visible light—hence pigments—and are changed thereby so as to yield a nervous excitation. The photo-

sensitive pigments must be continuously restored, or vision would cease soon after a light went on. The excitatory state must also be rapidly removed, or vision would continue long after a light went off. It would aid the economy of such a system if these reactions were coupled so as to complete a cycle but this, though an advantage, is not essential. All photoreceptor processes may therefore be formulated as follows:

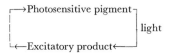

This is not only the basic arrangement for photoreception but, generalized to include stimuli other than light, it must also be the form of all neural excitation. Every irritable tissue must contain similar arrangements for reacting with the stimulus, for removing its effects and for restoring the original system. One may therefore expect to meet the same fundamental pattern of reactions at every level of the visual pathway; and the entire process of visual excitation from rods and cones to cerebral cortex may be conceived as a chain of such systems. The peculiar importance of the photoreceptor systems rests, therefore, not on their intrinsic form but on their unique sensitivity to light and their initial position in the chain, by virtue of which certain of their properties are imposed on the entire visual response.

Four visual pigments are known: rhodopsin and porphyropsin in rods, and iodopsin and cyanopsin in cones. All of them are built upon a common plan. They are all carotenoid-proteins—proteins bearing carotenoid chromophores to which they owe their color and sensitivity to light. The rhodopsin system will be described in some detail since it provides the

[1] The investigations from this laboratory were supported in part by the Rockefeller Foundation, the Office of Naval Research, and the Public Health Service. The author wishes to thank Dr. Ruth Hubbard for help with the preparation of this manuscript.

model for all the others. Once this system is under-stood, the others emerge as simple variants upon a common theme.

Rhodopsin

Franz Boll discovered the red pigment rhodopsin in the rods of frogs in 1876 (5). It is characteristic of the rods of marine fishes and land vertebrates (62). There is no evidence that it is ever found in cones.

Some years ago rhodopsin was shown to par-ticipate in a cycle of the following skeletal form (56):

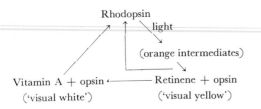

Rhodopsin bleaches in the light through orange intermediates to a mixture of the yellow carotenoid, retinene, and the colorless protein, opsin (fig. 1). The retinene is then converted to colorless vitamin A. Rhodopsin is resynthesized on the one hand from retinene and opsin, on the other from vitamin A and opsin.

Morton has shown that retinene is vitamin A aldehyde (3):

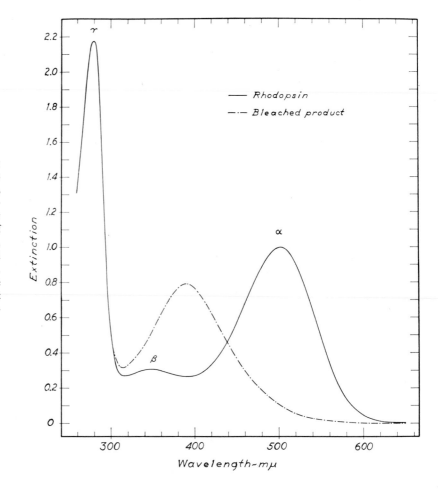

FIG. 1. Absorption spectra of bullfrog rhodopsin and of the product of its bleaching in aqueous digitonin solution, pH 5.55. Rhodopsin possesses three ab-sorption maxima: the α-band, mainly responsible for the spectral sensitivity of rod vision; the β-band, which, like α-, belongs to the prosthetic group; and the γ-band, due to the protein opsin. On bleaching the α- and β-bands are replaced by the retinene band at about 385 mμ; the opsin band remains un-changed. [From Wald (63).]

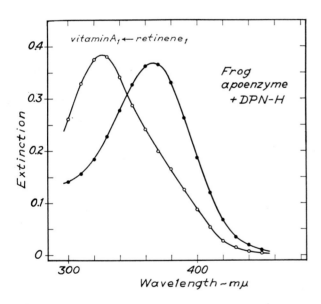

Retinene

The retinene formed by the bleaching of rhodopsin is reduced to vitamin A by the enzyme, alcohol dehydrogenase, working together with the coenzyme, DPN. This process is readily carried out in free solution (fig. 2). It involves only the transfer of hydrogen from reduced DPN to the aldehyde group of retinene, reducing it to the alcohol group of vitamin A (4, 64, 75):

$$C_{19}H_{27}CHO + DPN\text{-}H + H^+ \xrightarrow{\text{alcohol dehydrogenase}}$$

retinene

$$C_{19}H_{27}CH_2OH + DPN^+$$

vitamin A

FIG. 2. The reduction of retinene to vitamin A. Retinene was mixed in digitonin solution with the enzyme, alcohol dehydrogenase, extracted from frog retinas, and with reduced cozymase (DPN-H). A control mixture was also prepared which differed only in that the enzyme had been kept at 100°C for 0.5 min. Both mixtures were incubated, then extracted with hexane. The absorption spectra of the hexane extracts are shown. The control mixture (*solid circles*) contains unaltered retinene; the mixture containing active enzyme (*open circles*) shows complete conversion to vitamin A. [From Wald (64).]

DPN introduces a second vitamin into the chemistry of vision. Its active principle is nicotinamide, the antipellagra factor of the vitamin B complex. In the retina it is in the curious position of helping to regenerate vitamin A.

This completes the degradative processes in vision. Rhodopsin having been bleached by light to a mixture of retinene and opsin, the retinene is reduced to vitamin A. The problem now is to go back. Kühne already recognized this to be a dual problem (38). He described a resynthesis of rhodopsin from yellow precursors (anagenesis) which was relatively rapid and occurred not only in the intact eye but in the isolated retina and even slightly in solution. In addition there occurred a relatively slow synthesis of rhodopsin from colorless precursors (neogenesis) which Kühne could observe only in the intact eye and which seemed to require the cooperation of the pigment epithelium. These two processes can now be identified with the synthesis of rhodopsin from retinene and opsin, and from vitamin A and opsin.

The synthesis of rhodopsin from retinene and opsin is a spontaneous reaction. It requires neither an enzyme nor, as do most syntheses, an external source of energy. One has only to bring a mixture of these two substances into the dark to form rhodopsin (67). Like all spontaneous reactions, it is an energy-yielding process, which can therefore do work. The work it does in vision is to force the oxidation of vitamin A. The equilibrium between vitamin A and retinene lies far over toward the side of reduction—toward vitamin A. In the dark, however, opsin 'traps' retinene, removing it to form rhodopsin, so displacing the equilibrium in the oxidative direction. The basic mechanism of rhodopsin synthesis, therefore, is the energy-demanding oxidation of vitamin A to retinene, coupled with the energy-yielding condensation of retinene and opsin to form rhodopsin (33, 76).

One important consequence of this arrangement is that it is self-limiting. Vitamin A is oxidized to retinene only as long as opsin is available to trap the latter. Retinene therefore never accumulates. When all the opsin in the visual receptors has been converted to visual pigments, the oxidation of vitamin A automatically ceases.

The rhodopsin system in more detail therefore has the form shown in figure 3. Rhodopsin is converted by light to the orange-red intermediate, lumi-rhodopsin. At temperatures above −20°C this goes on to form meta-rhodopsin; and with access

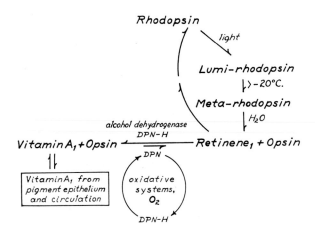

FIG. 3. Diagram of the rhodopsin system. [From Hubbard & Wald (33).]

to water, meta-rhodopsin yields retinene and opsin (74). The retinene is then reduced to vitamin A. In the dark, the spontaneous combination of retinene and opsin to form rhodopsin promotes the oxidation of vitamin A to retinene. This process is aided by the influx of new vitamin A from the pigment epithelium which obtains it from the blood circulation, by the provision of DPN, the oxidant of vitamin A, and by respiratory enzymes, which keep DPN oxidized. All these factors acting in concert sweep the system back toward rhodopsin (33).

It should be noted that light enters this scheme directly at only one point, the conversion of rhodopsin to lumi-rhodopsin. The other reactions follow from this initial act but are themselves 'dark' reactions, i.e. reactions which proceed equally well in light or darkness.

Judging from figure 3, it should be possible to assemble the rhodopsin system by mixing four substances in solution: vitamin A, opsin, alcohol dehydrogenase and DPN. The system has, in fact, been put together using highly purified vitamin A, crystalline alcohol dehydrogenase from horse livers and DPN from yeast. The only component that needs to be obtained from the retina, and indeed from the outer segments of the rods, is opsin. This mixture, placed in the dark, forms rhodopsin. Brought into the light it bleaches, and replaced in the dark it synthesizes more rhodopsin. It thus performs in solution all the reactions of the rhodopsin system (33).

However, in making up this mixture, not all vitamin A is effective. Vitamin A, like other carotenoids, exists in a number of different molecular

shapes, *cis-trans* isomers of one another (47, 83, 84). All-*trans* vitamin A (fig. 4), the predominant isomer in liver and blood (Wald, G. & P. S. Brown, unpublished observations), is ineffective in rhodopsin synthesis. Rhodopsin requires for its formation one of the *cis* isomers of vitamin A (34).

According to theory, only two of the four side-chain double bonds of vitamin A should be capable of forming stable *cis*-linkages, those marked 9 and 13 in figure 4. At the other double bonds, a *cis* linkage encounters serious steric hindrance, and the molecule must be twisted out of coplanarity. This interferes with resonance and should consequently lead to a lowered stability (42, 43). Only four geometrical isomers of vitamin A or retinene were therefore expected: all-*trans*, 9-*cis*, 13-*cis*, and 9,13-*dicis* (fig. 4).

Five *cis-trans* isomers of retinene, however, have been identified and crystallized (10, 32, 39, 48):

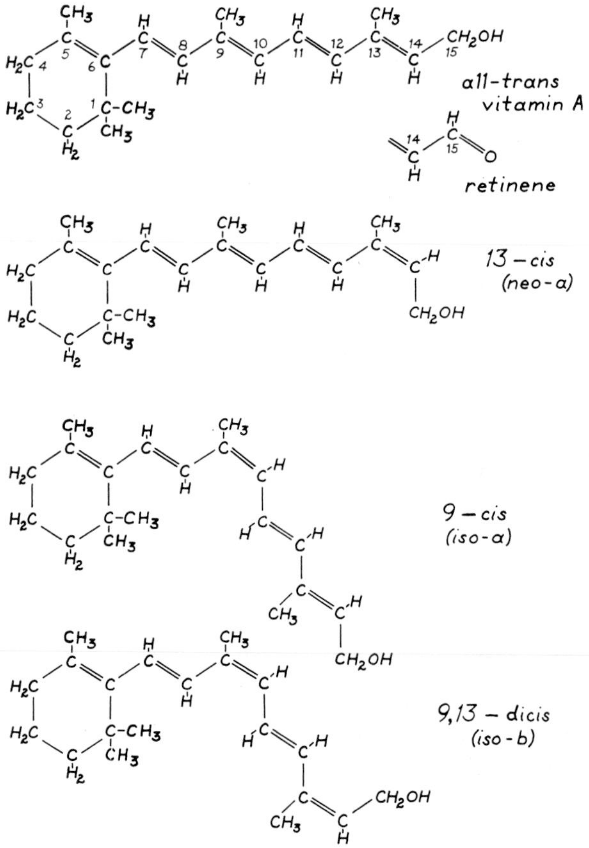

FIG. 4. Unhindered geometrical isomers of vitamin A. This molecule can assume the *cis* configuration only at double bonds 9 and 13 without encountering serious steric hindrance. At the other double bonds, groups come into conflict, and the *cis* configuration not only bends but twists the molecule [Modified from Hubbard & Wald (34).]

the all-*trans* isomer, originally prepared by Ball *et al.* (3); the three unhindered *cis* isomers—neo-*a* (13-*cis*), iso-*a* (9-*cis*) and iso-*b* (9,13-*dicis*); and a hindered *cis* isomer of the type which had been deemed improbable on theoretical grounds (fig. 5). This hindered *cis* isomer, neo-*b* (11-*cis*), is the precursor of rhodopsin (32, 39).[2]

The synthesis of rhodopsin proceeds in two stages. First, vitamin A is oxidized to retinene; then retinene couples with opsin. The first process is relatively indifferent to isomeric configuration. It is the coupling of retinene with opsin that is isomer-specific.

On incubation with opsin in the dark, neo-*b* retinene yields rhodopsin, indistinguishable from that extracted from the dark-adapted retina. On similar treatment, iso-*a* retinene yields a very similar, light-sensitive pigment, with its λ_{max} displaced about 13 mμ toward shorter wavelengths. This is called iso-rhodopsin. The remaining isomers are inactive (fig. 6).

When rhodopsin is bleached, the retinene which emerges is all-*trans*. This must be isomerized to the active isomer, neo-*b*, before it can resynthesize rhodopsin. A cycle of *cis-trans* isomerization is therefore an intrinsic part of the rhodopsin system.

A single passage through this cycle is shown in figure 7. On the left, a mixture of neo-*b* retinene and cattle opsin in aqueous solution incubated in the dark forms rhodopsin. On the right, the rhodopsin formed in this way is bleached to a mixture of all-*trans* retinene and opsin. The extinction of retinene which emerges on the right is much higher than that which enters on the left. That is because the specific extinction of all-*trans* retinene is higher than that of the neo-*b* isomer.

The mechanism by which the eye converts all-*trans* retinene, which results from bleaching rhodopsin, to neo-*b* retinene is not entirely clear. All-*trans* retinene is isomerized to a mixture of *cis* and *trans* isomers by simple exposure to light. This is a second photochemical process in the rhodopsin system. The eye tissues also contain an enzyme, retinene isomerase, which catalyzes specifically the interconversion of all-*trans* and neo-*b* retinene, and which is also light-sensitive (31). There probably are additional mechanisms for converting all-*trans* retinene or vitamin A to the neo-*b* isomer.

The rhodopsin system can therefore be formulated

as follows (34):

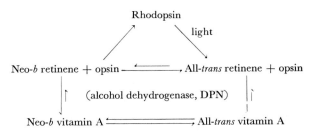

Vitamin A emerges from the bleaching of rhodopsin as the free alcohol; yet the great bulk of the vitamin

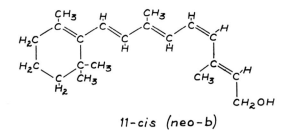

11-*cis* (*neo-b*)

FIG. 5. The sterically hindered neo-*b* (11-*cis*) isomer of vitamin A, precursor of rhodopsin and iodopsin. [From Oroshnik *et al.* (40).]

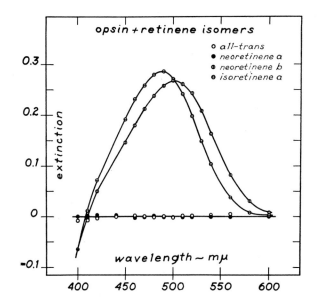

FIG. 6. The products of incubating various geometrical isomers of retinene with cattle opsin. Difference spectra are shown—differences in the absorption spectra before and after bleaching in the presence of hydroxylamine. All-*trans* and neo-*a* retinene yield no light-sensitive pigment. Neo-*b* retinene yields rhodopsin; iso-*a* retinene, iso-rhodopsin. Iso-*b* retinene, though itself inactive, isomerizes preferentially to iso-*a* which yields iso-rhodopsin. [From Hubbard & Wald (34).]

---

[2] A sixth isomer of retinene, called neo-*c* (11, 13-*dicis*), has since been synthesized by Oroshnik (39).

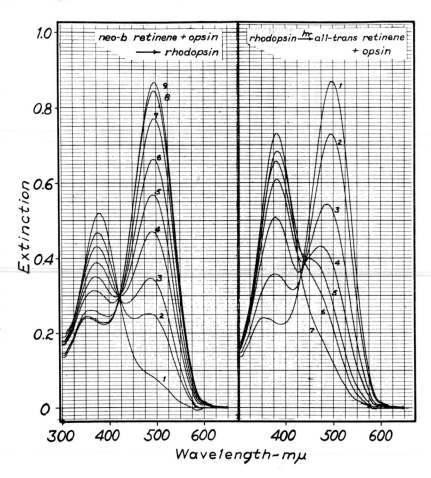

FIG. 7. Synthesis and bleaching of rhodopsin in solution (22.5°C, pH 7.0). *Left*: A mixture of neo-*b* retinene and cattle opsin was incubated in the dark, and absorption spectra recorded periodically, (1) at 0.3 min., (2) at 2.5, (3) at 5, (4) at 10, (5) at 18, (6) at 30, (7) at 60, (8) at 120 and (9) at 180 min. The absorption band of neo-*b* retinene (λ_{max} 380 mμ) falls regularly, while that of rhodopsin (λ_{max} 498 mμ) rises. *Right*: The rhodopsin formed at the *left* (1) is exposed to light of wavelengths >550 mμ for various intervals, and the spectrum is recorded immediately after each exposure. The total irradiations are: (2) 5 sec., (3) 10 sec., (4) 15 sec., (5) 30 sec., and (6) 120 sec. The residue was exposed for 45 sec. longer to light of wavelengths >440 mμ (7). [From Wald & Brown (70).]

A stored in the eye (primarily in the pigmented layers, choroid and pigment epithelium) is in the form of an ester. Recently a cell-free enzyme system has been prepared from cattle retinas and pigmented layers which esterifies vitamin A *in vitro* (38). The significance of this reaction for the visual cycle is still obscure. It is, however, noteworthy that the amount of vitamin A ester stored in the dark-adapted eye is roughly equivalent to its rhodopsin content on a molar basis, and that the neo-*b* isomer constitutes about one-half of this store (37; Wald, G. & P. S. Brown, unpublished observations).

Porphyropsin

The rods of vertebrates which live in, or better, spawn in fresh water—fresh-water fishes, spawning lampreys, and certain larval and adult amphibia—characteristically contain in place of rhodopsin a purple light-sensitive pigment called porphyropsin (62). Its λ_{max} in aqueous solution ordinarily is close to 522 mμ (fig. 8). On bleaching, it yields a mixture of opsin and a new retinene called retinene$_2$, and this in turn is reduced to a new vitamin A called vitamin A$_2$. It was the analysis of this visual system that led to the discovery of these carotenoids (57, 60). The structures of these substances have now been established by total synthesis (13). They differ from vitamin A and retinene[3]—sometimes called vitamin A$_1$ and retinene$_1$—only in possessing an additional double bond in the ring:

$$
\begin{array}{c}
CH_3 \quad CH_3 \\
\backslash \; / \\
C \\
/ \quad \backslash \\
H_2C \qquad C-C=C-C=C-C=C-C=C-C-OH \\
| \qquad \;\; | \qquad\qquad\qquad\qquad H \\
HC \qquad C-CH_3 \\
\backslash \quad / \\
C \\
| \\
H
\end{array}
$$

Vitamin A$_2$

---

[3] Throughout this discussion, the terms vitamin A and retinene will be used synonymously with vitamin A$_1$ and retinene$_1$.

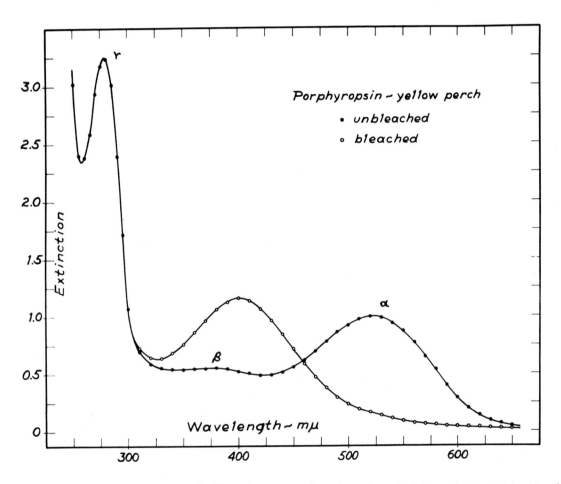

Retinene₂

The properties of the porphyropsin system are in general precisely parallel with those of the rhodopsin system. Alcohol dehydrogenase and DPN catalyze the equilibrium between retinene₂ and vitamin A₂

just as between retinene₁ and vitamin A₁ (64). The bleaching of porphyropsin yields an inactive form of retinene₂, apparently the all-*trans* isomer.

The geometrical isomers of retinene₂ have not been investigated as thoroughly as those of retinene₁. All-*trans* retinene₂ has been crystallized. Two *cis* forms of retinene₂ have been partially purified, though not crystallized. These resemble in their spectroscopic properties respectively the neo-*b* and iso-*a* isomers of retinene₁. Neo-*b* retinene₂, when incubated in the dark with opsin, yields porphyropsin, indistinguishable from that extracted from a dark-adapted fresh-water fish retina; whereas iso-*a* retinene treated similarly yields a comparable pigment, iso-

FIG. 8. Absorption spectra of porphyropsin and of the product of its bleaching (pH 7.0) from the fresh-water yellow perch, *Perca flavescens*. This preparation was extracted with 2 per cent digitonin from a suspension of rod outer segments, which had been previously hardened with alum, and pre-extracted with water and with petroleum ether. Porphyropsin, like rhodopsin, possesses three absorption bands: the α-band about 522 mμ at, the β-band at about 377 mμ, and the γ-band (opsin) at about 280 mμ. On bleaching, the α- and β-bands are replaced by the absorption band of retinene₂, at about 400 mμ. [From Wald, G., P. K. Brown & P. S. Brown, unpublished observations.]

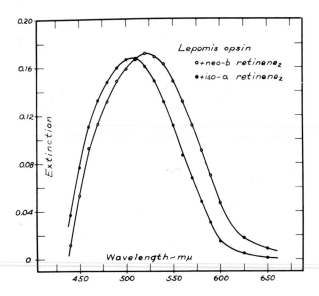

FIG. 9 Synthesis of porphyropsin and iso-porphyropsin. The neo-*b* and iso-*a* isomers of retinene₂, partially purified, were incubated with opsin from the sunfish, *Lepomis*. The difference spectra of the products are shown, measured in the presence of hydroxylamine. The neo-*b* isomer yields porphyropsin (λ_{max}, 522 mμ), the iso-*a* isomer iso-porphyropsin (λ_{max}, 507 mμ). [From Wald, G., P. K. Brown & P. S. Brown, unpublished observations.]

porphyropsin, with λ_{max} 507 mμ (fig. 9; Wald, G., P. K. Brown & P. S. Brown, unpublished observations).

In performing such syntheses it makes no difference whether the opsin is derived from a fresh-water fish, a frog or cattle. All these opsins when mixed with neo-*b* retinene₂ yield porphyropsin, while with neo-*b* retinene₁ they form rhodopsin. The pigments obtained with cattle opsin lie at slightly shorter wavelengths than those obtained with frog opsin: 'cattle porphyropsin' lies at λ_{max} 517 mμ, while 'frog porphyropsin' has λ_{max} 522 mμ. Cattle and frog rhodopsins display similar differences: the former has λ_{max} 498 mμ, the latter λ_{max} 502 mμ. Clearly species differences in the opsin affect the λ_{max} of the visual pigments.

The opsins of the rods that have been examined are so closely related that they must be regarded as belonging to the same family, the rod opsins or scotopsins. The rhodopsin and porphyropsin systems therefore share entirely the same proteins. Only their carotenoids differ and those only by one double bond in the ring. The porphyropsin system can therefore

be formulated:

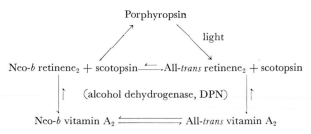

Iodopsin

The first light-sensitive pigment of cone vision was extracted from the chicken retina in 1937. It is a violet pigment (λ_{max} 562 mμ) called iodopsin. The chicken retina contains a few rods among a large predominance of cones and hence yields a mixture of iodopsin and rhodopsin (58).

The carotenoids of the iodopsin system are identical with those of the rhodopsin system, even to *cis-trans* configuration. Only the opsin is different. The cone opsins can be called photopsins. The replacement of scotopsin by photopsin changes the rhodopsin to the iodopsin system (72):

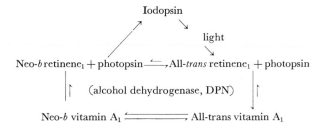

From the light-adapted chicken retina one can extract a colorless carotenoid-free mixture of the proteins of rod and cone vision, scotopsin and photopsin. On incubating this, or a wholly bleached extract of chicken retinas, in the dark with neo-*b* retinene₁, one obtains a mixture of rhodopsin and iodopsin indistinguishable from that extracted from the dark-adapted chicken retina (fig. 10).

Just as iso-*a* retinene₁ yields iso-rhodopsin when incubated with rod opsin, it yields a similarly displaced pigment, iso-iodopsin, on incubation with cone opsin. The λ_{max} of iso-iodopsin is at about 515 mμ. The remaining isomers of retinene are inactive (fig. 11).

Cyanopsin

Rod opsin combines with neo-*b* retinene₁ to yield rhodopsin, or with neo-*b* retinene₂ to yield por-

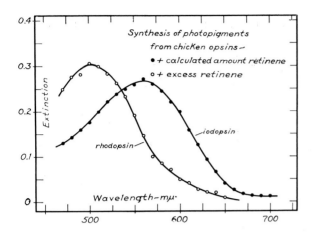

FIG. 10. Successive syntheses of iodopsin and rhodopsin in solution. An extract of chicken retinas was wholly bleached with an orange nonisomerizing light to a mixture of all-*trans* retinene and rod and cone opsins. To this mixture just enough neo-*b* retinene was added to regenerate iodopsin alone. This amount had been determined by preliminary trial. Iodopsin forms so much more rapidly than rhodopsin that its synthesis is complete when that of rhodopsin has scarcely begun (cf. fig. 21). The absorption spectrum of the product, formed within a few minutes in the dark, is shown with *solid circles*. Then a small excess of neo-*b* retinene was added, and the mixture was reincubated in the dark for 30 min. This yielded rhodopsin (*open circles*). [From Wald *et al.* (72).]

phyropsin. Cone opsin combines with neo-*b* retinene₁ to yield iodopsin. Clearly a fourth combination is possible: cone opsin with neo-*b* retinene₂.

This synthesis was recently performed in our laboratory. It yielded a blue photosensitive pigment called cyanopsin which absorbs maximally in the orange-red, at about 620 mμ (71). Always heretofore knowledge of a visual pigment had developed in the sequence: recognition, extraction, analysis, synthesis. With cyanopsin this history was reversed. A pigment was synthesized in solution which had never been identified in a retina. Had it a place in vision?

Where would one look? Obviously in retinas which provide its ingredients: cones, hence photopsin; and vitamin A₂. One might therefore look for cyanopsin in a fresh-water fish possessing cones, or in the all-cone retina of such a turtle as *Pseudemys*, which had been shown to contain vitamin A₂ (71).

Some years ago Granit measured electrophysiologically the spectral sensitivity of cone vision in a fresh-water fish, the tench, and in the European tortoise, *Testudo graeca* (15, 16). His measurements are shown as the points in figure 12; the line is the main absorption band of cyanopsin. There is little doubt

that cyanopsin is the pigment of cone vision in these animals.

Recapitulation

This phase of the chemistry of visual excitation ends on a very simple note. The visual systems which have been studied involve the interaction of four substances: a rod or cone opsin; the enzyme, alcohol dehydrogenase; the coenzyme, cozymase; and neo-*b* (11-*cis*) vitamin A₁ or A₂. They can be summarized:

$$\text{vitamin A}_1 \underset{\text{DNP-H}}{\overset{\text{DPN}^+}{\rightleftharpoons}} \text{retinene}_1 \begin{cases} + \text{rod opsin} \underset{\text{light}}{\rightleftharpoons} \text{rhodopsin} \\ + \text{cone opsin} \underset{\text{light}}{\rightleftharpoons} \text{iodopsin} \end{cases}$$

(alcohol dehydrogenase)

$$\text{vitamin A}_2 \underset{\text{DPN-H}}{\overset{\text{DPN}^+}{\rightleftharpoons}} \text{retinene}_2 \begin{cases} + \text{rod opsin} \underset{\text{light}}{\rightleftharpoons} \text{porphyropsin} \\ + \text{cone opsin} \overset{\text{light}}{\longrightarrow} \text{cyanopsin} \end{cases}$$

In addition there are the four iso-pigments, the carotenoid chromophores of which are stereoisomeric with those of the visual pigments. Since none of the iso-pigments has yet been found in a retina, they must for the present be regarded as artifacts. How does the retina avoid forming them? Preliminary measurements indicate that traces of iso-*a* vitamin A are present in liver oils, while in cattle blood the iso-*a* isomer accounts for about 6 per cent of the total vitamin A. No iso-*a* vitamin A has been detected in the retina and pigment layers of the eye, whereas the neo-*b* isomer is found only in the eye (Wald, G., P. K. Brown & P. S. Brown, unpublished observations). It is therefore likely that the eye actively forms neo-*b* vitamin A—presumably from the all-trans isomer—and actively excludes iso-*a* vitamin A.

Role of Opsin in Visual Excitation

To this point the visual pigments have been discussed mainly from the point of view of their carotenoid components. Their properties, however, depend greatly also upon the opsins. Though their color and sensitivity to light are mediated principally through the carotenoid prosthetic groups, almost everything else derives from their character as proteins. Light liberates retinene. Yet, like other carotenoids, retinene is a bland, relatively inert substance, hardly capable of initiating a nervous excitation. Furthermore, at physiological temperatures and pH it is released relatively slowly as the last step in a chain

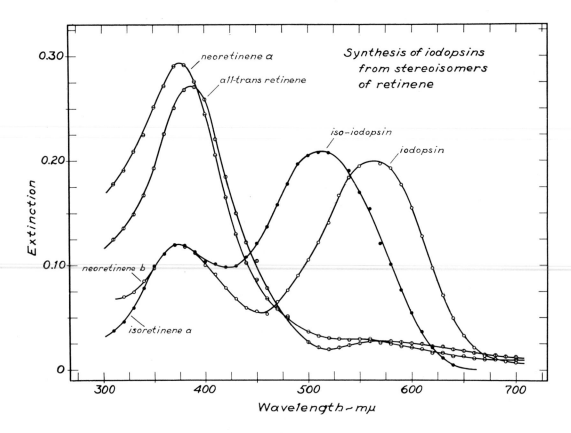

FIG. 11. Synthesis of iodopsin and iso-iodopsin. In a chicken retinal extract, the iodopsin alone was bleached with deep red light to a mixture of all-*trans* retinene and photopsin. This product was incubated in the dark with four geometrical isomers of retinene. The absorption spectra were then measured against the red-bleached solution as blank. All-*trans* and neo-*a* retinene synthesized no photosensitive pigments, hence remained almost as added. Neo-*b* retinene formed iodopsin (λ_{max} 562 mμ); iso-*a* retinene, iso-iodopsin (λ_{max} 510 mμ). Both photosensitive pigments are accompanied by residues of unchanged retinene, primarily responsible for the absorption bands at about 370 mμ. [From Wald *et al.* (72).]

of reactions initiated by light (viz fig. 3 and text above), whereas the nervous response, even in a cold-blooded animal, appears within a fraction of a second. Changes in the opsins therefore would seem to offer richer possibilities.

Rhodopsin has been studied most in this regard. Cattle rhodopsin has a molecular weight of about 40,000 and contains one molecule of retinene (30). It has a molar extinction of 40,600 (69). The iso-electric point of frog rhodopsin is at pH 4.47 and goes to pH 4.57 on bleaching (7); cattle rhodopsin is isoionic at pH 5.4 and goes to pH 5.5 on bleaching (45). Neither cattle rhodopsin nor opsin contains available N- or C-terminal amino acids (1).

The synthesis of rhodopsin from retinene and opsin requires the presence of free sulfhydryl (—SH) groups on opsin. Conversely, the bleaching of rho-

dopsin liberates 2 or 3 —SH groups per molecule. This is true equally for rhodopsins from cattle, frogs and squid (68, 69). Exposure of rhodopsin to light also immediately exposes an acid-binding group with a pK of about 6.6, close to the pK of the imidazole group of histidine (45). Furthermore, opsin is much more readily denatured by acid and alkali, or heat, than rhodopsin (31a, 46).

All of this means that the action of light on rhodopsin, in addition to splitting off carotenoid, profoundly affects the reactivity of the opsin. In the structural context of a rod outer limb, these or like changes are probably the ultimate source of excitation.

It is important to realize that rhodopsin is one of the principal structural components of a rod. It accounts for about 40 per cent of the dry weight of

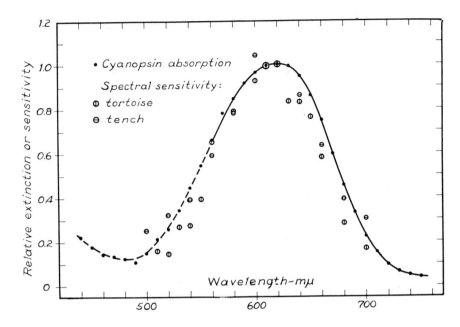

FIG. 12. The absorption spectrum of cyanopsin compared with Granit's electrophysiological measurements of the spectral sensitivity of cone vision in a fresh-water fish, the tench, and in the European tortoise, *Testudo graeca*. [From Wald *et al.* (71).]

the outer segment of a frog rod, or about 60 per cent of the nonlipid dry weight. In cattle rods, it accounts for about 14 per cent of the dry weight of the outer segment, or about 22 per cent of the nonlipid dry weight (30). The outer segments of the rods and cones are layered structures composed of several hundred to several thousand layers, apparently of protein, each about 40 to 160 Å thick (52). The membranes of the rod must be made in large part of rhodopsin (or porphyropsin). A cone has much the same construction, though in some cones the visual pigments may compose a smaller fraction of the membranes (65).

Two model systems have been described in which the bleaching of rhodopsin in solution registers directly as an electrical fluctuation (45, 68). Both are based on the fact that light exposes ion-binding groups on opsin, sulfhydryl groups in one case, an acid-binding group with pK 6.6 in the other, which affect the ion concentration in the medium. These models show that rhodopsin has the capacity to translate the absorption of a quantum of light into an electrical event. The effective utilization of this capacity depends entirely upon the structural framework within which it occurs. A dark-adapted rod is stimulated by the absorption of a single quantum of light (6, 29, 44). The same probably is true of a dark-adapted cone. One quantum of light is absorbed

by one molecule of visual pigment, and a rod or cone is so peculiarly constructed that so small a change can excite it.

PHYSIOLOGICAL CORRELATIONS

Every physiological function, normal and pathological, has its roots in biochemistry; conversely every facet of biochemistry finds expression in the properties and behavior of the organism. In a sense the organism is a macroscopic representation of certain of its component molecules, and one of the principal tasks of physiology is to learn to read its features in their features.

This is nowhere plainer than in vision. The reactions initiated by light in the rods and cones introduce a long train of nervous and synaptic processes which end in visual sensations. The primary events have been described in some detail. The visual apparatus as a whole is largely concerned with conducting the information they dictate. For this reason many of the basic properties of vision reflect simply and directly the properties of retinal molecules.

It is of the highest importance to explore these relationships. Needless to say, there is much more in vision than photochemistry, or indeed than any of the peripheral processes one can measure. Yet it is important to learn how far one can come with these if only to know that one must seek elsewhere for what remains.

Absorption Spectra and Spectral Sensitivity: Purkinje Phenomenon

The rise and fall of visual sensitivity throughout the spectrum is governed in the first instance by the capacity of the visual pigments to absorb light of various wavelengths, i.e. by their absorption spectra. When properly corrected, the spectral sensitivity should correspond closely with the absorption spectra of the visual pigments.

For such a comparison, the spectral sensitivity must be corrected for distortions caused by colored ocular structures, in the human eye principally the yellow lens and macula lutea and similar structures in the eyes of other animals. The spectral sensitivity also should be quantized. What is measured generally is the relative energy at each wavelength needed to evoke a constant response. The reciprocal of this is the relative sensitivity, and this divided by the wavelength is the sensitivity in terms of relative numbers of incident quanta. This is the form in which spectral sensitivity data can best be employed for the present purpose.

The spectra of the visual pigments should be stated in terms of percentage absorption rather than extinction (cf. 59). The point of this distinction is that all extinction curves are simple multiples of one another, whereas a percentage absorption curve has a unique shape depending upon the actual value of the absorption. However, extinction and percentage absorption are almost exactly proportional to each other up to 10 per cent absorption and depart only slightly from proportionality up to about 20 per cent absorption. All known cones and most rods seem to have absorptions below this value. Extinction therefore runs parallel with absorption for all cones and for all but the more densely pigmented rods. In the figures which follow, the absorption spectra of the visual pigments have been plotted in terms of relative extinction since the percentage absorption usually is not known. This introduces appreciable distortion only in comparison with frog rod vision (cf. fig. 14).

Figure 13 shows the comparison between the absorption spectra of chicken rhodopsin and iodopsin, and the spectral sensitivity of rod and cone vision in

the pigeon. It would, of course, be preferable to compare the spectral sensitivity of the chicken, but in the absence of accurate data measurements on the closely related pigeon have been used. They were obtained by inserting microelectrodes into the retina, following removal of the lens and cornea (11, 19). The pigeons were either dark-adapted 1 to 2 hours following the operation, or were light-adapted. At each wavelength, measurements were made of the energy needed to evoke a constant electrical response. The reciprocal of the energy, the sensitivity, was quantized by dividing by the wavelength.

The scotopic sensitivity agrees very well with the absorption spectrum of rhodopsin. The photopic sensitivity however is displaced about 20 mμ toward the red from the spectrum of iodopsin. This displacement must be caused in large part by the brightly-colored oil globules which lie in the cones of chickens and pigeons in the position of color filters (79, 80). The displacement seems larger than the color filters of the chicken retina should cause and may mean that many of the electrophysiological measurements happened to fall within the 'red field' of the pigeon retina, the dorsotemporal quadrant in which deep red oil globules predominate.

The shift of spectral sensitivity toward the red as one goes from scotopic to photopic conditions, from rod to cone vision, is the well-known Purkinje phenomenon. Except for the distortion just alluded to, this is accurately mimicked in solution by the absorption spectra of rhodopsin and iodopsin.

This comparison gains special force when made with retinas which do not possess obviously colored filtering pigments. In figure 14 the absorption spectra of chicken rhodopsin and iodopsin are compared with the spectral sensitivities of rod and cone vision in the frog, snake, guinea pig and cat, measured with electrical procedures by Granit and co-workers. The scotopic data agree very well with the absorption spectrum of rhodopsin. The photopic sensitivities agree so well with the absorption spectrum of iodopsin that it seems probable that this is the major pigment of cone vision in the frog, snake and cat.

Figure 14 shows that when colored ocular structures do not intervene, the Purkinje phenomenon emerges quantitatively from the absorption spectra of rhodopsin and iodopsin. In essence it involves nothing more than the transfer of vision from dependence on the absorption spectrum of rhodopsin in dim light to that of iodopsin in bright light.

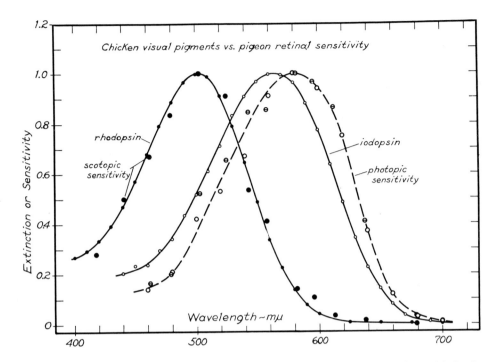

FIG. 13. Absorption spectra of chicken rhodopsin and iodopsin, compared with the spectral sensitivities of dark- and light-adapted pigeons. The latter were measured electrophysiologically and are plotted in terms of the reciprocals of the numbers of incident quanta needed to evoke a constant electrical response. The scotopic data are from Donner (11), the photopic data from the same source (*barred circles*) and from Granit (19) (*open circles*). The scotopic sensitivity agrees well with the absorption spectrum of rhodopsin. The photopic sensitivity is displaced about 20 mμ toward the red from the absorption spectrum of iodopsin, owing in large part to the filtering action of the colored oil globules of the pigeon cones. [From Wald (72).]

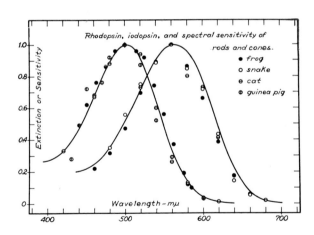

FIG. 14. The absorption spectra of chicken rhodopsin (λ_{max} 502 mμ) and iodopsin (λ_{max} 562 mμ) compared with the scotopic and photopic sensitivities of various animals. The *lines* show the absorption spectra of the visual pigments, the *points* electrophysiological measurements of spectral sensitivity (quantized). Scotopic data: frog (22); cat (12); guinea pig (18). Photopic measurements: frog (17); snake (20); cat (21). [From Wald *et al.* (72).]

Figure 15 shows this same comparison for the human eye. The spectral sensitivities were measured in the periphery of the aphakic (lensless) eye, to avoid distortions otherwise introduced by the yellow pigmentations of the lens and macula lutea (61, 63). The scotopic sensitivity agrees well with the absorption spectrum of rhodopsin, but the photopic sensitivity is displaced about 20 mμ toward the blue from iodopsin. This is hardly surprising, for the human photopic sensitivity is believed to be a composite function, the resultant of the spectral sensitivities of at least three classes of cone needed to account for trichromatic vision. These seem to possess maxima at about 450, 550 and 590 mμ (2, 53). Iodopsin, or a closely related pigment, may function as the middle member of this trio, but this must cooperate with at least two other cone pigments to provide the mechanism of normal color differentiation.

Finally, in figure 16, such a comparison is shown for the vitamin A$_2$ eye of a fresh-water fish, the tench. The spectral sensitivities, scotopic and photopic,

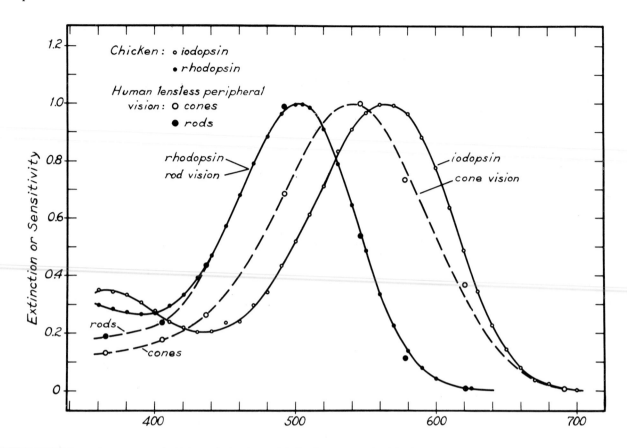

FIG. 15. Absorption spectra of chicken rhodopsin and iodopsin compared with the spectral sensitivity of human rod and cone vision. The spectral sensitivity measurements were made in a peripheral field in the aphakic (lensless) eye to avoid distortions caused by the yellow pigmentations of the lens and macula lutea. They represent as close an approximation to the sensitivities of the naked rods and cones as can be achieved in the living eye (cf. 61, 63). The scotopic (rod) sensitivity agrees with the absorption spectrum of rhodopsin over most of its course. The photopic (cone) sensitivity is displaced some 20 mμ toward the blue from the absorption spectrum of iodopsin; it represents the resultant of the spectral sensitivities of at least three groups of cones concerned with color vision. [From Wald *et al.* (72).]

measured electrophysiologically, are shown as large circles. The lines and small circles show the absorption spectra of porphyropsin and cyanopsin. The photopic sensitivity agrees very well with the absorption spectrum of cyanopsin; but for reasons which are still obscure, the scotopic sensitivity is displaced about 10 mμ toward the red from porphyropsin. The corneas and lenses had been removed from these preparations; possibly some yellow pigmentation in the retina or a trace of blood in the ocular fluids may account for this discrepancy.[4] In animals having vision based upon vitamin A₂, the

Purkinje shift is unusually large: about 90 mμ, from about 530 mμ in the scotopic eye to about 620 mμ in the photopic eye. This is consistent with the large displacement between the absorption spectra of porphyropsin and cyanopsin.

It can be concluded that the spectral sensitivities of rod and cone vision, and hence the Purkinje phenomenon, derive directly and quantitatively from the absorption spectra of the visual pigments.

Visual Adaptation and the Bleaching and Synthesis of Visual Pigments

It has been believed for many years that some simple relation connects the visual threshold, or

---

[4] Recently it has been shown that the absorption spectra of visual pigments *in situ* lie about 7 mμ toward the red from their positions in solution (9a, 70a).

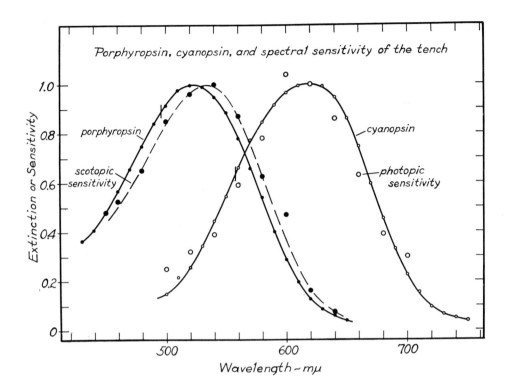

FIG. 16. Absorption spectra of porphyropsin and cyanopsin (*lines, small circles*) compared with the spectral sensitivities of rod and cone vision in a fresh-water fish, the tench (*broken line, large circles*). The spectral sensitivities were measured electrophysiologically by Granit (16) in opened eyes from which cornea and lens had been removed. The photopic sensitivity agrees well with the absorption spectrum of cyanopsin, but the scotopic sensitivity is displaced about 10 mμ toward the red from porphyropsin, perhaps because of some yellow pigmentation in the retina or ocular fluids.

better its reciprocal, the visual sensitivity, with the concentration of visual pigment. It has been assumed that in a steady illumination the visual pigments bleach to steady levels, maintained thereafter by regenerative processes. Simultaneously the visual sensitivity falls to a steady state value; this is light adaptation. Conversely, in the dark the visual pigments are synthesized to their maximal concentrations. Simultaneously the sensitivity rises to a maximum; this is dark adaptation.

Lately it has become apparent that whatever relation obtains between visual sensitivity and concentration of visual pigment is not as direct as simple proportionality. On the contrary, the bleaching of a very small fraction of rhodopsin in dark-adapted rods results in an extraordinarily large fall of sensitivity (51). Parallel 'light adaptations' conducted on a human subject and on a solution of cattle rhodopsin in a water model of the human eye show that, to a first approximation, the bleaching

of 0.006 per cent of the rhodopsin lowers the visual sensitivity 8.5 times; and the bleaching of 0.6 per cent of rhodopsin lowers the sensitivity 3300 times (65). Conversely the resynthesis of the last small fraction of rhodopsin must raise the sensitivity greatly. Indeed much of light and dark adaptation in the rods seems to involve the first small fraction of rhodopsin to be bleached, and the last small fraction to be resynthesized (cf. 23, 24).

Recently Rushton and his co-workers have succeeded by a most ingenious procedure in measuring directly the rise and fall of visual pigment in the living human eye (8, 49, 50). This permits a direct comparison between the rates of bleaching and synthesis of photosensitive pigments and the course of light and dark adaptation. For measuring rhodopsin, the method depends on comparing the reflection from the retina of a blue-green light strongly absorbed by rhodopsin with an orange light scarcely absorbed by rhodopsin. No change of retinal reflectance was detected on illuminating such rod-free areas as the fovea or the optic disc. On light-adapting areas known to contain rods, increases in the reflectance of blue-green light were recorded, apparently caused by bleaching rhodopsin. The variation in magnitude of this effect along the horizontal meridian, from nasal to temporal, can be correlated with the distribution of rod density (fig. 17).

When the eye is exposed to light, the rhodopsin content falls exponentially to a steady state level at which the rate of bleaching is balanced by the regeneration rate. As might be expected, the rhodopsin content at the steady state decreases as the level of illumination is raised (fig. 18). The time course of bleaching roughly parallels the course of light adaptation of human rod vision (cf. 73). Following light adaptation, the rhodopsin concentration rises regularly in the dark (fig. 18) and approaches a maximum value in about thirty minutes (50), in good agreement with the time required for human rod dark adaptation (fig. 19).

The course of bleaching and resynthesis of rhodopsin in the human retina, measured in this way, agrees with the course of human light and dark adaptation only when the latter is plotted in terms of log sensitivity. It is the logarithm of the visual sensitivity that rises and falls with time much as does the concentration of rhodopsin. A theory has been proposed which accounts for this relationship (65, 72). The rod is viewed as a compartmented structure. Each compartment contains a large quantity of rhodopsin and is discharged by the absorption of a first quantum of light. The residual rhodopsin of a discharged

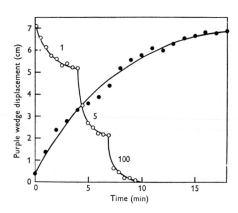

FIG. 18. Bleaching and resynthesis of rhodopsin in the human retina 15 degrees temporal to the fovea. *Open circles:* On exposing the eye successively to lights of increasing brightness (1, 5 and 100 units, where 1 unit = 20,000 trolands), the rhodopsin content falls each time to a new steady-state level at which the rate of bleaching is balanced by the regeneration rate. *Filled circles:* In the dark, rhodopsin regenerates. Complete recovery (not shown in figure) takes about 30 min. (50). [From Campbell & Rushton (8).]

compartment continues to absorb light and to bleach but can no longer contribute to excitation. A rod is rendered wholly inexcitable when each of its compartments has absorbed at least one quantum of light, i.e. when in each of its compartments at least one molecule of rhodopsin has been bleached. In this way the bleaching of very little rhodopsin can lead to a high state of light adaptation[5]. This hypothesis, pursued mathematically, leads to the expectation that the logarithm of the visual sensitivity should be approximately proportional to the concentration of visual pigment (72).

The same relationships appear to hold for cones. Rushton (49) has recently modified his method to measure cone pigments in the human fovea. He finds that in the dark, following exposure to a bright light, cone visual pigment is resynthesized much more rapidly than rhodopsin (fig. 20). The course of synthesis parallels human cone dark adaptation (fig. 19). It has long been known that in man and many other animals the cones dark-adapt much more rapidly than the rods. In the human eye the dark

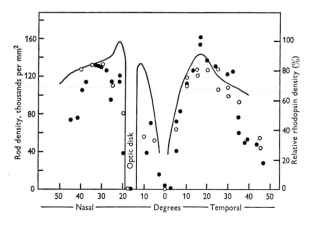

FIG. 17. Distribution of rhodopsin density in the human retina. *Circles:* measurements of rhodopsin density at the points shown along the horizontal meridian. *Line:* rod density per mm² in the same region. [From Campbell & Rushton (8).]

[5] The term bleach is here used loosely to involve the entire chain of effects that follows the absorption of light by rhodopsin. The first such effect is the production of lumi-rhodopsin; then by thermal reactions meta-rhodopsin (still without literal bleaching); and finally a mixture of all-*trans* retinene and opsin. The excitation process probably depends upon the first of these steps, the change to lumi- or at most meta-rhodopsin.

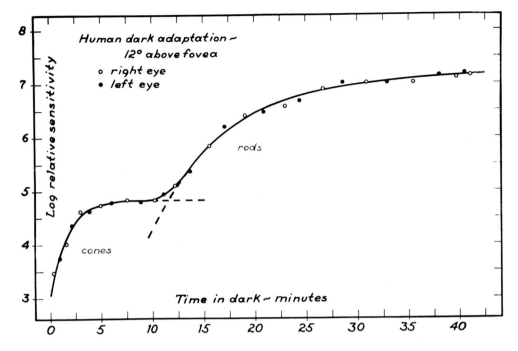

FIG. 19. Dark-adaptation of the human eye measured in a peripheral area which contains both rods and cones. The dark adaptation of the cones is completed within about 5 min., that of the rods within about 45 min. [From Wald *et al.* (72).]

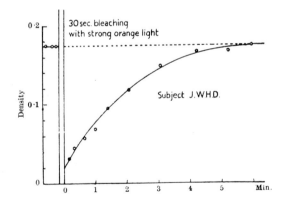

FIG. 20. Bleaching and resynthesis of visual pigments in the human fovea. Initial values after dark adaptation. Following a 30 sec. bleach with strong orange light, the density is at first very low but rises rapidly in the dark. Recovery is complete in 6 min. [From Rushton (49).]

adaptation of the cones is complete within 4 to 6 min., while that of the rods continues for over 45 min. The dark adaptation of a peripheral area of the human retina containing rods and cones is shown in figure 19. It is plotted in terms of log sensitivity (-log threshold) the better to expose its relationship to the rise of visual pigment concentration.

Another approach to this problem has been made by comparing the rates of synthesis of rhodopsin and iodopsin in solution. Figure 10 above shows a mixture of chicken iodopsin and rhodopsin made by incubating neo-*b* retinene in solution with a mixture of cone and rod opsins. The reason the visual pigments form separately in this instance is that iodopsin is synthesized with enormously greater speed than rhodopsin, about 530 times as fast at 10°C (72). Figure 21 shows the synthesis of the two pigments in solution at 23°C. The synthesis of iodopsin is complete within 5 min., while that of rhodopsin continues for well over an hour. The data are taken from the same experiment as figure 10 but with rhodopsin extinctions multiplied by 1.3. It is hardly necessary to labor the close relationship between these measurements, the synthesis of human rod and cone pigments *in vivo*, and the course of human dark adaptation, cone and rod. Again, however, what parallelism obtains involves the comparison of log sensitivity with the concentration of the visual pigments.

One must conclude from all these measurements that light and dark adaptation have their primary source in the bleaching and resynthesis of the visual pigments of the rods and cones. To be sure, more central phenomena—changes in the sensitivities of

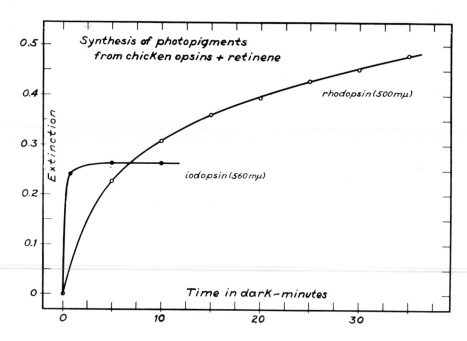

FIG. 21. Synthesis of iodopsin and rhodopsin in solution from a mixture of chicken opsins and neo-*b* retinene. 23°C. This is the same experiment as shown in figure 10 but with the rhodopsin extinctions multiplied by 1.3. At this temperature, iodopsin synthesis is complete within 2 to 3 min., whereas rhodopsin synthesis still continues after 35 min. [From Wald (72).]

neurons and synapses along the optic pathways—may also play a role. Of this possibility as yet very little is known. In general, neural adaptations are relatively rapid; if they enter at all, they should probably be completed during the earliest stages of visual adaptation. They probably are responsible also for only a minor portion of the range of visual adaptation. As a first approximation, light and dark adaptation seem to reflect the fall and rise of visual pigment; and specifically it is the log sensitivity which runs parallel with pigment concentration.

Vitamin A Deficiency and Night Blindness

Probably the earliest symptom of vitamin A deficiency in man and other animals is the rise of visual threshold known as night blindness. Because night vision is associated with the rods, it was once thought that dietary night blindness, so called to distinguish it from the idiopathic or congenital disease, is a failure specifically of rod vision. The first experimental studies of human night blindness, however, showed at once that in vitamin A deficiency cone vision deteriorates with rod vision, and both recover together on administration of vitamin A (figs. 22, 23) (26, 27, 77).

The realization that both iodopsin and rhodopsin are synthesized from the same form of vitamin A offers a substantial theoretical basis for this relationship. To be sure, iodopsin has not been demonstrated in human cones; if present, it is presumably accompanied by at least two other cone pigments needed to account for normal human color vision. Yet the observation that on administration of vitamin A, or carotene, night blindness is repaired as quickly and completely in the cones as in the rods (fig. 23) implies that the human cone pigments as a group are probably synthesized from vitamin A. Just as rhodopsin and iodopsin are constructed by joining the same prosthetic group to different opsins, so the cone pigments responsible for human color vision may well be composed of the same retinene combined with a variety of different opsins.

The opsins have been altogether a neglected component in the etiology of dietary night blindness. This disease and its cure have been thought of too much in terms of the removal and replacement of vitamin A, particularly since vitamin A was shown to be a precursor of rhodopsin. This preconception may be the source of some of the embarrassments that have attended the experimental study of night blindness: *a*) on beginning a vitamin A–deficient diet, some subjects immediately begin to become night-blind, whereas others show no effects, visual or otherwise, for many months; and *b*) on administration of vitamin A to night-blind subjects, some

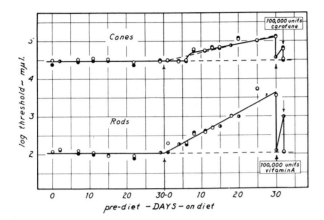

FIG. 22. Thresholds of completely dark-adapted cones and rods during 30 days of heavy vitamin A administration (*left*) and during 30 days on a vitamin A-deficient diet (*right*). *Open* and *closed circles* show thresholds of right and left eyes, respectively. On the thirtieth day of the deficient diet, one dose of vitamin A was administered; both rod and cone thresholds returned to normal. On the thirty-second day, the subject was again slightly night-blind and was given a dose of carotene; again both cone and rod thresholds returned to normal. [From Wald *et al.* (77).]

are cured completely within several hours, whereas others retain some degree of night blindness for months while receiving a high dosage of vitamin A. Figure 22 shows the rapid type of onset of night blindness, figure 23 the rapid type of cure. Unfortunately the other type of result is observed at least as often (28, 35, 66).

One must distinguish an acute from a chronic syndrome in vitamin A deficiency. The results of a current study of vitamin A deficiency in the rat are summarized in figure 24 (cf. 12a). When an animal is placed on a vitamin A-deficient diet, the liver stores slowly lose vitamin A until the liver has been emptied. Up to this time the blood level remains normal, but now it sinks within a few days to zero. To this point the rhodopsin content of the retina has remained normal, but now this too falls, marking the beginning of night blindness. For about three weeks longer the opsin level stays normal. Then it too begins to fall; at the same time the retina deteriorates anatomically, and the animal loses weight and displays other overt signs of vitamin A deficiency. All these disorders are reversed by administration of vitamin A.

The role of vitamin A as the precursor of visual pigments seems almost trivial compared with its general role in maintaining the integrity of the tissues. The mechanism of this action is still completely obscure. In vitamin A deficiency, various tissues all over the body begin to deteriorate, the

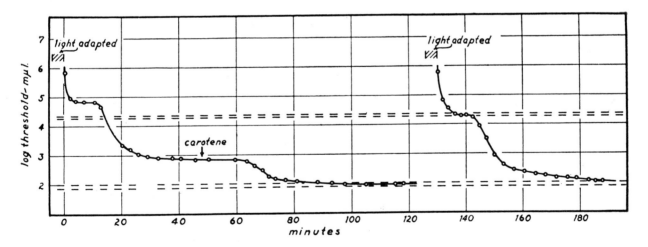

FIG. 23. The cure of night-blindness with carotene. Following a standard light adaptation, the measurement of dark adaptation shows both cone and rod plateaus to lie above their normal range (enclosed within the *upper* and *lower pairs of broken lines*). After dark adaptation was completed, 20,000 International Units of carotene in oil were administered in gelatin capsules orally. For 12 to 14 min. the rod threshold remained constant; then it fell rapidly to normal. Immediate repetition of the standard adaptation procedure showed both cone and rod plateaus to have entered their normal ranges. [From Wald & Steven (78).]

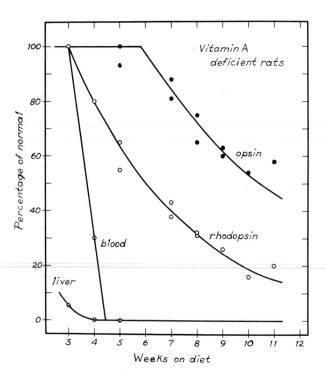

FIG. 24. Vitamin A deficiency in the rat. Blood vitamin A (⦶) falls precipitously as liver stores of vitamin A (⊖) are exhausted. At this point, the rhodopsin content of the dark-adapted eye (○) begins to decline, presumably because not enough vitamin A is available to convert all the opsin of the rods to rhodopsin. About three weeks later, opsin itself (●) begins to disappear, its concentration from then on paralleling the decreasing rhodopsin content. Disappearance of opsin may in part be responsible for the degeneration of rods and cones associated with chronic vitamin A deficiency. [From Dowling & Wald (12a).]

retina among others (36, 54). Johnson has reported that after 7 to 13 weeks of vitamin A deprivation in young rats, the rods in the retinal fundus exhibit marked changes. Many outer segments have disappeared and those that remain stain abnormally. As the deficiency progresses, the inner segments of the rods also degenerate, then successively the external limiting membrane and outer nuclear layer, the pigment epithelium, the outer molecular layer, and the inner nuclear layer. These changes progress much faster in the central retina than toward the periphery. Outer segments of rods which have suffered only slight degenerative changes seem to repair considerably within 24 hours of vitamin A therapy. Even rods which have degenerated completely appear to regenerate within 10 to 18 weeks of vitamin A administration.

The rod outer segment is composed in considerable measure of rhodopsin (see above). A loss of opsin might therefore profoundly damage its structural integrity; long before such changes are visible in the microscope they might become detectable physiologically as night blindness. In any case, night blindness clearly involves far more than the simple decline of vitamin A concentration in the retina. It introduces, particularly in prolonged deficiency, deep-seated anatomical changes and these might repair only very slowly.

In addition to deficiency in the diet, any interference with the flow of vitamin A to the retina, or with its utilization by the tissues can be expected to react on the visual threshold. This appears to be the case in certain chronic liver diseases (cf. 41). Bile is needed for the absorption of both carotene and vitamin A (25). In obstructive jaundice, in which bile fails to reach the intestine, vitamin A deficiency and hence night blindness may develop in spite of a diet adequate to meet normal requirements. In addition to producing the bile, the liver is the principal storage tissue for vitamin A. It is not surprising therefore that liver disorders may affect the extent, and apparently in some instances also the rate, of dark adaptation.

Recently it has been shown that the wall of the intestine is probably the principal site for the conversion of carotene to vitamin A (14, 55). It is not unlikely that conditions exist in which some failure of this process leads to visual disturbances.

Even when the diet is adequate, and the liver and intestine are performing their functions, this may not yet be enough. Vision depends, not merely on vitamin A, but on a particular shape of vitamin A, the neo-b isomer. This is not ordinarily present in the food, so that other isomers of vitamin A obtained in the diet must be converted into this special configuration. The neo-b isomer is continuously lost in the bleaching of the visual pigments and must be continuously replaced for vision to persist. It is not impossible that there exists a visual disorder that has its source in a failure to isomerize vitamin A. Furthermore, the fact that vitamin A is stored in the eye as an ester, which must presumably be hydrolyzed before entering the visual cycle, constitutes another point at which visual processes are vulnerable to metabolic failure.

It has repeatedly been suggested that retinitis pigmentosa, a degenerative disease which attacks primarily the layer of rods and cones, is due to some local failure in the supply or effective utilization of vitamin A (9, 81, 82). The lesions at one stage of vitamin A deficiency resemble somewhat those in retinitis pigmentosa. The layer of rods and cones is the first to deteriorate in vitamin A deficiency, and such deterioration is characteristic of the disease. In more advanced vitamin A deficiency, however, the inner retinal layers also succumb, while remaining apparently intact in retinitis pigmentosa. It is conceivable that these symptoms are due to a local failure in vitamin A metabolism which is not apparent elsewhere in the eye tissues.

The participation of vitamin A in the processes of visual excitation therefore introduces a whole series of special relationships. It renders vision dependent upon an ecological factor, the nutrition, and upon the entire network of internal arrangements that govern the absorption, metabolism and transport of vitamin A throughout the body.

Nicotinamide

A second vitamin plays a basic role in the visual processes: nicotinamide, the anti-pellagra factor of the vitamin B complex and the active principle of DPN, which is the coenzyme of the alcohol dehydrogenase system. Without this factor vitamin A presumably cannot be oxidized to retinene, a necessary step in the synthesis of rhodopsin and iodopsin.

Are there visual symptoms in pellagra? Is there, for example, some disturbance of dark adaptation in this disease? None has been reported; but it might be well to examine carefully the visual behavior of pellagrins with these considerations in mind.

REFERENCES

1. ALBRECHT, G. S. *J. Biol. Chem.* In press.
2. AUERBACH, E. AND G. WALD. *Am. J. Ophth.* 39: 24, 1955.
3. BALL, S., T. W. GOODWIN AND R. A. MORTON. *Biochem. J.* 42: 516, 1948.
4. BLISS, A. F. *Arch. Biochem. & Biophys.* 31: 197, 1951.
5. BOLL, F. *Arch. Anat. & Physiol.*: 4, 1877.
6. BOUMAN, M. A. AND H. A. VAN DER VELDEN. *J. Opt. Soc. Am.* 37: 908, 1947.
7. BRODA, E. E. AND E. VICTOR. *Biochem. J.* 34: 1501, 1940.
8. CAMPBELL, F. W. AND W. A. H. RUSHTON. *J. Physiol.* 130: 131, 1955.
9. COGAN, D. G. *Tr. Am. Acad. Ophth.*: 629, July–Aug. 1950.
9a. DENTON, E. J. *Nat. Phys. Lab. A. K. Proc.* Symp. 8. In press.
10. DIETERLE, J. M. AND C. D. ROBESON. *Science* 120: 219, 1954.
11. DONNER, K. O. *J. Physiol.* 122: 524, 1953.
12. DONNER, K. O. AND R. GRANIT. *Acta physiol. scandinav.* 17: 161, 1949.
12a. DOWLING, J. E. AND G. WALD. *Proc. Nat. Acad. Sc., Washington* 44: 648, 1958.
13. FARRAR, K. R., J. C. HAMLET, H. B. HENBEST AND E. R. H. JONES. *Chem. & Indust.*: 49, 1951.
14. GLOVER, J., T. W. GOODWIN AND R. A. MORTON. *Biochem. J. Proc.*, 41: xiv, 1947.
15. GRANIT, R. *Acta physiol. scandinav.* 1: 386, 1941.
16. GRANIT, R. *Acta physiol. scandinav.* 2: 334, 1941.
17. GRANIT, R. *Acta physiol. scandinav.* 3: 137, 1942.
18. GRANIT, R. *Acta physiol. scandinav.* 3: 318, 1942.
19. GRANIT, R. *Acta physiol. scandinav.* 4: 118, 1942.
20. GRANIT, R. *Acta physiol. scandinav.* 5: 108, 1943.
21. GRANIT, R. *Acta physiol. scandinav.* 5: 219, 1943.
22. GRANIT, R. *Sensory Mechanisms of the Retina.* London: Oxford, 1947, p. 292.
23. GRANIT, R., T. HOLMBERG AND M. ZEWI. *J. Physiol.* 94: 430, 1938.
24. GRANIT, R., A. MUNSTERHJELM AND M. ZEWI. *J. Physiol.* 96: 31, 1939.
25. GREAVES, J. D. AND C. I. A. SCHMIDT. *Am. J. Physiol.* 111: 492, 1935.
26. HAIG, C., S. HECHT AND A. J. PATEK, JR. *Science* 87: 534, 1938.
27. HECHT, S. AND J. MANDELBAUM. *Science* 88: 219, 1938.
28. HECHT, S. AND J. MANDELBAUM. *Am. J. Physiol.* 130: 651, 1940.
29. HECHT, S., S. SHLAER AND M. H. PIRENNE. *J. Gen. Physiol.* 25: 819, 1941–42.
30. HUBBARD, R. *J. Gen. Physiol.* 37: 381, 1953–54.
31. HUBBARD, R. *J. Gen. Physiol.* 39: 935, 1955–56.
31a. HUBBARD, R. *Nature, London* 181: 1126, 1958.
32. HUBBARD, R., R. I. GREGERMAN AND G. WALD. *J. Gen. Physiol.* 36: 415, 1952–53.
33. HUBBARD, R. AND G. WALD. *Proc. Nat. Acad. Sc., Washington* 37: 69, 1951.
34. HUBBARD, R. AND G. WALD. *J. Gen. Physiol.* 36: 269, 1952–53.
35. HUME, E. M. AND H. A. KREBS. *Vitamin A Requirements of Human Adults* (Medical Res. Council, Special Report Series No. 264). London: His Majesty's Stat. Off., 1949.
36. JOHNSON, M. L. *A.M.A. Arch. Ophth.* 29: 793, 1943.
37. KRINSKY, N. I. *J. Biol. Chem.* In press.
38. KÜHNE, W. In: *Handbuch der Physiologie*, edited by L. Hermann. Leipzig: Vogel, 1879, vol. 3, pt. 1, p. 312.
39. OROSHNIK, W. *J. Am. Chem. Soc.* 78: 2651, 1956.
40. OROSHNIK, W., P. K. BROWN, R. HUBBARD AND G. WALD. *Proc. Nat. Acad. Sc., Washington* 42: 578, 1956.
41. PATEK, A. J. AND C. HAIG. *J. Clin. Invest.* 18: 609, 1939.
42. PAULING, L. *Fortschr. Chem. org. Naturstoffe* 3: 203, 1939.
43. PAULING, L. *Helvet. chim. acta* 32: 2241, 1949.
44. PIRENNE, M. H. *Brit. M. Bull.* 9: 61, 1953.
45. RADDING, C. M. AND G. WALD. *J. Gen. Physiol.* 39: 909, 1955–56.
46. RADDING, C. M. AND G. WALD. *J. Gen. Physiol.* 39: 923, 1955–56.
47. ROBESON, C. D. AND J. G. BAXTER. *J. Am. Chem. Soc.* 69: 136, 1947.
48. ROBESON, C. D., W. P. BLUM, J. M. DIETERLE, J. D.

CAWLEY AND J. G. BAXTER. *J. Am. Chem. Soc.* 77: 4120, 1955.

49. RUSHTON, W. A. H. *Nature, London* 179: 571, 1957.
50. RUSHTON, W. A. H., F. W. CAMPBELL, W. A. HIGGINS AND G. S. BRINDLEY. *Optica acta* 1: 183, 1955.
51. RUSHTON, W. A. H. AND R. D. COHEN. *Nature, London* 173: 301, 1954.
52. SJÖSTRAND, F. S. *J. Cell. & Comp. Physiol.* 42: 15, 1953.
53. STILES, W. S. *Nederl. tijdschr. Natuurk.* 15: 125, 1949.
54. TANSLEY, K. *Proc. Roy. Soc., London. ser. B* 114: 79, 1933.
55. THOMPSON, S. Y., J. GANGULY AND S. K. KON. *Brit. J. Nutrition* 3: 50, 1949.
56. WALD, G. *J. Gen. Physiol.* 19: 781, 1935–36.
57. WALD, G. *Nature, London* 139: 1017, 1937.
58. WALD, G. *Nature, London* 140: 545, 1937.
59. WALD, G. *J. Gen. Physiol.* 21: 795, 1937–38.
60. WALD, G. *J. Gen. Physiol.* 22: 775, 1938–39.
61. WALD, G. *Science* 101: 653, 1945.
62. WALD, G. *Harvey Lectures.* Ser. 41: 117, 1945–46.
63. WALD, G. *Docum. ophth.* 3: 94, 1949.
64. WALD, G. *Biochimi. et biophys. acta* 4: 215, 1950.
65. WALD, G. *Science* 119: 887, 1954.
66. WALD, G., L. BROUHA AND R. E. JOHNSON. *Am. J. Physiol.* 137: 551, 1942.
67. WALD, G. AND P. K. BROWN. *Proc. Nat. Acad. Sc., Washington* 36: 84, 1950.
68. WALD, G. AND P. K. BROWN. *J. Gen. Physiol.* 35: 797, 1951–52.
69. WALD, G. AND P. K. BROWN. *J. Gen. Physiol.* 37: 189 1953–54.
70. WALD, G. AND P. K. BROWN. *Nature, London* 177: 174, 1956.
70a. WALD, G. AND P. K. BROWN. *Science* 127: 222, 1958.
71. WALD, G., P. K. BROWN AND P. H. SMITH. *Science* 118: 505, 1953.
72. WALD, G., P. K. BROWN AND P. H. SMITH. *J. Gen. Physiol.* 38: 623, 1954–55.
73. WALD, G. AND A. B. CLARK. *J. Gen. Physiol.* 21: 93, 1937–38.
74. WALD, G., J. DURELL AND R. C. C. ST. GEORGE. *Science* 111: 179, 1950.
75. WALD, G. AND R. HUBBARD. *J. Gen. Physiol.* 32: 367, 1948–49.
76. WALD, G. AND R. HUBBARD. *Proc. Nat. Acad. Sc., Washington* 36: 92, 1950.
77. WALD, G., H. JEGHERS AND J. ARMINIO. *Am. J. Physiol.* 123: 732, 1938.
78. WALD, G. AND D. STEVEN. *Proc. Nat. Acad. Sc., Washington* 25: 344, 1939.
79. WALD, G. AND H. ZUSSMAN. *J. Biol. Chem.* 122: 449, 1938.
80. WALLS, G. L. AND H. D. JUDD. *Brit. J. Ophth.* 17: 641, 705, 1933.
81. YUDKIN, A. M. *J. A. M. A.* 191: 921, 1933.
82. ZEAVIN, B. H. AND G. WALD. *Am. J. Ophth.* 42: part II: 254, 1956.
83. ZECHMEISTER, L. *Chem. Rev.* 34: 267, 1944.
84. ZECHMEISTER, L. *Experientia* 10: 1, 1954.

CHAPTER XXIX

Neural activity in the retina

RAGNAR GRANIT | *Nobel Institute for Neurophysiology, Karolinska Institutet, Stockholm, Sweden*

CHAPTER CONTENTS

OUTLINE OF RETINAL HISTOLOGY

THE RETINA consists of a surface layer of receptors, the rods and cones (fig. 1), joined to a nervous center which delivers an organized message in terms of impulses through the optic nerve. The great works of Ramón y Cajal (123, 124) and Polyak (122) should be consulted for details. The anatomy of the eye and retina throughout the vertebrates has been ably discussed by Walls (146). There is also a recent brief summary by Willmer (147).

In lower vertebrates it is not always easy to distinguish rods from cones (38, 146). In mammals rods end in knobs and cones in dendrites, but in frogs both types of receptor have dendritic terminals. Rods are generally more elongated and slender than cones but this criterion breaks down in some lizards and birds and in the fovea of the primates in which the elongated cones look like rods. Walls emphasizes that the outer cone segment is enclosed by a tubular process from the pigment epithelium cell opposite to it and holds this criterion to be universal and never found in rods. Differentiation between rods and cones seems possible by electron microscopy, at least in some species (132, 133, 134, 135). It has even been possible to distinguish two kinds of rods in guinea pigs (135) which would agree well with the electrophysiological observations on blue sensitivity existing in this species which has almost no cones. Photodichroism, an orientation of the light-absorbing molecules serving to aid absorption, has been observed in the rods (36, 129). The fresh cones, viewed end on, light up when the microscope is focused on the outer limbs which thus seem to serve as a focusing device operating by total internal reflection (138). This observation may explain why a pencil of light entering at an angle is dimmed if it enters cones, the Stiles-Crawford effect (136).

Double cones and twin cones have been described in fish but since these types do not occur in mammals, they have attracted little attention, physiological work rather tending to settle on universal characteristics. Schwalbe's 'green' rods found in frogs have recently been observed to contain a special blue-absorbing photosensitive substance (37) and may well be more general than one had thought.

The rods are integrating organs and converge in large numbers towards the bipolar dendrites. Bipolars in their turn converge towards the ganglion cells which give rise to the optic nerve fibers. In man there are some 125,000,000 rods as against 800,000 to 1,000,000 optic nerve fibers. Since man has only 4 to 7 million cones, it is clear that the amount of convergence is far less for them; this criterion seems to be general throughout the animal kingdom, signifying that cones, on the whole, are more discriminative, while rods are more integrative and designed to serve as collectors of light quanta in the dark (92, 127). The fundamental observation that rods actually do dominate the eyes of nocturnal animals and that an increasing number of cones is characteristic of diurnal habits was made by Schultze (131) on the basis of extensive histological studies. This, and later psychophysical work by Parinaud (117), König (99) and

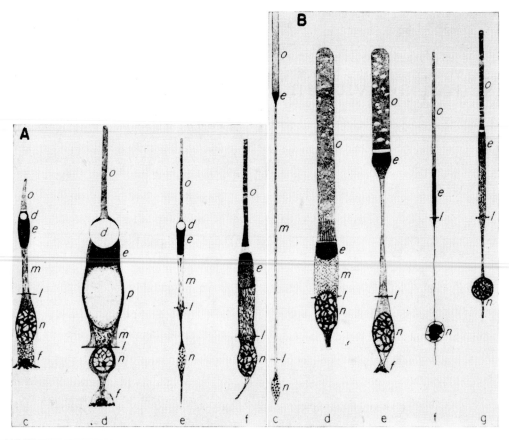

FIG. 1. *A.* Types of cones from the leopard frog, *Rana pipiens* (*c*); the snapping turtle, *Chelydra serpentina* (*d*); the marsh hawk, *Circus hudsonius* (*e*); and from the circumfoveal eminence of man (*f*). *B.* Types of rods from the goldfish, *Carassius auratus* (*c*); the leopard frog, a common or 'red' rod (*d*); the leopard frog, a so-called 'green' rod of Schwalbe (*e*); the flying squirrel, *Glaucomys v. volans* (*f*); and from the temporal side of the macula lutea of man (*g*). [From Walls (146).]

von Kries (145) led to the concept of a duplex retina for scotopic and photopic vision, respectively. Most eyes from this point of view are 'mixed', that is they contain two organs in one. When, at about the same period, Boll's (24) discovery of the light-sensitive visual purple (rhodopsin) was made and ably elaborated by Kühne (101), König (99) and their collaborators, this gave further support to the duplicity theory. Visual purple has been found only in the outer limbs of the rod. A historical review of this development is available (69).

In the external plexiform layer, between the receptors and bipolar cells, there are lateral connections, the horizontal cells (fig. 2), joining cones, each of which is embraced by a dendritic basket, to a larger group of rods and cones. There are several baskets to each horizontal cell and axons up to 0.8 mm in length have been found (123). The arrangement suggests a starting loop or positive feedback for general facilitation.

Polyak's (122) classification of bipolars is of interest because it is based on primates. There is, in the foveal area, the midget bipolar which is individual or private for a single cone. In the periphery each midget bipolar receives impulses from a small number of cones. At the opposite end it articulates with a midget ganglion cell by an axodendritic synapse, yet this midget system is not wholly isolated. Mop bipolars also run to the midget ganglion but this contact is axosomatic. These together with all the other bipolar types belong to the diffuse variety which receive a large number of receptors. The mop bipolars possess a kind of dendritic tuft, smaller in the fovea than in the periphery and forming a receptaculum for rod and cone pedicles. Its axosomatic projection is a crude shallow basket touching one or more ganglion cell

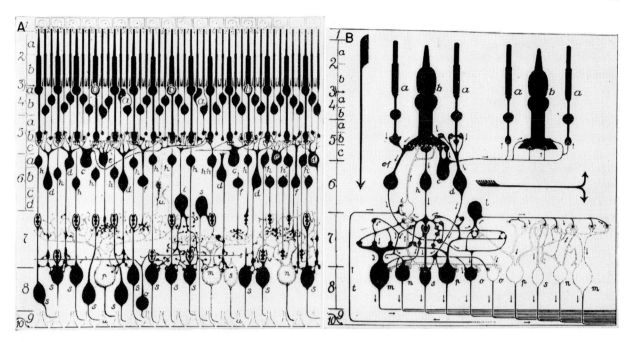

FIG. 2. *A*. Scheme of the structures of the primate retina as revealed by the method of Golgi. The layers and the zones are designated as follows: (*1*) pigment layer; (*2-a*) outer zone and (*2-b*) inner zone of the rod and cone layer; (*3*) outer limiting membrane; (*4-a*) outer zone and (*4-b*) inner zone of the outer nuclear layer; (*5-a*) outer zone, (*5-b*) middle zone and (*5-c*) inner zone of the outer plexiform layer; (*6*) inner nuclear layer with its four zones; (*7*) inner plexiform layer; (*8*) layer of the ganglion cells; (*9*) layer of the optic nerve fibers; and (*10*) inner limiting membrane. The nerve cells are designated as follows: (*a*) rods, (*b*) cones, (*c*) horizontal cells, (*d, e, f, h*) bipolar cells, (*i, l*) so-called 'amacrine cells', (*m, n, o, p, s*) ganglion cells and (*u*) 'radial fibers' of Müller. In this scheme the nervous elements are reduced to their essentials, with, however, the characteristic features of each variety preserved—the location of the cell bodies, the size, the shape, and the spreading of the dendrites and of the axis cylinders—and with the synaptic contacts presented accurately. [From Polyak (122).]

B. The structure of the primate retina reduced to its essentials, including the synopsis of the propagation of the retinal impulses from the photoreceptors to other parts of the retina, to the brain, and from the brain back to the retina (direction indicated by the arrows). The marking of the layers and the zones the same as in *A*. Labeling of the cells: (*a, b*) rods and cones, the photoreceptors where the nervous impulses are generated by physical 'light' (in the scheme only the left group of the photoreceptors is assumed to be stimulated by light); (*c*) horizontal cells which transmit the impulses to the surrounding rods and cones; (*d, e, f, h*) centripetal bipolar cells of the mop, brush, flat and midget varieties, which 'transmit' the impulses from the photoreceptors to the ganglion cells, the bipolars serving as 'analyzers'; (*i*) centrifugal bipolar cell, a variety of the 'amacrine cells,' which probably receives the impulses from the centripetal bipolars from the ganglion cells, and also from the brain by way of the centrifugal or efferent fibers (*t*) and transmits them back upon the photoreceptors (*a, b*); (*l*) an 'amacrine cell' which possibly intercepts a part of the bipolar impulses and spreads them over the surrounding territory; and (*m, n, o, p, s*) ganglion cells which receive impulses from the centripetal bipolars and transmit them to the brain along their axon called 'optic nerve fibers.' [From Polyak (122).]

bodies. The brush and flat bipolars resemble each other and occur everywhere in the retina from the fovea to the ora serrata. They have large dendritic territories. Their most interesting properties seem to be: *a*) a "reciprocal overlapping of each of the dendritic territories with its own kind" (122) and *b*) axodendritic articulations with the ganglion cells. The midget system also intermingles with this wide

axodendritic or plexiform (inner plexiform layer) network. The basic pattern consists of bipolar terminals, ganglion cell dendrites and the Golgi type II of cells called amacrines. Similar large plexiform networks with Golgi type II of cells are found elsewhere in the nervous system, including the cortex of the cerebellum.

The ganglion cells, for physiological correlations,

can be divided into two types, large and small, with two extremes, giant and midget. It is doubtful whether the midget system occurs in the common laboratory animals. The dendritic expansions of the giant ganglion cells may be "from 250 to 350 μ across and probably more" (Polyak).

The system of amacrine cells (i.e. cells without axons) seems highly organized. This, according to Ramón y Cajal, is particularly true for the stratified ones (Polyak's knotty amacrines) which form five to seven layers in the inner plexiform network. Their dendritic arborizations are similarly stratified at corresponding levels. There are also giant amacrines (Polyak's tasseled amacrines) some of which spread a 'daddy longlegs' mop extending over 1 mm above the plane of the ganglion cells. Polyak has also detected axons running from amacrine cells towards the pedicles of the receptors and regards them as bipolar cells conducting backwards. This raises the question of whether amacrines appear to lack axons merely because of difficulties in staining.

In this microcosm of a nervous center that we call a retina, the inner plexiform layer, as we have seen, is the meeting ground of three major systems and thus a critical region. It is difficult to imagine this layer to be wholly self-controlled by the chance play of light and shadow. And, as a matter of fact, this is the very region to which the centrifugal fibers of Ramón y Cajal (123) and Dogiel (50) were found to project. Ramón y Cajal studied them in the retina of the dog (fig. 3), while Dogiel worked on birds. They seem to be difficult to stain and their origin is unknown, yet Ramón y Cajal did not hesitate to postulate a central origin rather than to describe them as recurrent collaterals. Some centrifugal fibers are held to go as far as to the outer plexiform layer.

The briefest path in the retina clearly is disynaptic: receptor-bipolar-ganglion. A more fundamental issue seems to be the question of whether bipolar cells make axosomatic or axodendritic connections with the ganglion cells. Conduction is slow in dendrites (104) so that axosomatic latencies are likely to be shorter. In the probable absence of midget cells in the common laboratory animals, the size of the ganglion cell is likely to be an important property because the larger the cell, the greater the probability of axodendritic activation in the inner plexiform layer. Actually the ganglion spikes in the cat's retina fall into two main categories, large and small, the small ones as a rule having brief latent periods. The larger the spike caused by illumination, the later it tends to be discharged and the lower its absolute threshold to light. This is the author's general impression, not a result of systematic analysis.

If, in the cat's eye, one proceeds to send an antidromic (backward) shock into the optic nerve and places a microelectrode on the blind spot (74), the volley recorded consists of an early large and a later small group of spikes, similar to those recorded orthodromically at the central end of the optic nerve (22, 23, 107). The maximal conduction velocities of its fibers are 70 and 23 m per sec., respectively (22). Two main fiber sizes (as judged from the conduction velocities) suggest two main groups of sizes of ganglion cells. This is further evidence for subdividing the spikes into two main categories.

At the blind spot the optic nerve loses its myelin sheath and so conduction suddenly slows down as the antidromic impulse enters the fibers running across the retinal surface (74). Precise measurements by Dodt (42) gave mean values of 2.9 and 1.7 m per sec. for large and small spikes, respectively. The large spikes (see below) are the ones most easily influenced by centrifugal tetani (74) as also seems probable considering their wide dendritic expansions within the inner plexiform layer.

Another interesting point is that, on account of the slow conduction across the retinal surface, the impulses from the peripheral portions of the retina may be delayed by 4 to 6 msec. as compared with those arising in the region around the blind spot. This is of technical interest because it means that, unless special precautions are taken in studying retinal brain projections by evoked potentials, these are likely to be mainly determined by the fibers around the blind spot. Physiologically the delayed conduction means that, with a moving retina, space coordinates stand a good chance of being transformed into time coordinates. The eye always makes small oscillations in fixation (39, 125).

ELECTRORETINOGRAM (ERG)

The electroretinogram is a polyphasic mass response (fig. 4) with specific cornea-positive deflections at the onset and cessation of illumination. Standard leads in electroretinography are between the cornea and an 'indifferent' point on the body or behind the bulb (in the case of eyes excised from cold-blooded

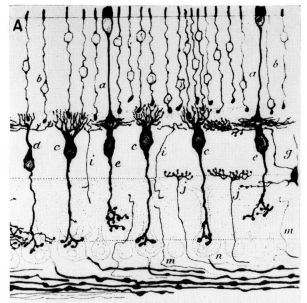

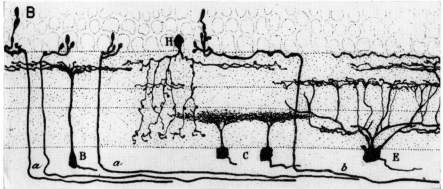

FIG. 3. *A*. Retina of the dog showing cone axons (*a*); rod axons (*b*); types of bipolars (*c–e*), o which *e* is Ramón y Cajal's cone bipolar; ganglion cells (*m, n*); ascending nerve fiber (*i*); and centrifugal fibers (*j*). *B*. Details of structure of ganglion cells (*B, C* and *E*) and of connections made by centrifugal fibers (*a*). [From Ramón y Cajal (123).]

animals). The ERG was discovered by Holmgren (94, 95). The literature has been twice summarized by the author (69, 73), the first time with a full historical review. Some of the more important classical papers are those of Kühne & Steiner (102, 103), Gotch (60, 61), Piper (119, 120, 121), Einthoven & Jolly (53), Frölich (56), Chaffee *et al.* (31), Chaffee & Hampson (32), Hartline (85), Adrian & Matthews (3) and Kohlrausch (98).

The ERG (which in such animals as cats and frogs reaches maximal cornea-positive values around 1 mv) begins with a small negative dip, the *a*-wave, then goes positive, the *b*-wave. If stimulus intensity is sufficiently high, there follows a very slow cornea-positive secondary rise or *c*-wave and, at the cessation of il-

lumination, another positive hump, the off-effect or *d*-wave (see fig. 4). There is some doubt as to whether the *c*-wave occurs in cone eyes. In mixed eyes it is not found in the state of light adaptation (144). Noell (114) appears to hold that it is always present but sometimes compensated for by an opposite negative potential of similar slow characteristics. There is no reason to believe any of the ERG waves to be absent in any kind of vertebrate eye; but they are very differently developed with respect to size and rate of rise and they vary with the experimental conditions so that, for instance, in rod eyes the *d*-wave is small or missing. The ERG has generally been thought to consist of components integrated in complex interference pictures. These are reasonably well-known

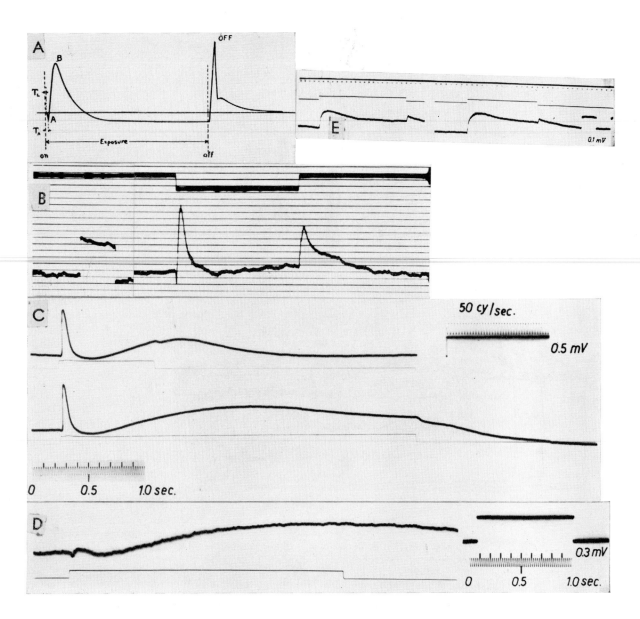

FIG. 4. Electroretinograms from various types of retinas. *A*. Cone retina of the cold blooded horned toad, *Phyronosoma*, showing a large diphasic *d*-wave. [From Chaffee & Sutcliffe (33).] *B*. Mammalian cone retina of the squirrel, *Sciurus carolinensis leucotis*, with marked *a*-wave and narrow pointed *b*- and *d*-waves (calibration: 0.5 mv; time, 1 sec.). [From Arden & Tansley (8).] *C*. Cat eye, dark-adapted, exposed to two flash durations at an intensity of about 700 meter-candles; *a*-wave is just visible, *b*-wave shows fast oscillation, followed by a drop below base line before the *c*-wave begins; *d*-wave or off-effect appears as a retarding of fall of response at cessation of illumination. [From Granit (73).] *D*. Guinea pig eye, dark-adapted, exposed to light intensity of about 900 lux, showing a definite *a*-wave and indication of double *b*-wave; in this eye the *c*-wave or secondary rise tends to be the most prominent phase of the response. [From Granit (73).] *E*. Gecko eye illuminated with an intensity of 1250 meter-candles; the first record represents 3.8 sec. illumination after 1 min. in the dark, the second record 2.8 sec. illumination after 2 min. in the dark (time marks 0.2 sec. apart). [From Dodt & Heck (47).] In records, *A* to *E* illumination periods are indicated by shift in the signal line.

for many types of eyes in different conditions. The reviews referred to should be consulted, supplemented with recent work (111, 114).

The problems of electroretinography have centered around the following main issues: a) differentiation of rod and cone ERG's, b) analysis of the transition from rod to cone dominance in mixed retinae, c) attempts to split the ERG into component responses, d) comparisons between the ERG and the discharge in the optic nerve and e) attempts to localize components of the ERG to specific structures in the retina. Under this heading also fall the recent experiments with penetrating capillary microelectrodes of the Gerard-Ling type. Finally as f) should be mentioned a steadily expanding literature on electroretinography in man from descriptive, theoretical and clinical points of view. All these aspects cannot be discussed with full attention to detail. Leading references will, however, be given within all of them.

The pure cone ERG's illustrated in figure 4 (A and B) are from the horned toad (33) and a squirrel (8) and are essentially alike. These types were called I-retinograms (69), as long as there were no pure cone mammalian ERG's available. The cone eyes of squirrel species (8, 9, 25) have since provided the evidence necessary for identifying the I-type with the cone ERG in mammals as well as other animals. There is no secondary rise or c-wave. Cone ERG's are often negative in between the b- and d-waves (cf. fig. 4A). They also tend to have large a-waves. The rod ERG's (C and D) are from guinea pig and cat eyes, the former having a practically pure rod retina, the latter with cones corresponding roughly to the number found in the human peripheral retina. The ERG labeled E is from the pure rod retina of the gecko (47). It differs from that of the guinea pig in showing a d-wave at 'off.' Now guinea pigs also have off-discharges in their optic nerves (a very striking feature of cone eyes) and so the absence of the corresponding d-wave in their ERG suggests that elements responding at 'off' are fewer in number than in cone eyes and many other types of rod eyes (cf. 69). In the ERG of the cat (C), for instance, the d-wave is reduced to a plateau, or a retardation at 'off' in the drop of potential towards the base line. Walls (146) holds the rods of the gecko to be transmuted cones. The a-wave seems to occur in all retinae, provided the light intensity is sufficiently high to elicit it.

By changing state of adaptation from scotopic to photopic it is also possible to demonstrate in mixed eyes that the on-off differentials, the a- and d-waves, become faster, the d-wave in addition becoming

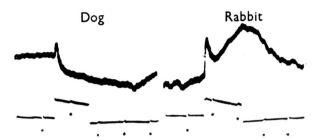

FIG. 5. A comparison of the electroretinogram of the red Irish setter and the rabbit. The upper tracing in each record gives the electroretinogram and the lower, the time mark. The light is 'on' when the time tracing is displaced upwards. The record shows that the normal positive c-wave of rabbits is replaced by a negative potential in dogs. Time mark: 0.5 sec. Calibration: 50 μv. [From Parry et al. (118).]

larger than before (41, 46, 80, 113). This is conveniently done by using flickering light. Rod ERG's tend to flicker with repeated positive b-waves, while in cone ERG's a-waves and d-waves (see below) also take part in the response to intermittent illumination.

By varying stimulus intensity from the threshold upwards it can easily be shown that both the b- and the d-waves consist of several components of different rates of rise and of different size though complete separation may be difficult to achieve. Systematic attention to this problem was first given in two papers on the frog eye (78, 84) and, by varying state of adaptation and wavelengths, the authors could show that some components belonged to rods (slow ones) and some to cones. Similar differentiations for the human eye were followed by Motokawa & Mita (110) and Adrian (1, 2). Variations in duration (149) and in rate of rise of the stimulating light (126) have recently been found to be convenient methods of separating scotopic and photopic components. (This matter is further considered below.)

Deteriorating ERG's tend to become cornea-negative, but in many animals the negative phase is also a normal feature of the response and then is always found to succeed the cornea-positive b-wave (see fig. 4A). In fact, a large negative phase occurs fairly generally in high intensity ERG's and, after light-adaptation, also in rod eyes. Figure 5 illustrates the ERG of a dog (118) which obviously contains a slow negative component not visible in the ERG of the rabbit inserted for comparison. Noell's (114) work is of particular interest from this point of view, as has been discussed by Granit (73).

The common occurrence of slow or semistationary negative phases during illumination has led most

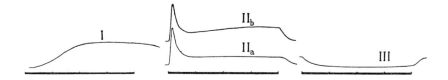

FIG. 6. Components of the cat ERG: PI, PII and PIII. The two alternatives for PII drawn on the basis of experimental results. [From Granit (64).]

workers to assume that the ERG is an algebraic sum of component processes of opposite signs. The methods used for analysis have been based on variations of stimulus intensity, duration and state of adaptation as well as on direct interference with the ERG by chemical agents and asphyxia. For an orientation in this field the reader is referred to the detailed discussion by Granit (69) supplemented by more recent work (7, 111, 114). The three components of the author's analysis (fig. 6) are based on many observations in the classical literature (quoted in the introduction) and certain of his own experiments (64, 80) and have served for some time now as a summary and a starting point for further work.

There is general agreement about the existence of a slow cornea-positive component such as PI which is responsible for the secondary rise or c-wave (see also 114, 144). This requires fairly high intensity and not too short exposures. There is much evidence to show that the cornea-negative a-wave is the first sign of illumination (cf. 3, 34, 69) and that it passes over into a slower negative phase which is often submerged below a mainly cornea-positive response but is sometimes visible. The component PIII appears to survive damage to the retina better than the other ones. Noell (114) uses poisoning with iodate to produce it in the rabbit's eye. It has been suggested (69, 73) that the negative PIII consists of two components, one fast and the other slow. This view has been elaborated in considerable detail by Noell (114), particularly with regard to the slow phase.

A convenient way of making the retina respond quickly to illumination by a fairly pure negative ERG is to drop potassium chloride solution into the opened bulb (83, 139). This is a well-known depolarizing agent and accordingly the remaining cornea-negative response to light cannot itself be a depolarization of already depolarized structures. The cornea-positive PII, however, is likely to represent depolarization by light. Both components are increased by running a polarizing current across the bulb, inside negative, and are decreased by reversal of this current (18, 28,

76). A negative ERG can be made positive by dropping alcohol into the bulb (19).

At cessation of illumination PIII returns towards the base line of the record (the so-called resting potential discussed below), first rapidly, then more slowly. At least in the isolated state the slow returning phase may appear as a kind of 'remnant negativity.' [There are apparently still slower changes of potential, both negative and positive (see 114), than the ones generally counted as belonging to the ERG proper.] At the same time the cornea-positive PII ends at cessation of illumination, either by returning to the base line or even going below it or else contributing to the d-wave that otherwise would have been due merely to interference between PII and PIII. There is evidence for both alternatives in the literature according to the view of Granit (73). Further experimentation with different eyes seems necessary to establish the dominant event in different types of eye (see 6, 82, 113, 141).

In considering questions of this kind it is necessary never to forget that the ERG is a mass response recorded at a distance from the sources generating its potential. Wirth & Zetterström (150) illuminated the cat's eye through perspex cones applied directly onto the retina and found that illumination of an area of 20 mm² was necessary for maximal responses. Considering that the diameter of the rods is 0.002 mm, there is ample margin for a large variety of elementary component responses to complicate the issue. A general analysis can merely aim at describing dominant features. Localized leads and localized light projections on the retina are necessary for a study of details. If one illuminates through a glass electrode applied directly onto the retina (20), the individual retinograms are very different in different places.

There are a number of interesting features by which the cornea-positive PII and the cornea-negative PIII of the general analysis differ from one another. Figure 7A, which illustrates for the frog retina the effect of reilluminating at different times after cessation of illumination (46, 80, 112), shows that the cornea-negative *a*-wave now is greatly increased and maximal when the off-effect has reached full size. The retina seems to show no refractoriness but is immediately ready to re-establish the level of negativity characteristic of that particular state of adaptation and stimulus strength. The cornea-positive PII (*b*-wave) behaves very differently. It fails to appear until some time has passed, as can also be very clearly seen with the cat retina (*D*) which is dominated by this component.

Figure 8 shows the full analysis of an experiment of this kind. The dotted lines represent the effects of the individual flashes of reillumination, *d* is the *d*-wave control; *b*, the level of the *b*-waves; *a*, that of the *a*-waves. Assuming *a* and *b* being generated in the same structures, it is difficult to understand why the former response is immediately ready to be re-established while the latter refuses to behave in the same fashion. Part of this difference has been found to be due to the *b*- and *d*-waves sharing generators in the sense that the one leaves refractoriness for the other (82).

In recent attempts to assign the origin of the ERG to definite retinal structures, experiments of this type have been neglected altogether. Yet, they seem to contain essential information about the components of the ERG which no discussion of these problems can

neglect. Perhaps this is the place for pointing out that the ganglion cells definitely seem to be excluded as sources of the ERG. From time to time since 1933 the author has stimulated antidromically the optic nerve of frogs and cats while recording the ERG in order

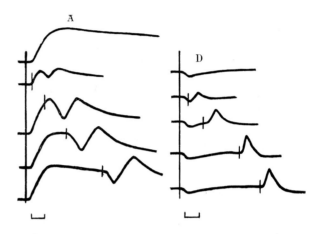

FIG. 7. Effect of increasing the interval between two stimuli on the electroretinogram of different types of retinae: *A*, frog; *D*, cat. Uppermost curve of each series shows the uninterrupted off-effect. Short vertical lines indicate the beginning of re-illumination. Time marking: 0.1 sec. [From Granit (65).]

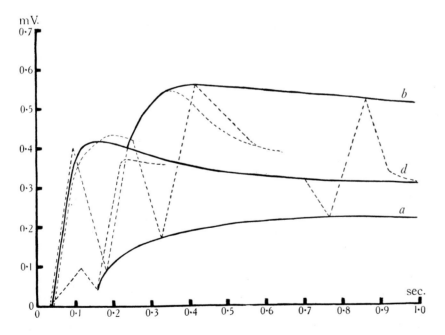

FIG. 8. Off-effect or *d*-wave given by *d* in the frog ERG. Reillumination by single flashes elicits the potential changes (*a*- and *b*-waves) shown in *dotted lines*. *a* and *b* trace maxima of *a*- and *b*-waves respectively. Note that curves *b* and *a* are drawn through peaks of *b* and *a* waves at different times of re-illumination and thus show that the *a*-wave reappears at once and is increased while the *b*-wave requires a long time for recovery. [From Granit & Riddell (80).]

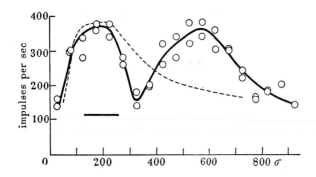

FIG. 9. Effect of a flash, superimposed on the off-discharge in the frog's optic nerve, plotted as average spike frequency in impulses per sec. against time in msec. *Dotted line*, off-discharge control. *Continuous line*, diminution in frequency (inhibition) caused by a flash, indicated by the *horizontal black line*, delivered at the height of the off-effect. [From Granit & Therman (81).]

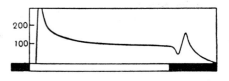

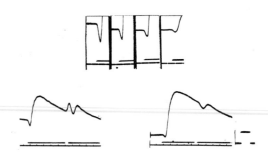

FIG. 10. Variation in impulse frequency of the eel optic nerve during stimulation. [From Adrian & Matthews (3).]

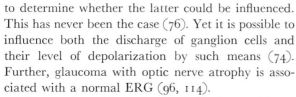

FIG. 11. Effect of alcohol on frog ERG. *Top record:* diminution of *a*-wave during alcohol treatment. *Left:* Light-adapted ERG with reillumination on top of the *d*-wave. *Right:* Same experiment after alcohol. Time, 0.2 sec. Light signal above time record. [From Bernhard & Skoglund (19).]

to determine whether the latter could be influenced. This has never been the case (76). Yet it is possible to influence both the discharge of ganglion cells and their level of depolarization by such means (74). Further, glaucoma with optic nerve atrophy is associated with a normal ERG (96, 114).

The question of how the ERG correlates with the discharge through the optic nerve can be profitably attacked by studying what happens in the nerve when these large *a*-waves are induced on top of the off-discharge. Figure 9 shows that there is inhibition of the off-discharge (81) and this was confirmed by Granit & Helme (76). This experiment provided the main argument for the view that PIII is concerned with inhibition rather than with excitation. The cornea-positive PII was held to signify excitation. The general likeness between the cornea-positive retinogram and the variation of the discharge-frequency through the optic nerve, first pointed out by Adrian & Matthews (3, 4, 5), supports the same inference (fig. 10). Granit & Therman (81) could find no effect in the optic nerve discharge corresponding to the large *c*-wave of the dark adapted eye.

In this connection the effect of alcohol on the frog retina is particularly interesting (19). The left record in figure 11 shows the light adapted ERG of a frog. A drop of alcohol into the opened bulb makes it change as shown in the right record. The upper record shows the change of the *a*-wave under alcohol. In this final stage it looks like the ERG of the fully dark adapted retina and, like the latter, has a small *d*-wave and responds only to slowly flickering light. Even an ERG made largely negative by potassium

chloride turns positive after alcohol. The interpretation of these changes is that alcohol diminishes PIII and augments PII, which agrees with the interpretation of the similar changes with state of adaptation. However, still more interesting from the present point of view is what happens in the test with reillumination in which, after alcohol, the negative *a*-wave will now be very small or absent. The experiment showed that the corresponding inhibitory pause in the discharge also was curtailed. The authors held their result to support the view that PIII (or what now may be called fast PIII) was inhibitory, i.e. as confirming the view that excitation and inhibition was characterized by opposite deflections of the ERG.

In this volume the vision of invertebrates is treated in Chapter XXVI by Milne and Milne. It is nevertheless of considerable interest here to mention the recent experiments of MacNichol & Benolken (105) with Hartline's so-called lateral inhibition in the plexus of nerve fibers behind the *Limulus* ommatidia (91). By means of interconnections in this plexus, illumination of one ommatidium suppresses the discharge of another (91). Now, MacNichol & Benolken find that alcohol removes this lateral inhibition reversibly.

For a final allocation of the retinal component potentials to definite structures (receptors or bipolar cells), it will be necessary to use nonpolarizable penetrating microelectrodes. Such work was initiated by Tomita (141, 142). Instead of a review of arguments from general electroretinographic work for which the author's summary (69) may be consulted, a brief discussion of the results obtained by such micromethods is given.

Tomita's work was criticized and ignored by Ottoson & Svaetichin (116) on the grounds that his penetrating microelectrodes were held to be too coarse. Tomita has since (142) repeated his experiments with the Ling-Gerard type of microcapillaries, used by Svaetichin, and confirmed his previous results. At the same time Brindley (28, 29, 30) has also published a careful study using the same technique. Ottoson & Svaetichin's conclusions as far as fundamental questions are concerned were: a) that slow potentials of the ERG type are obtained in the receptors only; this has since been definitely refuted by Brindley (30) and by Tomita & Torihama (142), who found large potential changes mirroring the ERG in the bipolar layer; b) that rods respond only with positive, and cones only with negative retinograms [cf. also Svaetichin (137)], disproved by Granit (73) as well as by Forbes et al. (55) and Brindley (29); c) that the resting potential of the retina is a receptor potential (115), since refuted by Brindley (28); d) that, from the fact that cocaine slowly attacks the ERG but immediately stops the discharge of impulses through the optic nerve, it is possible to conclude that the ERG is a pure receptor potential [from Kühne & Steiner (102) onwards the number of agents capable of blocking the impulse discharge without much effect on the ERG has been slowly multiplying, yet without suggesting to anyone such far-reaching conclusions]; e) that from the size of sudden potential gradients of the order of 20 to 30 mv within the fish retina (approached from the receptor end) it is possible to assume that the electrode recorded intracellularly from single cones. Now Brindley (28) has shown that there are characteristic steps in the radial resistance to a penetrating microelectrode, the largest one across the external limiting membrane (see below), and extracellular spike potentials of the order of 40 to 60 mv have been recorded by Granit & Phillips (79) by the same technique at the surface of the cerebellar Purkinje cells. Furthermore, an extracellular retinal microelectrode has been shown by Brindley (30) and Tomita & Torihama (142) to pick up its response from very distant illuminated regions. This is, of course, what one must expect. Light intensities and techniques of illumination are hardly ever mentioned in the papers by

Svaetichin & Ottoson but this, in itself, suggests that the whole retina or a large fraction of it was illuminated. Focal microillumination would be needed for localized responses and there is in its favor the further advantage that absence of a response within the bipolar layer shows whether damage has occurred (30, 142). Such damage probably explains why Ottoson & Svaetichin have missed the response inside the retina. In fact, Brindley (30) describes two types of responses in excised frog eyes of which the second agrees with the pictures of Svaetichin. This type Brindley holds to be characteristic of local damage because it alone is seen when the focal intraretinal response is absent. These remarks may suffice to show why it is felt that Ottoson & Svaetichin have underrated the analytical difficulties of the work they set out to do. For this reason individual good observations in their work, perhaps unjustly, lose their significance to a reviewer and can only be rescued by those who have undertaken microelectrode work with the same structure and thus can evaluate them critically against a background of specific experience.

Apparently retinal neurons do not differ from other neurons, all of them producing potential changes. Both Brindley and Tomita have arranged their experiments for comparison of precise focal microillumination around the microelectrode tip with illumination of larger areas. Unless an electrode within the bipolar area responds to focal illumination with a reponse of the intraretinal type, the region around this electrode is not likely to be in a normal state. Brindley suggests that this condition is due to damage of the external limiting membrane. The inside focal response has a maximum among the bipolar cells at a depth of 100 to 140 μ from the ganglion side. The large ERG elicited by general illumination is always obtained and tends to be positive. The two authors differ in that Tomita's response to diffuse light reverses sign within the inner nuclear layer, going from positive at the ganglion side to negative at the receptor side of the retina, while Brindley finds more variability in this regard. Now, is the focal response inside the retina identical with the ERG? Obviously this response is physiologically important but both Brindley and Tomita argue against identification. In the reviewer's opinion it is impossible at the present stage of our knowledge to be certain as to whether or not bipolar cells contribute to the ERG. Tomita, for instance, finds no focal response within the receptor layer. This is no crucial objection to a localization in the receptors, nevertheless it is a fact to be considered. Brindley holds the focal response to be caused by sources located tangentially within the retina and suggests, on the basis of electrical considerations too involved to discuss, that "only the rods and cones contribute substantially to the *a*-, *b*- and *d*-waves of the electroretinogram, although cells belonging to the inner nuclear layer can produce large electrical changes of similar time course" (30). He himself finds this hypothesis "somewhat surprising." Tomita localizes the same response to the bipolar layer with some contributions from other retinal layers, in particular the inner portion of the receptors [cf. also Noell (114)].

Particularly interesting are Brindley's (28) measurements of the passive electrical properties of frog retina for radial fields and currents and the method applied to make such measurements possible. The largest step takes place at around 230 μ from the ganglion side and is of the order of 270 Ω. This is Brindley's R-membrane which he provisionally identifies with the external limiting membrane. Its capacity is about 40 μ F. Across this membrane also is the largest step or component of the resting potential of the retina. Electron microscopy (134, 135) has led to the view that the external limiting membrane consists of rings or collars around the receptor base (inner segment), a fact difficult to harmonize with the high resistance and capacity if it really can be assumed that there has been no shrinkage in Sjöstrand's preparations.

These papers are thought-provoking and serious attempts to lay bare the considerable difficulties in arriving at evidence for final conclusions and thus form a structure of knowledge upon which further work can be built. There is a large body of information about the ERG as influenced by alcohol, potassium, state of adaptation, etc., which will have to be experimentally applied to microelectrode analysis before a final conclusion can be reached.

The crucial point in the present position is the identification of the R-membrane, it being highly unlikely that any intracellular potentials in the retina ever have been recorded. The recent findings by McNichol *et al.* (105a) show that the former cone-potential of Svaetichin actually is obtained below the layer of rods and cones and Tomita (141a) has shown that it can be obtained with electrodes far too big to penetrate individual cells successfully. However, the observations on effects of different wavelengths in fish seem interesting independently of present assumptions

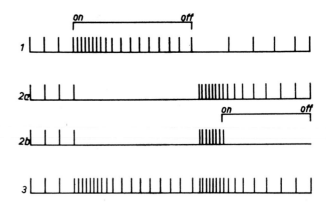

FIG. 12. Diagram illustrating three fibers in the optic nerve firing spontaneously and their responses to illumination as described in text. [From Granit (73).]

and also confirm the demonstration of dominators and narrow-banded modulators in this eye (65a).

NEURAL PATTERNS

Work on the spike discharge from the retina started with the classical papers by Adrian & Matthews (3, 4, 5) who used the long optic nerve of the eel *Conger* for a study of the massed discharge. The discovery of different discharge types was a consequence of Hartline's (86) successful attempts to split the frog optic nerve. This he did at the point where it enters the blind spot and is already naturally split into fibers coming from different parts of the retina. The types are shown in the schematic figure 12 in which account also is taken of the microelectrode records from mammals (see 69, 73) in which one often finds more activity between onset and cessation of light than in the frog and less stability of response types. Some fibers (*1* in fig. 12) respond to onset of light, others (*2*) are inhibited by onset of light and instead discharge at 'off.' The majority of them discharge to both onset and cessation of light (*3*). Reillumination during the off-discharge inhibits it, as shown by *2b*. It should be realized that, since the optic nerve fibers represent highly differentiated convergence structures, there are in actual practice almost as many discharge types as there are optic nerve fibers. Nevertheless the types illustrated show approximately what happens. The inhibition of the off-discharge, as stated, coincides with the large negative *a*-wave on top of the off-effect described above. In most eyes there is some spontaneous firing, generally greater in the scotopic state.

The salient point with regard to the general problem of response types is, as shown by Granit (71, 72) and Kuffler (100), that the retina contains two antagonistic systems, the on-system and the off-system, which, when made to clash on to the same ganglion cell, are mutually exclusive. One system is excited by light (the on-system), the other is inhibited by light (the off-system) and the latter behaves as if the longer, within limits, the duration during which inhibition is piled up, the more did this favor the subsequent off-discharge. Thus, during the time the off-discharge is inhibited by light something happens that makes it prone to respond when ultimately light is exchanged for darkness. Short exposures tend to give very brief off-effects. When a definite off-effect is seen in the ERG, e.g. in frogs, it also behaves similarly.

The anatomical convergence means that each fiber has a receptive field, first measured by Adrian & Matthews (3, 4, 5) and shown to be of the order of 1 mm in the eye of the conger eel, then more precisely with the single-fiber technique by Hartline (87). Figure 13 shows the exploring spot used by him and the field sizes obtained in the frog eye when stimulus strength was varied. Just as convergence varies from fiber to fiber, so do the dimensions of the receptive fields. In cats Kuffler (100) found them beautifully organized so that sometimes the on-, sometimes the off-effect occupied the center, the opposite response then occupying its periphery and on-off-responses occurring between the two. This provided Kuffler with a good opportunity to make on- and off-spots of the receptive field clash in various combinations and thus elegantly to demonstrate the antagonism between the two systems relative to the ganglion discharge. A very complete discussion of receptive fields and on-off systems has been given by Granit (73). Both principles of organization recur in the central structures to which receptors in other sense organs project.

Why then is the lining of receptors inside the eye connected to an intricate nervous center just behind it, while other receptor systems mostly have their first neural organization at the spinal cord level? Apparently receptors cannot do much by themselves; their messages must be organized somehow for discrimination and integration; and, since the little brain behind the rods and cones moves with the eye, it can because of its place in the retina aid better in the interpretation of the ever-changing boundaries of

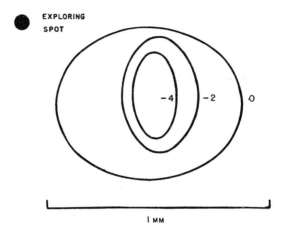

FIG. 13. Chart of the receptive field of a single optic nerve fiber of the frog. Each line encloses a retinal region within which the exploring spot light (relative size shown *above left*)—the log of the intensity is given on the line—produced a response from the fiber. On each line the indicated intensity was the threshold; the *set of curves* constitutes a contour map of the distribution of the retinal sensitivity to light with reference to this particular fiber. [From Hartline (89).]

light, darkness and color out of which the visual world is synthesized. The eye, as stated above, is never still and, if by artificial means the image is kept stationary (39, 125), it tends to fade out quickly, as if it needed the on-off differentials sharpening up contours during oscillations. Movement of an object or a point across the retina will light up a trail of on-off sparks, as well shown by Barlow (15, 16) in frog experiments set up to illustrate the biological significance of such factors for perception. Apparently also, it is necessary for this highly developed organ not to be forced to one single mode of working in coping with a range of illumination from dusk to bright sunlight. It has been shown that the receptive fields of the retina vary in width with state of adaptation (17).

From what has been stated it is clear that at least within a receptive field interaction can occur, as first shown by Adrian & Matthews (5) and then studied in detail by Hartline (87, 88). When spike frequency or latency is used as an indicator, area and intensity are found to be interchangeable within the field, whether from excitation or inhibition being unknown. These facts provide a likely explanation of the many old psychophysical observations on the interchangeability of area and intensity in vision. From what has been stated it will be realized that on-off interaction adds to the complexity so that over a large range of intensities the on-off ratio will undergo considerable variation. This variation has been held to support a mechanism of discrimination based on the overlapping receptive fields. Overlapping receptive fields, less elaborated than in the retina, also occur in other sense organs. These principles have been discussed at some length by Granit (73).

Many problems of retinal neurology have been clarified by Hartline's work on the much simpler *Limulus* eye, to which students of the vertebrate retina are advised to give careful attention. This in particular applies to the recent important analysis of the lateral inhibition (90) in the neural network below the ommatidia, because the suppression of the discharge of one ommatidium by its illuminated neighbor is clearly a mechanism of contrast. In the frog retina Barlow (15, 16) has found the discharge from a receptive field to be inhibited by illuminating retinal regions just outside it.

There are other aspects to the problem of inhibition than those connected with the organization of the receptive fields. There is, for example postexcitatory inhibition (73) and the generalized inhibition recently described by Dodt (43).

STIMULUS CORRELATES

The average electroretinographic response is roughly proportional to the logarithm of stimulus intensity. However, since most retinae contain two organs in one (rods and cones) and the ERG's of rods and cones do not relate similarly to stimulus intensity in addition to differing in latency and rate of rise (see above), too much should not be made out of this general logarithmic relationship. It does, however, suggest that the elementary generator potentials of which the total response is made up tend to be logarithmically related to stimulus intensity, and this, whenever they have been recorded, actually is the case [cf. the discussion by Granit (73)]. In *Limulus* the spike frequency emanating from the excentric cell of a single ommatidium is logarithmically related to stimulus intensity meaning that the level of ommatidial generator potential, at least when stabilized, is directly proportional to spike frequency [the corresponding relation for muscle receptors has been described (97)]. Many single fiber preparations representing receptive fields in frogs (86) and mammals (67) have shown a general logarithmic relation to stimulus intensity, superimposed, as it were, upon on-off complexities. The overall effect of an assembly

of cells is likely to follow this rule which, of course, is nothing but the well-known Fechner law looked at in a different way [for a full discussion, see Granit (73)].

The retina is a detector of so-called visible light which is visible because photochemical substances within the rods and cones absorb energy and transform it into a form appropriate for stimulation. Most color theories have assumed that different kinds of cones are provided with photochemical substances adjusted for absorption of light within different parts of the spectrum but the only substance known until fairly recently was Boll's visual purple or rhodopsin in the rod outer limbs, and these organs, on the duplicity theory, were assumed to be color blind. This was the situation until some experiments with the electroretinogram (78, 84) definitely proved that the frog light-adapted eye showed distributions of spectral sensitivity that required a minimum of three cone substances to be intelligible. This has since been confirmed in many other types of experiments with different eyes. In light-adapted frogs and in the cone eyes of the turtle, Forbes *et al.* (55) showed that, if they were illuminated by two 'white' lights, these could be exchanged without influencing the ERG but that certain pairs of colored lights never could be exchanged, whatever their intensity ratio, without a specific electroretinographic color response. Japanese workers (62, 63, 140) using frogs studied the multiple off-effects and wavelets on top of the off-effect, mentioned above, and found evidence for a representation of differential spectral sensitivity in the different crest times of such wavelets. There was a minimum of three humps appearing in the order red, green and blue, as also shown in the recent work of Heck & Rendahl (93). A similar order had previously been observed by Donner (51) working with the spike frequency-time differentials of single ganglion cells in the cat retina and by Motokawa and his group (108, 109, 143). There is a critical review of Motokawa's work by Gebhard (59). Motokawa's measurements were based on the rate of rise of retinal sensitivity to a brief polarizing current after preillumination with different wavelengths.

Recent work with the human electroretinogram is definite in showing that the ERG contains components of different color sensitivity, even in the light-adapted state (10, 11, 93, 130). However, all work with a mass response such as the ERG suffers from the difficulty of isolating the spectral components in a quantitative way.

Color vision as an electrophysiological problem contains two different aspects: *a*) the primary sensitivity distributions of individual receptors and *b*) their representation in the organized message delivered by the ganglion cells through the optic nerve. The latter delivers the information which the striate area has to interpret and so problem *b* is as important as problem *a*. The act of interpretation itself is at the moment beyond the reach of electrophysiological approach. Solution of the first problem requires more reliable microelectrode records of individual receptor potentials than is found in any paper hitherto presented. Our most definite quantitative data are still the ones obtained from individual optic nerve fibers of animals (66, 68, 69, 73). It is necessary to understand how a spectral distribution is defined in order to comprehend the color problem. A simplified presentation of this question can be given in the following way.

Assume that a color-sensitive substance absorbs light along a spectral distribution curve represented in every wavelength by S_λ. Dependent upon the lamp used and upon other properties of the spectrum (e.g. slit width, diffraction) each of these wavelengths tested represents an amount of energy E_λ. Finally, again, each of the wavelengths tested elicits an effect L_λ. It is immaterial now if this effect is considered in terms of a receptor potential, a spike frequency or as perceived brightness. This effect L_λ will be proportional to the sensitivity S_λ and the amount of energy E_λ so that $L_\lambda = E_\lambda \cdot S_\lambda$. In order to measure S_λ which is the function we want to study and which clearly is $S_\lambda = L_\lambda/E_\lambda$ we must first of all measure E_λ of the spectrum used (which should be of a high degree of purity). The next step is to set up the biological experiment so that the physiological effect L_λ is kept constant in every wavelength. Then, with L_λ and E_λ known, the equation can be solved, i.e. S_λ can be calculated. It is proportional to $1/E_\lambda$. For quantitative work it is therefore not enough to keep the energy E of the spectrum constant and measure the physiological effect L, even though such results may have indicative value and can be approximately corrected if the relation between E and L initially has been measured over the working range for each wavelength. Very serious errors can also be introduced by filters of which even the best have narrow color bands over one or two log units only. Therefore spectra should be used for quantitative work. A good method is to measure $1/E_\lambda$ for a constant response (L_λ) such as the threshold. This was the method employed in the experiments on the discharge from individual nerve fibers.

These results, for which a large number of different species of animals were used, some with pure cone

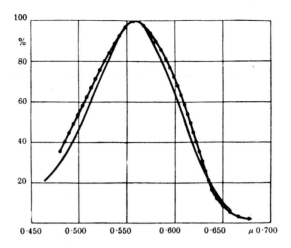

FIG. 14. Photopic dominator curves of the frog (——) and the snake *Tropidonotus natrix* (●——●). Equal quantum intensity spectrum. Sensitivity plotted against wavelength. [From Granit (66).]

retinae, others with mixed retinae (after light-adaptation), led to the dominator-modulator concept. The optic nerve fibers were found to deliver two types of curves, broad-band dominators and narrow-band modulators. Figure 14 shows photopic dominators of the snake cone eye and the light-adapted frog eye which are of interest because the photochemical systems of these eyes seem to be very similar to our own. Actually their photopic dominators agree very well with the average photopic distribution of sensitivity of the human eye. When the mixed eye is dark-adapted, the same fiber that previously gave a photopic dominator now gives a scotopic one with maximum around 5000 Å which agrees with the sensitivity distribution of visual purple or rhodopsin. We recall that Polyak (122) had shown that both rods and cones converge towards the same ganglion cell. Thus the dominators are the carriers of the Purkinje shift of retinal sensitivity with state of adaptation. In man the point of maximum shifts from 5560 to 5100 Å, just as in frogs and cats. The photochemical aspects will be discussed elsewhere in this volume (Wald, Chapter XXVIII), but it deserves to be pointed out that dominators in various systems have been synthesized by Wald out of vitamin A aldehydes and rod and cone proteins with the aid of various enzymes and that these synthesized products have absorption spectra in good agreement with the experimental results obtained from optic nerve fibers [see also the summaries by Granit (73, 75)].

Examples of modulators from different animals are

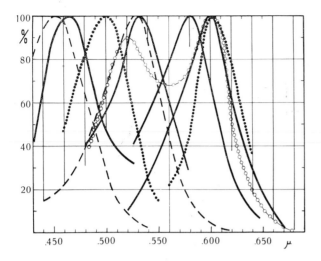

FIG. 15. Modulator curves. *Dots*, rat; *broken line*, guinea pig; *continuous line*, frog; ○—— ○, snake. Equal quantum intensity spectrum. Sensitivity plotted against wavelength. [From Granit (66).]

given in figure 15. The modulator at 5000 Å was obtained after light-adaptation from the rat, an animal with rod eyes. In the dark-adapted state it had been a dominator of the ordinary rhodopsin type. It is by no means rare to find, in practically pure rod eyes such narrow curves with maximum around 5000 Å, when visual purple activity has been suppressed by light-adaptation. The other modulators very clearly occupy three regions of predilection which have recurred since in many other measurements. The narrowest modulators ever seen were found by Donner (52) in the pigeon cone retina where they also occurred in three regions of predilection and shifted slightly towards wavelengths which are long compared with those of frogs. Donner suggested that this shift was due to colored oil globules. Modulators have also been obtained by selective adaptation to different wavelengths as well as by electrical polarization.

A much debated question is whether these modulators represent the more or less pure absorption curves of photochemical substances or are products of neural interaction based, for instance, on a minimum of three broad-band curves. The simplest basis for such interaction would obviously be overlap of broad-band curves, such as those of Dartnall (35), the pathways of one set of cones synaptically suppressing or exciting those of the neighbor cones with which they overlap in spectral sensitivity. As to such interaction, it is true that it has been shown to exist (43, 71), especially by polarization methods (70), but

this does not necessarily constitute proof that it actually did occur under the circumstances of threshold experiments of the type used to establish the concepts. On the other hand, retinal photochemistry, though highly developed in many interesting experiments by several workers [see Wald's summary in Chapter XXVIII of this volume; also Granit (73, 75)], has not yet reached the point when it would be possible to state that narrow-band photochemical substances do not occur in living retinae. The most that could be said is that broad-band curves seem to be easier to demonstrate. Further work will no doubt solve this problem.

Much work has lately been devoted to the study of the action of intermittent or flickering light. In general, rod eyes have been found to fuse flicker at lower values than cone eyes. In a mixed eye in the dark adapted state rod sensitivity is high, for example in the frog retina with roughly equal numbers of rods and cones. Fusion frequency of the ERG to a light of some 2000 lux in this animal will then be around 7 to 10 flashes per sec. But if this light is allowed to shine for a while so as to light-adapt the eye, the fusion frequency will soon rise to values around 20 flashes per sec. Now why could not the faster cones also participate in the dark-adapted state and raise the fusion frequency to their higher rate? Why was light-adaptation necessary, particularly if the ERG is a pure receptor affair and not influenced by interaction? Perhaps the reply is that interaction does occur so that highly sensitized rods suppress the cones, as was suggested by Granit & Riddell (80) when they made this experiment. They also demonstrated that the flickering wavelets change character as light-adaptation proceeds and, besides, are different in rcd and cone eyes. The same changes can be seen in the ERG of man (41).

Figure 16 is from experiments with ERG in guinea pigs, cats and pigeons (45, 49) and shows a graph of fusion frequency against light intensity in double logarithmic plotting. Clearly there are two branches of the curve in cats and guinea pigs. Much evidence, presented in Granit's summary (73), goes to show that the lower branch is a scotopic and the steeper portion a photopic function. The less the number of cones (their being far fewer in guinea pigs than in cats), the higher the intensity at the kink of the curve. The pigeon with cone dominance in the ERG has no low-intensity branch but the curve rises steeply towards values as high as around 150 per sec.

Records from the large retinal ganglion cells of cats have shown (54) that fusion frequency is pro-

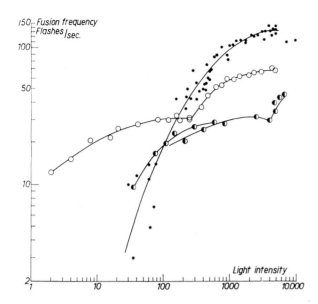

FIG. 16. Double logarithmic plot of fusion frequency of the electroretinogram against stimulus intensity in meter candles. ○, cat; ◑, guinea pig (two animals); ●, pigeon. [From Granit (73).]

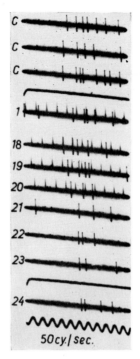

FIG. 17. *Encéphale isolé* given curare. Collicular stimulating electrodes on contralateral side at depth H 2 in Horsley-Clarke coordinates. *C*, controls with test light of 3 lux alone. *1*, and *18–20* show first and three last records of stimulation period 22 sec. in duration, at a rate of 47 per sec. Note, no driving, as shown by isolated shock artifacts; afterwards diminution of spike frequency. Sweep interval in sec. [From Granit (74).]

portional to impulse frequency set up by the individual flashes just before the moment of fusion when impulse frequency still can be measured. Fusion itself is defined as the flicker frequency at which effects of individual flashes on the spike frequency are no longer discernible. Flicker and fusion in electrical records has recently been discussed by Granit (73).

CENTRIFUGAL CONTROL

The inner plexiform layer, which forms a network of dendrites between ganglion cells and bipolar cells densely interspersed with amacrine cells, also receives the terminals of the centrifugal fibers (see fig. 2). Their central station in the brain is unknown. However, experiments have shown that it is possible to obtain different kinds of centrifugal effects on the ganglion cell discharge (44, 74). These are partly excitatory, partly inhibitory but quite often mixed, excitation followed by inhibition, and generally require an array of antidromic stimuli to the optic nerve before a definite effect is noticed. This is not surprising. We are best informed about centrifugal effects from the brainstem to the muscle spindles (77) through the so-called gamma neurons and these too mostly require iterative stimulation. Similarly the suppression of the cochlear nerve discharge (58) by

stimulation of the centrifugal olivocochlear bundle is fully developed only after it has been stimulated for about half a second at the optimal rate of 100 per sec. The effect on the retina is very similar independently of whether the site of stimulation is the optic nerve where it is spread out in the pretectum or the brainstem reticular substance. In the former case there is, of course, also driving of the ganglion cells by antidromic stimulation which seems to facilitate excitatory components on the driven cells. On the other hand, from lower portions of the optic nerve inhibitory effects are quite common. When the effect is excitation, it tends to be an increase of level of excitability so that a greater number of impulses are discharged between 'on' and 'off'. The on-off differentials tend to disappear in this general outburst. Again, when the final result is suppression, the whole effect of light is suppressed. An inhibitory effect from the brainstem reticular formation is shown in figure 17. High-frequency on- or off-bursts cannot be much altered by centrifugal stimulation.

Recently further work by Dodt (44) on the rabbit eye has led to the actual demonstration of a centrifugal spike picked up in the retina. This spike is from 8 to 20 msec. delayed with respect to antidromic impulses recorded from the ganglion cells. These also are positive-negative and much larger than the centrifugal spikes which are purely negative as if they started below the recording electrode itself. It is impossible to elicit the centrifugal spike by light. It is at the moment too early to put forth a theory of the role of centrifugal control.

ERG OF MAN: ITS CLINICAL USE

ERG's of man have been recorded from the very earliest time of electroretinography but the first really good records were published by Hartline (85). The work gradually got under way, particularly when the first more differentiated responses separating rods and cones were published by Motokawa & Mita (110) and Adrian (1, 2) and when Karpe (96) started clinical electroretinography. In 1956 this subject gathered a large number of European continental and British students of the human ERG to a first symposium in Hamburg (128). The contributions to this symposium provide a convenient introduction to the literature of electroretinography, particularly in its clinical aspects.

Since in man it is impossible to open the eye and use microillumination of selected spots and, at the same time, the dominant phase of the human ERG is a rod response requiring dark-adaptation, the question of whether the ERG is a generalized response to stray light or is focally elicited has created considerable interest. Contributions to this discussion by Fry & Bartley (57), Boynton & Riggs (27), Asher (13), Boynton (26), Wirth & Zetterström (150), Marg & Heath (106) and Brindley (29) should be consulted. There is general agreement that stray light is unavoidable at the strength needed for an ERG to be recorded in the human eye, i.e. from the cornea; in particular, clinical work shows that evidence of large scotomata may fail to appear in the ERG (96). In cats, as stated, an area of 20 mm² must be illuminated for a maximum ERG (150). With regard to localized focal stimuli in opened eyes of animals and whether they can interact or not, opinions still differ (29, 106).

Much recent theoretical work on the human ERG has been devoted to the identification of its various deflections and components, particularly with regard to rods and cones (12, 14, 21, 40, 41, 48, 130, 148), and to a study of its sensitivity to colored lights (as mentioned above).

The clinical values are both diagnostic and prognostic. Karpe (96) initiated the work by bringing together the data necessary for establishment of normal standard values for the b-wave and for defining a number of fundamental pathological types of initial deflections. There has since been much systematic work done, and in many eye hospitals recording of the ERG is a routine procedure, not only when the eye media are opaque but also for the prognosis of varieties of tapetoretinal degenerations, to decide whether treatment should be surgical or not, in children (151), etc. It seems that early changes in the ERG or failure of such changes when the ophthalmoscopic picture suggests a pathological retina are of considerable prognostic value.

REFERENCES

1. ADRIAN, E. D. *J. Physiol.* 104: 84, 1945.
2. ADRIAN, E. D. *J. Physiol.* 105: 24, 1946.
3. ADRIAN, E. D. AND R. MATTHEWS. *J. Physiol.* 63: 378, 1927.
4. ADRIAN, E. D. AND R. MATTHEWS. *J. Physiol.* 64: 279, 1927.
5. ADRIAN, E. D. AND R. MATTHEWS. *J. Physiol.* 65: 273, 1928.
6. ANDRÉE, G. AND H.-W. MÜLLER-LIMMROTH. *Ztschr. Biol.* 106: 395, 1954.
7. ARDEN, G. B. AND D. P. GREAVES. *J. Physiol.* 133: 266, 1956.
8. ARDEN, G. B. AND K. TANSLEY. *J. Physiol.* 127: 592, 1955.
9. ARDEN, G. B. AND K. TANSLEY. *J. Physiol.* 130: 225, 1955.
10. ARMINGTON, J. C. *J. Opt. Soc. Am.* 42: 393, 1952.
11. ARMINGTON, J. C. *J. Opt. Soc. Am.* 45: 1058, 1955.
12. ARMINGTON, J. C., E. P. JOHNSON AND L. A. RIGGS. *J. Physiol.* 118: 289, 1952.
13. ASHER, H. *J. Physiol.* 112: 40P, 1951.
14. AUERBACH, E. AND H. M. BURIAN. *Am. J. Ophth.* 40: 42, 1955.
15. BARLOW, H. B. *J. Physiol.* 119: 58, 1953.
16. BARLOW, H. B. *J. Physiol.* 119: 69, 1953.
17. BARLOW, H. B., R. FITZHUGH AND S. W. KUFFLER. *J. Physiol.* 125: 28P, 1954.
18. BENOIT, P. H. AND L. CORNU. *Compt. rend. Soc. de biol.* 147: 454, 1953.
19. BERNHARD, C. G. AND C. R. SKOGLUND. *Acta physiol. scandinav.* 2: 10, 1941.
20. BEST, W. *Ztschr. Biol.* 106: 171, 1953.
21. BEST, W. *Acta ophth.* 31: 95, 1953.
22. BISHOP, P. O., D. JEREMY AND J. W. LANCE. *J. Physiol.* 121: 415, 1953.
23. BISHOP, P. O. AND J. S. O'LEARY. *J. Neurophysiol.* 1: 391, 1938.
24. BOLL, F. *Monatsber. Akad. Wiss. Berlin* 41: 783, 1876.
25. BORNSCHEIN, H. *Naturwissenschaften* 41: 435, 1954.
26. BOYNTON, R. M. *J. Opt. Soc. Am.* 43: 442, 1953.
27. BOYNTON, R. M. AND L. A. RIGGS. *J. Exper. Psychol.* 42: 217, 1951.
28. BRINDLEY, G. S. *J. Physiol.* 134: 339, 1956.
29. BRINDLEY, G. S. *J. Physiol.* 134: 353, 1956.
30. BRINDLEY, G. S. *J. Physiol.* 134: 360, 1956.

31. CHAFFEE, E. L., W. T. BOVIE AND A. HAMPSON. *J. Opt. Soc. Am.* 7: 1, 1923.

32. CHAFFEE, E. L. AND A. HAMPSON. *J. Opt. Soc. Am.* 9: 1, 1924.

33. CHAFFEE, E. L. AND E. SUTCLIFFE. *Am. J. Physiol.* 95: 250, 1930.

34. COBB, W. AND H. B. MORTON. *Electroencephalog. & Clin. Neurophysiol.* 4: 547, 1952.

35. DARTNALL, H. J. A. *J. Physiol.* 134: 327, 1956.

36. DENTON, E. J. *J. Physiol.* 124: 16P, 1954.

37. DENTON, E. J. AND J. H. WYLLIE. *J. Physiol.* 127: 81, 1955.

38. DETWILER, S. R. *Vertebrate Photoreceptors.* New York: Macmillan, 1943.

39. DITCHBURN, R. W. AND B. L. GINSBORG. *J. Physiol.* 119: 1, 1953.

40. DODT, E. *von Graefes Arch. Ophth.* 151: 672, 1951.

41. DODT, E. *von Graefes Arch. Ophth.* 153: 152, 1952.

42. DODT, E. *Experientia* 12: 34, 1956.

43. DODT, E. *Acta physiol. scandinav.* 36: 219, 1956.

44. DODT, E. *J. Neurophysiol.* 19: 301, 1956.

45. DODT, E. AND C. ENROTH. *Acta physiol. scandinav.* 30: 375, 1953.

46. DODT, E. AND J. HECK. *Arch. ges. Physiol.* 259: 212, 1954.

47. DODT, E. AND J. HECK. *Arch. ges. Physiol.* 259: 226, 1954.

48. DODT, E. AND L. WADENSTEN. *Acta ophth.* 32: 165, 1954.

49. DODT, E. AND A. WIRTH. *Acta physiol. scandinav.* 30: 80, 1953.

50. DOGIEL, A. S. *Arch. mikroskop. Anat.* 44: 622, 1895.

51. DONNER, K. O. *Acta physiol. scandinav.* 21: Suppl. 72, 1950.

52. DONNER, K. O. *J. Physiol.* 122: 524, 1953.

53. EINTHOVEN, W. AND W. A. JOLLY. *Quart. J. Exper. Physiol.* 1: 373, 1908.

54. ENROTH, CH. *Acta physiol. scandinav.* 27: Suppl. 100, 1952.

55. FORBES, A., S. BURLEIGH AND M. NEYLAND. *J. Neurophysiol.* 18: 517, 1955.

56. FRÖLICH, F. W. *Grundzüge einer Lehre vom Licht- und Farbensinn. Ein Beitrag zur allgemeinen Physiologie der Sinne.* Jena: Fischer, 1921, 86 pp.

57. FRY, G. A. AND S. H. BARTLEY. *Am. J. Physiol.* 111: 335, 1935.

58. GALAMBOS, R. *J. Neurophysiol.* 19: 424, 1956.

59. GEBHARD, J. W. Proc. 29th Meeting Armed Forces National Research Council Vision Committee, 1951.

60. GOTCH, F. *J. Physiol.* 29: 388, 1903.

61. GOTCH, F. *J. Physiol.* 31: 1, 1904.

62. GOTO, M. AND N. TOIDA. *Jap. J. Physiol.* 4: 123, 1954.

63. GOTO, M. AND N. TOIDA. *Jap. J. Physiol.* 4: 221, 1954.

64. GRANIT, R. *J. Physiol.* 77: 207, 1933.

65. GRANIT, R. *J. Physiol.* 85: 421, 1935.

65a. GRANIT, R. *Acta physiol. scandinav.* 2: 334, 1941.

66. GRANIT, R. *Nature, London* 151: 11, 1943.

67. GRANIT, R. *J. Physiol.* 103: 103, 1944.

68. GRANIT, R. *Proc. Phys. Soc. London* 57: 447, 1945.

69. GRANIT, R. *Sensory Mechanisms of the Retina.* London: Oxford, 1947, 412 pp.

70. GRANIT, R. *J. Neurophysiol.* 11: 253, 1948.

71. GRANIT, R. *Acta physiol. scandinav.* 18: 281, 1949.

72. GRANIT, R. *Année Psychol.* 50: 129, 1951.

73. GRANIT, R. *Receptors and Sensory Perception.* New Haven: Yale, 1955, 367 pp.

74. GRANIT, R. *J. Neurophysiol.* 18: 388, 1955.

75. GRANIT, R. Proc. XXth Internat. Physiol. Congress, Brussels, 1956, p. 65.

76. GRANIT, R. AND T. HELME. *J. Neurophysiol.* 2: 556, 1939.

77. GRANIT, R. AND B. R. KAADA. *Acta physiol. scandinav.* 27: 130, 1952.

78. GRANIT, R. AND A. MUNSTERHJELM. *J. Physiol.* 88: 436, 1937.

79. GRANIT, R. AND C. G. PHILLIPS. *J. Physiol.* 133: 520, 1956.

80. GRANIT, R. AND L. A. RIDDELL. *J. Physiol.* 81: 1, 1934.

81. GRANIT, R. AND P. O. THERMAN. *J. Physiol.* 83: 359, 1935.

82. GRANIT, R. AND P. O. THERMAN. *J. Physiol.* 91: 127, 1937.

83. GRANIT, R. AND P. O. THERMAN. *J. Physiol.* 93: 9P, 1938.

84. GRANIT, R. AND C. M. WREDE. *J. Physiol.* 89: 239, 1937.

85. HARTLINE, H. K. *Am. J. Physiol.* 73: 600, 1925.

86. HARTLINE, H. K. *Am. J. Physiol.* 121: 400, 1938.

87. HARTLINE, H. K. *Am. J. Physiol.* 130: 690, 1940.

88. HARTLINE, H. K. *Am. J. Physiol.* 130: 700, 1940.

89. HARTLINE, H. K. *J. Opt. Soc. Am.* 30: 239, 1940.

90. HARTLINE, H. K., H. G. WAGNER AND F. RATLIFF. *J. Gen. Physiol.* 39: 651, 1956.

91. HARTLINE, H. K., H. G. WAGNER AND T. TOMITA. Proc. XIXth Internat. Physiol. Congress, Montreal, 1953, p. 441.

92. HECHT, S., S. SHLAER AND M. H. PIRENNE. *J. Gen. Physiol.* 25: 819, 1942.

93. HECK, J. AND I. RENDAHL. *Acta physiol. scandinav.* 39: 167, 1957.

94. HOLMGREN, F. *Upsala läkaref. förh.* 1: 177, 1865–66.

95. HOLMGREN, F. *Upsala läkaref. förh.* 6: 419, 1870–71.

96. KARPE, G. *Acta Ophth.* Suppl. 24: 1945, 118 pp.

97. KATZ, B. *J. Physiol.* 111: 261, 1950.

98. KOHLRAUSCH, A. *Handb. norm. path. Physiol.* 12, Pt. 2: 1393, 1931.

99. KÖNIG, A. *Gesammelte Abhandlungen zur physiologischen Optik.* Leipzig: Barth, 1903, 443 pp.

100. KUFFLER, S. W. *J. Neurophysiol.* 16: 37, 1953.

101. KÜHNE, W. *Handb. Physiol.* 3: 235, 1879.

102. KÜHNE, W. AND J. STEINER. *Unters. physiol. Inst. Heidelb.* 3: 327, 1880.

103. KÜHNE, W. AND J. STEINER. *Unters. physiol. Inst. Heidelb.* 4: 64, 1881.

104. LORENTE DE NÓ, R. *J. Cell. & Comp. Physiol.* 29: 207, 1947.

105. MacNICHOL, E. F. AND R. BENOLKEN. *Science* 124: 681, 1956.

105a. MacNICHOL, E. J., JR. AND G. SVAETICHIN. *Am. J. Ophth.* 46: 26, 1958.

106. MARG, E. AND G. G. HEATH. *Science* 122: 1234, 1955.

107. MARSHALL, W. H. *J. Neurophysiol.* 12: 277, 1949.

108. MOTOKAWA, K. *J. Neurophysiol.* 12: 291, 1949.

109. MOTOKAWA, K., K. IWAMA AND S. TUKAHARA. *Tohoku J. Exper. Med.* 53: 399, 1951.

110. MOTOKAWA, K. AND T. MITA. *Tohoku J. Exper. Med.* 42: 114, 1942.

111. MÜLLER-LIMMROTH, H.-W. AND G. ANDRÉE. *Ztschr. Biol.* 105: 348, 1952.

112. MÜLLER-LIMMROTH, H.-W. AND G. ANDRÉE. *Arch. ges. Physiol.* 257: 216, 1953.

113. MÜLLER-LIMMROTH, H.-W. AND W. WIRTH. *Ztschr. Biol.* 107: 444, 1955.

114. NOELL, W. K. *Studies on the Electrophysiology and the Me-*

tabolism of the Retina. Randolph Field Texas: USAF School of Aviation Medicine, 1953, 122 pp.

115. OTTOSON, D. AND G. SVAETICHIN. *Cold Spring Harbor Symp. Quant. Biol.* 17: 165, 1952.

116. OTTOSON, D. AND G. SVAETICHIN. *Acta physiol. scandinav.* Suppl. 106, 29: 538, 1954.

117. PARINAUD, H. *La Vision*. Paris: Doin, 1898, 218 pp.

118. PARRY, H. B., K. TANSLEY AND L. C. THOMSON. *J. Physiol.* 120: 28, 1953.

119. PIPER, H. *Arch. Anat. Physiol.* Suppl. Bd. 1905, p. 133.

120. PIPER, H. *Arch. Anat. Physiol.* Suppl. Bd. 1910, p. 461.

121. PIPER, H. *Arch. Anat. Physiol.* 1911, p. 85.

122. POLYAK, S. *The Retina*. Chicago: Univ. Chicago Press. 1941, 607 pp.

123. RAMÓN Y CAJAL, S. *Die Retina der Wirbeltiere*. Wiesbaden: Bergmann, 1894, 168 pp.

124. RAMÓN Y CAJAL, S. *Trav. Lab. Rech. Biol. Univ. Madrid* 28: Appendice, 1933.

125. RIGGS, L. A., F. RATLIFF, J. C. CORNSWEET AND T. N. CORNSWEET. *J. Opt. Soc. Am.* 43: 495, 1953.

126. RONCHI, L. AND S. GRAZI. Istituto Nazionale di Ottica, Firenze, Technical Note No. 5, 1956.

127. RUSHTON, W. A. H. *J. Physiol.* 134: 30, 1956.

128. SAUTTER, H. AND W. STRAUB (editors). *Elektroretinographie*. Basel: Karger, 1957.

129. SCHMIDT, W. J. *Kolloid-Ztschr.* 85: 137, 1938.

130. SCHUBERT, G. AND H. BORNSCHEIN. *Ophthalmologica* 123: 396, 1952.

131. SCHULTZE, M. *Strickers Handb. d. Lehre von den Geweben.* 2: 977, 1871.

132. SJÖSTRAND, F. S. *J. Appl. Physiol.* 19: 1188, 1948.

133. SJÖSTRAND, F. S. *J. Cell. & Comp. Physiol.* 33: 383, 1949.

134. SJÖSTRAND, F. S. *J. Cell. & Comp. Physiol.* 42: 15, 1953.

135. SJÖSTRAND, F. S. *J. Cell. & Comp. Physiol.* 42: 45, 1953.

136. STILES, W. S. AND B. H. CRAWFORD. *Proc. Roy. Soc., London. ser. B* 112: 428, 1933.

137. SVAETICHIN, G. *Acta physiol. scandinav.* Suppl. 106, 29: 601, 1954.

138. TANSLEY, K., AND B. K. JOHNSON. *Nature, London* 178: 1285, 1956.

139. THERMAN, P. O. *Acta Soc. Scient. Fenn.* Nova Ser. B. 2: 1, 1938.

140. TOIDA, N. AND M. GOTO. *Jap. J. Physiol.* 4: 260, 1954.

141. TOMITA, T. *Jap. J. Physiol.* 1: 110, 1950.

141a. TOMITA, T. *Jap. J. Physiol.* 7: 80, 1957.

142. TOMITA, T. AND Y. TORIHAMA. *Jap. J. Physiol.* 6: 118, 1956.

143. TUKAHARA, S. *Tohoku J. Exper. Med.* 54: 11, 1951.

144. VON BRÜCKE, E. T. AND S. GARTEN. *Arch. ges. Physiol.* 120: 290, 1907.

145. VON KRIES, J. *Handb. norm. path. Physiol.* 12, Pt. 1: 678, 1929.

146. WALLS, G. L. *The Vertebrate Eye and its Adaptive Radiation*. Michigan: Cranbrook Press, 1942, 785 pp.

147. WILLMER, E. N. *Ann. Rev. Physiol.* 17: 339, 1955.

148. WIRTH, A. *von Graefes Arch. Ophth.* 151: 662, 1951.

149. WIRTH, A. *Arch. sc. biol.* 40: 163, 1956.

150. WIRTH, A. AND B. ZETTERSTRÖM. *Brit. J. Ophth.* 38: 257, 1954.

151. ZETTERSTRÖM, B. *Studies on the Postnatal Development of the Electroretinogram in Newborn Infants*. Stockholm: Akademisk Avhandling Karolinska Institutet, 1956.

CHAPTER XXX

Central mechanisms of vision

S. HOWARD BARTLEY | *Department of Psychology, Michigan State University, East Lansing, Michigan*

CHAPTER CONTENTS

THE PRESENT CHAPTER, devoted to central mechanisms of vision, must deal with two diverse sets of phenomena. One set comprises the phenomena that, taken together, we call vision. The other is the group of neurophysiological phenomena that constitute the activities of the central end of the optic pathway. The visual phenomena must be considered first, for they are the items to be accounted for, if possible, by what we know about the optic pathway and its associated systems.

Vision is the behavior of the organism that stems more or less directly from optic pathway activity. Vision includes both the introspective (the experiential) and the motor. Visual behavior in question is divisible in still another way. Part of it is the immediate discriminatory reaction which we call visual perception. Perception is not only experiential but also motor in expression. Another part of behavior is in the form of imagery, etc., that is, a function of the visual mechanism when the eye is not stimulated.

Material appropriate in the discussion of central visual mechanisms stems first from what we know about visual phenomena in accord with the definition of vision just given and from what we have found out from direct investigation of the activity of the entire optic pathway. We may also legitimately include certain inferences that seem to be necessary to bridge the gaps in our knowledge and to provide a basis for further investigation.

TYPES OF DATA

In this portion of the chapter we must specify, at least in general, the kinds of phenomena with which we shall deal. They are of two kinds so diverse that they generally are dealt with in entirely separate discourses. The one class is visual and includes the experiential outcomes of the action of the optic pathway activated by photic radiation. The other class of phenomena is neurophysiological. The task of the present chapter seems to be one of relating the two classes of phenomena.

Commonality in Modes of Study

The fundamental requirement in relating vision to the various phenomena in the optic pathway is for the two sets of events to be initiated by the same external event (stimulus). In this way, one can say that a given visual end result is occasioned upon such and such events in the bodily mechanism involved.

It is fortunate that the same stimulus conditions can and have been used to study the behavior of the two categories of events. This is to say that not only are photic stimuli used in both cases, but the very same manipulations are used and seem effective in giving us the data we need.

The following remarks have to do with modes of studying both vision and the neural mechanisms that underlie them. Vision can be studied only in the intact or near-intact animal. Neurophysiological mechanisms can be studied in the reduced animal and in animal preparations. Vision is to be studied only by use of retinal stimulation with photic radiation. Neurophysiological mechanisms (including central mechanisms) may be studied by stimulating either the retina or by eliminating it and stimulating the optic nerve directly by electrical energy, or by directly stimulating regions farther along in the pathway. The electrical method provides for stricter control than the photic and, though 'unnatural' in the temporal pattern of impulses delivered, the central end of the pathway is helpful in analyzing the nature of the mechanisms involved. Eliminating the retina eliminates the selective features employed by it in producing the optic nerve discharge. The retina selects or emphasizes certain channels in the optic nerve according to the distribution of the discharge into the various channels in keeping with its own principles of divergence and convergence in its neural circuits. Virtually no discharge initiated by the retina involves all channels simultaneously. They are activated in temporal succession of some sort or another.

When the optic nerve is stimulated directly (electrically), all available channels may be activated together in time and thus a very different reception of the afferent input may occur at the stations along the pathway. To discover just how nearly alike the two forms of stimulation, in effect, can be is a matter of empirical test.

At this point, it may be appropriate to point out one of the more salient features of the retina-initiated optic nerve discharge, namely that it is composed of three temporal orders. *a*) One is the maintained discharge, a series of impulses lasting throughout the life of the photic impingement on the retina. *b*) Another is the on-off discharge, occurring at the beginning and also at the termination of the photic impingement. *c*) The third type is the off discharge, occurring only following the termination of impingement. There are certain visual end results that seem to be explained

on the basis of these differences. The retina is also responsible for an unexpected end result, the seeing of two flashes when the photic impingement (pulse) is brief, moderate in intensity and singular, owing to the fact that the two sets of sense cells do not have the same latency.

Modes of study involve not only the two forms of setting up the optic nerve message but also manipulations in the photic impingements themselves. In general, three forms of timing may be employed: *a*) single isolated stimuli; *b*) paired stimuli, in which the two members of the pair are variously separated in time; and *c*) trains of stimuli, often called intermittent stimulation. In intermittent stimulation, time intervals between stimuli may be varied, and the ratio between the stimulus (pulse) duration and the length of the cycle of intermittency may also be varied.

These three forms of manipulation have turned out to be much more than empty differences in form of stimulation as will be seen later. The use of method *a* provides for a response from a resting system, at least as far as intended activation is concerned. Method *b* provides for the determination of the effect of the first stimulus on the second, or otherwise stated it provides for discovering how long it takes for the reacting system to complete its response and reassume *status quo*. Method *c* provides for still another aspect of the reacting system to become manifest. Since the optic pathway consists of a number of parallel channels, each with finite limits in the rate at which it can be reactivated, it is possible that, when a whole train of stimuli is delivered at a rate beyond which single channels can repeatedly respond, a redistribution of the relationships between repeated pulses and the responses to them occurs as stimulation progresses.

Phenomena of Vision

The phenomena of vision are the items to be ultimately accounted for, hence it is necessary that we have in mind what they are. Vision consists in the appreciation of the surrounds via the use of the eye, the nervous system, and in turn the effector muscles. The feature of the environment to which response is made is, of course, photic radiation. The dimensions involved are spatial, intensive and temporal. Hence it could easily be supposed that these would be the experimental variables to be used.

In vision a field is responded to in terms of intensive components that, when they evoke experience, are perceived as lightness and darkness of various degrees. These qualities need not be stable but may be perceived as appearing and disappearing. Vision is also response to spatial relationships of radiation originating in various directions from the eye. When these relationships are experienced, we see objects at various locations, manifesting various movements and assuming various directions from us. We are also visually responsive to manipulations in timing of radiation coming from various parts of the field. When this response is in the form of experience, events are seen as occurring in succession, or together in time, and lasting for various durations. Photic radiation may also be differentially responded to in terms of its wavelength. The experience then is of color, hue, saturation and brightness.

It is meant to be clear to the reader that vision, i. e. perceptual response, may occur in the form of clear immediate experience, in the form of inarticulate gross incipient reactions or in the form of articulate differential motor responses. In the last analysis, the sharp dichotomizing between the experiential and the motor is only one of the possible ways of dealing with behavior. It would seem that when one looks carefully at the kinds of behavior which the human manifests, it is more appropriate to postulate a kind of spectrum of kinds rather than two opposite kinds with no form intervening between them.

The following are some of the essential types of problems which we must handle as best we can with our present information and interpretations. a) The first problem is that of seeing various brightnesses. b) Next we have the problem of seeing continuously. It is known that many neurophysiological processes are discontinuous. Were these the only processes we could discover in the nervous system, the problem of getting continuity from discontinuity would seem to be a cardinal one. We are beginning to learn of sustained activity or sustained state of potential, and this may help a great deal. c) This is followed by the problem of differential response to various parts of the space field, since response to the field as a whole is not what would be expected were the response to isolated parts either independent or summative. d) The problem of fine resolution is the question of how closely adjacent parts of the field are seen as separate. e) Finally, we have the problem of differential response to various parts of the spectrum—both local response to an isolated part of the field and response to the whole field.

While the problems that have just been listed are fundamental, they are in the form of generalizations and cannot be dealt with as directly and as concretely as is the case when particular visual phenomena are

chosen. For most of our considerations, we have chosen phenomena that are fairly specific but stand for the broader classes to which they belong.

The first general phenomenon appropriate for mention is that of gross response to the simplest major intensity differentiations in the field. This is the response merely to one large part of the field as more intense than the others.

Whereas the foregoing item may be thought to have to do with brightness, brightness is an experience. It and any overt response that seems to be related to it in an experimentally approachable way had better be put in a class by themselves. Hence, in the present category, we refer to the higher order responses to intensity relations in the stimulus field. These responses would be expected to be based on cortical function, whereas those in category above may be subcortical.

The observer experiences undulations of darkness and lightness in temporal sequence. This is flicker. At high rates of intermittent stimulation this experience is lost, a fact implying that the neural or some other mechanism is unable to keep pace. Differential response to the intermittent stimulation of the optic mechanisms of subhuman species also are quite common and manifest many close parallels or similarities to the quantitative features of the experiential responses of the human subject.

Brightness enhancement is another feature of human experiential response. It is the case in which intermittent stimulation results in a higher brightness than continuous stimulation of the same intensity.

Bilateral functions involving the use of the two eyes result, of course, in a different input into the central nervous system than the involvement of one eye alone. It has been found that both the experiential and the oculomotor outcomes differ in the two cases.

Brightness contrast occurs when fields made up of certain patterns and intensities of radiation are presented. They are reacted to in ways not predictable from the separate local intensities of the parts of the field. These parts are not independent in effect nor are the results simply additive when they are interdependent. The major phenomena in this category are often known as brightness-contrast phenomena.

Visual movement creates complexities. Portions of the visual field are not stable. They quickly appear and disappear as segregated portions that may or may not undergo spatial displacement. When movement is seen under conditions where no visual target elements are displaced, it has been customary to call the movement 'apparent movement.' When displacement is involved, the movement is said to be 'real.' Again it may be said that subhuman species respond in motor ways so as to indicate they are differentially sensitive both in cases of displacement and in cases of stationary localization of targets.

Color vision is the name given to the fact that both human and some subhuman species give evidence of being differentially sensitive to various portions of the visible spectrum. Color as an experience may also be evoked in the human by nonspectrally selected radiation, hence the color end result stems also from conditions of nonspectral selection.

Phenomena of the Optic Pathway

BRAIN WAVES: SPONTANEOUS AND EVOKED. One of the major considerations in dealing with the neurophysiology of central phenomena, 'brain waves,' for example, is the assignment of their origin. All the activities which we deal with can be put into two classes: those that occur when no intended peripheral input to the brain is involved (spontaneous activity), and the specific activity that occurs when known inputs are delivered through intended stimulation (specific or evoked responses).

What do the characteristic waves found in the record of spontaneous activity represent? What elements produce them? There are two quite obvious alternative possibilities. One is that these rhythmic patterns of potential are the summed record of the primary impulses of unit neuronal responses occurring somewhat out of phase and producing wave envelopes of much longer duration than the unit impulses themselves. The second alternative is that the recorded waves are the manifestations of slower longer-lasting processes that are more nearly similar in duration to the recorded waves than would be the case in the first alternative. These waves would apparently be something like after-potentials in elements where activity would fall short of the kind of discharge that produces spikes. Bishop & Clare (21) believe that the first alternative is preferable in accounting primarily for spontaneous activity. They believe that this activity may incidentally include slower potentials suggested in the second alternative. As for evoked responses, the slow surface-negative portions may be an example of a slow potential of the character suggested in the second alternative.

Whichever alternative may operate, the next question is whether the spontaneous and the evoked activities as the result of well-controlled peripheral stimulation occupy the same cortical elements. Of course, there are two alternatives here. At first, it was inferred that they did not, but it has later appeared possible that the two activities share at least some common elements (15, 21).

The conclusions just given are in line with the findings of Adrian & Moruzzi (1). They reported that groups of impulses were discharged via axons in the pyramidal tract in unison with the alpha cycle of the motor cortex. Thus it appears that whatever may be said about the cortical waves themselves, impulse volleys are associated with them. Primary impulses of cortical cells are involved in spontaneous activity. The conclusions are also consistent with the finding of Bartley (4) that, following the cortical response to the afferent input via the optic nerve and radiation, the cortex is refractory to a second stimulus, the degree depending upon elapsed time. The moment of full recovery coincides with the point at which the alpha-like portion of the typical evoked response develops. This alpha-like portion may be spoken of as a sequel to the specific response (21) or be considered as a less specific but true portion of the response. The conclusions are also in line with Bishop's (18) finding that responses to stimulation of the optic nerve waxed and waned in such a way as to imply that the spontaneous alpha wave left a depression of the same temporal character as the evoked response just mentioned (4).

Interpretations that may be added in this connection are those of Bremer (31), Eccles (40), and Gastaut *et al.* (42). The first of these attributed spontaneously occurring rhythmic potentials in connection with excitability changes, plus axon discharges to account for the brain waves observed in 'resting' records. The second supposes that the activity in the cortex can be interpreted as being analogous to that in the spinal cord where neuronal activity involves recovery from depression. The interpretation is that rhythmicity results from successive re-excitations following periods of depression. Apparently closed neural chains form the sources of the re-excitations. The third, in studying what is ordinarily called photic driving of the cortex, inferred that the spontaneous cycle is an expression of refractoriness following discharge.

OPTIC PATHWAY. The optic pathway consists of: *a)* the tract, including the optic nerve; *b)* the relay nuclei of the lateral geniculate, the pretectal area and the superior colliculus; *c)* the radiation to cortex, and paths to thalamus and tectal area; and *d)* the projection areas including the cortical, thalamic and tectal projections. In addition to these, there are *e*) the association areas. Just where to delimit the visual system is problematic, depending upon how one views neural functions.

Omitting retinal structures, the first way station is the geniculate body. Saggitally, the dorsal nucleus of the lateral geniculate body of the cat possesses three layers: A, A_1 and B. The middle layer has been further differentiated by Rioch (62). Layers A and B receive terminals of tract fibers of the contralateral retina. The middle layer, A_1, is the terminus of fibers from the homolateral retina. It would seem that the development of binocular vision has involved increased stratification of the dorsal nucleus of the geniculate. The rabbit nucleus possesses scarcely any, if any, and thoes of monkey and man present six layers. Part of the process of development seems to have involved an increase in homolateral representation of the retina.

There are four groups of fibers in the optic tract (24). These groups distribute to four different regions and are unlike in range of cross-section size and in conduction rate. The fastest conducting groups innervate layers A and A_1 of the lateral geniculate. These fibers relay to the projection area of the striate cortex.

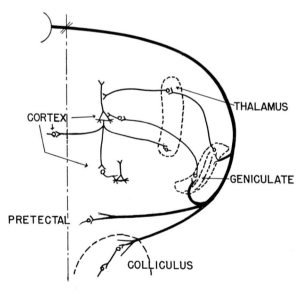

FIG. 1. Diagram to indicate distribution of optic activity to structures beyond the optic tract. The first relay neurons in the geniculate, pretectal area and colliculus are indicated for four tract components. Neurons for projection are represented in the striate cortex, lateral nucleus of thalamus and tectum. From the striate cortex paths are indicated to elaborative structures of opposite cortex, association cortex, pulvinar, etc. In cortex a short-axon cell is inferred on the basis of other work to relay the impulse from afferent fiber to pyramid cell. [From Bishop & Clare (24).]

The next slower group synapses in layer B of the geniculate, and relays to the lateral nucleus of the thalamus. The third group goes to the pretectal area and the fourth group terminates in the superior colliculus. Figure 1 is Bishop & Clare's schematization of these connections. (See also figs. 2 and 3.)

The conduction rates step down by ratios of one half from group to group. Neither in the frog nor the cat, for example, can four distinct fiber-size maxima be demonstrated. No qualitative sensory differences, such as are found to be correlated with fiber size in the somesthetic system, have yet been found in the visual system. Sensation is likely mediated by the direct path to the cortex via the large fiber group.

Strong stimulation of the contralateral optic nerve elicits two definite spikes, sometimes followed by a prolonged diminishing potential recordable just prior to the dorsal nucleus of the lateral geniculate. The second spike is propagated at about one half the rate of the first, and the threshold of its elicitation is about $2\frac{1}{2}$ times as high as for the first. Corresponding to these two spikes, there are two postsynaptic spikes manifested by the cells and axons of the dorsal nucleus (27, 28).

Single shocks to the optic nerve induce complete cortical responses even when such stimuli are weak enough to activate only the large-fiber group, inducing the first of the two tract spikes. The time of arrival at the cortex of the response to the second group of radiation fibers does not tally with any of the prominent spike components of the cortical record. Instead, the activity induced in layer B of the geniculate is propagated to the lateral nucleus of the thalamus. It first emerges when stimuli just strong enough to elicit the second spike are used, and thus the activity is not a response induced there by activity coming back from the cortex.

When records are obtained from the postsynaptic elements in the geniculate, the response to the first tract spike from the contralateral eye arises mainly from layer A and the response to the second spike from layer B. Thus the ensuing responses from the activation by the first tract spike reach the cortex, and those from the second spike reach the thalamus. This represents a functional differentiation of the two geniculate layers. These two layers are also different histologically (59), but we do not yet know the significance of the difference.

The response of the middle layer A_1 to the stimulation of the homolateral optic nerve is mainly to the first tract spike. When occasionally a second postsynaptic spike is elicited, its threshold is the same as

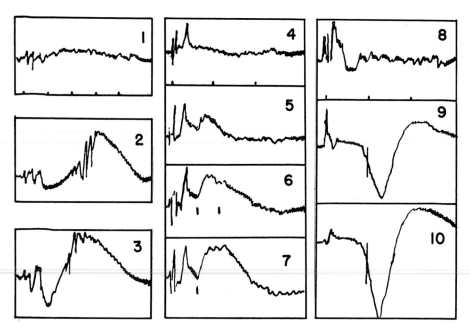

FIG. 2. Postsynaptic responses following single stimuli to the optic nerve from the pretectal area (*records 1 to 3*), from the colliculus (*8 to 10*) and from both (*4 to 7*). The presynaptic responses are usually too low to detect. Time scale is in 10 msec. intervals. In each column the first record is below threshold for the major responses to be recorded but nearly maximal for the second tract spike. For *record 2*, stimulus strength is 1.5 times that for *1*, for *3* it is twice. For *5 to 7*, strengths are 3, 5, and 6 times that for *4*. For *9 to 10*, strengths are 3 and 5 times that for *8*. Ratios of thresholds depend materially upon durations of square-wave pulse stimuli, the ratios increasing with shorter duration of pulses. *First column:* Records from electrodes, one at the surface above pretectal area and one below surface. The wave form varies widely with different positions of electrodes, and the spikes recorded here are not usually as prominent. *Second column:* Critical electrode in anterior border of superior colliculus where it evidently recorded activity both of pretectal character (with latency of 7 msec., shown in the *first column*) and of colliculus type (latency 11 msec., *third column*). Reference electrode in the medial geniculate body. Note growth of second potential in *records 6* and *7* as a wave starting beyond the crest of the first (starts marked by vertical lines) when stimulus strength is increased. *Third column:* The second only of the two waves of *record 6* is recorded from a critical electrode just below the surface of the colliculus proper against a reference electrode at a distance. Critical electrode negative. Record *8* is at high amplification, *9* and *10* at one quarter of this amplification. [From Bishop & Clare (24).]

the first response. Layers A and A₁ are homologous in function, both being activated by the first tract spike and both relaying to the cortex. Both retinas, however, send fibers to each colliculus, though many more arrive from the contralateral retina than from the other (24, 59).

Bishop *et al.* (29) and Bishop & McLeod (30) also have studied the response of the lateral geniculate body, finding it repetitive under the conditions used. They attribute repetitiveness to origins outside the geniculate, possibly to excitation over reverberatory circuits leading back from the cortex. Such paths have not been established anatomically.

The responses of structures beyond the relay nuclei (the cortex, the lateral thalamic nucleus and the tectum) differ from those up to and including the relay nuclei. Instead of being mainly spikes, they are extended responses involving complex pictures of chains of neurons, each link active in turn.

In the cat, it is at present feasible to distinguish histologically only three fiber-size ranges in the optic tract. The large-size group includes fibers ranging from 8 to 12 μ, and these pass only to the dorsal geniculate nucleus and are included in the first of the four functional groups of fibers already mentioned. The middle histological group with fibers ranging from 4 to 8 μ also makes up some of those in the first functional group as well as some in the second spike group. The small-fiber group constitutes the fibers in the third and fourth functional groups. Although the

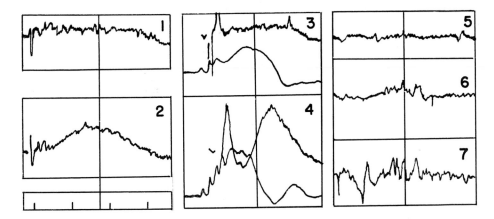

FIG. 3. Responses from the lateral nucleus of the thalamus to the second postsynaptic volley from dorsal nucleus of the geniculate with single optic nerve stimuli. The *first record* in each column was from a stimulus just below threshold for the second postsynaptic spike as recorded from the dorsal nucleus. Strength of stimulus for *record 2* was 5 times that for *1*; for *4*, 3.5 times that for *3*; for *6*, 2.5 times that for *5*. *Record 7* is a duplicate of *6* at 1.5 and higher amplification. In the *second column* the cortical record appears on the second oscillograph beam. In the *third column* the response consists of a sequence of brief spikes. Time scale for thalamic records in 10 msec. intervals. Latency of response cannot be accurately determined but is not over 6 msec. Form of response varies widely with location of electrodes and with depth below the surface of the thalamus, and varies considerably at one locus following identical stimuli. All records presented were from a critical electrode in the dorsal or dorsolateral region of the lateral nucleus approximately at the level of the anterior tip of the dorsal nucleus of the geniculate. The reference electrode was deeper in the thalamus or in white matter lateral to it. [From Bishop & Clare (24).]

locations of the fiber groups in the cross section of the tract are known (24), it is not necessary to delineate them here.

CORTICAL RESPONSE. The cortical response of the cat to a peripheral input as simple as it is possible to deliver is exceedingly complex. The simplest pattern may be shown by the recorded events in the optic cortex following single stimuli to the stump of the optic nerve. The afferent radiation fibers conduct impulses mainly to the fourth layer of the cortex. Activity, of course, immediately spreads to the other cortical layers. This is pictured in the record as a sequence of three definite spikes interpretable as indicating that three groups of cell bodies are discharging in sequence (20). More intimate examination (23) of the early part of the response shows that a second spike sequence also occurs. It, of course, is less prominent than the one just mentioned. In the record, the second series (the small spikes) alternates with the first. The authors have reason to infer that the small spikes represent the short-axon cells of the cortex. These cells do not possess long apical dendrites as do the pyramid cells. Their axons are short and mingle with the adjacent pyramid cells. It is supposed that they

conduct activity from one group of pyramids to another.

The model of activity that Clare & Bishop (37) suggest is as follows and is pictured in figure 4. Afferent radiation fibers first activate the short axon cells of the fourth layer of the cortex. These, in turn, innervate a group of pyramid cells at about the same cortical level. These cells discharge into their axons. The main branches of these leave this level of the cortex via the subcortical white matter, activating other parts of the central nervous system. The pyramid-cell axons possess recurrent branches that arborize within the cortex activating a second group of short axon cells. These, then, activate a second group of pyramidal cells. This alternation occurs until the sequence first mentioned has been completed. Since the synaptic periods between each two successive spikes is less than 1 msec., the transmission is thought to be from axon to cell body.

When activation of the pyramidal cells is intense enough, the dendrites of these cells are definitely involved. When so, they conduct their effects toward their terminals. Clare & Bishop (37) state that this produces the slow wave sequence typical of the response of the visual cortex. If stimulation is slight, pyramidal cells may become active without activity of their apical dendrites resulting. They suggest the possibility that in normal cortical behavior dendritic activation is minor. Activation of dendrites via paths in addition to the afferent radiation must also be considered, although in the present case the radiation impulses form the major component.

Neurons exert their influences on their surrounds by way of their axon discharges, but neurons may re-

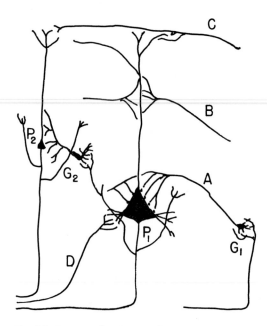

FIG. 4. Possible patterns of activation of neurons in the cortex. The afferent radiation axon entering at right activates the Golgi cell G_1, the axon A of which in turn activates the pyramidal cell P_1 at its cell body and induces a brief spike response. A recurrent branch of the axon of P_1 is shown activating G_2, which in turn activates P_2, etc., accounting for the alternate high and low spike sequences of the response. Circuits from other sources are able to activate the dendrites of P_1 and set up slow wave responses. B is such a circuit ending along the apical dendrite, C ending at its terminals and D ending on the basal dendrites. [From Clare & Bishop (37).]

ceive their effects either through cell body synapses or through their dendritic synapses. Activation through cell body synapses has been considered to require more than a single impulse. The required number may reach the cell body via several branches of one axon synapsing with the given cell body, or via several axons, or several impulses via one axon. The above mentioned authors deduce that when a cell body is intensely activated, its continued firing for a time after input has ceased depends upon the behavior of dendrites. These dendrites were activated by the cell

body and now in turn are reactivating the cell body or, as we might say, keeping it active. The dendritic contribution acts like a steady current stimulus to the cell body.

What has already been said in describing the initial spikes in the nerve has been interpreted as picturing a sequence of activations from lower levels in the cortex to the surface. A slow surface positive wave associated with the spikes is another component of the response. A negative wave immediately follows the positive one, and it is found in the lower third of the cortex, probably originating in layer IV. Prior to this negative wave, there is another negative wave. It occasionally shows up in a normal record and becomes the most conspicuous part of a record under strychninization in which case it occupies the whole depth of the cortex. Not only do the two negative waves seem to have different origins, but the late negative wave is believed to arise from cells other than those responsible for the positive components in the record. The first negative wave is attributed to conduction from cell bodies via apical dendrites toward the surface of the cortex. When not present in the normal record, its absence is a sign that such conduction is not induced by cortical stimulation. In weakly strychninized preparations, before any detectable effect is produced upon the surface positive components, the response represented by the negativity in question is made evident. When large positive responses are induced, they are followed immediately by the early negativity. Lower responses are characterized by a delay between the positive and negative waves. In these records, the two negative waves are distinguishable.

Bishop & Clare (20) interpret the early positive wave as representing the activity of the basal dendrites of the neurons of which the spikes indicate the activity of cell bodies. In figure 5 is presented the diagram given by Bishop & Clare to indicate the nature and origin of the five components of the cortical response of the cat. Figure 6 shows the findings of Bishop & O'Leary (25) on the rabbit. In both the cat and the rabbit, the final component of the response may repeat several times at the rate of the alpha rhythm.

Chang & Kaada (33) also analyzed the cortical response to optic nerve stimulation. The description is much like the one we have just given. Some of their interpretation was different from that of Bishop's laboratory. The authors did point out, however, that it is only the slow waves of the various components of the response that are reduced by agents affecting the cortex. This is in line with findings of Bishop's laboratory over the years.

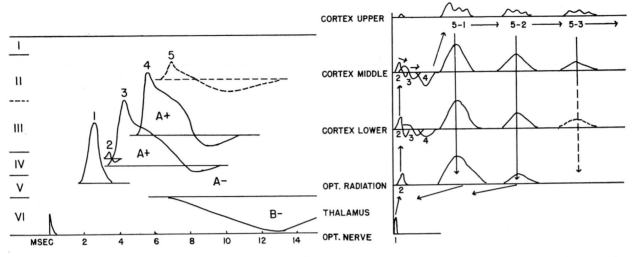

FIG. 5. *Left:* Tentative inferences concerning the origin of cortical responses drawn from experimental data. *Roman numerals at left* indicate conventional cortical layers and furnish a scale of depth. *Numerals 1 to 5* refer to cortical spikes; *A+* refers to underlying surface-positive waves; *B−* refers to late surface-negative wave which appears to arise from lower layers of cortex; *A−* represents the early surface-negative wave only occasionally seen well-developed in normal cortex, but large under strychnine where it becomes the most prominent potential element of the record. [From Bishop & Clare (20).]

FIG. 6. *Right:* Diagram of responses of the optic pathway of the rabbit. At least four elements of the response, following the activation of the optic nerve, can be distinguished in some records although any two adjacent elements, each presumably complex, may be confluent in a single response. The last of these four may be repeated several times at intervals of about 0.2 sec. following a single shock. There is a discharge of the corticofugal fibers during at least the first of these repetitive cortical discharges which appears to facilitate the thalamic neurons to a second discharge from the optic nerve. This is indicated by the *long vertical arrows* pointing downward. (*Abscissae,* time; *ordinates,* voltage.) [From Bishop & O'Leary (25).]

Chang attributes deflections 2, 3 and 4 in his record to the activities of three different geniculocortical pathways and suggests that they may conduct the respective impulses of trichromatic vision. He uses to support this interpretation the findings of Pieron (60) to the effect that latencies for seeing the three fundamental colors are different. This is thought to be evidence that the impulses signalling these travel at independent and different velocities.

We prefer to follow Bishop & Clare (19, 20, 23), Clare & Bishop (37) and Bishop & O'Leary (25, 26). Bishop & Clare (19) made it a point to check the findings of Chang & Kaada in regard to the kind of potentials found in the geniculocortical radiation and found only a single and rapidly conducting spike. When a later tract spike resulting from use of higher stimulus strengths is elicited, it represents impulses distributed mainly to the pulvinar, pretectal area and colliculus. Hence they conclude that all the successive spikes up to five in number, except the first one, that can be recorded from the cortex represent groups of neurons active within the cortex itself.

Bishop & Clare (22) stimulated the optic and parietal cortex in cats at various depths below the surface. They found that when the cortex is stimulated at the surface, the response obtained from two electrodes, one at the surface and the other at any depth, is a simple negative wave. When stimulation is presented below the surface, a diphasic wave with its initial phase surface-positive is obtained. When stimulation is presented half way or more down through the cortex, first a single and then two or three short spikes are manifested in the response. These are comparable to those elicited from activation of the radiation pathway. As the radiation terminals are approached, the complete cortical response to peripheral afferent stimulation is simulated. This procedure is thus a way of showing the transition from direct cortical stimulation to the indirect or peripheral.

The main difference between direct and indirect stimulation, in addition to the possible simultaneous activation by the direct stimulus of elements that respond successively to indirect stimulation, pertains

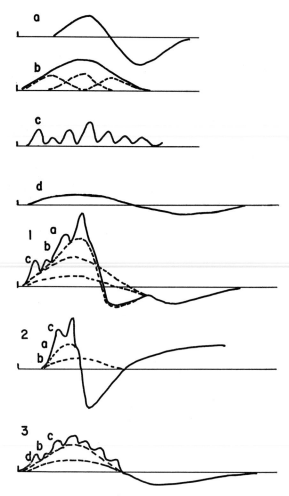

FIG. 7. Diagrammatic reconstruction of typical records, led from surface to white matter, by addition of what are inferred to be their chief potential components. *a.* Diphasic response assignable to conduction along apical dendrites when these only are activated below the surface of the cortex; negative phase is early negative component. *b.* Summation of surface-positive potentials inferred to be caused by activity of successively activated basal dendrites at successively higher levels of the cortex. *c.* Spike sequence detectable in responses to near-threshold stimulation of the optic nerve, later responses of which are usually obscured following stronger stimuli. *d.* Slow, presumably diphasic process arising from deeper layer of cortex, the second phase of which appears as a late negativity in many responses. *1.* From addition of all four of above components, a reconstruction of a record of response to optic nerve stimulation which shows considerable early negativity. *2.* Similar reconstruction of response to direct stimulation fairly deep in the cortex, but above layers V and VI, eliminating component *d*; negative phase of diphasic component *a* is exaggerated, as appears to be the case in records from direction stimulation, and the first spikes are telescoped. *3.* Reconstruction as in *1*, but for record showing minimal or no early negativity, from which therefore component *a* is eliminated. [From Bishop & Clare (22).]

to the way the apical dendrites behave (see fig. 7). When these structures are directly activated from the region of the neuron's cell bodies, the dendrites always conduct toward the surface of the cortex. When indirectly activated, by way of the radiation, this conduction often does not materialize, even following maximal optic nerve stimulation. It generally fails in connection with very weak stimulation. They deduced that in normal (nonsynchronous) activation conduction does not occur from cell body to apical dendrite. On the other hand, supposedly when a sufficient number of dendrites are activated, some kind of mutual facilitation provides for antidromic conduction.

These authors believe that when strychnine or any other convulsive drug is applied, the spike manifestation is primarily the indication of a conducted response in apical dendrites. The essence of the convulsive state lies both in the heightened irritability of the dendrites and in the mutual facilitation and activation to the point of a massive and well synchronized discharge.

The cortical response, recorded from leads from brain surface to white matter, is a composite (summation) of many primary sources of potential. The response to a single brief stimulus to the optic nerve producing a volley of impulses may produce a record that is an inadequate representation of cortical function in normal behavior. The brief stimulus produces a degree of synchronization that, in itself, is an artificial distribution of impulses from the start. This sort of volley could be considered more appropriate for producing convulsions than for the usual response (23). One of the justifications for this, however, aside from procedural necessity, is that the normal observer can make a visual discrimination from such stimuli which are shorter than might ordinarily be thought effective. Actually, for certain comparisons between perceptions very short pulses of photic stimulation are found usable and analytically helpful. Of course, none of such stimuli is actually as brief as the electric shocks used.

While the investigations of Bishop & Clare cited in this chapter indicate a general propagation of mass impulse from cell to cell upward from the neighborhood of the terminals of afferent fibers and apparently downward also to lower cortical layers, the normal stratification may be less sharp than has been described. Apparently, as more and more minute regions are explored with closely located microelectrodes, an increasing heterogeneity in the directions of propagated impulses becomes evident. Marshall (55) has shown a remarkable degree of temporal summation of the optic pathway to be recordable at the geniculate. Bishop & Clare (19, 20) have done likewise for the effects manifested at the cortex. The latter authors have pointed out that, with graded stimulation, a large effect reaching the geniculate neurons is required to produce even a threshold response in them. Furthermore, supraliminal activity of the afferent radiation is needed to produce a threshold response at the cortex. Increasing the strength of stimulation upward from this level prolongs the cortical response with its spikes and waves.

They also point out that weak stimulation is, in effect, the stimulation that fails to produce much spatial summation. In normal activity of the optic pathway, this lack of summation ought to be characteristic and, accordingly, lead to incomplete or brief cortical responses. But the fact that normal stimulation is characteristically prolonged rather than abbreviated to a very small fraction of a second, would provide for temporal summation that ought to compensate for the lack of the spatial variety. Relevant to this, Chang (32) has demonstrated the extreme effectiveness of 'potentiation' by photic stimulation of the retina of responses to individual brief stimuli at the geniculate. This steady photic stimulation seemed to maintain a raised level of excitation and this made incidental impingements more effective. We know that exceedingly weak excitation of the retina transmits something to the cortex. Not only does this slight effect get through to the cortex but certain effects from adjacent cortical areas are also produced in order that the activity in the visual cortex be given a context that would provide meaning for the terminal input. Bishop & Clare (23) describe well how the experimental conditions of the laboratory emphasize the effects of spatial interaction at the expense of what may occur via temporal interaction.

From their work and knowledge of cytoarchitecture, Bishop & Clare (23) depict the kind of interaction between cortical elements that would plausibly occur. The description is as follows. The elements in the cortical network can be supposed to constitute a system of both parallel and series connections. Each afferent channel (fiber) at any given synaptic level would be in connection with a number of postsynaptic elements, the arrangement involving definite overlapping. This would be the parallel set of connections. In addition to this, elements at each synaptic level send axons to the next higher level, and this provides

series connections. The authors suggest two further features of the system. Afferents from sources collateral to the visual projection system surely connect at some or all levels. What they call 'jumpers' may be involved. These are collaterals affecting more than a single synaptic level. An example may be the recurrent axons of the pyramidal cells. Some authors have reported afferent radiation fibers terminating not only at the usual layer IV but also at the two successive layers above it. Bishop & Clare inject an additional assumption, namely, that the mass of impulses traversing the one-step circuits are more effective than those involving a jump of two or three synapses. Perhaps the latter pathways should be considered to need assistance even to fire the synapses. The activity just suggested is pictured in figure 8, schematized in figure 9. The evidence for the scheme consists in a double series of spikes, ones of low amplitude alternating with ones of high amplitude when certain submaximal records are obtained from potentiometer leads and from electrodes subtending only small fractions of the total cortical depth. The timing of the spikes is about 1.4 msec. between those of the same series, and 0.7 msec. between any two of the alternate series. Bishop & Clare's suggestion is that this double series is made up of pyramidal cells alternating in discharge with short axon cells (Golgi II). Since the latter cells are oriented in random fashion, their potentials would tend to be registered by the leads as lower in amplitude. The pyramids extend in a single direction. This description differs from that of Thomas & Jenkner (66) in which records were interpreted as evidencing repetitive firing of the same cells.

ACTIVATION OF CORTEX BY STIMULATION OF RADIATION. Instead of initiating activity in the optic pathway by stimulating the optic nerve, it is possible to eliminate the geniculate and stimulate the radiation and note the cortical effects. By stimulating at this site, Bishop & Clare (23) found that the same cortical response was obtainable as when the cortex is stimulated through the geniculate. Certain features of cortical response must be independent of the geniculate cycle.

To single stimuli constant in intensity, the initial cortical response spike attributable to radiation axons was constant in amplitude. Throughout a period of a few milliseconds, the specific response to a second stimulus manifested only slight diminution of amplitude in its positive phase. The early negative wave of the second response was depressed nearly to the vanishing point, and this effect covered the whole de-

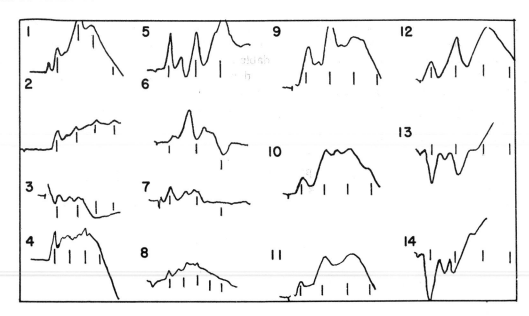

FIG. 8. Records of cat optic cortex to show minor spike series. *1.* Total cortex, stimulation of radiation above the geniculate. *2.* Same, but stimulation of the optic nerve; negativity failed to develop in a weak response, and between each pair of spikes there occurs a minor disturbance. *3.* Radiation stimulus; potentiometer balance to accentuate first minor spike. *4.* Like *2* (in a different cat), a submaximal response of total cortex thickness showing a succession of spikes at half the intervals of major sequence. *5.* Balanced record showing first and second minor spikes. *6* and *7.* Stimulus at the radiation, different fractions, similarly balanced. *5* to *7.* From same cat as *1* to *3.* *8.* Weak response like *4* (from a different cat), showing double sequence. Major spike intervals marked on *4* and *8* were obtained from other records of the respective preparations of form of record *1.* *9.* Total cortex, submaximal stimulus to radiation, like *2*, first and second minor spikes recorded. *10.* Balanced record accentuating second of these. *11.* Maximal response, lower amplification, same cat. *12.* Total cortex. *13.* Record as in *12* but balanced to accentuate the first and second minor spikes. *14.* Same as *13* but at half the stimulus strength and recorded at twice the amplification. [From Bishop & Clare (23).]

pression period. Negativity representing antidromic conduction via apical dendrites toward the cortical surface appears to be depressed more easily by prior activity than the other features of response.

In the period of depression, the base line slowly became negative during which responses to second stimuli were diminished. Following the depression, the positive phase of the specific cortical responses to second stimuli returned to normal amplitude.

Clare & Bishop, from these and other results, concluded that most of the features of the cortical response can be attributed to the excitability cycle of the cortex itself. On the basis of this information on the cortical cycle and Marshall's (55) analysis of the geniculate cycle, cortical responses to optic nerve stimulation were studied.

The degree of depression in the geniculate response to a second stimulus varies greatly from one animal to another as well as to varying intensities of optic nerve stimulation. Aside from the possibility that some

of the variation may be due to anesthesia differences, the variability may arise from the contextual or background excitation upon which the activation is superimposed.

If two stimuli are delivered very close together, a single supramaximal response may occur. Even when an initial maximal stimulus is involved, there seem to be a number of elements that were not activated but only possibly excited subliminally. These can be activated by the second stimulus, hence producing a supermaximal response to the paired shocks. This principle is more pronounced when the shocks are submaximal. The facilitation period soon ends and beyond it a period of depression ensues. It may last as long as 5 sec.

We may inject here the idea that this period may possibly bring about perceptual (visual) end results simulating adaptation in the retina. Some of the many visual experiments labeled those of adaptation have to do with short term effects. The various experiments of Schouten and Ornstein, and of Fry and colleagues are the ones referred to.

Clare & Bishop (34) noted that even during the deepest depression, a second stimulus may find that a first one, though maximal, may have left some elements that were not stimulated. This is as if at no time can any stimulus deliverable to the optic nerve fire all channels in the radiation pathway. The opposite extreme of this may take place. A second stimulus may cause a large geniculate response at any instant following a maximal first one. From this, they infer that many, though not all, elements represented in the first response are likewise involved in the second. When the second stimulus is made weaker, the second response manifests first a more marked diminution than when the first stimulus is applied alone. Ultimately, the response disappears completely at a stimulus strength otherwise able to elicit a large response if not preceded by an earlier stimulus. If, now, the first stimulus is diminished the response to the second grows, indicating the activation of elements not activated by the first stimulus.

ACTIVITY IN REGIONS OTHER THAN OPTIC CORTEX. Clare & Bishop (35) studied the activity of a portion of the lower half of the medial wall of the suprasylvian gyrus in the cat. This is an area responding only secondarily to activity in the striate cortex. They recorded from this area, first to optic nerve stimulation and second to direct electrical stimulation of points in the striate area itself.

They found that this region responds quite similarly to the striate area, but with an amplitude about one eighth or less. The response with all its components appears about 1 msec. later than does the striate response, when the activation is induced by the impulses in the optic nerve. The response to striate stimulation is late by only a very short conduction time. Experimentation showed that this region was fired by the discharge of the second major spike of the optic cortex response to optic nerve stimulation, which is to say, the activity of the pyramids in layer IV and probably in layer II. This activity probably represents an association area interrelating acoustic and optic activities.

Jasper et al. (48), utilizing repetitive activation producing local convulsive activity in the striate cortex of the monkey, did not disclose active pathways across the cortex from striate to parastriate and other areas. They did find activity transmitted to the pulvinar. When this region is activated by direct experimental

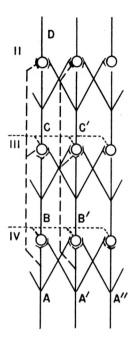

FIG. 9. Schematic diagram of cell network suggested by analysis of spike responses. *Solid lines:* A, afferent radiation; B to D, sequence of cell groups. Differences between short axon cells and pyramids are ignored in the interest of diagrammatic simplicity. *Dashed lines:* Collateral 'jumpers' impinging on cells falling later in sequence than next adjacent cell. *Dotted lines:* Afferents from sources other than geniculate. Axons leaving the cortex are omitted. Lines ending blindly indicate synaptic connections similar to those represented. This fundamental assumption is required to render the diagram functionally applicable; insofar as impulses at synapses are equivalent, a minimal number (more than one) is required to fire a cell at which they arrive simultaneously. From A simultaneous impulses arrive at B and C. B will be activated if A' fires with A, and C will not until activated by synchronous firing of B and B', or A and B, etc. Activated by a synchronous volley of impulses from radiation fibers, a simple succession of synchronized discharges should ensue. Activated by a barrage of impulses from same source, a much more scattered discharge should result, owing to arrival of impulses at each level over different paths (*solid* and *dashed lines*), and with different delays. Arrival of impulses from other sources (*dotted lines*) should further modulate the patterns. [From Bishop & Clare (23.)]

stimulation, it was found to activate areas of cortex alongside the optic cortex.

Marshall et al. (57), on the other hand, in exploring the cat's cortex found an area of the cortex overlapping with the acoustic cortex. From it, they were able to obtain response both to the acoustic and to optic stimuli. Bishop & Clare (24) found that the relay fibers responding to the second spike in the optic tract terminate in the thalamus.

Chang & Kaada (33) interpreted the three spikes of the cortical record following single shock stimulation as attributable to separate groups of fibers from the thalamus. They assume that each of the three spikes is followed in turn by a surface positive wave, but that these three longer-lasting effects sum in the record to a single surface positive wave. Bishop & Clare (19) re-examined the matter. To do this, they recorded the impulses in the radiation directly, following optic nerve stimulation, using diphasicity as a criterion for propagation in radiation fibers. It was from this technique that they found only one spike conducting in the radiation from geniculate to cortex and that this was the relay from the first spike in the optic tract prior to the geniculate.

There are possibly three subcortical pathways the activities of which directly or indirectly affect the optic cortex in a demonstrable way. There is, of course, the direct relay path, the optic pathway itself; the collateral path of the brain stem to association nuclei in the thalamus (65); and possibly a collateral circuit from thalamic relay nuclei to others in the thalamus to the cortex (38, 47).

Bishop & Clare (24) describe a bundle of fibers leaving the pulvinar and terminating in the temporal lobe of the cortex. When the optic nerve is stimulated, a weak and extended discharge is recorded in this bundle. The activation of the bundle was presumably from brain-stem or thalamic nuclei responding to optic tract activation. The exact origin of the discharge is not yet known, but its temporal features tally with the pretectal or lateral nucleus.

CORTICAL LOCALIZATION. Bartley (4), using photic stimulation of the retina in which two discrete retinal areas were tested, showed that one part of the cortex responded maximally to the activity in one retinal area A, and another part of the optic cortex responded maximally to another retinal area B. Stimulation of A would not usually activate the cortical area responding to B, and vice versa. When any sign of response under these conditions was detected, it was merely an irregular train of indefinite waves.

When A and B were stimulated simultaneously, the corresponding cortical areas did not manifest any summation. The responses were simply of the usual size. On the other hand, when the two stimuli were separated by an interval of 150 to 175 msec., the response to the second was enhanced; and if the interval was lengthened, a value could be found at which inhibition or depression of the second response was manifested.

At a retinal point C, intermediate between A and B, responses to both stimuli were recordable, both responses being discernible when enough temporal separation was allowed for the two response waves to be seen in two parts of the record. When simultaneous, the record representing the response to the two retinal areas was a single wave larger than either of the two responses individually recorded.

In one experiment, for instance, cortical point C later came to respond only to the stimulation of the second retinal area. At first, the two stimuli produced an enhanced result when simultaneous. When the two were separated by about 15 msec., the entire response almost disappeared. This continued to be the case as the separation was made considerably greater. It did not matter which of the two stimuli was delivered first. When finally the first retinal area failed to produce a response of its own, it still could augment B, when applied simultaneously, and reduce the size of B, when definitely out of phase with it. Still other examples of the interaction of cortical areas were obtained.

Since this material relates not only to cortical localization but also to the visual experience of movement, it will be discussed in the section on that subject.

PROPERTIES OF DENDRITES. Stimulation of the cortex at various depths has led Clare & Bishop (36, 37) to make certain inferences about the behavior of cortical dendrites. These were given in the section devoted to the cortical response. The following is a statement of the picture they paint of the behavior of the various parts of the neuron. In referring to intercortical paths that terminate only on apical dendrites of pyramidal cells, they found cases in which only the terminal portions near the cortical surface are activated. When the dendrites are activated indirectly by way of these paths, or directly by artificial stimuli, dendritic conduction is not of the all-or-none type. The conduction occurs more readily away from the cell body than in the reverse direction. Its rate is less than 1 m per sec.

After initial indirect activation, a stimulus finds the dendrites activatable at all times later than the absolutely refractory period of the axons involved. Following a 20 msec. facilitation period, depression sets in and the sign is positive. The authors inferred that, in general, the depression following neuron activation is attributable mainly to its dendrites. Apical dendrites manifest no refractoriness, and so later activation sums with the first. Continuous negativity may be perpetuated by repetitive stimulation. All that would be required to produce waves of potential of any temporal proportions would be modulation of stimulation of the dendrites. The authors suggest this principle in the production of the waves of the cortical record.

The influence of a neuron on its surrounds is brought about only through the impulses it causes to be discharged by the cell body into its axon. These effects are variously distributed via the ramification of axon branches. Activation of the neuron may occur via two avenues. The one is by way of cell-body synapses; the other by way of dendrite synapses. These two avenues ought to affect the pattern of axonal discharge from the cell.

The conditions applying to activation of the neuron via cell-body synapses are as follows. More than one impulse must be delivered to the cell body in order to activate it. When the discharge is once set up, it is of the all-or-none type. The impulses required for cell-body activation may arrive via a single axon branch, or via several of them, provided that they arrive within the required time limits.

As just implied, when once set into action, the cell body discharges once or more without receiving further activation. The authors (36, 37) infer that, when once a cell body is set into action, its action may be sustained by its own dendritic activity. They say that the cell body once sufficiently activated can activate its own dendrites, and they in turn can sustain activity in the cell body. The duration of the dendritic impulse seems to be of the order of 15 msec. This length of time provides for the dendrites acting like a steady-current stimulus to the cell body while it builds and discharges several times.

In cases of stimulation of dendrites only, the dendrites do not exhibit all-or-none conduction to the cell body which, therefore, would not be expected to be activated. It is presumed that some effect, nevertheless, would be exerted by dendrites upon the cell body by reason of the excited state of one and unexcited state of the other. The various excitations induced in dendrites would sum. The authors suppose it proble that, if the dendrites are excited from enough converging sources, they might begin to conduct and activate cell bodies. The role of the dendrite seems to be to raise the level of excitation of the cell body and thereby lower its threshold to influences arriving via axons impinging on it. The chief characteristic of dendritic action is its graded character in contrast to the all-or-none manifestations of cell body and axon. This provides for a great deal more flexibility and variety in action than a system limited to all-or-none activity.

VISUAL PHENOMENA TO BE EXPLAINED

Gross Response to Gross Intensity Relations

One of the major considerations in the study of vision and its mechanism is the question of what characteristics of vision require the striate cortex and what characteristics are demonstrable when the cortex is removed. It has been found that in some animals response to gross intensity relations in the stimulus field are re-

acted to in the absence of the occipital cortex. This is not at all surprising in the light of what we know about the bifurcation of the optic pathway, some fibers going to cortex and some going to motor centers that are subcortical, and in the light of our findings on pupillary responses which parallel Fechner's paradox (see the subsequent section on bilateral functions). It would seem possible that the structuring of response to gross flux differences could occur in the motor sphere and in the sensory spheres somewhat parallel to each other, according to our interpretation of the parallelism described in connection with Fechner's paradox. If one of the two channels were to be destroyed, the other might be able to mediate an end result. With the cortical channels destroyed, motor behavior of some effective kind might still be able to be exhibited. With the motor channel destroyed, one could experiment only on man, for he alone could tell whether experiential reactions to intensive features of stimulation were altered. We should not expect them to be in gross situations.

The following are some of the characteristics of the behavior of monkeys in response to visual stimuli when their occipital cortices are removed, eliminating the geniculostriate systems, as described by Klüver (50). In such animals, the eyelid reflex to photic stimulation is abolished permanently. The pupillary reflex to photic stimulation is retained, however. The sudden appearance of a stationary or moving photic source does not elicit a turning of the head or eyes towards it, although movements of the head and eyes are elicited by nonphotic stimuli.

Conjugate movements of the eyes are not destroyed; neither does destruction of the superior colliculi abolish such movements in response to stimulation of the cortical eye fields. Visual placing reactions are lost. Nevertheless, animals rarely bump into objects when they are left to themselves or are not excited.

When the bilaterally decorticate monkey is in a limited familiar habitat, its behavior in jumping, swinging and climbing is so readily executed that the unsuspecting observer would suppose the animal to be normal. Variation in the position of some familiar object in its cage elicits considerable fumbling until the animal's hands come into contact with it.

Such a monkey can respond discriminatively to the more or less intense of two photic sources whether they are indefinitely present or appear suddenly, or whether their presentation is simultaneous or successive. Responses to weak photic stimuli have demonstrated that the absolute threshold in the occipitally operated

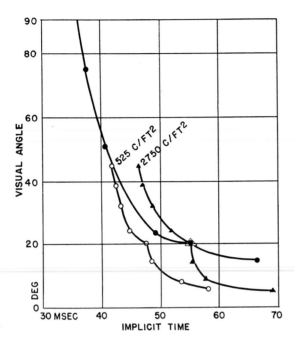

FIG. 10. The relation between implicit time of the rabbit's cortex and the visual angle of the target. Note break in curves at or near 20 degrees. This suggests that the increase in target size beyond this point does not involve further spatial summation at the retina, and that further reduction in implicit time is a continuation of the effect from increasing the intensity of incidental stray illumination of the retina. [From Bartley (3).]

monkey is not essentially different from that of the normal monkey or of man.

The decorticated monkey responds differentially to two equally intense and equally large targets if their distances from the eye are quite different. This is to say, the animal is able to use differences in total flux as a factor. This reaction, like the others in which familiarity with the stimulus is absent, has to be learned rather than immediately apprehended.

Responses to targets differing in shape, preoperatively established, are lost through the removal of the occipital lobes. Neither can new differential responses be learned if the new targets are compact and do not differ greatly in any dimensional respect. A decorticate animal, taught to respond to a target having a greater amount of flux, will continue to do so regardless of whether the flux is continuous or intermittent. Thus a source with an on-off rate of 4 per sec. is equivalent to a continuous one just so long as the total flux per second is the same.

Color vision is permanently lost in the decorticate animal. Klüver would say, from his many studies, that brightness vision is destroyed in the animal

without occipital cortices. What such an animal does is to respond on the basis of total flux.

Area of Target

When a photic source (target) subtending some known visual angle at the eye is used as a stimulus, the resulting response of an animal may be that which we could call the perception of brightness, or it may be simply the response to the stimulus as total flux. Brightness is the response to flux per unit area of target, and may be expressed as an experience or as a differential motor response on the basis of flux per unit area. It is not difficult to determine which of the two possible responses is being made when the human is a subject, and not too difficult when certain subhuman species are being tested. It is a little more uncertain when inferred in some cases such as from the cortical response to photic stimulation of the retina.

The experiments of Bartley (3) on manipulating the target area to measure the implicit time of the cortical response will be presented here. Implicit time is the time elapsing between the beginning of stimulus and the peak of the initial large wave of response. In this investigation, target area was varied from 1 to 90 degrees of visual angle. Throughout this range increments in visual angle reduced implicit time of the cortical response. One of the significant findings was that the relation between target area and implicit time was not a simple function throughout the range used as was the function of target intensity. To explain this, it was pointed out that the image of the target on the retina was not the only site of retinal stimulation. The retina as a whole received stray radiation as well as focused radiation. Thus the curve showing the relation between implicit time and stimulus area is a composite of the increasing spatial summation within the image and the increasing intensity of stray photic flux on the retina as a whole.

If the target area operates as just indicated, one ought not to expect the resulting curves relating area to implicit time and intensity to implicit time to coincide. Since spatial interaction and stimulus intensity are both varied when target area is manipulated and stimulus intensity alone when photic intensity is manipulated, the curve for the former would lie to the left of the latter. Thus, if interaction (spatial summation) would operate over part of the range of target manipulation and not over the whole range, then a break in the response curve would be expected. This is what resulted, as appears in figure 10. In all experiments in which the target was increased beyond about 20 degrees, a break in the curve appeared. The question of how far across the retina spatial summation may operate has been dealt with by Adrian and others. To say the least, spatial summation has come to be considered to possess definite limitations. The limiting subtense in this investigation seemed to be in the region of 20 degrees. The curve in each experiment shows that when targets of broad angular subtense are reduced in size, the implicit time is lengthened. This continues until the target is reduced to about 20 degrees and then, fairly quickly, implicit time becomes much shorter than expected for further target area reductions.

While the present investigation offered no way to eliminate the stimulation outside the retinal image, it did present evidence of the operation of two stimulus components (increase in image area and increase in stray radiation intensity). The same evidence demonstrated that the two factors operated at different rates. In the demonstration that two factors were in operation, the author showed intensity per unit area of retinal image was involved in determining implicit time. Thus it can be said it was not merely flux as such that produced the response as recorded but that the response was in a way a brightness response. While it was not doubted that the rabbit has brightness vision, it was a question from the beginning as to whether it could be demonstrated by the neurophysiological experiments of the kind being performed.

Brightness

The experience of brightness or a motor response based on the same principle is something different than the response to mere flux differences in two major portions of the photic field. Brightness is the result of manipulation of intensity per unit area of visual target. Hence an area can be seen as brighter than another even though the total flux of the first area is less than that of the second. This would be the case if the flux per unit area were greater. Klüver's monkeys, devoid of the geniculostriate system, gave no evidence of being able to do this. They could learn to distinguish between two equal-sized and equally intense targets when one was removed to a greater distance than the other, in which case its retinal image was smaller. A lesser total flux on the retina for it than for the near target was thus involved. Klüver states that he does not see any evidence in the behavior of cats and other animals that would indicate

that they can distinguish brightness at subcortical levels.

Electrophysiological experimentation upon the response of the optic pathway has not been of such a nature as to make the needed distinctions between response to total flux and to flux per unit area. One way to extract evidence on this point is to try to compare certain perceptual responses with the electrophysiological ones and make what deductions we can.

It now seems as though certain comparisons between brightness in perception and the amplitude of the response to specific brief stimulation can be made. In a later section we deal with brightness enhancement. In it we are comparing the experience that is evoked by steady continuous stimulation with one that is evoked by intermittent stimulation. So long as we keep the two areas equal, certain justifiable comparisons between the intensity needed in both cases to produce equally bright surfaces can be made. Many of the conditions for producing the various levels of effectiveness of the intermittent stimuli seem to be the very same as those similarly varying the amplitude of the cortical response to such stimuli.

Since continuous steady stimulation produces nothing in the extended record of cortical activity, the amplitude of which we can measure, we are prevented from making the same amplitude-brightness comparisons for steady photic impingements. With the concrete evidence at present available, we seem unable to go beyond the gross comparison just described. Perhaps we do not know enough regarding the measurement of steady states and the relation of steady states in one part of the cortex to those in others. Steady states seem, at the present state of our knowledge, to be quite dead and processless. To explain some things, however, they seem to be just what is required. (For further discussion of cortical response to continued peripheral stimulation, see the later section on brightness enhancement.)

Flicker and Fusion

When a series of photic pulses is delivered to the retina, the experience is flicker, except when the rate of delivery reaches a critical value. Obviously, the intact human and even certain subhuman species can distinguish between an intermittent and a steady photic source. This is true at least down to arthropods and crustaceans. How the discrimination is accomplished must differ in detail at the various phylogenetic levels. It would seem from Klüver's observations that a monkey, deprived of the geniculocortical apparatus, can not distinguish between a steady source and one the intermittency of which is as low as 4 cps, just so long as the total flux per unit time is the same in the two cases. Hence, although much has been said about the photochemical basis for flicker and its elimination, the ultimate crucial point of determination of critical flicker frequency (c.f.f.) appears to be in the cortex.

During flicker, the activity in the optic nerve waxes and wanes with sufficient amplitude and at such rates that the cortical activity may also vary in its temporal aspects in significant ways. It has been noted that whereas the response of the optic pathway up to and including the postsynaptic elements in the lateral geniculate body are brief and spike-like, response beyond this is somewhat extended in time and involves certain complexities absent in its precursors. This in itself would be a kind of evidence for believing that the cortex cannot respond at the same high rate as the peripheral mechanisms.

Be this as it may, a rate can be attained that results in the perception of uniform continuous light. The point at which this is reached (c.f.f.) is also known as the fusion point. All rates above this maintain fusion. This means that at the fusion point any temporal undulations in cortical activity that may occur are so slight as to be of no ultimate effect.

Talbot found that when fusion was reached, the level of perceived brightness of the light field was less than for a continuous and uniform stimulus of the same intensity. The effect is as if the input instead of being intermittent were uniform and spread evenly throughout the cycle. Thus, if the PCF (pulse-to-cycle-fraction) is one-half, the level of brightness is one-half. Whereas those devoted to photochemistry have shown how this effect might be attributed to the manner in which photochemical systems react to photic impingements, certain features of the behavior of the optic pathway have been overlooked. One of these is the way the neuroretina behaves. It rearranges the temporal distribution of the sense-cell discharge effects of the retina. Since we are not dealing primarily with peripheral responses, we cannot go into this matter further. Needless to say, the cortex must take a hand in even the determination of critical flicker frequency and the Talbot effect (7, 8).

Since the Talbot effect represents the simplest possible smoothing-out result from a waxing and waning stimulus, we can suppose that the cortex operates on the simplest principle in that respect.

The following investigations in which cortical response was elicited by stimulation of the retina rather than electrical stimulation of the optic nerve was used to give some information relative to the mechanisms at work in flicker and fusion. Bartley (3–5) measured the latency of the cortical response to various forms of photic stimulation. One of the factors varied was the duration of a 'dark' interval. When these intervals were very short, the off-response to the termination of the photic pulse and the on-response to the beginning of the succeeding pulse were both evident in the record when the interval was as short as 12 msec. When this interval was shorter than the implicit time of the off-response, the resumption of stimulation did not preclude the appearance of the off-response, nor the appearance of the on-response to the beginning of the next pulse. Since 12 msec. compare to the interval between pulses when pulse frequency is 40 per sec., if the pulse-to-cycle fraction is one-half, it would seem as though under the conditions dealt with, Bartley was reaching the point called critical flicker frequency in human flicker experiments.

The implicit times of the on- and off-responses are not equivalent. It would seem from the results (4, 5) that for similar conditions the implicit times of the on-response are shorter than those for the off-response. Thus, as the 'dark' interval in the cycle is made shorter and shorter, the off-response to the termination of the one pulse and the on-response to the beginning of the succeeding pulse finally becomes concurrent. This might be one factor in bringing about fusion in flicker experiments, since in some way these two responses might counteract each other at some final level in the cortex.

That the two forms of response (on and off) could be concurrent is to be understood from the finding of Bartley that the two responses occupy separate channels all the way from the retina to the cortex. One of the evidences for this was the finding that an on-response can follow an off-response as closely as 12 or fewer msec., whereas an on-response to a second stimulus cannot follow unless the two are at least 80 msec. apart. Electrograms of the retina have been interpreted as showing that a second pulse presented shortly following the termination of the first will inhibit the off-response to the first. Bartley (4) showed in a number of ways that phenomena that were detectable in the cortical record are not discernible in the electroretinogram recorded under the same conditions. It would thus seem logical to rely on the cortical record in cases where differential responses in the electroretinogram fail to show up.

Bartley also measured the implicit time of cortical on-response when duration was the variable (2) and

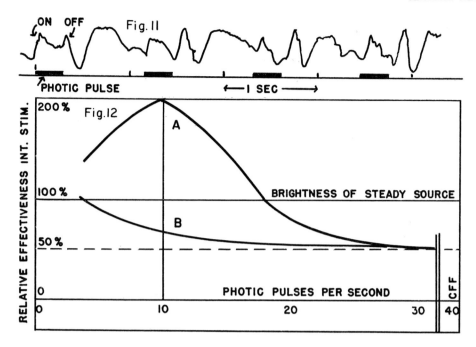

FIG. 11. The cortical response of the rabbit to intermittent stimulation of the eye in which the photic pulse occupied one quarter of the cycle. Note responses both to onset and to termination of the photic pulse. [From Bartley (9).]

FIG. 12. Brightness enhancement, the greater relative effectiveness of intermittent stimulation than of steady stimulation at low photic pulse rates. This is shown in *curve A* but not in *curve B*. *B* shows the effect under some conditions of weak stimulation. [From Bartley (7).]

when area of the target was a variable (3). For variation in duration of photic pulse to affect implicit time, it must be as short as 4 or 5 msec. for targets with luminosities as great as 2400 candles per square foot, and which subtend 6 or 7 degrees. Increasing area reduced implicit time and thus would be expected to work in the direction of raising critical flicker frequency.

Jasper (46) recorded potentials from the occipital cortex in man following pulse rates of 55 to 60 per sec., and thus was near the critical flicker frequency under the conditions. This was not interpreted as being a demonstration of driving the cortical alpha rhythm beyond its normal 8 to 13 per sec. frequency. He found that the amplitude of the waves at 20 per sec. was about one-half of what it was at 10 per sec., and waves at 40 per sec. were about one-fourth as high as those at 10 per sec. A further very crucial observation also supporting his interpretation of the impossibility of driving the cortex was the following. As the stimulus rate was slowly increased, there were stages at which the waves would undergo what he called desynchronization. For example, at frequencies of from 14 to 15 per sec., this would happen and the result would in-

clude a shift in amplitude so that at from 18 to 20 per sec., the amplitude would drop to one-half the height up to that time.

Halstead and colleagues (44, 45, 67) reported that although the dominant brain waves (alpha) in the monkey could be 'driven' up to rates comparable to critical flicker frequency only, the pathway prior to the cortex could follow input intermittencies beyond the c.f.f. Obviously, the records of Halstead and colleagues manifest waves at the rates indicated and thus, in essence, tally with those of Jasper. Whether this is driving depends upon one's definition of the term. A standard definition has not yet been put into the literature.

The foregoing tallies with Bartley's observations and his alternation of response theory (which is considered in the section on brightness enhancement). For example, one observation (3) was that if the rate of intermittent retinal stimulation suddenly delivered to the retina was definitely above 5 per sec. (the rabbit's alpha rate), the following would occur. A large cortical response to the first pulse would appear. No response to the second pulse would result. Then, the responses to the following few pulses would wax and wane or be entirely absent in random order. Finally, all pulses would be responded to by equal waves but of a reduced size, the amplitude in keeping with the rate. If the rate was high the amplitude would be low, and vice versa. This irregular initial period was looked upon as a reorganization period during which redistribution of the various retina-to-cortex channels responsive to successive stimuli was brought about so that all stimuli were responded to.

Bartley (9) obtained a very definite cortical off-response as well as an on-response in the rabbit when using a slow photic pulse rate and a pulse-to-cycle-fraction of 1 to 4. The results are pictured in figure 11. In it, the shape and temporal characteristic of the wave following the off-response would suggest that it is the usual final slow component of a typical cortical response or, in other words, an alpha wave. If this be the case, then it is suggested that the off-response may institute an alpha series in the same sense as it can be said that a brief electric stimulus to the optic nerve may do so. The fact that an off-response is at all discernible in the cortical record makes the supposition that the off-response plays a role in controlling critical flicker frequency all the more plausible.

Brightness Enhancement

When intermittent photic stimulation is used at rates below those producing the experience of steady light (i.e. at subfusional pulse frequencies), it may become more effective than steady stimulation in producing brightness. This increased effectiveness we call 'brightness enhancement' which is pictured in figure 12. With intense pulses, effects such as shown in

curve *A* will occur. With weaker photic radiation, results shown in curve *B* will occur. While it is to be taken for granted that photochemical processes in sense cells play their usual roles in determining the magnitude of afferent input over the optic nerve, they do not account for the nature of brightness enhancement. We must look to neurophysiological processes for this.

It will be seen from the diagram in figure 12 that the effectiveness of intermittent stimulation increases as pulse rate is reduced, and that under some conditions it becomes maximum in the human in the region of 10 pulses per sec. This region is the peak and still slower rates result in reduced effectivenesses. One might well start off with these findings and make various manipulations of pulse rate, pulse-to-cycle-fraction, pulse intensity, etc., to further one's understanding of brightness enhancement in general. The study of brightness enhancement has not proceeded on this basis. The work that has provided the impetus for brightness enhancement investigation lay in the findings of neurophysiology of the optic pathway. On this account, it may well seem much clearer to the reader were we to describe behavior of the visual response apparatus before continuing to deal with brightness enhancement.

Bishop and Bartley, in their study of cortical response to precise stimulation of the optic nerve in the rabbit, disclosed a number of temporal and intensive features of the behavior of the cortex. Bishop (18) first demonstrated the rhythmicity for the cortex in relation to peripheral stimulation. Stimuli presented to the optic nerve at intervals without regard to cortical events produced random-sized responses. He showed that stimuli could be tuned to the cortex, so that all responses would be essentially the same; either all small, all large or all medium-sized, depending upon the phase to which the input was tuned. He showed that if the first stimulus in a train was maximal, that it would, in effect, 'drive' the cortex. This is to say, it would be able to start off a sequence of cortical consequences having the properties of the natural rhythm but shifted somewhat in time from it. Subsequent closely-following stimuli would obey the laws of the rhythmicity but according to the shifted timing. Bartley (4) mapped the nature of the rhythm by using paired stimuli systematically varied in their separation. He found that the size of a second maximal stimulus to the optic nerve did not produce a cortical response the same size as the first until the temporal interval became equal to the cortical period found by the means earlier discovered. The findings of Bartley

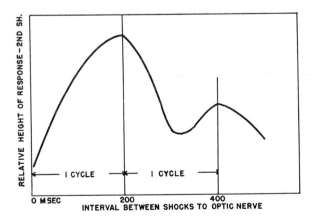

FIG. 13. The cycle of responsiveness of the optic cortex of the rabbit as determined by paired stimulation. [From Bartley (4).]

(4) are shown in figure 13, in which it is indicated that the rhythm could be followed through at least about two cycles. Since maximal stimuli were used, it was inferred that the behavior of the optic nerve as a whole represented the way the single parallel channels in it react. This deduction rested upon the idea that all parallel channels in the nerve were activated simultaneously. This cycle represented the rhythm of single channels while being the rhythmicity of the system as a whole under these conditions.

The more specific portion of the evoked response to brief stimulation is followed by a long-lasting surface-negative potential (14). It is during this time that a second brief peripheral impingement evokes either no response or else one of reduced amplitude (25). The repetition of the cycle implied here may be demonstrated at the frequency of the spontaneous alpha sequence. Use of repetitive stimulation at twice alpha frequency (4) showed that an original inability of the system to respond at intervals half the alpha value slowly changed into submaximal response following each stimulus. The shift was as if the channels available for response became differently distributed in time, so that finally part were ready to respond at the presentation of one stimulus and the other part at the presentation of the succeeding stimulus. Stimulation at higher multiples of the alpha rate resulted in what appeared to be a further redistribution, such that each stimulus was responded to in some degree but, of course, more weakly than when rates were slower (see fig. 14).

This phenomenon could be expected to have a parallel in perceptual response. Whereas a certain rate of intermittent stimulation (c.f.f.) is required to obliterate flicker fully once the visual system is exposed to a considerable number of photic pulses, an even slower rate may fail to be responded to as individual pulses at the very onset of the stimulus train. Wilkinson (68) studied this problem and found that

the rate at which the first few pulses were seen as individual flashes or produced flicker was much below the rate at which the pulses could still produce definite flicker after the train had progressed for awhile. The perceptual responses to the first few pulses manifested some of essentially the same irregularity as was manifested in the cortical response (4) under the same conditions.

In some cases, as in the rabbit, the long-lasting surface-negative wave is replaced by a series of briefer waves (25). Something like this was observed in the cat by Bishop & O'Leary (26). Prior to the onset of the depression following a specific cortical response, it was found that a short period of facilitation to a second stimulus occurs in the radiation response (27). For example, as the strength of an initial stimulus is increased, the response of the radiation increases more rapidly than does the tract response. With a second stimulus, it and the first, being 'maximal' for the tract, may elicit a larger radiation response than a single stimulus. Even below maximal, a second stimulus is typically more effective than the first when falling within the short time limits implicit. This indicates that spatial and temporal summation are operative in the geniculate even with 'maximal stimuli.' This, although indubitable, is inconsistent with the idea of a one-to-one fiber channel from retina to cortex in the functional sense. It is consistent with the theory of partially shifted overlap suggested by Lorente de Nó (53). Similar results were reported by Marshall & Talbot (56).

Facilitation may occur also at the cortical level. The matter is far more complex, however, for at least two reasons. In the first place, the type of facilitation just described for the geniculate occurs at each cortical synapse. That is, facilitation builds up step by step at each synapse in the sequence, even though the facilitation at each synapse in the cortex may be no greater than the geniculate synapse facilitation. The

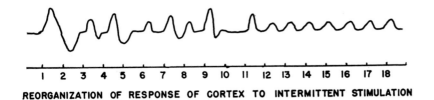

REORGANIZATION OF RESPONSE OF CORTEX TO INTERMITTENT STIMULATION

FIG. 14. The response of the optic cortex of the rabbit to rapidly repeated stimulation of the optic nerve. At first the pulses are delivered more frequently than the cortex is able to respond. Later to this same rate, the several channels capable of being activated become distributed in time in such a way that no single channel needs to respond to successive pulses for there to be a cortical response. [From Bartley (4).]

second reason is that the size of the cortical response varies independently from the amplitude of the response of the geniculate, owing to the phase of the spontaneous alpha rhythm that is involved at the time. The greater responses are elicitable during the final surface-positive phase of the cycle (18).

The depression phase following activation of a pathway may be a more general thing than merely a phenomenon of the optic pathway. Such a phenomenon was dealt with by Pitts (61) in respiratory function. Phasic fluctuations of response to a second click stimulus have been observed in the auditory tract by Rosenzweig (63).

As an extension of the description of the phasic nature of cortical activity both spontaneous and evoked, and thus as a furtherance of the understanding of the mechanisms that possibly underlie brightness enhancement, we shall describe the changes in spontaneous activity of the cortex following a single optic nerve stimulus.

The spontaneous picture in the rabbit and cat differs (21). Whereas in the rabbit extended periods of alpha wave activity are typical, in the cat similarly dealt with one may find short trains of alpha waves, but more often this is replaced by a continuous rapid sequence of low-amplitude waves varying in frequency from 20 to 80 per sec. This sort of sequence tends to appear during the intervals between the 'spindles' of alpha wave activity.

If stimulation is presented during this fast-wave activity, the cortex undergoes a characteristic alteration. The waves just mentioned disappear and slowly come back over a period of from 100 to 200 msec. At the end of this period, the amplitude of these waves may be far above normal in some cases. Sometimes the waves may coalesce into longer waves as if two or more had summed. These may be of a higher amplitude and are frequently diphasic. The whole sequence, in amplitude variation and in temporal features, often presents the over-all envelope of the typical alpha wave.

In the rabbit also, the typical alpha wave may be replaced at times by three or more peaks with the same over-all duration as the alpha wave (26). The differences in the two animals presumably consists in a smoother summation in the one than the other, rather than in the presence or absence of the alpha cycle. The depression cycle in both animals seems to be a recovery from the peripheral input and a return to spontaneous activity.

When submaximal rather than maximal stimuli are used, the response to a second stimulus of a pair is less depressed. The spontaneous activity is also less depressed. The amplitude of the specific response during the depression period is a function of depression in both the geniculate and cortex, but the recovery in the cortex seems to be dependent upon events in the cortex alone.

The basic picture of how the overall systems must react to intermittent inputs was summarized by Bartley (6) in what he called the 'alternation of response' theory. The essentials of the theory are as follows. a) There is a fixed number of parallel channels in the optic pathway from eye to brain. b) These channels can be activated simultaneously or they can be activated according to the various temporal distributions. c) Certain maximally intense, but abrupt and brief, stimuli may activate all available channels while submaximal stimuli do not. d) Any given single channel from eye to cortex cannot be reactivated until it has recovered. This requires about 0.2 sec. for the rabbit and 0.1 sec. for man. e) The period represented in the cycle is of the same length as the animal's alpha rhythm. In fact, it is the alpha rhythm, as was indicated in the work of Bartley (15). f) Brief stimuli delivered at the alpha rate would be expected to produce maximal brightness effects. g) Not only must the stimuli be intense (maximal or in the upper range of intensity) but they must be relatively brief, else they would involve not only the initial activation of channels but also the reactivation of the same channels or the activation of still others, tending to spread the over-all activity out in time and reduce the number of channels participating in the responses at any single instant. h) Since the available channels, as has already been said, may be activated not only in unison but also in various temporal distributions, various patterns of the latter would result in corresponding levels of sensory brightness. This is to say that with continuous stimulation the activity of the available channels becomes uniformly distributed throughout the cycle. There would be as many channels going into action at all instants as are going into rest. This would provide for continuous uniform visual (sensory) response to continuous illumination. In fact, sensory continuity and steadiness may result before the full uniformity of channel activity is achieved.

Bartley (11, 12, 13, 16, 17) and colleagues have performed a number of sensory experiments, and in all cases the expectations of the alternation of response theory have been met.

It may be said, then, that in brightness enhancement and in the group of findings in regard to the way in which the optic pathway is able to react to timing of input, we have one of the more fully documented sets of the relationship between sensory behavior (perception) and neurophysiology of the central nervous system.

In the foregoing, it has been shown that stimulus conditions for obtaining various brightnesses and those for obtaining various amplitudes of cortical response are the same, but much still remains to be worked out. For example, the comparison seems to pertain to the quantitative features of continuous over-all brightness and the amplitude of a momentary feature of cortical activity, namely the specific brief response. As yet, there is no characteristic of recorded electrical response of the cortex to indicate the level of cortical activity in response to a continued peripheral stimulus. It is as if we are confined to dealing exclusively with momentary and brief effects in the central nervous system. They can be dealt with because they represent an observable change from previous or from subsequent activity as a reference. Continued stimulation does not result in any characteristics of prolonged cortical activity that lend themselves to useful quantification. One approach to this is, of course, the comparison of the appearance of the ongoing cortical activity during stimulation with activity in the absence of an intended experimental input. This, as was implied, does not give anything to quantify in a direct way. The chief difference between cortical records in the two sets of conditions seems to be the disappearance of certain forms of wave-like activity in the 'active' record. Various studies on 'blocking' the alpha rhythm are relevant here (64). They were also relevant in the earlier section on brightness.

Jasper & Cruikshank (49) studied the electro-encephalograms of human subjects exposed to a cross-target in a room in which this was the only photic stimulation. They ascertained the change in the cortical activity picture to the sudden exposure to the target and the subsequent sequence of changes that followed. They found the following: a) an occasional and varied short detectable cortical effect arising in a few milliseconds easily confused midst the features of the alpha rhythm; b) 'blocking' of the alpha rhythm after a latency of 160 to 520 msec.; c) gradual irregular recovery of the alpha rhythm if the stimulus continued for more than 3 to 5 sec.; d) the emergence of a second dubious positive effect that, since it followed the termination of exposure to the target, could be called an 'off' effect; e) sometimes a second 'blocking,' this time of the recovered rhythmic activity, following cessation of the stimulus; f) a continued depression or 'blocking' effect during the existence of reported

afterimages; g) a partial recovery toward the usual amplitude of alpha waves between successive afterimages; and h) a final total recovery of the normal alpha activity following the final afterimage. This recovery typically would begin as a train of small waves of higher frequency than those of the alpha rhythm. The amplitude of the alpha waves might even increase for a while before the full prior *status quo* would be reached. Here we have a set of results seeming to bear upon several matters: the nature of the cortical activity during continued stimulation, and the fact that one can detect cortical response during afterimages as being different than when they are absent. Others have been interested in the latency of the blocking effect, but we shall forego listing the authors or the exact latencies found.

To further the understanding of what constitutes the cortical response to continued stimulation, certain reference conditions for inactivity will have to be discovered. From these comparisons can be made. One of the possible leads in this direction may be the study of dendritic behavior. We have progressed from the exclusive concern with and ability to record spike-like, momentary, conducted all-or-none activity. The activity of dendrites seems to fall into the category of sustained potentials (36, 37). While sustained states seem to be 'inactive' ones, since we cannot detect them as ongoing processes, this static aspect may be only the over-all aspect of the whole complex of activities that is in operation, thus for us an 'illusion.'

When we realize that what is happening in any mass of central nervous tissue is a combination of various orders of process, having many origins and sustaining conditions, we may find added use, in our concept, for sustained states. They may be the substrata for the interplay of more highly particularized items of activity that occur differently and play different roles during one level of sustained potential than during another. It thus might become possible to conceive of the level of sustained dendritic potential in crucial areas as being the correlate of the experiential or motor outcome in the ultimate response called perceptual behavior.

In essence, the idea of a sustained state, varying in significance or potency according to its level, is nothing new. We have long had it in the central excitatory state and in the central inhibitory state of Sherrington. But, to understand the sustained state as being inherent in a neuron rather than in some sort of a chemical matrix outside it is very different. In dendritic activity, we may now have a basis for sustained potentials as an activity of neurons themselves.

Bilateral Functions

In viewing a single visual target, both sides of the optic pathway are generally involved. When corresponding portions of the two retinas receive photic radiation from this target, the results are as follows. If the photic flux is unequal to the two retinas, the surface seen will, of course, be singular but will not look as bright as though viewed by the eye receiving the greater radiation. That is, summation does not take place. This is Fechner's paradox. If, instead, equal radiation is received by both eyes, the result is summative. The brightness is greater than when one or the other eye views the target alone. Fechner did not make a full study of this matter. DeSilva & Bartley (39), and Fry & Bartley (41) manipulated stimulation so as to provide curves showing this function under a wide range of conditions (see fig. 15). Bartley (10) later studied a correlate phenomenon of Fechner's paradox, namely the way the pupil behaves under comparable conditions of stimulation. The same pattern of quantitative response was demonstrated. This is to say that if one eye alone is presented successive increments of photic radiation, the pupil constricts step by step. The same occurs in the unstimulated eye. Then, if the flux to the first eye is held at the final high level and step by step the flux to the second eye is increased from zero upward to the levelf for the first eye, at first, the paradoxical reversal o effect occurs. Instead of constricting further, the two pupils begin to dilate. They continue to do so as further steps of increment are added to the second eye. Finally, the paradox reaches a peak and further increments begin to cause constriction. When finally both eyes are receiving equal amounts of radiation, the two

pupils have constricted more than when the final level of radiation was directed to the one eye alone. This is, in quantitative pattern, the very thing that happens in perception.

It was also shown that the essentials of the paradox are manifested when noncorresponding points of the two eyes are involved and finally when two targets of differing intensity are imaged on two parts of a single retina.

It is not too startling to find the parallel between the perceptual and the motor phenomena when once it is remembered that the two end results stem from the same input, namely the discharge of the optic nerve. The same pattern of input must go to the geniculate and to the superior colliculus. In our illustration we have two simple aspects of the respective categories of response. Were we to try to compare other aspects of motion and perception (experience), we would be hard put to find modes of quantification. That is to say, it would be very difficult, if not impossible, to find convincing quantitative parallels in limb movement and in the concurrent perception of color or position of a seen object. Yet there must be rational (lawful) relations between what an organism sees and where it reaches to grasp the object seen.

Binocular relations of other sorts are brought out in other perceptual phenomena. If two fields differing in texture or color as seen separately are presented, one to the one eye and the other to the second eye simultaneously, the result may not be a fused single stable field but rather a single field that alternates in texture or color. This is called binocular rivalry. Some times this rivalry in lightness is replaced by a curious effect called 'luster.' Further analysis shows this luster to be a transparent light field behind which is a dark field.

FIG. 15. Binocular summation and subtraction in response to photic stimulation. The subtractive effect is Fechner's paradox. *Top line* indicates the seen brightness when both eyes are presented equal intensities. *Horizontal line* ('one eye alone') indicates the seen brightness when only one eye is exposed to the target. The *curve* shows the relative seen brightnesses when one eye is exposed to the full intensity of the target and the second eye is exposed to various fractions of full intensity shown on the horizontal axis. [From Da Silva & Bartley (39).]

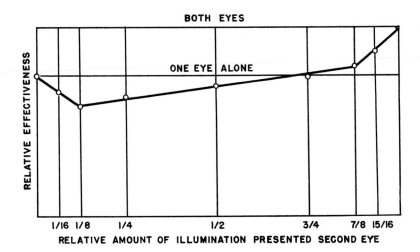

It is as if one can be seen through the other. This concurrent existence of the two fields is best brought out when one uses a temporal alternation of the targets for the two fields. Thus when the over-all binocular target is made up of a steady annulus surrounding an intermittent disk, luster eventuates when the intensity of the annulus is one-half that of the positive phase of the disk. Whether it shows up or whether one sees simply light and dark alternating is dependent partly upon the rate of stimulus intermittency. As one slowly shifts the rate, one can watch the phenomenon emerge.

Rivalry can occur even when the target viewed as first described constitutes only a small part of the visual field. Rivalry in this case occurs when the field surrounding the target is of medium brightness and the target seen via one eye is white and via the other is black. Apparently the neural contour processes for the two targets interact in some way that involves some sort of alternation, thus bringing about the rivalry (8).

It has been shown by Graham (43) that the absolute light threshold is no lower for the two eyes than for one. This finding, though it might be unexpected, is in line with the supposition of summation at a common central region, as found by Fry & Bartley (41). The latter pointed out that two thresholds must be recognized: *a*) the minimal radiation required to activate either of the two converging pathways, and *b*) the minimal frequency of impulses reaching a common central region to produce postsynaptic activity. The perceptual end result does not occur unless one or the other of the two pathways delivers the threshold frequency. If in either one of the two the minimum is reached, there is no lowering of the first threshold by adding a stream of impulses via the other converging pathway.

Brightness Contrast

Whereas the foregoing illustration (Fechner's paradox and its pupillary analogue) was meant to demonstrate intensive effects based upon the interaction of the two sides of the visual apparatus, it also exemplifies brightness contrast inasmuch as it has to do with adjacent as well as corresponding areas of the two retinas and with adjacent portions of a single retina. Brightness contrast pertains to adjacent portions of the visual target, but to explain it relevant adjacent portions of the visual apparatus must be dealt with. It would seem that whatever neural mechanism will account for Fechner's paradox will go a long way in accounting for brightness contrast.

Visual Movement

Brightness contrast, a spatial phenomenon, is a configurational one. The same principle would seem to apply to both perceptual and neurophysiological phenomena described in temporal terms. One order of temporal phenomena in perception is the experience of movement. Very often the crucial neural conditions underlying movement have been thought to be retinal and neuroretinal. These cannot be given space here. Be it sufficient to say that in this category lie some of the conditions for apparent visual movement. Apparent movement is defined as phenomenal (experienced) movement that is elicited by visual targets that do not undergo displacement. Real movement is the movement stemming from targets that do undergo displacement.

Despite all the patterning produced in the retina, there is still much left for the cortex to do. The cortex probably plays a part in making the end product resulting from optic nerve discharge under conditions of target displacement often very similar to that obtained with target fixity. We know that the perceptual end results, in some cases, are indistinguishable.

Since in beta movement (the form of apparent movement in which two spatially discrete targets are used) there is a temporal gap between the two portions of stimulation, the cortex was very definitely brought in by early workers to account for it. Supposedly some sort of spatial-temporal coalescence of the afferent discharge into the cortex was finally achieved in cortical activity much like that produced by the peripheral input from real-movement targets. An early form was called a short-circuit theory, but never has a theory been worked out to the point of being convincing. It would seem that in the recent establishment of the nature of dendrite activity, we have an essential tool for this purpose. Until recently, any theorist wishing to account for certain more persistent effects (those lasting up to seconds, minutes or longer) had to rely upon purely hypothetical processes such as those described by Köhler (51) or upon reverberative circuits. Now it would seem that with the demonstration that some tissue does maintain potential and not merely conduct potential via a fleeting impulse, certain more slowly changing active relations between tissue elements or central nervous regions are made more concretely thinkable.

The investigation (4) described in an earlier section on cortical localization is relevant here. Actually, the stimulus conditions used in this investigation were the very ones that produce apparent visual movement in the human subject, namely the exposure of two restricted local targets separated by an interspace and presented in sequence. To go with this target arrangement from conditions that are not productive of apparent movement to those that are is simply to adjust timing and spatial separation for the given intensity used (Korte's laws). In this investigation timing and spatial separation were manipulated, and it was demonstrated that cortical responses to two separate targets could be recorded at two separate cortical locations in the rabbit and that various interaction effects were obtainable when space separations were reduced and when the delivery of the stimuli was made close together in time. The elements of a study of apparent movement were demonstrated. The investigation did not go far enough to determine the conditions under which the rabbit responds to two stimuli as to a single moving target. A conditioning experiment would have been necessary for this. Thus, if the rabbit could be 'conditioned to apparent movement,' the cortical experiments, carried further than Bartley (4) was able to do, could possibly have given a picture of some of the cortical events involved in seeing movement.

Color Vision

No consideration of vision should bypass what is called color vision, the differential response to the spectrum. In discussing color vision, there is very often some confusion as to what is really meant, owing to the fact that the stimulus differentiators may lie not only at the periphery but also in the central nervous system, and owing to the possibility of setting up different criteria for color response. There are actually six items to keep in mind and make clear in a discussion of color vision. They will be mentioned here to set matters straight. *a*) There is the question of the existence of color sense cells and the number of kinds of such cells in the species in question. *b*) Often this discussion takes the form of whether some of the cells are differentially sensitive to the spectrum and some not sensitive (cones and rods). All of these matters have been studied on an anatomical basis. *c*) There is the question of directly or indirectly recording electrical responses to answer the questions in *a* and *b*. *d*) There is the problem of obtaining differential conditioning of overt responses to the spectrum in the species in question. *e*) In human subjects, there is the study of color experience. *f*) There is the realization of the possibility that any species might possess a well-developed spectral analyzer of which it can make

little or no use. For example, the eye of a rabbit or a cat or a monkey may be quite like that of a human, but this does not mean that in any or all of these cases there is the same color experience. In fact, we know nothing of subhuman experience in any case.

For our purposes here, we want to know the role played by central mechanisms in either muscular differential response to the spectrum or in the production of various color experiences. Obviously, even though we credit the retina in both its photochemical and neural mechanisms as being a keen analyzer and thus providing the central nervous system with a differentiated message, the central apparatus must also, in a way, be an analyzer, else it cannot make differential use of the message. The requirement of an analyzer applies both to the center and the periphery. This is made apparent to those possibly more difficult to convince by the fact that color experiences can be predictably elicited by nonspectral stimuli. Certain alternations in intensity of stimulation as produced by a rotating disk with high- and low-reflecting ('white' and 'black') portions are sufficient to produce color experience. The central apparatus responds to this nonspectral presentation in the same fashion as to certain spectral presentations.

The foregoing phenomena taken together, or many of them taken alone, lead us to the conclusion that for much of what we call vision we must include the central mechanisms that are not visual, else we have nothing that can be called vision. It is customary to call the surrounding areas association areas, but we see that their function is not to associate rigid units of activity each of which plays a single role but rather to participate in the overall differentiation of activity we call response.

Cortical as well as retinal responses to spectral stimulation (200 msec. in length) have been recorded by Lennox & Madsen (52). Simultaneous records from the cortex and retina were compared in wave form, amplitude and latency. The spectral points involved were 'blue' (445 mμ); 'green' (560 mμ); 'yellow' (575 mμ); and 'red' (620 mμ).

The recordable threshold of the cortex lay about one logarithm below the retinal threshold. The on-response of the cortical potential consisted in a diphasic wave, initially surface-positive. At low and moderate intensities, the positive response was double. At high intensities the initial phases contained four or five spikelets.

Increasing stimulus intensity decreased the latency of both the retinal and cortical responses and increased their amplitudes. The spectral composition of the stimulus affected shape, amplitude and latency. The two components of the positive response were most marked in response to 575 and 620 mμ stimuli. The amplitude of the cortical response to the 445 mμ stimulus was greater than to the 560 mμ stimulus when in the retina the two were the same. The latency of the cortical response to the 445 mμ stimulus was longer than for the greater wavelength when under the same circumstances the latencies were the same at the retina. The final conclusion was to the effect that variation in the cortical responses were not solely determined at the periphery.

The same two authors, Madsen & Lennox (54), studied cortical response to spectral stimuli still further. In this study, the anterior, mid and posterior optic cortices were compared by means of simultaneous recording. The double positive on-response mentioned earlier was found in the posterior and mid cortex. The response from the anterior cortex was single. The maximum of the wave corresponded to the latency of the second peak of the double waves found in mid cortex within a value of from 2 to 5 msec. Latencies on the anterior cortex were significantly longer than in posterior cortex, and the rate of reduction in latency with increase in intensity was more rapid. The authors attributed the difference in latency between the anterior and posterior cortex to the absence of the first positive peak of the on-response in the anterior cortex.

The latency of responses to the 445 mμ stimulus was shorter at the anterior position and that for red was longer than at the posterior position. The amplitude for the cortical response to the 445 mμ stimulus was relatively greater at the anterior than at the posterior cortical position.

The types of cortical responses obtained by these authors indicates that the cortex of the cat does respond differentially to spectral stimulation. In direct contrast to this, we have recent evidence for thinking that the over-all response of the cat (its overt behavior) does not utilize the differentials of cortical response just described. Meyer et al. (58) were unable to condition the cat differentially to the photic radiation passed by three Wratten filters (23A, 'red'), (47, 'blue') and (61, 'green'). One thousand trials were used for each of the comparisons of filter 23A with 61, and 47 with 61. As a check, a pure intensity comparison was used and conditioning was accomplished in 200 trials. This led the authors to believe that the cat does not possess color vision.

The fact that differential cortical responses to spectral stimulation can be detected and yet the same species cannot be taught to respond differentially in its overt behavior is a concrete example of the principle which we stated earlier in this section. It is an example of why we need to be quite definitive in what we mean when we use the term color vision.

To clarify matters, one had better never speak of color vision in subhuman species. If the animals in question can be trained to respond differentially to various parts of the spectrum, we can call the behavior overt spectral vision. Color vision is a term that should be reserved for the description of human experience. If neurophysiological experiments indicate differential response to the spectrum by any or all sense cells, then it should simply be called spectral response. Vision is not a term to apply to sense cell behavior. Thus we have three categories of behavior to talk about, spectral response, spectral vision and color vision, and it is in the interests of clarity that we use three terms.

REFERENCES

1. ADRIAN, E. C. AND G. MORUZZI. *J. Physiol.* 97: 153, 1939.
2. BARTLEY, S. H. *Am. J. Physiol.* 108: 387, 1934.
3. BARTLEY, S. H. *Am. J. Physiol.* 110: 666, 1935.
4. BARTLEY, S. H. *J. Cell. & Comp. Physiol.* 8: 41, 1936.
5. BARTLEY, S. H. *Am. J. Physiol.* 117: 338, 1936.
6. BARTLEY, S. H. *Proc. Soc. Exper. Biol. & Med.* 38: 535, 1938.
7. BARTLEY, S. H. *Psychol. Rev.* 46: 337, 1939.
8. BARTLEY, S. H. *J. Exper. Psychol.* 25: 462, 1939.
9. BARTLEY, S. H. *J. Exper. Psychol.* 27: 624, 1940.
10. BARTLEY, S. H. *J. Exper. Psychol.* 32: 110, 1943.
11. BARTLEY, S. H. *J. Psychol.* 32: 47, 1951.
12. BARTLEY, S. H. *J. Psychol.* 32: 217, 1951.
13. BARTLEY, S. H. *J. Psychol.* 34: 165, 1952.
14. BARTLEY, S. H. AND G. H. BISHOP. *Am. J. Physiol.* 103: 159, 1933.
15. BARTLEY, S. H., J. O'LEARY AND G. H. BISHOP. *Am. J. Physiol.* 120: 604, 1937.
16. BARTLEY, S. H., G. PACZEWITZ AND E. VALSI. *J. Psychol.* In press.
17. BARTLEY, S. H. AND F. R. WILKINSON. *J. Psychol.* 33: 301, 1952.
18. BISHOP, G. H. *Am. J. Physiol.* 103: 213, 1933.
19. BISHOP, G. H. AND M. CLARE. *J. Neurophysiol.* 14: 497, 1951.
20. BISHOP, G. H. AND M. H. CLARE. *J. Neurophysiol.* 15: 201, 1952.
21. BISHOP, G. H. AND M. H. CLARE. *Electroencephalog. & Clin. Neurophysiol.* 4: 321, 1952.
22. BISHOP, G. H. AND M. H. CLARE. *J. Neurophysiol.* 16: 1, 1953.

23. Bishop, G. H. and M. H. Clare. *J. Neurophysiol.* 16: 490, 1953.
24. Bishop, G. H. and M. H. Clare. *J. Comp. Neurol.* 103: 269, 1955.
25. Bishop, G. H. and J. O'Leary *Am. J. Physiol.* 117: 292, 1936.
26. Bishop, G. H. and J. O'Leary. *J. Neurophysiol.* 1: 391, 1938.
27. Bishop, G. H. and J. O'Leary. *J. Neurophysiol.* 3: 308, 1940.
28. Bishop, G. H. and J. O'Leary. *J. Cell. & Comp. Physiol.* 19: 315, 1942.
29. Bishop, P. O., D. Jeremy and J. B. McLeod. *J. Neurophysiol.* 16: 437, 1953.
30. Bishop, P. O. and J. B. McLeod. *J. Neurophysiol.* 17: 387, 1954.
31. Bremer, F. *Electroencephalog. & Clin. Neurophysiol.* 1: 177, 1949.
32. Chang, H. T. *J. Neurophysiol.* 15: 5, 1952.
33. Chang, H. T. and B. Kaada. *J. Neurophysiol.* 13: 305, 1950.
34. Clare, M. H. and G. H. Bishop. *Electroencephalog. & Clin. Neurophysiol.* 4: 311, 1952.
35. Clare, M. H. and G. H. Bishop. *J. Neurophysiol.* 17: 271, 1954.
36. Clare, M. H. and G. H. Bishop. *Electroencephalog. & Clin. Neurophysiol.* 7: 85, 1955.
37. Clare, M. H. and G. H. Bishop. *Am. J. Psychiat.* 111: 818, 1955.
38. Dempsey, E. W., R. S. Morison and B. R. Morison. *Am. J. Physiol.* 131: 718, 1941.
39. DeSilva, H. R. and S. H. Bartley. *Brit. J. Psychol.* 20: 241, 1930.
40. Eccles, J. C. *Electroencephalog. & Clin. Neurophysiol.* 3: 449, 1951.
41. Fry, G. A. and S. H. Bartley. *Am. J. Ophth.* 16: 687, 1933.
42. Gastaut, H., Y. A. Roger, J. Coriol and R. Naguet. *Electroencephalog. & Clin. Neurophysiol.* 3: 401, 1951.
43. Graham, C. H. *J. genet. Psychol.* 3: 492, 1930.
44. Halstead, W. C., G. W. Knox and A. E. Walker. *J. Neurophysiol.* 5: 349, 1942.
45. Halstead, W. C., G. W. Knox, J. I. Woolf and A. E. Walker. *J. Neurophysiol.* 5: 483, 1942.
46. Jasper, H. H. *XI Congr. Internat. Psychol., Rapp. et Communic.* 226, 1937.
47. Jasper, H. H. *Electroencephalog. & Clin. Neurophysiol.* 1: 405, 1949.
48. Jasper, H. H., C. Ajmone-Marsan and J. Stoll. *A.M.A. Arch. Neurol. & Psychiat.* 67: 155, 1952.
49. Jasper, H. H. and R. M. Cruikshank. *J. genet. Psychol.* 17: 29, 1937.
50. Klüver, H. *Biol. Symp.* 7: 253, 1942.
51. Köhler, W. *Dynamics in Psychology.* New York: Liveright, 1940.
52. Lennox, M. A. and A. Madsen. *J. Neurophysiol.* 18: 413, 1955.
53. Lorente de Nó, R. *J. Psychol. u. Neurol.* 46: 113, 1934.
54. Madsen, A. and M. A. Lennox. *J. Neurophysiol.* 18: 574, 1955.
55. Marshall, W. H. *J. Neurophysiol.* 12: 277, 1949.
56. Marshall, W. H. and S. A. Talbot. *Am. J. Physiol.* 129: 417, 1940.
57. Marshall, W. H., S. A. Talbot and H. W. Ades. *J. Neurophysiol.* 6: 1, 1942.
58. Meyer, D. R., R. C. Miles and P. Ratoosh. *J. Neurophysiol.* 17: 289, 1954.
59. O'Leary, J. L. *J. Comp. Neurol.* 62: 117, 1935.
60. Pieron, H. *Compt. rend. Soc. de biol.* 111: 380, 1932.
61. Pitts, R. F. *J. Neurophysiol.* 6: 439, 1943.
62. Rioch, D. McK. *J. Comp. Neurol.* 49: 1, 1929.
63. Rosenzweig, M. R. *Am. J. Physiol.* 163: 746, 1950.
64. Stamm, J. S. *Electroencephalog. & Clin. Neurophysiol.* 4: 61, 1952.
65. Starzl, T. E. and H. W. Magoun. *J. Neurophysiol.* 14: 133, 1951.
66. Thomas, L. B. and F. L. Jenkner. *Tr. Am. Neurol. A.* 77: 47, 1952.
67. Walker, A. E., J. T. Woolf, W. C. Halstead and T. J. Case. *J. Neurophysiol.* 6: 253, 1943.
68. Wilkinson, F. R. *The Organization of the Visual Response* (Thesis). East Lansing, Michigan: Michigan State University, 1955.

CHAPTER XXXI

Central control of receptors and sensory transmission systems

ROBERT B. LIVINGSTON | *National Institute of Mental Health and National Institute of Neurological Diseases and Blindness, National Institutes of Health, Bethesda, Maryland*

CHAPTER CONTENTS

IT IS A VERY OLD NOTION, which needs often to be repeated, that our sensory pathways are subject to error and hence may yield distorted sensations. This idea was succinctly stated three centuries ago by Descartes;[1] in point of fact, these essentially neurophysiological considerations provided the cornerstone of his philosophy of universal doubt. Nonetheless, little attention has been given to the possibility that the central nervous system may itself be able to exercise some measure of direct control over the traffic of nerve impulses ascending sensory pathways.

Recent experimental evidence indicates that such central influences do exist and can modify sensory input patterns all the way from receptors to whatever end point is chosen—from peripheral sense organs to at least the sensory cortex. Much additional study needs to be given to particular features of this mechanism, but already the implications are far-reaching.

Sensory impulses can apparently be interfered with at their point of origin and at synaptic junctions as a result of activity taking place in certain remote parts

[1] "I have learned from some persons whose arms or legs have been cut off, that they sometimes seemed to feel pain in the part which had been amputated, which made me think I could not be quite confident that it was a certain member which pained me, even although I felt pain in it. . . . In the same way, when I feel pain in my foot, my knowledge of physics teaches me that this sensation is communicated by means of nerves dispersed through the foot, which being extended like cords from there to the brain, when they are affected in the foot, at the same time affect the inmost portion of the brain which is their extremity and place of origin, and there excite a sensation of pain represented as existing in the foot. . . . If there is any cause which excites, not in the foot but in some part of the nerves which are extended between the foot and the brain, or even in the brain itself, the same action which usually is produced when the foot is detrimentally affected, pain will be experienced as though it were in the foot." RENÉ DESCARTES, *Discourse on Method*, 1637.

of the nervous system. This interference involves an active process that is usually inhibitory. In the waking state, the sensory pathways seem ordinarily to be under a tonic inhibitory influence; evidently a good deal of the potential content of sensory experience is being continuously reduced or eliminated within the initial stages of sensory integration. Inasmuch as activity along sensory pathways appears to be modifiable to some extent according to an animal's environmental experience and according to its overtly expressed direction of attention, the interference with sensory transmission appears to be regulatory and to constitute a goal-seeking physiological mechanism.

These findings call for some adjustment of current physiological, psychological and philosophical concepts relating to perception. Most such concepts have been based upon *a*) physiological findings derived from an examination of anesthetized animals, findings which usually reveal the activities of only a few parts of the nervous system at a time, and *b*) behavioral evidence obtained with waking unanesthetized animals in which the nervous system is treated as a whole. Some degree of closure between these two experimental realms of science was apparently achieved 30 years ago. Adrian and other physiologists discovered that the strength of a stimulus necessary to elicit action currents in peripheral sensory nerves of anesthetized animals was approximately equal to that found by psychologists for threshold perception in attentive human subjects (4, chapter VI). Comparable stimuli, again in anesthetized animals, were then found to yield evoked cortical responses that were localized to certain 'sensory receiving' areas of the cortical mantle (59). Detailed analysis in anesthetized animals of activity taking place within various relay stations between the peripheral nerves and the cortex revealed that the spinal (80), brain-stem (60) and thalamic synaptic relays (69) were quite reliable in their transmission of evoked signals.

Naturally such findings led to an interpretation that the sensory nerves and the central ascending paths reliably convey to the cortex whatever messages are generated by the sensory end organs. It was argued that only when the impulses reach the cortex are they then accessible to such psychological factors as habituation, focus of attention, suggestion, etc., long known to intervene in sensory perception. The cortex was believed to be only the first stage in the integration of sensation from sense data (7, pp. 39, 40, 62). This view fitted well with the traditional conception of hierarchical supremacy of the cortex—notions derived partly from the recognition of its topmost loca-

tion, enormous areal extent, anatomical complexity, phylogenetic recency, etc., and partly from the momentum of theoretical conceptions of Pavlov and others who assigned most psychological functions to the cortex (64).

Yet for more than 50 years anatomists have recognized that certain nervous pathways enter sensory nuclei and relay stations from above, and that nearly all sensory systems have efferent fibers passing from the neuraxis to receptor organs. When the individual anatomical features of these centrifugal projections are grouped together, they appear to constitute a series of descending neuronal cascades which conceivably might have an influence upon ascending sensory impulses. These descending and efferent sensory projections have usually been considered piecemeal and few conceptual generalizations are available. Perhaps the most prophetic of these appears in an interpretive discussion of neuropathology by Brouwer in 1933: "... We accept that there is also a centrifugal side in the process of sensation, of vision, of hearing, and so on. I believe that a further analysis of these descending tracts to pure sensory centers will also help physiologists and psychologists to understand some of their experiences" (10, p. 627).

CONTROL OF RECEPTOR ACTIVITY

Sympathetic Influence on Touch Receptors

Single touch receptor activity in isolated skin areas of the frog can be facilitated by stimulation of the sympathetic nerve supply to that region (56). Activity in these receptors can also be facilitated by the local application of epinephrine or norepinephrine, or by introducing these hormones into the circulation. Thus, individual receptors are evidently subject to generalized as well as local sympathetic influences. Sympathetic nerve influences have already been shown to be facilitatory to transmission across the neuromuscular junction (see 56 for references); their effects on touch receptor activity therefore appear to be parallel and to place the peripheral sensory as well as peripheral motor portions of the reflex arc under some degree of central control. By virtue of these influences, the reflex arcs relating to touch should no longer be considered such simple units of neurophysiological and behavioral systems. Since apparently all sensory receptors receive sympathetic fibers, it is perhaps not too extravagant a generalization to suppose that all of them may be found susceptible to this kind of central interference.

Efferent Control of Invertebrate Stretch Receptors

Another central control mechanism relating to peripheral afferent nerve discharge has been demonstrated in crustacean stretch receptors by Kuffler & Eyzaguirre (49). They have shown that the stretch-sensitive muscle afferent in the crayfish tail is itself innervated by an efferent inhibitory nerve fiber which can diminish or arrest the activity of the afferent fiber. The afferent nerve discharge that is ordinarily elicited by a given muscle stretch can be decreased or obliterated depending on the rate and number of impulses delivered to the inhibitory fiber. Presumably this sort of control can be effected by central ganglia in the intact crayfish.

Efferent Control of Mammalian Stretch Receptors

The rate of discharge of the large mammalian muscle-spindle afferent apparently depends upon the degree of tension developed by a small intrafusal muscle fiber contained within the spindle. This intrafusal fiber can be passively stretched or relaxed along with lengthening or shortening of the surrounding skeletal muscle. In addition, it has its own motor control by way of the small ventral root gamma efferents (40, 50–52). Thus, the discharge of spindle afferents, which play such an important role in proprioception, is determined both by the state of the skeletal muscle and by the rate of discharge of the gamma efferents.

The gamma efferents enable the spindle afferents to have a full range of discharge rates for any given muscle length, the end result being a better accommodation of different loads and rates of movements. It can readily be appreciated that this peripheral feedback or loop-gain system provides an exceedingly important measure of central control over sensory input.

Remote Central Control of Stretch Receptors

Granit & Kaada (30) discovered that the gamma efferents controlling muscle-spindle afferents are in turn regulated by a number of remote central structures. As shown in figure 1, muscle-spindle discharges are readily accelerated by stimulating the mesencephalic and diencephalic reticular formation—the brain-stem facilitatory region of Magoun (28, 30). When these structures are activated, a muscle-spindle afferent will continue to show facilitation for up to half a minute or more following discontinuation of the brain-stem excitation. Similar but less uniform

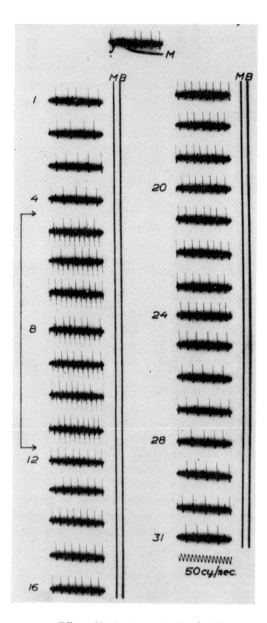

FIG. 1. Effect of brain-stem reticular (midbrain tegmentum) stimulation on a gastrocnemius muscle spindle afferent discharge. *Above:* Contraction of 134 gm at low myograph sensitivity to demonstrate silent period of the large muscle spindle afferent unit. Initial tension throughout, 52 gm. Light Dial-chloralose anesthesia. *1* to *4:* Control before reticular stimulation. *5* to *11:* During stimulation. *12* to *31:* After stimulation. Consecutive sweeps at 2 sec. intervals. Myograph (*M*) alongside film. Distance *M-B* (base line) corresponds to 10 gm. Note that stimulation of the brain-stem reticular formation, without altering the muscle tension, accelerates the spindle's rate of firing and that this effect persists more than half a minute. [From Granit & Kaada (30).]

effects are elicited by stimulating the motor cortex, the anterior lobe of the cerebellum, the habenular complex and the head of the caudate nucleus. Inhibition of spindle activity is readily elicited by stimulation of the medial part of the bulbar reticular formation—the brain-stem inhibitory region of Magoun —and by excitation of the anterior lobe of the cerebellum (17; 28, p. 103; 30). Eldred has painstakingly extended the exploration and analysis of these remote central spindle afferent control mechanisms (16).

Granit & Kaada showed that gamma efferent activity is facilitated by reticular stimulation at strengths considerably below those which will elicit a discharge of the large skeletal-muscle (alpha) motoneurons. Hence, motor facilitation by brain-stem mechanisms appears to take place first through an activation of the gamma efferents controlling sensory input from the muscle spindles, and then by both the direct descending influences which act upon the large motoneurons and the continuing indirect influence of brain-stem control over muscle-spindle afferent discharges which act back upon the same motor units. As in other sensory control systems, the gamma efferents appear to be normally under a tonic inhibitory influence from above.

In each example, the frog tactile receptor, the muscle stretch receptor in crustacea and the mammalian muscle-spindle afferent, there is evidence for efferent neuronal systems which exercise an important controlling effect upon the initiation of afferent nerve impulses. In the case of the muscle spindle, at least, the efferent fibers are in turn under the control of certain remote central mechanisms. The principle of central control of afferent activity is equally applicable to the special senses.

CONTROL OF ACTIVITY IN SPECIAL SENSE AFFERENTS

Auditory Nerve Activity

For many years a compact bundle of fibers traveling with the eighth cranial nerve pair was considered to be afferent (65, vol. I, figs. 319, 324). In a series of critical anatomical studies, Rasmussen proved that these are really efferent fibers. They arise in the vicinity of the superior olive and terminate within the contralateral cochlea (67, 68). Rasmussen's efferent fibers appear to make contact with the afferent auditory fibers as these pass from the hair cells to the spiral ganglion. Some of the efferents may pass directly to the inner hair cells but this point is un-

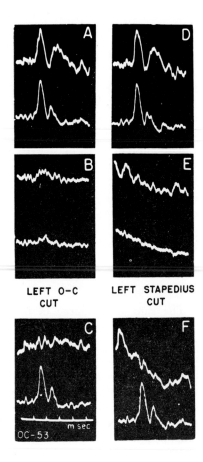

FIG. 2. Suppression of auditory nerve response by olivocochlear and stapedius mechanisms. *A.* Control auditory nerve responses to click applied to each ear, right recording above left. *B.* Suppression of both left and right responses with shocks at 100 per sec. delivered to the decussation of the olivocochlear bundle in the floor of the fourth ventricle. This high frequency of stimulation tetanizes the stapedius muscle so as to eliminate interference from that source (see *E* below). *C.* Following transection of the left olivocochlear bundle, the suppression shown in *B* occurs only on the right. *D.* Another control response showing that lesion made between *B* and *C* has not interfered with auditory nerve response from either ear. *E.* Single shocks to same medullary location 13 msec. prior to test clicks suppress the eighth nerve responses from either ear (stapedius effect). *F.* Following cutting of the tendon of left stapedius muscle the suppression shown in *E* is seen only on the right. [From Galambos (26).]

settled. Galambos has recently shown, as illustrated in figure 2, that stimulation of the medulla in the region of the superior olive, and along the course of the olivocochlear bundle, will cause a suppression of auditory nerve responses elicited by standard click stimulation (26). Such suppression does not occur following division of the olivocochlear bundle at a point peripheral to the locus of stimulation. The suppression reappears if the stimulus is reapplied peripherally to the point of division of the bundle. Rasmussen's efferent fibers are therefore evidently capable of suppressing activity in auditory afferents either at or near the point of impulse origin within the cochlea.

Optic Nerve Activity

Granit, by stimulating the midbrain tegmentum, induced a lasting augmentation of the frequency of firing of individual ganglion cells in the retina, whether the latter were spontaneously active or were made active by test flash illumination (29). Occasionally, from the same general region, inhibition is elicited. Both the facilitatory and inhibitory effects appear to be conveyed by fine efferent fibers described by Ramón y Cajal and others (e.g. 65, vol. II, fig. 211, p. 366). Dodt, by stimulating the optic tract in rabbits, elicited small, late-appearing retinal spikes which are unlike antidromic spikes; these he interpreted as due to impulses conveyed along the centrifugal fibers to the retina (15). The exact central origin of such centrifugal fibers is not yet determined. These efferent effects upon retinal activity are most readily initiated by stimulation of the reticular formation of the midbrain and are reliably obtained only in animals lacking central anesthesia (29, 39).

Olfactory Bulb Activity

The anterior commissure contains efferent fibers, described by Ramón y Cajal and others (e.g. 65, vol. II, p. 664, figs. 423–425; 66, p. 12), which apparently arise in basal rhinencephalic areas and pass out to the olfactory bulb. These and similar fibers coming from the opposite bulb are believed to terminate on granule cells and in the periventricular and external plexiform layers. In this location they have access to the synaptic junction between receptor-cell terminals and bulbar neurons. Kerr & Hagbarth (46) studied the effects of exciting this centrifugal system upon the electrical activity of the olfactory bulb, both in the resting state and following olfactory stimulation. Excitation of the anterior commissure, the prepyriform cortex, the cortical amygdaloid nucleus and the olfactory tubercle induces a diminution of olfactory-bulb activity. Efferent fibers apparently exercise a tonic inhibitory influence upon the olfactory bulb since the addition of central anesthesia or a surgical division of the anterior commissure is followed by an augmentation of olfactory-bulb activity.

CONTROL OF CENTRAL SENSORY RELAYS

Spinal Ascending Relays

Magoun observed in 1950 (58) that the "study of descending influences of the reticular formation has so far been preoccupied entirely with the pronounced effects exerted upon the discharge of spinal motor neurons. It would be of considerable interest to know whether or not these generalized reticulospinal influences are capable also of altering the transmission of afferent impulses within the cord." The effect of centrifugal influences upon the synaptic relay of impulses from dorsal root fibers to second order ascending neurons was first tested by Hagbarth & Kerr in 1954 (31). Using cats immobilized with curare and lacking central anesthesia, they applied test shocks to individual lumbosacral dorsal roots and analyzed the effects of intervening (conditioning) excitation applied elsewhere in the central nervous system. They found that stimulation in either the inhibitory or facilitatory zones of the reticular formation diminishes or abolishes responses being conveyed within both the ventral and lateral funiculi of the spinal cord. The relayed response in the dorsal columns is also affected although the primary dorsal column spike, representing conduction along primary afferent fibers, is unaltered. Stimulation of a number of other parts of the central nervous system, the sensorimotor cortex, the second somatic sensory area, the anterior part of the cingulate gyrus and the anterior vermis of the cerebellum, has similar but less pronounced effects. An example of this is shown in figure 3.

When central anesthetics are administered, there is an augmentation in amplitude of the relayed response as compared to preanesthetic levels (fig. 4). Additionally, if the spinal cord is divided in the cervical region in animals without central anesthesia, a similar 'release' appears, resulting in an increase of amplitude in the second order neuron responses to a standard dorsal-root volley (31). Evidently in anesthetized animals the high amplitude of sensory-evoked responses recorded within the classical sensory pathways is due to the anesthetic having interrupted a tonic descending inhibitory influence.

Dorsal Column and Other Bulbar Relays

Excitation of the brain-stem reticular formation induces a prolonged depression of transmission through the dorsal column relay nuclei (39, 71). A moderately intense 1-sec. stimulation causes a rapid onset and slow decay of depression, affecting impulses being relayed to the internal arcuate fibers. The initial spike of impulses arriving via the dorsal columns is not affected. Not only is the relayed response of the dorsal column nuclei modified, but the background activity of reticular neurons at the same level is affected, although with a different time course, by the same conditioning reticular stimulation. On the introduction of central anesthetics or the production of a mid-line pontine lesion, there is a notable increase in amplitude of evoked responses passing through the dorsal-column nuclei, indicating that ordinarily there

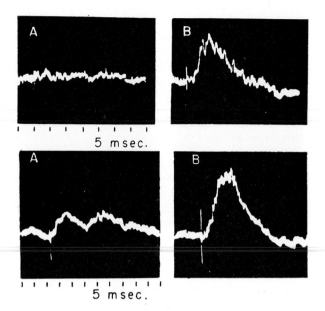

FIG. 4. 'Release' of tonic descending inhibitory influences by anesthesia and by cord transection. Curarized cats without central anesthesia. *Top row*: Left ventral column response to feeble L7 dorsal root stimulation (*A*) before, and (*B*) after injection of 45 mg chloralose per kg. *Bottom row*: Effect of high cord section on left ventral column response. *A* before, and *B* 1 hr. after transection. In each experiment the stimulus intensity and location were kept constant; the dorsal columns had been transected at the L4 level. [From Hagbarth & Kerr (31).]

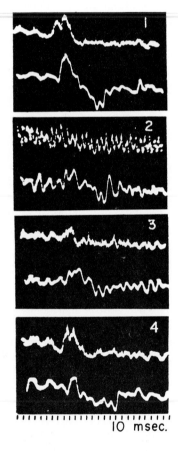

FIG. 3. Cerebellar influences on spinal sensory transmission. Responses are elicited by stimulation of the right dorsal root L7, and recorded from the left ventral column of the spinal cord (*upper beam*) and left sensory cortex (*lower beam*). Intercurrent stimulation is applied to the ventral part of the anterior vermis of the cerebellum. Test responses recorded (*1*) prior to cerebellar stimulation, (*2*) during cerebellar stimulation, (*3*) 1 sec. and (*4*) 3 sec. after termination of cerebellar stimulation. Dorsal columns of spinal cord were sectioned at L4. [From Hagbarth & Kerr (31).]

is a tonic descending inhibitory influence acting upon this relay station.

Impulses being relayed through the spinal root of the trigeminal nerve in response to test shocks applied to the ophthalmic branch of the trigeminal are also diminished by stimulation of the brain-stem reticular formation (36). Sensory-evoked responses in the adjacent reticular formation are sometimes depressed for more than a minute even though the trigeminal nuclear response is only transiently affected. Stimulation of the sensorimotor cortex will also bring about active inhibition of the trigeminal synaptic relay, as appears in figure 5.

Jouvet & Desmedt report that stimulation of the mesencephalic reticular formation will cause a marked reduction in amplitude of auditory-evoked responses recorded from the dorsal cochlear nucleus (44). This occurs even when the electrical responses recorded from the round window in response to the same sensory stimuli are unaffected. They conclude that

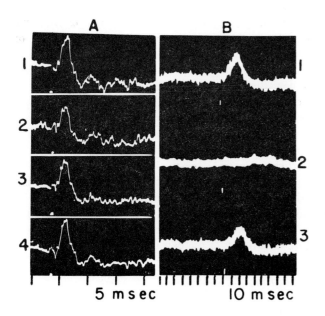

FIG. 5. Sensorimotor cortex influence on trigeminal relay and brain-stem reticular formation responses to infraorbital nerve stimulation. Curarized cats without central anesthesia. *A.* Bulbar recording from left spinal fifth tract. Afferent trigeminal response following stimulation of the left infraorbital nerve (*1*) before, (*2*) during, (*3*) 3 sec. after and (*4*) 6 sec. after repetitive stimulation of right sensorimotor cortex (100 per sec. for 3 sec.). In this record the trigeminal response is composed mainly of a secondary wave, the primary spike being hardly visible as an initial notch. *B.* Recording from the right side of the midbrain reticular formation. Reticular response evoked by infraorbital stimulation (*1*) before, (*2*) 13 sec. after and (*3*) about 20 sec. after repetitive stimulation of right sensorimotor cortex (100 per sec. for 3 sec.). [From Hernández-Peón & Hagbarth (36).]

the inhibitory effect is probably taking place at the level of the central (dorsal cochlear nucleus) relay.

Thalamic Relays

Recently the brain-stem reticular formation has been found capable of altering synaptic transmission through thalamic relay nuclei. In animals without central anesthesia, test-evoked responses being conveyed through the somatosensory relay (from the medial lemniscus to the internal capsule) develop a shortened latency and duration and a reduced amplitude during brain-stem activation (48). The peaks of facilitation that otherwise appear during recovery following a relayed volley are likewise obliterated. The converse, i.e. a long latency, high amplitude and prolonged duration response followed by successive

peaks of facilitation, holds for the thalamic relay of evoked responses during barbiturate anesthesia or following lesions placed in the brain-stem reticular formation. These alterations result from the 'release' from a tonic inhibitory reticular influence which evidently modulates the thalamic relay nuclei during wakefulness (48). Other evidence indicates that stimulation of the brain-stem reticular formation will affect the lateral geniculate as well as retinal relays of photically-evoked responses (39). Apparently evoked responses to the same flash signal may be augmented in the retina and yet depressed in the thalamus.

Altogether, these experiments suggest that each of the major stations which relay afferent impulses within the spinal cord, medulla and thalamus appears to be susceptible to interference by inhibitory influences, and that these influences are tonically active in the unanesthetized animal.

CEPHALIC INTERACTION SYSTEMS

Corticipetal Projection Systems

In addition to the primary somesthetic sensory responses which are highly resistant to deep anesthesia, there are the so-called 'secondary' responses which have longer latency, are more widespread and are somewhat less resistant to anesthesia (5, 20). These have been shown to be independent of the classical medial lemniscus pathway and to be dependent upon structures lying in the medial part of the cephalic brain-stem (14, 62). These secondary responses are recorded well beyond the boundaries of the classical somesthetic receiving cortex and may even be of higher amplitude in the surrounding association cortex (33, 42, 43, 76, 77, 79).

A number of additional studies have extended the analysis of the somesthetic secondary response and have found what appear to be analogous secondary responses relating to the auditory and visual systems as well. Recent studies, illustrated in figure 6, of Buser & Borenstein may be taken as exemplary of current insight into these mechanisms (11).[2] Primary

[2] Recent work confirms that the 'secondary discharge' of Forbes & Morison (20), observed in rather deeply anesthetized cats, probably involves a different mechanism from that responsible for the 'réponses sensorielles secondaires' of Buser & Borenstein (11), observed in animals lacking central anesthesia. Drs. Evarts and Fleming (personal communication) have established that by recording from implanted electrodes in the visual receiving cortex of the cat they can demonstrate a dis-

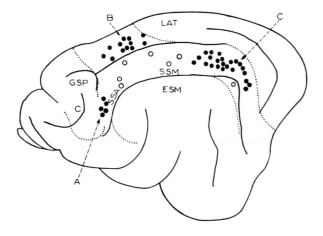

FIG. 6. Cortical zones showing reinforcement of responses between two heterogeneous sensory stimuli. Cats curarized, without central anesthesia or with a light dose of chloralose. When two heterogeneous stimuli occur nearly simultaneously, certain cortical loci outside of the primary receiving areas show an interaction between the two stimuli (potentially the effect is either facilitatory or inhibitory but is most readily identified if facilitatory). Auditory and somesthetic reinforcement in *A*; visual and somesthetic in *B*; auditory and visual in *C*. The principal primary receiving areas are outlined by *dotted lines*. *GSP*, posterior sigmoid gyrus; *C*, coronal gyrus; *SSA* and *SSM*, anterior and middle suprasylvian gyri; *LAT*, lateral gyrus; *ESM*, middle ectosylvian gyrus. [From Buser & Borenstein (11).]

and secondary response systems are differentiated by being *a*) independent in pathway (lemniscus and medial brain-stem reticular formation), *b*) different in susceptibility to anesthetic agents (primary responses are highly resistant, secondary responses are more vulnerable to barbiturate anesthesia), *c*) different in latency (for primary somesthetic responses, approximately 8 to 10 msec. as compared with those for secondary responses, approximately 40 to 80 msec.) and *d*) different in areal extent on cortex (primary localized to classical sensory projection area, secondary extending widely into association cortex where the modalities belonging to the different sensory systems overlap each other).

There is an important functional distinction between the classical sensory pathways and the ascending brain-stem reticular system. French & Magoun (22) found that monkeys with bilateral destruction of the classical lemniscal pathways in the midbrain are still aroused from sleep by sound and touch stimuli. When the reticular formation in the midbrain is destroyed, however, leaving the classical ascending sensory pathways intact, the monkeys remain in coma, even though sensory evoked potentials can be recorded in the auditory and somesthetic receiving cortices. Central anesthetics block conduction in certain extralemniscal pathways, and this undoubtedly represents an important basis for their action as anesthetics (23). These facts underline the importance to sensory evoked arousal, and presumably to sensation in general, of the extralemniscal pathways.

Cortical Interaction Systems

High frequency stimulation of the brain-stem reticular formation yields a generalized reduction in degree of synchronization among cortical neurons (63). The effect on the electrocorticographic patterns imitates the desynchronization that takes place during natural arousal. It has been shown that brain-stem activation is accompanied by an increase in the rate of discharge of neurons throughout the cephalic brain-stem, including the diffusely projecting thalamic system (57). As is well known, almost all individual cortical loci are reciprocally related to points that are symmetrically placed on the opposite hemisphere, as though in mirror image of each other. Chang discovered, as shown in figure 7, that when one records evoked potentials from a given cortical locus, an intervening stimulation of the homotopically related point on the opposite hemisphere will modify the evoked response (12, 13). von Euler & Ricci (81) have analyzed this capacity for interference with primary cortical sensory-evoked responses on the part of separate cortical inputs. By stimulating the classical thalamic relay nuclei and recording the primary evoked cortical responses, these investigators could then add conditioning stimuli to the contralateral homotopic cortical point. They find, as did Chang, that these systems converge and interact within the sensory cortex (81). Afferent impulses arriving in the sensory cortex are known to interact there with non-specific impulses from the thalamic recruiting system (43). Moreover, recruiting responses recorded from the cortex are found to be altered during behavioral alerting to sound stimuli (18).

All of these facts substantiate the general principle that within the cortical receiving areas, as at each of

---

continuity of secondary responses during the application of increasing increments of barbiturate anesthesia. An early secondary response which can be discerned when conditions are favorable in the completely unanesthetized cat disappears with light stages of anesthesia (pentobarbital, 15 mg/kg), and a much larger secondary response appears at a deeper stage of anesthesia (30 mg/kg) and after a substantially longer latency.

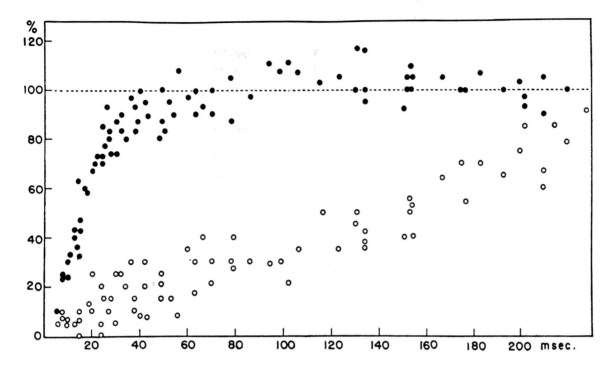

FIG. 7. Time course of blocking effect of callosal potential on positive and negative components of primary auditory response. *Abscissae*: Time after delivery of stimulus on contralateral cortex for callosal potential. *Ordinates*: Magnitude of auditory response expressed as percentage of control. *Dots* represent positive component and *circles*, negative component. Note that stimulation of the contralateral homotopic cortical locus modifies, by its callosal connections, the sensory-evoked response in a primary receiving area. [From Chang (13).]

the other stations along the sensory pathways, the character and extent of sensory-evoked responses are subject to intervention by activities taking place elsewhere within widespread regions of the brain.

Corticifugal Influences on Brain-stem Mechanisms

Bremer & Terzuolo (9) showed that stimulation of the cortex in cats without central anesthesia will induce electrocorticographic evidence of arousal. Jasper and co-workers (41), working with monkeys, had earlier shown a spread of localized cortically-induced after-discharges into the brain stem. It has subsequently been observed, in monkeys without central anesthesia, that single shock stimuli delivered to specific regions of the cortex will yield evoked potentials throughout a wide zone of the cephalic brain stem (1–3, 21). This zone is generally coextensive with the brain-stem region within which sensory responses from different sensory systems appear to converge. Blocking and facilitating interaction takes place in this general region among the various combinations of cortically and peripherally initiated signals (8, 21, 36, 70).

Examples appear in figures 8 and 9. The corticifugal projections not only interact with other signals converging upon the brain stem but also with signals intrinsic to the reticular formation, i.e. signals generated within and recorded from the brain-stem reticular formation itself (2), as may be seen in figure 10. The same corticifugal systems are known to be capable of initiating electrocorticographic (73) and behavioral (72) arousal, presumably by virtue of their connections with the cephalic brain-stem reticular formation.

It can be seen that not only are input and output patterns modifiable within the cortex, but the cortex itself can also modify activity taking place within the brain stem and thereby possibly have an indirect influence back upon sensory patterns as these are initiated and relayed at lower levels.

Organization of Centrifugal Sensory Control Mechanisms

Up to this point we have described mainly how activity in each of the sensory neurons linking together a given classical ascending sensory pathway

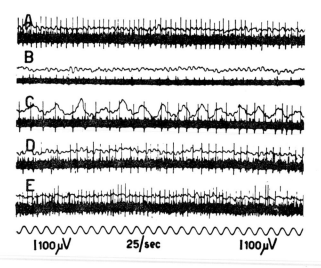

FIG. 8. Inhibition of reticular unit discharges by stimulation of the cerebellum and augmentation of reticular unit discharges by sensory stimulation. *Encéphale isolé* preparation, without central anesthesia. For each strip, the *top line* registers an electroencephalographic tracing recorded from the frontotemporal regions of a hemisphere; the *lower line* indicates unitary spike discharges picked up from the median bulbar reticular formation by a microelectrode. *A.* Activated electroencephalogram and continuous high frequency discharge of the reticular unit. *B.* Total inhibition of the unit by positive polarization of the anterior vermis of the cerebellum (0.5 ma); EEG trace not modified. *C.* Immediately after discontinuation of the cerebellar polarization. *D.* Same as C a few seconds later. The reticular unit reappears (*C*) and progressively increases in discharge frequency (*D*); during the early part of this period, slow high-amplitude waves appear in the EEG. *E.* Some minutes later, an intense tactile stimulation (brisk rubbing of the bridge of the nose) causes the appearance of a multiple reticular discharge (including recruitment of new units), and an increase in frequency of EEG waves. [From Mollica *et al.* (61).]

is subject to some degree of interference according to the state of activity in other parts of the nervous system. Now, is it possible to define somewhat more specifically the relationship between the classical sensory paths and these other parts? No final interpretations are warranted since the data are as yet incomplete for any one sensory system. Nonetheless, in each sensory system there can be identified certain centrifugal sensory control mechanisms which bear close analogy with structural or functional aspects of one or another of the other sensory systems. Generalizations that might not be permitted for one system alone seem to gain in strength when all of them are examined together.

Paralleling the classical succession of ascending neurons appears a descending system which links the same nuclear relay stations from above downward. Although analogous centrifugal projections have been identified anatomically for many individual parts of other sensory systems, the auditory pathway probably possesses the most completely documented succession of descending fibers. These pursue a course in reverse direction that roughly parallels the ascending auditory pathway. They pass step-by-step downward from the auditory cortex to the medial geniculate body and inferior colliculus, thence to the lateral lemniscus and trapezoid body and to the superior olive where they are succeeded by the olivocochlear efferent bundle. As Galambos says, "It is unlikely that these descending fiber systems—some reasonably powerful, some weak—perform no function in audition. What this function might be will unfortunately continue to remain entirely speculative until more anatomical and physiological data become available. One can hazard a guess, however, that the solution of certain problems of hearing resides as much in the understanding of the function of these descending pathways as in the knowledge of the ascending ones" (25, p. 503). Presumably centrifugal fiber projections which belong to the visual, somesthetic and olfactory systems might

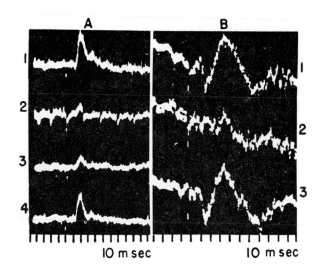

FIG. 9. Influence of hypothalamic and toe pad stimulation on sciatic nerve responses elicited within the brain-stem reticular formation. Recording from the right side of the midbrain reticular formation in a curarized cat without central anesthesia. *A.* Sciatic responses, (*1*) before, (*2*) during, (*3*) 8 sec. after and (*4*) 20 sec. after repetitive stimulation in the right hypothalamic region (50 per sec. for 3 sec.). *B.* Sciatic response (*1*) before, (*2*) during and (*3*) 10 sec. after pinching the toe pads of right hind limb (ipsilateral to reticular recording site). [From Hernández-Peón & Hagbarth (36).]

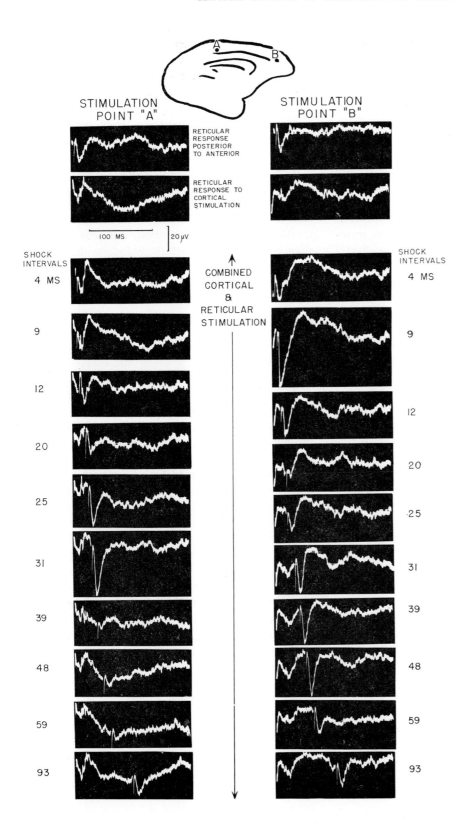

STIMULATION
POINT "A"

STIMULATION
POINT "B"

RETICULAR
RESPONSE
POSTERIOR
TO ANTERIOR

RETICULAR
RESPONSE TO
CORTICAL
STIMULATION

100 MS   20 μV

SHOCK
INTERVALS

4 MS

9

12

20

25

31

39

48

59

93

COMBINED
CORTICAL
&
RETICULAR
STIMULATION

SHOCK
INTERVALS

4 MS

9

12

20

25

31

39

48

59

93

FIG. 10. Corticifugal influences upon a conduction pathway in the brain-stem reticular formation. Responses recorded from bipolar electrodes in the anterior brain stem show effects of single cortical shocks on volleys ascending from a test stimulation site in the posterior brain stem. *Left column:* Effects of cortical shocks applied to point 'A' on the medial surface of the monkey hemisphere. *Right column:* Effects on the same pathway of shocks applied to a more anterior cortical site, point 'B'. Note that ascending brain-stem volley is facilitated when cortical shock is delivered to point 'A' 31 msec. prior to posterior brain stem test shock, whereas facilitation from point 'B' occurs at 9 and again at 48 msec. at which moments the brain-stem pathway is being inhibited from point 'A'. This illustrates the principle that a number of cortical sites can exert a controlling influence on ascending systems intrinsic to the brain stem, thereby being able, presumably, to interfere with mechanisms involved in sensation. [From Adey *et al.* (2).]

play an analogously important, but as yet undefined, role in the perception of each of these modalities.

It is generally accepted that the classical ascending sensory pathways connect directly or indirectly with the brain-stem reticular formation (78). Rasmussen reports that the centrifugal auditory projection system also sends branches into the same general region (personal communication). It may be by virtue of such collateral connections to the brain-stem reticular formation that most sensory pathways and certain zones of the cerebral cortex have indirect reciprocal relations with the cerebellum (6, 32, 74, 75). Each of the cerebral and cerebellar cortical areas which is capable of exercising an effect upon impulses transmitted along the classical ascending sensory pathways possesses projections to the brain-stem reticular formation. Moreover, stimulation of the brain-stem reticular formation is known to evoke very notable sensory control effects. This much is highly suggestive. But whether the descending sensory projections which parallel the classical ascending sensory pathways and the cerebral and cerebellar projections into the brain stem each have an influential access to the ascending sensory transmission systems must await definitive experimental proof.

To these considerations should be added the fact that there is really no physiological boundary between central sensory and motor mechanisms. Each central pattern for the initiation of movement has its neuronal repercussions upon central sensory patterns, and each performed movement introduces alterations in sensory input patterns. In this way sensory and motor systems are inextricably bound together both internally and externally.

Transactional Mechanisms Relating to
Sensory Control Systems

It is now possible to identify six extensive, mutually interacting systems: *a)* the classical ('lemniscal') ascending sensory pathways projecting finally upon the classical sensory receiving areas of the cortex, *b)* the parallel ('extralemniscal') ascending sensory pathways which reach more widespread regions of the cortex by way of the brain-stem reticular formation, *c)* the classical ('pyramidal') descending motor pathways projecting directly from cortex to lower motoneuron aggregations, *d)* the parallel ('extrapyramidal') motor pathways which descend to the motor nuclei indirectly by way of the basal ganglia and the brain-stem reticular formation, *e)* the brain-stem reticular formation which is known to exert

modifying influences upward upon both the cerebral and cerebellar hemispheres and downward upon both sensory and motor synaptic relays, and *f)* the centrifugal sensory control mechanisms which may involve fibers coursing in reverse direction parallel to the classical ascending sensory pathways and which may also implicate projections from cerebral and cerebellar loci through the brain-stem reticular formation.

The interdependence of these six systems is obvious. Evidently they are all knit together by the brain-stem reticular formation which could not be effectively studied in animals with central anesthesia. Because of this experimental limitation, antecedent conceptions had to deal with relatively independent sensory and motor systems which were more stable, imperious and reliable in their handling of signals than is the case in the unanesthetized brain.

Since collaterals from the classical ascending pathways influence the reticular formation and the reticular formation in turn modifies the initiation and transmission of impulses along the classical sensory pathways, since both of these systems interact with each other again in the sensory receiving cortex, since the reticular formation by way of the diffusely projecting thalamic nuclei modifies activity generally throughout the cortex and the cortex in turn modifies activity within the reticular formation, since the cerebellum is similarly linked both ways with the brain-stem reticular formation, etc., one can begin to visualize the extent of abstraction imposed by the experimental isolation of only a few elements of this entire complex. Moreover, it is not possible to define how such a 'transactional mechanism' (55) might operate on the basis of any single experimental approach. By adding evidence from studies that incorporate both neurophysiological and behavioral techniques, it is possible to add a new dimension to the conception of the mechanisms involved in the central control of sensory transmission.

SENSORY ATTENTION, HABITUATION AND CONDITIONING

Auditory Habituation

By means of electrodes implanted within the dorsal cochlear nucleus, Galambos, Hernández-Peón and their associates have recorded potentials elicited by acoustic stimulation during the course of behavioral studies on unanesthetized cats. Responses to the same tone pip show modest fluctuations in amplitude and

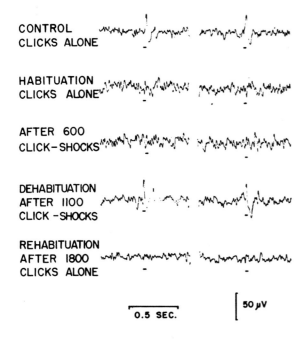

CONTROL
CLICKS ALONE

HABITUATION
CLICKS ALONE

AFTER 600
CLICK-SHOCKS

DEHABITUATION
AFTER 1100
CLICK-SHOCKS

REHABITUATION
AFTER 1800
CLICKS ALONE

0.5 SEC.

50 μV

FIG. 11. Modification of amplitude of click-evoked responses in dorsal cochlear nucleus according to experience of the animal. Unanesthetized cat with recording electrodes implanted in the dorsal cochlear nucleus. Amplitude of responses elicited by clicks repeated every second gradually declines over many trials. The animal exhibits behavioral as well as electrophysiological evidence of habituation to the click stimuli. After habituation, if weak electric shocks are applied to the foreleg of the same animal in temporal association with the clicks, the click-evoked responses gradually become increased in amplitude. The 'dehabituation' can occur within only a few trials if sufficiently powerful shock stimuli are applied, as shown by Galambos et al. (27). The 'dehabituation' is plastic in the sense that the amplitude of the click-evoked responses declines once more after the shock stimuli are discontinued. This kind of modification of sensory-evoked responses has been taken as an objective evidence of conditioning. [Modified from Jouvet & Hernández-Peón (45).]

undergo periods of waxing and waning. If the same tone signal is repeated many times, the amplitude of the evoked dorsal cochlear nucleus responses tends gradually to become reduced to a new lower level, although the fluctuations still persist (27, 37, 38, 45). The authors refer to this as auditory 'adaptation' or 'habituation.' If the tone is shifted up or down in pitch, the evoked potentials return to a higher amplitude once more, but rehabituation can be established to the new tone signal. After habituation to a particular tone has been thoroughly established and the tone is then associated with a nearly simultaneous signal, such as an electric shock to the foreleg or across the chest, a high amplitude cochlear response will re-

appear. This has been referred to as 'dehabituation' (35). After discontinuation of the electric shock, a slow rehabituation to the auditory signal takes place (27, 45), as is shown in figure 11.

Auditory Conditioning

These fluctuations in amplitude of the responses recorded within the first central relay stages along the auditory pathway may be reflected by roughly parallel shifts in the animal's behavior. When first introduced to the test-tone signals, an animal attentively alerts to each tone pip. As electrographic evidence of habituation occurs, the animal shows less behavioral evidence of devoting attention to the acoustic signals. When habituated and then given an unconditioned electric shock in association with the tone signals, the animal behaves as if it has suddenly acquired an increased interest in the associated tone. Growth in behavioral evidence of attention usually takes place a few trials in advance of the growth in amplitude of the evoked dorsal cochlear response, but the modified (conditioned) cochlear response lasts approximately as long, during extinction trials, as the overtly expressed attention. The electrophysiological plasticity in response of the nervous system has with some justification been taken as an objective indication of conditioning.

Using electrical shocks applied across the chests of cats, Galambos et al. (27) have found that only ten or twenty such unconditioned stimuli, applied in association with clicks to which the cats had previously become thoroughly habituated, were sufficient to cause electrographic as well as behavioral evidence of conditioning. Simultaneous recordings made in the cochlear nucleus, auditory cortex, hippocampus, septal area and head of the caudate nucleus show that electrographic changes associated with this kind of conditioning may occur at several different levels along the auditory pathway and in regions other than the classical auditory system. Cycles of associated behavioral and electrophysiological evidence for conditioning and extinction can apparently be repeated indefinitely. [Galambos et al. (27) may be consulted for additional evidence and commentary on conditioning in relation to modifications of electrical activity in the brain. This subject is also discussed by Galambos in Chapter LXI of this work.]

Shifts of Attention

Recording from electrodes implanted in the dorsal cochlear nucleus of the cat before habituation had been established, Hernández-Peón *et al.* (38) have tested the effects on auditory-evoked potentials of distraction by visual and olfactory stimuli. As may be seen in figure 12, when mice in a jar are placed before the experimental animals, or when fish odors are blown into the cage through a tube, the formerly high amplitude auditory responses are immediately reduced in amplitude. The effect is as if the cats had suddenly shifted from a naive to an 'habituated' state with reference to the auditory test-signal responses. But when the mice are removed or the odor blowing stopped, and after the cats are apparently relaxed once more, the evoked auditory potentials return again to their initial high level of amplitude. The duration of the reduced auditory potentials corresponds closely with the period when the animals are distracted by the nonacoustic signals.

Visual Responses

Using electrodes implanted in the brain-stem reticular formation, optic tract, lateral geniculate body and optic radiation, Hernández-Peón *et al.* (39) were able to analyze the effects of intercurrent brain-stem stimulation on the relay of flash-evoked responses through the retina and lateral geniculate body. When light flashes are reiterated over an extended period of time,

the flash-evoked responses at each point along the visual pathway tend to diminish in amplitude. This suggests that there is a mechanism of habituation operating in the visual system. Stimulation of the brain-stem reticular formation or behavioral distraction by nonvisual stimuli is associated with a reduction in amplitude of the nonhabituated photic response.

Behavior and Neurophysiology

Although these studies are quite recent, and only a few aspects of a potentially very rich field have been touched upon, certain features merit special comment. It is evident that the activity taking place along at least the auditory and visual pathways, and possibly the olfactory and somesthetic sensory systems as well, is vulnerable to systematic intervention in accordance with previous experience (habituation) and shift of attention (distraction) (11, 45 and other pertinent chapters in 19). It is inferred, but not yet firmly established, that these dynamic changes in activity within the sensory paths are accomplished by some mechanism involving the brain-stem reticular formation. The evidence is as follows: *a*) activation of the brain-

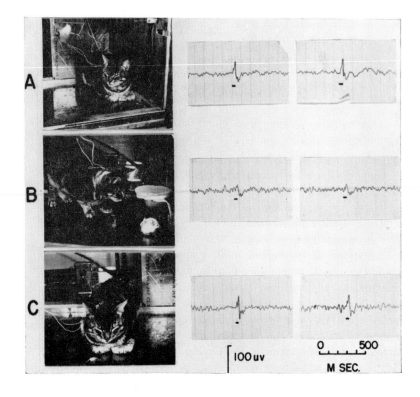

FIG. 12. Modification of click-evoked responses in the cochlear nucleus during 'attention' in the unanesthetized cat. Recording from implanted electrodes in the dorsal cochlear nucleus in an animal prior to habituation to click signals delivered every second. Photographs are simultaneous with potential recordings opposite. *Top* and *bottom*: Cat is relaxed; the click responses are large. *Middle*: While the cat is visually attentive to mice in a jar, the click responses are diminished in amplitude. [From Hernández-Peón *et al.* (38).]

stem reticular formation in unanesthetized animals has an effect on nonhabituated acoustic- or flash-evoked responses that is similar to distraction of attention by extraneous stimulation of the same animals; *b*) distraction of attention by extraneous sensory stimulation may very likely have its effect, as does arousal, by activation of the brain-stem reticular formation; *c*) animals given barbiturate anesthesia (known to interfere with activity in the brain-stem reticular formation) cannot be habituated; *d*) if animals are habituated prior to being anesthetized, the sensory-evoked potentials change from habituated (reduced) amplitude to the initial prehabituated height but typical habituated responses reappear following recovery from the anesthetic; *e*) in habituated animals, a lesion restricted to the pontine or mesencephalic brain-stem reticular formation is followed by permanent 'release' from the habituated pattern.[3]

Recently, Fuster (24) has reported that monkeys trained to do difficult tachistoscopic discriminations between two similar objects show improved performance in both their speed of response and percentage of correct choices when the test exposure is preceded by a very brief electrical shock applied to the mesencephalic brain-stem reticular formation. More prolonged stimulation in the same brain-stem location interferes deleteriously with both the reaction time and percentage of correct choices. These findings imply an alteration of visual sensory or possibly judgmental processes as a result of brain-stem activation. Although there is no way of being certain, in Fuster's experiments, where the effect takes place, it is possible that such changes occur within the first few synapses along the visual pathway. This might be inferred from the experiments of Granit (29) and Hernández-Peón *et al.* (39) cited above. More convincing evidence for improvement in the kind of differentiation demanded by tachistoscopic discrimination is reflected in experiments by Lindsley (53). He finds that two flashes which are placed close enough together to produce a single large-humped electrical wave in the lateral geniculate body are, on stimulation of the brain-stem reticular formation, separated into a two-peaked hump.

Taken as a whole, all of these behavioral experiments reinforce the neurophysiological evidence that the sensory pathways are relatively plastic rather than fixed in the transmission of impulses generated by a particular stimulus. Sensory transmission is apparently modifiable in accordance with waking experience. Moreover, the brain-stem reticular formation evidently plays an important role in the government of such neuronal plasticity.

INTERPRETATIONS

Remarkable changes take place within sensory circuits when one shifts from the use of anesthetized animals to animals without central anesthesia. In the anesthetized state the classical sensory pathways convey high amplitude signals with great reliability and consistency, and there is little activity within the brain-stem reticular formation. Cortical responses to sensory stimuli are greatly amplified and tend to be confined to the classical sensory receiving areas. In the waking brain, without central anesthesia, the classical sensory pathways convey signals that are less reproducible from one moment to the next. Indeed, over a period of some minutes or hours there may be remarkable alterations in the size of evoked responses to a given stimulus. In addition, there are widespread responses elicited throughout extensive cortical and subcortical regions. It seems obvious now that the classical sensory pathways and cortical projection systems, no matter how necessary they might be to perception, are not in themselves sufficient for perception.

The extralemniscal sensory pathways, coursing through the brain-stem reticular formation and diffusely projecting thalamic nuclei, appear to have a general function of providing an integrative background or context for perception. Their contribution in this respect may be likened usefully to the organizational contribution in movement and behavior that is made by the descending extrapyramidal projections. They may be thought to provide a general sensory awareness and feeling tone comparable to the background of excitability and motor tone generated by the extrapyramidal system. Nonetheless, they may convey more specific sense data too. Haugen & Melzack (34), for example, report persuasive evidence, some of which appears in figures 13, 14 and 15, that

---

[3] A note of caution. Much has been learned within the last few years which assigns important functions to 'the brain-stem reticular formation.' It must be remembered, however, that this region may well contain several functional systems. The studies of Adey, Amassian, Haugen, Moruzzi and their associates imply that this is the case (2, 8, 34, 47, 61). In the first stages of interpreting the functions of so large and complex a region of the brain, it is natural that somewhat overgeneralized and sweeping conclusions may be alluring. This does not deny the reliability of observations made to date but implies that, when this complex skein of reticular neurons becomes better understood, a greater precision in the localization and characterization of its functions may be possible.

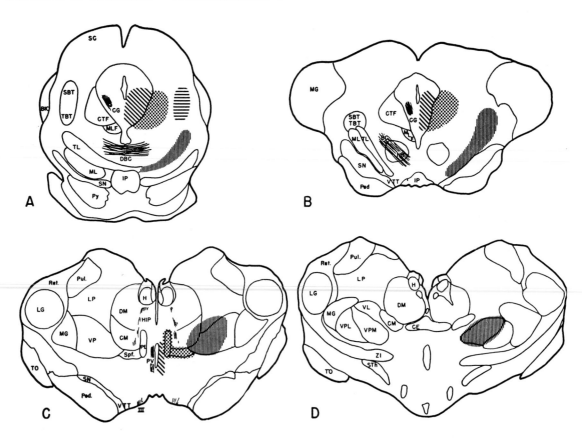

FIG. 13. Short and medium latency response areas of brain stem and thalamus responding to tooth pulp stimulation. *Narrow vertical stripes* identify the trigeminal lemniscus (medial lemniscus) which has a short latency and a dominantly contralateral projection. *Horizontal stripes* mark the trigeminobulbothalamic path (spinobulbothalamic), with short latency and bilateral projections. *Stippled areas* mark the ascending portion of the central tegmental fasciculus (dorsal secondary trigeminal pathway), with medium latency and bilateral projection. *Diagonal stripes* designate the ascending path within the central grey which possesses medium latency and bilateral projections. The reticular formation yields widespread responses characterized by long latency and bilateral character. The relevant structures are indicated on the left side of each level. Recording sites (except within reticular formation) are shaded on the right side. Abbreviations: *BC*, brachium conjunctivum; *BIC*, brachium of inferior colliculus; *CE*, centralis; *CG*, central grey; *CM*, center median; *CTF*, central tegmental fasciculus; *DBC*, decussation of brachium conjunctivum; *DM*, dorsalis medialis; *H*, habenula; *HIP*, habenulointerpeduncular tract; *IP*, interpeduncularis; *LG*, lateral geniculate; *LP*, lateralis posterior; *MG*, medial geniculate; *ML*, medial lemniscus; *MLF*, medial longitudinal fasciculus; *NR*, red nucleus; *Ped.*, peduncle; *Pf.*, parafascicularis; *Pul.*, pulvinar; *PV*, periventricular area; *Py*, pyramidal tract; *SBT*, spinobulbothalamic tract; *SC*, superior colliculus; *SN*, substantia nigra; *Spf.*, subparafascicularis; *STh*, subthalamicus; *TBT*, trigeminobulbothalamic tract; *TL*, trigeminal lemniscus; *TO*, optic tract; *VL*, ventralis lateralis; *VPL*, ventralis posterolateralis; *VP*, ventralis posterior; *VPM*, ventralis posteromedialis; *VTT*, ventral tegmental nucleus of Tsai; and *ZI*, zona incerta. [From Kerr *et al.* (47).]

particular portions of the reticular pathways may convey signals essential to pain perception.

It is clearly established that, whatever may be contributed by upward-streaming sensory-evoked impulses, the central nervous system possesses an important downstream sensory control mechanism which also undoubtedly contributes to the perceptual

content. The nervous system possesses some mechanism whereby the amplitude of sensory-evoked responses, and hence the number or synchrony of units responding, can be greatly modified. This mechanism exerts an effect within each of the classical sensory pathways, altering the initiation of impulses or their transmission through the entire succession of sensory synapses. There is good evidence, too, that this mechanism is discharged by way of the brain-stem reticular formation; the action might originate there or perhaps elsewhere within the cerebral and cerebellar hemisphears, but it undoubtedly funnels through and may be significantly modified by the reticular formation. The end effect of this mechanism may be facilitatory or inhibitory, but in many central relays it appears to be predominantly inhibitory. The mechanism clearly depends upon an active process; its effect can be interrupted by transection of the neuraxis above the level of testing, by deep anesthesia and, more specifically, by the placement of a lesion in the central core of the brain-stem reticular formation. The dynamic operation of this mechanism appears to be responsible during wakefulness for fluctuations in the amplitude of sensory-evoked responses.

Behavioral studies, too, indicate that this mecha-

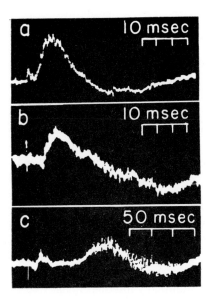

FIG. 14. Evoked potentials following tooth pulp stimulation recorded from three loci at the same mesencephalic level. *A.* Recorded from the portion of the central tegmental fasciculus ascending alongside the periaqueductal grey. *B.* Recorded from the pathway within the intermediolateral portion of the central grey. *C.* Small early response followed, after a long latency, by a second longer discharge, recorded from the region of the decussated brachium conjunctivum. Note differences in the time scale. Note also that, although all three of these individual loci may be considered parts subsumed within the general regional designation of the brain-stem reticular formation and each is a bilaterally represented pathway, they are nonetheless distinguished from one another by differences in latency, amplitude and duration of response. [From Kerr *et al.* (47).]

nism plays a dynamic role during wakefulness. Here its operational effect is usually a reduction of sensory signals, an effect that is active in inverse relation to the degree of attention or interest enlisted by that particular stimulus. The mechanism seems to be less active (to inhibit less) when a stimulus is novel or when a stimulus is given special significance, as by its association with an important unconditioned stimulus. The mechanism appears to be more active (to inhibit more) in relation to signals arising from stimuli to which habituation has been developed and other stimuli, even though not rendered ineffective by habituation from which attention has been withdrawn.

Briefly, this sensory control mechanism appears to provide the perceptual processes with an active organizing principle, including an element of purpose, which tends to select and modify sensory messages within the earliest stages of their trajectory. If overt behavior may be assumed to provide a cogent index for the interpretation of *telos*, then this sensory control mechanism is designed to diminish the engagement of higher centers with those signals that have the least significance to the individual.

A mechanism operating in this way requires that incoming signals be identified and given significance. How might this identification and attachment of value come about? Only partial answers can be provided at this time. Continuous electrographic recordings from multiple sites indicate that, when a behaving animal encounters a new situation, at first a very large territory of the brain is drawn into a novel activity. As the experience is repeated many times, there develops a significant economy in terms of the extent of brain involvement. Perhaps recognizable signals can eventually be reduced to a quite small number of impulses, representing minuscule abstractions of reality. Perhaps recognizable identity can be established even before the sensory-evoked impulses have time to ascend all the way to cortex and back. Something of a parallel sort appears to take place within motor circuits as one proceeds from the execution of a complex novel movement to that same movement when it is established as an ingrained motor habit. There is evidently an analogous economization and automatization of neuronal activity in relation to the habituated act as finally executed.

The attachment of value to such identified signals could presumably come about quite naturally through the activation, *pari passu*, of certain portions of the brain's primary reinforcement systems (see Chapter LXII by Stellar in this work). A number of the struc-

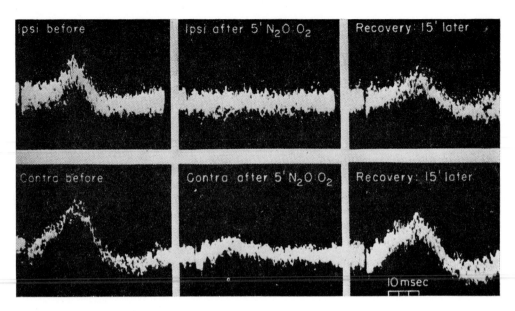

FIG. 15. Effect of nitrous oxide on long latency bilateral reticular formation responses to tooth pulp stimulation. Although the lemniscal response to tooth pulp stimulation is not perceptibly affected by nitrous oxide-oxygen inhalation, responses elicited within both ipsilateral and contralateral reticular formation practically disappear after 5 min. of such inhalation. Recovery is nearly complete 15 min. later. [From Haugen & Melzack (34).]

tures implicated in both positive and negative reinforcement undoubtedly participate in the central integration of both sensory and motor mechanisms. These structures are anatomically linked with the extralemniscal, diffusely projecting and extrapyramidal systems as well as the phylogenetically older parts of the cortex and brain stem.

There has long been a quest to know how nerve signals might be 'read' and how they might be given 'value.' We are now certainly closer to knowing where such events take place even though the how is still unanswered. Clearly the cortex is not the first step in sensory integration. During wakefulness sensory integration is taking place continuously and dynamically, beginning with the farthest afferent outposts. This involves an erosion of information that originally started into the nervous system and an intrusion of influences which are based upon the animal's previous experience as well as its momentary disposal of attention. This implies that there is a reduction and distortion of sensory-evoked signals from the actual nature of the stimulating world. Perhaps 'value' is likewise inserted into the complex at these early stages of sensory integration. Certainly significance to the organism appears to be a guiding principle with respect to the operation of sensory control mechanisms, hence a survival of incoming impulses in the

unanesthetized brain would appear to be *prima facie* evidence of their significance.

In order to bridge the gap between neurophysiology and psychology, it is necessary somehow to determine the neuronal mechanisms underlying behavior. A principal difficulty appears with the attempt to interpret the function of the whole out of its parts. Whereas the behavior of separate parts could be made out from an analysis of the interaction of one part with another, these parts will not add together in any simple fashion to account for the behavior of the whole. There have been recent attempts to characterize the differences between linear cause-and-effect relationships and the more involved dynamics of a large number of mutually interdependent systems in simultaneous action (55). The authors use the term 'trans-action' to signify the latter kinds of operations and to contrast them with more limited 'interaction' systems. Attempts have been made to interpret some of the transactional mechanisms involved in visceral sensation and emotional expression (54).

SUMMARY

Recent experimental evidence, drawn largely from the study of animals without central anesthesia, indicates that the nervous system is much more plastic in its action than previously believed. What may be taken for sensory pathways, because they convey sensory-evoked signals in a centripetal direction, turn out to be more variable and more widespread in their transmission of impulses in the waking state. The increased variability seems to be due to active interference by a centrifugal mechanism. The widespread distribution of sensory-evoked impulses allows a more elaborate intermingling of sensory with other signals throughout various parts of the brain. Experimental evidence favors a lessening of our conceptual isolation of sensory from motor and other central mechanisms. The nervous system appears to be made up less of independent linear pathways than of mutually interdependent loop circuits which stitch together the various parts of the brain into a functional whole.

Along ascending as well as descending projections, the brain-stem reticular formation and the cerebral and cerebellar systems linked closely with it seem to modulate impulse traffic in a continuous action that modifies the composition of perceptive as well as projective neural patterns. The losses and distortions of signals brought about by this mechanism favor the conclusion that some teleological mechanism is at work; this appears to be designed to diminish the involvement of higher centers with signals that have little immediate significance for the animal. Thus, sensory signals appear to be subject not only to error, in the sense projected by Descartes, but also to some purposive central control. A further examination of these mechanisms will help us to understand many problems of absorbing interest in neurology, psychiatry, psychology and philosophy.

REFERENCES

1. ADEY, W. R., N. C. R. MERRILLEES AND S. SUNDERLAND. *Brain* 79: 414, 1956.
2. ADEY, W. R., J. P. SEGUNDO AND R. B. LIVINGSTON. *J. Neurophysiol.* 20: 1, 1957.
3. ADEY, W. R., S. SUNDERLAND AND C. W. DUNLOP. *Electroencephalog. & Clin. Neurophysiol.* 9: 309, 1957.
4. ADRIAN, E. D. *The Basis of Sensation; the Action of the Sense Organs.* London: Christophers, 1928.
5. ADRIAN, E. D. *J. Physiol.* 100: 159, 1941.
6. ADRIAN, E. D. *Brain* 66: 289, 1943.
7. ADRIAN, E. D. *The Physical Background of Perception.* Oxford: Clarendon Press, 1947.
8. AMASSIAN, V. E. AND R. V. DEVITO. *J. Neurophysiol.* 17: 575, 1954.
9. BREMER, F. AND C. TERZUOLO. *Arch. internat. physiol.* 62: 157, 1954.
10. BROUWER, B. *J. Nerv. & Ment. Dis.* 77: 621, 1933.
11. BUSER, P. AND P. BORENSTEIN. *Electroencephalog. & Clin. Neurophysiol.* Suppl. 6: 89, 1957.
12. CHANG, H.-T. *J. Neurophysiol.* 16: 117, 1953.
13. CHANG, H.-T. *J. Neurophysiol.* 16: 133, 1953.
14. DEMPSEY, E. W., R. S. MORISON AND B. R. MORISON. *Am. J. Physiol.* 131: 718, 1941.
15. DODT, E. *J. Neurophysiol.* 19: 301, 1956.
16. ELDRED, E. AND B. FUJIMORI. In: *Reticular Formation of the Brain,* edited by H. H. Jasper *et al.* Boston: Little, 1958.
17. ELDRED, E., R. GRANIT AND P. A. MERTON. *J. Physiol.* 122: 498, 1953.
18. EVARTS, E. V. AND H. W. MAGOUN. *Science* 125: 1147, 1957.
19. FISCHGOLD, H. AND H. GASTAUT (editors). *Electroencephalog. & Clin. Neurophysiol.* Suppl. 6, 1957.
20. FORBES, A. AND B. R. MORISON. *J. Neurophysiol.* 2: 112, 1939.
21. FRENCH, J. D., R. HERNÁNDEZ-PEÓN AND R. B. LIVINGSTON. *J. Neurophysiol.* 18: 74, 1955.
22. FRENCH, J. D. AND H. W. MAGOUN. *A.M.A. Arch. Neurol. & Psychiat.* 68: 591, 1952.
23. FRENCH, J. D., M. VERZEANO AND H. W. MAGOUN. *A.M.A. Arch. Neurol. & Psychiat.* 69: 519, 1953.

24. FUSTER, J. M. *Fed. Proc.* 16: 43, 1957.
25. GALAMBOS, R. *Physiol. Rev.* 34: 497, 1954.
26. GALAMBOS, R. *J. Neurophysiol.* 19: 424, 1956.
27. GALAMBOS, R., G. SHEATZ AND V. G. VERNIER. *Science* 123: 376, 1956.
28. GRANIT, R. *Receptors and Sensory Perception.* New Haven: Yale Univ. Press, 1955.
29. GRANIT, R. *J. Neurophysiol.* 18: 388, 1955.
30. GRANIT, R. AND B. R. KAADA. *Acta physiol. scandinav.* 27: 130, 1952.
31. HAGBARTH, K.-E. AND D. I. B. KERR. *J. Neurophysiol.* 17: 295, 1954.
32. HAMPSON, J. L. *J. Neurophysiol.* 12: 37, 1949.
33. HANBERY, J. AND H. JASPER. *J. Neurophysiol.* 16: 252, 1953.
34. HAUGEN, F. P. AND R. MELZACK. *Anesthesiology* 18: 183, 1957.
35. HERNÁNDEZ-PEÓN, R. *Acta neurol. latinoam.* 1: 256, 1955.
36. HERNÁNDEZ-PEÓN, R. AND K.-E. HAGBARTH. *J. Neurophysiol.* 18: 44, 1955.
37. HERNÁNDEZ-PEÓN, R. AND H. SCHERRER. *Fed. Proc.* 14: 71, 1955.
38. HERNÁNDEZ-PEÓN, R., H. SCHERRER AND M. JOUVET. *Science* 123: 331, 1956.
39. HERNÁNDEZ-PEÓN, R., H. SCHERRER AND M. VELASCO. *Acta neurol. latinoam.* 2: 8, 1956.
40. HUNT, C. C. AND S. W. KUFFLER. *J. Physiol.* 113: 283, 1951.
41. JASPER, H., C. AJMONE-MARSAN AND J. STOLL. *A.M.A. Arch. Neurol. & Psychiat.* 67: 155, 1952.
42. JASPER, H. H. AND J. DROOGLEEVER-FORTUYN *A. Res. Nerv. & Ment. Dis., Proc.* 26: 272, 1947.
43. JASPER, H., R. NAQUET AND E. E. KING. *Electroencephalog. & Clin. Neurophysiol.* 7: 99, 1955.
44. JOUVET, M. AND J.-E. DESMEDT. *Compt. rend. Acad. sc., Paris* 243: 1916, 1956.
45. JOUVET, M. AND R. HERNÁNDEZ-PEÓN. *Electroencephalog. & Clin. Neurophysiol.* Suppl. 6: 39, 1957.
46. KERR, D. I. B. AND K.-E. HAGBARTH. *J. Neurophysiol.* 18: 362, 1955.

47. KERR, D. I. B., F. P. HAUGEN AND R. MELZACK. *Am. J. Physiol.* 183: 253, 1955.

48. KING, E. E., R. NAQUET AND H. W. MAGOUN. *J. Pharmacol. & Exper. Therap.* 119: 48, 1957.

49. KUFFLER, S. W. AND C. EYZAGUIRRE. *J. Gen. Physiol.* 39: 155, 1955.

50. KUFFLER, S. W. AND C. C. HUNT. *A. Res. Nerv. & Ment. Dis., Proc.* 30: 24, 1952.

51. KUFFLER, S. W., C. C. HUNT AND J. P. QUILLIAM. *J. Neurophysiol.* 14: 29, 1951.

52. LEKSELL, L. *Acta physiol. scandinav.* Suppl. 31, 10: 1, 1945.

53. LINDSLEY, D. B.: In: *Reticular Formation of the Brain*, edited by H. H. Jasper *et al.* Boston: Little, 1958.

54. LIVINGSTON, R. B. AND F. G. WORDEN. *Stanford M. Bull.* 13: 194, 1955.

55. LIVINGSTON, W. K., F. P. HAUGEN AND J. M. BROOKHART. *Neurology* 4: 485, 1954.

56. LOEWENSTEIN, W. R. *J. Physiol.* 132: 40, 1956.

57. MACHNE, X., I. CALMA AND H. W. MAGOUN. *J. Neurophysiol.* 18: 547, 1955.

58. MAGOUN, H. W. *Physiol. Rev.* 30: 459, 1950.

59. MARSHALL, W. H., C. N. WOOLSEY AND P. BARD. *Science* 85: 388, 1937.

60. MCKINLEY, W. A. AND H. W. MAGOUN. *Am. J. Physiol.* 137: 217, 1942.

61. MOLLICA, A., G. MORUZZI AND R. NAQUET. *Electroencephalog. & Clin. Neurophysiol.* 5: 571, 1953.

62. MORISON, R. S., E. W. DEMPSEY AND B. R. MORISON. *Am. J. Physiol.* 131: 732, 1941.

63. MORUZZI, S. AND H. W. MAGOUN. *Electroencephalog. & Clin. Neurophysiol.* 1: 455, 1949.

64. PAVLOV, I. P. *Lectures on Conditioned Reflexes.* New York: Internat. Pub., 1928.

65. RAMÓN Y CAJAL, S. *Histologie du Système Nerveux de l'Homme et des Vertébrés* (reprinted from original 1909–11 ed.). Madrid: Consejo Superior de Investigaciones Cientificas, 1952–55.

66. RAMÓN Y CAJAL, S. *Studies on the Cerebral Cortex [Limbic Structures]*, translated by L. M. Kraft. Chicago: Yr. Bk. Pub., 1955.

67. RASMUSSEN, G. L. *J. Comp. Neurol.* 84: 141, 1946.

68. RASMUSSEN, G. L. *J. Comp. Neurol.* 99: 61, 1953.

69. ROSE, J. E. AND V. B. MOUNTCASTLE. *Bull. Johns Hopkins Hosp.* 94: 238, 1954.

70. SCHEIBEL, M., A. SCHEIBEL, A. MOLLICA AND G. MORUZZI. *J. Neurophysiol.* 18: 309, 1955.

71. SCHERRER, H. AND R. HERNÁNDEZ-PEÓN. *Fed. Proc.* 14: 132, 1955.

72. SEGUNDO, J. P., R. ARANA AND J. D. FRENCH. *J. Neurosurg.* 12: 601, 1955.

73. SEGUNDO, J. P., R. NAQUET AND P. BUSER. *J. Neurophysiol.* 18: 236, 1955.

74. SNIDER, R. S. *A.M.A. Arch. Neurol. & Psychiat.* 64: 196, 1950.

75. SNIDER, R. S. AND A. STOWELL. *J. Neurophysiol.* 7: 331, 1944.

76. STARZL, T. E. AND H. W. MAGOUN. *J. Neurophysiol.* 14: 133, 1951.

77. STARZL, T. E., C. W. TAYLOR AND H. W. MAGOUN. *J. Neurophysiol.* 14: 461, 1951.

78. STARZL, T. E., C. W. TAYLOR AND H. W. MAGOUN. *J. Neurophysiol.* 14: 479, 1951.

79. STARZL, T. E. AND D. G. WHITLOCK. *J. Neurophysiol.* 15: 449, 1952.

80. THERMAN, P. O. *J. Neurophysiol.* 4: 153, 1941.

81. VON EULER, C. AND G. RICCI. *J. Neurophysiol.* 21: 231, 1958.

INDEX

Index